MW01012824

The ASQ Certified Six Sigma Black Belt Handbook

The ASQ Certified Six Sigma Black Belt Handbook

Fourth Edition

Mary McShane-Vaughn, editor

ASQExcellence
Milwaukee, Wisconsin

Published by ASQExcellence, Milwaukee, WI
Produced and distributed by Quality Press, ASQ, Milwaukee, WI

Publisher's Cataloging-in-Publication Data

Names: McShane-Vaughn, Mary, editor.
Title: The ASQ certified six sigma black belt handbook , fourth edition / Mary McShane-Vaughn, Editor.
Description: Includes bibliographical references and index. | Milwaukee, WI: ASQExcellence, 2022.
Identifiers: LCCN: 2022947810 | ISBN: 978-1-63694-023-6 (hardcover) | 978-1-63694-025-0 (e-pub) | 978-1-63694-024-3 (pdf)
Subjects: LCSH Quality control--Statistical methods--Handbooks, manuals, etc. | BISAC BUSINESS & ECONOMICS / Quality Control | STUDY AIDS / Professional
Classification: LCC TS156 .A87 2022 | DDC 658.4/013--dc23

ASQ advances individual, organizational, and community excellence worldwide through learning, quality improvement, and knowledge exchange.

Bookstores, wholesalers, schools, libraries, businesses, and organizations: Quality Press books are available at quantity discounts for bulk purchases for business, trade, or educational uses. For more information, please contact Quality Press at 800-248-1946 or books@asq.org.

To place orders or browse the selection of all Quality Press titles, visit our website at: http://www.asq.org/quality-press.

Printed in the United States of America
26 25 24 23 22 LS 6 5 4 3 2 1

Quality Press
600 N. Plankinton Ave.
Milwaukee, WI 53203-2914
Email: books@asq.org
Excellence Through Quality™

For Mick, the next engineer in the family.

Table of Contents

Part VI: Analyze

Part VIII: Control

Part IX: Design for Six Sigma (DFSS) Framework and Methodologies

Part X: Appendices

List of Figures and Tables

Preface to the Fourth Edition

I am honored to present the fourth edition of *The Certified Six Sigma Black Belt Handbook*. The handbook has been updated to reflect the Six Sigma Black Belt Body of Knowledge released in 2022.

I want to thank the previous authors, T. M. Kubiak and Donald W. Benbow, for creating the handbook from scratch in 2005 and updating it for the second and third editions. We appreciate the breadth and depth of the source material we had for the editing effort. To paraphrase Isaac Newton, if our team has reached far, it is because we have stood on the shoulders of giants.

CHANGES TO THE BODY OF KNOWLEDGE

There have been some significant changes to the 2022 Black Belt Body of Knowledge (BoK). These changes stem from the results of the ASQ Job Survey completed by certified Black Belts in late 2021. Respondents were asked how important each tool in the BoK was in their work, and how often they used it. In addition, they were asked if any tools or topics should be added to the BoK. The Black Belt Body of Knowledge is thus a living document that reflects the current state of the practice of Six Sigma in a wide range of industries. The updated version of the BoK can be found at the end of the front matter.

Based on the importance the Black Belts placed on the tools in each major category of the BoK, the number of exam questions by section has changed as follows:

BoK Section	2015 BoK Test Questions	2022 BoK Test Questions	Delta
I. Organization-Wide Planning and Deployment	12	12	0
II. Organizational Process Management and Measures	10	12	+2
III. Team Management	18	15	–3
IV. Define	20	20	0
V. Measure	25	25	0
VI. Analyze	22	22	0
VII. Improve	21	21	0
VIII. Control	15	17	+2
Design for Six Sigma (DFSS) Framework and Methodologies	7	6	–1

Topics or tools removed from the most recent BoK include the foundations and history of lean Six Sigma, hoshin kanri, portfolio analysis, PEST, circle diagrams, data coding and imputation, contingency tables, and nonparametric testing. Note, however, that these deleted topics remain in the glossary.

Topics and tools that have entered the BoK for the first time include business planning and return on investment (ROI) in the strategic planning section, key behavior indicators (KBIs) and objectives and key results (OKR), the roles of coaching and finance in projects, process decision program charts (PDPCs) and interrelationship digraphs, audit MSA, A3 analysis, maturity models, types of risk, and RASCI matrices.

There were also changes in the Bloom's cognition levels for several of the statistical topics:

Topic	2015 Bloom's Level	2022 Bloom's Level
Basic probability concepts	Apply	Understand
Additional distributions, to include hypergeometric, bivariate normal, exponential, lognormal, and Weibull	Evaluate	Understand
Multivariate tools: factor analysis, discriminant analysis, and MANOVA	Evaluate	Understand
One-factor experiments	Evaluate	Understand
Full-factorial experiments	Evaluate	Understand
Two-level fractional factorial experiments	Evaluate	Understand

EDITORIAL GOALS

As editor, my goals for this edition were to produce a handbook that:

- adhered to the updated Body of Knowledge
- reflected the latest technology and applications of Six Sigma and lean tools
- presented thorough explanations of statistical concepts in a straightforward way
- used a variety of software packages to create output for examples
- offered a larger number of shorter, more diverse examples illustrating key concepts
- provided an excellent resource for the certification test, both for study prep and on exam day
- created a handbook that would be a valuable addition to any quality practitioner's professional library

Please let me know if I have achieved these goals by dropping a note to books@asq.org.

WHAT'S NEW?

There are some changes to the look and feel of the handbook.

We attempted to produce a more focused volume without losing any vital information. We've incorporated the former Glossary of Japanese Terms into the general glossary, and removed appendices, tools, and chapters that were no longer applicable to the BoK.

We reordered some features, moving the BoK and acronym glossary to the front of the handbook, and refining and reordering the appendices to follow the order of the text. The appendices also feature new standard normal and Student's *t* tables that include more values.

To help candidates prepare for the exam, we numbered equations for easier reference and focused the examples on hand calculations as much as possible. We also present computer output using Minitab®, JMP®, and Design Ease® software.

The companion CD containing practice questions and example files that was included with past editions has been discontinued.

Here is a summary of the content changes in each chapter:

Chapter 1 Organization-Wide Considerations—Added maturity models, and examples from the quality literature representing a wide range of industries and countries.

Chapter 2 Leadership—Added a section on critical success factors taken from the quality literature and expanded the section on force-field analysis and change management.

Chapter 3 Impact on Stakeholders—Expanded the section on stakeholder classification.

Chapter 4 Benchmarking—Streamlined the presentation of benchmarking.

Chapter 5 Business Measures—Expanded the discussion of key performance indicators (KPIs), added key behavior indictors (KBIs) and Objectives and Key Results (OKRs), and customer loyalty metrics such as the net promoter score. Added a major expansion of the financial measures to include net present value for whole year, partial year, and continuous compounding, and discounted ROI.

Chapter 6 Team Formation—Refreshed

Chapter 7 Team Facilitation—Expanded the discussion to include Lencioni's five dysfunctions of a team.

Chapter 8 Team Dynamics—Added individual disruptive behaviors, tips on facilitating group discussions, Eckes's escalation scale and methods for diffusing disruptive behaviors, and the Vroom-Yetton decision-making model.

Chapter 9 Team Training—Added the ADDIE training development model, the lean learning model, training matrices, training plans, the Ebbinghaus's forgetting curve, and the Kirkpatrick evaluation model, and updated training delivery modalities and methods.

Chapter 10 Voice of the Customer—Updated listening posts to reflect today's technology.

Chapter 11 Business Case and Project Charter—Updated the project charter template and expanded the tips on crafting problem statements.

Chapter 12 Project Management—Refreshed examples, added the RASCI matrix.

Chapter 13 Analytical tools—Added language to emphasize the process decision program chart and interrelationship digraphs that are now part of the BoK.

Chapter 14 Process Characteristics—Refreshed the flow chart and spaghetti diagram examples.

Chapter 15 Data Collection—Reworked the data categorization section, added cluster sampling, and reworked the block sampling and check sheet sections.

Chapter 16 Measurement Systems—Refreshed and refined definitions and examples.

Chapter 17 Basic Statistics—Reworked the definition of the central limit theorem, added new examples for descriptive statistics, updated the definition of kurtosis, simplified the normal plot example, and streamlined the examples of plots for other distributions.

Chapter 18 Probability—Created an all-new chapter adapted from Mary McShane-Vaughn's *The Probability Handbook* (Milwaukee, WI: ASQ Quality Press, 2016).

Chapter 19 Process Capability—Created an all-new chapter with updated formula presentations, examples, and analogies for the indices.

Chapter 20 Measuring and Modeling Relationships Between Variables—Created an all-new chapter using a simple data set for the examples, emphasizing interpreting output, not on one particular software package.

Chapter 21 Hypothesis Testing—Created an all-new chapter with extended discussion of the interpretation of the *p*-value, sensitivity and specificity, and short examples for each confidence interval and hypothesis test covered. Added flowcharts to help candidates select appropriate hypothesis tests.

Chapter 22 Risk Analysis and Management—Added new sections on risk management, identifying risk, assessing prioritizing risk, mitigating risk, supplier risk, cybersecurity risk, and the action priority table.

Chapter 23 Additional Analysis Methods—Updated examples added A3 analysis and helpful waste mnemonics.

Chapter 24 Design of Experiments—Extensively edited to add and refine definitions of important terms and added thorough background on key concepts. Created new and updated examples using JMP®, Minitab®, and Design Ease® statistical software.

Chapter 25 Lean Methods—Updated examples and formulas, updated the overall equipment effectiveness (OEE) example, and added the Six Big Losses.

Chapter 26 Implementation—Updated the simulation section.

Chapter 27 Statistical Process Control—Refreshed explanations and expanded information on Type I errors.

Chapter 28 Other Controls—Updated the visuals and examples.

Chapter 29 Maintain Controls—Refreshed.

Chapter 30 Sustain Improvements—Added a section on replication.

Chapter 31 Common DFSS Methodologies—Streamlined the presentation of DFSS methods.

Chapter 32 Design for X (DFX)—Added reference to design for service.

Chapter 33 Robust Designs—Refreshed.

Chapter 34 Retained Knowledge—Removed chapter.

THE HANDBOOK TEAM

I was lucky enough to be able to assemble a team that applied their years of experience in data analysis, statistics, editing, training, lean, and design for Six Sigma to help me craft this new edition of the handbook.

Mr. Mark Anderson is an Engineering Consultant at Stat-Ease, Inc. Previously, he spearheaded an award-winning quality improvement program for an international manufacturer, generating millions of dollars in profit. He offers a diverse array of experience in process development, quality assurance, marketing, purchasing, and general management. Mark is also the lead author of three popular books on design of experiments, response surface methods, and formulation. He is also a guest lecturer at the University of Minnesota Chemical Engineering & Materials Science department and the Ohio State University Fisher College of Business.

Dr. Mark Bailey currently works in statistical software development at JMP Statistical Discovery LLC. He pursued research and development of medical diagnostics at Eastman Kodak and Abbott Laboratories and helped Abbott Diagnostics adopt Six Sigma in R&D activity. He taught training courses in data visualization and analysis, statistical programming and modeling, design of experiments, and predictive modeling for more than 20 years at SAS Institute.

Dr. Sandra L. Furterer is Professor of Practice in the Department of Integrated Systems Engineering at The Ohio State University. She is an ASQ Certified Six Sigma Black Belt, Certified Manager of Quality/Organizational Excellence, Certified Quality Engineer, and an ASQ fellow. Sandy is also a certified Six Sigma Master Black Belt. She is immediate past chair of the CQE exam committee. She is also the editor of ASQ's CMQ/OE and CQIA handbooks, and a prolific speaker.

Dr. Karen J. Hulting is Distinguished Statistician and Design for Six Sigma (DFSS) Coach at Medtronic. She is an ASQ Certified Six Sigma Black Belt, Certified Quality Engineer, and Certified Reliability Engineer, as well as an ASQ Fellow. She is immediate past chair of the CRE exam committee, and a past SSBB exam chair.

Mr. Daniel J. Obermiller is a senior manager for SAS Institute in the Education Department and a senior member of ASQ. He earned his Master Black Belt certification in 2002 from the Dow Chemical Company and later served as a Six Sigma Technology Leader for the company. As a manger in SAS Education, he has taught and developed training courses in statistical analysis, data visualization, design of experiments, predictive modeling, and machine learning for more than ten years. He holds a master's degree in statistics from The Ohio State University.

Mr. Paul O'Mara is a Senior Global Account Analyst, Global Sales, at Manpower Group. He is an ASQ Certified Quality Improvement Associate and Certified Six Sigma Green Belt, and a former managing editor of ASQ Quality Press.

Mr. Chad A. Smith is owner and Master Black Belt at Continuous Improvement Solutions, LLC. Chad has 34 years of continuous improvement experience, and is an ASQ Certified Master Black Belt, Certified Six Sigma Black Belt, and an ASQ Fellow. Chad is also a Certified Scrum Master. He is past chair of both the ASQ Master Black Belt exam committee and the ASQ Six Sigma Forum Technical Community.

Ms. Mary Beth Soloy is the President of Nexus Quality and Productivity Specialists. Her professional career includes positions in Manufacturing, Engineering, Reliability, and Quality at General Motors Corporation and Ford Motor Company. An ASQ Fellow, she is also an ASQ Certified Quality Engineer, Certified Reliability Engineer, Certified Six Sigma Black Belt, and Certified Master Black Belt. She is a past chair of the CMBB exam committee. Currently, Mary Beth serves as Secretary for the ASQ Automotive Division and is the Past Chair and Treasurer for the ASQ Six Sigma Forum Technical Community as well as a member of the Editorial Review Board for ASQ Lean Six Sigma Review Magazine.

As editor of the handbook, any errors that may appear in the text are all mine. Please submit suggestions, additions, corrections, or deletions for the handbook to books@asq.org.

—The Editor

Preface to the Third Edition

In the spirit of customer–supplier relationships, we are pleased to provide our readers with the third edition of *The Certified Six Sigma Black Belt Handbook.* The handbook has been updated to reflect the most recent Six Sigma Black Belt Body of Knowledge released in 2015.

As with all ASQ certification–based handbooks, the primary audience for this work is the individual who plans to prepare to sit for the Six Sigma Black Belt certification examination. Therefore, the book assumes the necessary background and experience in quality and Six Sigma. Concepts are dealt with briefly, but facilitated with practical examples. We have intentionally avoided theoretical discussion unless such a discussion was necessary to communicate a concept. As always, readers are encouraged to use additional sources when they are seeking much deeper levels of discussion. Most of the citations provided in the references section will be helpful in this regard.

A secondary audience for the handbook is the quality and Six Sigma professional who would like a relevant Six Sigma reference book. With this audience in mind, we have greatly expanded the appendices section:

- Although the Body of Knowledge was updated in 2015, we have elected to keep both the 2001 and 2007 bodies of knowledge so that readers can compare changes and perhaps offer recommendations for future changes.
- All tables were developed using a combination of Microsoft Excel and Minitab 15. As such, the reader may find some differences between our tables and those published in other sources. Note that many statistical tables were produced years ago either by hand or using rudimentary calculators. These tables have been handed down from author to author and have remained largely unchanged. Our approach was to revert to the formulas and algorithms that produced the tables and then re-develop them using statistical software.
- Additional exercises have been included particularly to address the more difficult concepts.
- Additional tables and figures have been added to clarify concepts. Tables, in particular, are used to help collect concepts and to make comparisons and contrasts more easily accomplished.
- Additional content has been added between the DMAIC parts of the book (that is, Parts IV–VII) to help smooth the transition between

phases and to better relate the underlying concepts of the DMAIC methodology.

- Content that was removed in the 2015 Body of Knowledge was retained and placed in the last chapter of the book for preservation of knowledge purposes.
- Additional content has been added that is not part of the body of knowledge because of direct relevance. Such content has been identified as not being in the body of knowledge.
- Additional content has been added to ensure that the Black Belt is fully trained in concepts taught to the Green Belt. Inconsistencies between the two bodies of knowledge were noted. For example, the Green Belt body of knowledge may discuss material not covered in the Black Belt body of knowledge. The additional content is meant to address such gaps.
- The glossary has been updated where appropriate.
- An acronym glossary is now included in the Appendix.
- The CD* now includes both Excel and Minitab files for most exercises. This will permit our readers to work the examples more easily and, hopefully, facilitate the learning process. However, this book is not intended to serve as a learning tool for Excel or Minitab.
- The supplemental and simulated exam problems are now fully worked so that readers can more readily follow the problem-solving process.

We are confident readers will find the above improvements useful.

As you might expect, the number of the chapters and sections follows the same method used in the SSBB Body of Knowledge. This has made for some awkward placement of discussions (for example, the normal distribution is referred to several times before it is defined). In some cases, redundancy of discussion exists. However, where possible, we have tried to reference the main content in the handbook and refer the reader there for the primary discussion.

After the first edition was published, we received several comments from readers stating that their answers did not completely agree with those given in the examples. In many instances, we found that discrepancies could be attributed to the use of computers with different bits, the number of significant digits accounted for by the software used, the sequence in which the arithmetic was performed, and the propagation of errors due to rounding or truncation. Therefore, we urge the reader to carefully consider the above points as the examples are worked. Also, it should be noted that due to software updates and improvements by Minitab, the results shown in charts and graphs in the third edition may differ slightly with the second edition. These differences are minor and can be ignored.

However, we do recognize that errors occasionally occur. We ask that readers recommend suggestions, additions, corrections, or deletions, as well as

*As of 2021, CD components to any editions no longer exist. Customers may contact help@asq.org to request a hyperlink to ancillary materials.

seek out any corrections that may have been found and published, by emailing books@asq.org.

Finally, the enclosed CD* contains supplementary problems covering each chapter and a simulated exam that has problems distributed among chapters according to the scheme published in the Body of Knowledge. It is suggested that the reader study a particular chapter, repeating any calculations independently, and then do the supplementary problems for that chapter. After attaining success with all chapters, the reader may complete the simulated exam to confirm mastery of the entire Six Sigma Black Belt Body of Knowledge.

—The Authors

*As of 2021, CD components to any editions no longer exist. Customers may contact help@asq.org to request a hyperlink to ancillary materials.

Preface to the Second Edition

In the spirit of customer–supplier relationships, we are pleased to provide our readers with the second edition of *The Certified Six Sigma Black Belt Handbook.* The handbook has been updated to reflect the most recent Six Sigma Black Belt Body of Knowledge, released in 2007.

As with all ASQ certification–based handbooks, the primary audience for this work is the individual who plans to prepare to sit for the Six Sigma Black Belt certification examination. Therefore, the book assumes the individual has the necessary background and experience in quality and Six Sigma. Concepts are dealt with briefly but facilitated with practical examples. We have intentionally avoided theoretical discussion unless such a discussion was necessary to communicate a concept. As always, readers are encouraged to use additional sources when seeking much deeper levels of discussion. Most of the citations provided in the references will be helpful in this regard.

A secondary audience for the handbook is the quality and Six Sigma professional who would like a relevant Six Sigma reference book. With this audience in mind, we have greatly expanded the appendices section:

- Although the Body of Knowledge was updated in 2007, we have elected to keep the 2001 Body of Knowledge so that readers can compare changes and perhaps offer recommendations for future Bodies of Knowledge.
- All tables were developed using a combination of Microsoft Excel and Minitab 15. Thus, the reader may find some differences between our tables and those published in other sources. Appendices 29–33 are examples of where such differences might occur. Note that years ago many statistical tables were produced either by hand or by using rudimentary calculators. These tables have been handed down from author to author and have remained largely unchanged. Our approach was to revert to the formulas and algorithms that produced the tables and then redevelop them using statistical software.
- The table for control constants has been expanded to now include virtually all control constants. To the best of our knowledge, this handbook is probably the only reference source that includes this information.
- Tables for both cumulative and noncumulative forms of the most useful distributions are now present—for example, binomial, Poisson, and normal.

- Additional alpha values in tables have been included. For example, large alpha values for the left side of the F-distribution now exist. Thus, it will no longer be necessary to use the well-known conversion property of the distribution to obtain critical F values associated with higher alpha values. Though the conversion formula is straightforward, everyone seems to get it wrong. We expect our readers will appreciate this.
- The glossary has grown significantly. Most notable is the inclusion of more terms relating to lean.
- A second glossary has been added as well. This short glossary is limited to the most common Japanese terms used by quality and Six Sigma professionals.

We are confident that readers will find the above additions useful.

As you might expect, chapter and section numbering follows the same method used in the Six Sigma Black Belt Body of Knowledge. This has made for some awkward placement of discussions (for example, the normal distribution is referred to several times before it is defined), and in some cases, redundancy of discussion exists. However, where possible, we have tried to reference the main content in the handbook and refer the reader there for the primary discussion.

After the first edition was published, we received several comments from readers who stated that their answers did not completely agree with those given in the examples. In many instances, we found that discrepancies could be attributed to the following: use of computers with different bits, the number of significant digits accounted for by the software used, the sequence in which the arithmetic was performed, and the propagation of errors due to rounding or truncation. Therefore, we urge the reader to carefully consider the above points as the examples are worked.

Finally, the enclosed CD* contains supplementary problems covering each chapter and a simulated exam that has problems distributed among chapters according to the scheme published in the Body of Knowledge. It is suggested that the reader study a particular chapter, repeating any calculations independently, and then do the supplementary problems for that chapter. After attaining success with all chapters, the reader may complete the simulated exam to confirm mastery of the entire Six Sigma Black Belt Body of Knowledge.

—The Authors

*As of 2021, CD components to any editions no longer exist. Customers may contact help@asq.org to request a hyperlink to ancillary materials.

Preface to the First Edition

We decided to number chapters and sections by the same method used in the Body of Knowledge (BOK) specified for the Certified Six Sigma Black Belt examination. This made for some awkward placement (the normal distribution is referred to several times before it is defined), and in some cases, redundancy. We thought the ease of access for readers, who might be struggling with some particular point in the BOK, would more than balance these disadvantages.

The enclosed CD* contains supplementary problems covering each chapter and a simulated exam that has problems distributed among chapters according to the scheme published in the Body of Knowledge. It is suggested that the reader study a particular chapter, repeating any calculations independently, and then do the supplementary problems for that chapter. After attaining success with all chapters, the reader may complete the simulated exam to confirm mastery of the entire Six Sigma Black Belt Body of Knowledge.

—The Authors

*As of 2021, CD components to any editions no longer exist. Customers may contact help@asq.org to request a hyperlink to ancillary materials.

Acknowledgments

I want to thank Michael Byrnes, Executive Director of Certification Operations at ASQE, for offering me the opportunity to edit this handbook. The ASQ Black Belt Body of Knowledge has been a particular interest of mine ever since I worked on the Six Sigma Black Belt exam committee and served as the exam chair way back in 2010.

I've been writing about and teaching Six Sigma topics for the past 20 years. However, taking on the task of updating a 912-page handbook on a deadline was a unique challenge. One of my Black Belt students commented that the text was so big, we should call it a "two-hand" book. The editing exercise stretched my project management skills, writing ability, and knowledge of the field. I leveraged the power of Zoom for editorial meetings and Google sheets to meticulously track the status of the chapter changes.

Most importantly, I was able to surround myself with a team of professionals who were smarter than me. Over the course of seven months, the team and I read and discussed each existing chapter, mapped out changes we wanted to make, and then went about editing, rewriting, commenting, cross-checking, re-reading, and finalizing each chapter. Each of us was motivated by our love of the subject matter as well as a profound sense of responsibility to the ASQ Black Belt community. I am extremely proud of the outcome.

Thanks to my stellar team of subject matter experts who volunteered their time, intellect, and energy to make this handbook possible:

Mr. Mark J. Anderson, PE, MBA, CQE
Stat-Ease, Inc.

Dr. Mark Bailey
JMP Statistical Discovery LLC

Dr. Sandra L. Furterer, MBA, CQE, CSSBB, CMQ/OE, ASQ Fellow, MBB
The Ohio State University

Dr. Karen J. Hulting, CQE, CRE, CSSBB, ASQ Fellow
Medtronic

Mr. Daniel J. Obermiller, MS, MBB
SAS Education

Mr. Chad A. Smith, CSSBB, CMBB, ASQ Fellow
Continuous Improvement Solutions, LLC

Ms. Mary Beth Soloy, MBA, CRE, CQE, CSSBB, CMBB, ASQ Fellow
Nexus Quality and Productivity Specialists

Team member contributions are shown below:

Chapter	Contributor
1 Organization-Wide Considerations	Mary Beth Soloy
	Mary McShane-Vaughn
2 Leadership	Mary Beth Soloy
	Mary McShane-Vaughn
3 Impact on Stakeholders	Sandra L. Furterer
	Mary McShane-Vaughn
4 Benchmarking	Sandra L. Furterer
	Mary McShane-Vaughn
5 Business Measures	Sandra L. Furterer
	Mary McShane-Vaughn
6 Team Formation	Mary McShane-Vaughn
7 Team Facilitation	Mary McShane-Vaughn
8 Team Dynamics	Mary McShane-Vaughn
9 Team Training	Mary McShane-Vaughn
10 Voice of the Customer	Mary Beth Soloy
	Mary McShane-Vaughn
11 Business Case and Project Charter	Mary Beth Soloy
	Mary McShane-Vaughn
12 Project Management (PM) Tools	Mary Beth Soloy
	Mary McShane-Vaughn
13 Analytical Tools	Mary Beth Soloy
	Mary McShane-Vaughn
14 Process Characteristics	Mary McShane-Vaughn
15 Data Collection	Mary McShane-Vaughn
16 Measurement Systems	Daniel J. Obermiller
17 Basic Statistics	Daniel J. Obermiller
18 Probability	Mary McShane-Vaughn
19 Process Capability	Karen J. Hulting
	Mary McShane-Vaughn

Chapter	Contributor
20 Measuring and Modeling Relationships Between Variables	Mary McShane-Vaughn
21 Hypothesis Testing	Mary McShane-Vaughn
22 Risk Analysis and Management	Chad A. Smith
	Mary McShane-Vaughn
23 Additional Analysis Methods	Chad A. Smith
24 Design of Experiments	Mark Bailey
	Mark A. Anderson
	Mary McShane-Vaughn
25 Lean Methods	Chad A. Smith
26 Implementation	Chad A. Smith
27 Statistical Process Control	Sandra L. Furterer
	Mary McShane-Vaughn
28 Other Controls	Chad A. Smith
29 Maintain Controls	Chad A. Smith
30 Sustain Improvements	Chad A. Smith
31 Common DFSS Methodologies	Mary Beth Soloy
32 Design for X	Mary Beth Soloy
33 Robust Designs	Mary Beth Soloy

A special thank-you goes to Paul O'Mara, MA, MS, CQIA, CCCGB, who is the rarest of people: a current data scientist and a former managing editor. Paul was the editor of my previous two Quality Press books, and he was a delight to work with once again. Paul has never been disheartened by my requests for help. His encouragement, suggestions, and insights were invaluable as I wrestled with the sheer size of the project.

Thanks also to Marge Goodrich and Lisa Stanick. We met as 17-year-old freshman at General Motors Institute in Flint, Michigan, and have been dear friends ever since. I co-opted our online book club in early 2022 by suggesting that we read and comment on chapters of the Black Belt handbook instead. Marge and Lisa each graciously gave their time to provide many suggestions that increased the impact and readability of the chapters.

A shout-out to Dr. Dave Goldsman, Director of Master's Programs, and Coca-Cola Foundation Professor in the Industrial and Systems Engineering Department at Georgia Tech, who put the word out to the graduate students that I was looking for assistance. A hearty thanks to Mr. Yunlang Zhu, MS student in Operations Research, and Mr. Surya Dhanvantari Ramakrishna Pantula, MS student in Supply Chain Engineering, who both did a superb job of checking the equations and examples in the statistics chapters. Go Jackets!

Thank you to Kush Shah, immediate past Black Belt exam chair; April Schmidt, Black Belt exam committee community liaison; and Mike Sage, psychometrician at ASQE, for fielding questions we had about the changes in the Body of Knowledge.

Thanks to Katelyn Andersen and Team Ahlman at the Six Sigma Ranch & Winery in Lower Lake, CA, for helping me provide the perfect thank-you gifts for the team.

A special thanks to Dr. Steven P. Bailey for reading every word of the draft and making insightful comments and vital additions. It was a pleasure discussing some the stickier points of the statistics chapters with him and absorbing some of his vast knowledge. The handbook is better because of his input. In addition, I would like to thank the Quality Press management staff, Lillian McAnally and Erica Barse, for their cheerful support during the entire project, and for providing references when they were needed. Finally, I'd would like to thank the staff at The Froebe Group for steering this handbook from draft to final form. Their efforts have produced a final product worthy of the ASQ Quality Press family of publications.

—The Editor

About the Editor

Mary McShane-Vaughn is Principal at University Training Partners, a company that designs and delivers online and in-person training for Six Sigma. Previously, Dr. McShane-Vaughn was a tenured professor at Southern Polytechnic State University (now Kennesaw State). For eight years she directed and grew the MS in Quality Assurance program and taught statistics, design of experiments, and statistical process control in the graduate program. Before her career in academics, Mary worked for 15 years as a quality engineer and statistician in the automotive, medical device, consumer product testing, and revenue management industries.

Mary is currently the chair of the ASQ certified quality engineer exam committee and a member of the technical program committee. She is immediate past chair of the ASQ Sacramento section and served as the Black Belt exam chair from 2010–2012. She is the author of *The Probability Handbook* and *The Probability Workbook*, and co-author of *The Certified Quality Inspector Handbook*, all published by Quality Press. She is also the author of *Leadership Tools for Black Belts* and several other Six Sigma course companion books. Mary also serves on the editorial review board of the *Lean & Six Sigma Review*. She is an ASQ certified Six Sigma Black Belt, Quality Engineer, and Reliability Engineer.

Dr. McShane-Vaughn earned her Ph.D. in Industrial Engineering and MS in Applied Statistics from the Georgia Institute of Technology, and a BS in Industrial Engineering from Kettering University. She is a senior member of ASQ, and a member of the Institute of Industrial and System Engineers, and the American Statistical Association.

Acronym Glossary

5S (Five S)—seiri (sort; also sifting), seiton (set in order), seiso (shine; also sanitize or scrub), seiketsu (standardize), and shitsuke (sustain; also self-discipline).

5Ws & 1H—who, what, where, when, why, and how.

6Ms—machines, manpower, materials, measurements, methods, and Mother Nature.

7Ms—machines, manpower, materials, measurements, methods, Mother Nature, and management.

ABC—activity-based costing.

ACWP—actual cost of work performed.

ADDIE—instructional design model steps of analysis, design, development, implementaion, and evaluation.

AIAG—Automotive Industry Action Group.

AND—activity network diagram.

ANOM—analysis of means.

ANOVA—analysis of variance.

ANSI—American National Standards Institute.

APC—automated process control.

AS-9100—a standard for the aeronautics industry embracing the ISO 9001 standard.

ASQ—American Society for Quality.

AV—actual value.

BAC—budget at completion.

BB—Black Belt.

BCWP—budgeted cost of work performed.

BCWS—budgeted cost of work scheduled.

BPM—business process management.

CBA—cost–benefit analysis.

CFM—continuous flow manufacturing.

CLT—central limit theorem.

COPQ—cost of poor quality.

COQ—cost of quality.

COV—components of variation.

CPI—cost performance index.

CPL—lower process capability index.

CPM—critical path method.

CPU—upper process capability index.

CSF—critical success factors.

CSSBB—Certified Six Sigma Black Belt.

CSSGB—Certified Six Sigma Green Belt.

CSSYB—Certified Six Sigma Yellow Belt.

CSSWB—Certified Six Sigma White Belt.

CTQ—critical-to-quality.

CUSUM—cumulative sum (control chart).

CV—cost variance.

CV—coefficient of variation.

DFA—design for assembly.

DFC—design for cost.

DFM—design for manufacturability or design for maintainability.

DFMEA—design failure mode and effects analysis.

DFP—design for producibility.

DFQ—design for quality.

DFSS—design for Six Sigma.

DFT—design for testability.

DFX—design for X.

DMADOV—define, measure, analyze, design, optimize, verify.

DMADV—define, measure, analyze, design, verify.

DMAIC—define, measure, analyze, improve, control.

DOE—design of experiments.

DOX—design of experiments.

DPMO—defects per million opportunities.

DPU—defects per unit.

DTC—design to cost.

EAC—estimate at completion.

ETC—estimate to complete.

EV—earned value.

EVOP—evolutionary operations.

FMEA—failure mode and effects analysis.

FPY—first-pass yield.

FTY—first-time yield.

GB—Green Belt.

GD&T—geometric dimensioning and tolerancing.

GLM—general linear model.

GR&R—gage repeatability and reproducibility.

ICC—intra-class correlation coefficient.

ID—interrelationship digraph.

IDOV—identify, design, optimize, validate.

IRR—internal rate of return.

ISO—International Organization for Standardization.

ITIL—information technology infrastructure library.

JIT—just-in-time.

KBI—key behavior indicator.

KBD—key business driver.

KJ method—affinity diagram.

KPI—key performance indicator.

LCL—lower control limit.

LNTL—lower natural tolerance limit.

LSL—lower specification limit.

LTL—lower tolerance limit.

MAD—mean absolute deviation.

MANOVA—multiple analysis of variance.

MAPE—mean absolute percentage error.

MBB—Master Black Belt.

MBNQA—Malcolm Baldrige National Quality Award.

MRB—materials review board.

MSC—Manpower Services Commission.

MSD—mean squared deviation.

MTBF—mean time between failures.

MTTF—mean time to failure.

MTTR—mean time to repair.

NGT—nominal group technique.

NIST—National Institute of Standards and Technology (U.S.).

NPS—net promoter score.

NPV—net present value.

NVA—non-value-added.

OOC—out of control.

OKR—objective and key result.

PDCA—plan–do–check–act.

PDPC—process decision program chart.

PDSA—plan–do–study–act.

PERT—program evaluation and review technique.

PFMEA—process failure mode and effects analysis.

PIT—process improvement team.

PONC—price of nonconformance.

ppb—parts per billion.

PPL—lower process performance index.

ppm—parts per million.

PPU—upper process performance index.

PTR—precision-to-tolerance ratio.

PV—present value.

QFD—quality function deployment.

ROE—return on equity.

ROI—return on investment.

RTY—rolled throughput yield.

SEI—Software Engineering Institute.

SIPOC—suppliers, inputs, process, outputs, customers.

SMART—specific, measurable, achievable, relevant, timely.

SMED—single-minute exchange of die.

SOW—statement of work.

SPC—statistical process control.

SPI—schedule performance index.

SQC—statistical quality control.

SV—schedule variance.

SWOT—strengths, weaknesses, opportunities, threats.

T—specification target, specification nominal.

TOC—theory of constraints.

TPM—total productive maintenance.

UCL—upper control limit.

UNTL—upper natural tolerance limit.

USL—upper specification limit.

UTL—upper tolerance limit.

VA—value-added or value analysis.

VE—value engineering.

VIF—variance inflation factor.

VOC—voice of the customer.

VOP—voice of the process.

VSA—value stream analysis.

VSM—value stream map.

YB—Yellow Belt.

WB—White Belt.

ASQ Six Sigma Black Belt Certification Body of Knowledge (2022)

The topics in this Body of Knowledge include additional detail in the form of subtext explanations and the cognitive level at which test questions will be written. This information will provide guidance for the candidate preparing to take the exam. The subtext is not intended to limit the subject matter or be all-inclusive of what might be covered in an exam. It is meant to clarify the type of content to be included in the exam. The descriptor in parentheses at the end of each entry refers to the maximum cognitive level at which the topic will be tested. A complete description of cognitive levels is provided at the end of this document.

I. Organization-Wide Planning and Deployment (12 Questions)

A. ***Organization-wide considerations***

1. *Fundamentals of six sigma and lean methodologies.* Define and describe the value and goals of these approaches and describe the integration and complementary relationship between them. Identify and understand an organization's lean six sigma maturity model. (Understand)
2. *Six sigma, lean, and continuous improvement methodologies.* Describe when to use six sigma instead of other problem-solving approaches and describe the importance of aligning six sigma objectives with organizational goals. Describe screening criteria and how such criteria can be used for the selection of six sigma projects, lean initiatives, and other continuous improvement methods. (Apply)
3. *Relationships among business systems and processes.* Describe the interactive relationships among business systems, processes, and internal and external stakeholders, and the impact those relationships have on business systems. (Understand)
4. *Strategic planning and deployment for initiatives.* Define the importance of identification and strategic planning of six sigma projects and lean initiatives as part of the business planning process taking into consideration outcomes such as return on investment and measured intangibles. Use strengths, weaknesses, opportunities, and threats analysis (SWOT), contingency planning, and business continuity planning to enhance strategic planning and deployment. (Apply)

B. ***Leadership***

1. *Roles and responsibilities.* Describe the roles and responsibilities of executive leadership, champions, sponsors, process owners, master black belts, black belts, and green belts in driving six sigma and

lean initiatives. Understand the importance of coaching multiple levels of leadership and belts on appropriate six sigma tools and techniques. Understand the importance of finance and its role supporting a project and confirming its outcome. Describe how each group influences project deployment in terms of providing or managing resources, enabling changes in organizational structure, and supporting communications about the purpose and deployment of the initiatives. (Understand)

2. *Organizational barriers*. Describe how an organization's structure and culture can impact six sigma projects. Identify common causes of six sigma failures, including lack of management support and lack of resources. (Apply)

3. *Change management*. Apply and facilitate change management techniques, including stakeholder analysis, readiness assessments, proactive change management, and communication plans to overcome barriers and drive organization-wide change. (Apply)

II. Organizational Process Management and Measures (12 Questions)

A. ***Impact on stakeholders***. Describe the impact six sigma projects can have on customers, suppliers, and other stakeholders. (Understand)

B. ***Benchmarking***. Define and distinguish between various types of benchmarking, e.g., best practices, competitive, collaborative, and breakthrough. Select measures and performance goals for projects resulting from benchmarking activities. (Apply)

C. ***Business measures***

1. *Performance measures*. Define and describe balanced scorecard, key performance indicators (KPIs), key behavior indicators (KBIs), objectives and key results (OKRs), customer loyalty metrics, and leading and lagging indicators. Explain how to create a line of sight from performance measures to organizational strategies. (Analyze)

2. *Financial measures*. Define and use revenue growth, market share, margin, net present value (NPV), return on investment (ROI), and cost–benefit analysis (CBA). Explain the difference between hard cost measures (from profit and loss statements) and soft cost benefits of cost avoidance and reduction. (Apply)

III. Team Management (15 Questions)

A. ***Team formation***

1. *Team types and constraints*. Define and describe various teams, including virtual, cross-functional, and self-directed. Determine what team type will work best for a given a set of constraints, e.g., geography, technology availability, staff schedules, time zones. (Apply)

2. *Team roles and responsibilities*. Define and describe various team roles and responsibilities for leader, facilitator, coach, and individual member. (Understand)

3. *Team member selection criteria.* Describe various factors that influence the selection of team members, including the ability to influence, openness to change, required skills sets, subject matter expertise, and availability. (Apply)
4. *Team success factors.* Identify and describe the elements necessary for successful teams, e.g., management support, clear goals, ground rules, and timelines. (Apply)

B. ***Team facilitation***

1. *Motivational techniques.* Describe and apply techniques to motivate team members. Identify factors that can demotivate team members and describe techniques to overcome them. (Apply)
2. *Team stages of development.* Identify and describe the classic stages of team development: forming, storming, norming, performing, and adjourning. (Apply)
3. *Team communication.* Describe and explain the elements of an effective communication plan, e.g., audience identification, message type, medium, frequency. (Apply)
4. *Team leadership models.* Describe and select appropriate leadership approaches (e.g., direct, coach, support, and delegate) to ensure team success. (Apply)

C. ***Team dynamics***

1. *Group behaviors.* Identify and use various conflict resolution techniques (e.g., coaching, mentoring, and intervention) to overcome negative group dynamics, including dominant and reluctant participants, groupthink, rushing to finish, and digressions. (Evaluate)
2. *Meeting management.* Select and use various meeting management techniques, including using agendas, starting on time, requiring pre-work by attendees, and ensuring that the right people and resources are available. (Apply)
3. *Team decision-making methods.* Define, select, and use various tools (e.g., consensus, nominal group technique, and multi-voting) for decision making. (Apply)

D. ***Team training***

1. *Needs assessment.* Identify the steps involved to implement an effective training curriculum: identify skills gaps, develop learning objectives, prepare a training plan, and develop training materials. (Understand)
2. *Delivery.* Describe various techniques used to deliver effective training, including adult learning theory, soft skills, and modes of learning. (Understand)
3. *Evaluation.* Describe various techniques to evaluate training, including evaluation planning, feedback surveys, pre-training and post-training testing. (Understand)

IV. Define (20 Questions)

A. *Voice of the customer*

1. *Customer identification.* Identify and segment customers and show how a project will impact both internal and external customers. (Apply)
2. *Customer data collection.* Identify and select appropriate data collection methods (e.g., surveys, focus groups, interviews, and observations) to gather voice of the customer data. Ensure the data collection methods used are reviewed for validity and reliability. (Analyze)
3. *Customer requirements.* Define, select, and apply appropriate tools to determine customer needs and requirements, including critical-to-X (CTX when "X" can be quality, cost, safety, etc.), CTQ tree, quality function deployment (QFD), supplier, input, process, output, customer (SIPOC), and Kano model. (Analyze)

B. *Business case and project charter*

1. *Business case.* Describe business case justification used to support projects. (Understand)
2. *Problem statement.* Develop a project problem statement and evaluate it in relation to baseline performance and improvement goals. (Evaluate)
3. *Project scope.* Develop and review project boundaries to ensure that the project has value to the customer. (Analyze)
4. *Goals and objectives.* Identify SMART (specific, measurable, actionable, relevant, and time-bound) goals and objectives on the basis of the project's problem statement and scope. (Analyze)
5. *Project performance measurements.* Identify and evaluate performance measurements (e.g., cost, revenue, delivery, schedule, and customer satisfaction) that connect critical elements of the process to key outputs. (Analyze)
6. *Project charter review.* Explain the importance of having periodic project charter reviews with stakeholders. (Understand)

C. ***Project management (PM) tools.*** Identify and use the following PM tools to track projects and document their progress. (Evaluate)

1. Gantt charts
2. Tollgate reviews
3. Work breakdown structure (WBS)
4. RACI Model (responsible, accountable, consulted, and informed)

D. ***Analytical tools.*** Identify and use the following analytical tools throughout the DMAIC cycle. (Apply)

1. Affinity diagrams
2. Tree diagrams

3. Matrix diagrams
4. Prioritization matrices
5. Activity network diagrams
6. Process decision program chart (PDPC)
7. Interrelationship digraph (ID)

V. Measure (25 Questions)

A. ***Process characteristics***

1. *Process flow metrics*. Identify and use process flow metrics (e.g., work in progress (WIP), work in queue (WIQ), touch time, takt time, cycle time, and throughput) to determine constraints. Describe the impact that "hidden factories" can have on process flow metrics. (Analyze)
2. *Process analysis tools*. Select, use, and evaluate various tools, e.g., value stream maps, process maps, work instructions, flowcharts, spaghetti diagrams, and gemba walk. (Evaluate)

B. ***Data collection***

1. *Types of data*. Define, classify, and distinguish between qualitative and quantitative data, and continuous and discrete data. (Evaluate)
2. *Measurement scales*. Define and use nominal, ordinal, interval, and ratio measurement scales. (Apply)
3. *Sampling*. Define and describe sampling concepts, including representative selection, homogeneity, bias, accuracy, and precision. Determine the appropriate sampling method (e.g., random, stratified, systematic, subgroup, and block) to obtain valid representation in various situations. (Evaluate)
4. *Data collection plans and methods*. Develop and implement data collection plans that include data integrity, accuracy, and processing tools, e.g., check sheets and data normalization. Avoid data collection pitfalls by defining the metrics to be used or collected, ensuring that collectors are trained in the tools and understand how the data will be used, and checking for seasonality effects. (Analyze)

C. ***Measurement systems***

1. *Measurement system analysis (MSA)*. Use gauge repeatability and reproducibility (R&R) studies and other MSA tools (e.g., bias, correlation, linearity, precision to tolerance, and percent agreement) to analyze variable measurement system capability. Use audit MSA for attribute measurement systems. (Evaluate)
2. *Measurement systems across the organization*. Identify how measurement systems can be applied to all functional areas of the organization (e.g., marketing, sales, engineering, research and development (R&D), supply chain management, operations and customer experience). (Understand)

3. *Metrology.* Define and describe elements of metrology, including calibration systems, traceability to reference standards, and the control and integrity of measurement devices and standards. (Understand)

D. ***Basic statistics***

1. *Basic statistical terms.* Define and distinguish between population parameters and sample statistics, e.g., proportion, mean, and standard deviation. (Apply)
2. *Central limit theorem.* Explain the central limit theorem and its significance in the application of inferential statistics for confidence intervals, hypothesis tests, and control charts. (Understand)
3. *Descriptive statistics.* Calculate and interpret measures of dispersion and central tendency. (Evaluate)
4. *Graphical methods.* Construct and interpret diagrams and charts, e.g., box-and-whisker plots, scatter diagrams, histograms, normal probability plots, frequency distributions, and cumulative frequency distributions. (Evaluate)
5. *Valid statistical conclusions.* Distinguish between descriptive and inferential statistical studies. Evaluate how the results of statistical studies are used to draw valid conclusions. (Evaluate)

E. ***Probability***

1. *Basic concepts.* Describe and apply probability concepts, e.g., independence, mutually exclusive events, addition and multiplication rules, conditional probability, complementary probability, and joint occurrence of events. (Understand)
2. *Common distributions.* Describe, interpret, and use normal, Poisson, binomial, chi-square, Student's *t*, and F distributions. (Evaluate)
3. *Additional distributions.* Identify hypergeometric, bivariate, exponential, lognormal, and Weibull distributions. (Understand)

F. ***Process capability***

1. *Process capability indices.* Define, select, and calculate C_p and C_{pk}. (Evaluate)
2. *Process performance indices.* Define, select, and calculate P_p, P_{pk}, C_{pm}, and process sigma. (Evaluate)
3. *General process capability studies.* Describe and apply elements of designing and conducting process capability studies relative to characteristics, specifications, sampling plans, stability, and normality. (Evaluate)
4. *Process capability for attributes data.* Calculate the process capability and process sigma level for attributes data. (Apply)
5. *Process capability for non-normal data.* Identify non-normal data and determine when it is appropriate to use Box-Cox or other transformation techniques. (Apply)

6. *Process performance versus specification.* Distinguish between natural process limits and specification limits. Calculate process performance metrics, e.g., percent defective, parts per million (PPM), defects per million opportunities (DPMO), defects per unit (DPU), first pass yield, and rolled throughput yield (RTY). (Evaluate)

7. *Short-term and long-term capability.* Describe and use appropriate assumptions and conventions when only short-term data or only long-term data are available. Interpret the relationship between short-term and long-term capability. (Evaluate)

VI. Analyze (22 Questions)

A. ***Measuring and modeling relationships and variables***

1. *Correlation coefficient.* Calculate and interpret the correlation coefficient and its confidence interval and describe the difference between correlation and causation. (Evaluate)

2. *Linear regression.* Calculate and interpret regression analysis and apply and interpret hypothesis tests for regression parameters. Use the regression model for estimation and prediction, analyze the uncertainty in the estimate, and perform a residual analysis to validate the model. (Evaluate)

3. *Multivariate tools.* Understand sources of variation through multivariate (e.g., factor analysis, discriminant analysis, multiple analysis of variance (MANOVA)). (Understand)

B. ***Hypothesis testing***

1. *Terminology.* Define and interpret the significance level, power, type I, and type II errors of statistical tests. (Evaluate)

2. *Statistical versus practical significance.* Define, compare, and interpret statistical and practical significance. (Evaluate)

3. *Sample size.* Calculate sample size for common hypothesis tests: equality of means and equality of proportions. (Apply)

4. *Point and interval estimates.* Define and distinguish between confidence and prediction intervals. Define and interpret the efficiency and bias of estimators. Calculate tolerance and confidence intervals. (Evaluate)

5. *Tests for means, variances, and proportions.* Use and interpret the results of hypothesis tests for means, variances, and proportions. (Evaluate)

6. *Analysis of variance (ANOVA).* Select, calculate, and interpret the results of ANOVAs. (Evaluate)

7. *Goodness-of-fit (chi-square) tests.* Define, select, and interpret the results of these tests. (Evaluate)

C. ***Risk analysis and management***

1. *Types of risk.* Identify, assess, and prioritize various types of risk such as enterprise, operational, supplier, security, product, and cybersecurity. (Analyze)

2. *Failure mode and effects analysis (FMEA).* Describe the purpose and elements of FMEA, including risk priority number (RPN), and evaluate FMEA results for processes, products, and services. Distinguish between design FMEA (DFMEA) and process FMEA (PFMEA) and interpret their results. (Evaluate)

D. ***Additional analysis methods***

1. *Gap analysis.* Analyze scenarios to identify performance gaps, and compare current and future states using predefined metrics. (Analyze)
2. *Root cause analysis.* Define and describe the purpose of root cause analysis, recognize the issues involved in identifying a root cause, and use various tools (e.g., 5 whys, Pareto charts, fault tree analysis, cause-and-effect diagrams, and A3) to resolve chronic problems. (Analyze)
3. *Waste analysis.* Identify and interpret the seven classic wastes (overproduction, inventory, defects, over-processing, waiting, motion, and transportation) and resource under-utilization. (Analyze)

VII. Improve (21 Questions)

A. ***Design of experiments (DOE)***

1. *Terminology.* Define basic DOE terms, e.g., independent and dependent variables, factors and levels, response, treatment, error, and nested. (Understand)
2. *Design principles.* Define and apply DOE principles, e.g., power, sample size, balance, repetition, replication, order, efficiency, randomization, blocking, interaction, confounding, and resolution. (Apply)
3. *Planning experiments.* Plan and evaluate DOEs by determining the objective, selecting appropriate factors, responses, and measurement methods, and choosing the appropriate design. (Evaluate)
4. *One-factor experiments.* Understand when to use completely randomized, randomized block, and Latin square designs. (Understand)
5. *Two-level fractional factorial experiments.* Understand these types of experiments and describe how confounding can affect their use. (Understand)
6. *Full-factorial experiments.* Understand these types of experiments. (Understand)

B. ***Lean methods***

1. *Waste elimination.* Select and apply tools and techniques for eliminating or preventing waste, e.g., pull systems, kanban, 5S, standard work, and poka-yoke. (Analyze)
2. *Cycle-time reduction.* Use various tools and techniques for reducing cycle time, e.g., continuous flow, single-minute exchange of die (SMED), and heijunka (production leveling). (Analyze)

3. *Kaizen.* Define and distinguish between kaizen and kaizen blitz and describe when to use each method. (Apply)
4. *Other improvement tools and techniques.* Identify and describe how other process improvement methodologies are used, e.g., theory of constraints (TOC), and overall equipment effectiveness (OEE). (Understand)

C. ***Implementation.*** Develop plans for implementing proposed improvements, including conducting pilot tests or simulations, and evaluate results to select the optimum solution. (Evaluate)

VIII. Control (17 Questions)

A. ***Statistical process control (SPC)***

1. *Objectives.* Explain the objectives of SPC, including monitoring and controlling process performance, tracking trends, runs, and reducing variation within a process. (Understand)
2. *Selection of variables.* Identify and select critical process characteristics for control chart monitoring. (Apply)
3. *Rational subgrouping.* Define and apply the principle of rational subgrouping. (Apply)
4. *Control chart selection.* Select and use control charts in various situations: $\bar{X} - R$, $\bar{X} - s$, individual and moving range (ImR), p, np, c, u, short-run SPC, and moving average. (Apply)
5. *Control chart analysis.* Interpret control charts and distinguish between common and special causes using rules for determining statistical control. (Analyze)

B. ***Other controls***

1. *Total productive maintenance (TPM).* Define the elements of TPM and describe how it can be used to consistently control the improved process. (Understand)
2. *Visual controls.* Define the elements of visual controls (e.g., pictures of correct procedures, color-coded components, and indicator lights), and describe how they can help control the improved process. (Understand)

C. ***Maintain controls***

1. *Measurement system reanalysis.* Review and evaluate measurement system capability as process capability improves, and ensure that measurement capability is sufficient for its intended use. (Evaluate)
2. *Control plan.* Develop a control plan to maintain the improved process performance, enable continuous improvement, and transfer responsibility from the project team to the process owner. (Apply)

D. ***Sustain improvements***

1. *Lessons learned.* Document the lessons learned and benefits realized from all phases of a project and identify strategies for reinforcing and replicating improvements. (Apply)

2. *Documentation*. Develop or modify documents including standard operating procedures (SOPs), work instructions, and control plans to ensure that the improvements are sustained over time. (Apply)
3. *Training for process owners and staff*. Develop and implement training plans that are handed off to process owners to ensure consistent execution of revised process methods, KPIs to confirm sustained benefits, and standards to maintain process requirements. (Apply)
4. *Ongoing evaluation*. Identify and apply tools (e.g., control charts and control plans) for ongoing evaluation of the improved process, including monitoring leading indicators, lagging indicators, and additional opportunities for improvement. (Apply)

IX. Design for Six Sigma (DFSS) Framework and Methodologies (6 Questions)

A. ***Common DFSS methodologies***. Identify and describe DMADV (define, measure, analyze, design, and validate) and DMADOV (define, measure, analyze, design, optimize, and validate). (Understand)

B. ***Design for X (DFX)***. Describe design constraints, including design for cost, design for manufacturability (producibility), design for test, and design for maintainability. (Understand)

C. ***Robust designs***. Describe the elements of robust product design, tolerance design, and statistical tolerancing. (Understand)

LEVELS OF COGNITION—BASED ON BLOOM'S TAXONOMY—REVISED (2001)

In addition to content specifics, the subtext for each topic in this BoK also indicates the intended complexity level of the test questions for that topic. These levels are based on "Levels of Cognition" (from Bloom's Taxonomy—Revised, 2001) and are presented below in rank order, from least complex to most complex.

Remember

Recall or recognize terms, definitions, facts, ideas, materials, patterns, sequences, methods, principles, etc.

Understand

Read and understand descriptions, communications, reports, tables, diagrams, directions, regulations, etc.

Apply

Know when and how to use ideas, procedures, methods, formulas, principles, theories, etc.

Analyze

Break down information into its constituent parts and recognize their relationship to one another and how they are organized; identify sublevel factors or salient data from a complex scenario.

Evaluate

Make judgments about the value of proposed ideas, solutions, etc., by comparing the proposal to specific criteria or standards.

Create

Put parts or elements together in such a way as to reveal a pattern or structure not clearly there before; identify which data or information from a complex set is appropriate to examine further or from which supported conclusions can be drawn.

Part I

Organization-Wide Planning and Deployment

Chapter 1
Organization-Wide Considerations

Six Sigma is a quality program that, when all is said and done, improves your customers' experience, lowers your costs, and builds better leaders.

–Jack Welch

FUNDAMENTALS OF SIX SIGMA AND LEAN METHODOLOGIES

> Define and describe the value and goals of these approaches and describe the integration and complementary relationship between them. Identify and understand an organization's lean six sigma maturity model. (Understand)
>
> **Body of Knowledge I.A.1**

Six Sigma

In the first edition of this handbook, Kubiak and Benbow proffered this definition of Six Sigma:

> *Six Sigma is a fact-based, data-driven philosophy of improvement that values defect prevention over defect detection. It drives customer satisfaction and bottom-line results by reducing variation and waste, thereby promoting a competitive advantage. It applies anywhere variation and waste exist, and every employee should be involved.*

Linderman et al. (2003) define Six Sigma as "an organized and systematic method for strategic process improvement and new product and service development that relies on statistical methods and the scientific method to make dramatic reductions in customer defined defect rates."

Magnusson et al. (2003) define Six Sigma as "a business process that allows companies to drastically improve their bottom line by designing and monitoring everyday business activities in ways that minimize waste and resources while increasing customer satisfaction by some of its proponents."

Regardless of the exact definition, companies from a wide range of industries have found that when the Six Sigma approach is fully embraced, the enterprise thrives. What is this Six Sigma approach? Upon studying the various definitions, we notice the following common threads:

- The use of teams that are assigned well-defined projects having direct impact on the organization's bottom line.
- Training in statistical thinking at all levels with key people extensively trained in advanced statistics and project management. These key people are designated as Black Belts.
- An emphasis on the five-step problem-solving approach of Define, Measure, Analyze, Improve, and Control (DMAIC).
- A management environment that supports these initiatives as a business strategy.

The literature is replete with examples of projects that have returned high dollar amounts to the organizations involved. According to Harry and Schroeder (2000), in large organizations, each Black Belt brings savings of around $230,000, with many Black Belts completing four to six projects per year.

Six Sigma also has been described as a management philosophy, a problem-solving methodology, and a statistical standard of quality:

Philosophy

The philosophical perspective views all work as *processes*. Processes are a series of steps that take various inputs and produce outputs such as a product or a service. Understanding the relationship between the inputs and outputs is a key concept in Six Sigma. By controlling the inputs, an enterprise can control the outputs. This notion can be expressed as the concept of $Y = f(X)$, where Y is the output, X is the input or input(s) and f is the function, or process, which transforms the inputs into outputs, as shown in Figure 1.1.

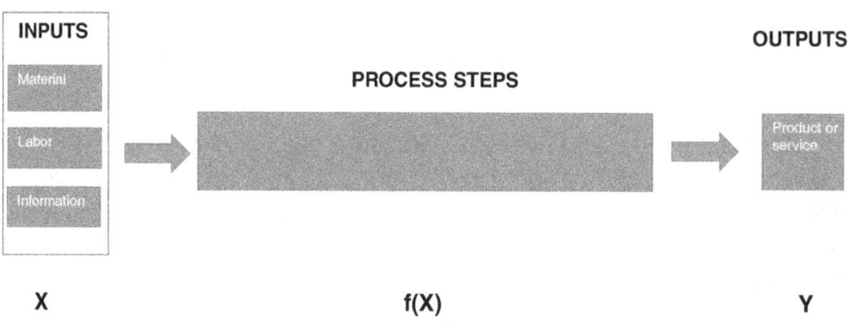

Figure 1.1 Inputs, process steps, and outputs.

Methodology

The methodological view of Six Sigma describes the rigorous five-step project-solving approach of Define, Measure, Analyze, Improve, and Control, or DMAIC, as shown in Figure 1.2. DMAIC defines the steps a Six Sigma practitioner is expected to follow, starting with identifying the problem and ending with implementing long-lasting solutions. While DMAIC is not the only Six Sigma methodology in use, it is certainly the most widely adopted and recognized.

Statistical Standard

In simple terms, a Six Sigma-level of quality performance translates into 3.4 defects per million opportunities (accounting for a 1.5-sigma shift in the mean). This concept is explained in more detail in Chapter 19.

Lean

Lean is a separate methodology and philosophy from Six Sigma. However, Six Sigma has incorporated several lean tools into its toolbox. Lean can trace its origins to post-WWII Japan, in which the recovering industry was forced to do more with less. NIST (2000) defines lean as "a systematic approach to identifying and eliminating waste through continuous improvement, flowing the product at the pull of the customer in pursuit of perfection."

At its heart, lean has five pillars, or principles:

1. *Specify value.* Define value from the customer's point of view.
2. *Identify the value stream.* Map the flow from customer order to delivery and payment, showing activities that add value for the customer, and those that do not. ASQ defines the term "non-value-added" as a process step or function that is not required for the direct achievement of process output. These steps or functions are identified and examined for potential elimination.

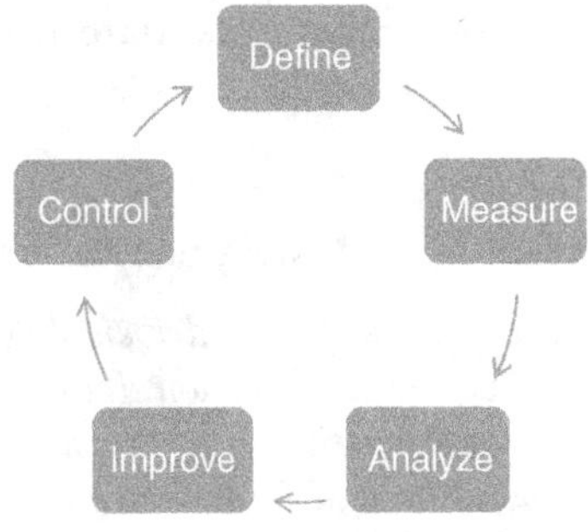

Figure 1.2 The DMAIC cycle.

3. *Create flow.* Concentrate on having pieces flow through the process without stopping or being put into inventory. Avoid creating large batches with the ultimate goal of one-piece flow.
4. *Pull from the customer.* Pulling from the customer means matching production output to customer demand. Here, organizations will only produce an item when it is required downstream in the flow.
5. *Seek perfection.* Unlike the Six Sigma goal of 3.4 defects per million opportunities, lean has zero defects as its goal. Organizations strive to continuously improve processes in the pursuit of perfection.

The term "lean thinking" expands the ideas originally used on the manufacturing floor into all areas of an organization. Lean is often thought of as a set of practices focused on the elimination of waste by concurrently reducing supplier, customer, and internal variability (Shah and Ward, 2007).

While Six Sigma emphasizes reducing variation, lean concentrates on reducing waste. These wastes can be categorized under the Eight Wastes: transportation, inventory, motion, waiting, overprocessing, over-production, defects, and skills. These wastes will be discussed in more detail in Chapter 23.

A lean organization is characterized by teamwork in which well-informed, cross-trained, and valued employees participate directly in improving processes. Work areas are clean and organized to allow for problems to be spotted more readily. Production systems are designed around flow instead of batch and queue, with the ultimate goal of one-piece flow. Work is centered around a pull system in which replenishment is based on what the customer has consumed. Finally, lead times are reduced due to concentration on efficient processing, setups, and scheduling.

Lean and Six Sigma have the same general purpose of providing the customer with the best possible quality, cost, and delivery, as well as a newer attribute, nimbleness. There is a great deal of overlap, and disciples of both disagree as to which techniques belong to which approach.

The most successful users of implementations have begun with the lean approach, making the workplace as efficient and effective as possible, reducing wastes, and using value stream maps to improve understanding and throughput. When process problems remain, the more technical Six Sigma statistical tools may be applied. Both methodologies require strong management support to ensure that the quality approaches become the standard way of doing business.

Lean and Six Sigma

A combined definition of lean and Six Sigma might read:

> *Lean Six Sigma is a process-focused, data-driven philosophy of improvement that values defect prevention over defect detection. It drives customer satisfaction and bottom-line results by reducing variation, waste, and cycle time while promoting the use of work standardization and flow, thereby creating a competitive advantage. It applies anywhere variation and waste exist, and every employee should be involved.*

Lean Six Sigma Maturity Model

Employing a maturity model for lean Six Sigma implementation helps organizations identify strengths and gaps in their lean Six Sigma deployment, and determine the steps required to move to the next stage of maturity. In addition, these maturity models can be used to benchmark against other companies (Raje, 2016). There are many models from which to choose. We outline three examples here.

Raje (2016) lists ten dimensions with which to measure an organization's lean Six Sigma maturity: leadership support, training, people, project selection, financial impact, reporting, software used, strategy maturing, beyond DMAIC, and culture change. The resulting scores are used to place an organization onto a five-stage progression:

1. Launch
2. Early Success
3. Scale and Replication
4. Institutionalization
5. Culture Transformation

During the Launch phase (ideally driven from the top down), training of belts is begun, often with the help of outside consultants. Here, the first set of improvement projects is launched.

The second phase is Early Success, in which the first projects have shown to improve processes and contribute to bottom-line results. These projects are often concentrated on low-hanging fruit.

Once the proof of concept is complete, the organization moves to the Scale and Replication phase of the maturity model. Here, projects are pursued in more areas of the company, more belts are trained, and more formal reporting mechanisms are in place.

The fourth phase is Institutionalization, in which Six Sigma is consistently applied to solve process problems. The problem-solving approaches are also extended beyond DMAIC and include Design for Six Sigma (DFSS) as well.

In the final phase, Cultural Transformation, Six Sigma has become engrained into the fabric of the organization.

He (2009) refined Raje's model to include a comprehensive scoring mechanism across seven dimensions, listed below.

1. Six Sigma leadership
2. Customer focus
3. Six Sigma strategy
4. Six Sigma project management
5. Evaluation and motivation
6. Six Sigma infrastructure
7. Business results

These dimensions were further broken down into 26 subcategories and 47 assessment items, as shown in Table 1.1. For each item, the organization is scored from 0 to 5, with 0 mapping to very poor and 5 being excellent. Scores for each dimension are tallied according to the points scale noted in the table.

<table>
<tr><th>Category Total</th><th>Subcategory</th><th>Item</th><th>Item Possible Points</th></tr>
<tr><td rowspan="4">1. Six Sigma Leadership</td><td rowspan="2">1.1 Organization vision and core values 20%</td><td>a. Vision</td><td>10</td></tr>
<tr><td>b. Core values</td><td>10</td></tr>
<tr><td rowspan="2">1.2 Executive leadership 80%</td><td>a. Visible resource support</td><td>40</td></tr>
<tr><td>b. Participation in Six Sigma</td><td>40</td></tr>
<tr><td colspan="3">Category Total</td><td>100</td></tr>
<tr><td rowspan="3">2. Customer focus</td><td>2.1 Voice of the Customer and organization's response to customer requirements</td><td>a. VOC and organization's response to customer's requirements</td><td>40</td></tr>
<tr><td rowspan="2">2.2 Customer satisfaction</td><td>a. Customer satisfaction metrics</td><td>20</td></tr>
<tr><td>b. Customer satisfaction measurement</td><td>20</td></tr>
<tr><td colspan="3">Category Total</td><td>80</td></tr>
<tr><td rowspan="4">3. Six Sigma Strategy</td><td rowspan="2">3.1 Six Sigma strategy development</td><td>a. Strategy development process</td><td>20</td></tr>
<tr><td>b. Six Sigma and organization strategy alignment</td><td>20</td></tr>
<tr><td rowspan="2">3.2 Six Sigma strategy deployment</td><td>a. Deployment process</td><td>20</td></tr>
<tr><td>b. Key performance metrics</td><td>20</td></tr>
<tr><td colspan="3">Category Total</td><td>80</td></tr>
<tr><td rowspan="2">4. Six Sigma project management</td><td rowspan="2">4.1 Project selection</td><td>a. Opportunity identification</td><td>15</td></tr>
<tr><td>b. Project selection procedure</td><td>15</td></tr>
</table>

Table 1.1 Six Sigma maturity model scoring template
Source: adapted from He, "Progress Report, Learn Something About Your Six Sigma Program's Maturity," Quality Progress, August 2009, pp. 22-28.

	4.2 Project team	a. Team building	15
		b. Team work	15
	4.3 Problem-solving procedure and tools	a. Problem-solving procedure	20
		b. Problems-solving tools	20
	4.4 Project plan and execution	a. Project plan	20
		b. Project process review	20
	4.5 Project evaluation	a. Project evaluation	30
Category Total			170
5. Evaluation and motivation	5.1 Performance evaluation system	a. Team performance assessment	30
		b. Performance of people in charge of Six Sigma deployment	10
	5.2 Motivation	a. Award and recognition	30
		b. Career development	30
Category Total			100
6. Six Sigma infrastructure	6.1 Six Sigma deployment structure	a. Structure	20
		b. Objective, responsibilities and resource allocation	20
	6.2 Six Sigma management system and procedures	a. Six Sigma management system and procedures	40
	6.3 Six Sigma training system	a. Training system and management	10
		b. Body of Knowledge	10
		c. Contribution of training to Six Sigma projects	10
	6.4 Communication and employee involvement	a. Communication	5
		b. Exchanging with outside organizations	5
		c. Employee involvement	20

Table 1.1 *Continued*

	6.5 Data management	a. Quality and availability of data	20
		b. Data-processing system	10
	6.6 Information system and sharing	a. Support of information system	10
		b. Knowledge management and sharing	20
	6.7 Six Sigma in supply chain	a. Deployment in supply chain	20
		b. Deployment with strategic partners	10
Category Total			230
7. Business results	7.1 Customer satisfaction results	a. Customer satisfaction results	40
	7.2 Financial results	a. Financial results	60
	7.3 Human resource development	a. Talent cultivation	20
		b. Employee satisfaction	20
	7.4 Internal business process improvement results	a. Internal business process improvement results	40
	7.5 Supply chain improvement results	a. Supply chain improvement results	30
	7.6 Corporate culture transformation results	a. Corporate culture transformation results	20
		b. Corporate social responsibility results	10
Category Total			240
Grand Total			1000

Table 1.1 *Continued*

Total Score	Category
< 400	Poor
400 to 600	Marginally qualified
601 to 800	Qualified
> 800	Excellent

Table 1.2 Six Sigma maturity categorization based on total maturity score.

The overall score is then calculated and categorized as shown in Table 1.2.

This model can be used to compare maturity across divisions of the same company.

SIX SIGMA, LEAN, AND CONTINUOUS IMPROVEMENT METHODOLOGIES

> Describe when to use six sigma instead of other problem-solving approaches and describe the importance of aligning six sigma objectives with organizational goals. Describe screening criteria and how such criteria can be used for the selection of six sigma projects, lean initiatives, and other continuous improvement methods. (Apply)
>
> **Body of Knowledge I.A.2**

The demarcation between Six Sigma and lean has blurred. We are hearing about terms such as "Lean Six Sigma" with greater frequency because process improvement requires aspects of both approaches to attain positive results. Six Sigma focuses on reducing process variation and enhancing process control, whereas lean—also known as *lean manufacturing*—drives out waste (non-value-added) and promotes work standardization and flow. Six Sigma practitioners should be well versed in both. More details of what is sometimes referred to as lean thinking are given in Chapters 25 and 26.

Using Lean Six Sigma

The two initiatives approach their common purpose from slightly different angles:

Lean focuses on waste reduction, whereas Six Sigma emphasizes variation reduction. Lean achieves its goals by using less technical, hands-on tools such as kaizen, workplace organization, and visual controls, whereas Six Sigma tends to use statistical data analysis, design of experiments, and hypothesis tests.

The most successful implementations of lean and Six Sigma are driven from the top down, with upper management having an awareness of both lean and Six Sigma principles. An oversight group with top management representation and support then defines and prioritizes problems and establishes teams to solve them. The oversight group is responsible for maintaining a systemic approach. It also provides the training, support, recognition, and rewards for teams. The following are examples of projects that would be assigned to teams across various industries. Note the wide array of tools used to realize the project outcomes.

EXAMPLE 1.1

Financial Services

Several customers of an accounting firm have complained about the amount of time the firm takes to perform an audit. The oversight group forms a team consisting of three auditors (one of them a lead auditor), two cost accountants, and two representatives from the firm's top customers. The oversight group asks the team to determine whether the lead time is indeed inordinate and to propose measures that will reduce it. The team begins by benchmarking a customer's internal audit process. After allowing for differences between internal and external audits, the team concludes that the lead time should be shortened. The team next constructs a value stream map (VSM), which displays work in progress, cycle times, and communication channels. A careful study of the map data shows several areas where lead time can be decreased.

EXAMPLE 1.2

Manufacturing

A team has been charged with improving the operation of a shuttle brazer. Automotive radiators are loaded onto this machine and shuttled through a series of gas-fired torches to braze the connections. The operator can adjust the shuttle speed, wait time, gas pressure, torch angle, and torch height. There is a tendency to adjust one or more of these settings to produce leak-free joints, but no one can agree on the best settings. The team decides to conduct a two-level full-factorial experiment with four replicates during a planned plant shutdown.

EXAMPLE 1.3

Public Transportation

Kuvvetli and Firuzan (2019) present a case study in which the DMAIC methodology is used to reduce traffic accidents involving public buses. Upon collecting data from bus accidents over the previous year, the team used Pareto analysis to identify the top three causes of traffic accidents: driver error, route type, and bus type. A logistic regression analysis was used to predict the probability of accidents based on various conditions and driver behaviors. Based on the analysis, the team implemented driver training and made changes to accident-prone routes. The accident rate then decreased from 4.73 per 100,000 bus km to 3.77 per 100,000 bus km.

EXAMPLE 1.4

Food Service

Chen and Chen (2016) describe how Six Sigma methods were used to improve customer satisfaction at a university campus restaurant. A Pareto analysis revealed that the top three customer complaints were long wait time (42.5%), food quality defects (19.8%), and missing meals (14.4%). A Six Sigma project was launched to address the top customer complaint, wait time. During the Measure phase of the project, the team found that the average wait time was 21 minutes, with over 10% of customers waiting longer than 30 minutes. In the Analyze phase, the team brainstormed causes of the excessive wait times using a fishbone diagram. The causes were broadly categorized as Staff, Facilities, Preparation Methods, and Operation Procedures. Countermeasures were devised for each of the causes identified. For example, under Staff, it was found that staffing was uneven: There were an inadequate number of staff at peak dining times and too many during times of low demand. Schedules were thus revised to match customer demand. Under Operation Procedures, the team found that the kitchen facilities were disorganized, and ingredients were poorly labeled. A 5S (sort, straighten, shine, standardize, and sustain) exercise was conducted on the kitchen to assure that the ingredients and supplies were easily accessible when needed. The countermeasures implemented resulted in average wait time of 18.6 minutes, with only 35.4% waiting for more than 21 minutes, and only 7% waiting longer than half an hour.

EXAMPLE 1.5

Manufacturing

Cabrita et al. (2016) describe a bolt manufacturer that aimed to increase its manufacturing capacity. The team developed a value stream map of production flow, starting with delivery of raw materials, through fabrication, heat treatment, surface treatment, sorting a packaging, and final storage and shipping. The VSM revealed large variation in stock levels between the raw material pickling process and stamping processes. A Pareto analysis of downtime confirmed the primary cause of downtime to be lack of raw material, which was housed in another building. A kanban system was instituted that allowed the production of the material to be synchronized with demand. The kanban system reduced the average stock level between the two workstations by 50% and there was a 10% decrease of downtime due to raw material shortages.

EXAMPLE 1.6

Software Development

A company is plagued with failure to meet deadlines for software projects. A team is formed to study and improve the design/code/test process. The team splits into three sub-teams, one for each phase. The design sub-team discovers that this crucial phase endures excess variation in the form of customer needs. This occurs because customers change the requirements and because sometimes the software package is designed to serve multiple customers whose needs aren't known until late in the design phase. The sub-team helps the designers develop a generic Gantt chart for the design phase itself. It also establishes a better process for determining potential customer needs. The design group decides to develop configurable software packages that permit the user to specify the functions needed.

The coding sub-team finds that those responsible for writing code are often involved with multiple projects, leading to tension between project managers. This results in spurts of activity and concentration being split across several projects with the resulting inefficiencies. The sub-team collaborates with the project manager to establish a format for prioritization matrices, which provide better guidance for coders.

The testing sub-team determines that there is poor communication between designers and testers regarding critical functions, especially those that appeared late in the design phase. After discussions with those involved, it is decided that for each project a representative of the testing group should be an ex officio member of the design group.

EXAMPLE 1.7

Healthcare

Arthur (2016) describes how a hospital reduced lab turnaround time using lean methods. The team conducted a 5S exercise (sort, straighten, shine, standardize, and sustain) in the lab, removing unneeded supplies, expired materials, and broken equipment, and standardizing where supplies and instruments were stored. The team then redesigned the process and lab layout using a detailed process map and a spaghetti diagram that tracked the movement of lab technicians and samples. Staff movement was reduced by 54%, sample travel was reduced by 55%, and floor space was reduced by 17%.

EXAMPLE 1.8

Banking

Vijaya Sunder (2016) details how a bank rejected an excessive number of account applications from its customers. The goal was to reduce the rejection rate from 10% to 4.5% within six months. The team created a detailed swim lane chart of the application acceptance processes. This chart revealed overprocessing and transportation waste from multiple levels of inspection and physical movement of account application forms from branches to the central office. A measurement system analysis for attributes, attribute agreement analysis, was then performed to determine the repeatability, reproducibility, and accuracy of judging a customer's qualification for approval. Overall repeatability and reproducibility were each 80%, and accuracy was 50%. A fishbone diagram was created to list potential causes of the higher rejection percentage, with categories being sales, process, service providers, and policy. Pareto analysis showed that 60% of the rejections occurred due to signature-related and names-related mismatches. Several improvements were implemented, including installing new signature matching software and changes in the name mismatch policy. After improvement, the rejection percentage was reduced to 3.4%.

Screening Criteria

Six Sigma projects are aligned with the company's strategic goals, which stem from the enterprise's customer requirements and the organization's business strategy. Organizational goals must be consistent with the long-term strategies of the enterprise. The enterprise is driven by its long-term strategic objectives and its customer requirements. These in turn inform the organization's goals. Each Six Sigma project should be aligned with the company's goals, which in turn feed into the business strategy and serve to meet customer requirements, as shown in Figure 1.3.

Once Six Sigma projects have started making a positive impact, there will usually be more project ideas generated than an organization can undertake at one time. Some sort of project proposal format may be needed, along with an associated process for project selection. It is common to require that project proposals include precise statements of the problem definition and some preliminary measures of the seriousness of the problem, including its impact on the goals of the enterprise.

A project-selection group that usually includes Master Black Belts, Black Belts, organizational champions, and key executive supporters establishes a set of criteria for project selection. The project selection criteria may include customer impact, return on investment, ease of implementation, and availability of resources, among others. Projects can then be compared according to these criteria using a prioritization matrix, presented in Chapter 13.

One key to gauging both the performance and the health of an organization and its processes lies with its selection and use of metrics. These are usually converted to financial terms such as return on investment, cost reduction, and increases in sales and/or profit. More details on project metrics are covered in Chapter 11.

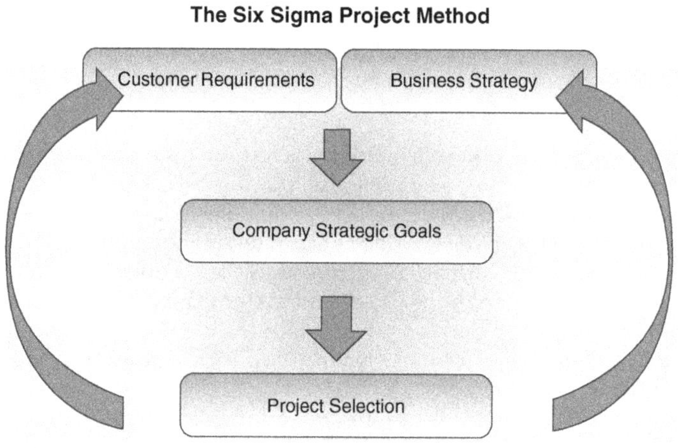

Figure 1.3 The Six Sigma project method.
Source: Adapted from Mary McShane-Vaughn, *Lean Six Sigma Leadership Tools* (Folsom, CA: University Training Partners Press, 2017), p. 23.

In some companies the project-selection group assigns some projects to Six Sigma teams and other projects to teams using other methodologies. For example, problems involving extensive data analysis and improvements using designed experiments would be assigned to a Six Sigma team, whereas a process improvement not requiring these techniques might be assigned to a lean manufacturing team employing kaizen tools. Details on new product design should follow the Design for Six Sigma (DFSS) guidelines as detailed in Chapters 31 and 32.

RELATIONSHIPS AMONG BUSINESS SYSTEMS AND PROCESSES

> Describe the interactive relationships among business systems, processes, and internal and external stakeholders, and the impact those relationships have on business systems. (Understand)
>
> **Body of Knowledge I.A.3**

Business Systems

A business system is designed to implement a process or a set of processes. The business system must coordinate the often-conflicting forces on the design and implementation of its processes. This means that the business system must consider the goals and objectives of the enterprise as it provides resources and guidance. Business systems make certain that process inputs are in the right place at the right time so that each step of the process has the resources it needs. A business system must also have as its goal the continual improvement of its processes, products, and services. To this end, the business system is responsible for collecting and analyzing data from the process and other sources that will help in the continual incremental improvement of process outputs.

Each part of a system can be broken into a series of processes, each of which may have subprocesses. The subprocesses may be further broken into steps. In addition, the business system imposes performance expectations on the process and its designers in terms of safety, cost, quality, and delivery. The performance of a process, in turn, is a determining factor in the success of its business system. The Six Sigma Black Belt is often called on to help teams improve process performance. Much of this handbook is devoted to presenting tools that can be used in response to such requests.

Processes

A process is a series of steps that takes inputs and converts them into a product or service. A process is often diagrammed with a flowchart depicting inputs, the path that material or information follows, and outputs. An example of a flowchart for a payroll process is shown in Figure 1.4. Understanding and improving processes is a key part of every Six Sigma project.

A Six Sigma project is completed using five clearly defined steps: Define, Measure, Analyze, Improve, and Control, or DMAIC. These steps constitute the cycle Six Sigma practitioners use to manage problem-solving projects. The steps help practitioners assure that data-driven decisions are made, root causes are identified, improvements are vetted, and controls are placed on the process, as well as to assure that data is driving improvement decisions. The individual parts of the DMAIC cycle are explained in Chapters 10-30.

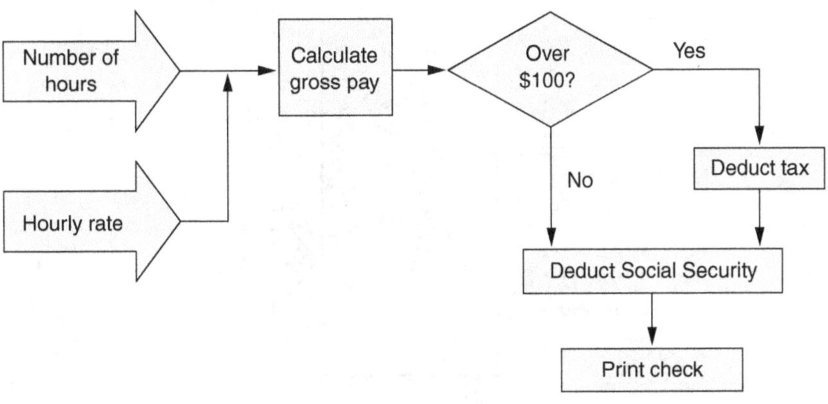

Figure 1.4 Example of a process flow chart.

Internal and External Stakeholders

Once a product or service has been designed, the next step is to develop a process to produce it. In some fields the process is referred to as a set of procedures or routines. Regardless of the name used, process design is a critical step for all stakeholders. As the terms suggest, *internal stakeholders* are departments or individuals within the organization and *external stakeholders* are entities outside the organization that will be affected by the change or have expectations concerning the change. Stakeholders and their expectations may include:

- The *customer* who needs a process that provides a quality output in an acceptable time frame and at an acceptable cost.
- The *producer* who needs a process that uses reasonably priced inputs and that reliably generates output that meets or exceeds customer expectations.
- The *employees* who need a process that is well designed, efficient, repeatable, safe, and effective.
- The *marketplace* that requires a quality product or service at a competitive price as an output from a process that is agile enough to meet changing customer requirements.
- The *suppliers* who need a dependable market for their products that are the inputs to the process.
- The *regulatory agencies* that require proof of the process's efficacy, safety, and adherence to standards.

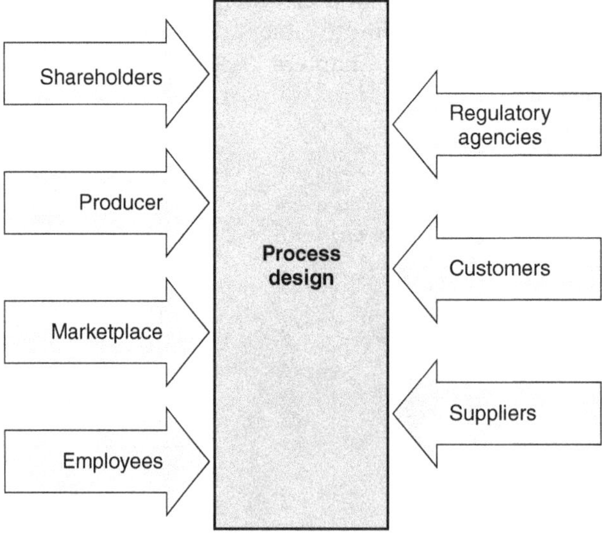

Figure 1.5 Some of the forces impacting process design.

- The *shareholders* who require a return on their investment.

These stakeholders can sometimes generate conflicting forces on the process, as shown in Figure 1.5.

Stakeholders are presented in more detail in Chapter 3.

STRATEGIC PLANNING AND DEPLOYMENT FOR INITIATIVES

> Define the importance of identification and strategic planning of six sigma projects and lean initiatives as part of the business planning process taking into consideration outcomes such as return on investment and measured intangibles. Use strengths, weaknesses, opportunities, and threats analysis (SWOT), contingency planning, and business continuity planning to enhance strategic planning and deployment. (Apply)
>
> **Body of Knowledge I.A.4**

Strategic planning must be a priority of top management. For strategic planning to be successful, senior management must be actively engaged in the process. Successful strategic planning must create a line of sight from strategic to tactical to operational activities. This does not mean that individuals executing activities at the lowest level of the organization must understand the details of the strategic plan. However, it does mean that their actions are traceable back to the strategic plan itself.

In general, the strategic planning process involves three activities:

1. Studying the current state (that is, the business environment in which we operate)
2. Envisioning the ideal future state (that is, where we'd like to be in three to five years)
3. Planning the path (that is, how we'll get from here to there)

Various strategic planning tools can enhance the strategic planning and deployment operation. These are described in the following subsections.

Return on Investment

A key component of Six Sigma project is delivering bottom-line results, either in increased efficiency or market share, or both. A financial results section is included in each project charter. Return on investment, or ROI, is used as a criterion for choosing which projects to pursue. In its simplest form, ROI can be calculated by dividing the expected net financial benefits (Income – Cost) of the project by the expected cost. This ratio is then multiplied by 100%, as shown in Equation 1.1.

Equation 1.1

$$\text{ROI} = \frac{(\text{Income} - \text{Cost})}{\text{Cost}} \times 100\%$$

Return on investment can be negative, which means that the cost of the project outweighs the income generated from the project. A return on investment equal to 30%, for example, means that the project will bring in financial benefits that cover the cost of the project plus an additional 30%. This metric will be covered in more detail in Chapter 5.

Measured Intangibles

In addition to hard dollar savings, Six Sigma projects can bring intangible financial benefits, also referred to as soft savings, such as improved customer satisfaction and goodwill. These benefits can be measured in several ways, such as customer satisfaction surveys, net promoter scores, complaints and returns reports, warranty charges, and market share.

SWOT Analysis

A strengths, weaknesses, opportunities, and threats (SWOT) analysis is an effective strategic planning tool applicable to a business or project objective.

Strengths and weaknesses are identified with respect to the internal capabilities of an organization. They provide an introspective view. Strengths and weaknesses should not be considered opposites.

On the other hand, opportunities and threats look outside the organization. Quite simply, we are trying to identify opportunities for the organization and threats to the organization.

When analyzing a SWOT, the question to ask is, "How can the organization leverage its strengths or improve its weaknesses to take advantage of the opportunities while mitigating or eliminating the threats?"

EXAMPLE 1.9

A private higher-education institution has experienced declining enrollment for four consecutive years, particularly from the two major cities in the state where it is located. This declining enrollment has impacted cash flow. The president is feeling pressure from the foundation board, which wants answers as to why the enrollment levels are declining. The industrial engineering department has proposed a Six Sigma project aimed at improving the enrollment rate for students from the two major cities. As the department begins its study of the current situation, it produces the SWOT analysis shown in figure 1.6. The team's next steps would be to devise a plan to leverage its internal academic and fundraising strengths to take advantage of its opportunities and to mitigate its weaknesses.

	Strengths	Weaknesses
Internal	• High academic entrance requirements • Strong general education program • High percentage of full-time faculty • New endowments for faculty chairs • Fundraising goals are being met each year • Well-designed internship and study abroad opportunities	• Print communications for prospective students are bland and generic • Recruitment staff is too passive in contacting prospective students • Uneven implementation of assessment and program review methods • Student-centered customer focus is not recognized throughout the institution
	Opportunities	**Threats**
External	• Metropolitan area location has population advantages • Area corporations offer tuition reimbursements • Reputable business program with a global studies focus is not marketed as well as it could be	• The number of traditional-age prospective students is expected to decline • With the cost of education escalating, community colleges have recently become viable competitors • Public universities have undertaken significant marketing efforts to position themselves as comparable in experience to private colleges

Figure 1.6 SWOT analysis for Example 1.9.

Contingency and Continuity Planning

Tools and techniques discussed earlier in this chapter enable long-range planning, but a crisis that occurs in minutes can change everything if the organization isn't prepared. A contingency plan (also called a *Plan B*) can be divided into three topics:

1. Crisis management
   - Natural disasters
   - Terrorism

- Pandemics
- On-the-job injuries/accidents
- Positive events such as a huge order that can't be met with current resources

2. Business continuity
   - Loss of key personnel
   - Sudden change in customer/supplier/marketplace
   - Strike by bargaining unit personnel
3. Asset security
   - Loss of intellectual property or other assets
   - Loss of data
   - Mismanagement (neglect, theft)
   - Product recall

A contingency planning team should address each of these areas using the following steps:

1. Use a cause-and-effect diagram for each of the areas to generate lists of events that could cause disruption of business.
2. Prioritize the items. One method might be to:
   a. Assign each item a score of 1 to 10 to reflect the impact on the business, using 10 for the most impactful.
   b. Assign each item a score of 1 to 10 to reflect the probability of occurrence, using 10 as the most probable.
   c. Multiply the two scores to provide a priority index.
3. Beginning with the highest-priority items, develop a plan for each that will address the following:
   a. *Reaction.* How to protect people and property during the event. Include activities like evacuation, accounting for all personnel, and equipment damage assessment.
   b. *Continuity.* How to maintain the business after the event. Include activities like contracting out some work, temporary warehousing, logistics, security measures, and data back-up and recovery procedures.

Chapter 2

Leadership

A leader is one who knows the way, goes the way, and shows the way.

—John C. Maxwell

ROLES AND RESPONSIBILITIES

> Describe the roles and responsibilities of executive leadership, champions, sponsors, process owners, master black belts, black belts, and green belts in driving six sigma and lean initiatives. Understand the importance of coaching multiple levels of leadership and belts on appropriate six sigma tools and techniques. Understand the importance of finance and its role supporting a project and confirming its outcome. Describe how each group influences project deployment in terms of providing or managing resources, enabling changes in organizational structure, and supporting communications about the purpose and deployment of the initiatives. (Understand)
>
> **Body of Knowledge I.B.1**

The definition and role of leadership have undergone major shifts in recent years. The leadership model that is most effective in the deployment of Six Sigma envisions the leader as a problem solver. The leader's job is to implement systems that identify and solve problems that impede the effectiveness of the processes. This requires two steps:

1. Allocate resources to support team-based problem identification and solution
2. Allocate resources to install corrections and ensure that the problems do not recur

This concept of leadership implies a good understanding of team dynamics and Six Sigma problem-solving techniques. Deployment of a culture-changing initiative such as the adoption of Six Sigma rarely succeeds without engaged, visible, and active senior-level management involvement. Initiatives starting in the lowest levels of the organization seldom gain the critical mass necessary to sustain and fuel their own existence.

Enterprises with successful Six Sigma programs have found it useful to delineate roles and responsibilities for people involved in project activity. Although titles vary somewhat from company to company, the following list represents the general thinking regarding each role.

Executive Leadership

An executive is a company leader, often a White Belt, who will drive the implementation and set the tone for Six Sigma in an organization. Successful implementations of Six Sigma have unwavering support from the company-level executives. Executives demonstrate their support for Six Sigma through their communications and actions.

Champion or Sponsor

A champion or sponsor is a Six Sigma role associated with a senior manager who ensures that their projects are aligned with the organization's strategic goals and priorities, provides the Six Sigma team with resources, removes organizational barriers for the team, participates in project tollgate reviews, and serves as the team's backer. A champion is typically a top-level manager who is familiar with the benefits of Six Sigma strategies and provides support for the program.

Process Owner

A process owner is a Six Sigma role associated with an individual who coordinates the various functions and work activities at all levels of a process, has the authority or ability to make changes in the process as required, and manages the entire process cycle to ensure performance effectiveness.

Process owners are those managers who are responsible for a process and who have the authority to make decisions on process changes. It is only natural that managers responsible for a particular process frequently will have a vested interest in keeping things as they are. They should be involved in any discussion of change. In most cases, they are willing to support changes but need to see evidence that recommended improvements are for the long-term good of the enterprise. A team member with a "show me" attitude can make a very positive contribution to the team. Process owners should be provided with opportunities for training at least to the Green Belt level.

Master Black Belts

The Master Black Belt (MBB) is a Six Sigma role associated with an individual typically assigned full-time to train and mentor Black Belts. In addition, MBBs lead the strategy to ensure that the improvement projects chartered are the right strategic projects for the organization. Master Black Belts are usually the authorizing body to certify White, Yellow, Green, and Black Belts. Master Black Belts have advanced knowledge in statistics, process improvement, and project management, and provide technical support to the Black Belts.

Black Belts

The Black Belt (BB) is a Six Sigma role associated with an individual typically assigned full-time to train and mentor Green Belts. Black Belts also lead improvement projects using specified methodologies such as DMAIC, and Design for Six Sigma (DFSS).

In many larger organizations, Black Belts work full-time on Six Sigma projects. These projects are often prioritized based on their potential fiscal impact on the enterprise and their alignment with the organization's objectives. Individuals designated as Black Belts must be thoroughly trained in statistical methods and be proficient at leading teams to achieve project goals. Breyfogle (2003) suggests that the number of Black Belts should equal about 1% of the number of employees in the organization.

Green Belts

A Green Belt (GB) is a Six Sigma role associated with an individual who retains their regular position within the firm but is trained in the tools, methods, and skills necessary to conduct Six Sigma improvement projects either individually or as part of larger teams. A Green Belt usually works under the direction of a Black Belt, assisting with all phases of project operation. Green Belts typically are less adept at statistics and other more technical problem-solving techniques than Black Belts.

Yellow Belts

A Yellow Belt (YB) is a Six Sigma role associated with an individual who is familiar with many problem-solving tools and can serve as a valuable project team member. Yellow Belts are assigned to work under Green or Black Belts on a team.

White Belts

A White Belt (WB) is a Six Sigma role associated with an individual who has a basic understanding of Six Sigma principles. Executives who are White Belts can advocate for implementation across the organization and can serve as project champions.

Finance

Because Six Sigma projects have an emphasis on improving bottom-line results for the organization, the finance department is a natural partner in the effort. Finance plays a vital role in helping a team establish accurate baseline financial metrics, vetting estimated savings, and working to procure funds for process improvement. Each Six Sigma project should have sign- off from the finance department to assure that proposed cost savings are realistic and achievable estimates.

Coaches

Most Six Sigma teams comprise a cross-functional team with members having varying degrees of experience with the Six Sigma project cycle and tools. Because of their considerable experience, Master Black Belts and Black Belts serve as coaches, providing guidance on selecting and using proper tools and techniques. This guidance may include on-the-spot training of a tool, facilitating a brainstorming session, or advising a team leader when he or she is unsure of next steps. In addition, a coach may help a team prepare for tollgate meetings and serve as a sounding board for project-related issues. A coach may also be involved in resolving team conflicts.

ORGANIZATIONAL BARRIERS

> Describe how an organization's structure and culture can impact six sigma projects. Identify common causes of six sigma failures, including lack of management support and lack of resources. (Apply)
>
> **Body of Knowledge I.B.2**

Leaders must understand that change, like any movement, generates friction and resistance. Awareness of this resistance and the ability to mitigate it are important skills.

Organization Structure

Many organizations have a structure and culture that center around maintaining business as usual. A highly centralized organizational structure tends to have more of this inertia than a decentralized one. Such a structure and culture tend to resist any change. An unintended consequence is that fundamental improvements are difficult to achieve. Some symptoms of such a system are listed here, with suggested remedies.

Symptom: A system that requires many signatures for expenditures discourages or delays improvements, particularly when signatories are busy or travel frequently.

Proposed Remedies:

- A multiple-signature e-mail procedure can be instituted.
- Teams can be empowered with budgets.

Symptom: Adherence to an "if it ain't broke, don't fix it" philosophy serves as a barrier to change.

Proposed Remedies:

- A company begins to encourage employees to stop the assembly line when they see a problem or an opportunity for improvement. A wall clock reflects the number of minutes the line was stopped during the shift. They try to have 30 to 40 minutes of downtime per shift, because only when the line is down are they solving problems and making improvements.
- Everyone must understand that an important part of their job is to make improvements. Incentives for these improvements must be provided.

Symptom: Managers are not properly trained as change agents.

Proposed Remedy: All personnel with management responsibilities need to understand the basics of change management.

Project champions are often the ones best able to break roadblocks. In many situations, the motto "No champion, no project" is valid. Typically, the champion is at an executive level of the organization, and often a White Belt. Sometimes, the champion is the process owner.

Organization Culture

There was a time when a manager's job was to keep things running the way they always did—in other words, to prevent change. Today it is widely understood that change is critical to an enterprise, and the management of changing processes has become a science of its own. Some common errors that managers need to avoid include:

- Inadequate communication about coming changes. Management may assume that a single memo or meeting is appropriate, but people need to have time and an opportunity to digest and react to changes.
- Assigning the change-management function to people without the preparation or resources to execute it.
- Improper or inadequate explanation of the change. Employees tend to fear and resist change that they do not understand.

For best results, a team with executive leadership should be charged with leading the change and advising top management of necessary actions. Effective communication is essential to success. The following steps are typical in the management of change:

1. Communicate the need for change. Use data regarding market share, competition, and prospects for expansion. Benchmarking (see Chapter 4) is a useful tool.
2. Communicate a view of a future state with a successful change.

3. Establish and communicate near-term, intermediate-term, and long-term goals and metrics.
4. Identify and use forces for change; identify and reduce barriers to change.
5. Communicate early successes and recognize those responsible.
6. Lock in improvements.
7. Establish the need to be a nimble, changing organization.

Causes for Six Sigma Failures

Many Six Sigma implementations do not perform as well as expected. In fact, many fail. Generally, Six Sigma failure can be traced to a failure in leadership and/or a failure in implementation.

Six Sigma is driven from the top down, so continued support of executive leadership is necessary for Six Sigma to thrive. If the executive leadership in an organization treats Six Sigma as a fad, there may be initial enthusiasm but no lasting commitment.

Implementation failures can take the form of faulty rollout of training programs, arbitrary requirements set for teams, lack of resources, or poor choice of projects.

Training Programs

A company may train so many employees in Six Sigma at the beginning of implementation that not every belt can be assigned a project. With no project to work on, the employees' new skills fade, and momentum is lost.

Arbitrary Requirements

Requiring Black Belts to complete a set number of projects per year or to save a minimum dollar amount may lead to unintended consequences. For example, if management requires a Black Belt to complete a set number of projects in a year, he or she may gravitate toward projects that can be completed quickly, but don't have much monetary or customer-facing impact. Or, to meet minimum savings requirements, Six Sigma teams may incorporate cost avoidance or be forced to be creative in their accounting, while not adding real dollars to the bottom line.

Lack of Resources

A company can have too many employees assigned to work on Six Sigma projects, to the detriment of their other, customer-facing jobs. Or, overly stretched resources may result in teams abandoning projects due to lack of time and energy.

Poor Project Selection

In addition, projects may be selected that are not focused or are not tied to the strategic plan. Another common implementation failure is to assign root causes and solutions to projects prematurely. For example, a team could be given the project, "Reduce defects on production line #2 by installing a new welding robot." This project skips the first three DMAIC steps and lands on Improve. Assigning a root cause and solution without doing the D and M and A work may result in simply treating a symptom, or suboptimizing the process. These suboptimal solutions are then incorrectly blamed on Six Sigma.

In some cases, the solution to the problem is well understood. In this situation, a project would be classified as a JDI, or Just Do It project, and there is no need to go through the DMAIC cycle.

Gray and Anantatmula (2009) surveyed Six Sigma project leaders currently working in the healthcare, information technology, and manufacturing fields. Two-thirds of the respondents had experienced at least one Six Sigma project failure. Reasons given for these failures mirror those given above and included:

- Failure to identify and mange project stakeholders and their expectations
- Inadequate project selection process
- Inability to align projects with critical organizational priorities
- Lack of project management facilitation
- Lack of leadership
- Scope creep
- Availability of project resources
- Lack of accountability on the part of project team members.

Critical Success Factors

We have listed how Six Sigma programs can fail. Now we focus on what factors can create Six Sigma success. Maneesh et al. (2011) identify the top five criteria for Six Sigma readiness as:

1. Leadership
2. Customer focus
3. Measurement and process
4. Systems and control
5. People management

Tlapa et al. (2014) conducted a meta-analysis of 234 studies of Six Sigma implementation spanning a wide range of industries and company sizes. They identified the top ten most frequently cited *success factors* for Six Sigma implementation:

1. Top management involvement and commitment
2. Training and education
3. Cultural change/change management

4. Team communication
5. Project leadership/leadership
6. Customer focus/customer involvement
7. Project management skills
8. Team involvement and commitment
9. Project selection and prioritization
10. Choosing the right team

Laureani and Antony (2012) conducted a survey of 600 lean Six Sigma professionals with 101 responses. The top ten success factors found from their study include:

1. Management commitment
2. Organizational culture
3. Linking LSS to business strategy
4. Leadership styles
5. Communication
6. Linking LSS to customers
7. Awareness
8. Selection of LSS staff
9. Data-based approach
10. LSS project selection/prioritization

CHANGE MANAGEMENT

> Apply and facilitate change management techniques, including stakeholder analysis, readiness assessments, proactive change management, and communication plans to overcome barriers and drive organization-wide change. (Apply)
>
> **Body of Knowledge I.B.2**

Stakeholder Analysis

The success of any proposed change depends on the buy-in by impacted stakeholders. Internal and external stakeholders should be involved in the problem-

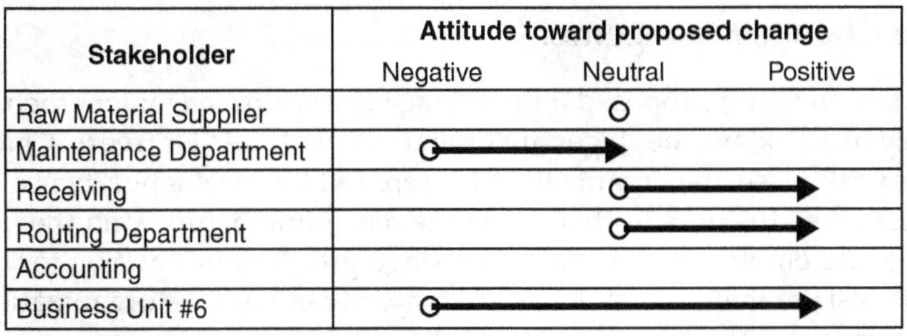

Stakeholder	Attitude toward proposed change		
	Negative	Neutral	Positive
Raw Material Supplier		O	
Maintenance Department	O ⟶	⟶	
Receiving		O ⟶	⟶
Routing Department		O ⟶	⟶
Accounting			
Business Unit #6	O ⟶	⟶	⟶

Figure 2.1 Example analysis of stakeholders' attitudes.

solving and decision-making processes to the extent possible. At a minimum, they need to be in the communication loop from the beginning. Additional information on stakeholder analysis can be found in Chapter 3.

Through interviews, surveys, group meetings, and any other ways deemed feasible, the stakeholders' attitudes toward the proposed change should be assessed and analyzed. A format for summarizing results is shown in Figure 2.1, where the current attitude of the stakeholder is indicated by the open circle, and the arrow shows where the attitude needs to be for the project to be successful. Change management is often the most challenging aspect of process improvement.

Readiness Assessment

Understanding the causes of resistance to change and taking steps to address them are crucial to the success of the proposed change. Determining organizational readiness for change involves assessment of several traits. This assessment tends to be subjective, and the traits will vary depending on the situation. Figure 2.2 displays an example of a readiness assessment. The readiness assessment provides guidance regarding communication and information decisions.

Trait	Score (1–10)
Alignment with organizational goals	9
Awareness of the need for change	3
Commitment to change	4
Openness to change	6
Willingness to be involved in change	5
Willingness to enable change	3

Figure 2.2 Example of a readiness assessment.

Proactive Change Management

Kurt Lewin (1947) proposed a three-stage change management theory that is still widely used today. The stages are often referred to as "Unfreeze, Change, Freeze." In the first phase, the organization is prepared for the change, hence "unfreezing" its current status quo. In this phase the reasoning behind and the benefits of the change are emphasized. Ideally, this stage provides motivation for the change. It is at this stage that Lewin's *force-field analysis* can help the organization lay out the plan to prepare the organization for change.

In a force-field analysis, the desired state is written in the middle of the whiteboard, and then the team brainstorms driving forces that will help move the organization toward the change listed on the left-hand side. The team then brainstorms the restraining forces, or forces that will impede the change, and lists those on the right-hand side. After the forces are identified, their strength can be rated from 1 (weak) to 5 (strong). The ratings for the driving and restraining forces are then added up, as shown in Figure 2.3. The team then evaluates each force to identify ones that can be influenced. The team then develops a strategy to mitigate the restraining forces and strengthen the driving forces. The exercise ends with a list of action steps to effect changes to the forces.

Common driving forces for a lean Six Sigma project may include management support, increased efficiency, lower costs, and increased customer satisfaction. Examples of common restraining forces include organizational culture, resistance to change, time and resource constraints, and training costs.

The second phase in the theory is Change. Lewin characterizes change not as an event, but a process (Connelly, 2020). Finally, once the change is achieved, the organization moves to the final stage and "freezes" or locks in the change to make it part of the new culture.

A force-field analysis can be performed at any level and is useful when there are two opposing sides to an issue that need to be considered. Identifying which forces can and cannot be changed will help reduce wasted energy. Focusing energy on removing or reducing forces that are restraining change or ensuring that the driving forces are maintained increase the team's probability of success.

Another change management model was proposed by Hiatt (2003), consisting of five necessary elements for achieving change, called the ADKAR model:

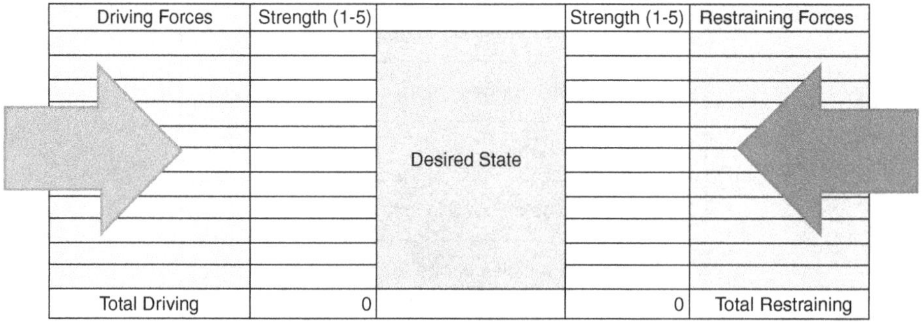

Driving Forces
Strength (1-5)
Strength (1-5)
Restraining Forces
Desired State
Total Driving
0
0
Total Restraining

Figure 2.3 Force-field analysis template.

1. Awareness of the need to change
2. Desire to support and participate in the change
3. Knowledge of how to change
4. Ability to implement the change
5. Reinforcement to sustain the change

Kotter (1996) proposed an eight-step strategy for change management:

1. Create a sense of urgency
2. Build a guiding coalition
3. Form a strategic vision and initiatives
4. Enlist a large volunteer force for change
5. Enable action by removing barriers
6. Create short-term wins
7. Sustain acceleration
8. Institute changes

Communication Plans

The Six Sigma Black Belt should develop the ability to effectively communicate the strategic need for change. Communication and transparency are so critical to the success of a proposed change that they require a formal plan. Key issues include the following:

- All stakeholders should be informed of the need for the change at the earliest possible time. This may involve meetings, articles in newsletters, or the use of social media.
- Involvement in determining the need and the requisite change to meet the need aids communication. Involvement, even by means of representatives, can help.
- Continuous communication of the status throughout the change cycle is key to maintaining support.

Additional information on communication plans can be found in Chapter 7.

Part II

Organizational Process Management and Measures

Chapter 3
Impact on Stakeholders

Change is not made without inconvenience, even from worse to better.

–Samuel Johnson

> Describe the impact six sigma projects can have on customers, suppliers, and other stakeholders. (Understand)
>
> **Body of Knowledge II.A**

This chapter will address stakeholders from two perspectives: the impact projects can have on stakeholders, and the impact stakeholders can have on projects.

IDENTIFYING STAKEHOLDERS

A stakeholder can be defined as anyone with an interest in a project, or anyone who can effect a change, or be affected by an action or change. Stakeholders may be individuals or groups, and internal or external to the organization. Notice that this definition may include workers up, down, across, and outside the organization. Stakeholders may be internal customers, external customers, end users, suppliers, distributors, frontline workers, administrators, government entities, and regulatory bodies, for example. It is best to err on the side of inclusion in identifying potential stakeholders. The following questions can be used to identify project stakeholders (Tague, 2005):

- Who might receive benefits from this project?
- Who might experience negative effects from the project?
- Who might have to change behavior?
- Who has goals that align with the project goals?
- Who has goals that conflict with the project goals?
- Who has responsibility for actions or decisions concerning the project?
- Who has resources or skills that are important to this project?
- Who has expectations for this project?

STAKEHOLDER ANALYSIS

It behooves the Black Belt to conduct a stakeholder analysis in the Define stage of a project, casting the net as wide as possible to capture all the people and groups who will be affected by the project. Too often, well-intentioned projects fail because the leaders did not consider the people involved. A thorough stakeholder analysis can help the project leader anticipate pushback or reluctance, identify key players who can contribute to the team, and assure that changes brought by the project will be fair and well received.

Once the project stakeholders have been identified, a template such as the one shown in Table 3.1 below can be used to capture relevant information about the stakeholders:

- *Stakeholder.* The list provided above is an excellent starting point for identifying stakeholders. There are two types of stakeholders: primary and secondary.

  Primary stakeholders are directly affected by the project. *Secondary stakeholders* are involved in implementing, funding, monitoring, and so on, and are considered intermediaries. Consider identifying each stakeholder as primary or secondary.

- *Project impact.* Clarify the impact of the project on the stakeholder. This establishes the relationship between the stakeholder and the project. For example, will the project change a stakeholder's daily workflow?

- *Level of influence.* Rate the level of influence the stakeholder has in the organization: stakeholders with profit and loss (P&L) responsibility, management responsibility, or who control access to funds, or have control over the process. Frontline workers tend to have low influence, while process owners and financial decision makers have a high influence. Consider a scale from 1 to 5, or low, medium, and high. Alternatively, one could rate influence simply as low and high.

- *Level of importance.* Rate the level of importance each stakeholder has to the project's success. Here, the people directly interacting with the process will have high importance, such as subject matter experts (SMEs), frontline workers, maintenance personnel, and engineers, for example. Consider a scale from 1 to 5; or low, medium, and high; or low and high.

- *Current attitude.* Rate the attitude the stakeholder has toward the project. Consider a scale from 1 to 5; or low, medium, and high; or low and high.

- *Action plan.* Outline different strategies for dealing with each stakeholder. The strategies should focus on reducing opposition and increasing support.

Once Table 3.1 has been completed, the rating from the level of influence and importance columns can be transferred to Table 3.2. Table 3.2 provides the added benefit of classifying stakeholders and offering a suggested behavioral approach for each type:

Stakeholder	Project impact	Level of influence	Level of importance	Current attitude	Action plan

Table 3.1 A simple form for completing a stakeholder analysis.

		Influence	
		High	**Low**
Importance	**High**	Collaborate	Protect and defend
	Low	High risk	Do not spend resources

Table 3.2 Example of an influence-importance stakeholder table.
Source: Adapted from Tague (2005).

- *High influence/high importance.* Collaborate with these stakeholders.
- *High influence/low importance.* Work with these stakeholders to involve them and increase their level of interest. These stakeholders are capable of sabotaging plans and escalating problems and are considered high risk.
- *Low influence/high importance.* Protect and defend these stakeholders. Work to give them a voice and help increase their level of influence.
- *Low influence/low importance.* Monitor these stakeholders, but don't spend resources on them.

Andersen (2007) suggests another means of classifying stakeholders. His method provides additional insight and is depicted in Table 3.3. In this table, stakeholders are classified as to their potential impact on the organization versus their potential for cooperation with the organization. Again, this requires categorizing each stakeholder as either low or high. Once complete, stakeholders can be charted and viewed as:

		Potential to impact	
		High	**Low**
Potential for cooperation	**High**	Mixed blessing	Supportive
	Low	Nonsupportive	Marginal

Table 3.3 Example of an impact-cooperation stakeholder table.
Source: Adapted from Collins and Huge (1993).

- *High impact/high cooperation.* These stakeholders are considered a "mixed blessing" and should be handled through cooperation.
- *High impact/low cooperation.* These individuals are considered "non-supportive." Minimize dependency on this type of stakeholder through a defensive strategy.
- *Low impact/high cooperation.* These stakeholders are considered "supportive" and should be involved in relevant discussions and decisions.
- *Low impact/low cooperation.* These stakeholders are considered "marginal" and should be monitored. Similar to Tague's low influence/low importance quadrant, don't spend resources on them.

Black Belts as well as Master Black Belts may find that a sizable portion of their time is dedicated to engaging project stakeholders. As Covey (1989) would say in his fifth habit, "Seek first to understand, then to be understood." The stakeholder analysis is a highly structured method dedicated to this purpose. However, if done properly, it can be a sensitive document. Care needs to be taken to keep the analysis confidential: If left open to public consumption within the organization, it can be damaging or hurtful, or perceived as offensive. Use this tool effectively but use it with discretion.

Chapter 4
Benchmarking

Benchmarking means outmaneuvering your competitors.

—Allan Sayle

> Define and distinguish between various types of benchmarking, e.g., best practices, competitive, collaborative, and breakthrough. Select measures and performance goals for projects resulting from benchmarking activities. (Apply)
>
> **Body of Knowledge II.B**

Improving processes and products is often aided by comparing the current state with outstanding processes or products. In some cases, the comparison will be with other divisions within the same company. In other cases, external comparisons are more appropriate. The use of these comparisons is called *benchmarking*. The *benchmark* is the recognized or accepted measurement value that establishes the best performance for a given process.

Benchmarking often assists a Six Sigma team in setting targets and finding new ways to achieve them. It is an especially helpful technique when a quality improvement team has run out of innovative ideas. For example, a payroll department team is charged with making improvements in the quality and efficiency of the department's work. The team seeks out a company known for the quality of its payroll work. With that company's agreement, the team studies the payroll function, looking for ideas it can use in its home department.

The information for benchmarking may come from various sources, including publications, professional meetings, university research, customer feedback, site visits, and analysis of competitors' products. A downside of benchmarking within a particular industry is that it tends to put one in second place, at best.

Benchmarking helps teams strive toward excellence while reducing the tendency to feel that locally generated ideas are the only ideas worth considering. Moreover, benchmarking gives the organization the opportunity to see what level of process performance is possible. Seeing this gap in process performance helps an organization determine its desired rate of improvement and allows it to set meaningful intermediate stretch goals or targets. Benchmarking is useful for driving breakthrough improvement over continuous improvement.

TYPES OF BENCHMARKING

Camp (1995), the recognized father of benchmarking, has defined the following four types of benchmarking:

Internal benchmarking. The process of comparing your own processes to similar ones within your own organization. Westcott (2014) notes that the data for internal benchmarking are easy to collect, but the focus is limited and possibly biased. The search for exceptional performance is often limited by the company's culture, norms, and history.

Competitive benchmarking. The process of comparing your own processes to similar ones of competitors within your own industry. This type compares direct competitors at the local, regional, national, or even global level. Thus, legal concerns may be a consideration, and ethical issues become overly complicated at global levels.

Noncompetitive benchmarking. The process of comparing your own processes to similar ones of noncompetitors outside your industry. Westcott (2014) refers to this as functional benchmarking: the act of comparing the process or performance of a business function (for example, finance, IT, or human resources) in two or more organizations.

Generic process benchmarking. Similar to noncompetitive benchmarking but seeks to identify who does each process absolutely the best. Finding organizations that have best-in-class processes and approaches from which one may learn and translate to improvements at one's own organization.

Other types of benchmarking include:

Best practice benchmarking. Most authors who are authorities on the subject of benchmarking do not consider this a specific type of benchmarking, probably because there is not universal agreement on what constitutes "best practices." APQC (2014-3) places the concept of "best practice" in perspective when it writes, "[T]here is no single 'best practice' because best is not the same for everyone. Every organization is different in some way—missions, cultures, environments, and technologies. What is meant by 'best' are practices that have produced superior results. Best practices are then adapted to fit a particular organization."

Competitive benchmarking. A recognized type of benchmarking, competitive benchmarking forces organizations to take an external perspective. However, focusing on industry practices may limit opportunities to achieve high levels of performance, particularly if a given industry is not known for its quality. Competitive benchmarking forces organizations to take an external perspective.

Collaborative benchmarking. Although generally not considered a type of benchmarking since, by definition, all benchmarking is collaborative, this refers to the cooperation between various organizations to achieve benchmarking results. Collaborative benchmarking may permit access to specific benchmarking partners that may not exist with the other types of benchmarking.

Breakthrough benchmarking. The concept of "breakthrough" is often associated with benchmarking because it makes organizations aware of what's possible and, more specifically, what's achievable. Consequently, organizations that act through projects based on their effective use of benchmarking have been able to achieve significant (that is, breakthrough) levels of improvement. These organizations understand that routinely setting low improvement goals of, say, 10% are trivial and likely to be considered managerially irresponsible in today's highly competitive economic environment.

BENCHMARKING METHODOLOGIES

Benchmarking is not a haphazard activity, but one that requires the use of a strict methodology that must be planned and funded. Organizations that approach it any other way will likely fail. Camp (1993) has outlined steps required to perform a benchmarking study:

1. Determine what to benchmark.
2. Determine whom to benchmark against.
3. Exercise all data sources that will help you do this kind of work.
4. Analyze the gap between what you do and what the sum of the practices would say you should look like.
5. Revise your internal performance measurements and goals.

DANGERS OF BENCHMARKING

Benchmarking does not provide a shortcut to success: It is important to note that wholesale copying of processes from one organization to another rarely succeeds. Often, processes are adopted but not given adequate time, money, or manpower to succeed. Systems may be incompatible. Another consideration when transplanting processes is the culture, norms, and history of the receiving organization.

For example, consider a five-step machining process that must be accomplished on five different machines. Machine shop A has the benchmark machine process. It is family-owned, staffed entirely by family members, located in rural Arkansas, and non-union. Machine shop B, located in upstate New York, has just reopened after a two-week machinist union wildcat strike. Do the culture, norms, and history of machine shop B have an impact on the successful transplantation of the process used by machine shop A?

Another danger associated with benchmarking is that organizations become exposed to potential breaches of confidentiality. Such breaches may occur by conduct of their partners or their own employees. Trade secrets and process patents may be involved, and certain restrictions may need to be established and respected. Furthermore, with competitive benchmarking, legal aspects may need to be considered to prevent any improprieties or the appearance of improprieties.

At the outset of benchmarking, organizations must establish a code of conduct. One such code is provided by Westcott et al. (2014), shown in Figure 4.1. Notice that it is quite thorough. One portion of the code deals with not wasting a partner's time. During the early days of benchmarking, many organizations simply window-shopped—their intent was to take without giving. It is only when partners cooperate and collaborate that they achieve the full benefits of benchmarking.

SELECTING MEASURES AND PERFORMANCE GOALS

While the actual measures for a project are selected based on the process being improved, benchmarking can be a valuable tool in helping an organization recognize and set the desired levels of improvement to be achieved.

Historically, many organizations have set mundane process improvement goals. Usually, they accomplish this by reviewing the annual performance data and selecting one of the following methods:

- Guessing
- Guessing without looking at the annual performance data
- Always using a 10% improvement
- Using the previous annual goal
- Using what the boss provides
- Using what corporate provides
- Using some other equally sophisticated method

Benchmarking, however, allows organizations to set breakthrough improvement goals or otherwise meaningful and defensible targets and goals. Figure 4.2 illustrates the relationship that exists among goals, targets, and benchmarks.

Organizations aim for benchmarks as the ultimate measure of success. However, many organizations do not realize that benchmarks are dynamic. More specifically, those organizations setting the benchmarks are usually engaged in a continual process of improving them. Thus, any given organization shooting for a benchmark needs to aim higher, or it will forever be chasing the benchmark.

A *target*, in the context of benchmarking, is some intermediary goal that lies between the goal and the benchmark. Occasionally, a target is known as a *stretch goal*. A target is useful when the prospect of achieving the benchmark is infeasible, perhaps due to cost, manpower, or other limitations. For example, Company A's widget product line is operating at 65% yield, though it has taken years to achieve that level due to attempts to increase the yield through an annual project goal of 10% per year. The company has recently implemented a benchmarking initiative and discovered from a noncompetitive partner (who is in the same industry) that a yield of 98% is quite feasible. Such a benchmark represents an increase

Preamble—To guide benchmarking encounters and enhance the professionalism and effectiveness of benchmarking, many organizations have adopted this common Code of Conduct. All organizations are encouraged to abide by this Code of Conduct. Adherence to these principles will contribute to efficient, effective, and ethical benchmarking.

1. *Principle of Legality.*
   - If there is any potential question on the legality of an issue, don't do it.
   - Avoid discussions or actions that could lead to or imply an interest in restraint of trade, market and/or customer allocation schemes, price fixing, dealing arrangements, bid rigging, or bribery. Don't discuss costs with competitors if costs are an element of pricing.
   - Refrain from the acquisition of trade secrets by any means that could be interpreted as improper, including the breach or inducement of a breach of any duty to maintain secrecy. Do not disclose or use any trade secret that may have been obtained through improper means or that was disclosed by another in violation of a duty to maintain secrecy or limit its use. Do not, as a consultant or client, extend one benchmarking effort's findings to another company without first obtaining permission from the parties of the first effort.
2. *Principle of Exchange.*
   - Be willing to provide the same type and level of information that you request from your benchmarking partner to your benchmarking partner.
   - Communicate fully and early in the relationship to clarify expectations, avoid misunderstanding, and establish mutual interest in the benchmarking exchange. Be honest and complete.
3. *Principle of Confidentiality.*
   - Treat benchmarking interchanges as confidential to the individuals and companies involved. Information must not be communicated outside the partnering organizations without the prior consent of the benchmarking partner who shared the information.
   - A company's participation in a study is confidential and should not be communicated externally without its prior permission.
4. *Principle of Use.*
   - Use information obtained through benchmarking only for purposes of formulating improvement of operations or processes within the companies participating in the benchmarking effort.
   - The use or communication of a benchmarking partner's name with the data obtained or practices observed requires the prior permission of that partner.
   - Do not use benchmarking as a means to market or sell.
5. *Principle of First-Party Contact.*
   - Initiate benchmarking contacts, whenever possible, through a benchmarking contact designated by the partner company.
   - Respect the corporate culture of partner companies and work within mutually agreed-on procedures.
   - Obtain mutual agreement with the designated benchmarking contact on any hand-off of communication or responsibility to other parties.
6. *Principle of Third-Party Contact.*
   - Obtain an individual's permission before providing his or her name in response to a contact request.
   - Avoid communicating a contact's name in an open forum without the contact's permission.
7. *Principle of Preparation.*
   - Demonstrate commitment to the efficiency and effectiveness of benchmarking by completing preparatory work prior to making an initial benchmarking contact, and follow a benchmarking process.
   - Make the most of your benchmarking partner's time by being fully prepared for each exchange.
   - Help your benchmarking partners prepare by providing them with an interview guide or questionnaire and agenda prior to benchmarking visits.

Figure 4.1 Benchmarking code of conduct.
Source: Westcott et al. (2014).

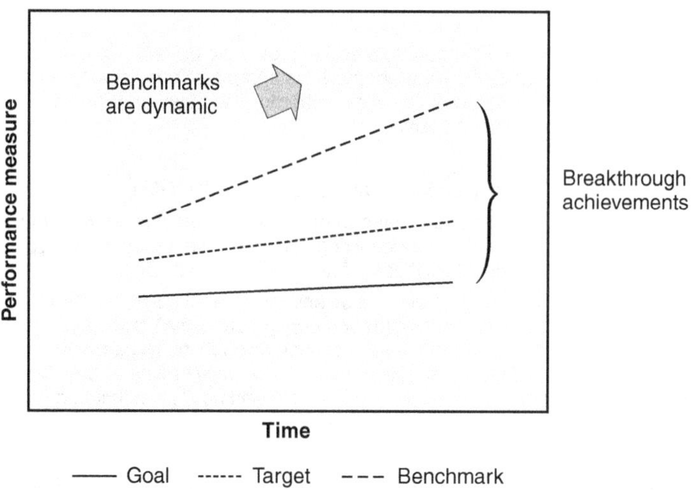

Figure 4.2 Selecting performance levels for projects resulting from benchmarking.

of almost 50%. The director of production is reluctant to accept the benchmark as the project goal. However, he agrees to the project goal of a 30% increase (goal yield of 85%), a target increase of 40% (target yield of 91%), and the benchmark of 50% increase (benchmark yield of 98%).

Chapter 5
Business Measures

What gets measured gets improved.

—Peter Drucker

Many Lean Six Sigma tools deal with analyzing numerical values. The metrics the organization chooses reflects its business philosophy and, in large part, determines its success. Unfortunately, many organizations use too many metrics, often lagging in nature, which may drown them in data and cause them to be unable to change with customer needs. This section lists some tools that will help in the selection and use of business performance measures.

PERFORMANCE MEASURES

> Define and describe balanced scorecard, key performance indicators (KPIs), key behavior indicators (KBIs), objectives and key results (OKRs), customer loyalty metrics, and leading and lagging indicators. Explain how to create a line of sight from performance measures to organizational strategies. (Analyze)
>
> Body of Knowledge II.C.1

Balanced Scorecard

The *balanced scorecard,* a term coined by Kaplan and Norton (1992), separates organizational metrics into four perspectives:

- *Financial perspective: How do we look to shareholders?* This provides the organization with insight into how well its goals, objectives, and strategies are contributing to shareholder value and the bottom line. It provides shareholders with a direct line of sight into the health and well-being of the organization. Common metrics used for this perspective are given in the next section.
- *Customer perspective: How do customers see us?* This perspective defines an organization's value proposition and measures how effective the organization is in creating value for its customers through its goals,

objectives, strategies, and processes. The customer perspective is not easily obtained. Multiple approaches and listening posts are frequently required and must be compared and reconciled to ensure a correct understanding of the customer's stated and unstated needs and expectations of the organization's products and services, and the strength of its customer relationships.

- *Internal business processes perspective: What must we excel at?* Internal business processes include all organizational processes designed to create and deliver the customer's value proposition. Organizations that perform these processes well generally have high levels of customer satisfaction and strong customer relationships since efficient and effective internal processes can be considered predictors of the metrics included in the customer perspective.
- *Innovation and learning perspective: Can we continue to improve and create value?* This perspective includes the capabilities and skills of an organization and how it is focused and channeled to support the internal processes used to create customer value. The development and effective use of human resources and information systems, as well as the organizational culture, are key aspects of this perspective.

By monitoring metrics from these perspectives, managers get a broad, balanced view of the health of the organization in one report. Because it presents all the important measures across the organization, the scorecard guards against suboptimization.

Common metrics in each benchmark category are shown in Table 5.1.

These examples should be considered a starter set and subjected to the criteria identified earlier to ensure their appropriateness. Also, note that the metrics in these perspectives are not necessarily mutually exclusive and may very well overlap. For example, quality and on-time delivery rates appear in both the customer and internal business process perspectives. Customers judge an organization by these metrics and make determinations regarding the continuance of a business relationship with a supplier. On the other hand, these same metrics may be used by a supplier as a predictor of the customer satisfaction levels that might be achieved because of its internal business processes.

Key Performance Indicators (KPIs)

There are three categories of key performance indicators (KPIs) (Eckerson, 2006). From the lowest to highest levels, they are *operational, tactical,* and *strategic* metrics.

Operational key performance indicators are measurements that are the closest to the actual work being performed. These metrics are out on the shop floor or the call center, for example, and are close to real time monitoring. Operational metrics can be used to trigger alerts and alarms.

Tactical KPIs provide a single version of the truth and are consolidated. They allow for proactive analysis and action. These metrics are what first-level managers rely on to track progress and make decisions.

Perspective	Metrics
Financial	Return on investment
	Return on capital
	Cash flow
	Quarterly sales growth
Customer	Customer satisfaction levels
	Retention rates
	Net promoter score
	Spend
	On-time delivery
Internal Business Processes	Cycle time
	Unit cost
	Throughput
	Defect rates
	Quality level
Innovation and Learning	Time to market for new products
	Employee satisfaction
	Percentage of internal promotions
	Number of new products in pipeline
	Sustainability

Table 5.1 Common metrics in benchmarking categories.

Then, at the highest level, we have strategic metrics, such as financial or customer metrics, which allow companies to make long-range plans.

Table 5.2 lists examples of each type of key performance indicator across a variety of industries.

Features of Good KPIs

How can we choose good KPIs for a dashboard report, or for Six Sigma projects? The best KPIs are (Eckerson, 2006):

- *Aligned* to the business's goals, or the project goals.
- *Owned* in terms of data collection, analysis, and responsibility to act.
- *Predictive* of the future (leading).
- *Actionable.*

Indicator Level	Key Performance Indicator
Operational	Daily production counts
	Daily hospital admissions
	Control chart measurements
	Number of new website visitors
	Number of new trouble tickets
Tactical	Number of inventory turns
	Average length of hospital stay
	Weekly average call length
	Monthly absentee rates
	Monthly budget variances
Strategic	Market share
	Customer satisfaction
	Revenue growth
	Price-to-earnings ratio

Table 5.2 Examples of operational, tactical, and strategic indicators.

- *Limited* in number.
- *Transparent.* Indices are sometimes too complex. When people can't understand what goes on under the hood in a formula, they won't be able to act to improve an index.
- *Balanced and linked.* This will help us avoid suboptimizing a process.
- *Standardized.* This will allow us to compare departments across divisions, and cuts down on gaming the system by choosing different denominators in our rates, etc. We need one consistent version of the truth.
- *Timely.* Will the metric be updated often enough for it to be actionable? Is the data easy to collect?

Choosing KPIs

Taking the features of a good KPI into consideration, how might we choose metrics? We must answer these questions (Eckerson, 2006):

- What is the business justification and strategic importance of this metric?
- Who is the metric's business owner?

- Who collects, reviews, and reports data? Is this metric owned?
- What are the metric goals? (target and stretch)
- Who approves goals?
- How is the metric calculated? Is it clear? Standardized?
- What is the data source? How is it collected? When is data available? How easy is it to collect? How often will the metric be refreshed? How reliable is the data? Who must clean the data?
- Are there detailed reports to support the metric? Do we have a data trail?
- What are the related metrics (upstream and downstream)? We need to have our KPIs balanced and linked.

Organizational metrics do not end with KPIs. Lower-level metrics down to the individual process level may be required to support KPIs and to provide deep, meaningful, and actionable insight in order for organizations to effectively conduct and run their businesses.

Suboptimized Systems

A system may be thought of as the set of processes that make up an enterprise. When improvements are proposed, it is important to take a systems approach. This means that consideration should be given to the effect the proposed changes will have on other processes within the system, and therefore on the entire enterprise. Operating a system at less than its best mode is called *suboptimization.* Changes to a system may optimize individual processes but suboptimize the system as a whole. It is important to put measurement systems in place that reflect unintended consequences of proposed actions.

For example, a team may have a goal to improve the throughput for process A. However, the throughput might be increased to a point that overwhelms process B, creating a bottleneck and increasing work in process inventory dramatically.

In another example, a distribution center loads its trucks in a manner that minimizes its work. This savings in work, however, requires the receiving organization to expend more time, energy, resources, and money to unload the trucks. Taking a systematic approach, a different loading arrangement may increase the costs for the distribution center but minimize the overall costs to the system.

Key Behavior Indicators (KBIs)

Organizations that track key behavior indicators (KBIs) recognize that performance is for the most part driven by people. Once an organization understands the type of behavior that leads to high-level performance, it can set up systems to assure those behaviors are performed.

For example, a company measures sales growth as a key performance indicator, and can study the behavior and habits of its top salespeople, also known as the *positive deviants.* The behaviors and habits that set this group apart can then be codified and used to train or coach the other less successful salespeople. These KBIs then become leading indicators of the performance metric.

Key behavior indictors can also be used in a broader sense to track cultural change in an organization. Leaders communicate what types of behaviors they expect at all levels of the organization and work with team members to establish ways to track this type of behavior.

Objectives and Key Results (OKRs)

Objectives and key results (OKRs), created by Andy Grove at Intel and popularized by John Doerr, is a collaborative method used to develop and track goals. The objective is what is to be achieved, stated in concrete terms. The key results are written so that they are specific, measurable, achievable, relevant, and time-bound (SMART). An OKR begins with an objective statement, under which three to five key results are listed. The OKRs are reviewed quarterly, often using a yes/no or red, yellow, green scoring approach. These OKRs can be written for broad organization goals or used for specific departmental or individual goals.

For example, a food delivery company may have a mission to be the premier company in its industry segment. To fulfill this mission, it has set an objective of having the best customer service in its industry. The resulting OKR may look something like this:

Objective: Deliver the best customer service in the industry

Key Result: Reduce delivery time by 40%

Key Result: Increase order accuracy by 100%

Key Result: Increase the number of food items available by 120%

Key Result: Increase app usage by 300%

Key Result: Increase customer satisfaction scores by 50%

On a more personal level, a Six Sigma Black Belt candidate may create an OKR as follows:

Objective: Earn an ASQ Six Sigma Black Belt certification this year

Key Result: View instructional videos at least three hours per week

Key Result: Answer 25 practice questions per week

Key Result: Read 50 pages of Certified Six Sigma Black Belt Handbook per week

Key Result: Increase testing speed by 50%

Key Results: Increase number of correct answers by 60%

Doerr (2018) describes the benefits of OKRs using the acronym FACTS:

- *Focus*. The team is represented with a small number of meaningful objectives.
- *Alignment*. Goals are aligned at each level of the organization.

- *Commitment.* Achieving the goals requires commitment from the entire team.
- *Tracking.* Teams are able to track progress and make adjustments.
- *Stretching.* Teams are empowered to stretch to make significant changes.

Common Customer Loyalty Metrics

Customer loyalty is a term used to describe the behavior of customers—in particular, customers who exhibit a high level of satisfaction, conduct repeat business, or provide referrals and testimonials. It results from an organization's processes, practices, and efforts designed to deliver its services or products in ways that drive such behavior.

Many organizations recognize that it is far easier and less costly to retain customers than to attract new ones. Hence, customer loyalty drives customer retention and, by extension, has a financial impact. However, customer loyalty can be a double-edged sword. Some organizations strive blindly to retain all their customers, including those that are unprofitable. Chapter 10 discusses the concept of customer segmentation. In one context of segmentation, customers may be classified as profitable or unprofitable. Conceptually, the idea of unprofitable customers is difficult to understand. Moreover, severing ties with this customer segment may be even more difficult, as it may be seen as highly unusual or simply "not done." Enlightened organizations understand this distinction well and act accordingly. Such organizations have gained insight into the cost of maintaining customer relationships through extensive data collection and analysis. This insight has given rise to such terms as "relationship costs" and "relationship revenue."

Organizations must be careful not to confuse loyal customers with tolerant customers. Customers have a zone of tolerance whereby a single bad experience or even a series of bad experiences spread over a sufficiently long timeframe may strain the customer–supplier relationship yet keep it intact. However, the cumulative effects of such experiences may push a customer beyond its zone of tolerance, resulting in customer defection or a reduction in business. At this point, a customer may deem that it is no longer worth maintaining the business relationship. Consider your own banking relationship for the moment. How many times would it take for your bank to provide bad service before you are willing to forsake convenience and take your business elsewhere?

Organizations, especially those in a niche market or those that may be a single/sole-source provider, should have a deep understanding of what drives their customer satisfaction levels and relationships. Limited competition or the cost of changing suppliers or service providers may be all that is keeping customers loyal. Given the right opportunity, these "loyal" customers might readily defect.

There are numerous customer loyalty metrics used by organizations. However, when scrutinized, we find that they are not always a direct measure of customer behavior. Consequently, we offer the following basic customer loyalty metrics as a starting point:

- *Net promoter score* (NPS). This score is calculated based on the response to the following customer survey question using a 1-10 Likert scale response:

  How likely are you to recommend [brand or product] to a friend or colleague?

  Here, a score of 1 maps to *Not at all likely* and 10 maps to *Extremely likely*. Scores are divided into groups:

  - *Promoters (score 9-10).* These customers are loyal and enthusiastic, and will refer others to the brand, fueling growth.
  - *Passives (7-8).* These customers are satisfied but unenthusiastic. They may be enticed by offers from competitors.
  - *Detractors (1-6).* These are unhappy customers who can damage the brand and impede growth by posting negative reviews and by word of mouth.

  The Net Promoter Score is then calculated by subtracting the percentage of detractors from the percentage of promoters. The score can range from a low of negative 100 (all customers are detractors) to a high of +100 (all customers are promoters).

- *Customer referrals.* Customers are often reluctant to refer individuals or organizations unless their confidence is high that the individual or organization will provide a superior product or service in the same manner that they themselves received. "Customer referrals" is an excellent measure of customer loyalty, particularly when it can be expressed as a rate.

- *Customer abandonment rate.* This is the complement of the customer retention rate. Some organizations prefer the abandonment rate because it focuses effort on customer issues and tends to have a stronger internal impact, whereas the use of the retention rate can sometimes lull organizations into a false sense of security. It is sometimes called *customer churn* or the *customer churn rate.*

- *Customer retention rate.* This metric has applicability when customers have an active role in staying with an organization. For example, membership dues with the American Society for Quality must be actively paid each year to retain membership. There is no automatic renewal process. Members elect to stay as members because they see value in retaining themselves as members. ASQ has retained them as members due to a concerted effort as part of a strategy that is in place to generate membership value. Because the strategy works, it influences the member (customer) retention rate.

  However, caution is required when using the retention rate as a customer loyalty metric, particularly when:

  - No real alternative to leaving the organization exists; such is the case of monopolies (for example, utilities) or sole/single-source suppliers.

- The cost or difficulty of leaving the organization is very high; consider the sole/single-source supplier, or just the matter of moving your financials from one bank to another. This may sound simple, but suppose you have several integrated checking and savings accounts that you transfer funds between and use for all your bill paying. The difficulty involved in switching banks could be very high and quite time-consuming.

Organizations using the retention rate metric with customers facing these conditions have a retention rate that is likely to be overstated and they should be concerned about possible future mass customer defections when the conditions change.

- *Customer renewal rate.* The renewal rate is a useful metric when customers must actively engage with the organization to demonstrate their loyalty. If we continue with the ASQ membership example from above, members must actively renew their membership each year.
- *Repeat customers.* When we talk about repeat customers, we are talking about the time between purchases of the product or service relative to the durability of the product or need for the service. Examples on the product side include the purchase of an automobile or refrigerator. Generally, such purchases happen infrequently and there is a lot of competition for the customer's attention. To be a repeat customer with long spans of time between purchases makes a positive statement about the customer experience. This metric is particularly useful if it can be expressed as a rate.
- *Share of wallet.* This refers to customers extending their loyalty to the purchase of other products and services within the same organization based on their experience with a given product or service. However, when the customer cannot sufficiently distinguish supplying organizations (that is, suppliers of products and services) apart, this extension of loyalty is sometimes conducted as a matter of convenience on the part of the customer rather than being earned on the part of the receiving organization.

Leading and Lagging Indicators

Within each category of key performance indicators, there are two types of indicators: *leading,* which are used to predict future outcomes, and *lagging,* which are measurements taken following an event. We can influence a leading indicator, whereas a lagging indicator is purely informational, telling us how we did in the recent past.

We can view leading and lagging indicators through the lens of $Y = f(X)$, in which f is the function that converts the inputs (X) into outputs (Y). Understanding the relationship between inputs and outputs can help us choose leading metrics (X) that are predictive of process outputs (Y). Table 5.3 shows a few examples of leading metrics and what they can be used to predict.

Leading indicator (X)	Predicts	Outcome (Y)
Number of sales meetings with prospects	⇒	Future sales
Website engagement	⇒	Future sales
Booked revenue	⇒	Future income
Number of product returns	⇒	Net promoter score
Abandoned call rates	⇒	Future customer satisfaction scores
Employee absenteeism rates	⇒	Future employee satisfaction scores

Table 5.3 Examples of leading indicators.

Lagging Indicator (Y)
Defect rates
Average cycle time
Warranty claims
Number of accidents
Monthly sales
Market share
Margin

Table 5.4 Examples of lagging indicators.

Examples of lagging indicators are shown in Table 5.4. These indicators are considered "after the fact" and provide information, but no means to change their outcome.

It is interesting to note that indicators can be both *lagging and leading* depending on how they are viewed. For example, defect rates or warranty claims are a lagging indicator of quality but can be a leading indicator of customer satisfaction scores, or market share.

Creating Line of Sight from Measures to Strategies

The details of this subsection were addressed in Chapter 1. However, it is important to keep in mind that an organization must have an effective strategic planning methodology that aligns the organization both horizontally and vertically while decomposing the plan downward from strategic to tactical to operational plans and into projects.

At each level, measures or metrics are developed to ensure accountability, and responsibility is maintained. Concurrently, the strategic, tactical, operational, and project plans are integrated with other plans as necessary, such as the capital plan and strategic human resource plan.

When the above occurs, line of sight must be maintained. See Chapter 1 for specific details.

FINANCIAL MEASURES

> Define and use revenue growth, market share, margin, net present value (NPV), return on investment (ROI), and cost-benefit analysis (CBA). Explain the difference between hard cost measures (from profit and loss statements) and soft cost benefits of cost avoidance and reduction. (Apply)
>
> **Body of Knowledge II.C.2**

Since Six Sigma project emphasize bottom-line results, Black Belts need to have a solid understanding of the various financial measures that may be used to cost-justify projects, and higher-level business performance metrics that may weigh upon project selection.

This section will address some of the key tools needed to support such an analysis and will discuss some of the advantages and disadvantages of each. Remember, as with any analysis, it is critical to enumerate all assumptions on which it is based since it may be necessary to revisit them from time to time. Also, whenever possible, work with the organization's financial department. The financial department is a valuable partner that will serve to instill confidence and credibility into the project numbers.

While financial aspects usually dominate the benefit section of a project charter or report, some benefits cannot be stated financially. For example, it is difficult to quantify the effects of improved morale or team-building skills. However, these types of benefits should be included since they may be used to break ties between projects with equal financial benefits.

Revenue Growth

Revenue growth is the projected increase in income that will result from the project. Revenue growth may be stated in dollars per year or as a percentage per year.

Market Share

An organization's *market share* of a particular product or service is that percentage of the dollar value that is sold relative to the total dollar value sold by all organizations in a given market. A project's goal may be to increase this percentage. During a market slowdown, market share is often watched closely because an increase in market share, even with a drop in sales, can produce an increase in sales when the slowdown ends.

Margin

Margin, or gross profit, is equal to revenue minus cost. We can also calculate a percent margin to compare the margins across projects, shown in Equation 5.1 and Equation 5.2.

Equation 5.1 Margin

$$\text{Margin} = (\text{Revenue} - \text{Cost})$$

Percent margin. This metric provides an overall sense of how efficiently an organization converts sales into profits. It is computed as follows:

Equation 5.2 Percent Margin

$$\text{Percent Margin} = \left(\frac{\text{Revenue} - \text{Cost}}{\text{Revenue}}\right) \times 100\%$$

Simple ROI

In basic terms, the *return on investment* (ROI) metric measures the effectiveness of an organization's ability to use its resources to generate income. If we want to know what the return on investment is for a short-term project, we can use the *Simple ROI* formula. This formula ignores the time value of money and can be used for projects in which the effect of compound interest is negligible, such as projects that are less than a year in duration.

To calculate Simple ROI, we take the financial benefits of the project, which could be dollar savings, and/or an increase in revenue or profit, and subtract off the cost of the project, yielding net benefit. Then we divide the net benefit by the project cost. The resulting Simple ROI gives us an idea of the benefit of the project's monetary outlay, shown in Equation 5.3:

Equation 5.3 Simple ROI

$$\text{Simple ROI} = \frac{(\text{Benefit} - \text{Cost})}{\text{Cost}}$$

EXAMPLE 5.1

A Six Sigma improvement project costs $68,000 to implement, but it produces a one-time increase in sales and an improvement in delivery time equal to $100,000. The Simple ROI is calculated as:

$$\text{Simple ROI} = \frac{(\text{Benefit} - \text{Cost})}{\text{Cost}}$$
$$= \frac{(100{,}000 - 68{,}000)}{68{,}000} = 0.47$$

This is a 47% return on investment, meaning that we recouped not only the entire cost outlay of $68,000, but we also brought in benefits equal to 47% of the cost.

A positive ROI indicates that we have made money on the project. An ROI of zero means that we have broken even. A negative ROI indicates that the benefits of the project were not enough to recoup the cost of the project.

Net Present Value

More sophisticated financial analyses consider the time value of money. If a benefit will be received in the future, it must be brought back to today's dollars using a *net present value* calculation so we can properly evaluate its merits. The net present value is calculated using Equation 5.4:

Equation 5.4 Net present value

$$NPV = \frac{A}{(1+r)^n}$$

where A is the future payment amount, r is the annual rate of inflation, and n is the number of years in the future the payment will be made.

EXAMPLE 5.2

An individual will receive a payment of $35,000 20 years from now. We can calculate the *net present value* to find what the future $35,000 payment would equal in today's dollars, based on the inflation rate. Assume the inflation rate is 3.5%.

The variable A is the value of the future payment, $35,000. The variable r is the rate, expressed as a decimal: 0.035. The variable n, the number of years in the future the payment will be made, is equal to 20. As each year goes by, the buying power of that $35,000 will slowly erode.

The *net present value* (NPV) is calculated using Equation 5.4:

$$NPV = \frac{A}{(1+r)^n}$$
$$= \frac{\$35{,}000}{(1+0.035)^{20}} = \$17{,}589.81$$

Continued

Continued

The resulting NPV is $17,589.81, which is about half of the buying power if we were to receive the $35,000 payment today.

Alternatively, we can use the = *npv* formula in Excel, shown in Figure 5.1. The arguments for this formula include the rate, and Value1, which is an array of the value of payments received. In this case, the payments for the first 19 years are equal to zero, and the twentieth payment is equal to $35,000. Create a column in Excel with 19 zeroes and $35,000 entered into the twentieth row. Use this cell range for Value1. The formula will return the net present value.

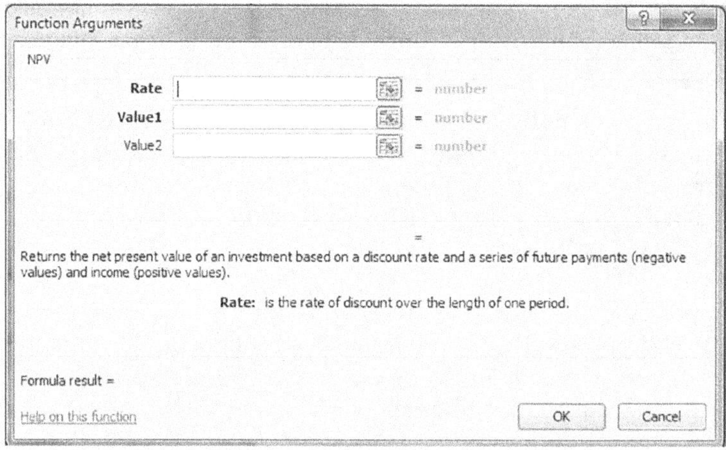

Figure 5.1 *NPV* function in Excel.

Note that the formula we used for NPV assumes that money is compounded once a year. We can use a more general formula to consider that there may be an annual rate of return *r*, but the interest might be compounded monthly, quarterly, etc.

We now introduce a new variable, *t*, which is the number of times that the interest is compounded annually. If we let *t* equal 1, we get the formula presented in Equation 5.4. The new, more general formula shown in Equation 5.5 can be used in all situations.

Equation 5.5 Net present value, general form

$$NPV = \frac{A}{\left(1+\frac{r}{t}\right)^{nt}}$$

EXAMPLE 5.3

A company will receive a payment of $225,000 in four years. The interest rate is equal to 4.5%, compounded every six months (twice a year, so $t = 2$). Here, $A = \$225,000$, $r = 0.045$, $t = 2$, and $n = 4$. We can use Equation 5.5 to calculate the net present value of the payment:

$$NPV = \frac{A}{\left(1+\frac{r}{t}\right)^{nt}}$$

$$= \frac{\$225,000}{\left(1+\frac{0.045}{2}\right)^{4\times 2}} = \frac{\$225,000}{(1.0225)^{8}} = \$188,311.13$$

We can also calculate ROI in the situation of *continuous compounding* using Equation 5.6:

Equation 5.6 Net present value, continuous compounding

$$NPV = \frac{A}{e^{rn}}$$

where A is the future amount, n is the time period, and e is Euler's number, the irrational constant 2.71828 …

EXAMPLE 5.4

A payment of $25,000 will be made in 6 years, and the interest rate is 1%, continuously compounded. The variable $A = \$25,000$, $r = 0.01$, and $n = 6$. The net present value is calculated using Equation 5.6:

$$NPV = \frac{A}{e^{rn}}$$

$$= \frac{\$25,000}{e^{0.01\times 6}} = \frac{\$25,000}{e^{0.06}} = \$23,544.11$$

We can also find the NPV for a series of payments over several years using the formula shown in Equation 5.7:

Equation 5.7 Net present value for a series of payments

$$NPV = \sum_{i=0}^{n} \frac{A_i}{(1+r)^i}$$

where A_i is the amount received in year i, r is the rate, and n is the number of years.

EXAMPLE 5.5

A Six Sigma project requires an initial outlay of $9,500 and delivers savings of $5,500 in the first year, and $8,000 in the second year. Required rate of return is 4.0%, compounded annually.

First, we write out the cash flow by year, and then apply the NPV formula in Equation 5.7.

Year	Cash Flow (A_i)
0	– $9,500
1	$5,500
2	$8,000

The interest rate $r = 0.04$, and $i = 0, 1, 2$.

$$NPV = \sum_{i=0}^{n} \frac{A_i}{(1+r)^i}$$

$$= \frac{-\$9,500}{(1+0.04)^0} + \frac{\$5,500}{(1+0.04)^1} + \frac{\$8,000}{(1+0.04)^2}$$

$$= \frac{-\$9,500}{1} + \frac{\$5,500}{1.04} + \frac{\$8,000}{(1.04)^2} = \$3,184.91$$

Note that any value to the zero power equals 1.

Remember it is best to round the answer at the end, not in the intermediate calculations.

Discounted ROI

Using the NPV, we can calculate a *discounted ROI* that takes the time value of money into account.

$$\text{Discounted ROI} = \frac{(\text{Total present value of benefits} - \text{Total present value of costs})}{\text{Total present value of costs}}$$

Here, benefits in future years are brought back to the present, as are all the future costs. The formula for discounted ROI is shown in Equation 5.8:

Equation 5.8 Discounted ROI

$$\text{Discounted ROI} = \frac{\sum_{i=0}^{n} \left(\frac{\text{Benefit}_i - \text{Cost}_i}{(1+r)^i} \right)}{\sum_{i=0}^{n} \left(\frac{\text{Cost}_i}{(1+r)^i} \right)}$$

The use of the discounted ROI formula is illustrated in Example 5.6.

EXAMPLE 5.6

A company is considering leasing a new piece of equipment with a two-year contract. The initial cost is $60,000 with maintenance fees of $5,000 in years 1 and 2. The immediate benefit is equal to $85,000, and then $6,000 for each of the next two years. What is the overall discounted ROI? Assume the discount rate is 5.0%. We first write out the cash flow table for years 0, 1 and 2:

Year	Benefit_i	Cost_i
0	$85,000	$60,000.00
1	$6,000	$5,000.00
2	$6,000	$5,000.00

Note that $r = 0.05$ and $n = 2$. Next, we plug the values into the discounted ROI formula using Equation 5.8:

$$\text{Discounter ROI} = \frac{\sum_{i=0}^{n}\left(\frac{\text{Benefit}_i - \text{Cost}_i}{(1+r)^i}\right)}{\sum_{i=0}^{n}\left(\frac{\text{Cost}_i}{(1+r)^i}\right)}$$

$$= \frac{\frac{(\$85,000 - \$60,000)}{(1+0.05)^0} + \frac{(\$6,000 - \$5,000)}{(1+0.05)^1} + \frac{(\$6,000 - \$5,000)}{(1+0.05)^2}}{\frac{\$60,000}{(1+0.05)^0} + \frac{\$5,000}{(1+0.05)^1} + \frac{\$5,000}{(1+0.05)^2}}$$

$$= \frac{(\$25,000 + \$952.38 + \$907.03)}{(\$60,000 + \$4,761.91 + \$4,535.15)}$$

$$= 0.388$$

We will realize a return on investment equal to 38.8%.

Cost–Benefit Analysis (CBA)

Top management must approve funding for projects that require significant financial resources. Therefore, before a proposed project is initiated, a cost–benefit analysis using projected revenues, costs, and net cash flows is performed to determine the project's financial feasibility. This analysis is based on estimates of the project's benefits and costs and the timing thereof. The results of the analysis are a key factor in deciding which projects will be funded. Upon project completion, accounting data are analyzed to verify the project's financial impact on the organization. In other words, management must confirm whether the project added to or detracted from the company's financial well-being.

In today's competitive global environment, resource allocation is complicated by the fact that business needs and opportunities are greater and that improvements are often more difficult to achieve. Many of the easier projects have already been done. Therefore, top management requires that project benefits and costs be evaluated so that projects can be correlated to overall revenues, costs, customer satisfaction, market share, and other criteria. These factors are analyzed to maximize business returns and to limit risks, costs, and exposures. Therefore, quality improvement projects are considered business investments—as are all cash or capital investments—in which benefits must exceed costs. Quality managers are additionally challenged in that many of these benefits and costs are not easily quantifiable, as is normally expected by executives, accountants, and financial officers.

A *cost–benefit* (also known as a *benefit–cost*) *analysis* attempts to evaluate the benefits and costs associated with a project or initiative. Two types of benefits can be evaluated: direct or indirect. Direct benefits are easily measured and include items such as increased production, higher quality, increased sales, reduced delivery costs, higher reliability, decreased deficiencies, and lower warranty costs. Indirect benefits are more difficult to measure and include such items as improved quality of work life, increased internal customer satisfaction, and better-trained employees. Similarly, two types of costs can be evaluated. Direct costs include equipment, labor, training, machinery, and salaries. Indirect costs include downtime, opportunity costs, pollution, and displaced workers.

The simple formula for computing a benefit–cost ratio is shown in Equation 5.9:

Equation 5.9 Benefit–Cost Ratio

$$\text{Benefit–Cost Ratio} = \frac{\sum \text{NPV of all benefits}}{\sum \text{NPV of all costs}}$$

EXAMPLE 5.7

We now calculate the benefit–cost ratio for the scenario described in Example 5.6. A company is considering leasing a new piece of equipment with a two-year contract. The initial cost is $60,000 with maintenance fees of $5,000 for years 1 and 2. The immediate benefit is equal to $85,000, and then $6,000 for each of the next two years. What is the benefit–cost ratio? Assume the discount rate is 5.0%.

We first write out the cash flow table for years 0, 1, and 2:

Year	Benefit_i	Cost_i
0	$85,000	$60,000.00
1	$6,000	$5,000.00
2	$6,000	$5,000.00

We note that $r = 0.05$ and $n = 2$. Using Equation 5.9:

Continued

Continued

$$\text{Benefit–Cost Ratio} = \frac{\sum_{i=0}^{n}\left(\frac{\text{Benefit}_i}{(1+r)^i}\right)}{\sum_{i=0}^{n}\left(\frac{\text{Cost}_i}{(1+r)^i}\right)}$$

$$= \frac{\frac{(\$85,000)}{(1+0.05)^0} + \frac{(\$6,000)}{(1+0.05)^1} + \frac{(\$6,000)}{(1+0.05)^2}}{\frac{\$60,000}{(1+0.05)^0} + \frac{\$5,000}{(1+0.05)^1} + \frac{\$5,000}{(1+0.05)^2}}$$

$$= \frac{(\$85,000 + \$5,714.29 + \$5,442.18)}{(\$60,000 + \$4,761.91 + \$4,535.15)}$$

$$= 1.388$$

If the formula above yields a value greater than 1, the project is generally worth considering. The benefit–cost ratio of 1.388 means that there is a benefit of roughly $1.39 for every dollar expended. Note that this ratio is equal to 1 plus the discounted ROI.

Typically, a cost–benefit analysis is conducted to:

- Assist in the performance of a *what-if analysis*
- Compare the benefits, costs, and risks of competing projects
- Allocate resources among multiple projects
- Justify expenditures for equipment, products, or people

Because many indirect benefits and costs are difficult to quantify, and time is needed to identify such costs, some worthwhile quality projects or initiatives could fail to obtain the necessary funding.

Quality professionals are expected to help their organizations profit from quality investments, so no project should receive automatic approval and resource allocation. To be competitive, companies must find ways to increase profitability while providing customers with high levels of satisfaction. The challenge for improvement projects, programs, and initiatives is to find the link between critical business performance measurements, such as profitability, and quality investments. Although some quality benefits and costs are difficult to measure or are unknowable, the quality manager still must help determine and measure quality's effect on the organization's finances.

Defining Hard versus Soft Dollars

What constitutes hard and soft dollar savings is a long-standing debate. So many organizations have defined them differently over the years that confusion abounds. Ashenbaum (2006) noted that "[g]enerally speaking, cost savings are understood as tangible bottom-line reductions resulting in saved money that could be removed from budgets or reinvested back into the business. There also needs to be a prior baseline or standard cost for the purchased product or service so that these savings could be measured against the spend of a prior time period's spend." (Note: In the context in which Ashenbaum offered this definition, cost savings are synonymous with hard dollar savings.) Based on this definition, let's extract the key characteristics of *cost (hard dollar) savings:*

- A prior baseline of spending must be established, typically 12 months.
- The dollars must have been planned and in the budget. This goes along with the baseline requirement above.
- The cost savings must affect the bottom line (that is, the profit and loss statement or balance sheet).

Unexpectedly, this definition also settles the question regarding whether spent or reinvested cost savings were ever savings at all. Some organizations tend to empty the savings pot as soon as it's filled. Then they wonder or even complain about the lack of savings from the Lean Six Sigma strategic initiative. Once a project books its hard savings, these savings exist regardless of what the organization chooses to do with them thereafter.

Soft dollar savings are *cost avoidance savings* and are, by exclusion, everything that is not hard dollar savings. Ashenbaum (2006) offers some additional clarity on the subject:

- Avoidance is a cost reduction that does not lower the cost of products or services when compared against historical results, but instead minimizes or avoids the negative impact to the bottom line that a price increase would have caused.
- When there is an increase in output-capacity without increasing resource expenditure, in general, the cost avoidance savings are the amount that would have been spent to handle the increased volume/output.
- Avoidances include process improvements that do not immediately reduce costs or assets but provide benefits through improved process efficiency, employee productivity, customer satisfaction, improved competitiveness, etc. Over time, cost avoidance often becomes cost savings.

We can expand our view by considering that "cost avoidance" depends on whether it has a budget impact or not. Let's consider the following examples:

- *Cost avoidance (budget impacting).* This type of cost avoidance eliminates or reduces items in the budget marked for future spending. For example, three engineers are budgeted for hire in the fourth quarter. The cost of the three engineers is not in the baseline, nor has any spending for these engineers occurred. Eliminating these planned expenses has an impact on the future budget and is thus cost avoidance.
- *Cost avoidance (non–budget impacting).* This type of cost avoidance results from productivity or efficiencies gained in a process (that is, reduction of non-value-added activities) without a head count

reduction. For example, the process cycle time that involved two workers was reduced by 10%. Assuming the 10% amounts to two hours per worker per week, the two workers save four hours per week. These four hours are allocated to other tasks.

Another way to impact the bottom line is through revenue or top-line growth. How might a Lean Six Sigma project affect such growth? Consider a project that identifies and removes a production bottleneck or constraint. As a direct consequence of removing that constraint, the organization can accept new customer orders (something it wasn't able to do previously) or work off backlogged orders. In this situation, revenue growth is achieved, and the reason is the constraint removal as an outcome of the project. It would seem that "revenue growth" would be a desirable category to which to attribute the dollar impact of Lean Six Sigma project dollars.

Some organizations further refine cost savings into the third category of working capital/cash flow. Projects falling into this category might improve internal invoicing processes, resulting in lower accounts receivable, or reduce inventory requirements through increased process efficiency and reduced claims. Figure 5.2 reflects all the possible impacts to the bottom line and the types of cost avoidance discussed.

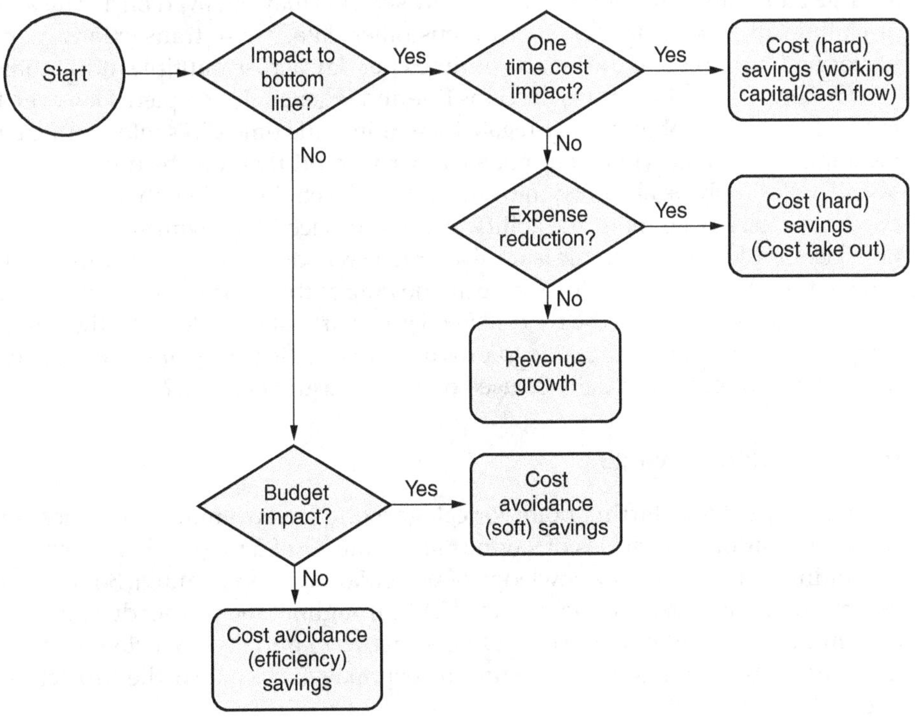

Figure 5.2 Expanded definition of cost savings.

In summary, there are two major categories of savings, each of which can be further refined:

- Hard savings (cost savings)
  - Cost take-out
  - Revenue growth
  - Working capital/cash flow
- Soft savings (cost avoidance)
  - Cost avoidance (budget impacting)
  - Cost avoidance (non–budget impacting)

False Savings

One of the most troubling and abused areas of savings is cost avoidance (non–budget impacting). This area of savings is typically generated from productivity or efficiency gains. Many organizations will save a small slice of time in an employee workday, multiply that by the number of workers performing the same job and extend that over a year. Voilà! Enormous savings are generated and booked. This approach is common in many transaction-based organizations such as large banks and call centers where a few seconds may be saved on a transaction or calling up a computer screen with customer data. These transactions may be performed hundreds of thousands of times per day across multiple individuals.

On the surface, this approach seems fine and is generally accepted. However, the fallacy lies with the ability to aggregate these miniscule time slices into a sufficiently meaningful size that will accommodate other work. If this can't be done, the "time saved" will simply be absorbed into adjacent work activities. Then they are not even paper savings. Furthermore, the ability to measure such time savings might be questionable. Consider trying to measure five or ten seconds saved from a two- to three-minute transaction. In many cases, we are dealing at the noise level. Yet, these types of savings are reported all the time, in Six Sigma particularly. Although they may be categorized as cost avoidance due to productivity or efficiency gains, are they really that if the gains cannot actually be used or even measured reliably?

Identifying Project Savings

Table 5.5 provides a starting point for categorizing improvement in business metrics to the various categories of savings at the outset of a project. However, at the beginning of a project our knowledge of potential savings is limited. Some categories of savings by business metric may hold throughout the project duration, with only minor increases or decreases. Others that were initially projected may never materialize. Still others that were unforeseen may surface near the project's end and yield healthy returns.

It is important to remember that any given project may have a wide variety of savings. Therefore, it is crucial to involve the financial representative to ensure that potential savings are not overlooked and to provide or enhance the credibility of the statement of benefits.

Business metric	Savings categories				
	Cost (hard) savings			Cost (soft) avoidance	
	Cost take out (bottom line)	Revenue growth (top line)	Working capital/ cash flow	Cost avoidance (budget)	Cost avoidance (non-budget)
Labor					
The amount of labor required to perform a process decreases					
Shift premium decreases or is eliminated					
Overtime decreases					
Less rework occurs					
Material					
Less material is consumed (for example, solvents, office supplies, and so on)					
Less raw materials are purchased					
Less material is stocked in inventory					
Shelf life is extended/ expirations are reduced					
Reduced lead time in acquiring parts					
Reduced price of raw materials					
Increased inventory turns					
Inventory carrying costs are reduced					
Capacity					
Machine cycle time decreases					
Available capacity increases and can be used					
Overhead					
Travel expenses are reduced or eliminated					
Reduction of floor space					

Table 5.5 Business metrics and savings categories. *Continued*

Business metric	Savings categories				
	Cost (hard) savings			Cost (soft) avoidance	
	Cost take out (bottom line)	Revenue growth (top line)	Working capital/ cash flow	Cost avoidance (budget)	Cost avoidance (non-budget)
Improvement in building and grounds					
Reduction in expenses and supplies					
Fewer utilities are used (for example, electric, gas, water)					
Equipment					
Capital requirements are reduced or eliminated					
General and miscellaneous					
Less scrap is produced					
Customer penalties are decreased or eliminated					
Planned future costs are reduced or eliminated					
Less office supplies consumed					
Customer					
Improvement in customer satisfaction					
Improvement in voice of the customer					
Reduced warranty claims					
Increased OEM acceptance rates					
Process					
Increased yields					
Improvement in voice of the process					
Revenue growth					
Increased capacity					
Removal of process bottlenecks					

Table 5.5 *Continued*

Part III

Team Management

Chapter 6

Team Formation

If everyone is moving forward together, then success takes care of itself.

–Henry Ford

This chapter will address the various aspects of forming a team, including team types, constraints placed on teams, team roles and responsibilities, criteria for selecting team members, and factors that make teams successful.

TEAM TYPES AND CONSTRAINTS

> Define and describe various teams, including virtual, cross-functional, and self-directed. Determine what team type will work best for a given set of constraints, e.g., geography, technology availability, staff schedules, time zones. (Apply)
>
> **Body of Knowledge III.A.1**

The two general types of teams are *formal* and *informal. Formal teams* have a specific goal or goals linked to the organization's plans. The goal is referred to as the *mission* or *statement of purpose* of the team. The formal team may also have a charter that includes its mission statement, a listing of team members, and a statement of support from management. *Informal teams* usually have none of these documents and may have a more fluid membership depending on their needs.

Virtual teams are made up of people in different locations who may never meet in person. Instead, the team may hold online meetings, often augmented by asynchronous communication through virtual collaboration platforms and e-mail. Virtual teams can bring specific benefits to the organization such as:

- Reduced travel expenses
- Reduced office equipment requirements
- Increased flexibility
- Increased number of potential team members

Process improvement teams are formed to identify and propose changes in specific processes. These teams are usually *cross-functional,* involving representation from various groups likely to be impacted by the changes.

Self-managed work teams and *work group teams* usually have a broader and more open-ended mission involving day-to-day operations. These teams often own a work process and are collocated. These work teams typically make decisions about safety, quality, maintenance, scheduling, personnel, and so on.

Management cannot simply declare that a work group is a self-managed work team and then expect success. Successful self-management comes only with the proper preparation and infrastructure. According to Westcott (2014), self-managed work teams "require more up-front planning, support structures, and nurturing. The transition will usually take a significant time period and needs consistent support from management."

There are different constraints that affect the efficiency and effectiveness of each type of team. Let's look at each constraint type briefly:

- *Geography.* Geography might include team members in their home offices, or groups of workers at different sites.
- *Technology availability.* The technology available may differ vastly depending on the organization's resources and culture. Technologies that enable virtual meetings and collaboration are dependent upon reliable and fast Internet connections, which may not be available in all areas.
- *Staff schedules.* Team members may be on different shifts or work different weekly schedules. This adds a layer of complexity to meeting scheduling and communication.
- *Time zones.* Today's virtual team members may operate in widely different time zones. In today's global organizations, there may be as much as a 12- to 16-hour time difference between team members. In these situations, asynchronous collaboration can be used to meet team deliverables.

TEAM ROLES AND RESPONSIBILITIES

> Define and describe various team roles and responsibilities for leader, facilitator, coach, and individual member. (Understand)
>
> **Body of Knowledge III.A.2**

Teams seem to work best when members understand their assigned roles and the team dynamics. Some standard team roles with typical duties include:

Champion. As discussed in Chapter 2, a champion or sponsor is a senior manager who ensures that their projects are aligned with the organization's strategic goals and priorities, provides the Six Sigma team with resources, removes organizational barriers for the team, participates in project tollgate reviews, and serves as the team's executive sponsor. This individual does not usually attend regular team meetings.

Team leader. A team leader is often a Black Belt, although smaller scale projects can be led by Green Belts. The team leader:

- Chairs team meetings and maintains team focus on the goal.
- Monitors progress toward the goal and communicates this to the organization.
- Manages administrative and record-keeping details.
- Establishes and follows up on action assignments for individual team members.

Facilitator. There may be a separate team member designated to fulfill the facilitator role. Often, the team leader also acts as the facilitator based on resources available and the skill level needed. The facilitator:

- Makes certain all members have an opportunity for input and that a full discussion of issues occurs. In some cases, the facilitator chairs the meeting.
- Helps the team leader keep the team on track.
- Summarizes progress using visual aids as appropriate.
- Provides methods for reaching decisions.
- Mitigates nonproductive behavior.
- Helps resolve conflicts.

Scribe/recorder. This may be a temporary or rotating position. The scribe:

- Maintains and publishes meeting minutes. May communicate action assignment reminders to individuals.
- May use visual aids to record discussion points so all can see and react.

Timekeeper. This role is used when a timed agenda is used. The timekeeper:

- Keeps track of the time elapsed.
- Notifies the team leader or facilitator of the time remaining on each agenda item.

Coach. In the case of a Lean Six Sigma team, the coach is likely to be the Master Black Belt. The coach:

- Works with the team leader and facilitator to move the team toward the objective.

- Helps provide resources for completion of team member assignments.
- Evaluates the team's progress.

Team member: A successful team member:

- Participates in team meetings.
- Communicates ideas and expertise.
- Listens openly to all ideas.
- Completes action assignments as scheduled.

TEAM MEMBER SELECTION CRITERIA

> Describe various factors that influence the selection of team members, including the ability to influence, openness to change, required skills sets, subject matter expertise, and availability. (Apply)
>
> **Body of Knowledge III.A.3**

Organizations can use several criteria to select the appropriate members for a team. Such criteria are important because their use is foundational to making a team successful. Typical criteria include:

- *Ability to influence.* The ability to influence is important in that this skill helps keep the team moving forward by building consensus on decisions.
- *Openness to change.* Team members that hunker down and dig into a position even when presented with facts that contradict their position can create great frustration for the team. Team members that are open to change create harmony and keep the team moving forward.
- *Required skill sets.* Teams usually require a variety of skill sets. Possessing a required skill set fills a void and keeps the team moving forward.
- *Subject-matter expertise.* A subject-matter expert is an individual who is intimately familiar with the detailed workings of the process under investigation. This individual will bring facts and knowledge to the team when needed.
- *Availability.* Teams cannot be staffed simply by whomever is available. Unfortunately, many organizations do this. A team must select the right individual, one who has the ability to influence, is open to change, and

possesses the right skill set. This individual may or may not be a subject matter expert. Alternately, teams are often staffed with members who delegate their attendance to subordinates who are not in a position to make decisions. Such actions stall teams or even cause them to fail.

- *Team orientation.* It is not uncommon that some individuals find the role of "team member" to be troublesome. More specifically, they may find that they do not know how to behave in this role. As this information becomes known, it is imperative that the team leader takes immediate action. Such action might include "team (member) training." This training would provide instruction regarding how to serve on a team, what is expected of a team member, and so on. Such training may be formal or informal depending on the extent of the need.

Other Considerations

In some situations, team composition will change over the life cycle of the project. For example, design engineers may be involved in the concept phase of a new product, and production personnel would be brought in for the preproduction/launch phase. Some team members may be in one, some, or all phases depending on the nature of the project. Of course, care must be exercised to ensure that team members are brought in at the appropriate times. For example, waiting too long to involve production personnel may result in an elegant yet non-buildable product.

A team must be provided with the resources needed to complete team activities and assignments. This includes ensuring that team member participation is viewed as part of a team member's job and that adequate time is allotted for completing team assignments.

Finally, teams should be staffed with actively involved members who can make decisions on behalf of the organizations they represent. If team members are not empowered to make decisions, then other members should be chosen, or the team should not be launched.

TEAM SUCCESS FACTORS

> Identify and describe the elements necessary for successful teams, e.g., management support, clear goals, ground rules, and timelines. (Apply)
>
> **Body of Knowledge III.A.4**

Using teams to work through Lean Six Sigma projects has become commonplace. Team members and team dynamics bring resources to bear on a project and yield results that people working individually would not be able to produce.

However, even well-selected teams with the best intentions may still perform suboptimally without careful preparation. There seems to be no standard list of preparation steps, but the following items should be addressed at a minimum:

Management support. Teams can succeed only if management wants them to. If clear management support is not in place, the wisdom of launching the team is in question. Team members must know that they have the authority to gather data, ask difficult questions, and, in general, think differently.

Sponsorship. All teams should have a sponsor who has a vested interest in the project. The sponsor reviews the team's progress, provides resources, and removes organizational roadblocks.

Team purpose and goals. The team should have a clear purpose and a set of goals. These should be directly related to the project charter. Teams should not be asked to define their own purpose, although intermediate goals and timetables can be team generated. Teams often flounder when their purpose is too vague. If team members have been selected to represent groups or supply technical knowledge, these roles should be announced at the initial or kickoff meeting.

Team initiation. The formation of the team should be communicated in a written document from an individual at the executive level of the organization. Sign-off from each member's immediate supervisor is also very helpful in providing up-front recognition that the team member's participation is important for the success of the team.

Team-building training. Time should be allocated in the project plan for team training. Without an understanding of how a team works and the individual behavior that advances team progress, the team will often get caught in personality concerns and turf wars.

Team meeting schedule. A schedule of team meetings should be published early, and team members should be asked to commit to attending all meetings. Additional subgroup meetings may be scheduled, but full team meetings should be held as originally scheduled.

Team ground rules and norms. The establishment of team norms is a helpful technique that is often initiated at the first team meeting. Team norms provide clear guidelines regarding what the team will and will not tolerate, and often define the consequences of violating the norms. These norms can be captured in a team-created Team Charter. Examples of team norms include:

- Be on time. (A consequence of being late may be to put a dollar into a collection jar that will be used at the team's discretion later.)
- Hold one conversation at a time.
- Demonstrate civility and courtesy to all members.
- Accomplish assigned tasks on time.
- Provide advance notice of not being able to attend a meeting.

- Actively participate in each meeting.
- Follow a prepared agenda.
- Put all phones, tablets, and laptops away.
- For online meetings, turn cameras on and mute microphones when not speaking. If someone requests that the meeting be recorded, notify all team members and ask for their approval.
- Discussions in the meeting are confidential. What is said in the room stays in the room.

Once a Six Sigma team has been selected and launched, the Black Belt must then work to guide the individuals through the team growth stages, facilitate discussions to uncover root causes, lead the team meetings, and deliver training on Six Sigma tools. We discuss these topics in Chapters 7–9.

Chapter 7
Team Facilitation

The new leader is a facilitator, not an order giver.

—John Naisbitt

This chapter will cover various aspects of team facilitation, from motivation techniques, demotivating factors to avoid, the stages of team development, team communication modes, facilitation behaviors to avoid, and team leadership models.

MOTIVATION TECHNIQUES

> Describe and apply techniques to motivate team members. Identify factors that can demotivate team members and describe techniques to overcome them. (Apply)
>
> **Body of Knowledge III.B.1**

In many enterprises people feel like anonymous cogs in a giant machine. They become unwilling to invest much of themselves in a project. An important part of team leadership is generating and maintaining a high level of motivation toward project completion. The following recognition and reward techniques have proved successful.

Recognition

Some forms of recognition include:

- Letters of appreciation sent to individuals and placed in personnel files
- Public expressions of appreciation via meetings, newsletters, and so forth
- Positive feedback and comments from management
- Inclusion in the performance appraisal, which is important, particularly because this type of recognition tells the individual that the project was not separate from their "regular" job and was

important to the organization. Also, it can be a means of reinforcing a Lean Six Sigma deployment.

Ideally, the type of recognition given should be tailored to the individual to be most effective. For example, shy individuals would probably not appreciate public recognition. The responsibility lies with the individual providing the recognition to determine the best type to deliver.

Rewards

Rewards fall into two categories: monetary and nonmonetary. Monetary rewards are effective, especially when considerable personal time or sacrifice is involved. However, particular care must be taken with this type of reward. Frequently, the individual giving the reward delivers the same dollar amount to each team member without considering the amount of personal time, sacrifice, or results achieved by each team member.

This is the easy route for the giver, but it may generate hard feelings within the team because all the members know the degree to which each team member participated. One way around this issue is to provide a set monetary limit for the entire team and allow the members to determine how the money is spent or divided.

Monetary rewards can include:

- Bonuses based on milestones met
- Percentage of the project savings
- Fixed or scale-based dollar amounts

When monetary rewards are involved, it is recommended that an objective means of determining the reward is established or, at least, an agreement is made in advance. Otherwise, recipients may tend to second-guess the reward structure. This can set morale on a downward spiral.

Nonmonetary rewards include tokens of appreciation such as trophies, gifts, apparel, vacations, and so on. Nonmonetary rewards, like monetary rewards, must be thought out in advance.

Relationships Within the Team

During team meetings, facilitators and other team members can enhance motivation by setting an example of civility and informality, relaxing outside roles, and exhibiting a willingness to learn from one another. Simply, they can serve as role models.

It is also helpful if one of the team ground rules is to "leave your stripes at the door." This translates to a level playing field during the meeting, because all titles and ranks are left outside the meeting room. All team members become equals.

Celebrating the achievement of a project milestone may enhance teamwork. Some team leaders have found that the adage "celebrate early, celebrate often" is highly effective. In addition, some authorities suggest that participation and motivation are improved simply by referring to team sessions as workshops rather than meetings.

Westcott (2014) notes that "[a]n effective team leader can provide an environment in which team members feel motivated. This can be achieved by applying the *six R's*:

1. *Reinforce.* Identify and positively reinforce work done well.
2. *Request information.* Discuss team members' views. Is anything preventing expected performance?
3. *Resources.* Identify needed resources, the lack of which could impede quality performance.
4. *Responsibility.* Customers make paydays possible; all employees have a responsibility to the customers, internal and external.
5. *Role.* Be a role model. Don't just tell; demonstrate how to do it. Observe [team members'] performance. Together, critique the approach and work out an improved method.
6. *Repeat.* Apply the above principles regularly and repetitively."

One of the most important motivating factors is *communication,* which will be discussed in a later section in this chapter.

DEMOTIVATING FACTORS

There are many factors either working independently or in combination with others that can demotivate team members. The following are some of the more significant ones:

- *Constantly changing scope.* Often, the source of this issue is leadership. In this case, it would be the project sponsor. When project scope changes constantly, it is likely due to the lack of a signed project charter by the project sponsor. Revisit the project charter with the sponsor and the team, working the issue until agreement is achieved and the charter is signed. If necessary, use the project coach for assistance.
- *Unclear problem statement.* Hopefully, this is just a matter of poor writing. However, unclear problem statements can occur when the pain point is not defined. In some cases, this points to "pet" projects. When this occurs, engage your project coach. Lean Six Sigma team resources should not be expended on projects such as these.
- *Unclear scope.* Work with the project sponsor to clarify the scope. Don't let this issue linger. In fact, projects with unclear scopes should never launch.
- *Insufficient resources.* This insufficiency may be in terms of dollars and/or available workers. A quick way of dealing with this issue is to adjust the project plan to reflect the constraints and present the

revision to the project sponsor. If the adjusted plan is not acceptable to the sponsor, it is the sponsor's responsibility to secure the appropriate resources so that the plan can be modified accordingly.

- *Failure to achieve goals.* Decompose the goals into smaller, intermediate, and more achievable milestones. Celebrate these milestones when they're accomplished.
- *Team members' supervisors preempt team's work.* This can and does create significant problems for teams in many organizations. In addition, it sends a mixed message to the organization regarding the importance of the work of the team. Furthermore, it creates a dilemma for the team member. As soon as these issues occur, the team leader must work through the sponsor who will, in turn, work with the appropriate supervisors to resolve it.
- *Team members who aren't team players.* Occasionally, there will be a time when the application of motivation techniques fails to improve the behavior of a team member. When this occurs, it is usually best to have a private conversation with the team member with the express intent of notifying them that their future participation is in question. Furthermore, contingent upon a turnaround in behavior, their participation on the team will be terminated. This drastic step will usually yield the desired result for most team members. However, there are those stubborn few for which this approach does not work. In this case, the team leader must be prepared to replace the team member. Removing a team member actually takes a courageous leader. Many team leaders would be reluctant to take this necessary action due to the high level of conflict involved. Consequently, the morale and productivity of the entire team suffers.

The Five Dysfunctions of a Team

To function at a high level, teams must overcome what Lencioni (2012) describes as the *Five Dysfunctions of a Team*. These dysfunctions build upon one another, as shown in Figure 7.1.

1. *Absence of trust.* As shown in Figure 7.1, trust is the bedrock of a successful team. If members do not feel comfortable sharing their opinions, or making mistakes, then the team will not be successful. If there is an absence of trust, none of the other dysfunctions can be overcome.
2. *Fear of conflict.* Only after trust has been established can team members feel secure enough to disagree with each other (this is aligned with the storming phase of team development). Trusted team members can challenge each other's views without creating resentment. If there is a fear of conflict, then the team will lapse into groupthink, which rarely results in the best solutions.

Figure 7.1 Lencioni's five dysfunctions of a team.

3. *Lack of commitment.* Teams that engage in healthy discussions foster commitment from members. These discussions, in which everyone's opinion is heard, lead to decisions that are more likely to get buy-in from members. Fear of conflict leads to lack of commitment and direction, which can lead to frustration among team members.
4. *Avoidance of accountability.* If team members are committed to a plan of action, they will be willing to be held accountable for their actions. Member goals will align with the team's decisions, and team members will work to achieve the desired result. If there is lack of commitment, then members will avoid accepting accountability for their actions and the team's progress.
5. *Inattention to team results.* Finally, team members that trust one another, are not afraid to disagree, are committed to the team goals and decisions, and are accountable to the group will pay attention to the team's results. When team members are not held accountable for results, they will put their individual needs over the team's objectives.

TEAM STAGES OF DEVELOPMENT

Identify and describe the classic stages of team development: forming, storming, norming, performing, and adjourning. (Apply)

Body of Knowledge III.B.2

According to Tuckman (1965), teams progress through several growth stages:

- *Forming.* In this initial stage, members are hesitant participants, and may struggle to understand the team goal and its meaning for them individually. In this stage, members will look to the leader to help them understand their roles.
- *Storming.* Teams then progress to the storming stage in which there can be intragroup conflict. Members may be competitive or defensive, expressing their own opinions and ideas and often disagreeing with others. Team members are thinking based on individual experiences, and collaboration has yet to occur. Members may want to redefine the team's purpose and goals, and some will test the leader's authority.
- *Norming.* In this stage, team members cultivate group cohesion, and begin to understand the need to operate as a team rather than as a group of individuals. Members feel comfortable expressing themselves and listening to others. Interpersonal conflicts are becoming less frequent, and work toward goals is beginning to proceed.
- *Performing.* At this stage, the team works together as a cohesive unit to reach their common goal. Members understand one another and recognize each other's strengths and weaknesses.

Two additional stages have since been added to Tuckman's original model:

- *Adjourning.* Tuckman expanded his original model (Tuckman and Jensen, 1977) to include this final stage. This stage acknowledges the "life cycle" model of team development in which there is a distinct end point for the team. In this stage, a final team meeting is held, during which management decisions regarding the project are discussed, and other loose ends are tied up. This is a critical step. Formal closeout of teams is important in that it generates a feeling of accomplishment. All too often, team members are left hanging, not knowing whether their role on a team is complete or if they can reallocate their valuable time.
- *Recognition.* This team stage was added to the expanded Tuckman model to assure that after the team has adjourned, it is properly recognized for its accomplishments. The team's contribution is acknowledged using the techniques of recognition and reward discussed earlier in Motivation Techniques.

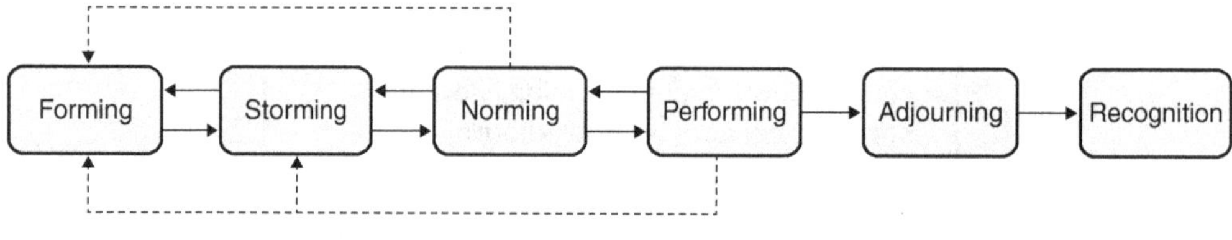

Figure 7.2 Team stages and their flow.

In Figure 7.2, the horizontal arrows indicate the standard stages of team development. The dashed arrows show alternate paths taken by teams in some circumstances. For example, once a team has reached the performing stage, the addition of an ad hoc member who attends a few meetings to share their expertise may move the entire team down a level (to norming), as it tries to incorporate this new member. Recognize that any new members added start off in the forming stage, and the team leader must bring the new members through the stages as quickly as possible, so that they can "catch up" with the rest of the team and be effective additions.

If a team leader or facilitator observes signs of regressing, they should remind the group of the goals and agenda and the need to press forward. Team members accustomed to working with one another on similar projects may skip the storming stage, and possibly the norming stage.

TEAM COMMUNICATION

> Describe and explain the elements of an effective communication plan, e.g., audience identification, message type, medium, frequency. (Apply)
>
> Body of Knowledge III.B.3

Lack of effective communication is one of the most frequently noted causes of team failure. Sincere effort toward improving communication should be made at each stage of team development. In some situations, such as large projects or those with geographical barriers, it is necessary to develop a formal communication plan.

It was noted in Chapter 6 that at the time a team is initiated, a clear statement of the goals and purpose of the team is critical. If team members have been selected to represent groups or supply technical knowledge, these roles should be announced at the initial or kickoff meeting. The team's initiation should be in the form of a written document from an individual at the executive level of the organization. A separate document from each member's immediate supervisor is also helpful in reinforcing that the team member's participation is important for the success of the team.

Ongoing communication throughout the duration of a project is essential. This includes:

- Announcements of team meetings—including time, location, agenda, and such—must be made as early as possible.
- Minutes or a summary of the meeting should be provided immediately after each session.
- Disposition of action items.

Who delivers	What message	To whom	By what method	How often

Table 7.1 Constructing a communications plan.

- Routine status reports and presentations to management.
- Feedback from management to the team.
- Feedback to the team from the team leader, coach, or sponsor.
- Routine status reports from the team members to the team leader.
- Final reports and closeout memos.

One particularly useful document for facilitating communication is the communications plan shown in Table 7.1. This document helps direct the flow of communication both within and outside of the team.

A communications plan defines who will deliver and what will be communicated, to whom, how often, and by what means. Communications could include status reports, presentations, newsletters, and so on. Methods may be either formal or informal. In all cases, though, the communications plan must reflect the needs of the receiver.

Communicating Within the Team

Communication within the team should take place on a regular basis. All communication within the team should be open, honest, and with no fear of retribution. In general, team members should be aware of any project problems or issues before anyone outside of the team. No team member should ever be blindsided because project information bypassed them.

In addition, team members should be kept apprised of their own performance. Too often, this valuable activity is ignored. The project leader may feel uncomfortable providing constructive criticism, or because of limited human capital resources, the project leader may be reluctant to alienate a team member by providing less than positive feedback.

As noted previously, lack of adequate communication is one of the most frequently noted causes of team failure. In some situations, such as large projects or those with wide geographical boundaries, the development of a formal communications plan is critical to success. This is particularly true in the case of virtual teams.

Many teams operating in today's large organizations may never be face to face or, for that matter, ever see one another. Fortunately, technology facilitates team interaction. However, careful planning for communication is still required.

Who delivers	What message	To whom	By what method	How often
Team leader	Progress report	Project sponsor	Face-to-face presentation	Second Tuesday of each month
Team leader	Progress report	Project sponsor subordinates	E-mail	Second Wednesday of each month
Team scribe	Team meeting minutes	Team members	E-mail	Within 24 hours after each team meeting
Coach	Team evaluation	Team members	Face to face	Quarterly

Table 7.2 Example of a communications plan.

Accommodations for extreme time zone differences might be necessary, and technologies may be new or challenging to some sites and localities. Therefore, it is important to test any form of technical communication before operating it in a live environment.

The irony is that we now have technology that facilitates round-the-clock, worldwide contact, but this technology can also make the communication process more difficult or prone to misunderstanding. If the communication process is conducted via audio only, team members have no ability to read body language or facial expression. They are limited to verbal cues and voice intonations. Even in video meetings, reading body language is more difficult than with an in-person setting. Consequently, some team members may find it difficult to function as a virtual team member. In these cases. team communication must be carefully planned, monitored, and adjusted, as necessary.

Table 7.2 provides an example of how a communication plan may be used by a team. Notice that it is used for communicating both within and outside of the team.

Communication Outside the Team

As with communication within the team, communication outside the team should also take place on a regular basis. Such communications typically include status reports and presentations. Status reports should be brief. A bullet format is usually sufficient when grouped under a series of headings. Typical headings include:

- Accomplishments since last report
- Problems, issues, or concerns
- Actions being taken
- 30-day plans

A recipient of a status report in the above format might conclude that the project leader is indeed making progress, has incurred problems but has recognized them (some leaders don't), has taken mitigating action (therefore, no need to intervene), and is proceeding forward once more.

The recipient reads the status report and is left with a feeling of confidence in the project leader. Poorly written status reports invite criticism and, occasionally, unwarranted scrutiny and intrusion.

Presentations are another format commonly used to communicate outside the team and are usually delivered to higher levels of the organization. The project leader may request a spot on the sponsoring executive's staff meeting agenda or may be invited to attend.

While the above bullet format is acceptable, more detail is required. Remember, the presentation will be interactive and usually face to face. Therefore, messages need to be clear and crisp. There is no room for ambiguity.

Furthermore, the presenter should expect interruptions and questions out of order, which may interrupt the intended delivery sequence. Hence, the presenter's motto is "Be prepared!" As with poorly written status reports, a poorly delivered presentation can be a disaster that makes recovery difficult and often brings unwanted help.

TEAM LEADERSHIP MODELS

> Describe and select appropriate leadership approaches (e.g., direct, coach, support, delegate) to ensure team success. (Apply)
>
> **Body of Knowledge III.B.4**

Blanchard et al. (1999) developed what is described as a *situational leadership* model. This model is illustrated in Figure 7.3. In this model the leadership style is categorized by quadrant according to the leader's degree of supportive and directive behavior. *Supportive behavior* involves two-way communication and focuses on emotional and social support, while *directive behavior* establishes a clear path to the goal by specifying what is to be done, how it is to be done, and who is going to do it.

Each leadership style now will be addressed:

- *Directing.* This style is characterized by high directive and low supportive behavior. It is suited for individuals who possess low competence and high commitment. Such individuals are often described as *enthusiastic beginners.* They are new to a task and motivated about it.
- *Coaching.* This style is characterized by high directive and high supportive behavior. It is suited for individuals who possess moderate competence and low commitment. Such individuals are often

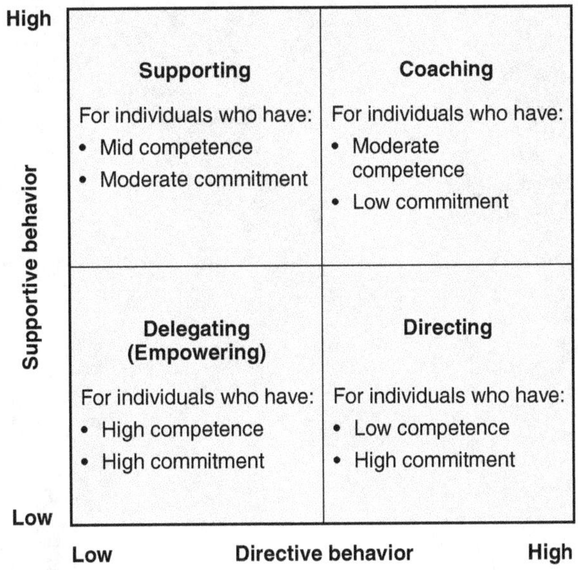

High

Supporting

For individuals who have:
• Mid competence
• Moderate commitment

Coaching

For individuals who have:
• Moderate competence
• Low commitment

Supportive behavior

Delegating (Empowering)

For individuals who have:
• High competence
• High commitment

Directing

For individuals who have:
• Low competence
• High commitment

Low

Low Directive behavior High

Figure 7.3 Situational leadership model.
Source: Adapted from Blanchard et al. (1999).

described as *disillusioned learners*. They are new to a task, but not motivated about it.

- *Supporting*. This style is characterized by low directive and high supportive behavior. It is suited for individuals who possess mid-level competence and moderate commitment. Such individuals are often described as *capable, but cautious, performers*. They know their task but are not motivated about it.
- *Delegating (Empowering)*. This style is characterized by low directive and low supportive behavior. It is suited for individuals who possess high competence and high commitment. Such individuals are often described as *self-reliant achievers*. They are proficient in their task and are highly motivated about it.

It is important to note that leadership styles are highly dynamic and depend on the competency or commitment level of an individual at any given time. For example, an individual who is competent at a specific task may vary in their commitment toward that task over time depending on their motivation. Similarly, an individual who is committed to their task will likely demonstrate an increase in competency as they gain proficiency over time. Consequently, leaders should recognize these shifting dynamics and adjust their styles accordingly.

Chapter 8

Team Dynamics

Coming together is a beginning; keeping together is progress; working together is success.

—Henry Ford

This chapter will cover group and individual disruptive behaviors as well as conflict management techniques that can be used to overcome them. Meeting management and group decision-making approaches are also presented.

GROUP BEHAVIORS

> Identify and use various conflict resolution techniques (e.g., coaching, mentoring, and intervention) to overcome negative group dynamics, including dominant and reluctant participants, groupthink, rushing to finish, and digressions. (Evaluate)
>
> **Body of Knowledge III.C.1**

Group Disruptive Behaviors

Once teams have been formed, they must be built, because a true team is more than a collection of individuals. A team begins to take on a life of its own that is greater than the sum of its parts.

The building of a team begins with well-trained members who understand their roles and responsibilities within the team and how they may differ from their roles outside the team. For example, a first-line supervisor might find himself deferring to team members during team sessions more than he would outside team meetings. Teams are built with understanding and trust in fellow team members; therefore, an early step in team building should be informal introductions of each member.

Various ice breakers can be used in the first team meeting such as *give your name, a non–job related interest, and what you hope the team accomplishes.* This last request sometimes uncovers so-called hidden agendas. These are goals individuals have in addition to the team's stated goals and purposes. Whether or not such agendas are verbalized, team members must recognize their existence and importance. The most successful teams suppress the hidden agendas in favor of team progress on the stated ones.

The best model for team leadership is the coach who strives to motivate all members to contribute their best. Productive teams occur when team coaches facilitate progress while recognizing and dealing with obstacles. Team leaders or team facilitators, or both, may perform the coaching function. Table 8.1 contains common team obstacles and associated solutions.

Individual Disruptive Behaviors

Within the team, there may be individuals who exhibit behaviors that are not productive (Eckes, 2003). The types of behaviors can be characterized by the following personas:

- *The whisperer* turns and has private conversations with their neighbor. Others on the team may feel the whisperer is speaking negatively about team members.
- *The storyteller* is well liked, but gets off on tangents, or must recount the entire history of a problem—often putting themselves front and center as the main character or hero.
- *The dropout* is not engaged in the team. This team member may have been on the losing side of a previous decision and has decided not to cooperate.
- *The naysayer* often has a long tenure with the company and is quick to point out that a particular solution will not work because it was tried unsuccessfully ten years ago. This team member may react negatively to ideas to make themselves feel more knowledgeable than the rest of the team.
- *The verbal attacker* insults other team members and uses intimidation to try to get their way.
- *The politician* sees every decision as a way to get ahead. They may agree with whomever they are currently speaking with to curry favor.
- *The team clown* wastes a lot of time in meetings with asides and jokes. Comic relief is often welcome, especially when a discussion is intense, but the clown may use humor to deflect attention away from their lack of productivity.

Leading Group Discussions

An experienced facilitator can lead group discussions to get the most from each team member. Eckes (2003) describes several techniques that can be used to help team members generate ideas and keep the discussion flowing.

Obstacle	Solutions
• A person or group dominates the discussion	• Go around the team, asking each person for one comment or reaction. • Ask dominating people to summarize their positions or proposals and e-mail them to all team members. • If the dominating people tend to react negatively to the suggestions of others, ask them for their ideas first or adopt the "no judgments allowed" rule from the brainstorming technique. • Speak to the dominating people between team meetings, requesting their assistance and cooperation in making sure all voices are heard.
• A person or group is reluctant to participate	• Be sure to welcome and express appreciation for every comment or contribution. • Form small subgroups that report to the full team. • Make action assignments for each person, with brief reports at the beginning of the next team meeting. • Speak to the reluctant people between team meetings, requesting their assistance and cooperation in making sure all voices are heard.
• A tendency exists to accept opinions without data	• Emphasize the importance of basing decisions on facts from the first meeting onward. • Raise questions such as: – Are there data that can support that? – How do we know that? – How could we verify that? – Who could collect some data on that?
• Groupthink: emphasis on consensus building has influenced a team to seek consensus too early or members are more concerned with avoiding a conflict	• Provide full opportunity for the expression of all views. • Seek out dissenting views. • Ask individuals to play devil's advocate by opposing early consensus. • Be sure a preliminary written conclusion includes dissenting views. • Ensure that the team ground rules call for multiple alternatives to be examined.
• Team members begin to air old disputes	• Make sure ground rules state the need for a fresh start, keeping history in the past. • Have a printed agenda, possibly with scheduled times for agenda items. A facilitator may say, "It's 3:10; let's move on to item number 2." • Assign team members the job of collecting data regarding the issue in dispute.

Table 8.1 Negative group dynamics–team obstacles and solutions. *Continued*

Obstacle	Solutions
• The team is floundering because it has lost sight of its goals and objectives	• Make sure goals and objectives are clear and well understood at the first team meeting. • Start team meetings by revisiting goals and objectives and offering a reminder as to where the team is in its journey and which objective is next. • Use graphics based on PERT and Gantt charts to help keep teams focused. • Bring in an outside voice, which often generates new ideas and approaches. • Consider using a facilitator.
• The team is rushing to meet its milestones or designated accomplishments without the benefit of a thorough study or analysis Note: When the above occurs, the team risks: • Suboptimizing • Unintended consequences (that is, solving one problem but creating others • Missing root causes	• Encourage the team to study a far-ranging list of approaches and solutions. Use divergent thinking tools such as brainstorming and cause-and-effect diagrams to broaden the perspective. • When a change is studied, be sure it is clearly communicated to all who might be impacted. Actively seek input regarding possible unintended consequences. • If a root cause is "turned off," the problem should go away. Try toggling the root cause on and off and observe whether the problem is toggling also.
• The team becomes troubled over the issue of attribution (that is, who should get credit for an accomplishment)	• If an idea comes from outside the team, that should be acknowledged. • If an idea was advanced before the team was formed, that should be acknowledged. • Often, the source of ideas and concepts developed during team sessions is not known, but if one person or group was responsible, that should be acknowledged.
• The team digresses too far from its goals and objectives	• Assign an individual or group to follow through on a side topic. • Set a specific time as a deadline beyond which no effort will be spent on the topic.

Table 8.1 *Continued*

- A leader can use a *direct probe* to get the discussion started. For example, a leader may ask, "What steps can we take to mistake proof this process?"
- A *redirect* is used to bring the conversation back to the topic at hand if it gets off track. For example, "Let's remember the goal of this meeting is to brainstorm the root causes of the problem, not solutions. Let's return to the fishbone diagram."
- A facilitator can ask a *leading question* that will force a response or challenge the group. For example, "We've only written down three ideas for improvement. Surely this group can think of more?"
- A *behavioral observation* can be used to point out team dynamics and have the team address them. For example, a leader may say, "I noticed that the conversation slowed down when we mentioned changing suppliers. Why is that?"
- *Idea floating* can be used to spark creativity when the group seems at an impasse. For example, a leader may ask, "What if we reconfigure an existing machine to produce the new part? How would we do that?"
- The *boomerang technique* is used to return the floor to a team member who is perhaps being negative. For example, a leader may say, "John, you say Mary's idea won't work. What do you think we should do instead?"
- The *lasso technique* is used by the leader to sum up what the team has discussed and decided upon.

Facilitation Behaviors to Avoid

Facilitating a cross-function team can be challenging. Eckes (2003) lists what he calls the "Ten Sins of Facilitation" to be avoided:

1. Choosing which comments are worthy of being documented
2. Showing bias toward one tool or technique
3. Permitting digressions
4. Permitting ground rules to be broken
5. Creating the impression that the facilitator has a bias toward one person or idea
6. Speaking in emotionally charged language
7. Allowing distrust or disrespectful behavior to occur
8. Failing to create a sense of purpose
9. Ignoring time keeping
10. Doing all the work for the team

Conflict Management

Conflict is inevitable, and every team must be prepared to deal with it. Bens (2011) notes that facilitating conflict has two steps:

1. *Venting emotions.* Individuals will not begin to resolve issues until they have vented their emotions. This step involves making people feel they have been heard and helping diffuse any pent-up emotions.
2. *Resolving issues.* It is important that a facilitator stay calm, neutral, assertive, and in control of the situation. Reference to the team norms is helpful, and a continued emphasis on effective listening is necessary. Slow things down and focus on a structured approach (for example, force-field analysis) for moving forward. Capture key points on a flip chart or other visual media and revisit when there is a need to regain control. Create closure by testing agreed-upon points and issues.

The following are the five basic approaches for resolving issues illustrated in Figure 8.1:

1. *Avoid.* Ignore the issue with the hope that it will go away. Employ this technique when the issue cannot be resolved profitably.
2. *Accommodate.* This involves asking people to try to get along. In truth, one person will ultimately have to give in to another. Employ this technique when keeping the peace is more important than finding a solution.
3. *Compromise.* This occurs when views are polarized, and each must meet somewhere in the middle. Compromise is not a consensus. Consensus-building will be discussed later in this chapter.
4. *Compete.* This creates a win/lose situation and is the least desirable means of attempting to resolve conflict.
5. *Collaborate.* This creates a win/win situation and encourages the participants to seek solutions that they can agree to. This approach is based on data, fact, and trust. Participants must be committed to finding a consensus-based solution that works.

Coaching

Coaching is a process by which a more experienced individual helps enhance the existing skills and capabilities that reside in a less experienced individual. Coaching is about listening, observing, and providing constructive, practical, and meaningful feedback.

During training, coaching helps the trainee translate the theoretical learning into applied learning while also helping the trainee develop confidence in their newly developing knowledge and skills. Post training, coaches help projects stay on track and advance toward completion in a timely manner.

Coaches provide guidance and direction on how to navigate organizational barriers, select and use the proper tools and techniques, prepare for tollgate

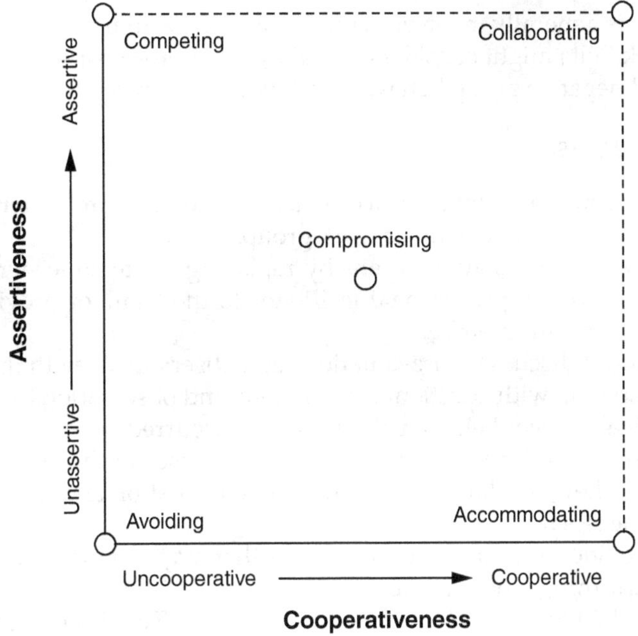

Figure 8.1 Conflict-handling modes.
Source: Furturer and Woods, 2021.

reviews, discover solutions on their own, provide intervention where needed, and generally serve as a sounding board for project-related issues. They are particularly useful in providing guidance regarding team conflict and facilitation issues given their considerable experience running project teams as both a Black Belt and Master Black Belt.

In some cases, the coach may find that the individual is unsuited to work on a specific project and consequently will have the project assigned to another Belt or request that the project champion have the project canceled if it no longer appears viable.

Mentoring

While coaching focuses on the individual as it relates to Lean Six Sigma, mentoring focuses on the individual from the career perspective. Mentors are usually experienced individuals (not necessarily in Lean Six Sigma) who have in-depth knowledge about the organization as well as the individual (that is, *mentee*). Usually, they come from within the organization, though not necessarily the same department as their mentee. Their role is to help provide guidance, wisdom, and a possible road map to career advancement.

Like the coach, the mentor also helps the individual navigate the organization. It would be conceivable that both a coach and a mentor would support an individual Black Belt concurrently. The coach would focus on the individual's role as a Belt and the mentor would focus on the individual's overall career. The mentor would be of great help to the individual in finding a suitable role elsewhere.

The mentor is generally involved with the Black Belt from a career standpoint. Therefore, Black Belts might consider only discussing project-specific issues such as conflicts and negative group behavior and dynamics with their mentor.

Intervention Strategies

An intervention is an action taken by a coach, facilitator, or team leader to support the effective functioning of a team or work group.

For example, a coach may intervene by replacing the team leader, replacing team members, adding a professional facilitator to the team, or providing additional training to specific members.

Coaches should discuss their evaluations and observations with the team frequently and follow up with additional evaluations and observations at later meetings to determine whether behavior changes have occurred.

By definition, team leaders and facilitators are closer to the everyday activities of the team. They may have to quickly assess a situation and decide whether intervention is necessary.

Table 8.2 provides a summary of conditions that may call for intervention and criteria for determining when to intervene.

Notice that the left column of Table 8.2 is bulleted. This is because the order of the conditions does not matter. The right column is numbered because it represents a serial thinking process. If the team leader or facilitator witnesses a possible situation described by the left column, they will mentally assess that situation by asking the series of questions outlined in the right column. Based on the answers to those questions, a decision is made, and the facilitator acts to intervene or not. Of course, this whole assessment takes place in seconds.

In Chapter 6 we discussed the concept of team norms and ground rules. Some teams gloss over this action swiftly. However, when done correctly, it makes team facilitation, and particularly intervention, much easier.

Often, situations requiring interventions are simply violations of team norms or ground rules. To ease the burden of facilitation, it is useful to post the norms and ground rules at each meeting. All that is required on the part of the facilitator is a minor interruption and a reference to the posting. Team members quickly understand and become accustomed to them. After a while, they begin to facilitate themselves.

The "three-knock rule" can be used as a team norm. This rule refers to a team member knocking three times on the table to interrupt the meeting for the sole purpose of gaining everyone's attention. With everyone's attention in hand, the team member explains that a team norm has been violated, such as too many side conversations, straying too far from the topic, and so on. The "three-knock rule" shares the facilitator's authority and role with all the team members. Once team members understand how this rule works, they will make adequate use of it, and meetings will begin to run smoothly.

Providing feedback is also an important way to address behaviors that violate team norms. Feedback to team members should be specific, address the behavior (and not the person), and be couched in terms of how the behavior makes the leader feel and why. Finally, the feedback should include a discussion of how the problem can be corrected in the future (Eckes, 2003). For example, a leader may

Conditions for intervening	Criteria for deciding to intervene
• A participant is not listening or paying attention or is distracting other participants • One or more side conversations are taking place • Participants are interrupting one another • Personal attacks, discourtesy, or incivility is occurring • The discussion is drifting off track • Violation of team norms or ground rules occurred • Violation of organization policy has occurred	1. Is this a serious problem? Consider whether this problem is a single serious problem or a series of recurring issues. 2. Will this problem go away by itself? 3. How much time will an intervention take, and do we have that much time? 4. How much of a disruption will the intervention cause, and can we recover from it? 5. Will the intervention impact team member relationships and/or the flow of the meeting? 6. Can the intervention hurt the climate of the meeting? 7. Will anyone's self-esteem be damaged? 8. What's the chance that the intervention will work? 9. Do I know these people well enough to do this? 10. Do I have enough credibility to do this? 11. Is it appropriate enough to intervene, given their level of openness and trust? 12. What will happen if I do nothing (that is, take no action)? Alternately, should I take action after the meeting?

Table 8.2 Deciding to intervene requires significant forethought.
Source: Adapted from Bens (1999).

say, "You've missed your last three deliverable deadlines. When you miss deadlines, I feel frustrated because the team cannot move on to the next phase of the project without the data we need. What can we do to make sure the next deadline is met?"

Eckes (2003) suggests methods and an escalation scale for leaders to use when trying to diffuse disruptor behaviors, as shown in Figure 8.2. At the lowest level, a leader can often stop an unwelcome behavior simply by making eye contact with the offender. If that is not effective, the leader can then stand up and walk halfway to the disruptor. Next, the leader can walk by the disruptor while making eye contact. If the behavior continues, the leader can ask the team member what they think about the current discussion. In most cases, these techniques will result in the offender realizing that their behavior is affecting the team. If further escalation is required, the leader can pull the member aside on a break and talk to them

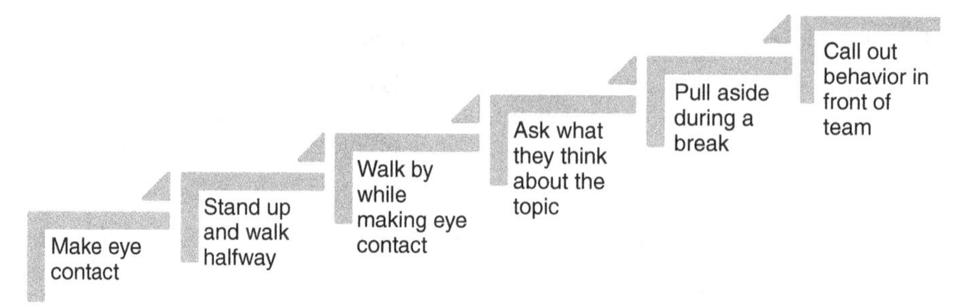

Figure 8.2 Escalation scale and methods for diffusing disruptive behavior.
Source: Eckes, 2003.

about their behavior directly. Calling out the disruptive behavior in front of the team should be the leader's last resort.

MEETING MANAGEMENT

> Select and use various meeting management techniques, including using agendas, starting on time, requiring pre-work by attendees, and ensuring that the right people and resources are available. (Apply)
>
> **Body of Knowledge III.C.2**

Time is often the most critical resource for any team. Team meeting time must be treated as the rare and valuable commodity that it is. It is up to the team leader and the facilitator to make every minute count, although every team member has this responsibility as well. Some practices that have proved useful follow:

- *Form an agenda committee.* This committee will generate the meeting agenda in advance of the scheduled meeting and will be responsible for getting the resources called for by each agenda item. For smaller teams, the team leader often prepares the agenda.
- *Publish timed meeting agendas.* A timed meeting agenda is simply a meeting agenda with time limits on each item. Assign a timekeeper and stick to the schedule as closely as possible. Leave five to ten minutes as a buffer at the end of the meeting and for conducting an end-of-meeting process check.

At times there will be agenda items that require more discussion time than allotted. There are two ways to handle these items. The first is to discuss within the time allotted and carry over the discussion into additional meetings until the issue is resolved. The second option is to spin off a sub-team and let the sub-team address the issue. Once the sub-team has completed its task, it will report to the main team with its resolution.

There are several methods to help keep a team productive and on track. Individually, each of the following techniques works well. Collectively, they keep teams effective, efficient, and moving forward. None of the techniques is difficult to learn or apply:

1. *Publish a project timeline.* Use a Gantt chart timeline displaying milestones and dates, updating as needed. This visual provides constant reinforcement of the milestones and due dates and retains a sense of urgency.
2. *Publish actions assigned.* In some cases, the team leader will want to review progress on these assignments between meetings.
3. *Publish reminders of assigned actions.* Intermediate reminders between meetings are helpful to ensure that actions are completed on time.
4. *Maintain a "parking lot" list.* This list contains important items that may not be relevant at the current time but should not be forgotten or may not be relevant to the team at all but should be forwarded to another authority for appropriate action or investigation.
5. *Start on time.* This may seem trivial, but it is of great importance—so much so that it should be incorporated into the team's norms. Lateness can be a great source of frustration and distraction for other members who are on time. Furthermore, some leaders have a propensity to backtrack for the benefit of late arrivals. This practice wastes time.
6. *Require pre-work.* Coming to a meeting with pre-work complete is like going to class with your homework complete. For example, if the meeting is to discuss a procedure, the pre-work should be to have each member review the procedure beforehand and come to the meeting prepared to discuss it. If necessary, the pre-work might include the member doing any related investigatory work that might be required to answer any of their own questions as well.
7. *Ensure that the right people and resources are available.* Occasionally, a meeting might require a special attendee, require a move to a special location for a particular meeting, and so on. Any unusual conditions or differences from normal meeting situations need to be given special attention and planned for in advance to ensure that meetings are executed smoothly and conducted effectively and efficiently.
8. *Assign prescribed roles.* This approach was covered in Chapter 6. Recall that the special roles include team leader, facilitator, scribe, timekeeper, and coach.
9. *Create the team norms.* The use of team norms was addressed in Chapter 6. Team norms describe the behavior we want team members to follow.

10. *Conduct in-meeting process checks.* Conduct periodic process checks during the meeting. Such checks include determining whether the team is making progress and whether it is moving at the right speed. It also provides the opportunity to ensure that all team members are moving forward together.

11. *Conduct end-of-meeting process check.* A few minutes are reserved at the end of each meeting and are included on the agenda to conduct a formal process check. This process check focuses on how well the meeting went and how it could be improved. Lessons learned from this activity are made effective with the next team meeting.

Apply a few of the preceding techniques in each meeting and before you know it, your team will be running smoothly and achieving its goals. When achieved, celebrate them!

TEAM DECISION-MAKING METHODS

> Define, select, and use various tools (e.g., consensus, nominal group technique, and multi-voting) for decision-making. (Apply)
>
> **Body of Knowledge III.C.3**

Consensus-Building

It is important to recognize that a consensus is not a compromise. Consensus creates a situation or outcome that all the participants can live with. If no situation or outcome can be found, discussion continues.

Bens (1999) provides an interesting take on consensus when she states, "Working toward consensus forces dissenters to collaborate. If they refuse and consensus isn't reached because of specific individuals, the minutes should reflect who blocked progress." She goes on to state, "Consensus isn't designed to make people happy or leave them in 100% agreement. Its goal is to create an outcome that represents the best feasible course of action given the circumstances."

Consensus requires a skilled facilitator who can, according to Bens (1999):

- Integrate and summarize complex ideas to the satisfaction of the group members
- Gain buy-in to the purpose of the meeting from all members
- Link people's ideas together so that they can see how they are saying the same thing

- Record ideas on a flip chart so that group members can see how they have contributed
- Draw out everyone's input into a clear goal and objective for the group's activities

While attempting to build consensus, the facilitator must simultaneously navigate the harsh waters of conflict management. It is for this reason that it is sometimes best that the roles of team leader and facilitator are split.

Nominal Group Technique (NGT)

The *nominal group technique* (NGT) is used to prioritize a list of items. The technique begins with all team members writing their ideas down on a slip of paper without any discussion. After a set period of time or when it appears that members have run out of ideas, the facilitator selects one idea from each team member and captures it on a flip chart. This process continues until all ideas have been collected. During this selection period, there is no discussion and ideas are not judged. When all the ideas have been captured, similar ideas can be consolidated with agreement from the contributing members.

Now it is time to prioritize the ideas. Each idea is designated with a letter, and each team member writes one letter on a slip of paper while assigning a priority to it. For example, if there are four items, each team member writes the letters A, B, C, and D on separate pieces of paper and then ranks each of the items, using a higher number for a higher ranking. The highest-ranking item would be marked "4," the next highest would be marked "3," and so on. (Conversely, ranks can be used with "1" being the highest priority. Either is acceptable. Make sure each member of the group understands the rating scale and which number maps to the highest rank.) The totals are compiled for each item and represent

EXAMPLE 8.1

Table 8.3 provides an example of the nominal group technique with four team members using a priority matrix with 4 being the highest priority. Note that team members 1 and 4 ranked item "A" high, while team members 2, 3, and 4 all ranked item "D" the highest. The resulting priority for the team, in order from highest to lowest, will be D, C, A, and B.

Item	Team member 1	Team member 2	Team member 3	Team member 4	Total
A	4	1	1	3	9
B	1	2	2	1	6
C	3	3	3	2	11
D	2	4	4	4	14

Table 8.3 Example of the nominal group technique.

the team's overall priorities. Items with the highest (lowest) totals are the priority items to be worked on by the team. If necessary, the process can be repeated for ties.

Multi-Voting

Multi-voting is a variation of nominal group technique (NGT) in which each team member has a set number of points with which to choose the items on the list that are most important in their view. Usually, the number of points assigned to the members is equal to one-third of the number of choices. For example, if there are 40 items to rate, each team member will be able to choose their highest 13 or 14 options from the list. After the allocations are complete, points assigned to each item are totaled and ranked accordingly. Items with the highest number of points are worked on first.

Another multi-voting technique is the "10-4" approach, in which each participant is allocated a total of ten points, regardless of the number of items on the list. Each participant then places anywhere from one to four points on their top items. For example, a team member can place four points on Item B, and two points on Item E, and one point each on items F, G, M, and P. The team's votes for each option are then tallied and ranked accordingly.

Note that multi-voting is easier to facilitate than the nominal group technique when there are more than ten items on the list, since it is difficult for most people to effectively rank more than ten items.

EXAMPLE 8.2

In this example, a four-person team is considering 15 items. Each member is given 15 × 1/3 = 5 points to choose the top five items in their view. Results are shown in Table 8.4. We note that Items G, E, and M earned the most votes, followed by items B, I, J, and K.

Item	Team member 1	Team member 2	Team member 3	Team member 4	Total
A	100	0	0	0	**100**
B	0	30	50	20	**100**
C	0	30	25	40	**95**
D	0	40	25	40	**105**

Table 8.4 Example of the multi-voting technique.

Votes can be placed individually, with each member allocating their points on a separate piece of paper that is then handed in to the team leader. If the team is a small, well-functioning group, and the items being prioritized are not controversial, the leader may choose to hand out different colored round stickers that represent points. (For example, a red dot equals four points, green equal three points, and yellow equals one point.) Team members can then approach the flip chart and openly vote for items with their stickers. The results will then be immediately apparent to everyone.

The Vroom-Yetton Decision-Making Model

Not every decision needs to be voted upon by the group. Vroom and Yetton (1973) developed a tree diagram to help leaders decide which decision-making technique best fits various situations. The types of decision-making approaches are listed and are based on four broad considerations: the quality of the decision required, commitment, problem information, and decision acceptance.

The model distinguishes between five decision-making approaches:

- *Autocratic* (A1). Use the information that you already have when making the decision, without reviewing any further input from your team.
- *Autocratic* (A2). Consult your team to obtain specific information that is needed, and then make the final decision.
- *Consultative* (C1). Inform the team of the situation and ask for members' opinions individually. The group is not brought in for a discussion. The leader then makes the final decision.
- *Consultative* (C2). The team is brought together to discuss the issue and give suggestions. The leader then makes the final decision.
- *Group-based* (G2). The leader works with the team to reach a group consensus. Here, the leader is mostly acting as facilitator to help team members reach a decision that they can all agree with.

Leaders provide yes or no answers to the following seven questions:

1. Is the quality of the decision (or solution) important? (e.g., is the solution critical?)
2. Is acceptance of the decision (or solution) by the team critical to its implementation?
3. Do I have sufficient information to make a high-quality decision?
4. Is the problem well structured?
5. If I were to make the decision by myself, would the team accept it?
6. Does the team share the organizational goals that will be obtained in solving the problem?
7. Is conflict among the team likely in obtaining the preferred solution?

The answers are then used to arrive at a suggested decision-making approach using the flow chart shown in Figure 8.3.

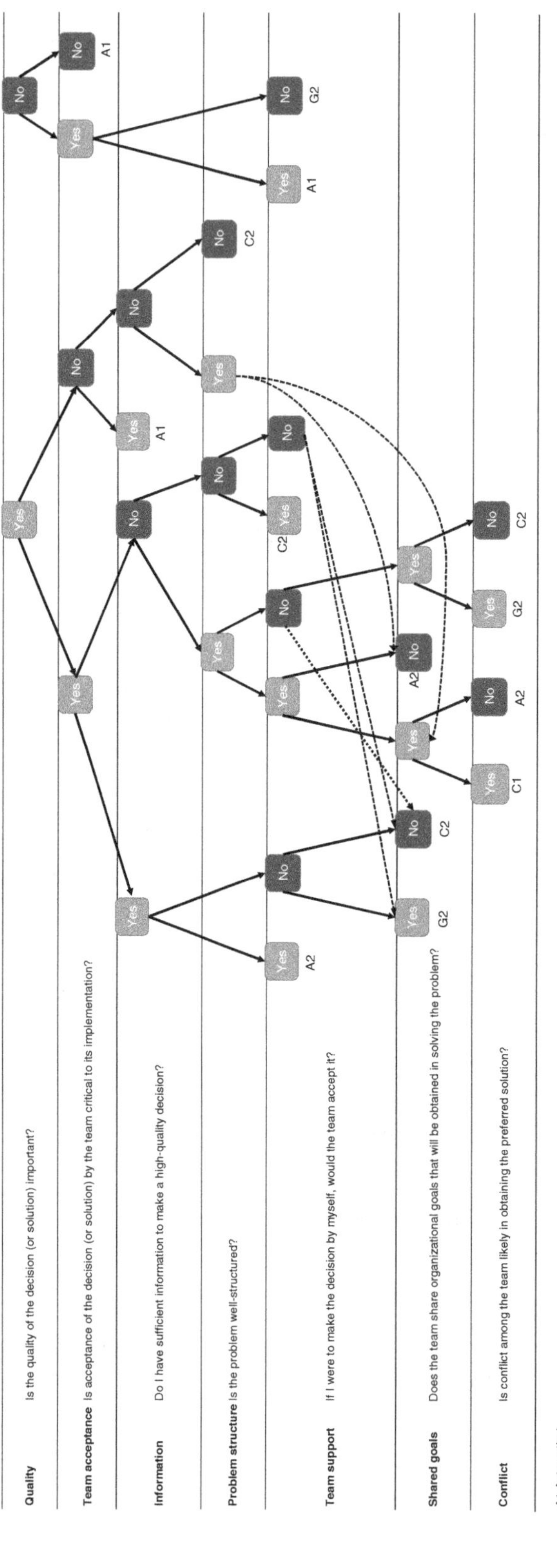

Figure 8.3 Vroom-Yetton decision-making model.

Chapter 9
Team Training

> Needs assessment. Identify the steps involved to implement an effective training curriculum: identify skills gaps, develop learning objectives, prepare a training plan, and develop training materials. (Understand)
>
> **Body of Knowledge III.D.1**

In theory there is no difference between theory and practice. In practice there is.

—Yogi Berra

This chapter will cover various approaches to design, implement, deliver, and evaluate an effective training program.

NEEDS ASSESSMENT

The terms "education" and "training" are often used interchangeably. However, *education* focuses on broadening an individual's knowledge base and expanding their thinking processes. Furthermore, education helps employees understand concepts, accept increased job responsibilities, and prepares them for future jobs and leadership roles. Simply, education helps individuals learn how to think.

Training is considered a subset of education that focuses on increasing proficiency in a skill. Training typically refers to skill-based instruction, addressing the specific skills employees need to perform a current job or task. Such skills can be highly diverse. For example, skills may include learning how to apply quality tools, implementing customer service principles, running a new piece of equipment, or facilitating a team. Training may take place in either a formal setting, such as a classroom, or an informal setting, such as on-the-job training.

The ADDIE Training Development Model

Careful design of the training program can help create a positive experience for learners. There are several instructional design paradigms in the adult education literature, but perhaps the best known is ADDIE model for training development, first used in the 1970s by the U.S. military (Biech, 2017). This five-step

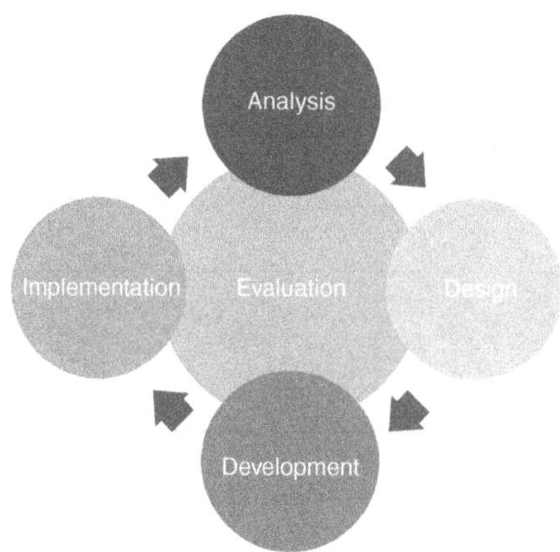

Figure 9.1 ADDIE instructional design model.

model includes Analysis, Design, Development, Implementation, and Evaluation, as shown in Figure 9.1. This model gives instructional designers a road map for creating successful training programs.

In the *analysis phase,* designers identify the learners and their characteristics, state the new behavior desired, identify learning constraints, list delivery options, and plan using project timelines, among other tasks.

In the *design phase,* a blueprint of the training is created. The learning objectives and assessment instruments are identified. Then, the designers plan the course content as well as group and individual exercises.

In the *development phase,* the designers create storyboards and bring the elements of the design blueprint to life.

In the *implementation phase,* trainers deliver the course to the learners.

The *evaluation phase appears* in the middle of the diagram, signifying that the results of the analyze, design, development, and implementation phases are each evaluated and adjusted before moving on to the next step. After the implementation phase is evaluated, the ADDIE model can be started again, this time incorporating feedback and results from the learners.

Lean Learning Model

Glaveski (2019) presents a training approach that he has named Lean Learning that draws upon the principles of lean manufacturing. The lean approach starts with the use of the Pareto Principle, in which 80% of the new behavior or skill can be accomplished by learning 20% of the available tools. For example, the Pareto Principle suggests that 80% of Six Sigma projects can be successfully led by using 20% of the available Six Sigma tools. Why put Green Belts through weeks of intensive training when they could accomplish the same improvements with one week of training on the most frequently used tools?

Another Lean training principle is to deliver the instruction at the time and place it is needed. This calls for on-the-spot training of tools as the team needs them or developing a suite of mini courses that train on a single tool. Finally, skills can be sustained by providing ways for learners to receive support after the training session via video conferences or e-mail correspondence.

Black Belts may be tapped to design a training module that teaches students how to use a specific tool. Even with this small-scale assignment, the ADDIE or Lean approach can be useful in developing the training session. Black Belts may also be tasked with designing and delivering entire Yellow and Green Belt programs for the organization.

Needs Assessment

Successful organizations understand and acknowledge the importance their human assets play in achieving their success. However, the degree of success depends on the appropriate level and relevance of their human assets' education and training. Remember, an organization's strategies are executed through its people. If the current education and training of the people cannot support the strategies, the organization must act on this gap via the training needs analysis.

The Importance of a Training Needs Analysis

A *training need* is essentially a performance gap between what people know or are able to do and what they should know or be able to do to perform their work competently. Therefore, a *training needs analysis* is a diagnostic method to identify the gap between current performance and desired performance. Organizational training needs stem from the strategic planning process, while individual training needs stem from both strategic planning and individual performance. A needs analysis is also known as a *needs assessment* or *training requirements analysis*.

A needs analysis uses a variety of tools and techniques to identify the training needs for a specific population, target group, or team. Through a systematic process, relevant data are collected and used to formulate a training plan for employees. In addition to identifying training needs for individual employees, a needs analysis also investigates how such training can support the organization's strategies.

A training needs analysis effort produces facts about the target audience, training needs, learning styles, and so on. However, a good needs analysis does more than merely gather information. It makes a case for training. To that end, a training needs analysis must be well executed to garner top-down support.

The Training Matrix

An organization can track core skills and competencies of its workforce using a visual tool such as a training matrix. A typical matrix will have columns listing employees, departments, employees and their roles, and core competencies and skills, as shown in Figure 9.2. Entries in the matrix then indicate the level of skills. This matrix can then be used to select team members according to their skills, spot deficiencies in skills sets, and create a training plan for employees.

			Required training		Skills				
Department	Employee	Role	A	B	A	B	C	D	E
101	321	Machine Operator	√	√					
101	322	Machine Operator		√					
101	344	Machine Operator	√	√					
101	355	Machine Operator	√	√					
101	357	Machine Operator	√	√					
101	368	Machine Operator	√						
101	369	Machine Operator	√						
101	371	Machine Operator	√	√					
101	380	Machine Operator	√	√					

Needs training
Progressing
Skilled

Figure 9.2 Example training matrix.

The Importance of Training Plans

When skills training is required, it is crucial to have a training plan. Every organization faces important decisions about the wide variety of organizational needs that might be supported, including new hire orientation; technical and process training; quality training; certification training; team, interpersonal, and communication skills training; diversity training; and management and leadership programs. Consequently, training dollars represent a significant budget item.

Despite their organizational importance, training expenditures are often vulnerable to cost-reduction pressures. When senior leaders do not view training as a strategic, cost-justified investment, business downturns can result in training budget cutbacks. Therefore, employee training should reinforce strategic plans with direct line of sight.

Training plans provide the road map for meeting critical training requirements. Without a plan, important organizational training requirements may go unnoticed, or may be poorly addressed or not addressed at all. In fact, many organizations with strategic plans that have training implications still leave such training to happenstance.

In large organizations, various business units, sites, functional groups, and departments may have individual training plans. All training plans, though, should be a result of a strategic business planning process and should provide a mechanism for ensuring that training and education build the organization's capabilities as well as enable employees to a make a positive contribution to the organization's success.

Components of an Effective Training Plan

Bee and Bee (1994) suggest that a viable training plan should comprise three critical components:

> *Statement of policy.* This constitutes a statement of direction for the time period covered by the training plan. For example, there may be a specific focus of training such as qualification or certification training, leadership

or first-line supervisory training, interpersonal skills training versus professional or technical skills training, and so on.

Training budget. This would include all costs associated with developing and executing the training plans. Also, it is important to specify how the training costs will be paid.

Operational plan. This covers all aspects of timing and non-financial resources. For example:

- Identify the need
- State objectives and outcomes
- Determine content and sequence of instruction, if designed internally, or select from qualified external suppliers
- Identify the target groups
- Develop schedules for all aspects of training, such as development, delivery, evaluation, and so on
- Specify resource requirements such as instructors, facilities, equipment, and materials
- Establish measurements
- Select training delivery methods
- Train instructors
- Deliver training
- Evaluate outcomes

Training Plan	Module: Project charter creation
Training objectives and outcomes	1. Participants will learn how to complete each section of a Six Sigma project charter
	2. Each participant will complete a project charter for their assigned Six Sigma project.
Training audience	Lean Six Sigma Yellow Belts & process owners working towards Green Belt designation
Instructional strategies	
Group exercises	Problem statement, goal statement, and metrics exercises
Case study	Analog Industries Case Study – Part 1
Assessment and exams	Instructor will assess/approve final project charter
Homework assignments	Financial results exercise
Team and individual work	Team will critique members' charters
Project work	N/A
Presentations	Power Point: Project Charter module
Training mode	In-person, instructor-led
Training schedule	Tuesdays 3:00–4:30pm for 3 weeks
Location	Training room #3

Figure 9.3 Training plan for project charter module.

- Modify training, as needed
- Conduct classes on lessons learned
- Add documentation to the organization's knowledge database

Remember, executing the training plan should be treated as any other project. That is, it should be managed properly using the appropriate project management tools and techniques. Therefore, planning for training should closely resemble the planning done for any other project. A training plan for a project charter module is shown in Figure 9.3.

Applying the Training Plan

In simplest terms, one of the key deliverables of a training plan will be a skills matrix. The matrix lists each identified skill and an associated level of competency. The "entry" level competency is the minimal level of competence required to be accepted into the training program or course. For example, in the Lean Six Sigma context, an entry-level skill might be basic math or algebra. Both are prerequisites to Lean Six Sigma training.

Developing Training Materials and Resources

Although some organizations may do well at conducting a training needs analysis and developing a training plan, most organizations invoke minimal effort when it comes to developing or evaluating existing training materials and resources. This occurs for one or more of the following reasons:

- They simply don't know how.
- It was overlooked and wasn't planned into the budget.
- It takes time and effort, and after all, it's the employee's responsibility to learn.
- If purchased, they assume that the high cost of training materials makes them high caliber.
- If developed in-house, "we only do good work, so why do we need to evaluate it?"
- They may use existing materials with some modifications due to cost constraints.

Developing training materials or evaluating already available training materials does take considerable planning and effort. To help organizations more effectively evaluate training materials and resources, the following checklist has been developed:

- Language
  - Is the language at the appropriate level for the target group?
  - Is the spelling correct?

  - Is the grammar correct?
  - Are idioms, slang, or excessive jargon used?
- Accuracy
  - Is the material technically accurate?
  - Is the material current?
  - Is the math correct?
- Format
  - Is the material consistent and uniform in design and presentation format?
  - Is the format easy to follow?
  - Is the material too dense?
  - Is there a mixture of words, illustrations, and graphics?
  - Is the material sufficiently modularized both in content and in time?
- Progression
  - Is an adequate foundation presented?
  - Does the material flow logically?
- Infrastructure
  - Does the material stand alone?
  - Are supplementary materials required?
  - Are instructors required, and if so, how many?
- Content
  - Is the content unambiguous?
  - Is the material presented without bias?
  - Does the content support the learning objectives and outcomes?
  - Is the material consistent with other material that either exists or is under consideration?
- Development and outcomes
  - Does the material address different learning styles?
  - Does the material address different generational preferences?
  - Will the material meet the objectives established by the training plan?
  - Will the material permit the target group to achieve the desired level of competency?

  - What target groups are suitable for the training materials?
  - Do the training materials require solution manuals, and if so, are they provided?
- Responsibilities and ownership
  - Who is responsible for updating the material (if the material is purchased)?
  - How often is the material updated (assuming the material is purchased, and the supplier is responsible for updates)?
  - How are errors in the materials handled (assuming the material is purchased, and the supplier is responsible for updates)?
  - Who owns the training materials (if delivered by a third party)?
  - Is there a one-time purchasing fee or recurring licensing fees (if purchased from a third party)?
- Delivery
  - Do instructors require certification?
  - Are the instructors knowledgeable in the subject matter?
  - Is the material available for delivery in different mediums (that is, classroom, electronic, and so on)?
  - Is the supplier accredited (assuming a third-party trainer and accreditation is required)?
  - Do the training materials require the training to take place in a special environment or require special facilities, tools, audiovisual equipment, computers, or software?
  - How much notification is required if delivered by a third party?
- Evaluations
  - Who evaluates the training materials and resources, and what are their qualifications for doing so?
  - How are students evaluated against training objectives?
  - How are the instructors evaluated?
  - Has the material been tested previously, and if so, what were the results?
- Duration
  - What is the course duration?
  - Is the course contiguous, periodic, or ad hoc (for example, three days in a row, the first week of every month for four months, or as time permits, respectively)?

A weighted criteria approach can be used for evaluating and selecting training material. This scoring method provides a more objective basis for the evaluation process that can facilitate meaningful discussions among the evaluators. Once training materials have been chosen, the decision can then be justified based on these quantitative evaluations.

The checklist provided is meant to be a starting point. Evaluating and selecting training materials and resources can take a significant amount of time and effort. Consequently, it should be incorporated into the training plan schedule and budget. Also, remember to choose developers and evaluators wisely—not everyone is capable of creating training material.

DELIVERY

> Describe various techniques used to deliver effective training, including adult learning theory, soft skills, and modes of learning. (Understand)
>
> **Body of Knowledge III.D.2**

Adult Learning Theory

Training has been defined as a subset of education that focuses on increasing proficiency in a skill. It is a "push" strategy in that it pushes knowledge, skills, and attitudes toward employees to enhance their job performance. By contrast, learning is a "pull" strategy by which the employee pulls knowledge, skills, and attitudes to enhance their job performance.

Olson and Hergenhahn (1997) state that "*learning* refers to a change in behavior potentiality, and *performance* refers to the translation of this potentiality into behavior." Rothwell (2008) states this more simply as "learning gives individuals the potential to get results. But performance is the actual realization of that potential."

Assumptions About Adult Learners

The following assumptions about adult learners are helpful in understanding how to design curricula, deliver material, and more effectively transfer knowledge. Adults may have one or more motivations to learn, such as:

- Building social networks
- Meeting expectations such as those that might be imposed by those in authority
- Advancing in their careers

- Seeking stimulation
- Helping others
- Learning for the sake of learning

At the outset of the training, the instructor should consider addressing the above topics with the learners to help gain a feel for the individual motivations for participating in the learning activity.

In general, adult learners:

- Prefer to focus on learning that centers on key ideas, principles, and experiences rather than on general learning topics.
- Prefer to learn in an environment that is both physically and psychologically comfortable.
- Face barriers to learning such as scheduling difficulties, money, management support, and so on.

Experience has shown that adult learners prefer to practice rather than just listen to lectures and that they prefer to interact with other learners when in a group learning environment.

Characteristics That Affect Adult Learners

Trainers need to be aware of any characteristics of adult learners that might impede their ability to learn or the trainer's ability to transfer knowledge and skills. Several key characteristics to be mindful of include hearing, seeing, memory, and specific learning disabilities, such as dyslexia.

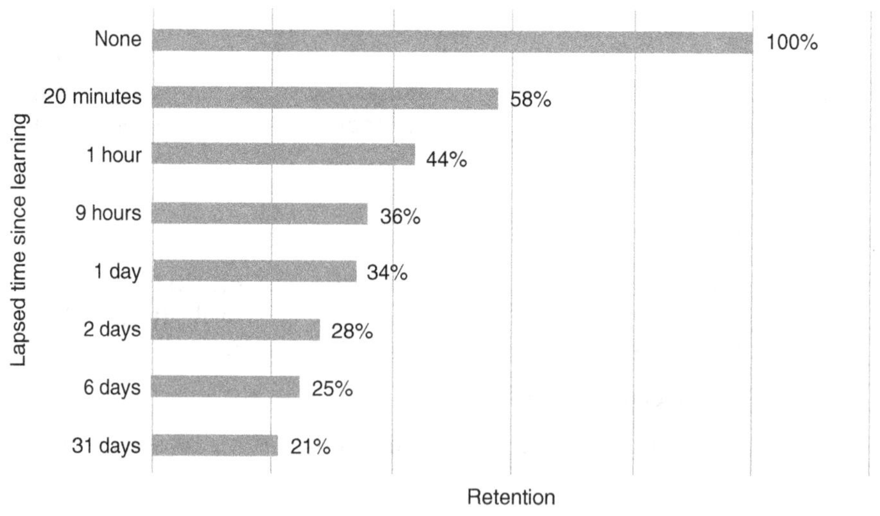

Figure 9.4 Ebbinghaus's Forgetting Curve.

The Forgetting Curve

Trainees perform best when they own their learning and are not made into passive recipients of knowledge. Adults learn best through experience and need to be shown how the knowledge being presented can be directly applied to their jobs. The "Forgetting Curve" was developed by German psychologist Hermann Ebbinghaus in the late nineteenth century and is shown in Figure 9.4. The curve demonstrates the negative effect of not applying what we have learned. After just six days, students forget 75% of what they have learned if the new knowledge is not applied.

Delivery Modalities

In-Person Learning

This type of learning occurs in a traditional classroom setup, in which participants are all physically together in the same room. Instructors can easily pick up on non-verbal cues to determine whether the class or a student is engaged or confused. In-person learners can interact with each other, work in groups, and get immediate feedback from peers and the instructor.

In-person learning does have disadvantages, however. Requiring all learners to be in the same physical space can be burdensome in terms of travel costs or time off the job. If a learner misses a point that the instructor makes, or is confused by an example, they can't "rewind" the lecture in real time.

Online Learning

Online learning has become much more popular because of technological advances and the increasing popularity of remote work. Once considered inferior to in-person training, online training courses offer several advantages to learners and instructors, as well as cost savings for the organization.

It is important to note that in-person and online learning are distinct delivery modes. Taking an in-person course and directly translating it into an online format simply combines the disadvantages of in-person learning with those of an online course. Resist the impulse to deliver a 5-hour lecture with a few 15-minute breaks. While this format is less than ideal for an in-person class, it is utterly exhausting for online learners. Instead, choose to leverage the many advantages and distinctive features of online learning that can improve student engagement and learning outcomes. We will cover three types of online learning: *synchronous, asynchronous,* and *combination.*

In *a synchronous online course,* all learners are logged into the course space at the same time to hear a presentation from the instructor. The instructor can use polls throughout the presentation to help learners stay engaged with the material. Communication between learners and the instructor can occur via the chat function or the audio feature. Often, the live presentations are recorded for future viewing.

The instructor can facilitate interactions and group participation in the course by assigning students to breakout rooms to complete an assigned activity. Once the allotted time is up, the class reconvenes, and each group presents and discusses their work.

Asynchronous online learning, or *self-paced courses*, usually consist of modules with pre-recorded videos and quizzes. Often, learners are given the opportunity to practice the skills presented in each module via activities or games that provide immediate feedback. This type of course allows adult learners to build toward achieving a desired competency level in required knowledge or skills. Asynchronous learning is cost-effective and can be offered on-demand across multiple locations and time zones. However, to be effective, learners must be self-motivated to work through the material. Consider offering instructor support for these types of classes so that students have a way to ask questions when they are stuck, or when they just need a boost.

In a *combination online course*, both synchronous and asynchronous components are incorporated. Often the combination course uses a *flipped classroom* delivery model. For example, throughout the week, students may be tasked to view a series of short, focused pre-recorded instructional videos, and answer questions in an asynchronous discussion forum. Then, in a weekly live online session, the instructor may answer questions posed by the class, facilitate group activities, or solve practice problems on a virtual white board. For this type of approach to be successful, students must be committed to finishing the pre-work before the live session each week.

The advantage of this combination approach is that throughout the week, students can view the instructional videos when they want, and as many times as needed to grasp the material. Posting to discussion forums requires students to connect with the module material and formulate a considered response. This type of interaction can allow more introverted learners to voice their views. In addition, students who are not native speakers can have time to craft their responses. The live sessions are kept short and engaging, and students can directly interact and discuss the material with instructor and each other.

Blended Learning

A blended learning approach refers to a course composed of online components and in-person classroom time. The blended learning model may follow the flipped classroom approach, as discussed previously. Blended learning can reduce training costs, hours in the physical classroom, and travel costs compared to strictly in-person training.

On-the-Job Training (OJT)

A significant amount of skills training occurs through on-the-job training (OJT). The learner is usually an employee who has been newly hired, transferred, or promoted into a position and lacks the knowledge and skill to perform some specific job component. A more experienced employee (for example, a peer or supervisor) is usually assigned to work with the trainee. Specific tasks are demonstrated and performed in the actual work environment to help the trainee gain the knowledge or skills previously lacking.

On-the-job training is highly regarded as a learning method. It matches the day-to-day realities of the organization and can be delivered just in time. However, it can be hampered by physical constraints of the job site, it may disrupt workflow, and it can create potential safety issues.

Because it is common OJT practice for an employee who is familiar with the job to train another employee, without objectives or a planned system, inconsistencies can result in the way employees perform their duties. In addition, the lack of structure can cause bad habits to be included in the training. Another problem occurs when a relatively inexperienced employee is responsible for training others. The employee might know how to do the job, but, as anyone who has done training knows, it is much more difficult to teach someone to do a job than to do it yourself.

Coaching

Used on a one-to-one basis, or for a small group or team, and conducted at the workplace, *coaching* is a teaching, learning, counseling relationship designed to develop job-related knowledge and skills and improve performance. It requires a continuous flow of instructions, comments, explanations, and suggestions from coach to employee, with the coach demonstrating, listening, questioning, relating learner's experiences, assisting, motivating, encouraging, and rewarding performance. The coaching option is used primarily to teach complex skills and operations—when there are few trainees, and the training is needed infrequently—and is a follow-on to other forms of employee training. It has the advantage of being flexible and adaptable. Its disadvantage is that its success depends on the competence of the coach.

Job Aids

Job aids are virtually any type of media that can substitute for formal training and/or provide reinforcement or reference after training. Often, providing a job aid can be the simplest and most cost-effective way to assist workers in doing their jobs. A few types of job aids are:

- Procedure manual
- Laminated checklist hung at a workstation
- Instructions printed on the back of a form providing details for completing the form
- Pertinent information for each critical step described on a shop work order or traveler
- QR Codes on machines that link to instructional videos

Overall, jobs aids can be cost-effective, available when and where they are needed, and easily kept current. They can also diminish the need for individuals to rely on memory. However, job aids are not a substitute for expertise or performance, and do not replace good judgment.

Soft Skills

Black Belts tasked with training must be well versed in their subject matter, but they also must possess sufficient "soft" or people skills to effectively teach learners. An instructor sets the tone for the course, and needs to create a friendly, welcoming environment in which students feel comfortable asking questions and making mistakes along the path to mastery.

Black Belts may also lead training sessions on soft skills themselves, helping others learn the tools of facilitation and coaching. Outside the classroom, Black Belts can model soft skills for others in how they conduct themselves and lead meetings, and how they handle challenging situations.

Delivery Methods

There is a wide array of training delivery methods available. We will discuss lectures and presentations, discussion formats, experiential learning, case studies, workbooks, as well as games, simulations, and role-playing.

Lectures and Presentations

A *lecture* is a one-directional transmission of information to students by an instructor, either in person or online. It is the most frequently used manner of conveying material to students and often is used in combination with other tools. Lectures are one type of presentation, but presentations can also include other oratorical or multimedia formats.

Lectures and presentations offer the advantage of being straightforward to develop, present, and revise. However, some learners find it difficult to master knowledge and skills by this means. Furthermore, learners do not retain information well when the lecture delivery method is used.

Discussion Format

The *discussion* format allows participants freedom to present views, opinions, and ideas in an unrestrained environment. Roundtables and panel discussions are variations. These methods normally work best with a knowledgeable and experienced discussion leader. The Socratic method of repeated questioning has been used successfully to elicit and share the accumulated knowledge and experience of course members. However, the discussion format requires a skilled facilitator in order to execute it successfully, and some participants may be reluctant to speak up in this environment.

Experiential Training

The *experiential* approach employs many types of structured experiences (for example, games, simulations, role-plays) to facilitate learning. Typically, participants assume roles within a stated scenario designed to surface one or more learning points. They then "play out" the scenario to a conclusion under the eye of a skilled facilitator. No outcome is prescribed, but a well-designed scenario will tend to produce a predictable range of responses highlighting the training content. Experiential training is often used to teach soft skills, but it is also effective in lean tools training.

Experiential training permits faster learning than on-the-job training and allows mistakes to occur without penalties. However, it requires a great deal of planning and can be costly to provide.

Case Studies

Case studies can be developed in-house or purchased from a variety of sources. When training learners with different industry backgrounds or experience levels, a case can provide a common ground for discussion. Often, class activities are based on the case, and tools taught are practiced using scenarios or data from the case study.

Workbooks

Workbooks contain a collection of discussion topics, exercises, extra readings, and other reference material. They may be designed in-house to supplement materials provided during classroom presentations. Well-designed workbooks are engaging and provide a useful takeaway from the course.

Instructional Games, Simulations, and Role-Playing

Instructional games are activities designed to augment other training methods to focus the participants' learning toward specific training outcomes. For example, teams can compete in a Jeopardy-style game to demonstrate their knowledge of the course material.

Simulations resemble instructional games but also include correspondence between some aspect of the game and reality. *Role-playing* consists of spontaneously performing in an assigned scenario. For example, instructors may lead teams through Dr. Deming's Red Bead experiment, or a lean exercise using Lego blocks. Various roles may be assigned to participants, such as operator, supervisor, inspector, etc.

EVALUATION

> Describe various techniques to evaluate training, including evaluation planning, feedback surveys, pre-training, and post-training testing. (Understand)
>
> **Body of Knowledge III.D.3**

Data Collection Methods

Numerous methods exist for collecting data for evaluating training. These include:

- Follow-up survey and questionnaires
- Observations on the job
- Follow-up interviews
- Follow-up focus groups

- Control group versus training group comparisons
- Testing (pre- and post-training)
- Performance monitoring
- Review of operational data (for example, scrap, rework)

The Kirkpatrick Evaluation Model

The Kirkpatrick training evaluation model, originally developed in the 1950s, is the industry standard for assessing training effectiveness. There are four levels of the evaluation (Kirkpatrick, 1998):

1. *Reaction*—What was the reaction of the students and their thoughts about the training experience? The focus of this measure contrasts with many post-training surveys that focus on the trainer and their abilities and delivery. Whether or not the students enjoyed the training can be assessed using post-training surveys known as *"happy sheets."*
2. *Learning*—Did knowledge transfer occur? The degree of student learning vis-à-vis the learning objectives of the training session can be assessed through pre- and post-tests.
3. *Behavior*—Did the training change the learners' behavior? This level assesses the degree to which the students apply the new knowledge in the workplace. This level can be assessed using a pre- and post-evaluation of learners' behavior.
4. *Results*—Did the training impact business results? This level measures tangible benefits of the training to the organization in terms of improved efficiency, reduced defects, reduced costs, employee retention or higher morale, among others. This level can be assessed by pre- and post-training measurements.

Phillips (2003) adds a fifth level to the standard evaluation:

5. *Return on investment*—Here we determine whether the training was worth the cost. The business results versus the training costs are evaluated through a cost–benefit analysis.

$$\text{ROI} = \frac{(\text{Total program benefits} - \text{Total program costs})}{\text{Total program costs}}$$

Part IV
Define

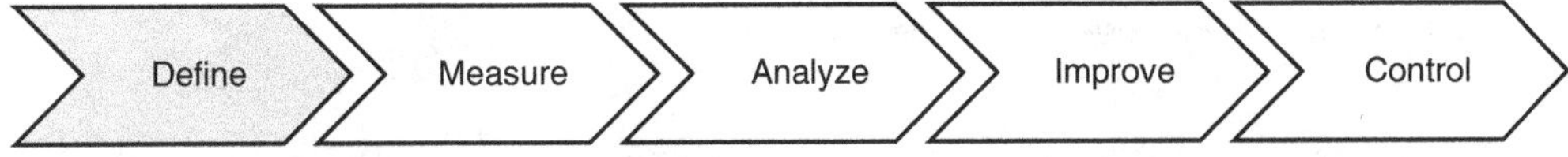

The purpose of this phase is to provide a compelling business case appropriately scoped, complete with SMART goals, and linked to a strategic plan. Common tools used in this phase are shown in Table IV.1.

As all Lean Six Sigma professionals know, DMAIC is the de facto methodology for improving processes using Lean Six Sigma. The reason for this is quite simple. The methodology is easy to understand, logical, and complete. Furthermore, it is sufficiently general to encompass virtually all improvement opportunities whether they are business or personal in nature.

When Black Belts first learn about DMAIC, they often see the phases depicted in a strict linear manner. Unfortunately, this is an illusion that leads inexperienced Black Belts to plow ahead from phase to phase, steamrolling weak champions, particularly if the Black Belts lack the support of a Master Black Belt to coach them. Projects conducted this way either fail or their results are not sustained.

Figure IV.1 depicts DMAIC in the real world. As we all know, tollgates occur after each phase. Diligent application of the proper tools and significant preparation are required to pass. Passing a tollgate is not a given. Notice that up to and including the *analyze* phase, the failure of a tollgate could set the project back one or two phases. This usually occurs when knowledge contrary to expectations is gained in a phase. In this case, the project team may be forced to retreat all the

5 whys	*Data collection plan*	Process decision program chart
Activity network diagrams	*Failure mode and effects analysis (FMEA)*	Program evaluation and review technique
Advanced quality planning	*Flowchart/process mapping (as is)*	Project charter
Affinity diagrams	Focus groups	*Project management*
Auditing	*Force-field analysis*	Project scope
Benchmarking	*Gantt chart*	*Project tracking*
Brainstorming	*Interrelationship digraphs*	Quality function deployment (QFD)
Cause-and-effect diagrams	Kano model	*Run charts*
Check sheets	Matrix diagrams	Sampling
Communication plan	*Meeting minutes*	Stakeholder analysis
Control charts	*Multivoting*	*Suppliers–inputs–process–outputs–customers (SIPOC)*
Critical-to-quality (CTQ) tree	*Nominal group technique*	*Tollgate review*
Customer feedback	*Pareto charts*	*Tree diagrams*
Customer identification	*Prioritization matrix*	*Y=f (X)*
Customer interviews		
Data collection		

Table IV.1 Common tools used in *define* phase.
Note: Tools shown in *italic* are used in more than phase.

way back to the *define phase* to restate the problem. Beyond the analyze phase, a failed tollgate usually results in correcting or performing additional work within the phase. However, at any phase, a project may be terminated. Project termination can happen when projects:

- no longer are synchronized with strategy
- are poorly scoped
- have potential savings that are less than expected, or
- have champions/sponsors who have lost interest or have transferred out.

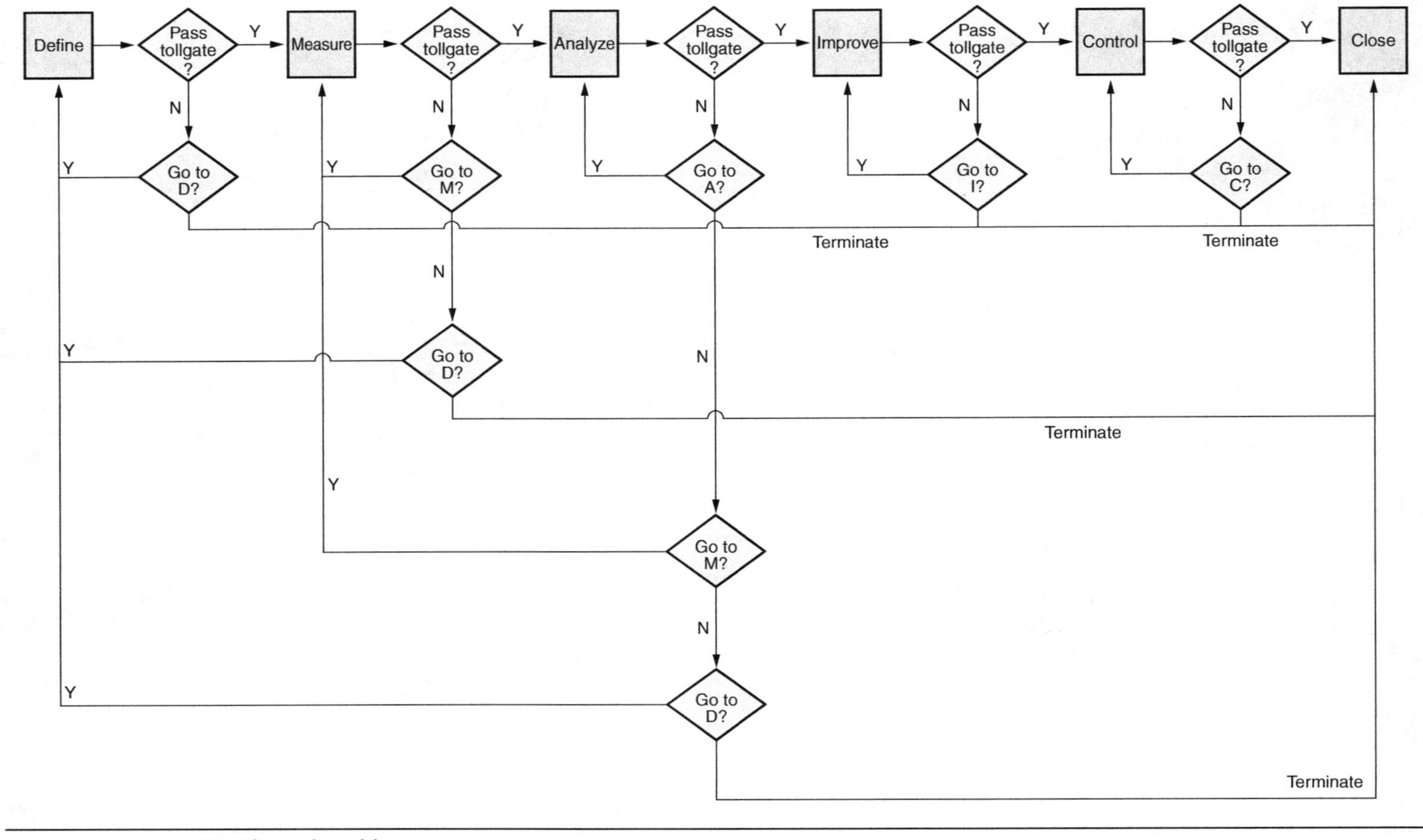

Figure IV.1 DMAIC in the real world.

Chapter 10

Voice of the Customer

The best way to understand your customer is to become your customer and walk a mile in his shoes.

—Ian D. Littman

Successful organizations consistently please their customers. In order to do this, organizations must first identify their target customers, and then determine their needs and wants. The customer information we collect, and the process by which we gather it, is known as *voice of the customer* (VOC). This data can be used as inputs into a design process and used to create specification limits.

In contrast to natural process limits, specification limits are customer determined or derived from customer requirements and are used to define acceptable levels of process performance. Specification limits are considered as the *voice of the customer* as well, and may be one-sided (that is, upper or lower) or two-sided. The difference between the upper and lower specification limits is known as the *tolerance*.

In some cases, customers provide specifications for products or services explicitly. This is often the situation when the customer is the Department of Defense or any of the military branches.

In others, customers express requirements in value terms, or the various components that influence the buying decision, such as price, product quality, innovation, service quality, company image, and reputation. In still other cases, customers may spotlight only their needs or wants, thus leaving it up to the organization to translate them into internal specifications. Tools such as quality function deployment, critical-to-quality analysis (also known as *customer requirements tree analysis*), and so on, often help with the last two situations.

CUSTOMER IDENTIFICATION

> Identify and segment customers and show how a project will impact both internal and external customers. (Apply)
>
> **Body of Knowledge IV.A.1**

An early step in any project is to seek the voice of the customer (VOC). The internal and external customers of a project include all those who are impacted by the project. For most projects, the customers can be grouped into categories and/or segments, with segments being a further breakdown within categories. This categorization and/or segmentation is driven by the similarity of customer requirements and often includes the following:

- Internal and external to the organization
- Customer demographics:
  - Age groups, especially for consumer goods
  - Geographical location, including climate, language and ethnic issues, and shipping considerations
- Industry types (for example, the project might impact customers in construction, agriculture, and stationary equipment industries)

When possible, a list of customers, or stakeholders in general, within a category and/or segment should be constructed. When a project team proposes changes of any type, all stakeholders, internal and external, must be consulted, or at a minimum, the stakeholders' concerns must be represented. This is usually accomplished best through the stakeholder analysis discussed in Chapter 3.

It is easy to underestimate the value of understanding and providing for customers' needs. It may be worth a reminder that without customers, we have nothing!

CUSTOMER DATA COLLECTION

> Identify and select appropriate data collection methods (e.g., surveys, focus groups, interviews, observations) to gather voice of the customer data. Ensure the data collection methods used are reviewed for validity and reliability. (Analyze)
>
> **Body of Knowledge IV.A.2**

Data Validity and Reliability

Because data errors can be difficult to detect, data validity and reliability considerations should be at the forefront of any data collection activity.

Data validity refers to the general correctness of a data set. *Data validation* refers to the process of validating data against a set of documented acceptance criteria, usually as the data are entered.

Common data validation checks include numeric versus alpha character checks, range checks, logic checks, spell checks, comparison checks, and lookup checks. When the data collection instrument is a survey, piloting can help reduce data validity issues that might arise by rewording questions that confuse the pilot group.

Data reliability refers to the overall consistency, stability, or dependability of a data set. In the context of data, reliability can be thought of as the extent to which data are reproducible.

EXAMPLE 10.1

The data field for the number of items sold per day is three characters long. The data are validated upon entry to ensure that a numeric value is entered between 0 and 999, inclusive. If an entry is coded incorrectly as 23r, for example, the validation method would flag the error.

If the number of items sold on a given day is 345, but is incorrectly entered as 258, the error would not be flagged since the validation method only checks to see if the entry is numeric. However, if unit sales per day never exceed 500 and a value of 572 is entered, it would be possible to validate an entry that exceeds the maximum value.

Reliability in data collection instruments such as surveys, for example, means that the survey will produce the same results regardless of when administered. Reliability problems in surveys can occur when respondents:

- Do not understand the question
- Are asked about something they don't recall
- Are asked about something that is not relevant to them
- Are asked compound questions (that is, questions containing "and" or "or")

Reliability problems often call for revision and improvement of the data collection instrument.

EXAMPLE 10.2

A certified 50-pound weight is used to test a scale (the data collection instrument) daily. Each day the scale reads 50 pounds. The scale is said to be both valid and reliable. It is valid because it gives the correct weight, and it is reliable because it gives the same weight consistently.

One day, the weight is placed on the scale, and it reads 40 pounds. Each day thereafter, the scale reads 40 pounds. Although the scale is now biased, it is still reliable because it is consistent, stable, and dependable. However, it is not valid anymore because it no longer gives the correct weight.

Now consider that the weight is placed on the scale, and it reads 70 pounds. Each day thereafter, the scale reads a different value than 50 pounds: 70, 30, 55, 60, etc. Now the scale is no longer valid or reliable. It is not reliable because it is not consistent, stable, or dependable in providing weight readings.

	Reliable	Not reliable
Valid	Best case	Not possible
Not valid	Biased	Worst case

Figure 10.1 Data validity and reliability.

There is a key aspect about data validity and reliability that should be noted. A data collection instrument can be reliable but not valid, but an instrument that is not reliable cannot be valid, as shown in Figure 10.1.

Regardless of the data collection instrument, the concepts of data validity and reliability must be considered. Furthermore, it is often useful to not only validate each data collection instrument unto itself, but also validate each against the others. For example, does the survey instrument provide data that is similar to the results gleaned from the focus group? If it doesn't, is there a logical reason for it? The ability to cross-validate data across multiple listening posts can provide increased assurance of the validity of critical customer issues and complaints and can create a sense of urgency in otherwise complacent organizations.

Designing a Data Collection System

Many organizations collect customer data but lack a systematic approach for doing so. Important data are often collected independently via many different departments, but never shared, collated, reconciled, or analyzed to draw meaningful conclusions that drive action.

When designing a customer data collection system, the following key considerations should be at the forefront regardless of the data collection instrument used:

- *Collect data as objectively and consistently as possible.* Essentially, minimize measurement error. This concept should permeate all data collection mechanisms such as surveys, data collection check sheets, and so on. Consider using scripts for interviews to ensure that the same questions are asked the same way each time.
- *Collect data at the right level of granularity.* Consider what type of analysis will be done, what questions you are trying to answer, or the type of requirements you are trying to discover. If data are collected at too high a level, information is lost. Data collected at too low a level is meaningless. Fortunately, it often can be summarized to an appropriate higher level for analysis. However, this creates additional work and consumes time.

- *Consider independent sources of data collection.* Multiple data collection mechanisms, or *listening posts,* should be used, as shown in Figure 10.2. This permits data regarding each customer category or segment to be validated. If the data cannot be validated, this is generally a signal that improvement in the mechanisms (for example, revised questions) is required.
- *Use multiple sources for collecting data.* Different customer categories or segments may favor different methods for providing feedback, as shown in Figure 10.3. The key is to determine how to best align listening posts with the most appropriate sources.
- *Make it easy for the customer.* Customers must have easy access to the organization to provide feedback. For example, suppose an organization uses an automated telephone system for collecting customer feedback. Customers may become frustrated with attempting to determine the correct routing path to take to provide the feedback. Consequently, they decide that their input and time is not worth the effort. As a result, the organization loses a source of valuable information regarding the performance of its products and services. Similarly, surveys that are too long or inappropriately designed may also cause customers to abandon participation.

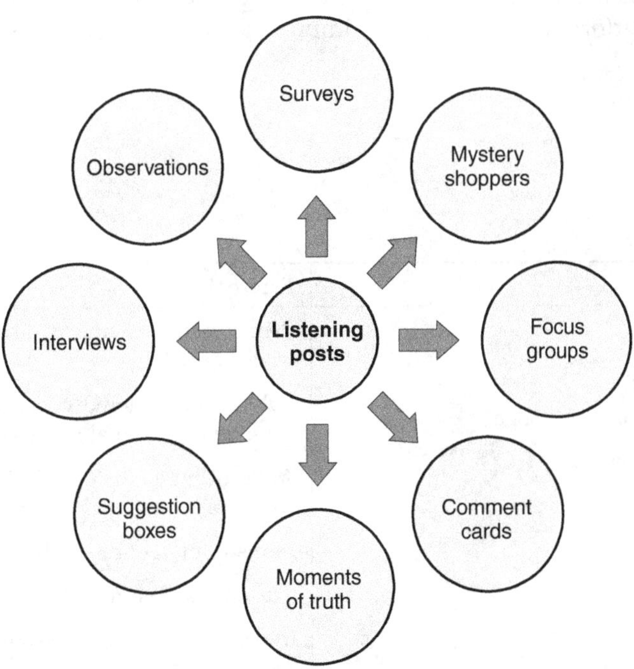

Figure 10.2 Examples of common listening posts.

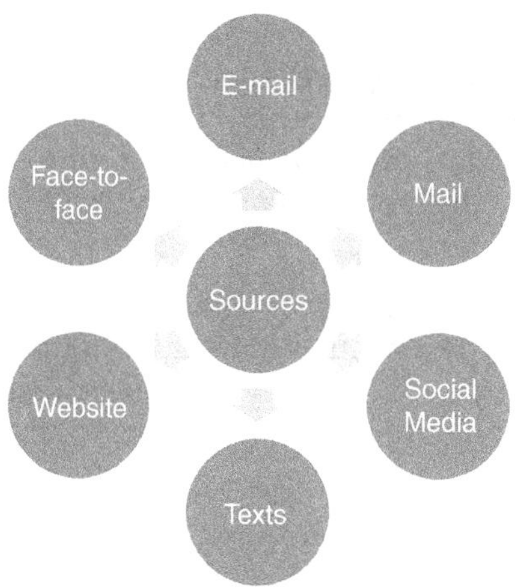

Figure 10.3 Examples of sources for listening posts.

Table 10.1 identifies both internal and external sources of customer data.

All customer data must be viewed in its entirety for meaningful conclusions to surface. Results from each data source should be compared to determine patterns of reinforcement or contradiction for each customer category or segment for each requirement, need, or want. Only then can an organization begin to translate requirements, needs, or wants into specifications. An added value of this analysis is the insight gained into the effectiveness of the listening posts. Listening posts that are performing poorly can be improved, modified, or even eliminated.

Internal	External
Complaints	Research (that is, magazines, newspapers, trade journals)
Claim resolutions	Public information (that is, customers' and competitors' annual reports)
Warranty and guarantee usage	Advertising media (that is, television, radio, websites)
Service records	Industry market research
Customer-contact employees	Customers of competitors
Listening post data	Industry conferences and forums
Market research	
Transaction data	
Defection data	

Table 10.1 Sources of customer data.

CUSTOMER REQUIREMENTS

> Define, select, and apply appropriate tools to determine customer needs and requirements, including critical-to-X (CTX when "X" can be quality, cost, safety, etc.), CTQ tree, quality function deployment (QFD), supplier, input, process, output, customer (SIPOC) and Kano model. (Analyze)
>
> Body of Knowledge IV.A.3

The best customer data collection and analysis is useless unless there is a system to use the data to effect changes. This system should study each item of customer feedback to determine which processes, products, and/or services will be impacted. The volume and/or urgency of customer concerns will help determine the requirements that customers deem critical. Some type of criticality rating system should be applied to the feedback data (for example, a phone call from a customer is rated higher than a response to a questionnaire).

For example, suppose that analysis of customer data identifies six areas where product quality is compromised. With the help of the criticality rating scale, perhaps two of the six would be deemed important enough to motivate immediate improvement projects.

CRITICAL TO X (CTX) REQUIREMENTS

The concept behind *critical to x* (CTX), where *X* is a variable, is simply that *X* represents an area or areas of impact on the customer. Critical customer requirements are usually expressed as expectations or needs, but not necessarily in quantifiable terms. Process CTXs represent measurable product or process performance characteristics and act to quantify the critical customer requirements. Let's look at some of the more familiar CTXs:

- *Critical-to-quality (CTQ).* CTQs may include the physical dimensions of height, width, depth, and weight. They may even include the electrical characteristics of a product, such as impedance. They describe the requirements of quality in general terms but lack the specificity to be measurable. However, CTQs can be translated into measurable terms or critical requirements through the inclusion of customer-defined specifications. For example, the customer may specify that the weight of the product be between 15 and 20 pounds. Products outside these specifications will not meet the customer's critical requirements.
- *Critical-to-cost (CTC).* CTCs are similar to CTQs but deal exclusively with the impact of cost on the customer. CTCs and CTQs may be similar yet stated by the customer for different reasons. For example,

the weight of the product may also serve as a CTC. Again, the customer might require the weight to be between 15 and 20 pounds. However, this specification is necessary to achieve an impact on cost. Products heavier than 20 pounds may require more power consumption, thus increasing the cost.

- *Critical-to-safety (CTS).* CTSs are stated customer needs regarding the safety of the product or process. Once more, consider the previous example of product weight. Product weight is the CTS variable. Though identical to the CTQ and the CTC, it is identified by the customer because any product heavier than 20 pounds has been shown to introduce a high rate of back injuries. Product weights less than 15 pounds have been shown to introduce a high rate of back injuries as well, since the lower weight induces the operator to pick up and transport multiple products. So far, we have seen that CTXs may be identical across categories, but for different reasons.
- *Critical-to-process (CTP).* CTPs are typically key process input variables. In terms of the process, we might think of CTPs as the critical X's in the $Y = f(X)$ equation. We may know and understand what the X's are (for example, temperature, pressure, humidity), but not necessarily their specific setting or level. Once the settings are determined or specified, they can be set to achieve a consistent process output, or Y.
- *Critical-to-delivery (CTD).* CTDs represent those customers with stated needs regarding delivery. Typically, one thinks of late deliveries. However, delivering too early may be a problem for some customers, as it represents excess inventory requiring payment before the need for such inventory arises. CTDs are translated into critical customer requirements through the quantification of these impact areas. For example, the customer may specify that products be received no

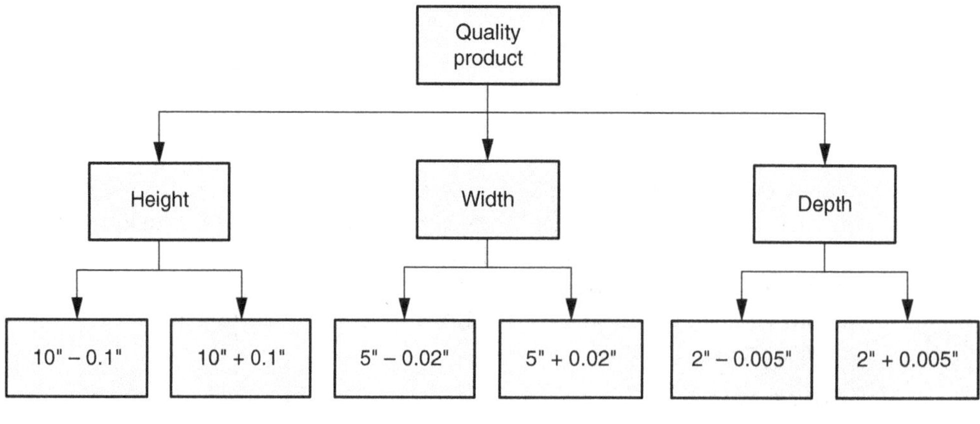

Figure 10.4 Example of a CTQ tree diagram.

earlier than two days prior to the delivery date and no later than one day after the delivery date.

Projects aligned with CTXs, and subsequently with critical customer requirements, have the biggest impact on the customer and often on the business directly. A useful tool for ensuring this alignment or translation from critical customer requirement to CTX is the tree diagram—an example using critical-to-quality (CTQ) is shown in Figure 10.4.

Critical-to-Quality Flow-Down

Customer satisfaction can be measured across three dimensions: quality, delivery, and cost. Cost and delivery are easy to quantify. Customers are willing to pay x per item and expect its delivery y days after they place the order. Quantifying quality characteristics presents more of a challenge.

One of the tools devised to help is called the *critical-to-quality* (CTQ) *flow-down.* Its purpose is to start with the high-level strategic goal of customer satisfaction and determine how this goal "flows down" into measurable goals. The nomenclature for the various levels is illustrated in Figure 10.5.

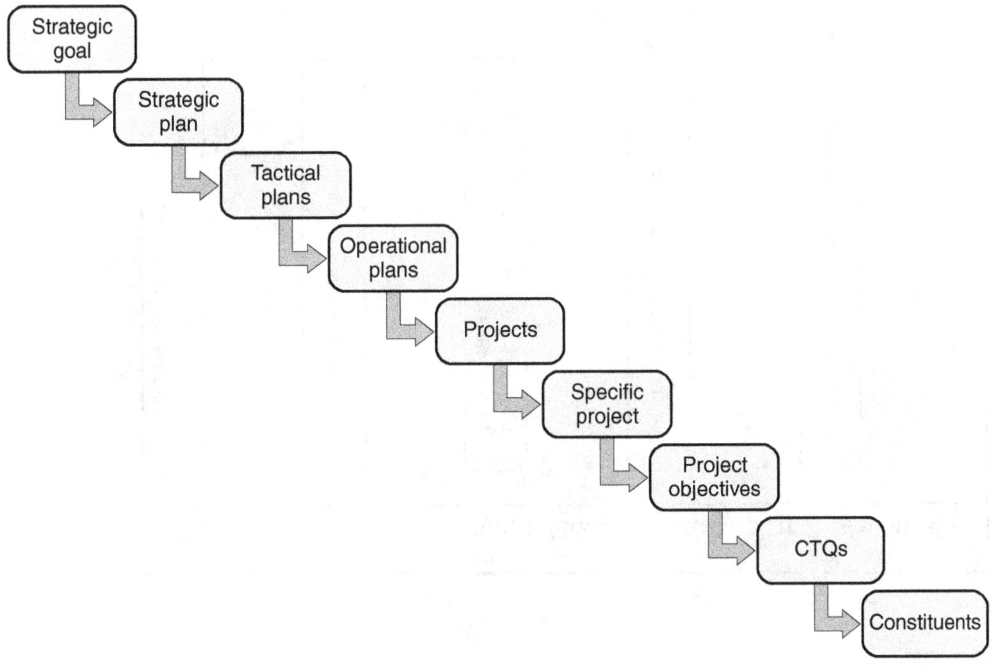

Figure 10.5 CTQ flow-down.

EXAMPLE 10.3

High on Mid-America Landscaping's list of strategic goals is customer satisfaction. A survey of past customers raised the need to establish a project team to ensure that customers understand the nature of the plants and trees they are purchasing. The team identifies several constituent parts to the problem. These constituents will guide the team. The CTQ flow-down diagram is shown in Figure 10.6.

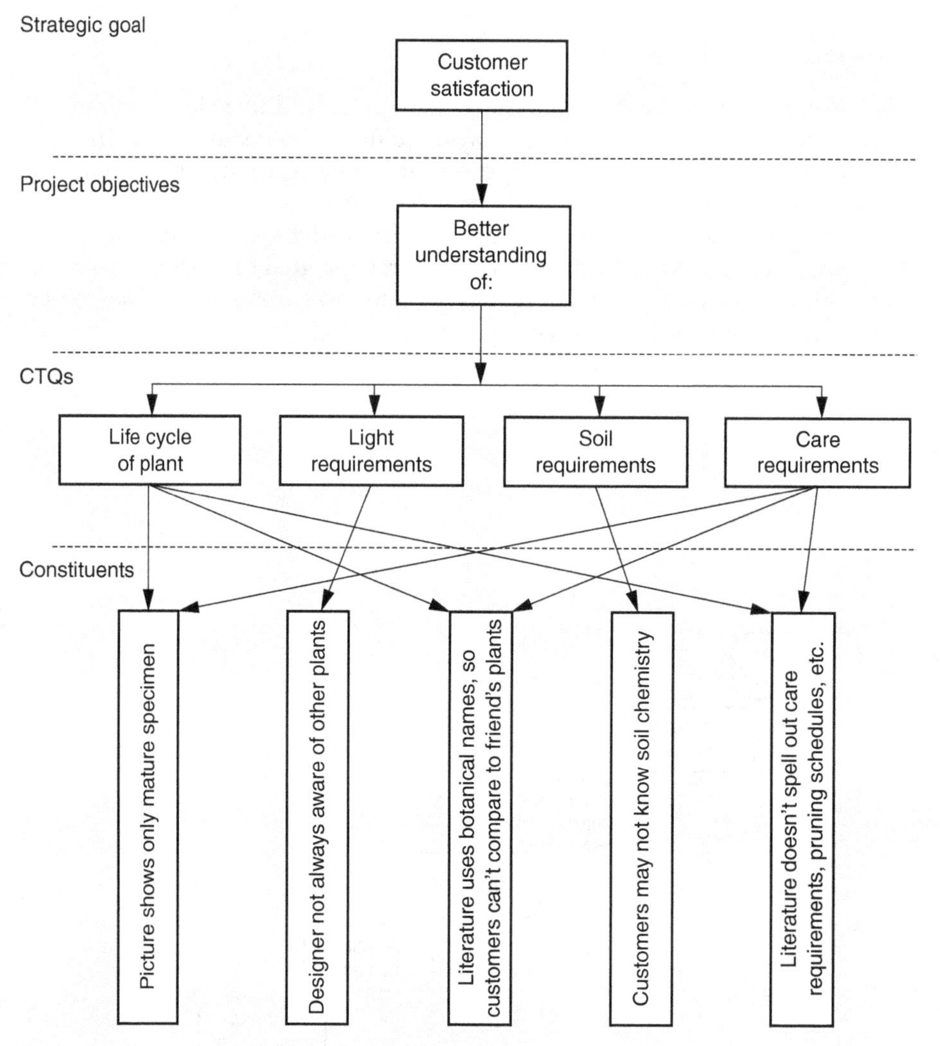

Figure 10.6 CTQ flow-down for Example 10.3.

QUALITY FUNCTION DEPLOYMENT

Quality function deployment (QFD) provides a process for planning new or redesigned products and services. The input to the process is the VOC. The QFD process requires that a team discover the needs and desires of its customer and study the organization's response to these needs and desires. The QFD matrix helps illustrate the linkage between the VOC and the resulting technical requirements. A map of the major sections of a QFD matrix are shown in Figure 10.7. As suggested by its shape, the QFD matrix may also be referred to as the *House of Quality*.

Figure 10.8 shows a completed QFD matrix for an animal trap. Let's look at each area, or room, individually:

- *Area 1: Customer requirements.* This area contains the customer requirements, which are developed from analysis of the VOC and often include a scale reflecting the importance of the individual entries.
- *Area 2: Technical requirements.* This area contains the technical requirements that are established in response to the customer requirements. The symbols on the top line in this section indicate whether lower (↓) or higher (↑) is better. A circle indicates that target is best.
- *Area 3: Comparison with competition.* This area plots the comparison with the competition for the customer requirements and is not always shown on QFD matrices.
- *Area 4: Relationship matrix.* This area displays the strength of the relationship between the technical requirements and the customer

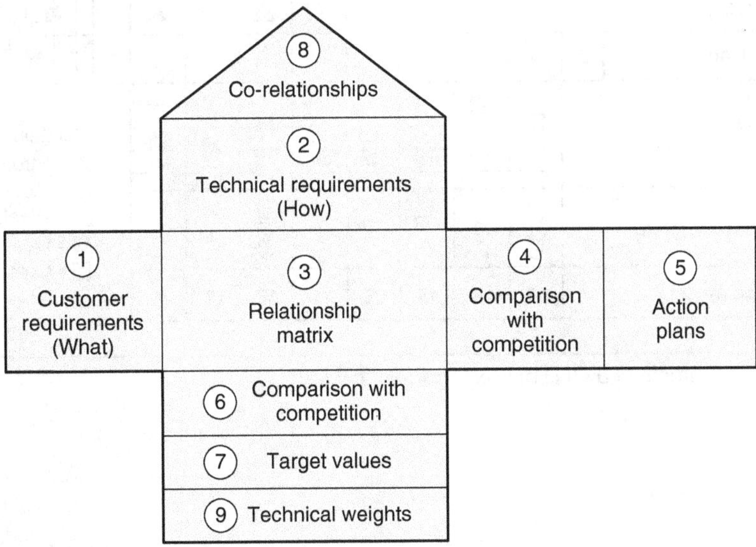

Figure 10.7 The structure of the QFD matrix (sometimes called the house of quality).

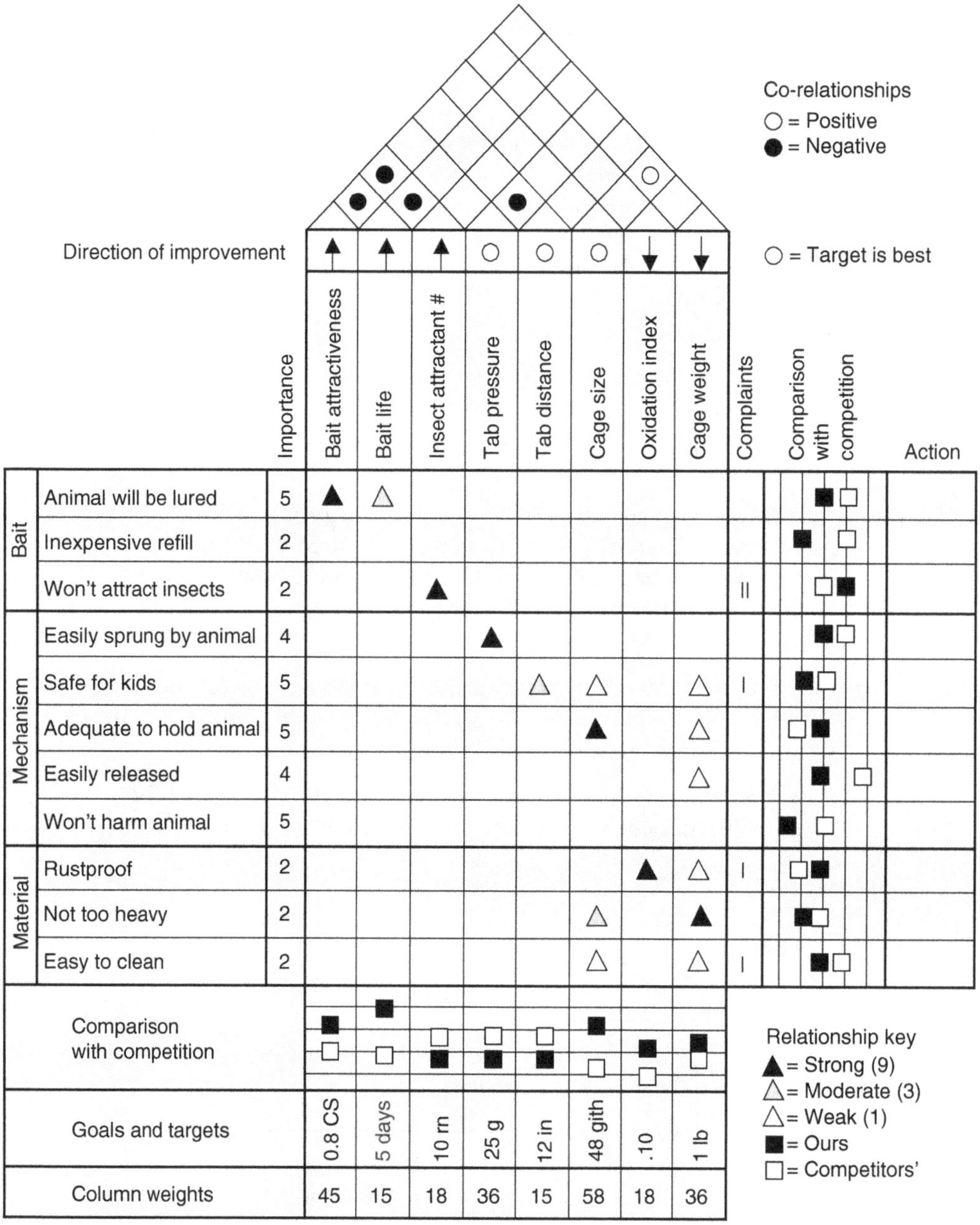

Co-relationships
○ = Positive
● = Negative

○ = Target is best

		Importance	Bait attractiveness	Bait life	Insect attractant #	Tab pressure	Tab distance	Cage size	Oxidation index	Cage weight	Complaints	Comparison with competition	Action
	Direction of improvement		↑	↑	↑	○	○	○	↓	↓			
Bait	Animal will be lured	5	▲	△								■□	
	Inexpensive refill	2										■ □	
	Won't attract insects	2			▲						||	□■	
Mechanism	Easily sprung by animal	4				▲						■□	
	Safe for kids	5					△	△		△	|	■□	
	Adequate to hold animal	5						▲		△		□■	
	Easily released	4								△		■ □	
	Won't harm animal	5										■ □	
Material	Rustproof	2							▲	△	|	□■	
	Not too heavy	2						△		▲		■□	
	Easy to clean	2						△		△	|	■□	
	Comparison with competition		■ □	■ □	□ ■	□ ■	□ ■	■ □	■ □	■□			
	Goals and targets		0.8 CS	5 days	10 m	25 g	12 in	48 gith	.10	1 lb			
	Column weights		45	15	18	36	15	58	18	36			

Relationship key
▲ = Strong (9)
△ = Moderate (3)
△ = Weak (1)
■ = Ours
□ = Competitors'

Figure 10.8 Example of a QFD matrix for an animal trap.

requirements. Various symbols can be used here. The most common are shown in Figure 10.8.

- *Area 5: Action plans.* This area contains notes or plans concerning improvement activities.
- *Area 6: Comparison with competition.* This area, like Area 4, is not always shown on QFD matrices. It plots the comparison with the competition for the technical requirements.
- *Area 7: Target values.* This area contains a list of the target values for each of the technical requirements.
- *Area 8 or Roof: Co-relationships.* This area shows the co-relationships between the technical requirements. A positive co-relationship indicates that both technical requirements can be improved at the same time. A negative co-relationship indicates that improving one of the technical requirements will worsen the other.
- *Area 9: Technical weights.* This area provides the column weights for each of the technical requirements. The column weights indicate the importance of the technical requirements in meeting customer requirements. The value in the "column weights" row is obtained by multiplying the value in the "importance" column in the customer requirements section by values assigned to the symbols in the relationship matrix. These assigned values are arbitrary. In the animal trap example, a strong relationship was assigned a 9, moderate 3, and weak 1.

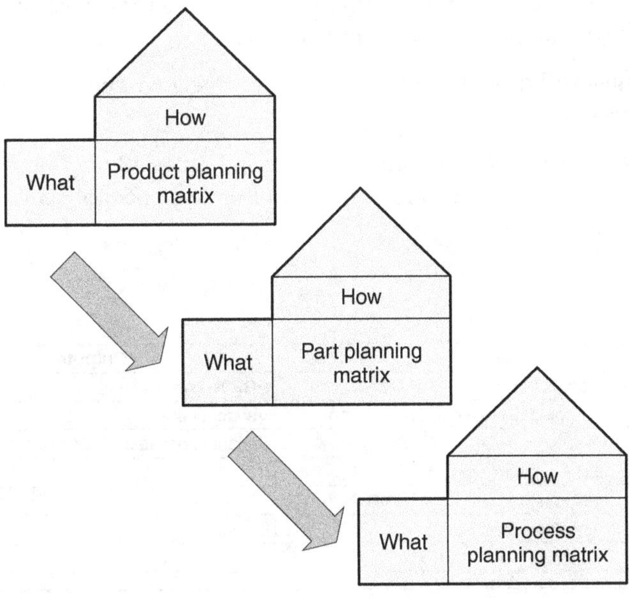

Figure 10.9 Using QFD for product planning and beyond.

The completed matrix can provide a database for product development, serve as a basis for planning product or process improvements, and suggest opportunities for new or revised product or process introductions.

The customer requirements section is sometimes called the "What," while the technical requirements section is referred to as the "How." This "what versus how" concept can be applied through a series of matrices intended to break down the technical requirements to lower levels that can eventually be assigned as tasks.

In addition, the basic QFD product-planning matrix can be followed with similar matrices for planning the parts that make up the product, and for planning the processes that will produce the parts. This concept is illustrated in Figure 10.9.

If a matrix has more than 25 customer voice lines, it tends to become unmanageable. In such a situation, a convergent tool such as the affinity diagram, presented in Chapter 13, may be used to condense the list.

SUPPLIERS–INPUTS–PROCESS–OUTPUTS–CUSTOMERS (SIPOC)

The *SIPOC* is another useful tool in the study of processes. The acronym stands for the key elements of a process:

- *Suppliers.* These are the internal and external providers of resources, materials, knowledge, and services.
- *Inputs.* These are the resources, material, services, and knowledge that feed that process. In the context of $Y = f(X)$, these are the X's.
- *Process.* This is the step or sequence of steps that is being investigated, analyzed, and improved.
- *Outputs.* These are the products and services produced by the process. In the context of $Y = f(X)$, these are the Y's.
- *Customers.* These organizations or users receive the final outputs of the process.

An example SIPOC diagram is shown in Figure 10.10 (Tague, 2005). Note that the SIPOC diagram can be augmented to capture specific requirements for both the inputs and outputs.

Suppliers	Inputs	Process	Outputs	Customers
Shipping	Vendor invoice	Acccounting	ERP Record	Cost centers
Receiving	Shipping system data	Operation	Vendor check	Vendors
Freight vendors	Shipper software	Freight	Freight expense allocated to cost center	
ERP software system	ERP software system	Invoice		
Shipping system	Shipping logs	Process		
Accounting Operations	Receiving logs			
	Labor			

Figure 10.10 Example of a completed SIPOC diagram.
Source: Tague, 2005.

A key benefit of the SIPOC is that it is much easier to complete than either a process map or a value stream map. However, SIPOCs can be used as a basis for constructing detailed process maps and value stream maps at future dates. Furthermore, SIPOCs help identify the voice of the customer as well as provide quick oversight into the initial *X*'s and *Y*'s.

KANO MODEL

Noriaki Kano's model of customer satisfaction identifies several types of requirements that impact customer satisfaction. They are illustrated in Figure 10.11 and described below:

- *Must-be requirements.* These are the requirements the customer assumes will be there, and when they aren't, the customer will be very dissatisfied. Such requirements are generally unspoken since they are basic expectations. Note that the line labeled "must-be" in Figure 10.11 is on the dissatisfied side when the requirement is missing. However, as the requirement becomes fulfilled, it does not improve customer satisfaction.

  Consider, for example, a shirt with a buttonhole that is sewed shut. Customers do not expect buttonholes to be sewed shut. When this occurs, customers are very dissatisfied. "Must-be" requirements are also known as *basic* requirements, *expected* requirements, *or must-have* requirements.

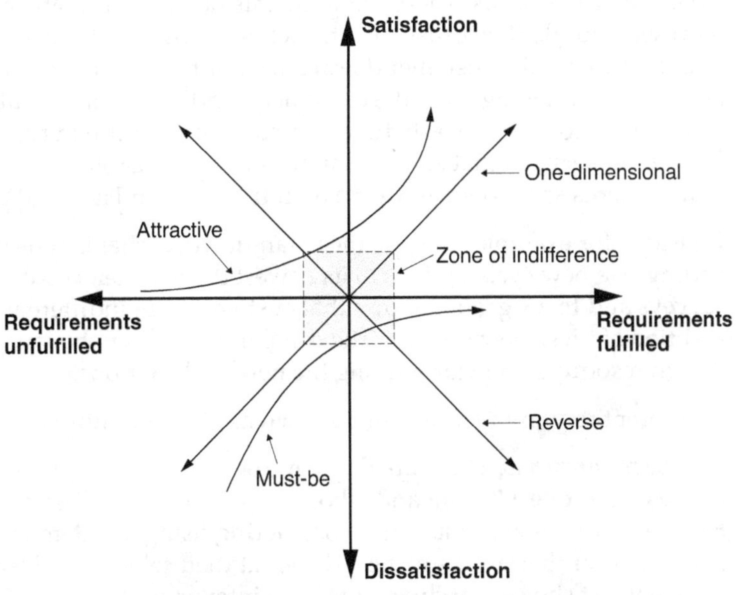

Figure 10.11 Kano model for customer satisfaction.

- *One-dimensional requirements.* These are the requirements in which the customer expects a certain level of fulfillment, and anything exceeding that level increases satisfaction. Such requirements can be articulated by the customer and determined by classic research methods.

  Consider, for example, a computer connection that may be advertised as having a certain data transfer rate. If the rate in use is less than the advertised rate, the customer is dissatisfied. However, as the transfer rate above the advertised rate increases, customer satisfaction will also increase.

  One-dimensional requirements are also known as *performance* requirements, *normal* requirements, *linear* requirements, and *satisfiers.* They are called linear requirements because satisfaction tends to increase linearly with the increase in the fulfillment of requirements.

- *Attractive requirements.* These are the requirements that get to the heart of the customer. When present, they increase satisfaction, but their absence does not cause dissatisfaction, because the customer does not expect them. Consequently, these are unspoken.

  Consider, for example, a hotel that stocks a complimentary welcome package in each room that includes sparkling water, cheese, crackers, and chocolates. This package is certainly not expected by the guests and will give them an "Oh wow!" moment.

  Attractive requirements are also known as *excitement* requirements, *exciters,* and *delighters.*

- *Indifferent requirements.* These requirements do not cause satisfaction if present, nor do they cause dissatisfaction if absent. This could refer to features the customer doesn't need or features the customer rarely uses. Knowing what the customer is indifferent about allows an organization to not waste time or resources providing product features or services that are not important to the customer. Indifferent requirements are shown as a zone of indifference in Figure 10.11.

  Consider, for example, an appliance manufacturer that is considering adding five new cycle options to its newest dishwasher. Feedback from surveys and focus groups shows that customers are indifferent to the addition of these new options. The company decides not to spend design resources on incorporating the new cycle options.

  Indifferent requirements are also known as *neutral* requirements.

- *Reverse requirements.* These are the requirements that refer to features the customer doesn't want and whose presence causes dissatisfaction. For example, a new restaurant is considering using a system in which patrons order their meals using a device at their table. Initial feedback of a pilot test shows that diners prefer to interact with waitstaff to ask questions about the dishes and make adjustments to the ingredients in their meals.

An awareness of these categories of customer satisfaction (and dissatisfaction) provides insight and guidance for the organization's goal of ever-improving customer satisfaction.

Chapter 11

Business Case and Project Charter

A goal without a plan is just a wish.

—Antoine de Saint-Exupéry

The *project charter,* though a simple living document, requires significant preparation time. It serves as a formal contract between the champion and the team, and helps the team stay on track with the goals of the project and organization. There are typically six key elements of a meaningful charter document:

1. Business case
2. Problem statement
3. Goal statement
4. Project scope
5. Project team
6. Project plan

Figure 11.1 displays a typical project charter template. Note how this form emphasizes baseline and goal performance and provides the opportunity to link the project directly to customer satisfaction.

Each element of the project charter will now be addressed.

BUSINESS CASE

> Describe business case justification used to support projects. (Understand)
>
> **Body of Knowledge IV.B.1**

The business case identifies the dollars to be saved and establishes how the project aligns to the organization's strategies. It also states how the organization will fare better when the project reaches its goals. Although the business case usually

Project Charter			
Project No.		***Black Belt / Green Belt / Yellow Belt:***	
Project Title:			
Project Leader:		***Email***	
Project Champion:		***Email***	
Start Date:		***Target Completion Date***	

	Element	**Description**			
1	**Business Case:**	Describe the business case for the opportunity.			
2	**Problem Statement:**	How long has the problem existed? What measurable item is affected? What is the performance gap? What is the business impact?			
3	**Project Goal:**	Describe the project goal. (SMART)			
4	**Objective:**	What improvement is targeted and which is/are the metric(s) to be used to evaluate progress?	**Metric**	**Current State (Before)**	**Proposed Future State (After)**
5	**Business Results ($):**	Include a breakdown of projected cost savings. (Attach a separate sheet if necessary.)			
6	**Team members:**	List the core team members and any SMEs who may be brought in to help the team.			
7	**Project Scope:**	Which part of the process will be investigated? What are the project boundaries? Attach a SIPOC diagram.			
8	**Resources needed:**	List resources that may be needed to accomplish project goals.			
9	**Schedule:**		**Preliminary Plan**	**Target**	**Actual**
			Start Date		
			Define		
			Measure		
			Analyze		
			Improve		
			Control		
			Completion Date		
10	**Approvals**		**Signature**		**Date**
	Process Owner:				
	Project Champion:				
	Finance:				

Figure 11.1 Project charter template.

appears first in a project charter, it is often easier to write the business case once the problem statement, goal statement, and project scope are defined.

EXAMPLE 11.1

The completion of this project will reduce the rework of product B on production line A by 57% and latent defects by more than 82%. Consequently, we expect to reduce in-process inventory by 35%, achieve on-time delivery to our top three customers, and eliminate their product complaints. Hard dollars savings are expected to be $2.75M in the first 12 months and efficiency savings are projected to be $65K. Most of the hard dollar savings are from eliminating a $1.9M capital expenditure, while the balance is from eliminating two hiring requisitions that were planned and opened for quality engineers to address these quality problems. Furthermore, the increased production yield will help advance strategy D of entering the emerging market in the southern region.

PROBLEM STATEMENT

Develop a project problem statement and evaluate it in relation to baseline performance and improvement goals. (Evaluate)

Body of Knowledge IV.B.2

The problem statement identifies what is not working, or where the pain point lies, and should be a concise explanation of a current state that adversely impacts the organization. A well-crafted problem statement should answer five questions:

1. Where does the problem exist?
2. How long has the problem existed?
3. What is the measurable item?
4. What is the performance gap?
5. What is the business impact? (In other words, why is this important?)

In many ways, the problem definition phase is the most important phase of the DMAIC cycle. If this phase is not done thoroughly, teams may move on to subsequent phases only to stall and cycle back through *define*. This phase should be emphasized, and teams should not move forward until the sponsor signs off on it.

In the goal section, we'll learn how to make meaningful goal statements so that baseline performance can be established.

EXAMPLE 11.2

Consider the following problem statement. Does it answer the five questions?

In Factory A, the reject rate for product X has increased by 1000ppm since the second quarter of this fiscal year and has caused us to lose 2% of our market share to competitor Z.

1. Where does the problem exist?

   Factory A

2. How long has the problem existed?

   Since the second quarter of the fiscal year

3. What is the measurable item?

   Reject rate for product X

4. What is the performance gap?

   Reject rate has increased by 1000ppm

5. What is the business impact? (in other words, Why is this important?)

   We have lost 2% of our market share to competitor Z.

This problem statement sufficiently answers each of the five key questions.

EXAMPLE 11.3

Consider the following problem statement. Does it answer the five questions?

Data entry errors for Form 122A have always been higher than they should be, resulting in $5,000 per month in rekeying costs.

1. Where does the problem exist?

   Form 122A

2. How long has the problem existed?

   Always? Need to do some digging here to find out when problem started.

3. What is the measurable item?

   Data entry errors for Form 122A

4. What is the performance gap?

   Higher than they should be? We need to know the extent of the deficiency to be able to determine the improvement the project achieves.

5. What is the business impact? (in other words, Why is this important?)

   $5,000 per month in rekeying costs.

The problem statement fails to adequately address two of the five questions. More investigation and data collection are needed before the project charter can be completed.

GOALS AND OBJECTIVES

> Identify SMART (specific, measurable, actionable, relevant, and timebound) goals and objectives on the basis of the project's problem statement and scope. (Analyze)
>
> **Body of Knowledge IV.B.4**

The *goal statement* identifies the project's objectives and targets and how the success of the project will be measured.

Goal statements must define at least one success (that is, primary) measure. However, baseline performance must be established for each primary measure. Frequently, primary measures are accompanied by secondary or countermeasures to ensure that when primary measures are improved, other measures (that is, secondary measures) do not suffer in the process. Likewise, baseline performance must be established for each secondary measure used.

The goal statement is constructed using the SMART model. SMART was discussed in Chapter 5, but will be recapped briefly here:

- *Specific.* This is not the place to be generic or philosophic. Nail down the goal.
- *Measurable.* Unless the team has measurable goals, they won't know whether they are making progress or whether they have succeeded.
- *Achievable,* yet aggressive. This is a judgment call, and experience with project planning and execution will help in meeting this requirement.
- *Relevant.* The goal must be specifically linked to the strategic goals of the enterprise.
- *Time-bound.* The goal must make sense in the time frame that the team has been given to work within.

Remember, all processes can be measured in terms of quality (that is, defects) and cycle time. The cost of the process flows from these two metrics. Reducing cost without focusing on reducing defects and cycle time is a recipe for disaster.

EXAMPLE 11.4

Consider the following SMART goal statements:

- Reduce the reject rate for product X from its baseline of 45% to 5% within six months. Note: Be careful when citing percentages since they can be misleading. This statement is referring to an absolute percentage reduction. The relative percentage reduction would be 88.9%. It is important to be clear when stating percentage changes.
- Reduce the cycle time of product B from 90 days to less than 10 days 95% of the time within three months.

Each of these goal statements meets the SMART criteria.

In many project charters there is a separate objective section, as shown in Figure 11.1. Metrics that will be tracked to determine project success are listed here with the current baseline values and the expected values based on the goal statement. In this section, it may be helpful to list more than one metric so that the team does not inadvertently suboptimize the process. For example, a project that aims to reduce processing time on loan applications should also track defect rates so that the faster system does not reduce the quality of the process. Suboptimized processes were discussed in Chapter 5.

PROJECT TEAM

The project team members should be chosen based on their interest and abilities to contribute to the project. The stakeholder analysis is an excellent resource for identifying team members. It is important to note each member's expected time contributions to the project. Knowing the total demand requirements placed on team members is essential to ensure they are not overloaded and that their "regular" jobs do not suffer from their contributions to projects.

PROJECT SCOPE

Develop and review project boundaries to ensure that the project has value to the customer. (Analyze)

Body of Knowledge IV.B.3

The project scope specifies the boundaries of the project. The most common scope limitations are budget, time, authority, and resources. Additional aspects of the scope are addressed below.

Lean Six Sigma projects sometimes suffer from a disagreement between the project team members and the sponsor regarding project boundaries. The process of defining scope, of course, can result in problems of extremes:

- Project definitions with scopes that are too broad may lead a team into a morass of connecting issues and associated problems beyond the team's resources. For example, "Improve customer satisfaction" with a complex product or service.
- Project boundaries that are set too narrow could restrict teams from finding root causes. For example, "Improve customer satisfaction by reducing variation in plating thickness" implies a restriction from looking at machining processes, which could be the root cause of the customer problems.

The tendency is to err on the side of making the scope too broad rather than too narrow. Extra attention, effort, and time may be needed to ensure a proper scope. Don't shortcut the process.

Several tools are available to assist in setting a project scope. These include:

- *Pareto charts* to help in the prioritizing processes and sometimes in support of project justification
- *Cause-and-effect diagrams* to broaden the thinking within set categories
- *Affinity diagrams* to show linkages between the project and other projects or processes
- *Process maps* to provide visualization and perhaps illuminate obvious project boundaries and relationships.

There are two methods useful in defining the scope of a project: the dimensional method and the functional method. We will now define each.

Dimensional Method

This approach identifies an initial eight possible dimensions for characterizing a project scope:

1. *Process.* Processes receive input from other processes and feed output to other processes. Tightly bound the process or subprocess associated with the project.
2. *Demographics.* This would consider factors such as employee categorizations, gender, age, education, job level, and so on.
3. *Relationships.* This would include such entities as suppliers, customers, contract personnel, and so on.
4. *Organizational.* Which business units, divisions, sites, or departments are included?

5. *Systems.* Which manual or computerized systems are included? For example, those using system A.
6. *Geographical.* Which country, region, or site is included?
7. *Customer.* Which segmentation or category will be considered?
8. *Combinations.* Any combination of the aforementioned.

The advantage of this method is that it communicates the scope in straightforward and easy-to-understand terms. Unfortunately, this method does not focus in on process inputs as well as the functional method.

> **EXAMPLE 11.5**
>
> Here is a project scope developed using the dimensional method.
>
> The project scope will entail process A, employee category B, at site C, which produce products D, E, and F for customer G. All other employee categories will be excluded.

In addition to defining what is in scope, it is often useful to define what is out of scope. Although one would seem to define the other, experience has shown that what is out of scope is frequently overlooked or not understood fully unless explicitly stated. Many sponsors, team members, and other stakeholders often fail to make this important connection. For example, process B is in scope, while processes A and C are out of scope.

Unwieldy scopes are one of the most frequent reasons cited for the demise of projects. When the scope is too large to be completed within the project plan time frame, or additional resources are not available, there may be a reluctance to go back and re-scope the project. When it is too small, projected savings may be overstated.

Functional Method

The functional method is rooted more in logic and functional relationships between input and output variables than the dimensional method. The intent is to isolate critical input variables. Other names for this method include *process mapping decomposition,* x–y *diagrams,* Y = f(X), and *big* Y *exercises.*

EXAMPLE 11.6

This method is best illustrated by an example provided by Lynch et al. (2003). The example deals with the issue of poor electric motor reliability. Figure 11.2 portrays the functional $Y = f(X)$ breakdown. Each of the X's should be supported by operational data and may be supported by subject matter expert opinions.

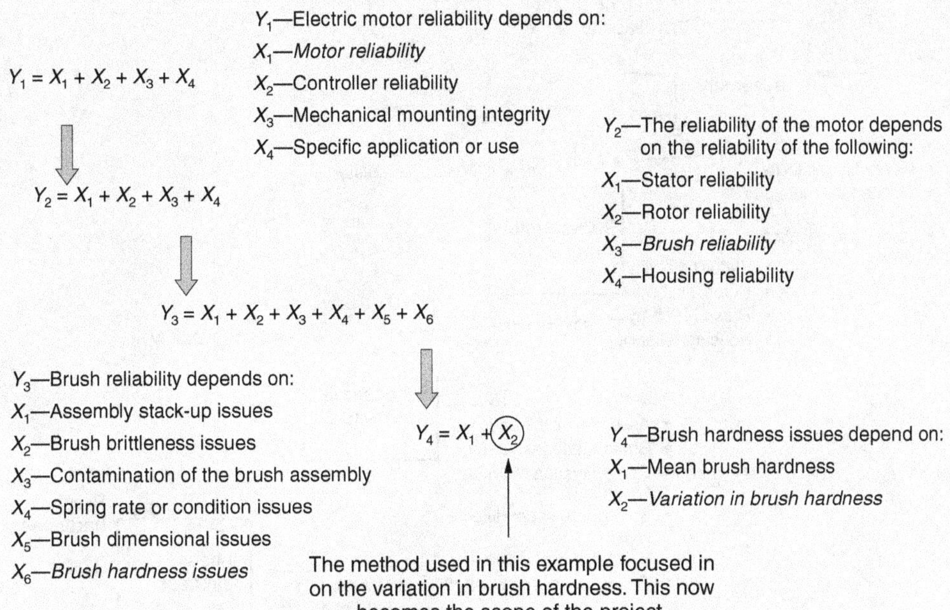

Figure 11.2 Example of project scoping using the cause-and-effect method $Y = f(X)$ format.
Source: Lynch et al. (2003).

The breakdown continues, in this example, until the smallest meaningful part with continuous data is identified. Keep in mind that another Y from the brush reliability equation could have been identified as well. This would have yielded an additional, but concurrent, project.

The disadvantage of using this approach lies in the difficulty of explaining it to senior leaders and other levels of management.

EXAMPLE 11.7

Figure 11.3 addresses the same project as Figure 11.2 but uses a process mapping decomposition breakdown format to isolate critical input variables. This format may be more appealing to senior leaders and management in general.

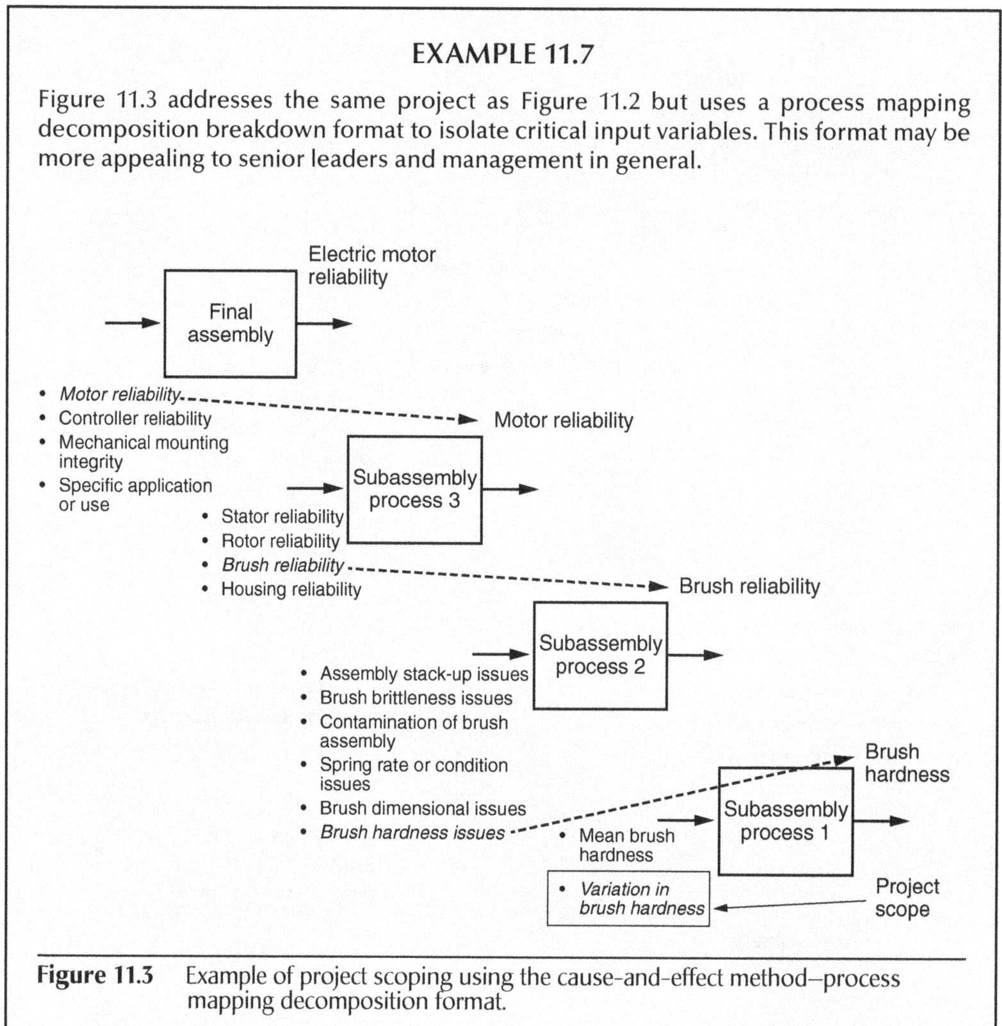

Figure 11.3 Example of project scoping using the cause-and-effect method–process mapping decomposition format.

PROJECT PLAN

The project charter sets forth a tentative schedule for the project timing after a thorough discussion and subsequent agreement with the project champion. This information is needed to facilitate the project pipeline creation and portfolio management process. Executives need to be aware that project time and completion dates are not easily manipulated since they may be part of an overall schedule that is being managed closely along with critical resources.

When a project plan is included, it becomes possible to manage the project from a portfolio perspective, particularly regarding cost, schedule, and resources.

Generally, a Gantt chart depicting the DMAIC phases and noting the resources required by phase will be sufficient. Gantt charts will be addressed in Chapter 12. However, at a minimum, an estimated start and completion date is required.

Charter Housekeeping Considerations

Furthermore, it is prudent to have charters replete with the appropriate signatures of authorization, not the least of which are the sponsor and financial representatives. The inclusion of the financial approval lends credibility and support to the proposed financial gains.

The project sponsor has the ultimate accountability for developing the project charter. He or she will likely seek counsel from a Black Belt or Master Black Belt. However, in the end, senior leaders will look to the project sponsor for the success or failure of the project.

PROJECT PERFORMANCE MEASUREMENTS

> Identify and evaluate performance measurements (e.g., cost, revenue, delivery, schedule, and customer satisfaction) that connect critical elements of the process to key outputs. (Analyze)
>
> **Body of Knowledge IV.B.5**

Projects exist for producing results. Portny (2010) states that three components must be present for an activity to be defined as a *project*. These components are depicted in Figure 11.4. Resources include both the financial component and the human capital component. These components define boundaries or constraints for the project. Without any one of them, the concept of a project evaporates. For example, consider a project without a scope. What would be accomplished? How about a project without a schedule? When would it be complete? Without any resources, who would do the project and how would it be paid for?

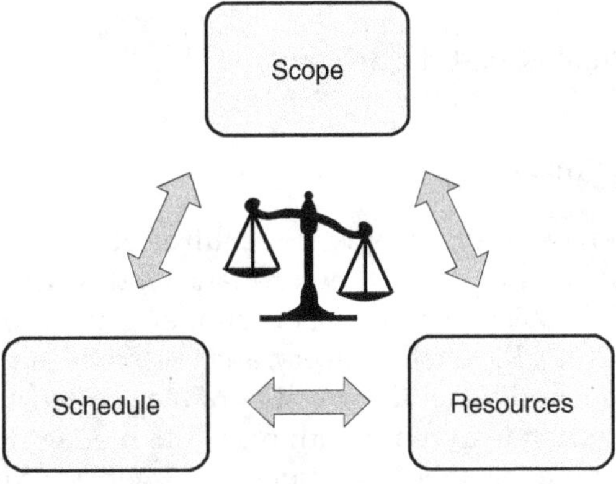

Figure 11.4 The components of any project.
Source: Adapted from Portny (2010).

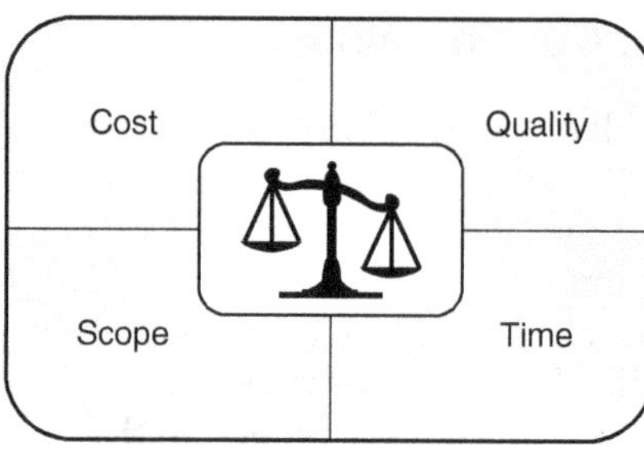

Figure 11.5 The balanced quadrant.
Source: Adapted from Williams (2008).

Williams (2008) offers what she calls the *balanced quadrant* concept depicted in Figure 11.5. Each quadrant represents one aspect of a project. Managing a project requires maintaining a balance among the four quadrants. Consider the following examples:

- An increase in scope results in an increase in time and cost
- An increase in quality results in an increase in cost and perhaps time
- A decrease in cost results in a decrease in scope, time, and/or quality

In most cases, the project manager or team leader cannot make balancing decisions alone. Often, the internal and external stakeholders must be consulted, particularly when cost is a consideration.

The above discussion raises a key point about Lean Six Sigma projects—that is, such projects are not managed by the DMAIC methodology alone. Like all significant projects, Lean Six Sigma projects must be managed using project management techniques. This includes using the following project performance measurements when appropriate:

- Cost
- Revenue
- Delivery (that is, on-time delivery)
- Schedule
- Customer satisfaction

Of the five above, cost and schedule are required at a minimum since they can be used to form the basis of the cost performance index (CPI) and schedule performance index (SPI). These two indices are fundamental project management indices. See Kubiak (2012). Revenue, delivery, and customer satisfaction, among others, may be needed depending on the specifics of the project.

A word of caution is in order with regard to managing Lean Six Sigma projects using project management techniques. The general concepts and techniques of project management work well. However, one must remember that these techniques were developed for projects where the plan, from start to finish, is well known. This is not the case for Lean Six Sigma projects.

Although the DMAIC methodology itself is rigorous, it is built upon the premise that we don't know the solution in advance and that we follow the data. Consequently, it is difficult to plan, resource, and cost out each phase with a high degree of precision. This does not mean we should abandon these planning tools and techniques—just recognize their limitations.

PROJECT CHARTER REVIEW

> Explain the importance of having periodic project charter reviews with stakeholders. (Understand)
>
> **Body of Knowledge IV.B.6**

It should be noted that the project charter is considered a living document and is adjusted as information is gained and learning takes place.

Stakeholders should be actively engaged in the review of Lean Six Sigma projects.

On one hand, champions must be engaged in a specific set of reviews related to the projects for which they are responsible. Recall that the role of the champions was addressed in Chapter 1. This set of reviews is known as *tollgates*, which will be addressed in detail in Chapter 12.

In addition to tollgates, many organizations instigate an integrated and routine set of reviews across all active projects. This set of reviews would include executive management, other senior leaders, middle management, and, of course, interested stakeholders other than champions.

If many projects are under way, half of the projects might be conducted one month and the other half the next month and rotated on this cycle thereafter. This permits stakeholders to view all the projects over a relatively short time frame. Projects not performing to plan may receive additional support and resources to rectify them.

Involving stakeholders in the review process helps ensure cooperation and buy-in and/or, at least, surfaces earlier an awareness of resistance that some stakeholders may harbor. When this awareness becomes known, the techniques of Chapter 3 can be applied.

Chapter 12

Project Management (PM) Tools

Time is the scarcest resource, and unless it is managed, nothing else can be managed.

—Peter Drucker

> Identify and use the following PM tools to track projects and document their progress: Gantt charts, tollgate reviews, work breakdown structure (WBS) and RACI model (responsible, accountable, consulted, and informed). (Evaluate)
>
> **Body of Knowledge IV.C.1-4**

This chapter will address a variety of basic project management tools, including Gantt charts, tollgate reviews, work breakdown structures, and the RACI matrix. When used fully, these tools provide a Black Belt with the capability to manage a project efficiently and effectively.

GANTT CHARTS

A *Gantt chart* is a project management tool that provides a high-level overview of the tasks needed to complete a project and their status. The chart displays planned and finished tasks in relation to time. As such, the Gantt chart provides an excellent visualization of time-based progress. It is also called a *milestone chart.*

The Gantt chart has the advantage of being easy to understand while conveying essential data and is often used for presentations to executive groups in addition to their use as tracking devices. Additional charts and diagrams can be produced for each of the activities listed. These graphical tools are also useful for tracking and evaluating the project at various phases and at final management reviews. *Storyboards* are sometimes used to convey project information involving changes that are easier to draw or photograph than to explain in words. A common application of storyboards is for before-and-after pictures, often called *current state* and *future state,* for a proposed project. This approach is appropriate for facility or product redesign projects. Storyboards for Six Sigma projects are often formatted into five sections labeled *define, measure, analyze, improve,* and *control* (DMAIC), with charts, figures, and documents illustrating the activity in each area.

EXAMPLE 12.1

Figure 12.1 shows an excerpt from a typical Gantt chart. Task numbers and names are listed in the first two columns, followed by a Resource column that lists the department or individual responsible for completing the tasks. The start and end dates, and duration in days are in the next three columns, followed by a Percent Complete column. A graphical display of the durations of the tasks, milestones, and task dependencies follows. Tasks that are dependent upon each other are connected by arrows, and milestones are depicted as diamonds. For a Six Sigma project, typical milestones would include the completion of each of the DMAIC steps.

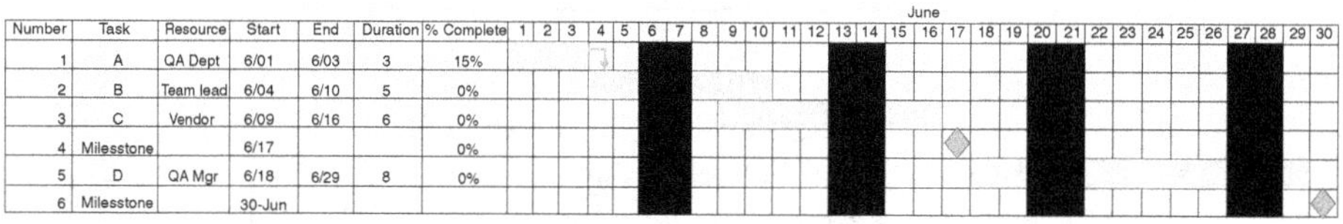

							June																													
Number	Task	Resource	Start	End	Duration	% Complete	1	2	3	4	5	6	7	8	9	10	11	12	13	14	15	16	17	18	19	20	21	22	23	24	25	26	27	28	29	30
1	A	QA Dept	6/01	6/03	3	15%																														
2	B	Team lead	6/04	6/10	5	0%																														
3	C	Vendor	6/09	6/16	6	0%																														
4	Milesstone		6/17			0%																														
5	D	QA Mgr	6/18	6/29	8	0%																														
6	Milesstone		30-Jun																																	

Figure 12.1 Gantt chart example.

Note that the first day of work on any activity is always available as a full day of work. For example, Task A begins on June 1 and ends on June 3. This activity has a duration of three days because June 1 is counted as a full day of work.

Note that like the project charter, a Gantt chart is a living document, and is updated frequently as tasks are completed or delayed.

TOLLGATE REVIEWS

Tollgate reviews are the bonds that hold the DMAIC framework together. They are a necessary part of the DMAIC infrastructure. Tollgates serve as meaningful checkpoints, facilitate communications, and ensure sponsor participation. They exist as a check and balance to ensure that teams are ready to transition from one phase to the next in an orderly manner. Tollgates focus projects on moving forward.

The *tollgate review* is a formal review process conducted by a champion who asks a series of focused questions aimed at ensuring that the team has performed diligently during a phase. The result of a tollgate is a *go* or *no-go* decision. The *go* decision allows the team to move forward to the next phase. If it is in the last phase, the *go* decision brings about project closure. If the decision is *no-go,* the team must remain in the phase, retreat to an earlier phase (in some instances), or perhaps the project is terminated or suspended. The concept of *go/no-go* decisions was illustrated in Figure IV.1 in the beginning of this Part.

Effective tollgate reviews are usually characterized by an objective evaluation of the work performed by the team during the phase, and the willingness to identify and resolve problems during the reviews. Poor preparation and incomplete documentation on behalf of the team typically characterize poor tollgate reviews. A poor review also can stem from a project champion desiring to change the scope, or a champion delegating a replacement to attend the meeting.

Many viewpoints exist regarding the purpose of tollgates, who should attend them, what questions should be asked, and what the exit criteria are from the tollgate phase. Table 12.1 provides a summary of one viewpoint. The "questions to address" are minimal in the table, but they are critical.

Note the first question asked: "Is the project consistent with the goals of the organization?" Project alignment to the strategy, and subsequently the goals and objectives, of the organization is critical. This question appears in every phase because of the highly dynamic nature of organizations. When the answer is "No," it is incumbent upon the champion to shut the project down and allow the project resources to be allocated elsewhere. However, notice that there is something unique about this question. Unlike the others in the table, this question should be both asked and answered by the champion, for it is simply a rhetorical question posed to the team. The champion is in the position to have direct access to the proper resources to be able to answer this question. The champion should come prepared at every tollgate to address this critical question.

Table 12.2 provides an additional set of questions the champion might ask during tollgate reviews. Of course, common to each phase are questions regarding budget and schedule. Also included is a question regarding what obstacles the team might have encountered and how the champion may be able to help. Recall that one job of the champion is the removal of organizational barriers the team might face.

Tollgate reviews, when executed well, provide real value to the Lean Six Sigma deployment. They keep projects focused and on track, and executives and champions engaged.

WORK BREAKDOWN STRUCTURE (WBS)

A *work breakdown structure* is a hierarchical decomposition of the work content for a given project. The WBS permits the project manager to systematically break the work into smaller, more manageable sizes that can be planned, executed, and tracked more efficiently. Figure 12.2 represents a generalized work breakdown structure. The project is first decomposed into small modules as shown in level 2. This level is subsequently broken down further into even smaller modules of work as shown in level 3. This process continues down to the level "n." This level represents the smallest work contents that must be tracked in order to manage the project successfully. At level "n," the tasks can be assigned to individuals for execution. Time, material, and expenses are collected at this level and can be summarized upward to any level desired. Thus, considerable thought must be given to the development of the WBS.

Component	Define	Measure	Analyze	Improve	Control
Purpose	Provide a compelling business case appropriately scoped, complete with SMART goals, and linked to a hoshin plan	Collect process performance data for primary and secondary metrics to gain insight and understanding into root causes and to establish performance baselines	Analyze and establish optimal performance settings for each X and verify root causes	Identify and implement process improvement solutions	Establish and deploy a control plan to ensure that gains in performance are maintained
Participants required	• Sponsor • Process owner • MBB/BB coach • Project champion • Project team • Finance partner	• Sponsor • Process owner • MBB/BB coach • Project champion • Project team	• Sponsor • Process owner • MBB/BB coach • Project champion • Project team • Finance partner	• Sponsor • Process owner • MBB/BB coach • Project champion • Project team	• Sponsor • Process owner • MBB/BB coach • Project champion • Project team • Finance partner
Questions to address	• Is this project consistent with the goals of the organization? • Do we have the right level of engagement from stakeholders and business partners?	• Is this project still consistent with the goals of the organization? • Do we have the right level of engagement from stakeholders and business partners?	• Is this project still consistent with the goals of the organization? • Do we have the right level of engagement from stakeholders and business partners?	• Is this project still consistent with the goals of the organization? • Do we have the right level of engagement from stakeholders and business partners?	• Is this project still consistent with the goals of the organization? • Have resources been allocated to move into replication?

Table 12.1 A brief summary of the tollgate process.

Continued

Component	Define	Measure	Analyze	Improve	Control
Questions to address (continued)	• Have resources been allocated to move to the next phase? • Do conflicts exist with other projects or activities?	• Have resources been allocated to move to the next phase?	• Have resources been allocated to move to the next phase? • What are the market and timing dependencies?	• Have resources been allocated to move to the next phase?	• Is the replication schedule and plan appropriate? • What are the market and timing dependencies? • Have responsibilities identified in the control plan been transferred to appropriate parties?
Exit criteria	• Sponsor approval • Finance approval • Funding approval	• Sponsor approval	• Sponsor approval • Finance approval	• Sponsor approval	• Sponsor approval • Finance approval • Hand-off to process owner

Table 12.1 *Continued*

Phase	Questions
Define	• Who are the stakeholders? • What are the primary and secondary measures? • Are you facing any barriers or obstacles I can help with? • Are we on schedule/budget?
Measure	• What is the process capability? • What data still remain to be collected? • What did the FMEA show? • What questions still remain to be answered about the process? • Are you facing any barriers or obstacles I can help with? • Are we on schedule/budget?
Analyze	• What are the critical X's? • What are the root causes? • Are you facing any barriers or obstacles I can help with? • Are we on schedule/budget?
Improve	• What is the process capability of the revised process? • What criteria will be used to select the optimum solution from the set of solutions? • Will we run a pilot? • Are you facing any barriers or obstacles I can help with? • Are we on schedule/budget?
Control	• Is the process documented? • Is the control plan completed? • Has the process been transitioned back to the process owner? • What lessons have we learned? • Do we know where we might be able to replicate our new process across the organization? • Are you facing any barriers or obstacles I can help with? • Are we on schedule/budget?

Table 12.2 Additional questions to be asked by the champion during tollgate reviews.
Source: Adapted and compiled from Phillips and Stone (2002).

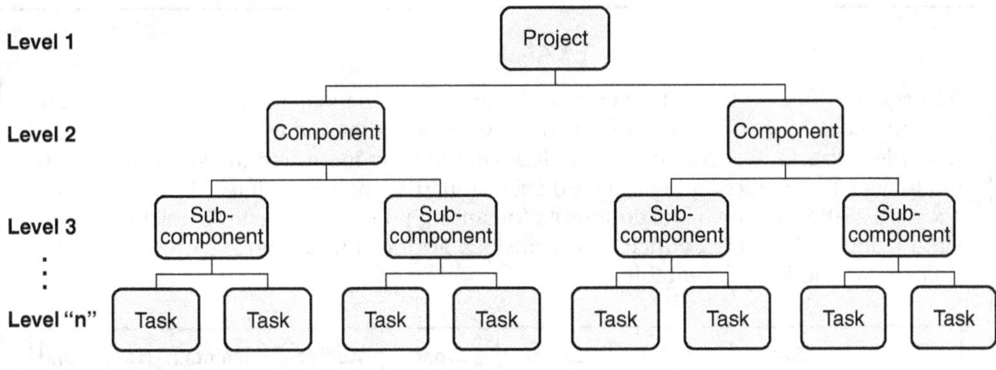

Figure 12.2 A generalized work breakdown structure.

Since the WBS is developed to assign and track work, the tasks should appear on the project schedule or Gantt chart. It should be noted that some of the integrated off-the-shelf software available permits the development and construction of a whole WBS and the subsequent translation into a project schedule, thus giving the project leader increased visibility into project performance.

RACI MODEL (RESPONSIBLE, ACCOUNTABLE, CONSULTED, AND INFORMED)

In addition to the communication plan described in Chapter 7, another effective tool for facilitating communication is the Responsible, Accountable, Consulted, and Informed (RACI) model. The RACI model is represented by a matrix in which stakeholders are categorized according to their involvement, or role, in a task. The roles include:

- *Responsible.* Individuals who actively participate in an activity. Notice that more than one individual at a time may be held responsible.
- *Accountable.* The individual accountable for results. Only one individual may be accountable at a time. This will become evident in the example given below.
- *Consulted.* Individuals who must be consulted before a decision is made. Sometimes this appears as *consultation* or *counselor.*
- *Informed.* Individuals who must be informed about a decision because they are affected. These individuals do not need to take part in the decision-making process.

The RACI matrix is completed by a team or committee, and in some cases, by an individual (for example, a project manager). Frequently, a RACI is distributed to team members to provide clarification. It is important to keep in mind that there should be single points of accountability with sufficient authority to make decisions.

EXAMPLE 12.2

An organization is in the initial stages of beginning its Lean Six Sigma deployment. Due to significant miscommunications and misunderstandings, the deployment incurred multiple setbacks. Consequently, the deployment team identified the set of stakeholders (players) and tasks and completed a RACI matrix, shown in Figure 12.3. The matrix shows that the executive is accountable for setting policy, the Master Black Belt is consulted, and the Quality council is responsible. For each task, there is only one stakeholder classified as accountable.

Task → Player ↓	Set policy	Identify projects	Select projects	Work projects	Achieve results	Maintain gains	Coach and mentor
Executive	A	C	I, C	I	I	I	
Sponsor		C	C	I	A	I	
Process owner		C	C	I, C	I	A, R	
MBB	C	R	R, C	C	I	I	A
BB		R	C	A, R	R	R	
GB		C		R	R		
Quality council	R	A	A	I	I	I	

Figure 12.3 RACI matrix for Example 12.2.

Because of the popularity and usefulness of the RACI matrix, it has evolved over the years, and numerous variants of it can be found. One popular version is RASCI (sometimes RASIC), which adds the Support role.

Chapter 13

Analytical Tools

We change our tools and then our tools change us.

—Jeff Bezos

> Identify and use the following analytical tools throughout the DMAIC cycle: affinity diagrams, tree diagrams, matrix diagrams, prioritization matrices, activity network diagrams, process decision program charts, interrelationship digraphs. (Apply)
>
> **Body of Knowledge IV.D.1-7**

This chapter will address what is commonly known as the *seven management and planning tools:*

1. Affinity diagrams
2. Tree diagrams
3. Matrix diagrams
4. Prioritization matrices
5. Activity network diagrams
6. Process decision program charts (PDPC)
7. Interrelationship digraphs (ID)

AFFINITY DIAGRAMS

The *affinity diagram* is a tool used to organize information and help achieve order out of the chaos that can develop in a brainstorming session. Large amounts of data, concepts, and ideas are grouped based on their natural relationship to one another. It is more a creative process than a logical process. The affinity diagram is also known as the *KJ method,* named after its originator, Kawakita Jiro.

The affinity diagram is useful when there are numerous ideas, bordering on chaos; the issues are large and difficult to grasp; and group consensus is necessary. See Tague (2005).

The basic procedure for developing the affinity diagram follows:

1. Conduct a brainstorming session and collect ideas on a sticky note or card.
2. Post ideas randomly on a large work surface or sheet of easel paper.
3. Gather all participants around the notes.
4. Without talking, participants should look for related ideas and gather them into logical groups. Also, participants may move notes that other participants have moved. If notes appear to belong to more than one group, replicate a note for each group. It is OK to have outliers or lone ideas.
5. At this point, participants may talk. Review all the notes within a group and look for a theme of the group. This theme may be already on a note. If not, capture this theme on a note and place it at the top of the group. Do this for all the groups. This is an important step as it is necessary to reach consensus on the groupings.
6. If appropriate, combine groups into supergroups.

The affinity diagram is a highly valued technique because it is evolutionary in nature. According to Tague (2005), it allows "groupings to happen," as well as allowing a group to "move beyond habitual thinking and preconceived categories." That's why it's important to avoid placing the notes in any order or developing any category headings in advance.

EXAMPLE 13.1

This example is taken from Tague (2005).

> The ZZ-400 manufacturing team used an affinity diagram to organize its list of potential performance indicators. Table 13.1 shows the list the team members brainstormed. Because the team works a shift schedule and members could not meet to do the affinity diagram together, they modified the procedure.
>
> They wrote each idea on a sticky note and put all the notes randomly on a rarely used door. Over several days, everyone reviewed the notes in their spare time and moved the notes into related groups. Some people reviewed the evolving pattern several times. After a few days, the natural grouping shown in Figure 13.1 had emerged.

Notice that one of the notes, "Safety," has become part of the heading for its group. The rest of the heading was added after the grouping emerged. Five broad areas of performance were identified: product quality, maintenance, manufacturing cost, safety and environmental, and volume.

Also, notice that "Maintenance costs" was placed into two groups, which are circled in Figure 13.1.

Possible performance measures			
% purity	% trace metals	Maintenance costs	Number of emergency jobs
Pounds produced	Environmental accidents	Material costs	Overtime costs
Number of pump seal failures	Viscosity	C_{pk} values	Safety
Days since last lost-time	% rework or reject	Hours downtime	% uptime
Number of OSHA recordables	Number of customer returns	Customer complaints	Overtime total hours worked
$ per pounds produced	Raw material utilization	Yield	Utility cost
ppm water	Color	Service factor	Time between turnarounds
Hours worked per employee	Pounds of waste	Housekeeping score	% capacity filled

Table 13.1 Affinity diagram for Example 1.3.

Continued

Continued

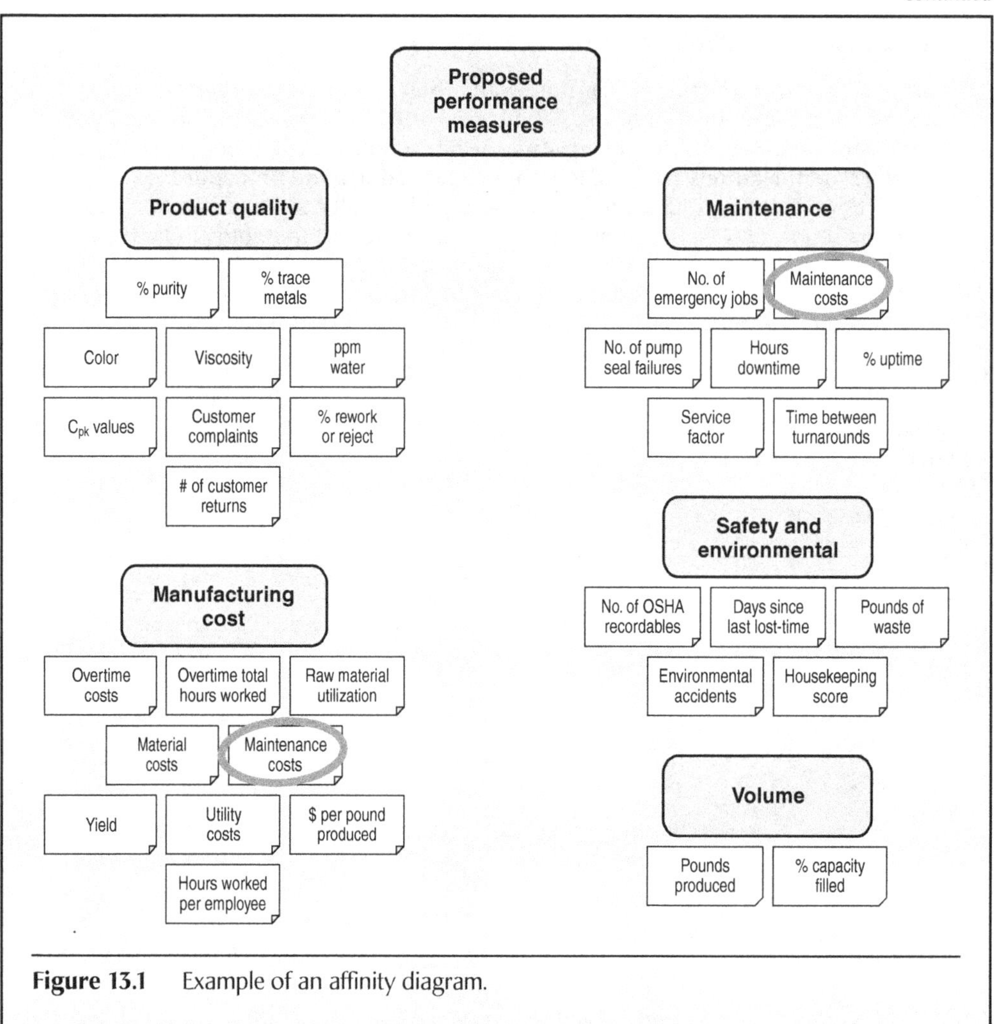

Figure 13.1 Example of an affinity diagram.

TREE DIAGRAMS

The *tree diagram* is a tool that depicts the hierarchy of tasks and subtasks needed to complete an objective. The finished diagram resembles a tree. Tree diagrams may be depicted either vertically top-down or horizontally left-to-right. When depicted top-down, tasks move from general (top) to specific (down), and when depicted left-to-right, tasks move from left (general) to right (specific).

Tree diagrams may be used in a wide variety of applications, including critical-to-quality tree, decision tree, fault tree analysis, organization chart, process decision program chart, five whys, work breakdown structure (WBS), and so on. Figure 13.2 illustrates the general structure of a tree diagram using the

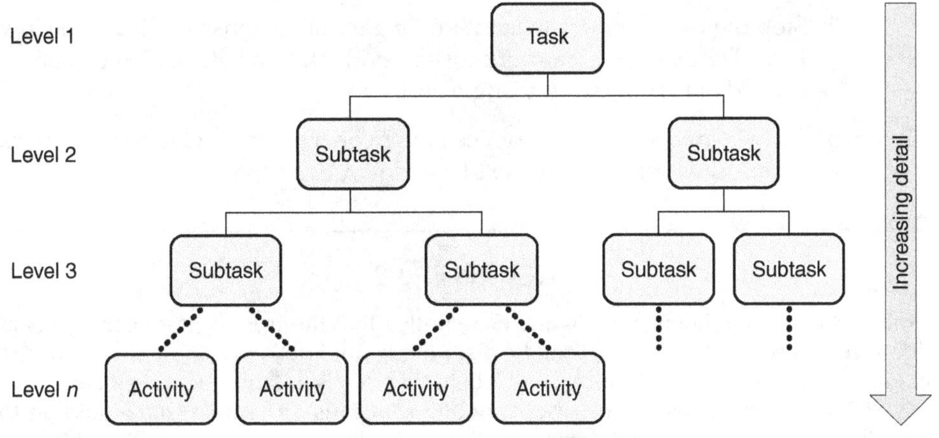

Figure 13.2 Example of the general structure of a tree diagram.

top-down format. "Tasks" were chosen in this figure. Had we chosen a "system" as the top tier, the second tier would have been subsystems, the third tier components, and the fourth tier parts.

The basic procedure for developing the tree diagram follows:

1. State the issue or problem to be explored. Write it on a note. This serves as the top of the tree.

2. Depending on the nature of the issue or problem, different questions must be asked to generate subsequent levels of the tree. For example, for each item at each level, Tague (2005) suggests:

   - If the top item of the tree is a WBS, plan, or goal, ask questions like "What tasks must be done to accomplish this?" or "How can this be accomplished?"

   - If the top item of the tree is a root cause analysis, ask questions like "What causes this?" or "Why does this happen?"

   Of course, the wording at each level might have to change to reflect the context of the level. For example, "components" might be replaced by "systems," "subsystems," or "parts."

   Brainstorm each item at each level until complete. When done properly, this technique could lead to very large tree diagrams.

3. Tague (2005) suggests:

   Do a "necessary and sufficient" check. Are all the items at this level necessary for the one the level above? If all the items at this level were present or accomplished, would they be sufficient for the one on the level above?

4. Stop the tree diagram when it no longer makes sense to divide the lowest level. For example, the root cause is evident, a specific action can be carried out, or a part is a single entity.
5. Draw connecting lines from each item on a given level to the appropriate supporting items on the next level down.

EXAMPLE 13.2

Consider the example given in Figure 13.3. Notice that the tree diagram completes at different levels. Also, notice that the best setting is not known for the viscosity of the paint. Consequently, it leads to runs, which, in turn, leads to tables being rejected.

This example has led to the discovery of a root cause. The next step would be to establish a project that would determine the optimal viscosity setting so that this root cause could be eliminated. A detailed review of this tree diagram would reveal other potential actions as well (for example, find the missing clamping instructions or create a new one, revise the tubing specification, and so on).

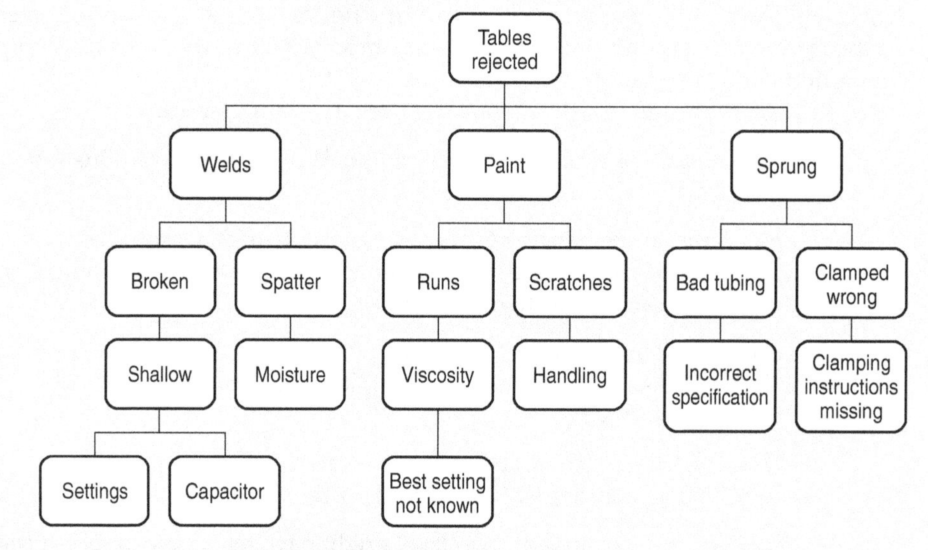

Figure 13.3 Tree diagram for Example 13.2.

MATRIX DIAGRAM

The *matrix diagram* is a tool that identifies the relationships that exist between groups of data. It can be also used to identify the strength of those relationships. The matrix diagram does not use a singular format. Instead, there are six different forms, including the C, L, T, X, Y, and roof-shaped format. The different shapes that can be selected depend on the number of variables to be compared, as shown in Table 13.2.

Matrix shape	Number of variables
C	3
L	2
T	3
X	4
Y	3
Roof	1

Table 13.2 Matrix diagram shapes by number of variables or groups compared.

Relationship	Symbol	Weight
Weak	Δ	1
Medium	○	3
Strong	⊙	9

Table 13.3 Relationship symbols and weights for matrix diagrams.

Strengths of relationships between variables can be depicted using different symbols, as shown in Table 13.3, and are used in the same manner as described in the discussion of quality function deployment in Chapter 10. Any choice of symbols can be used if they are sufficiently distinct. In some cases, users may only need to use two symbols depending on the comparison to be made, for example, high and low, or large and small.

The basic procedure for developing the matrix diagram follows:

1. Determine what type of variables or groups of items are to be compared.
2. Select the appropriate type of matrix: C, L, T, X, Y, or roof-shaped depending on the number of variables to be compared.
3. Complete the matrix headings using the items from each group as row and column headings.
4. Select the appropriate symbols for the matrix.
5. Complete each cell in the matrix by doing the appropriate comparisons and applying the necessary symbols.
6. Review the matrix for patterns and draw conclusions.

The following examples are taken from Tague (2005).

EXAMPLE 13.3

C-SHAPED MATRIX

Consider Figures 13.4 through 13.9. Think of C meaning, "cube." Because this matrix is three-dimensional, it is difficult to draw and infrequently used. If it is important to compare three groups simultaneously, consider using a three-dimensional model or computer software that can provide a clear visual image.

This figure shows one point on a C-shaped matrix relating products, customers, and manufacturing locations. Zig Company's model B is made at the Mississippi plant. (See Figure 13.4.)

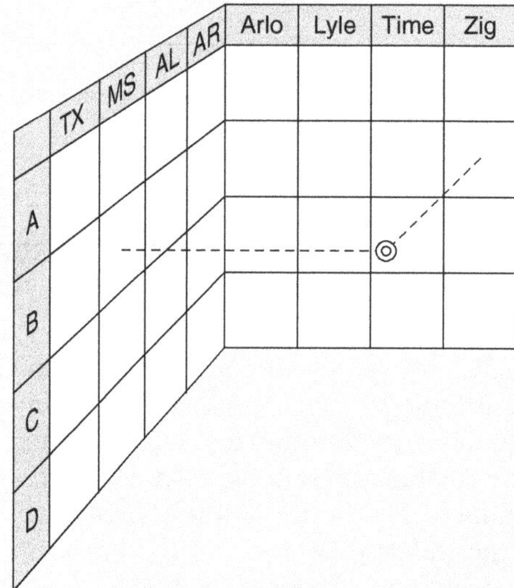

Figure 13.4 C-shaped matrix example.

EXAMPLE 13.4

L-SHAPED MATRIX

This L-shaped matrix summarizes customers' requirements. The team placed numbers in the boxes to show numerical specifications and used check marks to show choice of packaging. The L-shaped matrix actually forms an upside-down L. This is the most basic and most common matrix format. (See Figure 13.5.)

Customer Requirements

	Customer D	Customer M	Customer R	Customer T
Purity %	> 99.2	> 99.2	> 99.4	> 99.0
Trace metals (ppm)	< 5	—	< 10	< 25
Water (ppm)	< 10	< 5	< 10	—
Viscosity (cp)	20–35	20–30	10–50	15–35
Color	< 10	< 10	< 15	< 10
Drum		✔		
Truck	✔			✔
Railcar			✔	

Figure 13.5 L-shaped matrix example.

EXAMPLE 13.5

T-SHAPED MATRIX

This T-shaped matrix relates product models (group A) to their manufacturing locations (group B) and to their customers (group C).

Examining the matrix in different ways reveals different information. For example, concentrating on model A, we see that it is produced in large volume at the Texas plant and in small volume at the Alabama plant. Time Inc. is the major customer for model A, while Arlo Co. buys a small amount. If we choose to focus on the customer rows, we learn that only one customer, Arlo, buys all four models. Zig buys just one. Time makes large purchases of A and D, while Lyle is a relatively minor customer (see Figure 13.6).

Products—Customers—Manufacturing Locations

Texas plant	●		○	○
Mississippi plant		●		○
Alabama plant	○			●
Arkansas plant		○	●	
● Large volume ○ Small volume	Model A	Model B	Model C	Model D
Zig Corp.		●		
Arlo Co.	○	○	○	●
Lyle Co.			○	○
Time Inc.	●			●

Figure 13.6 T-shaped matrix example.

EXAMPLE 13.6

X-SHAPED MATRIX

This figure extends the T-shaped matrix example into an X-shaped matrix by including the relationships of freight lines with the manufacturing sites they serve and the customers who use them. Each axis of the matrix is related to the two adjacent ones, but not to the one across. Thus, the product models are related to the plant sites and to the customers, but not to the freight lines.

A lot of information can be contained in an X-shaped matrix. In this one, we can observe that Red Lines and Zip Inc., which seem to be minor carriers based on volume, are the only carriers that serve Lyle Co. Lyle doesn't buy much, but it and Arlo are the only customers for model C. Model D is made at three locations, while the other models are made at two. (See Figure 13.7.)

Manufacturing Sites—Products—Customers—Freight Lines

<table>
<tr><td>○</td><td></td><td>●</td><td>○</td><td>Texas plant</td><td>●</td><td></td><td>○</td><td>○</td></tr>
<tr><td></td><td>○</td><td>●</td><td>●</td><td>Mississippi plant</td><td></td><td>●</td><td></td><td>○</td></tr>
<tr><td></td><td></td><td>●</td><td>●</td><td>Alabama plant</td><td>○</td><td></td><td></td><td>●</td></tr>
<tr><td>○</td><td>○</td><td></td><td>○</td><td>Arkansas plant</td><td></td><td>○</td><td>●</td><td></td></tr>
<tr><td>Red Lines</td><td>Zip Inc.</td><td>World-wide</td><td>Trans South</td><td></td><td>Model A</td><td>Model B</td><td>Model C</td><td>Model D</td></tr>
<tr><td></td><td></td><td>●</td><td>○</td><td>Zig Corp.</td><td></td><td>●</td><td></td><td></td></tr>
<tr><td></td><td></td><td></td><td>●</td><td>Arlo Co.</td><td>○</td><td>○</td><td>○</td><td>●</td></tr>
<tr><td>○</td><td>○</td><td></td><td></td><td>Lyle Co.</td><td></td><td></td><td>○</td><td>○</td></tr>
<tr><td></td><td>○</td><td>●</td><td></td><td>Time Inc.</td><td>●</td><td></td><td></td><td>●</td></tr>
</table>

● Large volume

○ Small volume

Figure 13.7 X-shaped matrix example.

EXAMPLE 13.7

Y-SHAPED MATRIX

This Y-shaped matrix shows the relationships between customer requirements, internal process metrics, and the departments involved. Symbols show the strength of the relationships: primary relationships, such as the manufacturing department's responsibility for production capacity; secondary relationships, such as the link between product availability and inventory levels; minor relationships, such as the distribution department's responsibility for order lead time; and no relationship, such as between the purchasing department and on-time delivery.

The matrix tells an interesting story about on-time delivery. The distribution department is assigned primary responsibility for that customer requirement. The two metrics most strongly related to on-time delivery are inventory levels and order lead time. Of the two, distribution has only a weak relationship with order lead time and none with inventory levels. Perhaps the responsibility for on-time delivery needs to be reconsidered. (See Figure 13.8.)

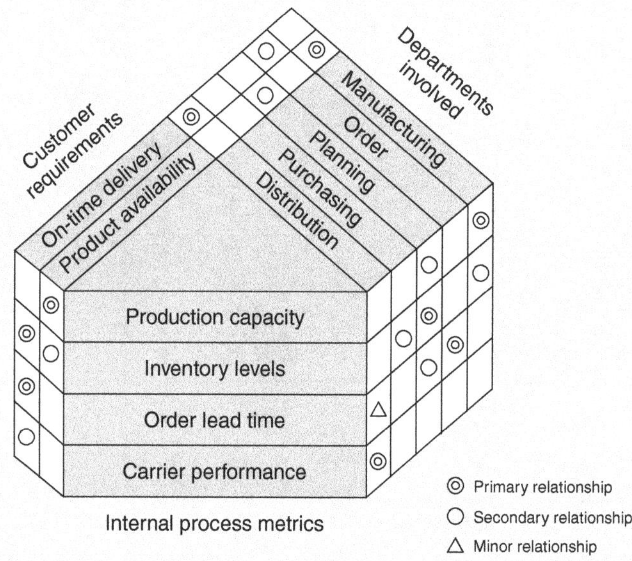

Figure 13.8 Y-shaped matrix example.

EXAMPLE 13.8

ROOF-SHAPED MATRIX

The roof-shaped matrix is used with an L- or T-shaped matrix to show one group of items relating to itself. It is most commonly used with a House of Quality, where it forms the "roof" of the "house." For example, a strong relationship links color and trace metals, while viscosity is unrelated to any of the other requirements. (See Figure 13.9.)

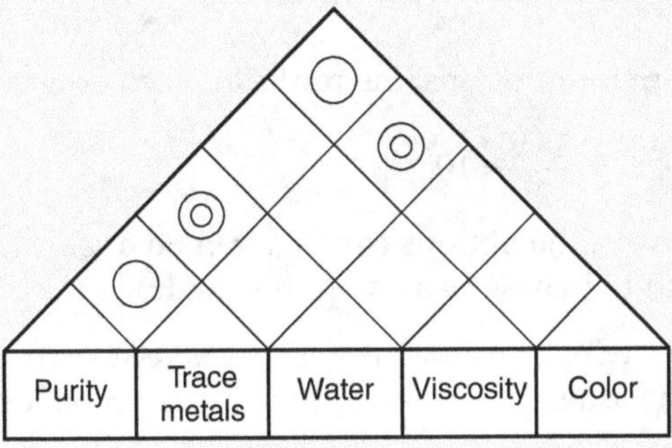

Figure 13.9 Roof-shaped matrix example.

The matrix diagram is a highly useful tool. The key lies with selecting the most appropriate one for conveying the proper message.

PRIORITIZATION MATRIX

The *prioritization matrix* is a tool used to choose between several options that have many useful benefits, but where not all of them are of equal value. The choices are prioritized according to known weighted criteria and then narrowed down to the most desirable or effective one(s) to accomplish the task or problem at hand.

The basic procedure for developing the prioritization matrix follows:

1. Identify the goal and clarify the options available.
2. Identify the criteria the decision must meet.
3. Develop the relative importance for each criterion (that is, weighting). This relative importance is a weighting between 0 and 1, denoted in 0.05 increments. The total weight must add to 1. There are many ways to obtain agreement on these weights. Multi-voting is one such method.
4. Create an L-matrix. List the relative importance weightings, criteria, and options as shown in Figure 13.10.
5. Rank each option within a criterion. If there are "n" options, we can rank the options with "1" being the best and "n" being the worst.

Make sure everyone is clear on the ranking scale. Rank the options for each criterion. As always, there are many ways to reach an agreement on the ranks. Select one that works best for your team. If there is a tie in the ranks between two options, we can score them using an average rank. For example, if there were a tie for first place for two options, each of these options would be ranked as 1.5, and then the third option would be given a rank of 3. Using this method, the ranks for each criterion should add to $\sum_{i=1}^{n} i = \frac{n(n+1)}{2}$. For example, if there are four options, the ranks for each criterion should add to

$(1+2+3+4) = \frac{4 \times 5}{2} = 10.$

Alternatively, the options can be rated on a scale from 1-5 or 1-10. There is no need to handle ties using this method.

No matter which approach is used, make sure that participants are clear on which values map to the highest and lowest levels.

6. When all criteria (that is, all columns) have been ranked, create another prioritization matrix with blank cells and cross-multiply the relative importance or weighting in each column by the rank for each option to create a new row value. Do this for all options. When complete, sum across to create a row total.
7. Select the option with the highest row total.
8. Conduct a sanity check to ensure the solution makes sense.

			Goal		
Relative importance	Weight 1	Weight 2	Weight 3	Weight 4	1.00
			Criteria		
Options	**Criteria 1**	**Criteria 2**	**Criteria 3**	**Criteria 4**	**Total**
Option 1					
Option 2					
Option 3					
Option 4					

Figure 13.10 Example of the general structure of a prioritization matrix.

EXAMPLE 13.9

Suppose a team is choosing among four software packages: A, B, C, and D. The team determines by consensus the criteria against which the options will be measured and the relative importance (that is, weighting) of each criterion. The criteria and their relative importance follows:

Compatibility: 0.20
Cost: 0.30
Ease of use: 0.40
Training time: 0.05
Total time: 1.00

The first step of the prioritization matrix is shown in Figure 13.11.

Determine the most suitable software package					
Relative importance	0.25	0.30	0.40	0.05	1.00
	Criteria				
Options	**Compatibility**	**Cost**	**Ease of use**	**Training time**	**Total**
Package A	4	1.5	3	3	N/A
Package B	1	4	2	2	N/A
Package C	3	1.5	4	4	N/A
Package D	2	3	1	1	N/A

Figure 13.11 First step of the prioritization matrix for Example 13.9.

Each option is ranked for each criterion, with 1 being the best and 4 being the worst. We see that packages A and C are tied for lowest cost. Therefore, packages A and C receive rank values of 1.5 each. Package D has the next highest cost, so it is assigned a rank value of 3. Package B has the highest cost (that is, worst rank), so it is assigned a rank value of 4.

The next step, as shown in Figure 13.12, is to multiply each of the option values by the relative importance (that is, weightings) and calculate the row totals. (Note in the sample calculations shown in Figure 13.12, the "4" and the "1" are obtained from the corresponding cells in Figure 13.11.) The option with the lowest total represents the team's consensus and therefore its software package selection. From Figure 13.12 we can see that the team will select software package D. Note that the weighted sums can be easily calculated using a spreadsheet.

Continued

Continued

Determine the most suitable software package					
Relative importance	0.25	0.30	0.40	0.05	1.00
	Criteria				
Options	Compatibility	Cost	Ease of use	Training time	Total
Package A	1.00	0.45	1.20	0.15	2.80
Package B	0.25	1.20	0.80	0.10	2.35
Package C	0.75	0.45	1.60	0.20	3.00
Package D	0.50	0.90	0.40	0.05	1.85

(0.25) × 4

(0.25) × 1

Figure 13.12 Second step of the prioritization matrix for Example 13.9.

For other methods of determining the best solution among several options using the prioritization matrix, see Tague (2005).

ACTIVITY NETWORK DIAGRAM

The *activity network diagram* (AND) is a tool used to illustrate a sequence of events or activities (nodes) and the interconnectivity of such nodes. It is used for scheduling and especially for determining the critical path through nodes. It is also known as an *arrow diagram.* The basic procedure for developing the activity network diagram (or arrow diagram) follows:

Note: The following is an excerpt from Tague (2005).

1. List all the necessary tasks in the project or process. One convenient method is to write each task on the top half of a card or sticky note. Across the middle of the card, draw a horizontal arrow pointing right.
2. Determine the correct sequence of the tasks. Do this by asking three questions for each task:

   a. Which tasks must happen before this one can begin?

   b. Which tasks can be done at the same time as this one?

   c. Which tasks should happen immediately after this one?

It can be useful to create a table with four columns—prior tasks, this task, simultaneous tasks, and following tasks.

3. Diagram the network of tasks. If you are using notes or cards, arrange them in sequence on a large piece of paper. Time should flow from left to right and concurrent tasks should be vertically aligned. Leave space between the cards.
4. Between each two tasks, draw circles for "events." An event marks the beginning or end of a task. Thus, events are nodes that separate tasks.
5. Look for three common problem situations and redraw them using "dummies" or extra events. A dummy is an arrow drawn with dotted lines used to separate tasks that would otherwise start and stop with the same events or to show logical sequence. Dummies are not real tasks.

   Problem situations:

   - Two simultaneous tasks start and end at the same events.

     Solution: Use a dummy and an extra event to separate them. In Figure 13.15, event 2 and the dummy between 2 and 3 have been added to separate tasks A and B.

   - Task C cannot start until both tasks A and B are complete; a fourth task, D, cannot start until A is complete, but need not wait for B. (See Figure 13.14.)

     Solution: Use a dummy between the end of task A and the beginning of task C.

   - A second task can be started before part of a first task is done.

     Solution: Add an extra event where the second task can begin and use multiple arrows to break the first task into two subtasks. In Figure 13.15, event 2 was added, splitting task A.

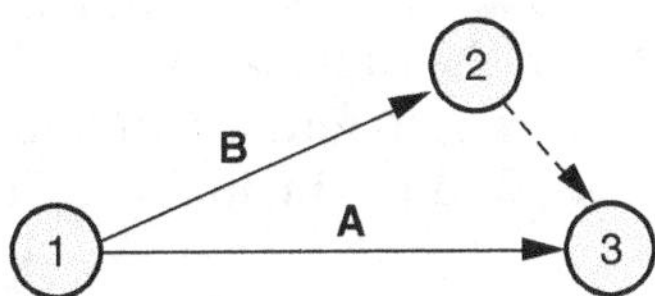

Figure 13.13 Dummy separating simultaneous tasks.

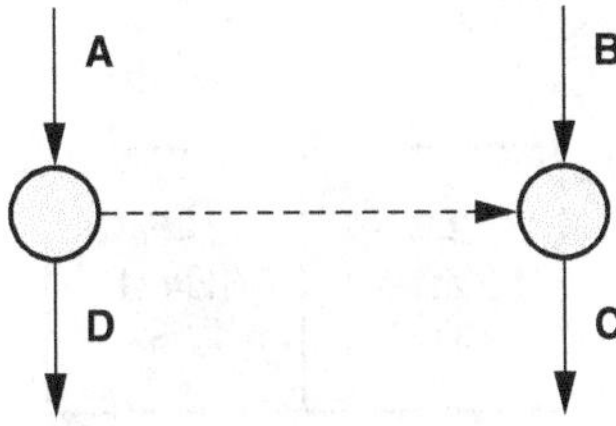

Figure 13.14 Dummy keeping sequence correct.

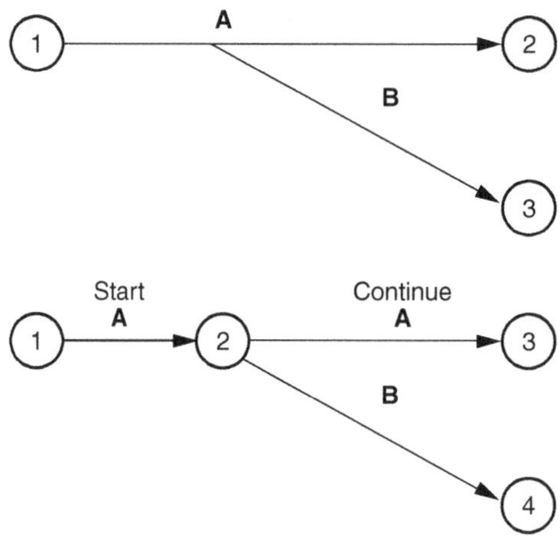

Figure 13.15 Using an extra event.

6. When the network is correct, label all events in sequence with event numbers in the circles. It can be useful to label all tasks in sequence, using letters.
7. Determine task times—the best estimate of the time that each task should require. Use one measuring unit (hours, days, or weeks) throughout, for consistency. Write the time on each task's arrow.
8. Determine the "critical path"—the longest path from the beginning to the end of the project. Mark the critical path with a heavy line or color. Calculate the length of the critical path: the sum of all the task times on the path.
9. Calculate the earliest times each task can start and finish, based on how long preceding tasks take. These are called earliest start (ES) and earliest finish (EF). Start with the first task, where ES = 0, and work forward. Draw a square divided into four quadrants, as in Figure 13.16. Write the ES in the top left box and the EF in the top right.

ES Earliest start	**EF** Earliest finish
LS Latest start	**LF** Latest finish

Figure 13.16 Arrow diagram time box.

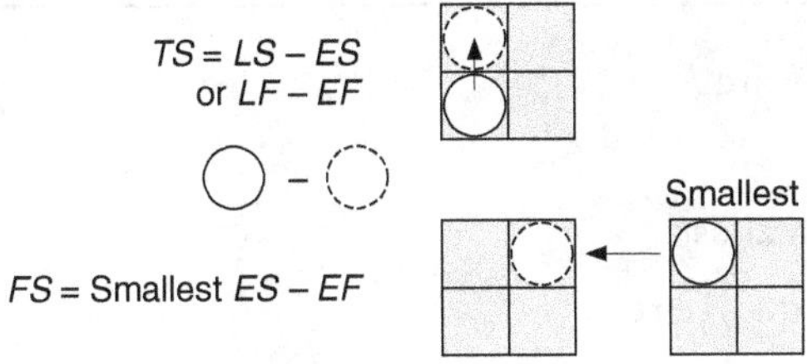

Figure 13.17 Remembering slack calculations.

For each task:

- Earliest start (ES) = The largest EF of the tasks leading into this one
- Earliest finish (EF) = ES + Task time for this task

10. Calculate the latest times each task can start and finish without upsetting the project schedule, based on how long later tasks will take. These are called latest start (LS) and latest finish (LF). Start from the last task, where the latest finish is the project deadline, and work backwards. Write the LS in the lower left box and the LF in the lower right box.
    - Latest finish (LF) = The smallest LS of all tasks immediately following this one
    - Latest start (LS) = LF – Task time for this task
11. Calculate slack times for each task and for the entire project.
    - *Total slack* is the time a job could be postponed without delaying the project schedule.
        - Total slack = LS – ES = LF – EF
    - *Free slack* is the time a task could be postponed without affecting the early start of any job following it.
        - Free slack = The earliest ES of all tasks immediately following this one – EF

Figure 13.17 shows a schematic way to remember which numbers to subtract.

EXAMPLE 13.10

A team uses a mailed survey to obtain information on customer preferences. The team identifies the following activities necessary for project completion:

A. Construct survey questionnaire

B. Decide whether to buy or build software to analyze the data

C. Print and mail questionnaire

Continued

D. Buy or build software

E. Test software

F. Enter data into database

G. Use software to analyze results

H. Interpret results and write final report

The order of these tasks is shown in the activity precedence table shown in Table 13.4.

Activity	Predecessor	Time
A		10
B		5
C	A	5
D	B	15
E	C	10
F	D	10
G	E, F	10
H	G	15

Table 13.4 Activity table for Example 13.10.

From this table, we can see for example that activity C occurs only after activity A is complete, and activity G occurs only after activities E and F are complete. The times for each activity are also listed. From this table we can sketch out the order of the tasks as shown in Figure 13.18. In addition, the entries in the time box for each activity have been calculated to show early start, late start, early finish, and late finish times. *Slack time* for an activity is defined as:

Slack time = Latest start time – Earliest start time

The program evaluation and review technique (PERT) and critical path method (CPM) have essentially merged in current software packages. The *critical path* is the path from start to finish that requires the most time. In Figure 13.18, there are just two paths:

- Path ACEGH requires 10 + 5 + 10 + 10 + 15 = 50 days
- Path BDFGH requires 5 + 15 + 10 + 10 + 15 = 55 days

Therefore, BDFGH is the critical path.

Continued

Continued

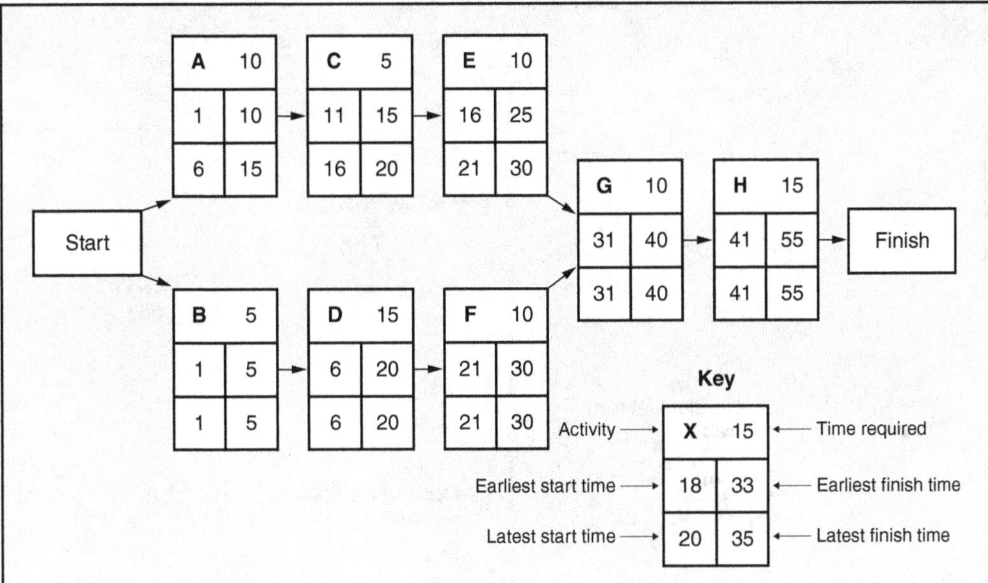

Figure 13.18 Activity network diagram.

Project management software is available to identify and calculate the critical path for projects with multiple paths. Critical path time is the time required to complete the project. If activities on the critical path are delayed, the entire project will be delayed.

One way to complete a project in less time is to decrease the time for at least one of the activities. This is usually accomplished by putting more resources into one or more activities on the critical path. This is sometimes referred to as "crashing" the project.

EXAMPLE 13.11

Figure 13.19 shows an arrow diagram for a benchmarking project.

Tasks. There are 14 tasks, shown as solid arrows. The number on the arrow is the task time in days, based on the experience and judgment of the group planning the project.

Continued

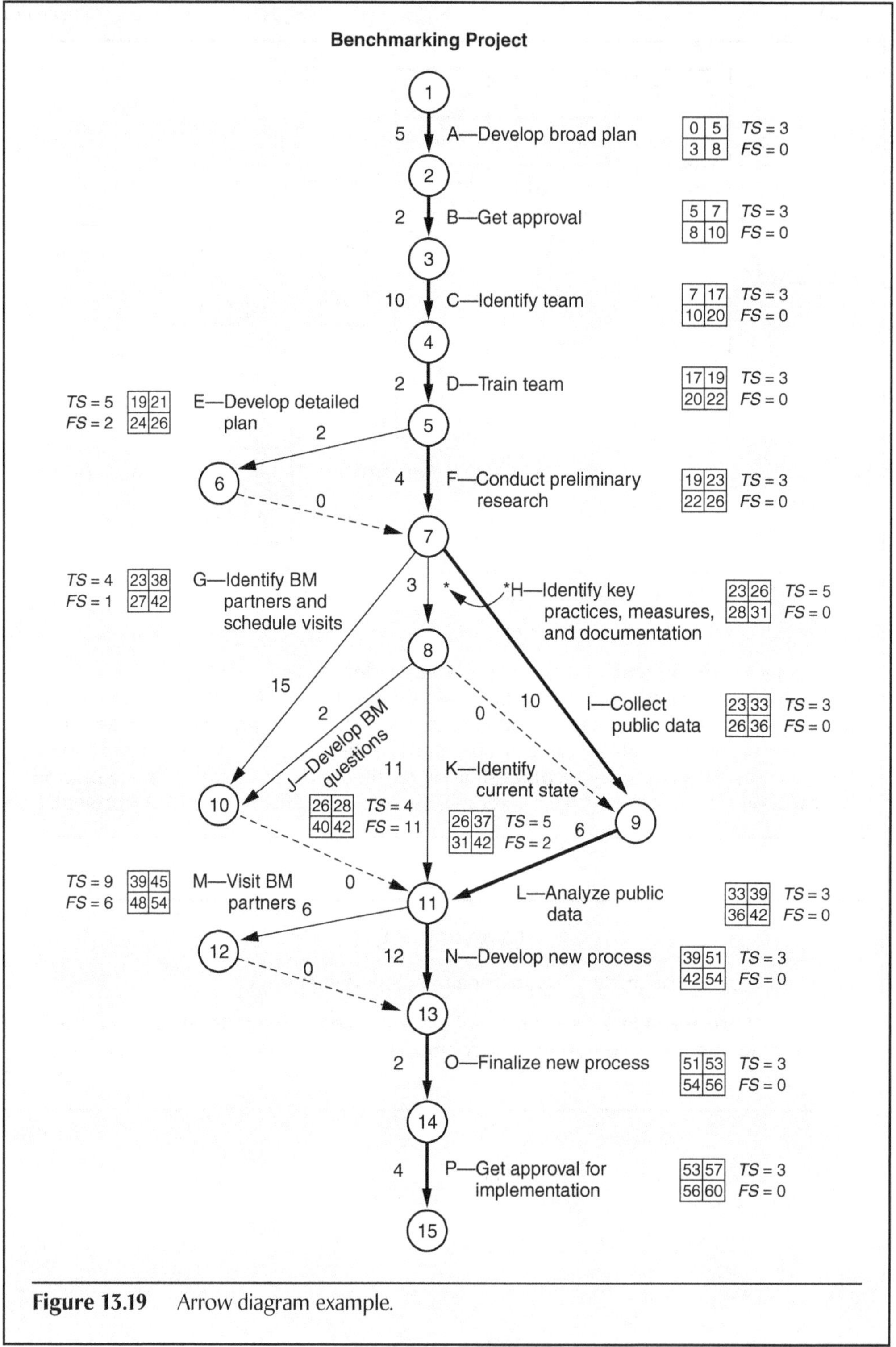

Figure 13.19 Arrow diagram example.

Continued

Events. There are 15 events, represented by the circled numbers. The events mark the beginning and ending times for the tasks. They will serve as milestones for monitoring progress throughout the project.

Dummies. Tasks E and F show the first kind of problem situation, where two tasks can occur simultaneously. Developing a detailed plan and conducting preliminary research can be done at the same time. Dummy 6-7 separates them. Task 10-11 is also a dummy to separate the simultaneous tasks J (develop questions) and K (identify current state).

The second kind of problem situation is illustrated around tasks H, I, J, K, and L. Task L (analyzing public data) cannot start until both tasks H (identifying key practices and measures) and I (collecting public data) are done. Task J (develop questions) and task K (identify current state) can start as soon as task H is complete. Task 8-9 is a dummy to separate the starting time of tasks J and K from that of task L.

The third kind of problem situation is illustrated around tasks M, N, and O. Originally, tasks N and O were one task—develop new process. Task M (visiting benchmark partners) can begin at the same time, but the visits need to be completed before final decisions can be made about the new process. To show this, subtask O (finalize new process) and extra event 13 were created. A dummy was also needed because tasks M and N are simultaneous. Now the network shows that the visits must be completed before the process can be finalized.

Critical path. The longest path, marked in bold, is the critical path. Its tasks and their times are:

A	B	C	D	F	I	L	N	O	P	Total
5	2	10	2	4	10	6	12	2	4	57

The team was surprised that the external visits, which members assumed would be a scheduling bottleneck, were not on the critical path—if they can schedule visits with a three-week lead time, as task G assumes. The entire project will require 57 days if all tasks on the critical path proceed as scheduled.

Earliest and latest start and finish times. The earliest times are calculated forward from the start. The ES is the largest EF of the tasks just before the one being calculated. The ES for the first task is zero, as shown in Table 13.5.

Continued

Task	ES +	Task time =	EF
A	0	5	5
B	5	2	7
C	7	10	17
D	17	2	19
E	19	2	21
F	19	4	23
G	23	15	38
H	23	3	26
I	23	10	33
J	26	2	28
K	26	11	37
L	33	6	39
M	39	6	45
N	39	12	51
O	51	2	53
P	53	4	57

Table 13.5 Calculation of earliest start and earliest finish times for Example 13.11.
Source: Adapted from Tague (2005).

The latest times are calculated backward from the end. LF is the smallest LS of the tasks just after the one being calculated. The project has a 12-week deadline, or 60 working days, so 60 is used as the LF for the last task as shown in Table 13.6. All these times are shown beside each task in the four-box grid.

Continued

Task	LF –	Task time =	LS
P	60	4	56
O	56	2	54
N	54	12	42
M	54	6	48
L	42	6	36
K	42	11	31
J	42	2	40
I	36	10	26
H	31	3	28
G	42	15	27
F	26	4	22
E	26	2	24
D	22	2	20
C	20	10	10
B	10	2	8
A	8	5	3

Table 13.6 Calculation of the latest start and latest finish times for Example 13.11.
Source: Adapted from Tague (2005).

Slack times. The slack times for each task are shown beside each grid. Because 60 days have been allotted for the project and the critical path adds up to 57 days, there is slack time for all the tasks. For each of the tasks on the critical path, the total slack time is three, the slack time for the entire project. The tasks not on the critical path have up to nine days total slack.

Surprisingly, there is free slack of six days for visiting the benchmark partners, so six days of scheduling problems with the partners can be tolerated without delaying later tasks. There is total slack of nine days for the visits, so if the project is on schedule up to that task, nine days' delay in making visits will not affect the project completion date. Table 13.7 shows the slack time calculations for the example.

Tables 13.5 and 13.6 were partially completed in Tague (2005). In addition, Table 13.7 was not part of the original example. However, we included it to help demonstrate how slack times are calculated.

Continued

Continued

Task	ES	LS	EF	LF	TS = LS – ES	FS
A	0	3	5	8	3	5 – 5 = 0
B	5	8	7	10	3	7 – 7 = 0
C	7	10	17	20	3	17 – 17 = 0
D	17	20	19	22	3	19 – 19 = 0
E	19	24	21	26	5	21 – 19 = 2
F	19	22	23	26	3	23 – 23 = 0
G	23	27	38	42	4	39 – 38 = 1
H	23	28	26	31	5	26 – 26 = 0
I	23	26	33	36	3	33 – 33 = 0
J	26	40	28	42	4	39 – 28 = 11
K	26	31	37	42	5	39 – 37 = 2
L	33	36	39	42	3	39 – 39 = 2
M	39	48	45	54	9	54 – 48 = 6
N	39	42	51	54	3	51 – 51 = 0
O	51	54	53	56	3	53 – 53 = 0
P	53	56	57	60	3	0

Table 13.7 Calculation of earliest start and earliest finish times for Example 13.11.
Source: Adapted from Tague (2005).

PROCESS DECISION PROGRAM CHART (PDPC)

The *process decision program chart* (PDPC) is a tool that identifies all events that can go wrong and the appropriate countermeasures for these events. It graphically represents all sequences that lead to a desirable effect.

The PDPC is based on a tree diagram (discussed below) and is often used when a plan is large and complex, must be on schedule, is being implemented for the first time, and the cost of failing is high.

Tague (2005) suggests the following procedure for developing a PDPC:

1. Obtain a high-level tree diagram of the proposed plan. This diagram should show the second level of main activities and the third level of broadly defined tasks.
2. Brainstorm what could go wrong for each third-level task.
3. Eliminate any problems that are improbable or whose consequences are insignificant. Show the problems as the fourth level on the diagram.

4. Brainstorm countermeasures for each problem. Such countermeasures might either prevent or remedy the problem. Show countermeasures at the fifth level by outlining in clouds or jagged lines as a convention.
5. Assess the practicality of each countermeasure in terms of cost, time, ease of implementation, and effectiveness. Use an "X" to depict those countermeasures that are impractical and an "O" for those that are practical.

EXAMPLE 13.12

This example is taken from Tague (2005).

A medical group is planning to improve the care of patients with chronic illnesses such as diabetes and asthma through a new chronic illness management program (CIMP). They have defined four main elements and, for each of these elements, key components. The information is laid out in the process decision program chart shown in Figure 13.20.

Dotted lines represent sections of the chart that have been omitted. Only some of the potential problems and countermeasures identified by the planning team are shown on the chart. In Figure 13.20 we see that one of the potential problems the team identified for patient goal setting is backsliding. The team liked the idea of each patient having a buddy or sponsor and will add that to the program design. Other areas of the chart helped the team plan better rollout, such as arranging for all staff to visit a clinic with a CIMP program in place. Still other areas allowed them to plan for problems, such as training the CIMP nurses how to counsel patients who choose inappropriate goals.

Continued

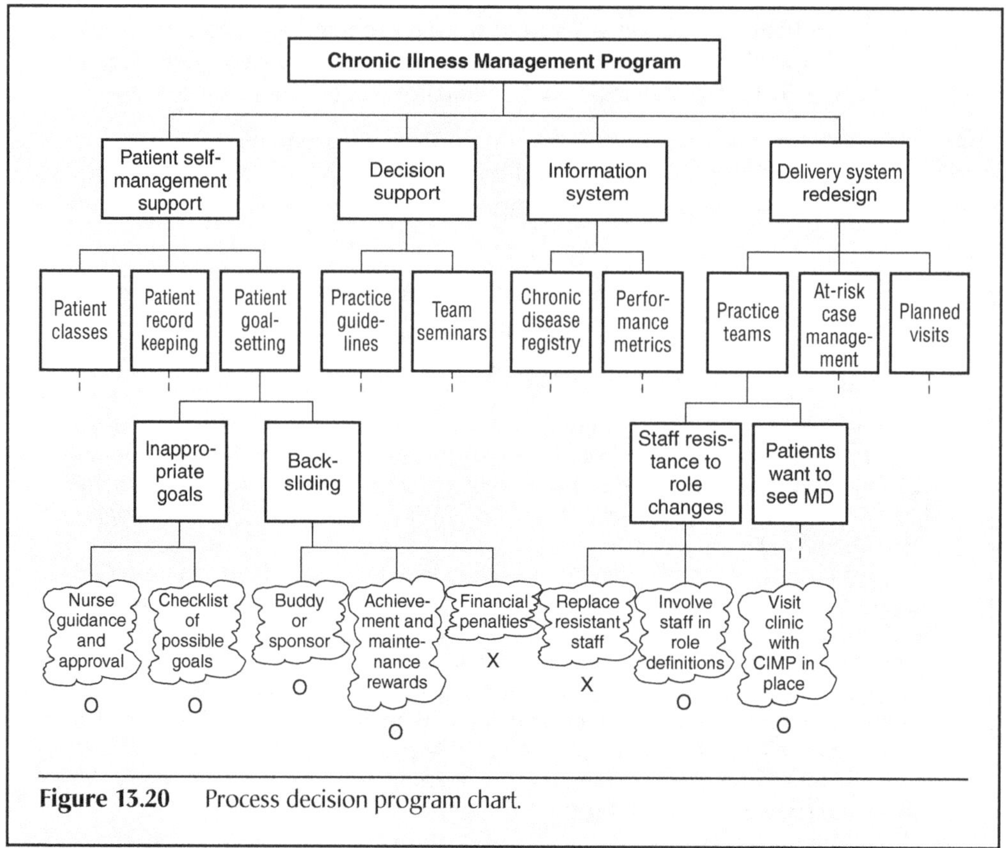

Figure 13.20 Process decision program chart.

INTERRELATIONSHIP DIGRAPH (ID)

The *interrelationship digraph* (ID) is a tool that displays the cause-and-effect relationships between ideas or factors in a complex situation. It identifies meaningful categories from a mass of ideas and is useful when relationships are difficult to determine. The ID is also known as a *relations diagram, circle diagram, or hand-off map.*

The basic procedure for developing the ID follows:

1. State the issue or problem to be explored.
2. Brainstorm the factors related to the issue or problem and list them individually on sticky notes.
3. Arrange the notes in a circle on a sheet of easel paper or something similar.
4. Start with the note at the 12 o'clock position, and moving clockwise, compare it with every other note (factor). Ask whether the current factor causes or influences the next factor, and so on. If it does, draw an arrow from the current factor to the one being compared and move on.

5. When all factors have been compared, count the number of incoming and outgoing arrows for each factor and designate as I/O (for example, 3/1). The factors that have the most outgoing arrows are the basic causes or drivers. The factors that have the most incoming arrows are the outcomes or final effects.
6. Begin improvement activities on the key drivers.

EXAMPLE 13.13

A team brainstormed the factors shown in this figure, identified the causal relationships, and counted the number of incoming and outgoing arrows for each factor. Notice that the number of incoming and outgoing arrows have been identified below each factor in Figure 13.21.

Since this ID is small, we can readily determine the drivers and the outcomes. The drivers have the largest number of outgoing arrows:

- Poor scheduling practices has seven outgoing arrows.
- Late order from the customer has five outgoing arrows.

The resulting outcome has the largest number of incoming arrows:

- Poor scheduling of trucker has four incoming arrows.

Now that two top drivers have been identified, the team can begin to formulate plans for its improvement efforts.

Continued

Continued

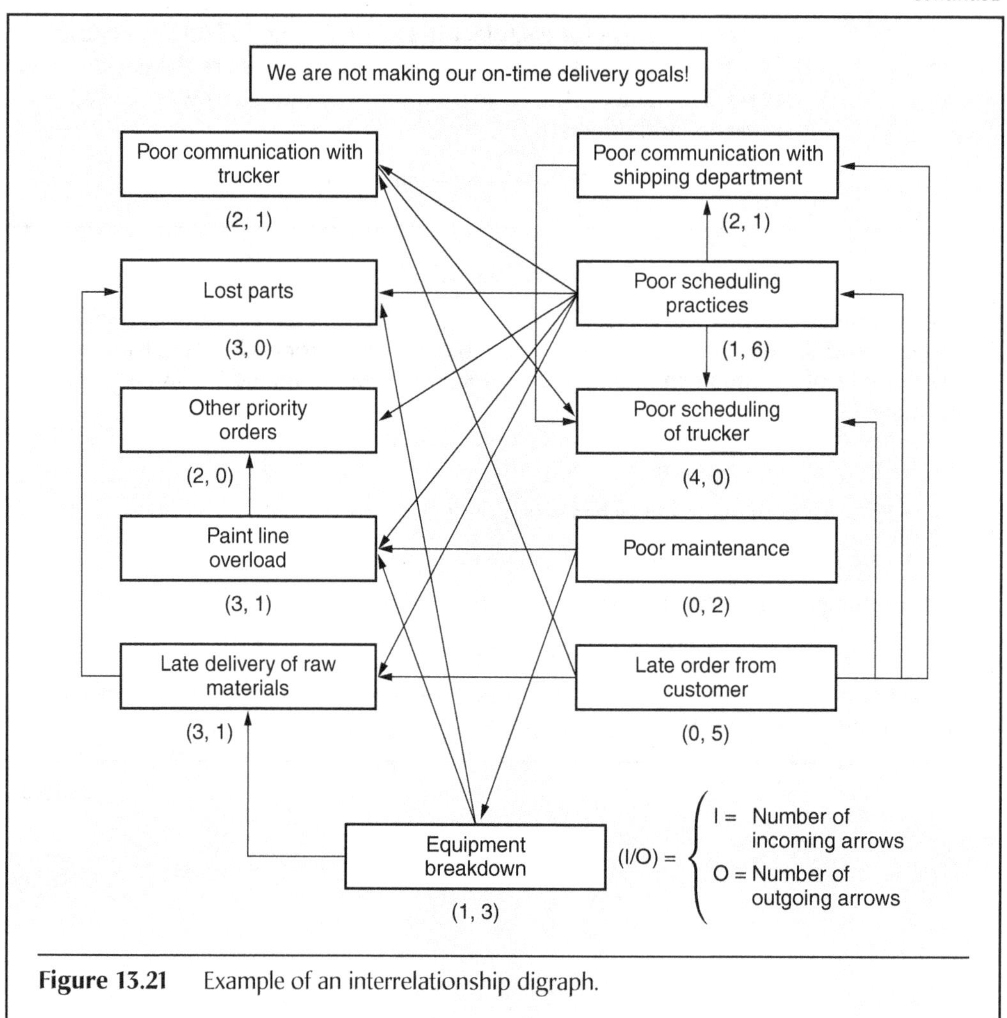

Figure 13.21 Example of an interrelationship digraph.

Part V
Measure

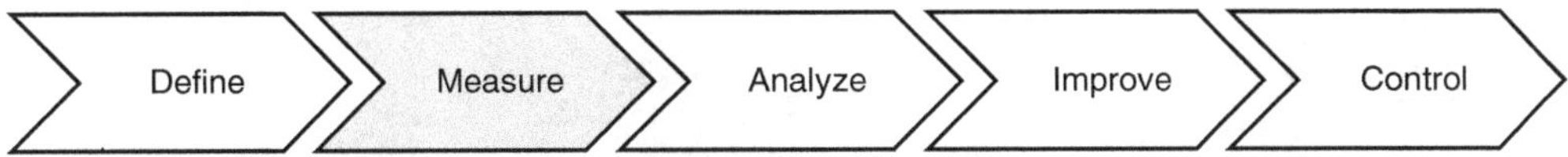

The purpose of this phase is to collect process performance data for primary and secondary metrics to gain insight and understanding into root causes and to establish performance baselines. Common tools used in this phase are shown in Table V.1.

Basic statistics	*Histograms*	*Project tracking*
Brainstorming	*Hypothesis testing*	*Regression*
Cause-and-effect diagrams	*Measurement systems analysis (MSA)*	*Run charts*
Check sheets	*Meeting minutes*	*Scatter diagrams*
Circle diagrams	Operational definitions	Spaghetti diagrams
Correlation	*Pareto charts*	*Statistical process control (SPC)*
Data collection	Probability	*Suppliers–inputs–process–outputs–customers (SIPOC)*
Data collection plan	*Process capability analysis*	Taguchi loss function
Failure mode and effects analysis (FMEA)	Process flow metrics	*Tollgate review*
Flowcharts	Process maps	*Value stream maps*
Gage R&R	*Process sigma*	
Graphical methods	*Project management*	

Table V.1 Common tools used in *measure* phase.

Note: Tools shown in *italic* are used in more than one phase.

Chapter 14
Process Characteristics

This chapter will address three key topics dealing with process characteristics: a variety of process flow metrics that can be used to gauge the health of a process, how these process flow metrics relate to the concept of the hidden factory, and visualization tools used to analyze process flow.

PROCESS FLOW METRICS

> Identify and use process flow metrics (e.g., work in progress (WIP), work in queue (WIQ), touch time, takt time, cycle time, and throughput) to determine constraints. Describe the impact that "hidden factories" can have on process flow metrics. (Analyze)
>
> Body of Knowledge V.A.1

Consider any business process such as generating an invoice; a government process such as serving a subpoena; a manufacturing process such as molding plastic parts; or a design process such as creating a new software application. The following metrics may be used to evaluate flow in the process:

- *Work in progress* (WIP). This is the all the material that has been input into the process, but that has not reached the output or finished stage. This includes the material being processed, waiting to be processed, or stored as inventory at each step. Work in progress is also known as *work in process.*

  In general, the larger the WIP, the longer the time required to complete the process. WIP, although considered an asset by some accounting systems, is in many ways a liability because it requires space, environmental control, labeling, record keeping, and other upkeep expenses.

- *Work in queue* (WIQ). This is the material waiting to be processed by one or more steps in the process and is one component of WIP. It is important to segment out the WIQ by step to help identify process bottlenecks or constraints. Also, it is desirable to maintain WIQ in "first in, first out" (FIFO) order depending on the shelf life of the inventory.
- *Touch time.* This is the time that a unit of product is being worked on at any step in the process. Again, it may be useful to segment out the total touch time by step so that processes with large touch times may be readily identified for improvement purposes. Touch time is usually considered *value-added,* which is covered later in this list.
- *Takt time.* This is rate at which units must be produced (or served) to achieve the customer demand. Takt is a German word meaning stroke or beat, referring to the constant rate of output. The takt time is calculated using Equation 14.1:

Equation 14.1 Takt time

$$\text{Takt time} = \frac{\text{Time available}}{\text{Number of units to be produced (or served)}}$$

If there are 420 available work minutes in a shift, and customer demand is equal to 200 units, then units must be produced at a rate of 2.1 minutes per unit.

$$\text{Takt time} = \frac{420 \text{ minutes}}{200 \text{ units}} = 2.1\,\text{min/unit}$$

- *Cycle time.* This is the time required to complete one unit from the beginning of the process to the end of the process. The average cycle time is computed over the completion of multiple units and thus cycles. If the cycle is greater than the takt time, the customer demand will not be met without a modification to the process. Such a modification might include an increase in labor.
- *Throughput.* This is the amount of output that passes through the process in a specified period of time. For example, a cycle time of ten minutes per invoice is equivalent to a throughput rate of six invoices per hour.

The following two definitions are not part of the body of knowledge, but are relevant to this subject matter and thus are included for completeness:

- *Value-added activity.* An activity that adds value to a product or service. In the case of a product, the value-added work changes the form, fit, or function of a product.

  In some instances, a valued-added activity is defined as an activity for which the customer is willing to pay. However, customers sometimes pay for activities that do not add value. Therefore, value-added activities should be defined independently of the customer.

All other activities that are not value-added are classified as non-value-added and should be examined for reduction, simplification, or elimination. Note that, based on the discussion above, touch time may not necessarily be the same as value-added time.

- *Setup time.* This is the time from the last unit on one job to the first good unit of the next job and includes the time it takes to remove all the dies and tooling from the previous job and replace them with the dies and tooling for the next job. Setup time is also known as *change-over time, turnover time,* or *prep time.* Although it usually refers to manufacturing machinery, setup time may be used in other types of businesses, such as the time it takes to a prepare a hospital operating room for the next patient.

These metrics are used alongside quality metrics to determine the health of a process. Both sets of metrics combined with improved design, manufacturing, and producibility techniques, in conjunction with Lean Six Sigma methodologies, will often result in moving the direction of the metrics as follows:

- Reducing work in progress
- Reducing work in queue
- Reducing touch time
- Reducing takt time
- Reducing cycle time
- Increasing throughput
- Increasing value-added activity
- Reducing setup time

Inevitably, there will be a time when improving one metric will come at the expense of another. When this occurs, it will be necessary to optimize the process according to some criterion. Usually, that criterion is cost. It is important to understand the cost dimension associated with the various elements of a process, particularly when it comes time to make trade-off decisions, for example, the costs associated with touch time, the inventory in progress, inventory in queue, and setup time.

Hidden Factory

The *hidden factory* constitutes the collection of activities in a process that generate waste. Consequently, the hidden factory results in lost time, money, and effort. The concept of waste will be discussed in detail in Chapter 23.

Most organizations that are aware of what constitutes the hidden factory have attempted to track components of waste such as scrap and rework. Some organizations have tried to implement cost-of-quality systems, but their progress can be limited by their accounting systems. Often, it takes creative approaches to allow their systems to track something simple such as the labor and material costs associated with a work group dedicated to rework and repair.

In the previous subsection we looked at a variety of process flow metrics. When the hidden factory exists (as it usually does), or is particularly large, these metrics are typically inflated. Consider the following examples of when defects occur along the process and rework must take place:

- Work in progress is increased because of defective raw material, and defective product occurs at various stages.
- Work in queue is increased for the same reason as work in progress.
- Cycle time is increased as defective products are being channeled off for rework and repair.
- Throughput is reduced because of rejected product due to defects.
- Setup time may increase because the time to produce the first good unit of the next lot takes longer because of defects being produced during the setup process.

These are examples of what happens to the process flow metrics considering the presence of just one of the Eight Wastes (that is, defects). When influenced by other waste factors as well, the hidden factory can have an enormous effect on the bottom line of an organization. Fortunately, if used properly, the process flow metrics can help highlight these waste factors in advance of serious trouble.

PROCESS ANALYSIS TOOLS

> Select, use, and evaluate various tools, e.g., value stream maps, process maps, work instructions, flowcharts, spaghetti diagrams, and gemba walk. (Evaluate)
>
> Body of Knowledge V.A.2

Flowcharts

A *flowchart* is a pictorial or graphical representation of a process and is used to help understand, communicate, document, improve, and/or manipulate a process off-line. Figure 14.1 shows a flowchart for a patient treatment process at a hospital. The flowchart is focused on activities and decision points. It is also known as a *process flowchart* or *flow diagram*.

Many symbols can be used when developing flowcharts, but the most common are shown in Figure 14.2.

Before any process flowchart is created, it is strongly suggested that the team walk the process (in person or via video) to see how the steps are performed in practice, as opposed to how they are documented in a standard operating procedure. This approach is also known as *going to gemba* and is addressed later in this chapter.

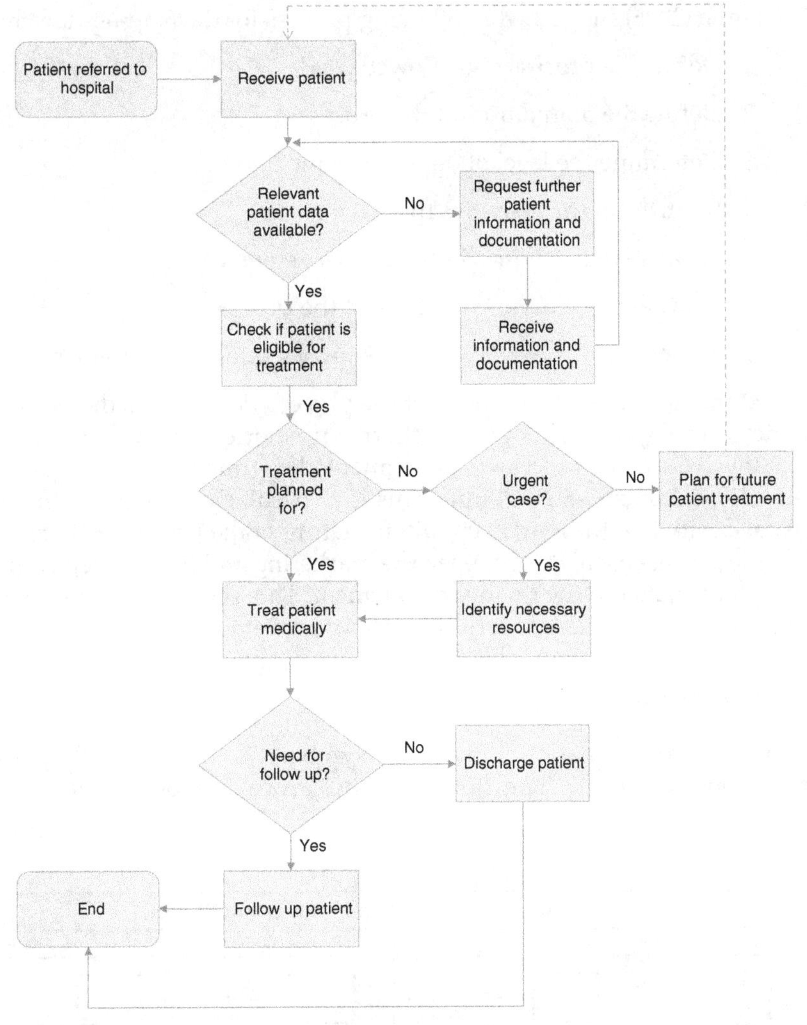

Figure 14.1 Patient treatment process.
Source: Adapted from Anderson et al. (2008).

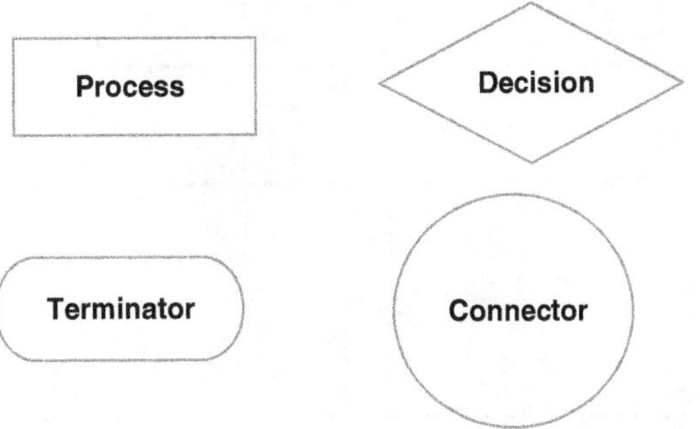

Figure 14.2 Most common flowchart symbols.

Tague (2005) suggests the following process for developing flowcharts:

1. Define the process to be flowcharted
2. Define the boundaries of the process
3. Determine the level of detail to be included
4. Brainstorm the activities that take place
5. Arrange the activities in the proper sequence
6. Draw arrows to show the flow of the process
7. Review the process with others involved to seek agreement

One of the most useful variations of the process flowchart is the swim lane chart, depicted in Figure 14.3. This flowchart can be oriented either vertically or horizontally. Notice that processes are segmented by functional group, department, or other logical organizational unit. This is particularly valuable in that it provides visual clarity into the overall circuitous nature of the process. For example, notice that the process oscillates between the marketing and finance departments before being terminated in the finance department. This raises questions regarding process flow and surfaces opportunities for improvement.

Process Maps

Although process maps use the same symbols as flowcharts, they reveal much more about a process than flowcharts do. Process maps provide the Black Belt

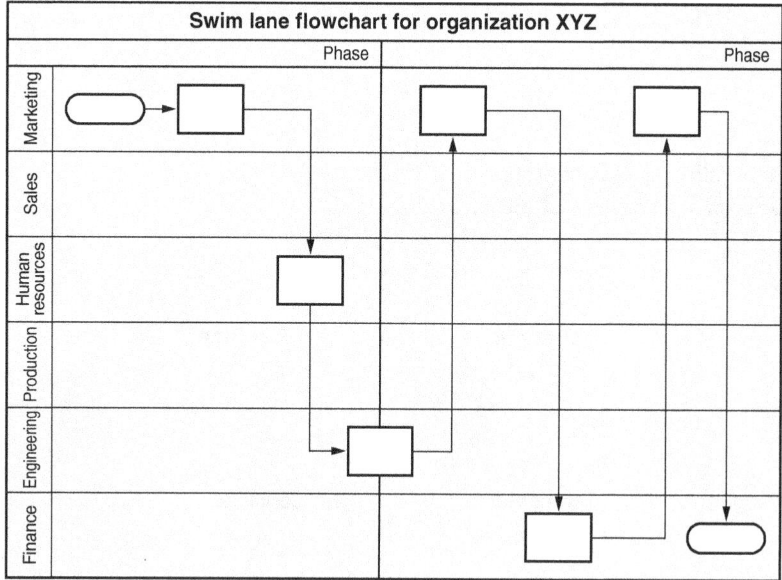

Figure 14.3 Example of a swim lane flowchart.

with more guidance because they address the key foundational concept of Lean Six Sigma: the concept of $Y = f(X)$, or simply, outputs are a function of inputs.

Categorizing and Classifying Process Input Variables

Kubiak (2007) describes the basic anatomy of a process map, as shown in Figure 14.4. *Input variables,* our list of Xs, flow into a transform function that we call a *process.* Flowing from the process is one or more desired *outputs.*

Notice that the inputs appear below the flow line, while outputs appear above the flow line. This is simply a matter of aesthetics. Otherwise, inputs and outputs appearing on the same line would significantly clutter the map, particularly when multiple process blocks appear adjacent to one another.

Notice the list of input variables. They should be familiar as they represent the typical categories (also known as the *six* Ms) of the main bones in a fishbone diagram. (Note: Some authors include "management" as another category and call the list the *seven* Ms.) Using the six Ms as a structured approach provides some assurance that few inputs will be overlooked. Table 14.1 identifies each of the Ms along with alternative terminology that may be used in service- or transaction-based industries, for example. Commentary and insight about each M have been included.

One important aspect of input variables not visible in Figure 14.4 is their classification. Classifying input variables helps Lean Six Sigma practitioners focus on those inputs that are controllable and guides practitioners away from spending time and energy on those that are not.

An example of a common classification scheme is shown in Table 14.2. Properly classifying input variables requires recognizing the need to fully understand a process in relation to the culture and business needs of the organization.

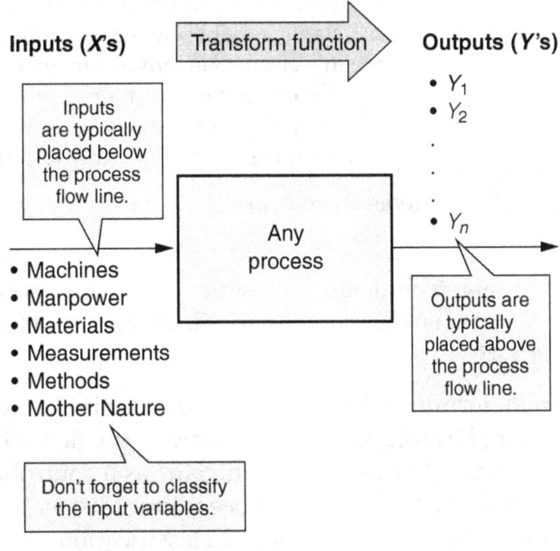

Figure 14.4 Demonstrating the $Y = f(X)$ concept.

Input (*X*)	Alternate terminology	Comment
Machines	Equipment	Machines or equipment need not be costly or even high-tech. Don't overlook the basics. For example, service and/or transactional-based processes might include the use of simple devices such as a stapler or highlighter. When considering input variables of this nature, it is often helpful to consider developing a list of "tools required."
Manpower	People	Human resources may take various forms such as skilled technicians, engineers, or administrative and clerical personnel. Even highly automated processes may occasionally call for human support when preventive or corrective maintenance or actions are required.
Materials	Materials	Materials may include raw materials or even intermediate subassemblies. Materials are often consumed or transformed during the execution of a process.
Measurements	Measurements	Always remember to ensure the measurement system is capable. If a measurement system is assumed capable when, in fact, it is not, erroneous results may occur. These include overlooking true critical input variables or concluding some variables are critical when they are not.
Methods	Processes	Processes come in all shapes and sizes. They may be well defined or very loosely defined. In the context of a manufacturing environment, there is a category of processes known as "special processes."
Mother Nature	Environment	Variables falling into this category can be associated with either an internal or external environment. This is an important distinction, particularly when determining whether such variables are "noise" variables. For example, temperature and humidity would likely be considered controllable variables when the underlying process takes place in a clean room environment. However, if another process is conducted outdoors, temperature and humidity might very likely be considered noise variables since they may be impossible or too costly to control.

Table 14.1 The six Ms: useful categories when thinking about input variables.

Let's assume that a technician represents the manpower required to perform a given process. What classification or variable designation from Table 14.2 should a Black Belt assign it?

- If the team determines that the skill and experience level of the technician can be assigned appropriately to the needs of the process, then the team would classify "technician" as a controllable input variable. It would appear in the process input list as "technician (C)." The input variable is followed by the classification designation in parentheses.

Variable designation	Type of variable	Comment
C	Controllable	These are variables over which the process owner has control (regardless of whether such control may ever be exercised). More specifically, characteristics or values of controllable variables can be set or manipulated in a manner that drives one or more output variables (Y's) in the desired direction.
N	Noise	Noise variables are those that either can not be controlled or perhaps are too expensive to control. It is important that such variables be defined so that the Green Belt team or project Black Belt knows which variables should not be addressed. Attempts to control "noise" variables often result in frustrated teams and/or failed projects.
SOP	Standard operating procedure	A standard operating procedure is a unique and predefined way of performing a process. For example, it may be an instruction document for assembling a bicycle or preparing an expense report. Just because an input variable is defined as an SOP, no inference should be drawn regarding the quality of the process encompassed by the procedure. SOP variables are a subset of controllable variables. Designating an input variable as SOP does not exclude it from the process owner's control. However, it does suggest that minimal variation is probably associated with it.
X	Critical	Critical input variables are a subset of the set of controllable variables. These are variables that have been determined to have a significant impact on one or more output variables (Y's). Significance may be demonstrated through statistical tools such as design of experiments, regression, and so on. Early in the DMAIC phase and particularly before the completion of *analyze*, use of this designation should be considered, at best, tentative. Only after the analyze phase has been completed will we have the knowledge to state with some degree of certainty that a variable is a "critical input." Be careful not to confuse this classification of variable with the "X" used in the equation $Y = f(X)$.

Table 14.2 Classifying input variables.

- If the team determines that management will not invest in training technicians and that the technician assigned to the process is fixed, the team may consider classifying "technician" as a noise input variable. If this were the case, then it would appear in the process input list as "technician (N)."

This example illustrates the need to revisit processes on a periodic basis since organizations continually change and evolve. New and insightful management may recognize the need to grow and improve the skill level of its technicians. Therefore, input variables previously classified as noise may now be considered controllable. Likewise, the opposite may become true.

It is more effective to focus on addressing whether an input variable can be controlled than trying to determine whether it will ever be controlled. This avoids the complications of having a team second-guess management.

Gaining Insights from the Process Map

Figure 14.4 demonstrated the basic architecture and components of the process map. If we expand Figure 14.4 so that it represents a series of linked processes or even subprocesses, we obtain something akin to Figure 14.5.

Though still simple in nature, Figure 14.5 depicts a representation of processes we are likely to encounter in any organization. For the sake of convenience, inputs and outputs in Figure 14.5 have been defined simply as letters. Since input variable classifications are not the focus of this section, they have been omitted.

A few immediate observations can be made upon reviewing Figure 14.5, including the following:

- Processes should have boundaries. Define them.
- Identical inputs may be required at different processes.
- Multiple process outputs may occur.
- Outputs of one process may become inputs of another process.
- Some may or may not be linked to processes outside of the process boundaries.

We can now extend the thinking captured in the previous bullets for each of the variables in Figure 14.5. These can be summarized easily in Table 14.3. Notice that some of the comments in the table are a statement of fact, while others demand action, seek information, or require further investigation.

A well-developed process map serves as an effective communication tool and is a constant reminder of where a team should and should not focus its time and energy.

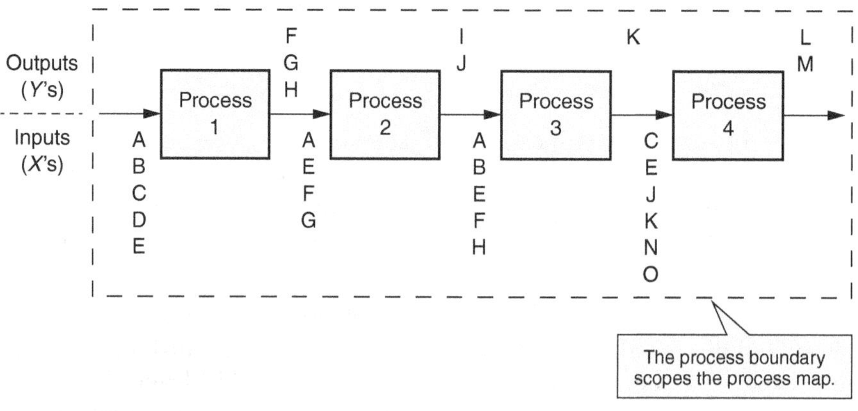

Figure 14.5 Analyzing inputs and outputs.

Variable	Comment
A	Input to processes 1, 2, and 3. However, it is not an output from any of the processes within the scope of the project at hand. If it is output from another process outside the scope, the project team should ascertain its source to ensure its availability when required.
B	Input to processes 1 and 3. However, it is not an output from any of the processes within the scope of the project at hand. If it is output from another process outside the scope, the project team should ascertain its source to ensure its availability when required.
C	Input to processes 1 and 4. However, it is not an output from any of the processes within the scope of the project at hand. If it is output from another process outside the scope, the project team should ascertain its source to ensure its availability when required.
D	Input to process 1. However, it is not an output from any of the processes within the scope of the project at hand. If it is output from another process outside the scope, the project team should ascertain its source to ensure its availability when required.
E	Input to processes 1, 2, 3, and 4. However, it is not an output from any of the processes within the scope of the project at hand. If it is output from another process outside the scope, the project team should ascertain its source to ensure its availability when required.
F	Output from process 1 and input to both processes 2 and 3.
G	Output from process 1 and input to process 2.
H	Output from process 1 and input to process 3.
I	Output from process 2. This variable is no longer found in the remainder of the process map. It might be an extraneous output that is no longer needed, and process 2 was never changed to eliminate its production. Alternately, it could be used in another process beyond the scope of the project at hand. Either way, action is required.
J	Output from process 2 and input to process 4.
K	Output from process 3 and input to process 4.
L	Output from process 4. It may or may not be used in another process.
M	Output from process 4. It may or may not be used in another process.
N	Input to process 4. However, it is not an output from any of the processes within the scope of the project at hand. If it is output from another process outside the scope, the project team should ascertain its source to ensure its availability when required.
O	Input to process 4. However, it is not an output from any of the processes within the scope of the project at hand. If it is output from another process outside the scope, the project team should ascertain its source to ensure its availability when required.

Table 14.3 Identifying potential issues with inputs and outputs.

Value Stream Maps

If the Lean Six Sigma project should take on more of a lean focus, the process map can evolve into a *value stream map* (VSM). According to Manos and Vincent (2012), a value stream is "all the actions (both value-added and non-value-added) currently required to bring a product through the main flows essential to every product: (1) the production flow from raw material into the arms of the customer, and (2) the design flow from concept to launch."

They go on to say, "Value stream mapping is simply an illustration of the sequential activities that take place within a value stream. At each step of the map the practitioner evaluates whether value is being created and whether one or more of the wastes exist. The purpose of the value stream map is to identify those activities that add value and those that create waste, with the latter being targets for elimination."

The general process for value stream mapping is given in Figure 14.6. Although the process appears simple, the map requires many details that often can only be gleaned by walking the process, perhaps many times. This practice will be addressed later in the section on *gemba walk.*

The following subsection on current and future states is excerpted from Manos and Vincent (2012).

Current State

The value stream map can be considered a flowchart on steroids. While a flowchart is a simple visualization of a process, the value stream map is a bigger picture of the flow of a given product/service throughout the entire organization. Before beginning to map the process, it is important to plan how the process will be mapped. The following are considerations for value stream mapping:

1. Collect information while walking the value stream. Customary practice is to use a cross-functional team of individuals who operate within the value stream, including the value stream owner and supporting functions at various levels. Everyone should carry an A3-sized piece of paper and document the value stream and information while walking the product/service flow and information flow, from beginning to end of the value stream.

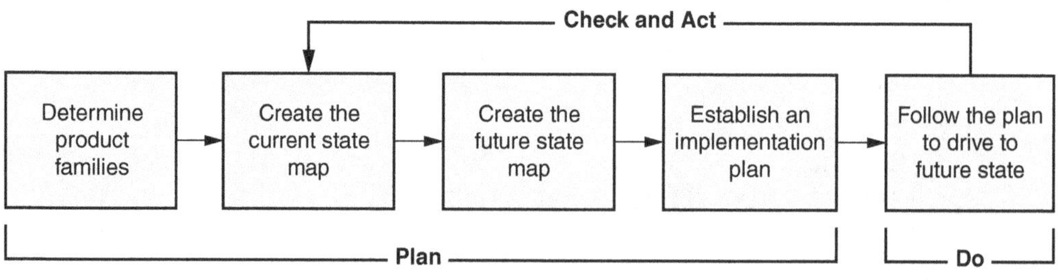

Figure 14.6 The process of value stream mapping.
Source: Manos and Vincent (2012).

2. It is customary to begin at the shipping end of the value stream, closest to the customer. This helps keep a customer focus throughout the entire value stream.
3. Obtain all information directly from the value stream through observations, time study, inventory counting, and so on. Bring a stopwatch and physically count work-in-process (WIP). Do not rely on standard times and inventory levels established for the existing financial system, as this information is typically inaccurate.
4. Draw the value stream manually during the mapping exercise. The team does not need to waste time while one plots on a computer and everyone else waits. Each person draws the value stream at the value stream. It is customary practice to use butcher paper, markers, and sticky notes on a wall for the entire team to participate in constructing the value stream for discussion and clarifications. Sometimes things can be overlooked by a team, but several individuals performing the same task will catch information missed by a group.

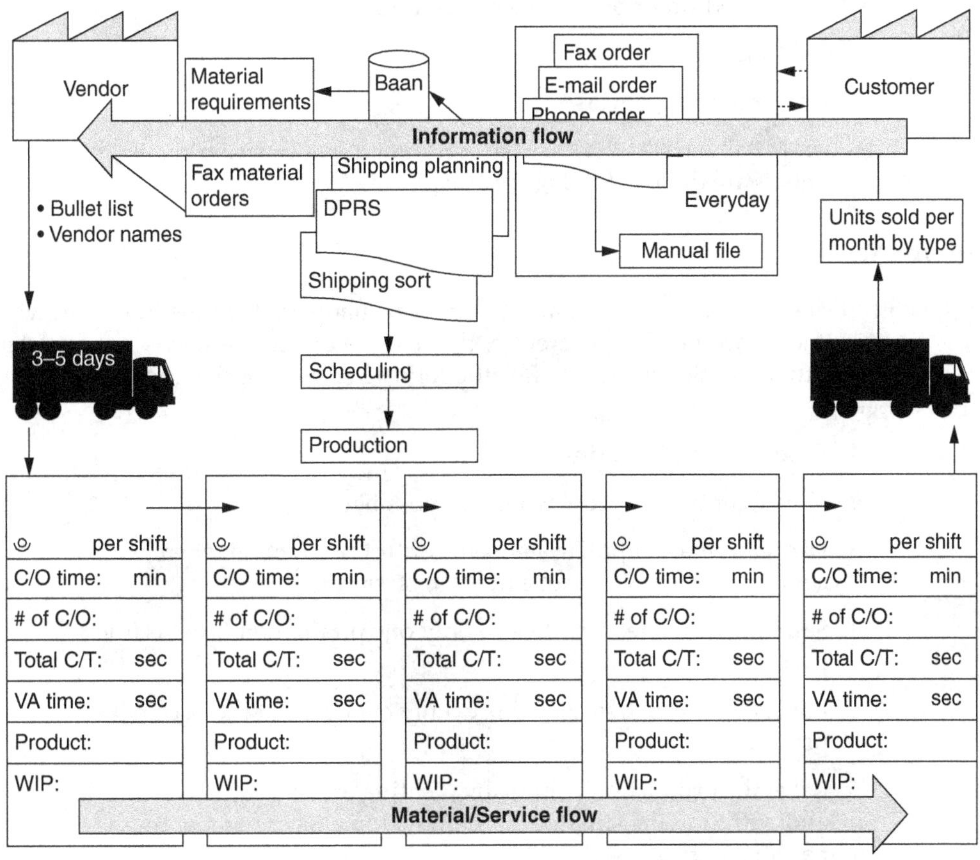

Figure 14.7 Basic structure of the value stream map.
Source: Manos and Vincent (2012).

The common mapping format is for material flow on the bottom from left to right and information flow at the top from right to left, as shown in Figure 14.7.

The following are examples of information commonly gathered during the value stream mapping of the current state:

- Cycle time
- Changeover time
- Number of people
- Uptime/downtime
- WIP
- Inventory
- Packaging size
- Scrap/defect rate
- Total operating time (minus breaks)
- Value-added time versus non-value-added time
- Lead time
- Number of changeovers

Figure 14.8 illustrates the basic structure of a value stream map, while many of the symbols are depicted in Figure 14.9.

Future State

With the current state of the value stream now mapped, it is time to look at what improvements are needed. Therefore, the lean value stream needs to be understood. Rother and Shook (2009) offer the following seven guidelines in Learning to See:

1. Produce to the takt time
2. Create continuous flow wherever possible
3. Use supermarket pull systems to control production where continuous flow does not extend upstream
4. Send the customer schedule to only one production process (the pacemaker process)
5. Level the product/service mix evenly over time at the pacemaker process
6. Level the production volume by creating an "initial pull," releasing and withdrawing small, consistent increments of work at the pacemaker process
7. Develop the ability to make "every part every day" in processes upstream of the pacemaker process

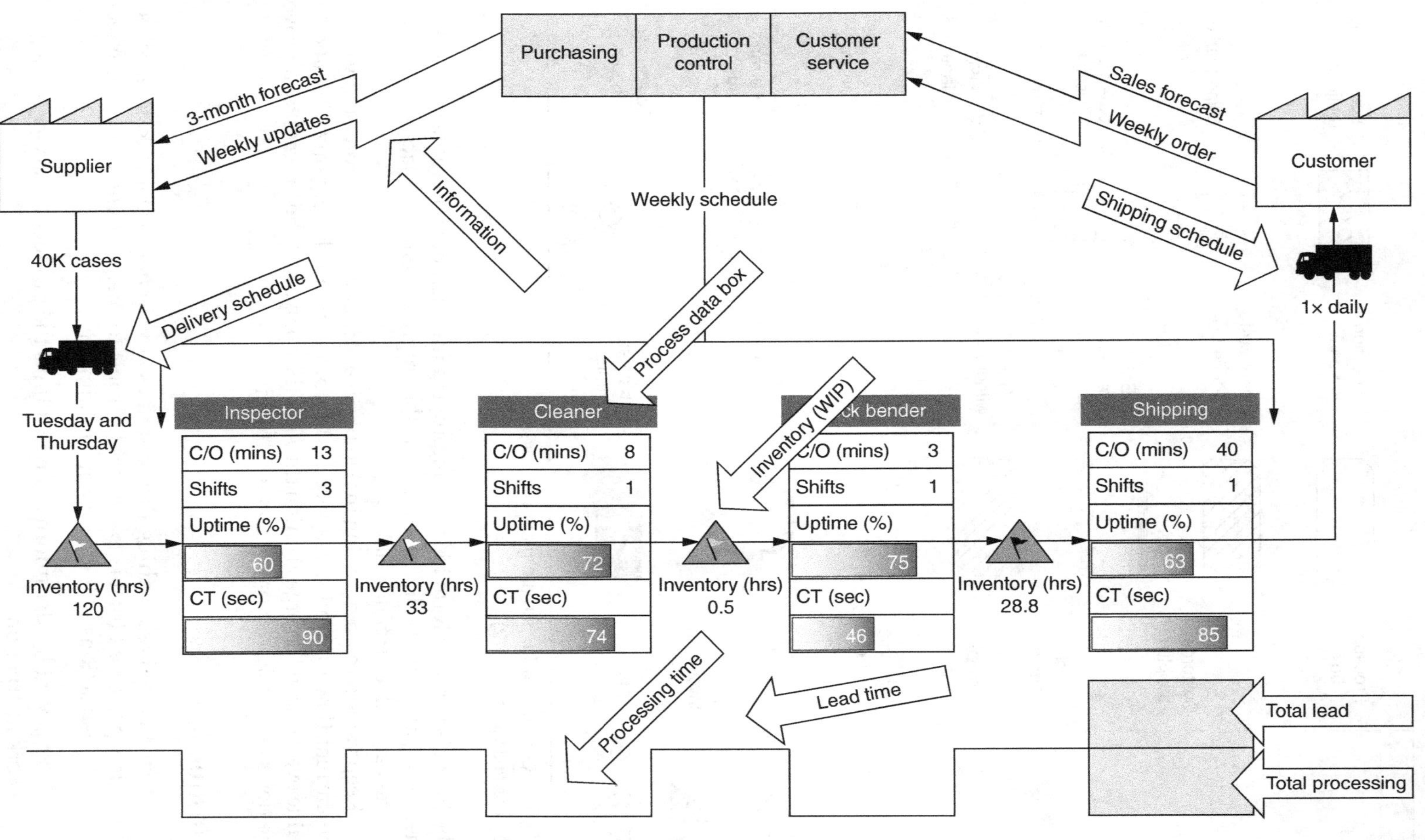

Figure 14.8 Value stream map components.
Source: Manos and Vincent (2012).

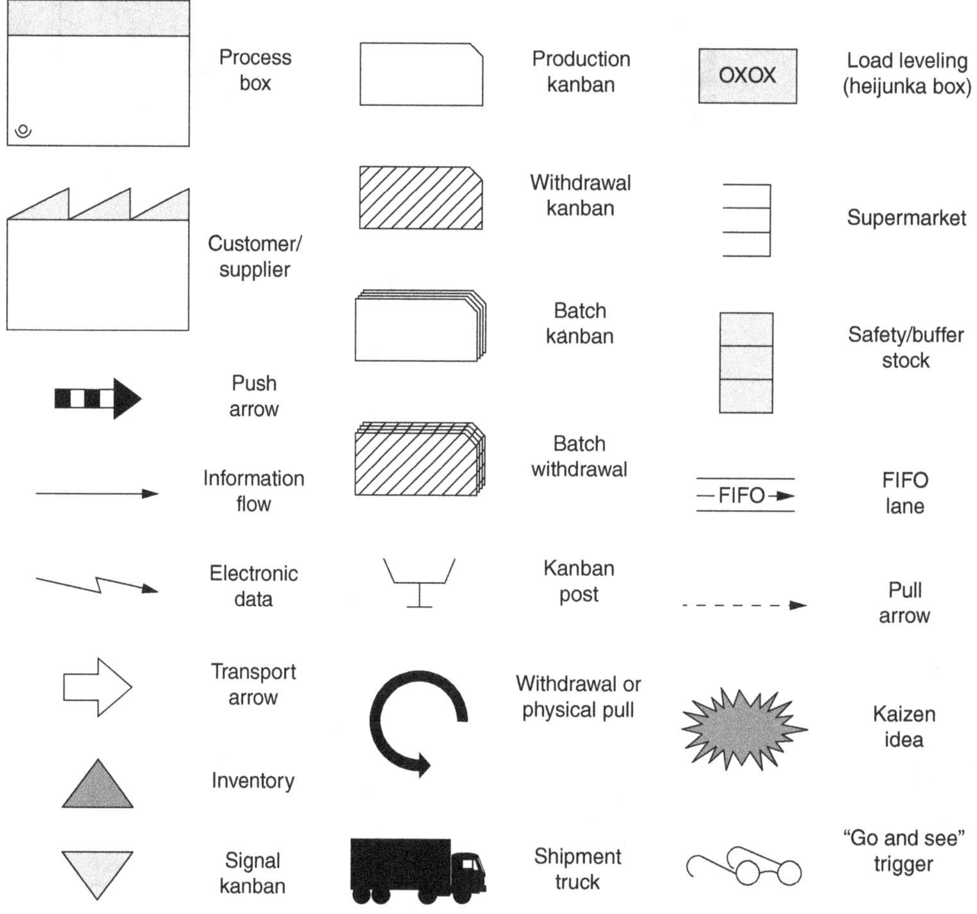

Figure 14.9 Common value stream mapping icons.
Source: Manos and Vincent (2012).

The intent is to brainstorm ideas for improving the current-state value stream and then reconstruct the value stream with the improvements in place (that is, the future-state value stream map).

Keep value stream mapping in perspective; it is simply a tool to visually show the current flow of product/service and information in the organization and to guide everyone in the organization through the analysis of the process to improve the flows and design improved value streams.

Work Instructions

A *work instruction* is something that describes how to perform a task. Regardless of how it is presented (that is, paper or electronic format, or something else), effective work instructions will identify at a minimum:

- All relevant header information that links the product or service to the work instruction

- All the parts required
- All the consumable raw materials
- All the tooling and fixtures required
- All the personnel required
- Potential safety hazards
- Potential opportunities to create defects
- Meaningful and properly annotated graphics and designs
- The exact sequence of steps required for assembling, manufacturing, producing, generating, and so on, the product or service governed by the work instruction
- A work instruction will contain a document number and revision number so that it can be properly identified. This is a critical piece of information so that proper work instruction documentation can be matched to the effectiveness of engineering changes.

Work instructions support lean activities through the creation of standardized work.

The question most often asked regarding work instructions is, "How much detail should be provided in a work instruction?" The answer to that question depends on how much variation an organization is willing or able to accept in the final output. Several key factors to consider are:

- How educated is the workforce that will be using the work instruction? The more educated, the less detail required. Consider "education" of the work force independent of a "trained" work force.
- How frequently will the workforce be using the work instruction? This must be considered in conjunction with the first bullet. However, in general, the less frequently, the less detail, if the workforce has some training.
- How much variation can the organization tolerate in the output? The less tolerance, the more detail in the work instruction and vice versa.

There is no magic answer for writing work instructions. Each organization must address its own issues and strike a meaningful balance. Note that work instructions support lean activities through the creation of standardized work.

An example of written work instructions is illustrated in Figure 14.10.

Spaghetti Diagrams

Spaghetti diagrams depict the physical flow of material, information, or people within a process. Figure 14.11 shows a spaghetti diagram representing the layout of the workstations in a diagnostic lab. The path a sample takes as it is being processed is shown by the lines in the diagram. We see that the sample returns to the same workstation in process steps 2, 4, and 6, and that this station is not

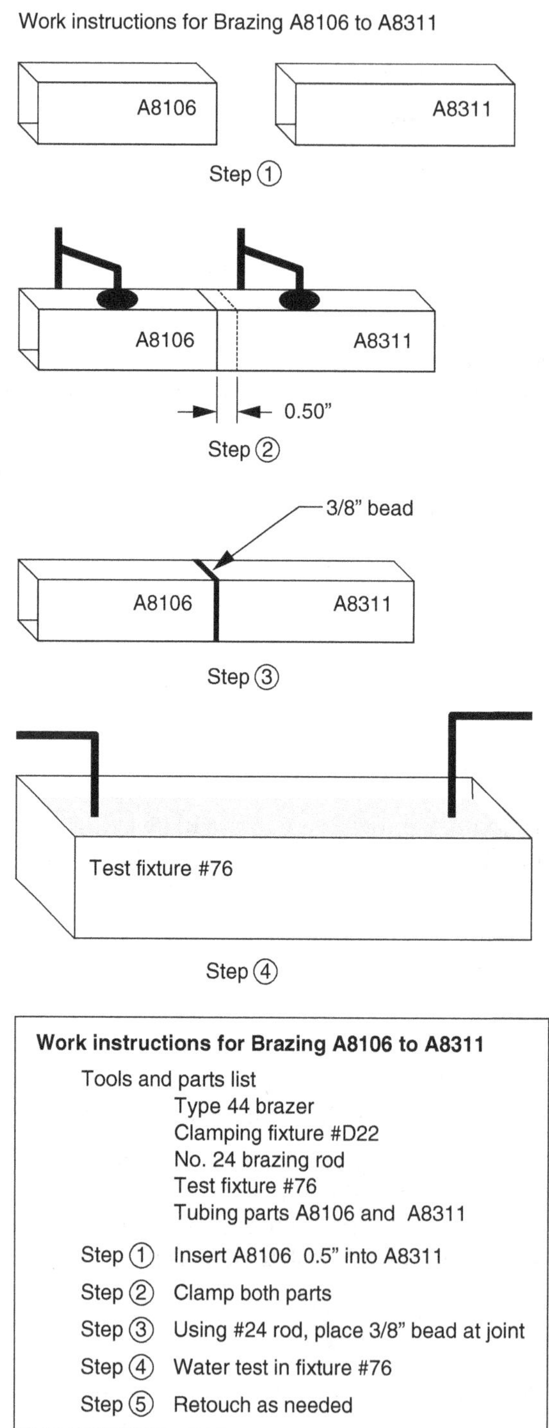

Figure 14.10 Example of work instructions.

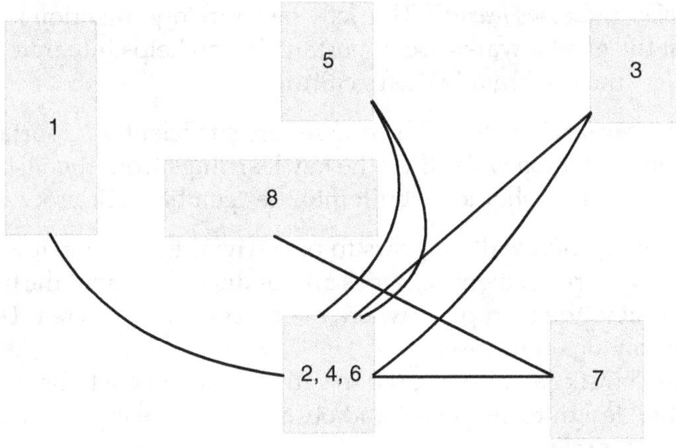

Figure 14.11 Example of a spaghetti diagram for a lab process.

centrally located. The diagram can be augmented by measuring the distance in feet that a sample travels through the process. The diagram can also be drawn from the worker perspective, depicting the movements of the lab technicians. Spaghetti diagrams often reveal convoluted and circuitous paths that are otherwise not noticed. Consequently, these diagrams are helpful in uncovering motion and transportation waste and streamlining process flow.

Gemba Walk

Gemba is a Japanese term that means "the actual place." In the context of process analysis tools, a *gemba walk* is conducted to see the process where and how it is being performed. Without this vital step, learning about a process is relegated to a conference room, a flip chart, and a half dozen conflicted subject matter experts arguing over how the process works.

Before beginning any gemba walk, it is important to establish a clear focus for the walk. The gemba walk is not the time to be critical, enforce policy, chastise, or solve problems. It is the time to learn, listen, and receive input.

If gemba walks are conducted on a regular basis independent of project improvement activities, it is important to consider the following:

- *Make the walks theme-based.* Change the focus of each gemba walk, such as housekeeping, up-to-date charts, safety, and so on.
- *Engage leaders.* Getting the leaders involved in the gemba walks helps them understand the processes and the value of the tool, and lets the organization know that gemba walks are sufficiently important to require their personal involvement.
- *Set expectations.* This sets the boundaries for what should and shouldn't be done on a gemba walk and how using gemba walks is beneficial.
- *Create a checklist.* The use of the checklist helps ensure that little is missed on the walk.

- *Publish what was learned.* This lets the entire organization know that the gemba walks are important. It also helps integrate their usage into the organization's culture.
- *Follow up on the process.* If processes are sufficiently important to receive a gemba walk, then the key learnings from the visit must be acted on. This should be built into the "gemba walk process."

Although the gemba walk appears to be a trivial technique, it is surprising how many process improvement activities are conducted without the benefit of a "look-and-see" visit to the workplace where the process is conducted. The improvement activity is conducted in absentia.

A gemba walk can also be used to gather "voice of customer" information that requires the design team to visit and observe how the customer uses the product in their environment.

Chapter 15
Data Collection

This chapter will cover aspects of data-related concepts and activities, including the types of data, the importance of understanding the different data measurement scales, various sampling designs and their uses, and effective approaches to collecting data.

TYPES OF DATA

> Define, classify, and distinguish between qualitative and quantitative data, and continuous and discrete data. (Evaluate)
>
> **Body of Knowledge V.B.1**

Qualitative and Quantitative Data

Data can be categorized into two types: qualitative and quantitative.

Qualitative data are data based on descriptive or verbal information rather than numerical information. This descriptive information can be in terms of the characteristics, attributes, properties, and qualities of an object. For example, an object may be described as "heavy," "blue," "smooth," "defective, "non-defective," and so on. As such, these descriptions categorize. Qualitative data can also be sequences of numbers if they serve as labels instead of measurements. For example, telephone numbers, social security numbers, and bank account numbers are numeric, but could be translated into alpha characters with no loss of information. Therefore, they are classified as qualitative data. Verbal information such customer reviews and recorded customer service calls are also classified as qualitative data.

Qualitative data can be collected by observations, interviews, surveys with open-ended questions, and narrative data from social media, for example. Often the customer feedback gleaned from open-ended survey questions or reviews provides the greatest insights. Qualitative data collected by these methods can be analyzed using advanced techniques such as computation linguistics and sentiment analysis.

Quantitative data are numerical data that can be measured, verified, and manipulated. For example, measurements such as height, mass, volume, temperature, impedance, and humidity are quantitative. Counts such as production volumes, inventory levels, and tallies of defect types are also quantitative.

Quantitative data can be further broken into two categories: continuous and discrete.

Discrete and Continuous Data

Discrete data can take on either a finite number of values or a countably infinite number of values. Two examples of finite sets of values follow. Say that the allowable values of a variable X are {–3/4, 0, 12}, then the variable X is discrete since it can take on only a finite number of distinct values. For the second example, we can consider the outcome of a single roll of a die. Here, the allowable values of X would include {1, 2, 3, 4, 5, 6}. On the other hand, if a variable X can take on the values of the set of counting numbers {0, 1, 2, 3 ...} then it is also considered discrete since the allowable values include distinct numbers that, while infinite, are countable. In the context of statistical process control charts, discrete data is also referred to as *attribute* or *attributes* data.

Continuous data are measurements taken from a variable that has a continuous scale, such as length, weight, or temperature. These scales are called *continuous* because there is an infinite number of values in between any two given values on the scale. For example, there is an infinite number of values between the measurements 1.537 inches and 1.538 inches since there is no limit to the number of decimal places for length. In effect, the number of decimal places we record for a continuous variable is only limited by the discrimination, or resolution, of the instrument we use for our measurement. Continuous data are often referred to as *variables* data in the context of statistical process control.

Note that continuous data can be transformed into discrete data, but the reverse is not true. We can group continuous data into categories, and then count the number in each category. For example, we can measure and record the lengths of parts. If we then classify any parts that exceed the specifications as defective, the tally of the defective parts is a discrete count. Note that the continuous measurements provide more information than the discrete data. Because we measured the parts, we know not only which ones are defective, but by how much they exceed the specification. However, if we were only given the count of the defectives, we would lose information about the severity of the nonconformities.

MEASUREMENT SCALES

Define and use nominal, ordinal, interval, and ratio measurement scales. (Apply)

Body of Knowledge V.B.2

To avoid analysis errors, it is important to recognize the type of measurement scale used to collect data. There are four types of measurement scales:

- Nominal
- Ordinal
- Interval
- Ratio

Nominal scales classify data into categories with no order implied—for example, a list of equipment such as presses, drills, and lathes is considered nominal. The nominal scale is qualitative and is simply a label. Mathematical operations performed on nominally scaled data will not have any meaning. For example, calculating an average of the telephone numbers in a business office will provide no useful information. When data are classified into two categories such as male/female, defective/non-defective, and so on, they are called *dichotomous*.

Ordinal scales refer to positions in a series, where order is important but precise differences between values aren't defined. An example might be the qualitative, subjective ranking of three light bulbs as bright (third), brighter (second), and brightest (first). Unless the light emitted from each bulb were measured in lumens, the difference between the first and second bulbs and the second and the third bulbs would be unknown. Only the ordering of the bulbs would matter. Ordinal data can also be represented by quantitative ranks, such as first, second and third place in a 5K race. While these ranks have numerical values, the difference in finishing times between the ranked runners cannot be determined.

Interval scales can be ordered and have meaningful differences but have no inherent zero point. Examples of this measurement scale include temperatures in degrees Fahrenheit and Celsius, since the zero points are arbitrarily chosen values. In addition, calendar years follow an interval scale, since the starting points vary between calendars used throughout the world, such as the Chinese, Gregorian, Islamic, and Jewish calendars. Because there is no inherent zero point, ratios between values on the interval scale are not meaningful. For example, a temperature measured as 20°F cannot be said to be twice as warm as 10°F.

Ratio scales can be ordered, they have meaningful differences, an absolute zero exists, and therefore, ratios are meaningful. For example, a length measured in inches is a ratio scale because zero length is defined as no length, and as a result, 20 inches can be said to be 4 times longer than 5 inches. Other examples of variables measured on a ratio scale include weight, dollars, age, or any variable in which zero means that there is none.

A summary of the four measurement scales along with other relevant information is given in Table 15.1.

	Measurement Scale			
Mathematical operations	**Nominal**	**Ordinal**	**Interval**	**Ratio**
$=, \neq$	✓	✓	✓	✓
$<, >$		✓	✓	✓
$+, -$			✓	✓
$\times, \div$				✓
Types of data	Qualitative	Qualitative or Quantitative	Quantitative	Quantitative
		Discrete	Discrete or Continuous	Discrete or Continuous
Measures of central tendency	Mode	Mode	Mode	Mode
		Median	Median	Median
			Mean	Mean
Measures of dispersion		Range	Range	Range
		Interquartile range	Interquartile range	Interquartile range
			Standard deviation	Standard deviation

Table 15.1 Comparison of measurement scales.

EXAMPLE 15.1

An organization wants to survey its customers using a five-point Likert scale, which, by definition, is ordinal. The general construct of the scale looked like:

Very unsatisfied	Unsatisfied	Neutral	Satisfied	Very satisfied
1	2	3	4	5

The organization could analyze the survey results treating the Likert categories as qualitative and report the percentage of customers who selected "very satisfied," "satisfied," and so on. Or the organization could transform the categorical data into discrete data using a 1 to 5 mapping. These data now follow an ordinal scale that is quantitative, and the sample median and range can be reported. Although technically incorrect, in practice Likert data are often analyzed as interval data, in which the sample mean and standard deviation are calculated.

SAMPLING

Define and describe sampling concepts, including representative selection, homogeneity, bias, accuracy, and precision. Determine the appropriate sampling method (e.g., random, stratified, systematic, subgroup, and block) to obtain valid representation in various situations. (Evaluate)

Body of Knowledge V.B.3

Sampling Concepts

In statistical analysis, our aim is to make statements about a population of interest whose parameters are unknown, and unknowable, to us. To do this, we take samples from the population and analyze them to make judgments about the population with a certain level of confidence. Therefore, sampling is the foundation of statistical analysis.

We introduce the following sampling concepts:

- *Sampling frame* refers to a complete list of the items in the target population from which a sample is drawn.
- *Representative selection* results in a sample that is representative of the target population. From a statistical point of view, a *representative sample* is a random sample that is drawn from a population so that observed values of the samples have the same distribution as the population. When samples are not representative of the population, valid statistical inferences cannot be made.

  True representative samples are sometimes difficult to accomplish. Consider a group of 32 suppliers, of which 16 are in located in the Midwest and 16 are in the South. A representative sample of size eight based on location alone would comprise four each in the Midwest and South. A nonrepresentative sample for example, would be eight Midwestern suppliers. If we added company size in terms of sales to the characteristics, finding a representative sample would become more difficult.
- *Homogeneity* refers to the similarity or sameness of specified characteristic(s) of the members of the targeted population. Homogeneity of subpopulations is important regarding stratified sampling, which is discussed in a later section.
- *Sampling bias.* Biased samples are not representative of the population. Bias can occur when the sample is selected in a nonrandom way, resulting in the sample statistics underestimating or overestimating the population parameter. Below are some types of sampling bias:

- Under (or over) coverage bias occurs when some members of the population are not proportionally represented in the sample. For example, an employee survey may be sent only to the workers on first shift and omit those working on the second shift.
- Self-selection bias occurs when individuals themselves decide whether to participate in the study. Those who choose to participate are often not representative of the population as a whole. For example, only those with strong opinions may respond to a survey.
- Survivorship bias occurs when the sample is comprised of units that pass the selection criteria while others are ignored. For example, a sample composed solely of assemblies that have survived 10,000 hours of use in the field will ignore the assemblies that have failed.
- Recall bias occurs when respondents do not remember events or information accurately. This type of bias can be reduced by collecting data in a timely manner.
- Exclusion bias occurs when specific groups are excluded from the sample if they have recently moved into the study or have left the study area.
- Convenience bias occurs when the sample collected is based on expediency. For example, a quality inspector who collects samples only from the production line closest to his office would be gathering a convenience sample.

A classic example of nonrepresentative sampling occurred in 1936 when a poll conducted by the *Literary Digest* predicted that Alf Landon would defeat Franklin Roosevelt by a landslide in the presidential election. The magazine sent out 10 million straw vote ballots, with recipients drawn mostly from automobile registration lists and telephone directories. More than 2.3 million ballots were returned. The poll results predicted Landon 55%, Roosevelt 41%, and Lemke 4%. (The actual results were Roosevelt 61% and Landon 37%.)

There were several factors that contributed to the poll being so wildly off the mark. The sample was based on readers of the magazine and was supplemented by records of registered automobile owners and telephone directories. Not surprisingly, this sample overrepresented wealthy individuals who at that time were more likely to vote for Landon, the Republican candidate. In addition, self-selection bias played a part, since voters who favored Landon were apparently more likely to return their straw vote ballots.

It is worth noting that a new pollster named George Gallup, who had founded his company in 1935, canvassed 50,000 voters and predicted Roosevelt with 54% and Landon with 46%. Remember that a smaller, representative sample is better than a larger, biased sample any day.

- *Accuracy* refers to how close the sample statistic is to the true population parameter. Accuracy is measured by the margin of error, E.
- *Precision* refers to how close estimates from different samples are to each other, or how close different measurements of the same sample

are to each other. Precision is inversely related to the standard error of the estimate, which is defined as the sample standard deviation divided by the square root of the sample size n. Precision is high when the standard error is small, and vice versa.

- *Margin of error.* This refers to the maximum expected difference between the sample estimate of the population parameter and the true population parameter. The margin of error, E, is equal to one-half of the width of a two-sided confidence interval used to estimate a population parameter. Confidence intervals are presented in detail in Chapter 21.
- *Stratum.* This refers to a mutually exclusive segment of the target population that is defined by one or more characteristics. The subpopulations in each stratum are considered homogeneous. In stratified sampling, all members of the targeted population are placed in a unique stratum, with the collection of strata being mutually exclusive and exhaustive of the population.
- *Cluster.* This refers to a mutually exclusive segment of the target population. In cluster sampling, the population is composed of clusters. These clusters are considered similar to each other, unlike strata, which are considered heterogeneous.

Types of Sampling

In this subsection, we present six sampling methods, the first five of which fall under the category of probability sampling. Block sampling, the sixth, falls under the category of non-probability sampling. These sampling methods include:

1. Simple random sampling
2. Stratified sampling
3. Systematic sampling
4. Subgroup sampling
5. Cluster sampling
6. Block sampling

Simple Random Sampling

This method involves drawing a sample from a targeted population in which each member of the population has an equal probability of being chosen for the sample. Furthermore, every member is selected independently of every other member.

The basic procedure for simple random sampling (SRS) follows:

1. Determine the sampling frame.
2. Assign each member of the population a number from 1 to N.
3. Generate a sample size of n different random numbers between 1 and N.

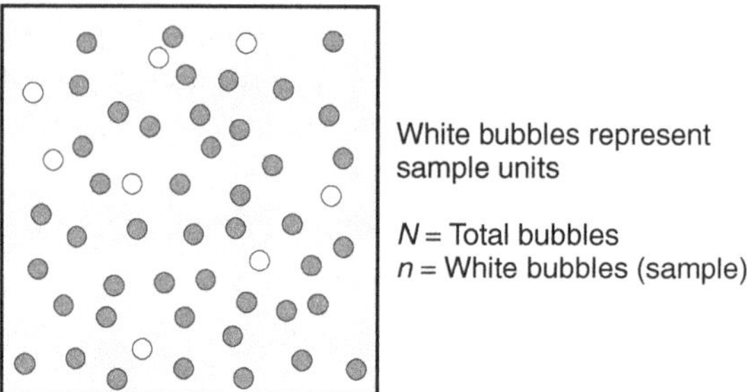

Figure 15.1 A graphical representation of random sampling.

4. Select the members of the population associated with the n random numbers. This constitutes the sample.

The simple random sampling concept is illustrated in Figure 15.1.

Stratified Sampling

This method first segregates the population into k mutually exclusive and exhaustive strata. These strata are dissimilar to each other, but members in each stratum are similar based on one or more characteristics. For example, a population of sub-assemblies could be stratified according to production line and/or shift, or the population of customers could be stratified by geographic region and/or spend level.

Each stratum is then sampled. Most often the sample size for each stratum is proportional to its relative size in the population. This type of stratified sample assures that each stratum will be proportionally represented in the sample.

Figure 15.2 depicts a stratified sample in which the strata represent size. Members of the population are segregated into the strata small, medium, and large.

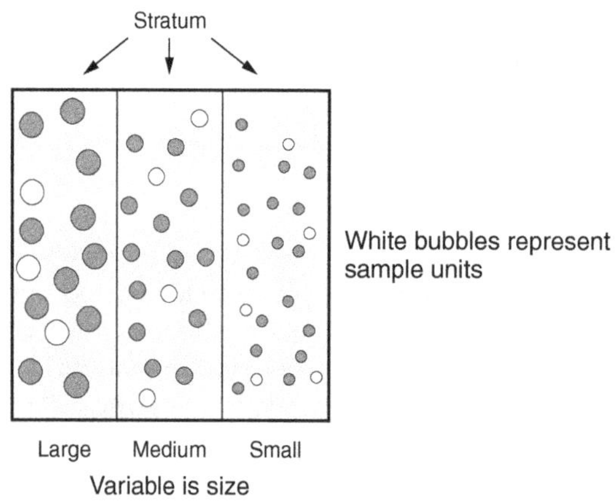

Figure 15.2 A graphical representation of stratified sampling.

The basic procedure for stratified random sampling follows:

1. Determine the sampling frame.
2. Select the stratification variable(s) and the number of strata, k.
3. Divide the entire population into k strata. Based on the classification variable, each member of the subpopulation is assigned to one of the k strata.
4. Determine the proportion of each stratum in the population:

$$p_i = \frac{N_i}{N}$$

   where N is the population size and N_i is the subpopulation size of the ith stratum.

5. Determine the total sample size, n.
6. Determine the sample size of each stratum, n_i, $i = 1, \ldots, k$, using

$$n_i = p_i n$$

   and round to the nearest integer.

7. In each stratum, number the members from 1 to N_i, $i = 1, \ldots, k$ where N_i is the subpopulation size of ith stratum.
8. Randomly draw samples of size n_i from each stratum (subpopulation) N_i, $i = 1, \ldots, k$ such that

$$\sum_{i=1}^{k} n_i = n; \sum_{i=1}^{k} N_i = N$$

Systematic Sampling

This method involves sampling from an ordered population at a specified sampling interval, *i*. This concept is shown in Figure 15.3. Systematic sampling is fast and efficient, but issues arise if, for some reason, the sampling interval synchro-

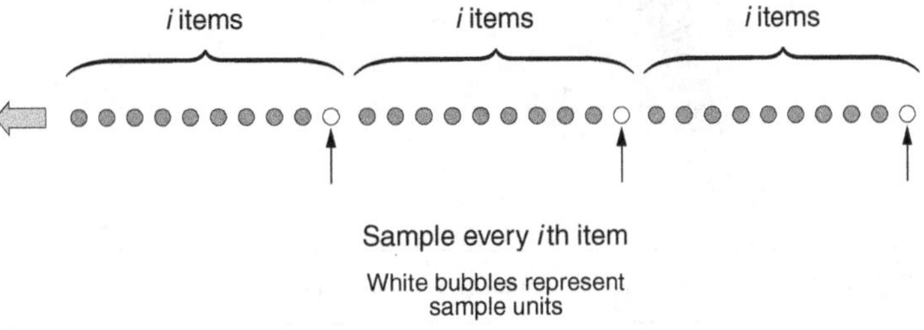

Figure 15.3 A graphical representation of systematic sampling.

nizes with a natural periodicity in the ordered population. The probability of this occurring can be minimized by randomly starting within the first interval. Systematic sampling is sometimes called *interval sampling*.

The basic procedure for systematic sampling follows:

1. Determine the sampling frame.
2. Assign each member of the population a number from 1 to N.
3. Determine the sampling interval, i. The sampling interval is defined by $i = N/n$ where n is the predetermined sample size. Round i to the nearest integer.
4. Generate a random number k between 1 and i. This will be used to create a random start.
5. Sample the following numbers: $k, k + i, k + 2i, k + 3i, \ldots, k + (n - 1)i$.

Subgroup Sampling

This method of sampling is performed in the context of statistical process control charts in which samples of size n are chosen at set time intervals. The samples are selected using a technique known as rational subgrouping. Here, the samples are selected to make the units with subgroups as homogeneous as possible. This technique is covered in detail in Chapter 27.

Cluster Sampling

This method separates the population into k clusters using some criterion such as proximity. The clusters are considered similar to each other. Then, a sample of n clusters is chosen, and 100% of the members of the chosen clusters are measured, as shown in Figure 15.4.

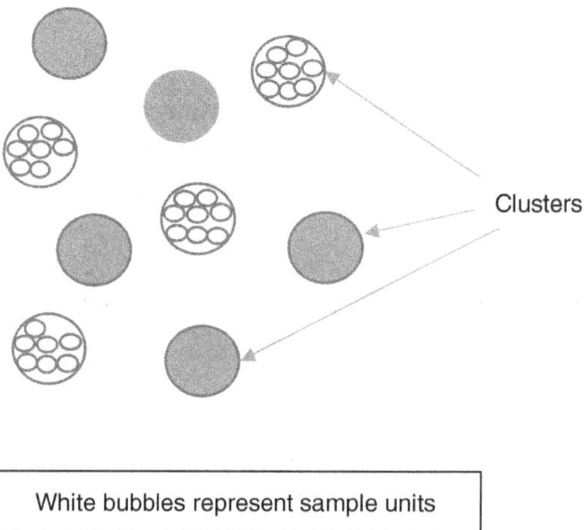

Figure 15.4 A graphical representation of cluster sampling.

The basic procedure for systematic sampling follows:

1. Determine the sampling frame.
2. Identify the k clusters in the population. Assign each cluster a number from 1 to k.
3. Select the sample size $n < k$.
4. Generate a sample size of n different random numbers between 1 and k.
5. Select the clusters associated with the n random numbers.
6. Sample all the units in the chosen clusters.

This type of sampling could be used when evaluating the efficacy of a new training program, in which scheduled classes are considered clusters. The makeup of each class is considered to be similar. If a class-cluster is chosen, each student in that class will receive training using the new program. The outcome of this new training program would then be compared to the outcome of the original program.

In another example, a new onboarding process could be evaluated by choosing three of a company's nine facilities. Here, the new hires in each facility would be considered similar in their makeup. All new employees at the chosen facility-clusters would then be onboarded using the new process. The efficacy of the new onboarding process would then be compared to the original process.

Block Sampling

Block sampling refers to a procedure in which an initial item is chosen from a population in sequential order and, consequently, the items in the balance of a defined block are automatically chosen, as depicted in Figure 15.5. Block sampling is most often used in auditing and falls into the category of non-probability sampling. It is considered an efficient technique since many documents can be gathered from one location. However, it is not considered as representative as a random sample.

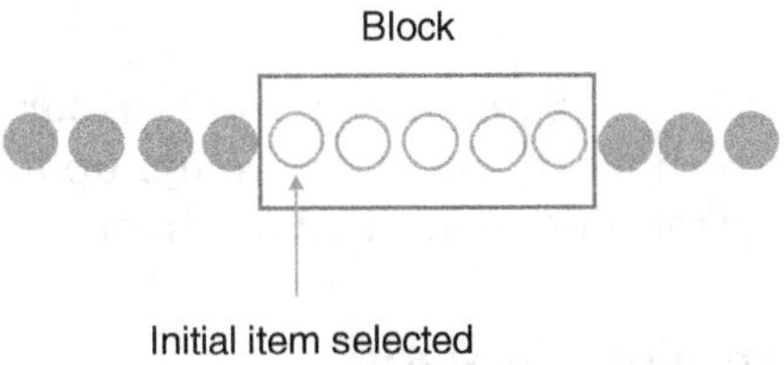

Figure 15.5 A graphical depiction of block sampling.

EXAMPLE 15.2

An auditor will be sampling 50 sequentially numbered purchase orders. He decides to sample purchase orders #230 - #279 for the audit. Note that as soon as the number of the first purchase order is chosen, the rest of the block is automatically defined.

Determining the Sample Size

A variety of factors can influence the sample size required. Some of these factors include:

- Nature of the study, including the sensitivity of the study, the time available to conduct it, and geographical considerations
- Sampling design adopted
- Size and characteristics of the population
- Difficulty in obtaining the sample data
- Resources available
- Precision and accuracy required
- Confidence and power required

For the purpose of being able to make statistical statements, readers are encouraged to calculate sample sizes. The correct sample size calculation to use depends entirely on the analysis planned for the data. When the population size N is a known quantity and the purpose of the study is estimating a mean with a confidence interval around it, Equation 15.1 can be used:

Equation 15.1 Sample size to achieve margin of error E

$$\lceil n = \frac{N}{1+NE^2}$$

where N = Population size, n = Sample size, and E = Margin of error. Note that $\lceil n$ is a ceiling function, which mean we always round up to the next highest whole number. Alternately, the formulas identified in Chapter 21 may be used.

What Makes a Good Sampling Design?

Many of the aspects of a good sampling design presented in this chapter are summarized as follows:

- Samples are drawn randomly from the targeted population.
- The sample is representative of the population from which it is drawn.

- The design is economical and efficient.
- The sampling design is sufficiently easy to conduct.
- The standard error is minimal.
- Bias is minimal.
- Statistical assumptions are not violated.
- Inferences can be made from the sample about the population with the desired level of confidence.
- The selection criteria are objective, not subject to data collector's bias.

These characteristics can be affected by sampling design. Table 15.2 summarizes the advantages and disadvantages of five of the sampling methods discussed in this subsection. We will leave a detailed look at subgroup sampling for Chapter 27.

DATA COLLECTION PLANS AND METHODS

> Develop and implement data collection plans that include data integrity, accuracy, and processing tools, e.g., check sheets, and data normalization. Avoid data collection pitfalls by defining the metrics to be used or collected, ensuring that collectors are trained in the tools and understand how the data will be used, and checking for seasonality effects. (Analyze)
>
> **Body of Knowledge V.B.4**

Establishing an Operational Definition

At the outset of any data collection activity, operational definitions should be established for each data element that will be collected. This is to ensure that the proper data elements will be collected and the opportunity for error will be minimized.

In the context of data collection and metric development, an operational definition is a clear, concise, and unambiguous statement that provides a unified understanding of the data for all involved before the data are collected or the metric is developed. It answers, "Who collects the data, how are the data collected, what data are collected, where are the sources of the data, and when are the data collected? " Additional "who," "how," "what," "where," and "when" answers may be required.

When the data are used to construct a metric, the operational definition further defines the formula that will be used, as well as each term used in the formula. As with data collection, the operational definition also delineates who provides

Method	Advantages	Disadvantages	Comments
Simple Random	• Easy to conduct • Requires minimum knowledge about the population • Human bias eliminated	• Identifying all members of the population can be difficult • Could be costly	• Can be performed with or without replacement • Population must be homogeneous
Stratified	• Higher sample accuracy • Higher sample precision • Assures that each stratum is represented	• Identifying all members of the population can be difficult • Identifying all members of a stratum may be difficult • May be difficult to select stratification variables	• There are both proportional and nonproportional stratified sampling methods • Random sampling is applied within each stratum • Each stratum is different from the others, but units within each strata are similar
Systematic	• Cost effective • Less time-consuming • Easy to conduct • If the order of the units is related to the characteristic of interest, representativeness of the sample is increased	• Not all members of the population have an equal chance of being included once sampling begins • If the order of the units produces a cyclic pattern, may reduce representativeness • Creates a risk of bias as there is a natural periodicity in the data, especially if it coincides with sampling interval	• Useful in survey sampling • Sample size typically known in advance to determine sampling interval • Frequently used with a random start
Cluster	• Effective for comparing programs • Cost effective • Less time-consuming • High reliability • Reduces logistical problems for program rollout	• Clusters may be difficult to define • Sample can be very large if cluster membership is large • May be difficult to implement • Sampling error can be high	• Clusters are considered similar groups • Each member of a chosen cluster is measured

Table 15.2 Comparison of sampling methods. *Continued*

Method	Advantages	Disadvantages	Comments
Block	• Cost effective • Less time-consuming	• Lack of objectivity and introduces bias • Sample may not be representative	• Not probability-based • Used in auditing

Table 15.2 *Continued*

the metrics and who is answerable to its results, how the metric is to be displayed or graphed, where the metric is displayed, and when it is available. Again, additional "who," "how," "what," "where," and "when" answers may be required.

Finally, the operational definition provides an interpretation of the metric, such as "up is good." While providing an interpretation of a metric seems trivial, this is not always the case.

For example, consider "employee attrition rate." How should this be interpreted? Is down good? Yes? How far down is "good"? Some authorities suggest that some amount of attrition is acceptable because it permits new thinking to enter the organization. A high level of attrition, however, can bleed the organization of institutional knowledge and memory.

In this example, the attrition rate metric may have boundaries in which:

- Above the upper boundary "down is good."
- Below the lower boundary "up is good."

Data Integrity

As quality or Lean Six Sigma professionals, we have been taught to address the issue of data accuracy and integrity from the statistical viewpoint. However, this section will address most of the elements of data integrity by discussing why data accuracy is important, the numerous causes of poor data accuracy, and various techniques for improvement and the placement of effective data collection points (Kubiak, 2008).

Importance of Data Accuracy

Poor data accuracy undermines two key precepts in a quality-focused or Lean Six Sigma organization: fact-based and data-driven decision making. When faced with data that have been rendered useless because of data accuracy issues, decision makers must revert to relying on intuition.

This might provide the naysayer with reason and justification to state, "This Lean Six Sigma approach won't work here." Remember, Lean Six Sigma drives cultural changes in organizations, and accurate data are necessary to accurately understand the current state to drive and sustain real improvement.

In addition, some organizations might be required to submit highly accurate data because of regulatory or reporting requirements, or because of contractual requirements. This is particularly true in industries such as aerospace, in which data, in addition to product, are a deliverable. In fact, most organizations have processes that deliver only data to other organizations.

Consider the example of payroll data regularly reported to the Internal Revenue Service. The consequences associated with poor data accuracy can be quite troublesome and can have a strong negative impact on the individual who is depending on the data.

Minimizing Poor Data Accuracy

There are many causes of poor data accuracy. Table 15.3 includes a few of the most significant causes. Consider how these issues relate to your own experience and create your own list so you can minimize the impact of poor data accuracy in your organization.

Table 15.4 lists data collection techniques used to minimize the occurrence of poor data accuracy or its impact.

Remember, processes are measurable and generate data. Treat poor data accuracy as you would any other quality defect: use the tools available to you as a quality or Lean Six Sigma professional to uncover the root cause or causes. Chart data defects as you would product defects. Make them available for all to see. Data accuracy is essential for managing and improving processes and achieving sustained results. Without it, decision making is, at best, uninformed. Consequently, poor data accuracy can adversely impact an organization. Data defects, like product defects, should be charted and improved using the variety of tools at the disposal of the quality or Lean Six Sigma professional.

Common Data Collection Points

Five common data collection points are summarized in Table 15.5 and are as follows:

- *End of process.* Traditionally, organizations have collected data to measure process performance at the very end when everything is said and done, and it's usually too late to take corrective action.
- *In process.* Over time, organizations that are more progressive have realized that data should be collected upstream and during the process. Data collection at critical subprocesses allows corrective action to be taken earlier when change is still an option. This move facilitates more effective process management and allows the organizations to better gauge the overall health of their processes.
- *Points of convergence.* This occurs when multiple streams of processes come together. Collecting data at this point makes sense because it helps organizations understand how each input stream affects the downstream subprocesses.
- *Points of divergence.* This is nothing more than a flip of the points of convergence. Keep in mind that a decision point is a specialized point of divergence with two distinct outputs. Decision points involving "yes or no" decisions are useful data collection points, particularly

Issue	Comment
Multiple points of entry	When data entry is centralized to a single individual, entry errors are usually minimized over time due to the experience of the individual and, often, the ability of the individual to contact the originator of the data for clarifications. When data originators become responsible for their own data entry, data accuracy usually diminishes, particularly when frequency of data entry decreases or there is high turnover among the data originators.
Limited use of data validation	Such validation would include the presence or absence of data, data ranges, inconsistent data, and other logical checks. Surprisingly, computer technology has not completely eliminated this cause.
Batching input versus real-time input/ synchronization of system updates	This scenario usually results in instantaneous differences, but the differences are usually reconciled with time. Consider the example of an individual inquiring about a checking account balance through an ATM, a bank teller, or online. Because of different cut-off and system update times, the individual will see up to three different account balances.
Multiple means of data correction access to upstream systems	When multiple data correction access points are present, the opportunity to have synchronization issues increases. For example, suppose there are three upstream systems prior to the current system. Label them 4, 3, 2, and 1 for the current system. If corrections are made to 4, then 3, 2, and 1 are updated. However, if corrections are made to 2, only 2 and 1 are updated.
Unclear directions	This issue becomes increasingly important when multiple points of data entry exist.
Lack of training	This issue becomes increasingly important when multiple points of data entry exist.
Ambiguous terminology	Ask an operations manager for monthly data and you get monthly data according to the calendar month. Ask for the same data from an accountant and you get monthly data by fiscal month. Different months' lengths yield different data.
Manual versus automated means of entry	Automated data entry is usually preferred over manual data entry, particularly if you accept the premise that people are fallible.
Rounding	Improper rounding, for example, when rounding up is appropriate instead of rounding down. Also, the cumulative effects of rounding can generate errors. For example, computers store and calculate using numbers to 16, 32, or even 64 digits. An individual using numbers rounded to four digits in the same calculations can arrive at a result that is substantially different than the results arrived at by a computer.
Order of calculations	Consider $\frac{36}{(1/9)}$. If you rewrite this equation as $36\left(\frac{9}{1}\right)$ and multiply through, you obtain 324. If you divide out 1/9 and round to four decimals, you obtain 0.1111. Dividing 36/0.1111, you obtain 324.0324. Different order, different answers.

Table 15.3 Common causes of poor data accuracy. *Continued*

Issue	Comment
Calculation errors	This is simply an arithmetic error or an error in the specification of the formula to be used. For example, I worked at two organizations that computed "associate turnover" incorrectly.
Inadequate measurement systems	This is an issue commonly known among Six Sigma professionals who have been taught to examine the adequacy of the measurement system first. Examples include Kappa studies and gage repeatability and reproducibility studies.
Units of measure not defined	This type of error occurs when the wrong use of measure is assumed or used, such as "foot" instead of "inch," "yard" instead "foot," or "box" instead of "each." The last example can significantly impact inventory levels.
Failing to use the proper system of measurement	On September 23, 1999, after a 286-day journey from Earth to Mars, NASA lost the $125 million Mars Climate Orbiter after the spacecraft entered orbit 100 kilometers closer than planned. NASA used the metric system, while its partner Lockheed Martin, the organization that designed the navigation system, used English units.
Field inconsistencies/ truncation among systems or data fields	Moving an *n* character field to an $n - 1$ character field or smaller can result in field truncation, which would impact all calculations that use it. For example, 100,789 is moved into a three-character numeric field. The result would be 789, not 100,789.
Similarities of characters	Several letters and numbers can easily be confused, particularly when handwriting is poor or when reading other than the top sheet of a no carbon required form. Common examples include: 0 O (oh) 4 H 8 B 1 l (el) 5 S 9 g (gee) or q 2 Z and occasionally Q 6 G 3 B 7 Z Examples of possible confusion between letters: c-e, C-O, E-F, m-n, M-N, O-Q, P-R, r-v, u-v, U-V, v-w, V-W, v-y
Copying errors	Duplicates of duplicates can result in image degradation and impact the readability of the copy. Also, copy truncation occurs when the image being copied is close to the edge of the paper. Try this with your credit card statement sometime. Ensure that the purchase amounts are adjacent to the edge of the copier glass.

Table 5.3 *Continued*

Technique	Comment
Walk the process first	Always walk the process first so everything that follows in this table has meaning and applicability.
Make the data collection process simple	Minimize the need to perform calculations and maximize the use of direct data collection. Direct data collection occurs when you take a reading from an instrument and log or enter that piece of data. In this case, a simple data transference has occurred.
Define collection points	Table 15.5 identifies typical and useful data collection points.
Use check sheets and checklists	These are simple but very effective tools and often overlooked. Perhaps they are too simple.
Bridge computer gaps	Some organizations still have processes requiring individuals to extract data from one computer report and enter it into a database residing on a different computer. In some cases, it is the same computer.
Minimize "other"	What is "other?" When collecting nominal or categorical data, it is often the last, and sometimes the largest, bar on a Pareto chart. A substantial amount of data classified as "other" usually indicates that data originators either don't understand clearly how to classify the data, or that categories are not mutually exclusive. The opportunity exists to classify data into multiple categories. As a result, data originators might disagree with one another, and the measurement system becomes inadequate.
Limit options	The more categories of data there are, the greater the possibility of a data collection error. This technique should be balanced against the previous "minimize other" technique.
Establish the rules	This technique is best illustrated by an example. Consider an organization that receives payments stating that any receipt received after 3:00 p.m. will be credited on the next business day.
Address timing and sequencing	This technique is important when a data collection point is inserted to collect data from multiple input streams. In this case, be particularly aware of the possibility of generating a bottleneck by waiting for a specific data input stream. Otherwise, it might be necessaryto collect the data at another point downstream. If this is not possible, rebalancing the upstream processes might be required.
Time-stamp data	This technique facilitates traceability of activities and events through time-based data and allows for more thorough root cause analysis.
Red-tag a unit of product or service	Track a specified unit of product or service through the entire process to understand how it is used to generate data or how data are collected from it.
Chart data accuracy	Remember, data collection is part of the process and therefore subject to charting techniques such as control charts and run charts.

Table 15.4 Useful data collection techniques.

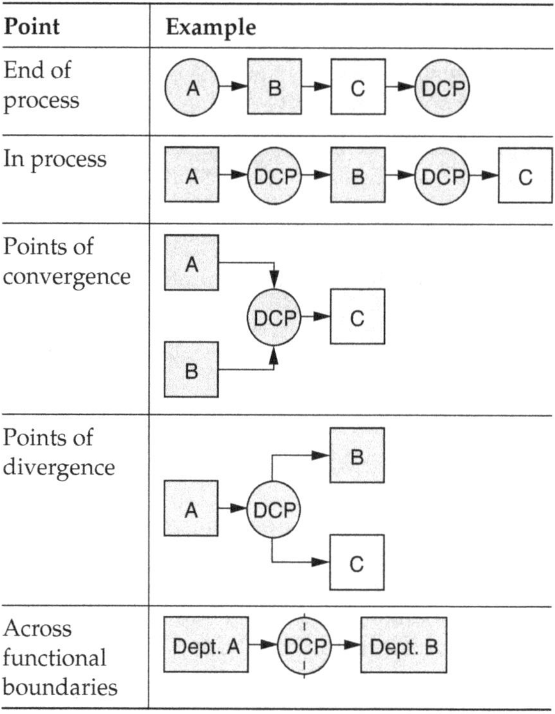

Point	Example
End of process	
In process	
Points of convergence	
Points of divergence	
Across functional boundaries	

Table 15.5 Common data collection points (DCPs).

when the "yes" path is the desired path and the "no" path is the undesired path. Understanding the percentage of products or services taking the "no" path becomes an important piece of data necessary for driving process improvement.

- *Across functional boundaries.* These are process hand-off points. Responsibilities and accountability usually change across functional boundaries.

Collecting data at these focus points helps organizations understand how each functional department supports or detracts from process efficiency and effectiveness. It also helps minimize organizational finger-pointing with data and fact.

Data Processing Tools

Check Sheets

One of the simplest tools for manual data collection is a check sheet, one of the seven Quality Tools. This tool, also referred to as a tally sheet, provides a listing of categories and space to enter tally marks for occurrences. Information on which process or products are being monitored, who is monitoring, and which dates, shifts, and times the monitoring is taking place should also be included on the sheet.

Shipping Department Check Sheet

Date collected: 9/07/20XX, first shift   Collected by: Marita R.

Defect Type		Total
Documentation missing	/ /	2
Shipping address incomplete	// //	4
Damaged box	/	1
Packaging inadeqate	///// /	6
Box too heavy	///// ///	8
Wrong item boxed	/	1
Missing items	/ /	2
Missing label	/	1
		25

Figure 15.6 Example of a check sheet for defect types.

The variable or variables monitored using the tally sheet should match the purpose of the study, and the categories should be selected to cover a wide range of possibilities. Inevitably, a situation will occur that is not covered by a category, so a few blank spaces should be included for the monitor to write these in. The check sheet for a shipping department is shown in Figure 15.6. The monitor was able to add the defect types "missing items" and "missing label" that occurred but were not on the original defect list.

Check sheets can be used to monitor the frequency of defect types for a product, the frequency of helpline calls by problem type, or the number of customers entering a showroom by day of week, for example.

The result of the check sheet shows which categories have the most frequent occurrences. The data from the check sheet can be used as input to a Pareto chart, or a chi-square goodness of fit test. Check sheets can be formatted so that

Defect Type	1	2	3	4	5	6	7	8	9	10	11	12	13	14	15	Total
Documentation missing																2
Shipping address incomplete																4
Damaged box																1
Packaging inadequate																6
Box too heavy																8
Wrong item boxed																1
Missing items																2
Missing label																1
																25

Figure 15.7 Check sheet, alternative recording method.

the completed check sheet is itself a graphical display of the data, as shown in Figure 15.7.

Data Normalization

A useful technique in data processing is *data normalization*, in which we transform data so that it is on a common scale. A normalization technique frequently used is the Z transformation, which results in a unitless, coded data set that has an average equal to zero, and standard deviation equal to 1. We first calculate the sample mean and standard deviation of the data and then apply the transformation to each data point, as shown in Equation 15.2.

Equation 15.2 Normalizing using a Z transformation

$$\hat{Z}_i = \frac{(x_i - \overline{x})}{s}$$

Note that "normalizing" a dataset does not make it normally distributed—it just puts the values on a common scale so they can be easily compared to other transformed variables.

Collecting Seasonal Data

When the data exhibit a seasonal effect, special consideration must be given to the data collection time frame. Figure 15.8 depicts a plot of data that exhibits a seasonal effect. In this figure, multiple seasons are shown, and the seasonal effects are fairly equal.

Figure 15.8 also shows three different data collection ranges that might correspond to three different data collection plans. The first data collection plan for data range 1 shows a very short time frame in which the data are collected. Notice

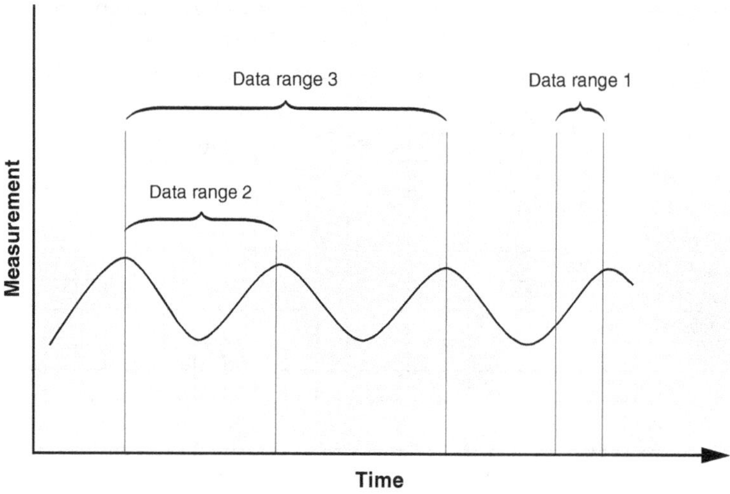

Figure 15.8 Collecting seasonal data.

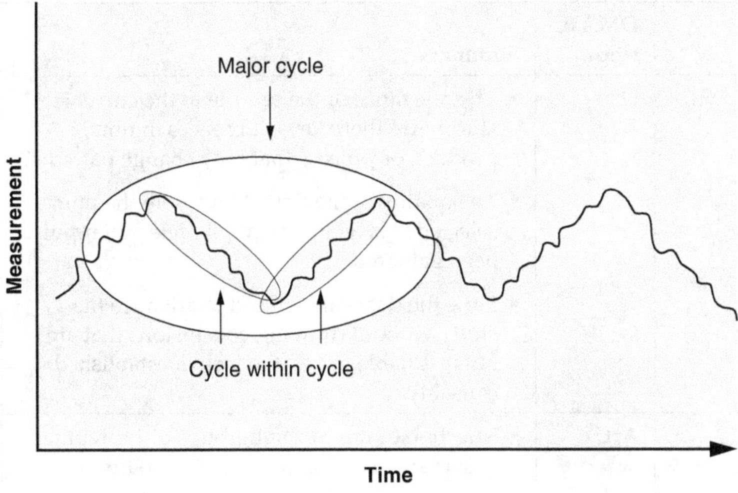

Figure 15.9 A seasonal effect within a seasonal effect.

that this data range captures a limited portion of the seasonal cycle and is not representative of the entire seasonal effect. Consequently, this would not be an appropriate data collection plan. The second data range depicts data being collected over one full seasonal cycle. This plan would capture all the data in a cycle and would be appropriate as a minimum data collection plan.

However, the third data collection plan encompasses multiple seasonal cycles and would be ideal if the data were available and the cost of data collection were acceptable. The presence of multiple cycles would permit us to explore variability with cycles. Another important aspect of seasonality effects is that there is the possibility that multiple cycles might exist and be embedded within each other, as shown in Figure 15.9. It is important to understand the nuances of the data before undertaking a major data collection effort.

Data Collection Strategies

Anderson-Cook and Borror (2013) identify seven data collection strategies, shown in Table 15.6. Notice that that each strategy is linked to one or more DMAIC phases. Furthermore, Anderson-Cook and Borror emphasize that the strategies are not mutually exclusive. Table 15.7 identifies the same strategies but includes advantages and disadvantages of each.

Collection strategy	DMAIC steps	Summary	Related strategies
1. Observational studies	D	• The relevance of the sample to the current study. Are there key differences in time, product, or process that may change patterns? • The quality of the data. How were the units selected? Have all potentially relevant inputs been gathered? • How the data can be used to advance the study without drawing conclusions that are not justifiable, given the lack of established causality.	2, 3, 4, 7
2. Monitoring techniques	A, C	• Selection of rational subgroups or individual observations to assess process stability • Action must be taken immediately (for example, when the monitoring technique is a control chart)	1, 3, 4, 5
3. Process capability	A, C	Selection of rational subgroups or individual observations to assess process stability	1, 2, 5
4. Measurement assessment	M	Assessment measurement of system capability and stability	1, 2 ,5 , 6
5. Sampling	A, C	Intentional selection of subset of population	2, 3, 4, 7
6. Design of experiments	I	Active manipulation of factors to establish causality	4
7. Complementary data and information	D, A	Qualitative, brainstorming, expert opinion, and informal assessment	1, 5

Table 15.6 A summary of data collection strategies.

Collection strategy	Advantages	Disadvantages
1. Observational studies	• Conveniently available data • Usually a large amount of data from which to sample	• Assuming a pattern observed in a convenience sample will be present in the larger population • Assuming causation between a set of inputs and its effect on the responses • Missing a lurking variable that wasn't measured and is driving change in both the input values and the response • Sampling from a portion of the total population, which might give a biased view of the relationship.
2. Monitoring techniques	• If used properly, these techniques can be highly beneficial to the organization • Can signal the need for swift action to be taken	• It is easy to misuse or select the wrong monitoring technique (for example, when the monitoring technique is a control chart) • Can easily fall into disuse
3. Process capability	• If used properly, this technique can be very effective in driving process improvement • Can provide estimates of short- and long-term variation	• It is easy to misuse or select the wrong process capability index • Much confusion exists around the use of this technique and associated indices such that the use of these indices might be a hard sell
4. Measurement assessment	• Provides insight into true process variation • Provides insight into the stability, bias, and linearity of the measurement system	• It is easy to misuse or select the wrong measurement assessment tool • Results may be difficult to interpret
5. Sampling	• Helps minimize costs • Can provide estimates of population parameters	• It is easy to select the wrong sampling technique • Once implemented, it is easy for production personnel to shortcut the sampling plan
6. Design of experiments	• Helps define the critical X's • Establishes the $Y = f(X)$ relationship	• It is easy to misuse or select the wrong experiment design • Can be expensive • May impact production
7. Complementary data and information	• Easy to teach and use • A little effort goes a long way	• Some techniques are subjective in nature

Table 15.7 Advantages and disadvantages of data collection strategies.

Chapter 16

Measurement Systems

This chapter will address the basics of measurement systems analysis. Both variables and attributes analyses will be included, and an example of each will be demonstrated. In addition, a firm foundation is provided of measurement systems analysis terminology, which is supplemented with ample use of graphics to solidify key points.

MEASUREMENT SYSTEM ANALYSIS (MSA)

> Use gauge repeatability and reproducibility (R&R) studies and other MSA tools (e.g., bias, correlation, linearity, precision to tolerance, percent agreement) to analyze measurement system capability. Use audit MSA for attribute measurement system. (Evaluate)
>
> **Body of Knowledge V.C.1**

Figure 16.1 depicts how the terminology in this section fits together. As you read this section, please keep this figure in mind, as it will help provide perspective and aid in the interpretation of the concepts discussed.

Terminology

To analyze a measurement system, it is important to understand several key concepts and terminology, as well as how they relate:

- *Accuracy* is how close the measurement is to the true value of the item being measured over the range of conditions for the measurement system. The components of accuracy are bias and linearity.
  - *Bias* is a systematic difference between the mean of the measurement results and a reference or true value. Bias may be either positive or negative. For example, if one measures the length of ten pieces of rope that range from one to ten meters multiple times, each time computing the average and always concluding that the length of each average is two meters shorter than the

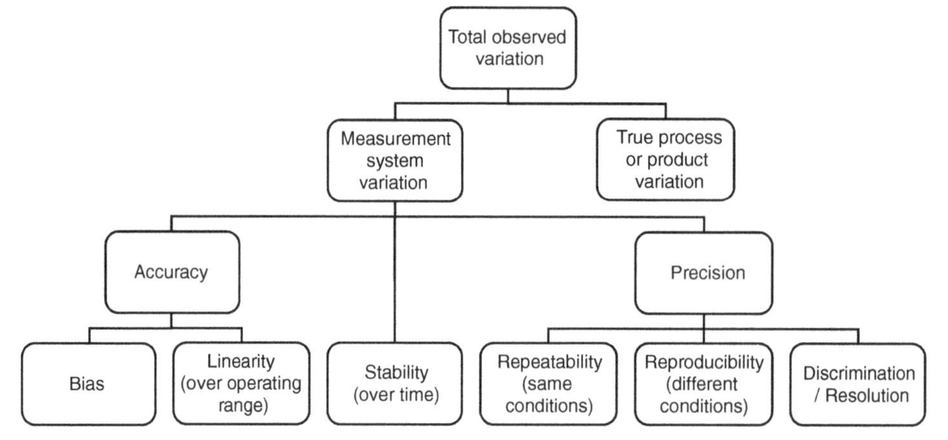

Figure 16.1 Measurement system hierarchy.

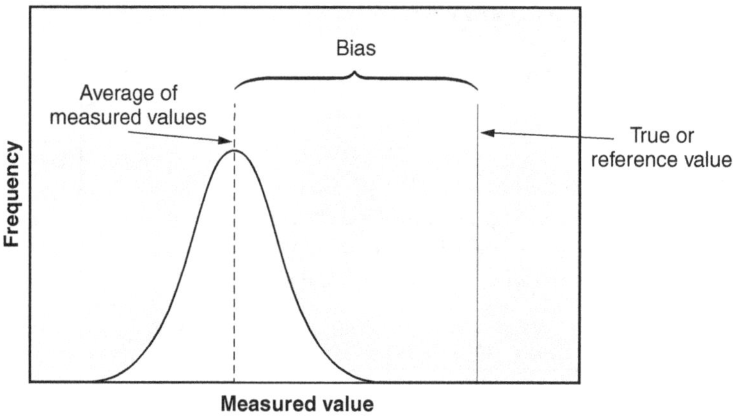

Figure 16.2 A graphical representation of bias.

true length, then the individual exhibits a bias of two meters. An organization's calibration process is used to control bias in a measurement system. The concept of bias is depicted in Figure 16.2.

- *Linearity* is the difference in bias through the operating range of measurements. A measurement system that has good linearity will have a constant bias no matter the magnitude of measurement. In the previous example, the range of measurement was from one meter to ten meters, with a constant linear bias of two meters. Figure 16.3 provides an example of linear bias. By contrast, Figure 16.4 illustrates nonlinear and varying linear bias. Notice that, in this example, the varying linear bias grows over the measurement range.

- *Stability (of a measurement system)* represents the accuracy and precision of a measurement system over time. A stable measurement system is one in which the bias and variation remain in statistical control, which

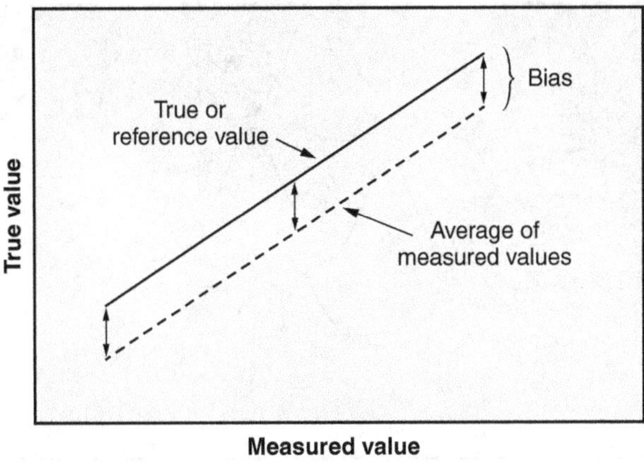

Figure 16.3 Example of a linear bias.

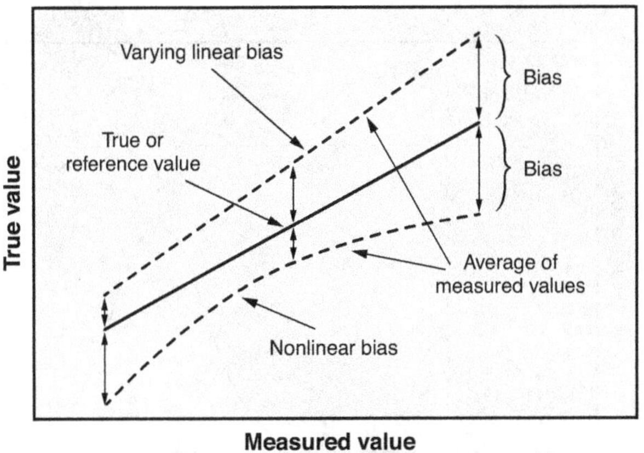

Figure 16.4 Examples of a nonlinear and varying linear bias.

is typically demonstrated in practice using control charts. The control charts can be used in conjunction with an organization's calibration process to help establish the calibration recall time frame for measurement instrumentation. The concept of stability is illustrated in Figure 16.5.

- *Precision* is the closeness of agreement between randomly selected individual measurement results. It is this aspect of measurement that addresses repeatability or consistency when an identical item is measured several times under identical conditions. Note that precision depends only on the distribution of random errors and does not relate to the reference or true value. Figure 16.6 illustrates the relationship between accuracy and precision. Figure 16.7 depicts a more traditional view of the relationship between accuracy and precision. This figure shows us how we can have low bias but not be precise, and vice versa.

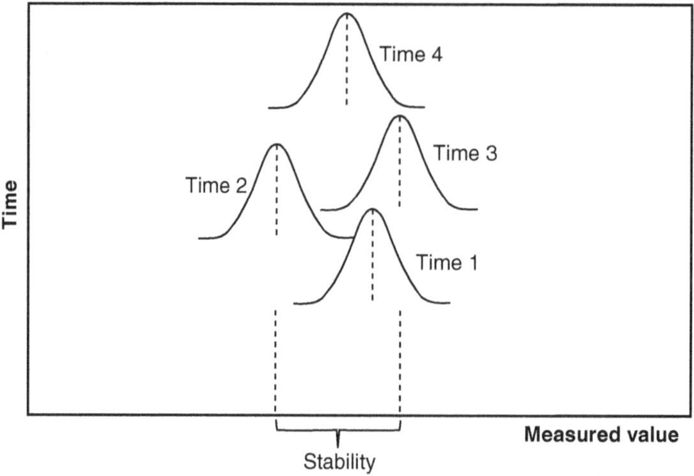

Figure 16.5 A graphical representation of stability.

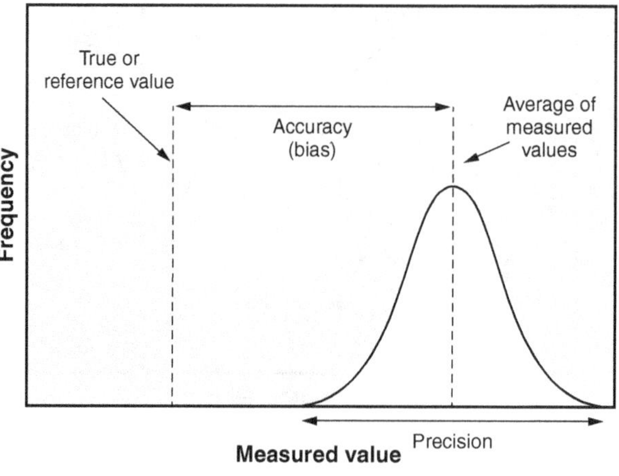

Figure 16.6 Precision and accuracy (bias).

The components of precision include:

- *Repeatability* is the precision under conditions where independent measurement results are obtained with the same method on identical measurement items by the same appraiser (that is, operator) using the same equipment within a short period of time. Although misleading, repeatability is often referred to as equipment variation (EV). It is also referred to as within-system variation when the conditions of measurement are fixed and defined (that is, equipment, appraiser, method, and environment). This concept is presented in Figure 16.8.
- *Reproducibility* is the precision under conditions where independent measurement results are obtained with the same method on

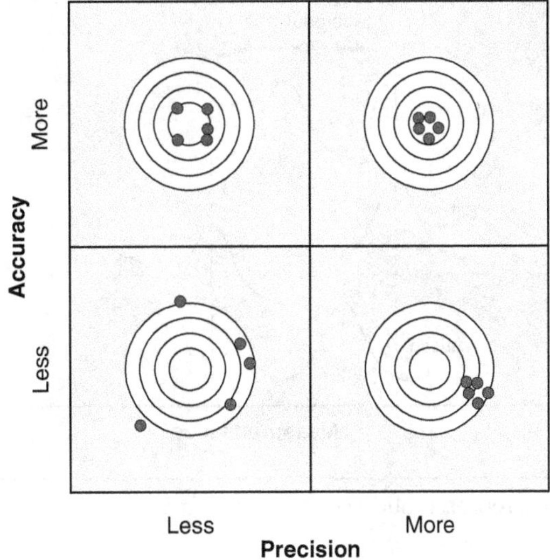

Figure 16.7 Accuracy versus precision.

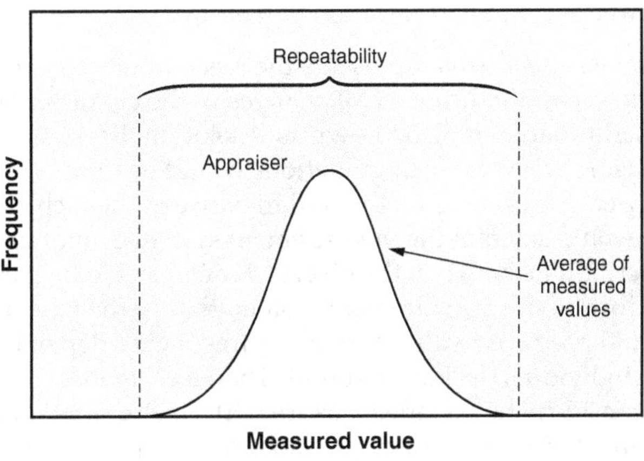

Figure 16.8 A graphical representation of repeatability.

identical measurement items under different conditions, such as different operators and different equipment. It should be stressed that reproducibility is the additional variation, above and beyond repeatability, due to different conditions, such as different operators or equipment. This concept is illustrated in Figure 16.9. Although misleading, reproducibility is often referred to as appraiser variation (AV). The term "appraiser variation" is used because it is common practice to have different operators with identical measuring systems. Reproducibility, however, can refer to any changes in the measurement system. For example, assume the same appraiser uses the same material, equipment, and environment,

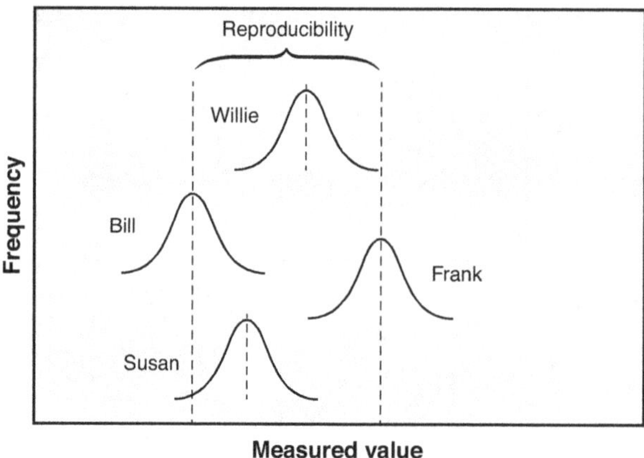

Figure 16.9 A graphical representation of reproducibility.

but uses two different measurement methods. The reproducibility calculation will show the variation due to a change in the method. It is also known as the average variation between systems, or between-conditions variation of measurement.

- *Discrimination*. This represents the measurement system's capability to detect and indicate small changes in the characteristic measured. Discrimination is also known as resolution. For example, a tape measure with one-inch gradations would be unable to distinguish between object lengths that fall in between the inch marks. Hence, we would say that the measurement system cannot properly discriminate between the objects. If an object to be measured is 2.5 inches, the measurement system (that is, the tape measure) would produce a value of two or three inches depending on how the individual decides to round. Therefore, to measure an object that is 2.5 inches, a tape measure with finer gradations would be required. Although there are more quantitative ways to measure discrimination, a quick check is to count the number of levels the measurement process is capable of distinguishing within the normal range of the process or specification. The number of measured values should be five or more for the measurement system to have adequate discrimination.

Several different approaches can be used to quantify the precision performance of the measurement system. The precision-to-tolerance ratio, Gage Repeatability and Reproducibility, and the EMP method are three such methods. The Precision-to-Tolerance ratio compares the measurement system standard deviation to a specification range or tolerance interval.

- *Precision-to-tolerance ratio (PTR)*. The PTR is a measure of the capability of the measurement system. The smaller the PTR value, the better. It can be calculated by:

$$\mathrm{PTR} = \frac{6\hat{\sigma}_{ms}}{\mathrm{USL} - \mathrm{LSL}}$$

where $\hat{\sigma}_{ms}$ is the estimated standard deviation of the total measurement system. In some industries, the PTR formula is given by:

$$\mathrm{PTR} = \frac{5.15\hat{\sigma}_{ms}}{\mathrm{USL} - \mathrm{LSL}}$$

where the 5.15 constant represents 5.15 standard deviations, which account for 99% of the measurement system variation if the metric is normally distributed.

Typically, PTR values less than 0.10 are considered good, while values greater than 0.30 require improvement in the measurement system.

- *Gage repeatability and reproducibility (GR&R) study.* A GR&R study is one type of measurement system analysis done to evaluate the performance of a test method or measurement system. Such a study quantifies the capabilities and limitations of a measurement instrument, often estimating its repeatability and reproducibility. It typically involves multiple appraisers measuring a series of items multiple times.
- *The Evaluating the Measurement Process, or EMP, method,* like the GR&R study, is a method of analyzing a test method. This type of study evaluates bias, stability, and precision, and is structured exactly like a GR&R study. The difference is in how the analysis is conducted. The EMP method focuses on graphical techniques resembling control charts to evaluate the measurement system. Details on this approach will not be given here but can be found in Wheeler (1989).
- *Percent agreement.* For a nominal or ordinal scale measurement system, percent agreement refers to the percentage of time in an attribute GR&R study that appraisers agree with (1) themselves (that is, repeatability), (2) other appraisers (that is, reproducibility), or (3) a known standard (that is, bias) when classifying or rating items using nominal or ordinal scales, respectively.

All the components of a measurement system that have been introduced are important. But there is one final piece to consider, *Audit MSA*. The history of the measurement data is important. Ensuring we know how and who input the data will ensure that the data is good. The purpose of Audit MSA is to create a series of questions to investigate where the data come from, who collected the data, and how the data came to be. Setting up an Audit MSA consists of six steps:

1. Find the initial data source. This is the "where."
2. Find the people inputting the data. This is the "who."
3. Create questions that describe "how" the data is generated or inputted.

4. Determine if those involved with the measurement system agree on the way data is entered. If not, this will affect the baseline.
5. Review any differences and findings with your team.
6. Ask the team if the data can be trusted.

Guidelines for Determining Whether a Measurement System Is Acceptable

Four criteria are used to assess the adequacy of a measurement system when conducting a GR&R study. These include:

1. *Total percent GR&R in the percent study variation.* In general, if the total percent GR&R in the study is less than 10%, the measurement system is considered acceptable. Between 10% and 30% inclusive, the measurement system is considered marginal and should be examined. Factors to be considered include the application, the cost of the measuring device, the cost of repair, and any other factors deemed relevant. If the percentage is greater than 30%, the measurement system is considered inadequate.
2. *Percent tolerance.* The percent tolerance is simply the precision-to-tolerance ration (PTR) expressed as a percentage. The criteria for percent tolerance are the same as for the GR&R. In general, if the percent tolerance is less than 10%, the measurement system is considered acceptable. Between 10% and 30% inclusive, the measurement system is considered marginal and should be examined. Factors to be considered include the application, the cost of the measuring device, the cost of the repair, and any other factors deemed relevant. Greater than 30%, the measurement system is considered inadequate.
3. *Percent contribution.* In general, if the percent contribution is less than 1%, the measurement system is considered acceptable. Between 1% and 9% inclusive, the measurement system is considered marginal and should be examined. Factors to be considered include the application, the cost of the measuring device, the cost of the repair, and any other factors deemed relevant. If the percent contribution is greater than 9%, the measurement system is considered inadequate.

   Note that percent contribution is redundant to the percent gage R&R since it is the square of the gage R&R proportion.
4. *Number of distinct categories (discrimination).* The minimum number of levels that is recommended is five. Any measurement system with fewer than five levels should be reviewed for improvement. The Automotive Industry Action Group (AIAG) established the above criteria. Therefore, unless your organization is part of this industry, you should consider the above criteria to be guidelines and dependent on the situation at hand.

Components of a Measurement System

Every measurement system consists of the following key components:

- Measurement instrument
- Appraiser(s) (commonly known as operators)
- Methods or procedures for conducting the measurement
- Environment

Each of the above components can introduce error into the measurement process.

TYPES OF MEASUREMENT SYSTEMS ANALYSIS

Measurement systems analysis can be categorized into two types:

1. Variables
2. Attributes

Three common methods fall into the variables category:

1. AIAG method
2. ANOVA method
3. Control chart method, sometimes called the EMP method

Each method will be addressed separately in the following subsections.

AIAG Method

The Automotive Industry Action Group (AIAG) developed its own GR&R study methodology. Example 16.1 illustrates this methodology step by step.

EXAMPLE 16.1

Figure 16.10 is an example of how to conduct a GR&R study. It uses the data collection sheet published by the AIAG in *Measurement System Analysis* (1995). These steps provide a widely accepted procedure for analyzing measurement systems:

1. Label ten parts with tags numbered 1–10 in such a way that the numbers on the tags aren't visible to the appraiser. Randomly place the parts on a work surface.
2. The first appraiser (we'll call her Susan) chooses a part, measures the designated dimension, announces the reading, and hands it to the recorder. The recorder looks at the number on the tag and records the reading announced by Susan in the appropriate column of row 1 (row labels are shown along the left margin).
3. Susan measures the remaining nine parts and announces the reading for each. The recorder enters the values in the columns of row 1 according to the tag number.
4. The ten parts are again randomly placed on the work surface with the tag numbers not visible. Frank, the second appraiser, measures each one. The recorder enters Frank's readings in row 6 of the form, which is the row for trial #1 for appraiser Frank.
5. Carlos, the third appraiser, repeats the procedure, and the recorder enters these values in row 11.
6. Now it's Susan's turn to measure the ten parts for trial #2. These readings are entered in row 2. Frank and Carlos follow with their second set of readings, which are recorded in rows 7 and 12, respectively. (The appraiser order can be randomized if desired rather than Susan, then Frank, and then Carlos as indicated here.)
7. Each appraiser completes the third trial of measurements, and these are recorded in rows 3, 8, and 13. This completes the data entry portion of the study. Figure 16.11 shows an example of the collected data.
8. Calculate the average and the range for each appraiser for each part tag number. The values go in rows 4 and 5, respectively, for Susan; 9 and 10, respectively, for Frank; and 14 and 15, respectively, for Carlos.
9. Calculate the values for row 16 by averaging the values in rows 4, 9, and 14.
10. Calculate the values for the "Average/range" column for rows 4, 5, 9, 10, 14, and 15 by averaging the ten values in their respective rows.
11. Calculate the value for the "Average/range" column of row 16 by averaging the ten values in that row.
12. Calculate the value for the "Average/range" column of row 17 by using the formula given in that row.

Continued

Gage Repeatability and Reproducibility Data Collection Sheet													
		Part											
Row	Appraiser/ Trial	1	2	3	4	5	6	7	8	9	10	Average/ Range	Appraiser/ Trial
1	A1												A1
2	A2												A2
3	A3												A3
4	**Average A**												$\overline{X}_A$
5	**Range A**												$\overline{R}_A$
6	B1												B1
7	B2												B2
8	B3												B3
9	**Average B**												$\overline{X}_B$
10	**Range B**												$\overline{R}_B$
11	C1												C1
12	C2												C2
13	C3												C3
14	**Average C**												$\overline{X}_C$
15	**Range C**												$\overline{R}_C$
16	**Part Average**												$\overline{\overline{X}}_{Part}$
17	Maximum part average – Minimum part average =												R_{Part}
18	$(\overline{R}_A + \overline{R}_B + \overline{R}_C)$ / Number of appraisers =												$\overline{\overline{R}}$
19	$\overline{X}_{DIFF} = Max(\overline{X}_A, \overline{X}_B, \overline{X}_C) - Min(\overline{X}_A, \overline{X}_B, \overline{X}_C) =$												$\overline{X}_{DIFF}$
20	$* \; UCL_R = D_4\overline{\overline{R}} = (2.574)\overline{\overline{R}} =$												
21	$* \; LCL_R = D_3\overline{\overline{R}} = (0)\overline{\overline{R}} = 0$												
22	$* \; D_3 = 0; D_4 = 2.574$ for 3 trials.												

Figure 16.10 Blank gage repeatability and reproducibility data collection sheet.

Source: Adapted from AIAG. Used with permission of AIAG.

13. Calculate the value for the "Average/range" column of row 18 by using the formula given in that row.
14. Calculate the value for the "Average/range" column of row 19 by using the formula given in that row.
15. Calculate the UCL_R by using the formula shown in line 20 along with the proper control chart constant values from row 22.

Continued

Gage Repeatability and Reproducibility Data Collection Sheet													
		Part											
Row	**Appraiser/ Trial**	**1**	**2**	**3**	**4**	**5**	**6**	**7**	**8**	**9**	**10**	**Average/ Range**	**Appraiser/ Trial**
1	A1	0.29	-0.56	1.34	0.47	-0.80	0.02	0.59	-0.31	2.26	-1.36	**0.19**	A1
2	A2	0.41	-0.68	1.17	0.50	-0.92	-0.11	0.75	-0.20	1.99	-1.25	**0.17**	A2
3	A3	0.64	-0.58	1.27	0.64	-0.84	-0.21	0.66	-0.17	2.01	-1.31	**0.21**	A3
4	**Average A**	**0.45**	**-0.61**	**1.26**	**0.54**	**-0.85**	**-0.10**	**0.67**	**-0.23**	**2.09**	**-1.31**	0.19	$\bar{X}_A$
5	**Range A**	**0.35**	**0.12**	**0.17**	**0.17**	**0.12**	**0.23**	**0.16**	**0.14**	**0.27**	**0.11**	0.18	$\bar{R}_A$
6	B1	0.08	-0.47	1.19	0.01	-0.56	-0.20	0.47	-0.63	1.80	-1.68	**0.00**	B1
7	B2	0.25	-1.22	0.94	1.03	-1.20	0.22	0.55	0.08	2.12	-1.62	**0.12**	B2
8	B3	0.07	-0.68	1.34	0.20	-1.28	0.06	0.83	-0.34	2.19	-1.50	**0.09**	B3
9	**Average B**	**0.13**	**-0.79**	**1.16**	**0.41**	**-1.01**	**0.03**	**0.62**	**-0.30**	**2.04**	**-1.60**	0.07	$\bar{X}_B$
10	**Range B**	**0.18**	**0.75**	**0.40**	**1.02**	**0.72**	**0.42**	**0.36**	**0.71**	**0.39**	**0.18**	0.51	$\bar{R}_B$
11	C1	0.04	-1.38	0.88	0.14	-1.46	-0.29	0.02	-0.46	1.77	-1.49	**-0.22**	C1
12	C2	-0.11	-1.13	1.09	0.20	-1.07	-0.67	0.01	-0.56	1.45	-1.77	**-0.26**	C2
13	C3	-0.15	-0.96	0.67	0.11	-1.45	-0.49	0.21	-0.49	1.87	-2.16	**-0.28**	C3
14	**Average C**	**-0.07**	**-1.16**	**0.88**	**0.15**	**-1.33**	**-0.48**	**0.08**	**-0.50**	**1.70**	**-1.81**	**-0.25**	$\bar{X}_C$
15	**Range C**	**0.19**	**0.42**	**0.42**	**0.09**	**0.39**	**0.38**	**0.20**	**0.10**	**0.42**	**0.67**	**0.33**	$\bar{R}_C$
16	**Part Average**	**0.17**	**-0.85**	**1.10**	**0.37**	**-1.06**	**-0.19**	**0.45**	**-0.34**	**1.94**	**-1.57**	**0.00**	$\bar{\bar{X}}_{Part}$
17	Maximum part average − Minimum part average =											**3.51**	R_{Part}
18	$(\bar{R}_A + \bar{R}_B + \bar{R}_C)$ / Number of appraisers $= (0.18 + 0.51 + 0.33)/3 =$											**0.3417**	$\bar{\bar{R}}$
19	$\bar{X}_{DIFF} = Max(\bar{X}_A, \bar{X}_B, \bar{X}_C) - Min(\bar{X}_A, \bar{X}_B, \bar{X}_C) = 0.19 - (-0.25) =$											**0.4447**	$\bar{X}_{DIFF}$
20	$* \; UCL_R = D_4\bar{\bar{R}} = (2.574)(0.3417) = 0.8795$												
21	$* \; LCL_R = D_3\bar{\bar{R}} = (0)(0.3417) = 0$												
22	$* \; D_3 = 0; D_4 = 2.574$ for 3 trials.												

Figure 16.11 GR&R data collection sheet with data entered and calculations completed for Example 16.1.

Source: Adapted from AIAG. Used with permission of AIAG.

16. Compare each of the ten *R*-values in row 5 to the UCL_R value calculated in row 20. Any *R*-value that exceeds the UCL_R should be circled. Repeat this for the *R*-values in rows 10 and 15. The circled *R*-values are significantly different from the others, and the cause of this difference should be identified and corrected. Once this has been done, the appropriate parts can be remeasured using the same appraiser, equipment, and so on, as for the original measurements. Recompute all appropriate values on the data collection sheet as necessary.

Continued

Continued

Recall that repeatability is the variation in measurements that occurs when the same measuring system—including equipment, material, and appraiser—is used. Repeatability, then, is reflected in the *R*-values as recorded in rows 5, 10, and 15, and summarized in row 17. Repeatability is often referred to as equipment variation, but the individual *R* averages may indicate differences between appraisers. In the example in Figure 16.11, R_A is smaller than R_B or R_C. This indicates that Susan has done a better job of getting the same answer upon repeated measurements of the same part than either Frank or Carlos. Perhaps Susan has a better technique, more skill, or sharper eyesight than the others. Investigation of this issue may provide an opportunity for variation reduction.

Reproducibility is the variation that occurs between the overall average measurements for the three appraisers. It is reflected by the $\overline{X}$-values in rows 4, 9, and 14 and summarized in the value of $\overline{X}_{Diff}$ in row 19. For example, had $\overline{X}_A$ and $\overline{X}_B$ been closer in value and $\overline{X}_C$ significantly different, then Carlos's measurements would exhibit a bias. Again, further investigation would be necessary.

The next step in the study is to complete the GR&R report shown in Figure 16.12. A completed report based on the data from Figure 16.11 is shown in Figure 16.13.

Each of the quantities in the "Measurement Unit Analysis" column will now be described:

- *Equipment variation* (EV) is an estimate of the standard deviation of the variation due to repeatability, and is sometimes denoted σ_E or σ_{rpt}.
- *Appraiser variation* (AV) is an estimate of the standard deviation of the variation due to reproducibility, and is sometimes denoted σ_A or σ_{rpd}.
- *Gage repeatability and reproducibility* (GR&R) is an estimate of the standard deviation of the variation due to the measurement system, and is sometimes denoted σ_M.
- *Part-to-part variation* (PV) is an estimate of the standard deviation of the variation due to part differences, and is sometimes denoted σ_P.
- *Total variation* (TV) is an estimate of the standard deviation of the total variation in the study, and is sometimes denoted σ_T.

The "Percent Total Variation" column in Figure 16.12 shows for each type of variation the percent of total variation it consumes. Sometimes, the right-hand column is based on the tolerance for the dimension. In this case, the value of *TV* is replaced by the tolerance.

ANOVA Method

The data depicted in Figure 16.11 can also be analyzed using the analysis of variance (ANOVA) methods, which are addressed in detail in Chapter 21.

With the ready availability of statistical analysis software, the ANOVA method represents a quick way to analyze data obtained from a GR&R study.

Gage Repeatability and Reproducibility Report					
Part No. and Name:		Gage Name:		Date:	
Characteristics:		Gage No.:		Performed by:	
Specifications:		Gage Type:			
From data sheet:	$\bar{\bar{R}}$ =		$\bar{X}_{DIFF}$		R_P

Measurement Unit Analysis			Percent Total Variation
Repeatability - Equipment Variation (EV) $EV = \bar{\bar{R}} \times K_1$ $= \_\_\_ \times \_\_\_$ $= \_\_\_\_$	Trials	K_1	$\%EV = 100(EV/TV)$ $= 100(\_\_\_/\_\_\_)$ $= \_\_\_\%$
	2	0.8862	
	3	0.5908	
Reproducibility - Appraiser Variation (AV) $AV = \sqrt{(\bar{X}_{DIFF} \times K_2)^2 - (EV^2/(nr))}$ $= \sqrt{(\_ \times \_)^2 - (\_^2/(\_ \times \_))}$ $= \_\_\_\_$	Appraisers	K_2	$\%AV = 100(AV/TV)$ $= 100(\_\_\_/\_\_\_)$ $= \_\_\_\%$ n = number of parts r = number of trials
	2	0.7071	
	3	0.5231	
Gage Repeatability & Reproducibility (GRR) $GRR = \sqrt{EV^2 + AV^2}$ $= \sqrt{\_\_\_^2 + \_\_\_^2}$ $= \_\_\_\_$	Parts	K_3	$\%GRR = 100(GRR/TV)$ $= 100(\_\_\_/\_\_\_)$ $= \_\_\_\%$
	2	0.7071	
	3	0.5231	
Part Variation (PV) $PV = R_{Part} \times K_3$ $= \_\_\_ \times \_\_\_$ $= \_\_\_\_$	4	0.4467	$\%PV = 100(PV/TV)$ $= 100(\_\_\_/\_\_\_)$ $= \_\_\_\%$
	5	0.4030	
	6	0.3742	
	7	0.3534	
Total Variation (TV) $TV = \sqrt{GRR^2 + PV^2}$ $= \sqrt{\_\_\_^2 + \_\_\_^2}$ $= \_\_\_\_$	8	0.3375	$ndc = 1.41(PV/GRR)$ $= 1.41(\_\_\_/\_\_\_)$ $= \_\_\_$ ndc = number of distinct categories
	9	0.3249	
	10	0.3146	

Figure 16.12 Blank gage repeatibility and reproducibility report.
Source: Adapted from AIAG. Used with permission of AIAG.

Gage Repeatability and Reproducibility Report		
Part No. and Name:	Gage Name:	Date:
Characteristics:	Gage No.:	Performed by:
Specifications:	Gage Type:	

From data sheet:	$\bar{\bar{R}} =$	0.3417	$\bar{X}_{DIFF}$	0.4447	R_{Part}	3.51

Measurement Unit Analysis			**Percent Total Variation**
Repeatability - Equipment Variation (EV) $EV = \bar{\bar{R}} \times K_1$ $= (0.3417)(0.5908)$ $= 0.2019$	Trials 2 3	K_1 0.8862 0.5908	$\%EV = 100(EV/TV)$ $= 100(0.2019/1.1458)$ $= 17.62\%$
Reproducibility - Appraiser Variation (AV) $AV = \sqrt{(\bar{X}_{DIFF} \times K_2)^2 - (EV^2/(nr))}$ $= \sqrt{((0.4447)(0.5231))^2 - ((0.2019)^2/(10)(3))}$ $= 0.2296$	Appraisers 2 3	K_2 0.7071 0.5231	$\%AV = 100(AV/TV)$ $= 100(0.2296/1.1458)$ $= 20.04\%$ n = number of parts r = number of trials
Gage Repeatability & Reproducibility (GRR) $GRR = \sqrt{EV^2 + AV^2}$ $= \sqrt{(0.2019)^2 + (0.2296)^2}$ $= 0.3058$	Parts 2 3	K_3 0.7071 0.5231	$\%GRR = 100(GRR/TV)$ $= 100(0.3058/1.1458)$ $= 26.69\%$
Part Variation (PV) $PV = R_{Part} \times K_3$ $= (3.51)(0.3146)$ $= 1.1042$	4 5 6 7	0.4467 0.4030 0.3742 0.3534	$\%PV = 100(PV/TV)$ $= 100(1.1042/1.1458)$ $= 96.37\%$
Total Variation (TV) $TV = \sqrt{GRR^2 + PV^2}$ $= \sqrt{(0.3058)^2 + (1.1042)^2}$ $= 1.1458$	8 9 10	0.3375 0.3249 0.3146	$ndc = 1.41(PV/GRR)$ $= 1.41(1.1042/0.3058)$ $= 5.09 \Rightarrow 5$ ndc = number of distinct categories

Figure 16.13 GR&R report with calculations for Example 16.1.

Source: Adapted from AIAG. Used with permission of AIAG.

EXAMPLE 16.2

Figure 16.10 is an example of how to conduct a GR&R study. It uses the data collection sheet published by the AIAG in *Measurement System Analysis* (1995). These steps provide a widely accepted procedure for analyzing measurement systems:

Gage R&R Study - ANOVA Method

Two-Way ANOVA Table With Interaction

Source	DF	SS	MS	F	P
Part	9	88.3619	9.81799	492.291	0.000
Operator	2	3.1673	1.58363	79.406	0.000
Part * Operator	**18**	**0.3590**	**0.01994**	**0.434**	**0.974**
Repeatability	60	2.7589	0.04598		
Total	89	94.6471			

First source table

Interaction term

α to remove interaction term = 0.25

Two-Way ANOVA Table Without Interaction

Source	DF	SS	MS	F	P
Part	9	88.3619	9.81799	245.614	0.000
Operator	2	3.1673	1.58363	39.617	0.000
Repeatability	78	3.1179	0.03997		
Total	89	94.6471			

Second source table

Gage R&R

Source	VarComp	**%Contribution** (of VarComp)
Total Gage R&R	0.09143	**7.76**
Repeatability	0.03997	3.39
Reproducibility	0.05146	4.37
Operator	0.05146	4.37
Part-To-Part	1.08645	**92.24**
Total Variation	1.17788	100.00

Third source table

Process tolerance = 8

Source	**StdDev (SD)**	Study Var (5.15 × SD)	**%Study Var** (%SV)	**%Tolerance** (SV/Toler)
Total Gage R&R	0.30237	1.55721	**27.86**	**19.47**
Repeatability	0.19993	1.02966	18.42	12.87
Reproducibility	0.22684	1.16821	20.90	14.60
Operator	0.22684	1.16821	20.90	14.60
Part-To-Part	1.04233	5.36799	**96.04**	**67.10**
Total Variation	1.08530	5.58929	100.00	69.87

Fourth source table

Number of Distinct Categories = 4 ← Discrimination

Figure 16.14 Gage R&R Study–ANOVA method: source tables for Example 16.2.

Continued

Continued

The third source table provides the variances for each component. Notice that the GR&R variation (that is, %Contribution) is relatively small with respect to the part-to-part variance. Most of the variation is due to the difference between parts. This is what we look (and hope) for in a measurement systems analysis.

The last source table in Figure 16.14 depicts how much each component contributes to the total variation. The "SD" column provides the standard deviation for each component. Compare this column with the "Measurement Unit Analysis" column in Figure 16.13. The numbers are similar though not exact.

The "%Study Var" column shows the percentage contribution of each component. The Total Gage R&R is 27.86%. While it is in the high marginal range, there may be some opportunity for improvement. Compare these numbers with the "Percent Total Variation" column in Figure 16.13. Again, the numbers are similar but not exact.

Although three of the criteria for this study are either acceptable or marginal, the number of distinct categories is four. Thus, the measurement system is unacceptable due to inadequate discrimination.

Figure 16.15 depicts what is called the "components of variation." Furthermore, it combines, in one graph, the three percentage criteria discussed previously. This graph confirms the discussion above.

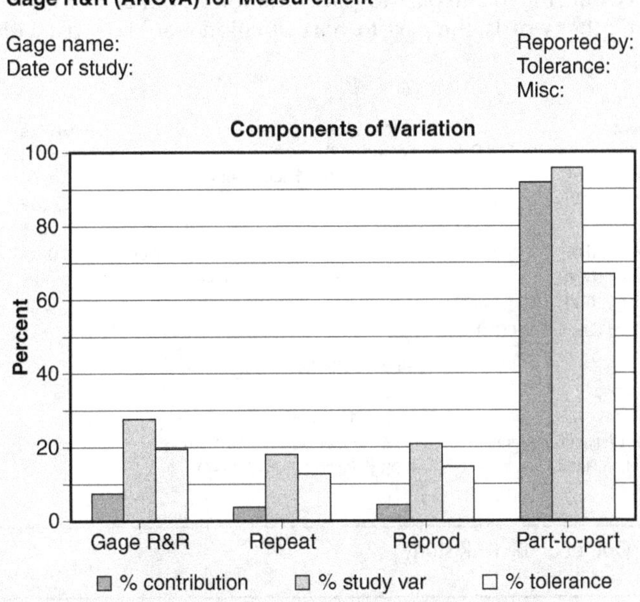

Figure 16.15 Gage R&R study–ANOVA method: components of variation for Example 16.2.

Control Chart Method

Another method for analyzing GR&R data is with control charts, which is sometimes called the Evaluating the Measurement Process (EMP) method. For a more detailed discussion on the use of the control chart method, see Pyzdek and Keller (2010).

EXAMPLE 16.3

Figure 16.16 provides the source tables for this method. Notice the similarities and differences between these two tables and the last two tables in Figure 16.14, as well as the "Percent Total Variation" column from Figure 16.13. The answers are, indeed, similar though not exact.

Note that, in contrast to Example 16.2, this method determines the number of distinct categories to be equal to four. However, for this particular data set, the ANOVA method would be more appropriate since it addressed the part–operator interaction.

Figure 16.17 is particularly interesting. Let's disregard the one out-of-control point on the range chart for Frank for the moment. Notice that each $\overline{X}$ chart is out of control. This is actually desirable since the R chart is based on repeatability error. If the $\overline{X}$ chart is in control, this would mean that part-to-part variation would be less than the repeatability variation. In other words, the part-to-part variation would be lost within the repeatability variation.

Measurement Source		Std Dev	Variation (5.15*StdDev)		Variance Component	% Total Var Comp
Repeatability	(EV)	0.2	1.03	Equipment Variation	0.04	3.39
Reproducibility	(AV)	0.227	1.17	Appraiser Variation	0.0515	4.37
Operator		0.227	1.17		0.0515	4.37
Gauge R&R	(RR)	0.302	1.56	Measurement Variation	0.0914	7.76
Part Variation	(PV)	1.04	5.37	Part Variation	1.09	92.2
Total Variation	(TV)	1.09	5.59	Total Variation	1.18	100

Summary and Gauge R&R Statistics

Source	Value	Definition
Sigma Multiplier	5.15	
% Gauge R&R	27.9	100*(RR/TV)
Number of Distinct Categories	4	Floor(Sqrt(2)*(PV/RR))
Discrimination Ratio	4.98	Sqrt(2*(PV/RR)^2+1)

Figure 16.16 Output of the R&R study.

Continued

Continued

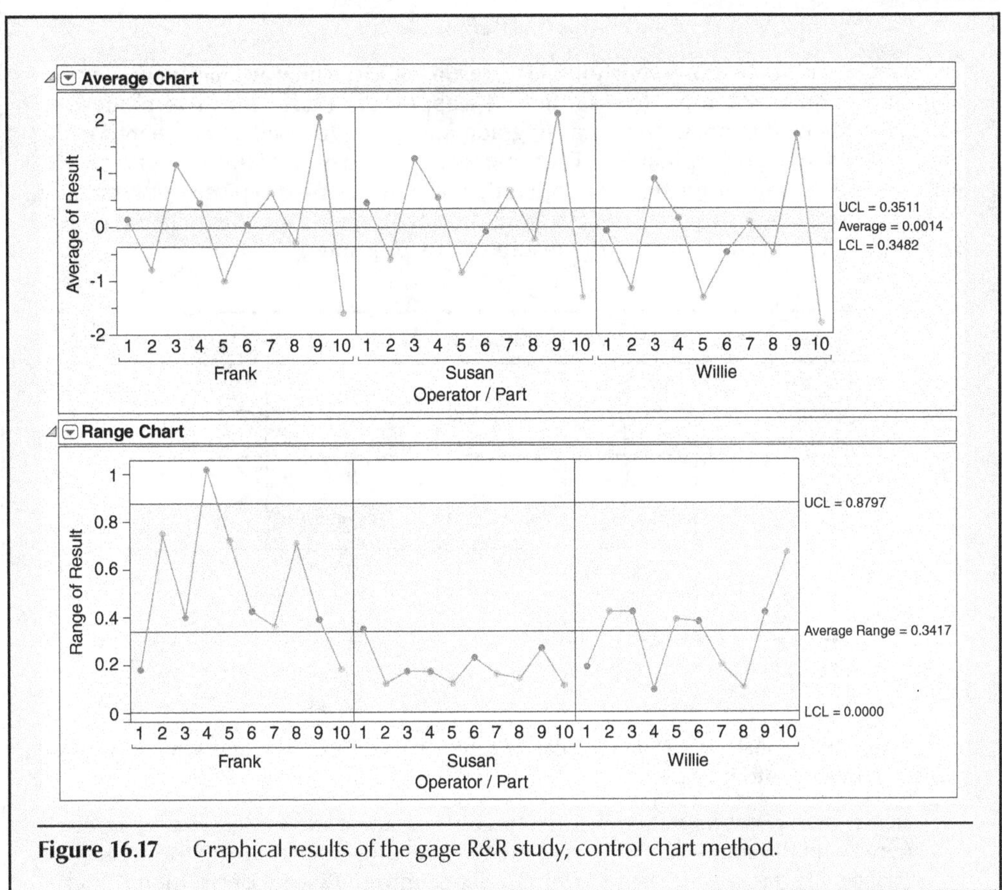

Figure 16.17 Graphical results of the gage R&R study, control chart method.

ATTRIBUTE AGREEMENT ANALYSIS

Now we will discuss two measurement analysis methods for attributes. The first is the *attribute agreement analysis.* This is an important type of analysis used to assess the level of agreement among appraisers grading on an ordinal scale. It is divided into four parts:

1. Each appraiser versus standard
2. Between appraisers
3. All appraisers versus standard
4. Within appraiser—how consistent is each appraiser within themselves?

The second method is the *attribute gage study—analytic method.* It is used to assess bias and repeatability in the measurement system.

Let's consider the following example.

EXAMPLE 16.4

The data in Table 16.1 show a portion of the results of three new appraisers grading the written portion of a 12th-grade essay test. The appraisers graded on a five-point scale: –2, –1, 0, 1, 2. In addition, each appraiser grade for a given test will be compared with a known standard grade for that test. Each appraiser graded each of the six tests. $\alpha = 0.05$ will be used. Note that for this type of study more tests would typically be graded in order to have a larger set of data for the comparisons. A smaller number of tests are used here just so that an illustration of the results can be presented.

Test Number	Standard	Simpson	Montgomery	Duncan
1	2	2	2	1
2	–1	–1	–1	–2
3	0	1	0	0
4	–2	–2	–2	–2
5	0	0	0	–1
6	1	1	1	1

Table 16.1 Attribute agreement analysis—data for Example 16.4.

Figure 16.18 illustrates some typical output for this type of analysis. The output is typically divided into four parts:

1. *Each appraiser versus standard.* The Effectiveness table shows the percent agreements with the standard. You can see that Montgomery agreed with the standard on all six assessments, followed by Simpson with five out of six, then Duncan with three out of six. Duncan is the only appraiser that did not do well against the known standard. These results are confirmed with the kappa statistics in the Agreement Comparisons report. Notice Duncan's overall kappa was only 0.379. Figure 16.19 depicts in graphical form these same results using confidence intervals. It is obvious that Duncan requires additional training on how to grade essay tests.
2. *Between appraisers.* The Agreement Across Categories report contains the *kappa statistic* that is a measure of agreement. The closer kappa is to 1, the stronger the agreement. The kappa statistic assumes the level of disagreement among scores is the same (that is, the difference between a score of –2 and –1 is the same as the difference between a score of –2 and 2). Therefore, the overall kappa statistic reflects a value that indicates an unacceptable measurement system (that is, 0.433). See Kubiak (2012) for details regarding when to use kappa statistics.
3. *All appraisers versus standard.* The Effectiveness table shows the overall effectiveness as 77.8%, which is 14 out of the 18 assessments. Overall, this number does not look too bad, but that is not too surprising since two of the three appraisers did a good job of matching the standard.
4. *Within appraiser.* This table is not shown because each appraiser assessed each test only once.

Continued

Continued

Agreement Comparisons

Rater	Compared with Standard	Kappa	Standard Error
Duncan	Standard	0.379	0.219
Montgomery	Standard	1	0
Simpson	Standard	0.793	0.186

Agreement within Raters

Agreement across Categories

Category	Kappa	Standard Error
-2	0.679	0.236
-1	0.2	0.236
0	0.357	0.236
1	0.446	0.236
2	0.438	0.236
Overall	0.433	0.122

Effectiveness Report

Agreement Counts

Rater	Correct(-2)	Correct(-1)	Correct(0)	Correct(1)	Correct(2)	Total Correct	Incorrect(-2)	Incorrect(-1)	Incorrect(0)	Incorrect(1)	Incorrect(2)	Grand Total
Duncan	1	0	1	1	0	3	0	1	1	0	1	6
Montgomery	1	1	2	1	1	6	0	0	0	0	0	6
Simpson	1	1	1	1	1	5	0	0	1	0	0	6

Effectiveness

Rater	Effectiveness	95% Lower CI	95% Upper CI	Error rate
Duncan	50	18.8	81.2	0.5
Montgomery	100	61	100	0
Simpson	83.3	43.6	97	0.167
Overall	77.8	54.8	91	0.222

Misclassifications

Standard Level	-2	-1	0	1	2
-2	.	1	0	0	0
-1	0	.	1	0	0
0	0	0	.	0	0
1	0	0	1	.	1
2	0	0	0	0	.
Other	0	0	0	0	0

Figure 16.18 Output for Example 16.4.

Continued

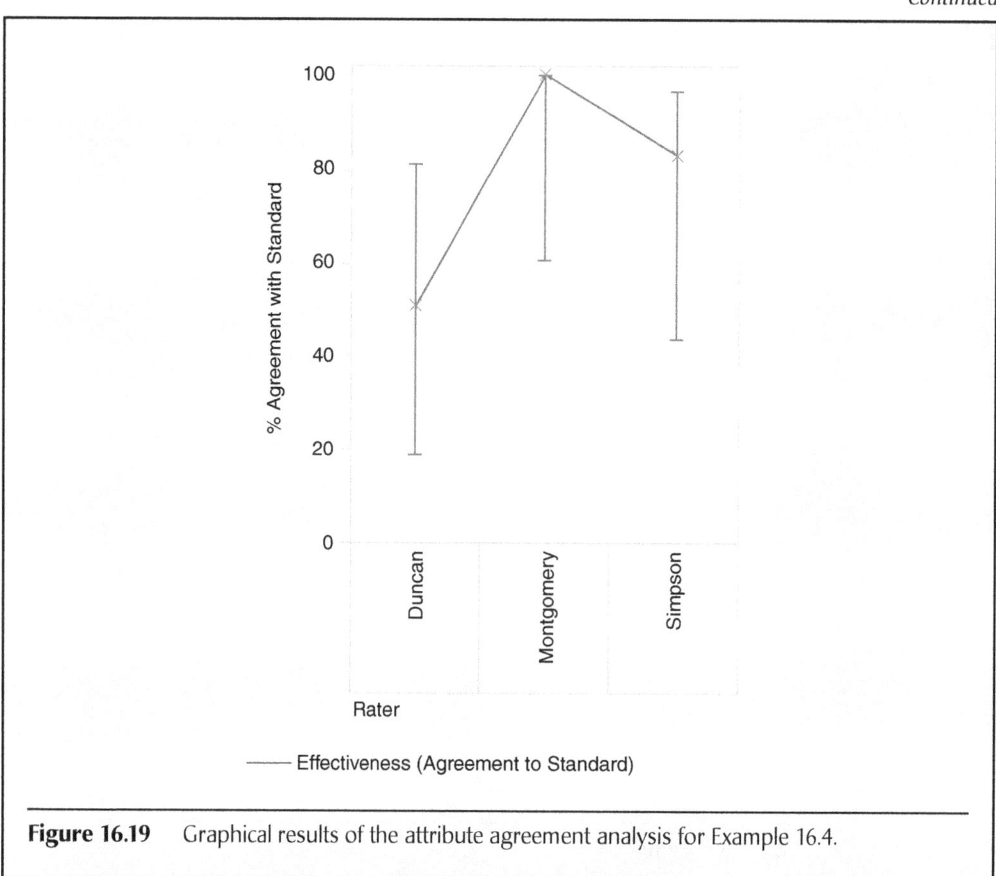

Figure 16.19 Graphical results of the attribute agreement analysis for Example 16.4.

Attribute Gage Study—Analytic Method

An attribute gage study is used to determine the amount of bias and repeatability of a measurement system when the response is an attribute variable (that is, accept or reject). In such studies, reference values are known for each part and are selected at equal intervals across the entire range of the gage.

Depending on the particular attribute gage study method chosen (for example, regression method or AIAG method), additional requirements may be placed on the characteristics of the parts, the number of parts per trial, and the number of parts used in the study. Therefore, for additional information when constructing an attribute gage study, the reader is referred to the tutorial or help files of the specific software used. Also, the reader will find the second edition of the AIAG *Measurement Systems Analysis Reference Manual* useful in understanding the underlying theory.

It should now be clear that whenever a process improvement project is undertaken, the measurement system should be one of the first things analyzed, for the following reasons:

- All data from processes are, in effect, filtered through measurement systems.
- Reducing measurement system variation often represents a cost-effective way to reduce the total observed variation.
- Time, cost, and energy spent on improving a process without ensuring an adequate underlying measurement system could very well be counterproductive.

MEASUREMENT SYSTEMS ACROSS THE ORGANIZATION

> Identify how measurement systems can be applied across all functional areas of the organization (e.g., marketing, sales, engineering, research and development (R&D), supply chain management, operations, and customer experience). (Understand)
>
> Body of Knowledge V.C.2

Measurement systems are widely found throughout most functions of an enterprise. Let's consider the following examples:

- *Human resources.* Though they are not often thought of as measurement systems in the context of Six Sigma, performance appraisal/evaluation systems are widely used throughout most organizations. More often than not, these systems are fraught with bias and lack repeatability. Managers, or *appraisers* as we call them, frequently must use ill-defined criteria to assess an employee's performance, usually on an annual basis. Such measurement systems can have a profound and deep impact on an individual and their career. In some instances, a single (annual) data point is used to determine whether to terminate an employee. In some organizational structures, employees may have multiple managers/appraisers who provide input that might be highly polarized. This discussion of a performance appraisal/evaluation system quickly raises questions regarding assessor agreement, such as manager repeatability, each manager to standard, and all managers to standard. These terms should be familiar, as they form the basis for the attribute agreement analysis discussed previously.
- *Marketing and sales/research and development/customer experience.* These functional organizations traditionally have used employee surveys to gauge levels of customer satisfaction, dissatisfaction, and loyalty, as well as customer needs, wants, and other behaviors. Survey results are often fed to research and development functions to support and justify changes to product features and capabilities. Therefore, it is desirable that such surveys are highly valid and reliable and well

defined. More than once, unreliable surveys have wreaked havoc on organizations. Consider the American automobile industry in the early 1970s. These companies continued to build large, gas-guzzling automobiles, missing the changing trend in consumer taste toward smaller, more fuel-efficient vehicles.

- *Operations.* This function is often responsible for conducting various GR&R studies similar to those discussed previously. In addition, departments within this function usually are accountable for equipment calibration.
- *Supply chain management.* Probably the most common measurement system found in a supply chain management function is that for evaluating supplier performance and/or issuing supplier report cards. Supplier performance may be assessed inaccurately for a variety of reasons, such as the inability to determine a defect, misclassification of defects, inaccurate data entry, or even poor definitions of what constitutes a defect or late delivery. Some organizations include subjective components of measurement for determining levels of service or the ease of doing business with the supplier. Measuring supplier performance is critical in many organizations, as such performance provides the foundation for determining rework and repair cost allocations and reimbursements and occasionally percentage of profit sharing.

These are just a few examples of where measurement systems are routinely found in organizations. Their widespread use makes it imperative that they be sound and adequate to support their intended purpose. Without adequate measurement systems, organizational decision making may result in completely erroneous decisions that send an organization down a treacherous path. Alternatively, the basis for decision making deteriorates and decision makers must rely on gut feeling or guesswork. Either way, the outcomes are undesirable.

METROLOGY

> Define and describe elements of metrology, including calibration systems, traceability to reference standards, and the control and integrity of measurement devices and standards. (Understand)
>
> Body of Knowledge V.C.3

The purpose of a gage traceability document is to show the relationship between a given measurement system and the standards maintained by the United States government at the National Institute of Standards and Technology (NIST). The traceability document quantifies the uncertainty involved in the various measurement transfers, from NIST calibration down to a measurement made on a part.

Measurement error is a source of variation. As such, it should be analyzed whenever a reduction in process variation is sought. It often happens that what was perceived as excess process variation was excess variation in the measurement system. When reducing the total observed process variation, improving the measurement system is often the most cost-effective strategy.

The causes of measurement error can be placed in the usual cause-and-effect categories with some typical examples of each:

- Machine (equipment)
  - *Lack of accuracy*
  - *Lack of precision*
  - *Gage instability over time*
- Methods (procedures)
  - *Wrong tool specified*
  - *Improper procedure specified*
  - *Failure to use specified tool or procedure*
- Manpower (appraiser)
  - *Lack of training*
  - *Lack of physical ability*
  - *Lack of motivation*
- Mother Nature (environment)
  - *Temperature, humidity, atmospheric pressure*
  - *Lighting, noise conditions*
  - *Vibration*
  - *Electronic emission*
- Materials (parts)
  - *Instability over time*
  - *Lack of homogeneity*
  - *Obsolescence*
- Measurement
  - *Measurement device not calibrated*
  - *Measurement device not "tared out," meaning it is not adjusted for the weight of the container*
  - *Parallax effect, meaning that the viewing angle of the measurement device reading affects the reported result.*

These causes are summarized in the fishbone diagram shown in Figure 16.20.

Whenever measuring equipment is used, a calibration system should be in place to help ensure that the measurement system does its job. The main thrust of a calibration system consists of a schedule that requires each piece of measuring equipment to be calibrated on a regular basis.

The time intervals between calibrations are based on the type of equipment and its uses. Calibration systems usually start with a relatively short interval for new equipment, with provisions for changing interval lengths depending on experience.

If, for instance, an instrument has been in for several successive calibrations with no adjustment needed, the calibration interval may be extended. On the other hand, instruments that frequently require adjustment may need shorter intervals.

Some organizations set calibration quality goals of, for example, 95%, meaning that 95% of the instruments scheduled for calibration need no adjustment.

Each instrument must have a label that plainly displays its due date. Some organizations install a procedure to notify users of pending calibration.

In addition, a record system is required to document calibration activity. A system must also be in place for maintaining the calibration standards and equipment. This system should include a schedule for verifying that the standards are usable by checking them against recognized master standards.

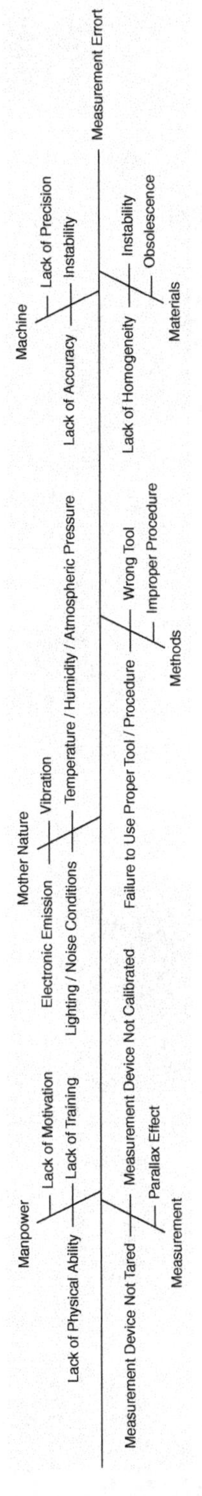

Figure 16.20 Fishbone diagram of some possible causes of measurement error.

Chapter 17

Basic Statistics

This chapter will address basic statistical concepts, including distinguishing between a population and a sample, measures of central tendency and dispersion, the central limit theorem and its practical application, various descriptive statistics, the difference between descriptive and inferential statistics, numerous graphical methods and how to interpret them, and, of course, how to draw valid conclusions.

BASIC STATISTICAL TERMS

> Define and distinguish between population parameters and sample statistics, e.g., proportion, mean, standard deviation. (Apply)
>
> **Body of Knowledge V.D.1**

In a statistical study, the word "population" refers to the entire set of items under discussion. For example, the population might be the set of parts shipped to customer B last Friday. When discussing "population," it must be placed into proper context. What does this mean? Friday's "population" would actually be a sample if we defined the population as the set of parts shipped in a week that included Friday. Similarly, the week would be a sample if we defined the population as the set of parts shipped in the month that included the week we just labeled as a population. And so on.

When it is not feasible to measure a characteristic on each item in a population, a statistical study will randomly select a sample from the population, measure each item in the sample, and analyze the resulting data. The analysis of the sample data produces *statistics*. Examples of sample statistics include sample mean, sample median, and the sample standard deviation. These sample statistics are then used to estimate the corresponding population *parameters*.

Traditionally, Latin letters are used to denote sample statistics and Greek letters are used to denote population parameters. However, there are many exceptions to this rule. While Greek letters always denote parameters, Latin letters can denote parameters as well. Table 17.1 shows commonly used symbols for the parameters and statistics used in this handbook.

	Population (Parameters)	Sample (Statistics)
Sample size	N	n
Mean	μ	$\bar{X}$ or $\bar{x}$
Standard deviation	σ	S or s or $\hat{\sigma}$
Median	None	$\tilde{X}$ or $\tilde{x}$
Mode	None	None
Proportion	p	$\hat{p}$

Table 17.1 Commonly used symbols for parameters and statistics.

The Greek letter μ is pronounced "mew." The Greek letter σ is a lowercase sigma. Note in Table 17.1 that some parameters and statistics have yet to be assigned symbols.

CENTRAL LIMIT THEOREM

> Explain the central limit theorem and its significance in the application of inferential statistics for confidence intervals, hypothesis tests, and control charts. (Understand)
>
> **Body of Knowledge V.D.2**

One of the most important and useful theorems in all of statistics is the Central Limit Theorem. It is invoked when we perform hypothesis testing, linear regression, analysis of variance, design of experiments, and control charting. Simply stated, the Central Limit Theorem (CLT) is:

> If the random variable X has a mean μ and variance σ^2, and we take n independent samples from the distribution, then the sum of the x's will approximately follow a normal distribution with mean equal to $n\mu$ and variance equal to $n\sigma^2$.

A few comments are in order. First, the reason why the CLT is so useful is that the underlying distribution of X can be *any* distribution that has a defined mean and variance. As long as we take enough independent samples and add them up, the distribution of the sum will become approximately normal with a known mean and variance.

Second, the distribution of the sum of the Xs is approximately normal, and this approximation will improve as n increases. If the underlying distribution of X is fairly symmetric, the approximation looks better faster as n increases. For very skewed distributions, it takes more samples in the sum to look normal. In general, using a sample of 30 for the calculations should make even the averages of the most skewed distributions look normal. Recognize that this is just a guideline, and there is nothing particularly magic about the number 30. Some distributions may need a larger sample size for the distribution of averages to look normal, others may need a smaller sample size. The more asymmetric the data distribution is, the larger the sample size will need to be for the sampling distribution of $\bar{X}$ to be approximately normal.

Many texts present the CLT in terms of the sample average. If we take n independent samples and then calculate their average, the sampling distribution of $\bar{X}$ will be approximately normal with mean μ and variance equal to $\frac{\sigma^2}{n}$.

For example, let X be the outcome of a single roll of a die. The random variable X thus follows a discrete uniform distribution, as shown in the shaded area in Figure 17.1. The mean of this distribution is equal to 3.5 and the variance is equal to 2.917.

If we roll the die four times and take the average, the resulting sampling distribution of $\bar{X}$ will approximately follow a normal distribution with mean 3.5, and variance equal to 2.917 ÷ 4 = 0.7293 and standard error equal to 0.8535. Note that the distribution of the averages shown is less variable than the distribution of the individual data values. The distribution of the averages will become less and less variable (have a smaller standard error) as we increase the sample size used to calculate the average. See Figure 17.1.

A more general presentation of the Central Limit Theorem states that *any* linear combination of independent samples from the distribution of X will approach a normal distribution. For example, we can take random, independent samples of $n = 3$ and calculate a new variable $y = x_1 + 2x_2 + 3x_3$. The resulting random variable Y will follow an approximate normal distribution with mean = 6μ and variance = $14\sigma^2$. The expectation and variance of a linear combination are presented in detail in Chapter 18. For now, we show without proof that the expectation of a linear combination of random variable can be calculated using:

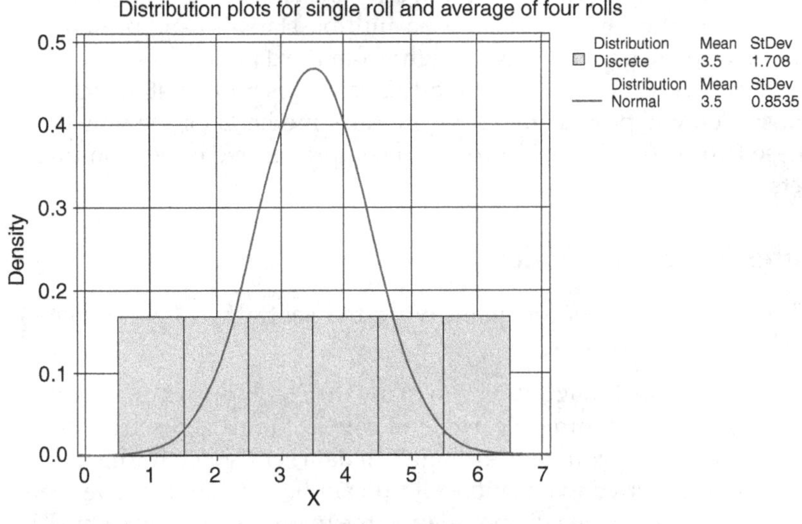

Figure 17.1 Probability distributions for the roll of one die and the average of four rolls.

$$E(Y) = \mu \sum_{i=1}^{n} a_i$$
$$E(Y) = E(x_1 + 2x_2 + 3x_3)$$
$$E(Y) = \mu + 2\mu + 3\mu = 6\mu$$

And, due to independence, the variance can be calculated by:

$$Var(Y) = \sigma^2 \sum_{i=1}^{n} a_i^2$$
$$Var(Y) = Var(x_1 + 2x_2 + 3x_3)$$
$$Var(Y) = \sigma^2 + 4\sigma^2 + 9\sigma^2 = 14\sigma^2$$

DESCRIPTIVE STATISTICS

> Calculate and interpret measures of dispersion and central tendency. (Evaluate)
>
> **Body of Knowledge V.D.3**

As presented, raw data provides little insight into underlying patterns, and limits our ability to draw meaningful conclusions. This is where descriptive statistics becomes useful.

Descriptive statistics is the collection of tools and techniques for displaying and summarizing data. There are many ways in which to display and summarize data. Therefore, it is important that one selects the best way to facilitate an understanding of the data. In some cases, multiple statistics and presentations or views are required to gain the most insight from the data.

This subsection will provide the basic descriptive statistics, while the next subsection will provide multiple graphical methods for viewing data. Combined, these two sections should provide a comprehensive understanding of most data sets.

Measures of Central Tendency

Three common ways for quantifying the centrality of a population or sample include the following:

1. *Mean.* Although there are many different types of statistical means, the most commonly used in Lean Six Sigma is the arithmetic mean or arithmetic average of a data set. Typically, the mean will be reported to one more significant figure than the data. The calculation for the population mean is given in Equation 17.1.

Equation 17.1 Population mean

$$\mu = \frac{\sum_{i=1}^{N} x_i}{N}$$

where N is the number of items in the population.

The sample mean is calculated using Equation 17.2.

Equation 17.2 Sample mean

$$\overline{X} = \frac{\sum_{i=1}^{n} x_i}{n}$$

where n is the sample size.

2. *Median*. The *median* is the middle value of an ordered data set. If the data are composed of an odd number of data points, the median is the middle value of the ordered data set. If the data are composed of an even number of data points, the median is the average of the two middle values of the ordered data set.

3. *Mode*. The *mode* is the most frequently found value in a data set. Note: There may be more than one mode present, or the mode of a data set may not exist if all values have the same frequency.

EXAMPLE 17.1

Consider the data given in Table 17.2 that represent a sample of diameters taken from a drilling operation. For convenience, this table has been sorted, but the data was collected in a random fashion. Compute all three measures of central tendency.

From Table 17.2, we see that the total of the diameters is 2.468. Using Equation 17.2, we have:

$$\text{Sample Mean} = \overline{X} = \frac{\sum_{i=1}^{n} x_i}{n} = \frac{2.468}{20} = 0.1234$$

From Table 17.2 we see there are an even number of data points in the ordered set of 20. Thus, the median is the average of points 10 and 11:

$$\text{Median} = 0.123$$

From Table 17.2, we see that the most frequently found value in the data set is 0.123. Thus, the mode = 0.123.

Continued

Continued

Number	Diameter	Number	Diameter
1	0.121	11	0.123
2	0.121	12	0.124
3	0.121	13	0.124
4	0.122	14	0.124
5	0.122	15	0.125
6	0.122	16	0.125
7	0.123	17	0.125
8	0.123	18	0.125
9	0.123	19	0.126
10	0.123	20	0.126
		TOTAL	**2.468**

Table 17.2 Data for Examples 17.1, 17.2, 17.3, 17.4, and 17.7.

Measures of Dispersion

Although there are many ways to determine the dispersion of data, the most common ways used in Lean Six Sigma include the following:

- *Standard deviation.* The standard deviation is best described in its computational forms:

  – *Population standard deviation.*

  We can calculate the population standard deviation using Equation 17.3:

Equation 17.3 Population standard deviation

$$\sigma = \sqrt{\frac{\sum_{i=1}^{N}(x_i - \mu)^2}{N}}$$

where N is the population size and μ is the population mean. Note that this measure is not calculated often since the entire population is seldom available.

– *Sample standard deviation.*

We can estimate the population standard deviation using Equation 17.4:

Equation 17.4 Sample standard deviation

$$s = \sqrt{\frac{\sum_{i=1}^{n} (x_i - \overline{X})^2}{n-1}}$$

where n is the sample size and $\overline{X}$ is the sample mean.

We can also use the following form of the formula when performing hand calculations, shown in Equation 17.5:

Equation 17.5 Sample standard deviation, calculation formula

$$s = \sqrt{\frac{\sum_{i=1}^{n} x_i^2 - n\overline{X}^2}{(n-1)}}$$

The standard deviation is typically recorded to two more significant digits than the raw data.

- *Range*. The *range* is simply the maximum value minus the minimum value.

$$R = x_{Max} - x_{Min}$$

Note that the range typically increases as the sample size increases, unlike the standard deviation. For this reason, the standard deviation is the preferred measure of dispersion for large samples.

EXAMPLE 17.2

Consider the data given in Table 17.2 that represent a sample of diameters taken from a drilling operation. Compute the standard deviation and range of the data.

Since the data are a sample, the standard deviation is given by either Equation 17.4 or Equation 17.5:

$$s = \sqrt{\frac{\sum_{i=1}^{n} (x_i - \overline{X})^2}{n-1}} = \sqrt{\frac{\sum_{i=1}^{27} (x_i - 0.1234)^2}{(20-1)}} = 0.00160$$

Continued

Continued

or,

$$s=\sqrt{\frac{\sum_{i=1}^{n} x_i^2 - n\bar{X}^2}{(n-1)}}=\sqrt{\frac{0.3046-(20)0.1234^2}{(20-1)}}=0.00160$$

Note: Readers may obtain slightly different answers depending on the manner in which calculations are performed, how the numbers are rounded, the number of significant digits used, and/or software used. To achieve the best results, keep all digits in the intermediate calculations, and then round at the end when reporting results.

The range of the data is the maximum value minus the minimum value. From Table 17.2, we see the maximum and minimum values are:

$$R = x_{Max} - x_{Min} = 0.126 - 0.121 = 0.005.$$

Other Useful Descriptive Statistics

Other useful descriptive statistics include the following:

- *Maximum*. As evident by the name, this is the maximum value in the sample.
- *Minimum*. As evident by the name, this is the minimum value in the sample.
- *First quartile* (Q_1). This is the point at which 25% of the data are less than or equal to this value. The first quartile does not have to be a value in the data set.
- *Second quartile* (Q_2). This is the point at which 50% of the data are less than or equal to this value. It is also known as the *median*. The second quartile or median does not have to be a value in the data set.
- *Third quartile* (Q_3). This is the point at which 75% of the data are less than or equal to this value. The third quartile does not have to be a value in the data set.
- *Fourth quartile*. This value is the maximum value in the data set, so no computations are necessary.
- *Interquartile range (IQR)*. The *interquartile range* is the third quartile minus the first quartile, meaning that the middle 50% of the data is within this range. It is considered a measure of dispersion.

- *Skewness.* This parameter measures the degree to which a set of data is not symmetrical. A skewness value may be negative, zero, or positive. When data are plotted as a histogram, a negative skewness value is depicted with the long tail of the distribution pointing toward the left, a positive skewness value is depicted with the long tail pointing toward the right, and a skewness value equal to zero indicates a symmetrical distribution. The computation formula for skewness is complex and better left to a spreadsheet or statistical software program. Figure 17.2 provides a pictorial representation of skewness.
- *Kurtosis.* This parameter measures the degree to which a distribution can produce outliers. Many references inaccurately refer to kurtosis as depicting how peaked or flat a distribution is. In reality, kurtosis gives scant information about the peak of a distribution.

  The kurtosis of the normal distribution is equal to 3. Often, the normal distribution is used as a baseline for measuring kurtosis, and most software calculates the *excess kurtosis,* which uses the kurtosis of the normal distribution as the standard. Hence, the excess kurtosis of the normal distribution is equal to 0. As such, excess kurtosis has the advantage of being easier to interpret.

  Values for excess kurtosis are in the range of $[-2,\infty)$. A negative excess kurtosis value indicates that the distribution has a lower proportion of data in the tails than that of the normal distribution. This type of distribution is described as *platykurtic.* The Bernoulli distribution with p = 0.50 achieves the minimum kurtosis possible, with excess kurtosis equal to –2.

  A distribution with a positive excess kurtosis value has heavier tails than the normal distribution, meaning it has a higher probability of outliers. This type of distribution is referred to *leptokurtic.* Note that there is no upper bound on excess kurtosis.

  The computation formula for kurtosis is complex and better left to a spreadsheet or statistical software program.

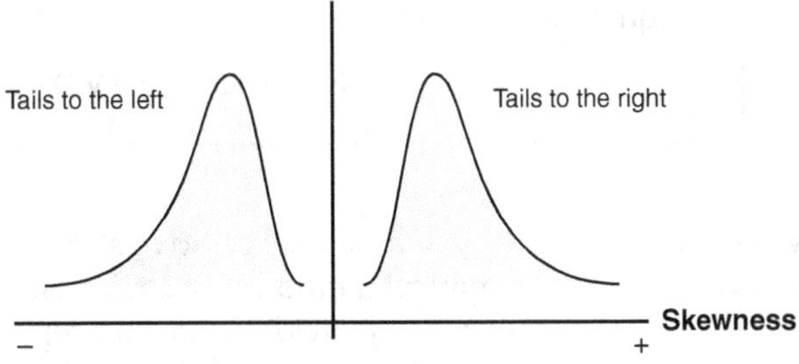

Figure 17.2 Pictorial representation of skewness.

EXAMPLE 17.3

Using the data given in Table 17.2, we can generate a histogram and compute the kurtosis and skewness of the data using Excel or a statistical software package.

A histogram of the data is shown in Figure 17.3. Notice the tail in the histogram in this figure is skewed slightly to the right and the distribution seems to have a large proportion of the data in the "tails." This is consistent with the calculated values of (excess) kurtosis = –1.029 and skewness = 0.031.

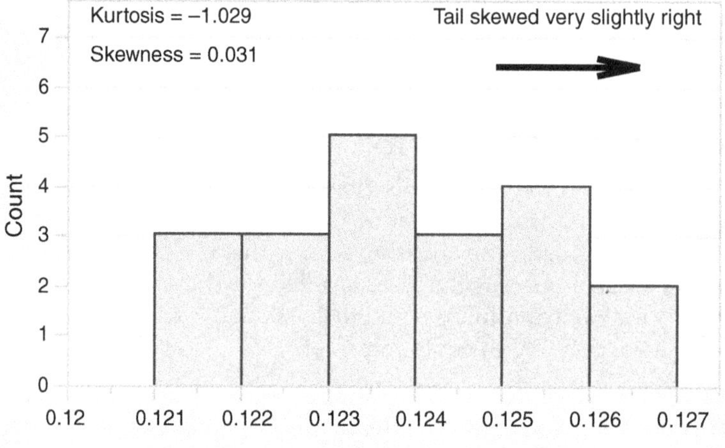

Figure 17.3 Histogram of data for Example 17.3.

GRAPHICAL METHODS

> Construct and interpret diagrams and charts, e.g., box-and-whisker plots, scatter diagrams, histograms, normal probability plots, frequency distributions, cumulative frequency distributions. (Evaluate)
>
> **Body of Knowledge V.D.4**

In the previous subsection, we discussed descriptive statistics. In this subsection, we will discuss a variety of graphical methods for depicting data. Graphical methods are quite appealing because they provide an instant representation of the data while giving the viewer an almost complete understanding with little room for misinterpretation.

Frequency Distribution

A *frequency distribution* is a tabular display of data in mutually exclusive and collectively exhaustive classes or intervals that summarizes the number of occurrences in each class. Additionally, classes must be continuous and of equal width. A frequency distribution table may also show the absolute and cumulative absolute frequency and the relative and cumulative relative frequency. The relative and cumulative relative frequencies can be converted into percentages by multiplying by 100. Generally, a frequency distribution table contains between 5 and 20 classes, although this is considered a guideline.

To fully understand the frequency distribution table, some additional terminology is required:

- *Class* or *class interval*. This is the range in which data in a frequency distribution table are placed or binned. Frequency distributions have a predetermined number of classes. A class is also known as a *cell*.
- *Class limits*. A class has an upper and lower class limit. The *upper class limit* is the largest data value that can go into a given class. Similarly, the *lower class limit* is the smallest data value that can go into a given class. Class limits have the same number of decimals as the data values.
- *Class mark*. This is the average value of the class limits. This concept becomes more useful when discussing the concept of measures of central tendency with respect to grouped data.
- *Class boundaries*. The class boundaries allow us to create mutually exclusive and adjacent classes without gaps between classes. They often have one decimal place more than the original raw data and typically end in "5." For example, if the data are whole numbers, then:

$$\text{Lower class boundary} = \text{Lower class limit} - 0.5$$

$$\text{Upper class boundary} = \text{Upper class limit} + 0.5$$

Notice that the interval formed by the class boundaries is larger than the class interval. For the example, the lowest class boundary is the minimum data point – 0.5 and the highest class boundary is the maximum data point + 0.5. The total range of all the class boundaries is greater than the total range of the raw data.

To calculate the class boundaries, we can employ the following approach:

1. Set your lower class boundary for your first class.
2. Determine your highest class boundary.
3. Calculate the range of the class boundaries.
4. Specify the number of classes or cells desired. This will be discussed in detail in the subsection on histograms.
5. Compute the class width using the formula

$$W = \frac{\text{Range of class boundaries}}{\text{Number of cells}}$$

6. Round *W* as appropriate; rounding up works best. You may also want to choose a number that is more convenient for creation of the histogram.
7. Compute your upper class boundary for your first class by adding *W* to your lower class boundary from step 1.
8. Set your lower class boundary for your second class equal to your upper class boundary for your first class.
9. Compute your upper class boundary for your second class by adding W to your lower class boundary.
10. Continue this process until you reach the upper class boundary that includes your largest data value.

EXAMPLE 17.4

Using the data given in Table 17.2, construct a frequency distribution table using four class intervals.

1. The smallest data value in our sample is 0.121. We will set the lowest class boundary equal to (0.121 – 0.0005) = 0.1205.
2. The maximum data value in the sample is 0.126. Our highest class boundary is equal to (0.126 + 0.0005) = 0.1265.
3. The range of the class boundaries is 0.1265 – 0.1205 = 0.006.
4. The problem statement sets the number of class intervals to four.
5. Compute the class width:

$$W = \frac{0.006}{4} = 0.0015$$

6. We do not need to round *W* for this example. So, $W = 0.0015$.
7. The first upper class boundary is the lower class boundary plus the class width:

$$0.1205 + 0.0015 = 0.122.$$

8. The lower class boundary for the second class is 0.122.
9. The upper class boundary for the second class is 0.122 + 0.0015 = 0.1235.

The remainder of the class boundaries are shown in Table 17.3 along with the completed frequency distribution table.

In general, we are not likely to develop a frequency distribution table with just four classes. Table 17.3 was completed to illustrate the process for developing the frequency distribution table.

Continued

Continued

Cell width	Lower class boundary	Upper class boundary	Tally	Data	Class interval	Class mark	Absolute frequency	Cumulative absolute frequency	Relative frequency	Cumulative relative frequency
0.0015	0.1205	0.1220								0.121, 0.121, 0.121, 0.122, 0.122, 0.122	0.1205 – 0.1220	0.1213	6	6	0.3	0.3
0.0015	0.1220	0.1235							0.123, 0.123, 0.123, 0.123, 0.123	0.1220 – 0.1235	0.1228	5	11	0.25	0.55
0.0015	0.1235	0.1250									0.124, 0.124, 0.124, 0.125, 0.125, 0.125, 0.125	0.1235 – 0.1250	0.1243	7	18	0.35	0.9
0.0015	0.1250	0.1265				0.126, 0.126	0.1250 – 0.1265	0.1258	2	20	0.1	1

Table 17.3 Example of a frequency distribution using the data given in Table 17.2.

Histogram

A *histogram* is a pictorial representation of data, the concepts of which are rooted in the frequency distribution. It is one of the seven basic tools of quality. Figure 17.3 provided an example of a histogram for the data given in Table 17.2. The figure was generated using software that uses its own set of rules and methods for determining the number of classes.

The advantage of using a histogram lies with its immediate visual feedback. With a brief review of Figure 17.3 we can quickly learn that the underlying distribution of the data is skewed right and tends to have heavy tails. The central tendency of the distribution is at or about 0.123. There is a single mode at 0.123. The data are quite compact and there are no outliers. Thus, the range can be readily determined.

A key disadvantage of the histogram is that it groups data into classes. Consequently, the values of the raw data are lost.

Typically, software is readily available to construct histograms. However, it is most likely that each software product constructs a histogram differently or provides the user with a plethora of options for calculating the number of class intervals. The goal of a histogram is to give us an idea of the shape of the distribution of the data. If we use too few categories, the resulting graph will be lumpy and not give enough detail. And if we use too many categories, the histogram will be disjointed. Consider the following methods for choosing the number of class intervals:

- *2 to the k rule.* Select the first integer value of k such that $2^k > n$ where n is the number of observations. Consider the data given in Table 17.2. There were 20 data values. Thus, $2^4 < 20$ and $2^5 > 20$, making $k = 5$.
- Sturges's formula.
  a. $k = 1 + 3.3\log_{10}(n)$ where k is rounded to the nearest whole number and n is the number of observations. From Table 17.2, $k = 5.29$, rounded to the nearest whole number 6.

  b. $k = \log_2(n) + 1$. This formula assumes an approximately normal distribution of the data and tends to perform poorly for $n < 30$. k is rounded to the nearest whole number. From Table 17.2, $k = 5.32$, rounded to 6.
- *Square root rule.* $k = \sqrt{n}$. From Table 17.2, $k = 4.47$, rounded to the nearest whole number 5.
- *Rice's rule.* $k = 2n^{1/3}$. From Table 17.2, $k = 5.43$. k is rounded to the nearest whole number, 6.

In addition to the above formulas, there are rules of thumb such as those given by Pyzdek (2003):

- Sample size of 100 or less 7–10 classes
- Sample size of 101–200 11–15 classes

- Sample size of 201 or more   13–20 classes

Other authors have suggested the following rules of thumb:

- Sample size of 50 or less   5–7 classes
- Sample size of 50–100   8–10 classes
- Sample size of 101–250   10–15 classes
- Sample size of 251 or more   15–20 classes

If one were to continue to research the number of classes relative to the sample size, numerous formulas and rules of thumb would continue to surface. In general, there appears to be little to no agreement in this area. Recall that Figure 17.3 had six classes in the figure.

Our recommendation is to become familiar with your preferred software and its method of producing histograms. If options are available for changing the number of classes, try them out. Use the number of classes that reveals the distribution the best.

Unlike the frequency distribution table, the histogram need not have equal class widths. However, most authors recommend equal class widths and most quality software provides only this option. Unequal class widths may be a consideration depending on the data density, skewness of the data, and presence of outliers.

Box-and-Whisker Plot

The *box-and-whisker plot* (also called a *box plot*), developed by Professor John Tukey of Princeton University, displays graphically the "five number summary" of the data. The five numbers that are displayed are

1. Minimum value
2. First quartile
3. Second quartile (as known as the median)
4. Third quartile
5. Maximum value

Since the quartiles are displayed, the interquartile range is automatically displayed. Commonly, the original box-and-whisker plot is modified to identify outliers. Depending on the software being used, other descriptive statistics may be available for display as well. An example of a box plot is depicted in Figure 17.4, which was constructed using the data from Table 17.2. However, an additional data point was added to depict the outlier at 0.117.

With a brief visual review of Figure 17.4 we quickly determine many of the descriptive statistics calculated previously. In addition, we notice that the data are compact, but skewed, and that an outlier is present.

Box-and-whisker plots are quite appealing and provide a lot of information about a data set in just a single diagram. They are also extremely useful as a means of comparing different samples or groups of data.

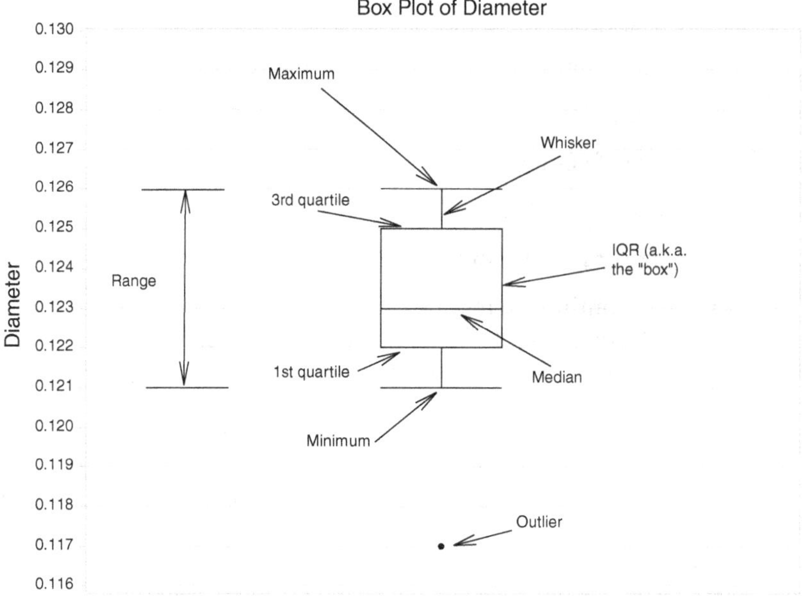

Figure 17.4 Basic components of a box-and-whisker plot (box plot).

EXAMPLE 17.5

A stainless-steel casting has a tight tolerance on the machined inside diameter (ID), which has been causing problems. The quality team has heard a number of proposed fixes. Some people believe the problem is caused by a slightly out-of-round condition on a cross-section of the casting. Others feel there is a taper, and still others insist the problem is too much part-to-part variation. The question is, which type of variation is giving the most trouble?

The team decides to measure the ID at three angles (12 o'clock, 2 o'clock, and 4 o'clock) at three locations along the bore (top, middle, and bottom) on five pieces. The data are shown in Table 17.4. Box plots created from these data are shown in Figure 17.5.

As we examine Figure 17.5, we notice that the within-part variation is quite small. However, the part-to-part variation is quite noticeable. For visual convenience, measurements within a part and from part-to-part have been connected with a mean connection line. This line helps enhance the interpretation of the two different types of variation.

Figure 17.5 confirms the problem to be part-to-part variation and the team can now take the appropriate corrective action.

Continued

Continued

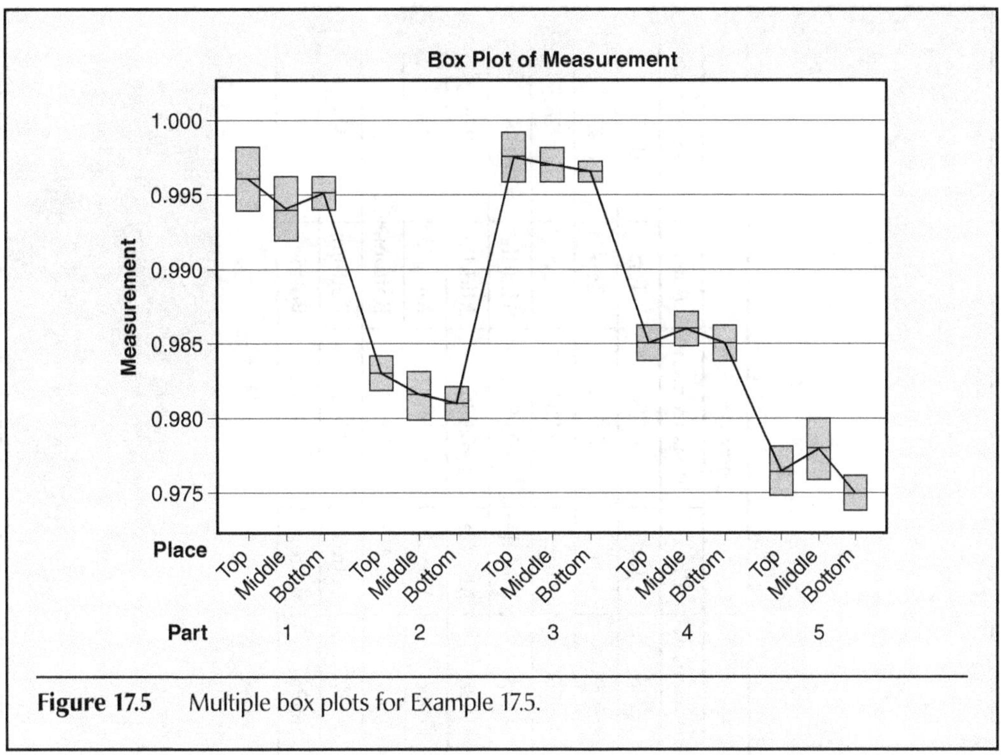

Figure 17.5 Multiple box plots for Example 17.5.

Continued

Scatter Plots

A *scatter plot* is a plot of two variables, one on the y-axis and the other on the x-axis. The resulting graph allows visual examination for patterns to determine whether the variables show any relationship or if there is just random "scatter." This pattern, or lack thereof, aids in choosing the appropriate type of model for estimation. It is important to note that evidence of a pattern does not imply that a causal relationship exists between the variables. The scatter diagram is one of the seven basic tools of quality.

As mentioned above, we look for evidence of patterns. Such patterns may be linear or nonlinear. If the plotted points appear to be generally linear in nature, then we can measure the strength of the linear relationship by using the sample correlation coefficient, denoted by the letter r. A positive correlation means that the line moves from the bottom left to the upper right. A negative correlation means that the line moves from the top left to the bottom right. If all the points fall exactly on a straight line that tips up on the right end, then $r = 1$. If all the points fall on a straight line that tips down on the right end, then $r = -1$. The value of r is always between -1 and $+1$, inclusive. This may be stated as $-1 \leq r \leq 1$. Therefore, the first step in analyzing a set of data for correlation is to construct a scatter diagram. If the points on this diagram tend to form a straight line, it makes sense to calculate the value of r.

Continued

Part #1		Part #2		Part #3		Part #4		Part #5	
Place	**Measurement**	**Place**	**Measurement**	**Place**	**Measurement**	**Place**	**Measurement**	**Place**	**Measurement**
Top	0.998	Top	0.984	Top	0.998	Top	0.986	Top	0.975
Top	0.994	Top	0.982	Top	0.999	Top	0.985	Top	0.975
Top	0.996	Top	0.984	Top	0.996	Top	0.984	Top	0.978
Middle	0.992	Middle	0.982	Middle	0.998	Middle	0.987	Middle	0.980
Middle	0.996	Middle	0.980	Middle	0.998	Middle	0.986	Middle	0.976
Middle	0.994	Middle	0.983	Middle	0.996	Middle	0.985	Middle	0.980
Bottom	0.996	Bottom	0.981	Bottom	0.997	Bottom	0.986	Bottom	0.976
Bottom	0.994	Bottom	0.982	Bottom	0.997	Bottom	0.986	Bottom	0.974
Bottom	0.995	Bottom	0.980	Bottom	0.996	Bottom	0.984	Bottom	0.974

Table 17.4 Data for Example 17.5.

The fact that a correlation exists does not imply that a cause-and-effect relationship exists. To conclude that there is a cause-and-effect relationship, we look to logic, scientific theory, or a designed experiment to explicitly look for the cause-and-effect relationships. When we obtain a high correlation coefficient, it means that we can predict one variable using the other. When we obtain a low correlation coefficient, the predictive ability of the variables is low, and we can generally, but not always, conclude that a cause-and-effect relationship does not exist. These concepts are covered more fully in Chapter 20.

Keep in mind that the correlation coefficient is a statistic. As such, we are able to place a confidence interval around this statistic and make a probabilistic statement regarding its significance. Confidence intervals for the correlation coefficient are presented in Chapter 20.

Normal Probability Plot

Many statistical hypothesis tests assume that the data follow a normal distribution. The central limit theorem is pivotal in turning non-normal data into approximately normal averages or sums, but only if we have enough data

EXAMPLE 17.6

Suppose an injection molding machine is producing parts with pitted surfaces. The following potential causes have been suggested:

- Mold pressure
- Coolant temperature
- Mold cooldown time
- Mold squeeze time

Values of each of these variables as well as the quality of the surface finish were collected on ten batches. These data are shown in Table 17.5.

Four graphs have been plotted in Figure 17.6. In each graph, "Surface finish" is along the y-axis and one variable (that is, mold pressure, coolant temperature, mold cooldown time, or mold squeeze time) is along the x-axis. Each data point on a graph represents one batch.

Let's briefly examine each of the graphs:

- *Scatter plot of surface finish versus mold pressure*. Notice the overall dispersion of the dot points. They are well dispersed and do not appear to present any noticeable pattern. The regression line for the variables is the solid black line in the middle of the graph. Notice that it is almost flat. This indicates that the y-value variation is almost completely unrelated to any change in the x-value. Consequently, there is little to no correlation present.
- *Scatter plot of surface finish versus coolant temperature*. The dot points are more tightly clustered together and clearly present a noticeable linear pattern. The addition of the regression line confirms a visually strong correlation coefficient.

Continued

Continued

Batch number	Mold pressure, PSI	Coolant temperature, °F	Cooldown time, minutes	Squeeze time, minutes	Surface finish, microinches
1	220	102.5	14.5	0.72	37
2	200	100.8	16.0	0.91	30
3	410	102.6	15.0	0.90	40
4	350	101.5	16.2	0.68	32
5	490	100.8	16.8	0.85	27
6	360	101.4	14.8	0.76	35
7	370	102.5	14.3	0.94	43
8	330	99.8	16.5	0.71	23
9	280	100.8	15.0	0.65	32
10	400	101.2	16.6	0.96	30

Table 17.5 Data for Example 17.6.

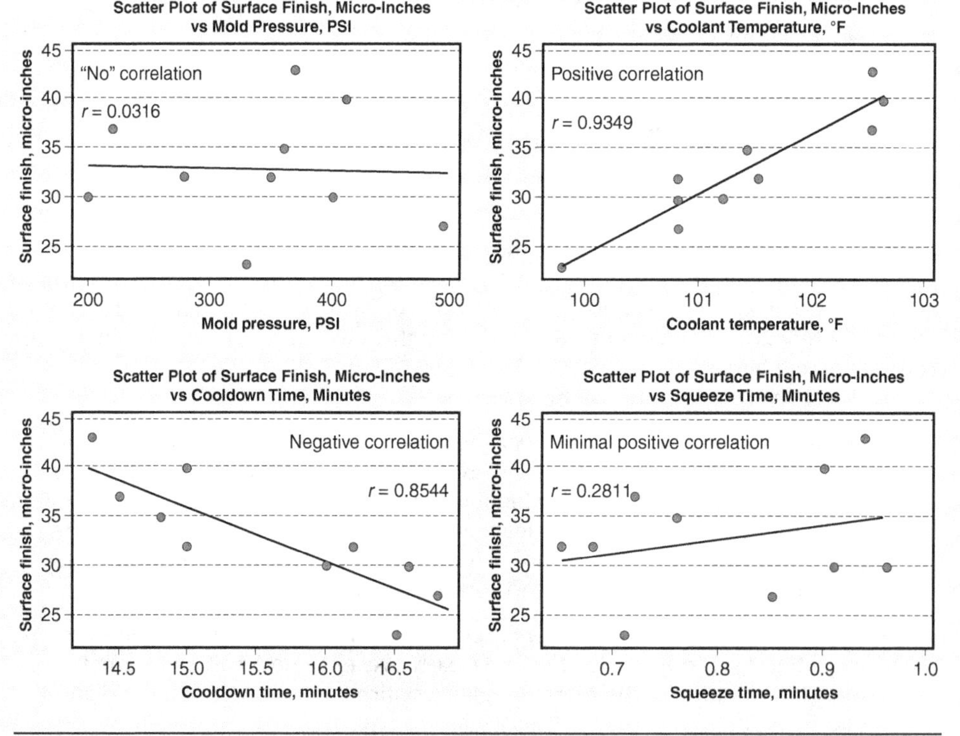

Figure 17.6 Scatter diagrams for Example 17.6.

Continued

- *Scatter plot of surface finish versus cooldown time.* The dot points in this graph are somewhat polarized in the lower and upper ends of the cooldown times, appearing to contribute to the correlation, which in this case is negative in nature.
- *Scatter plot of surface finish versus squeeze time.* Like the mold pressure, there is a lot of dispersion in the dot points, but a minor appearance of a linear pattern is present. The dot points are polarized and loosely clustered at the ends. An experienced eye might be able to determine the correlation to be minimally positive, but the aid of the regression line is certainly helpful.

points in the linear combination. How can we tell whether our data are normally distributed? We can create a normal probability plot of the data to see how well it fits a normal distribution. An example normal probability plot is shown in Figure 17.7.

The y-axis of this particular plot represents quantiles or percentiles of the normal distribution. For this reason, the graph is sometimes called a Normal Quantile Plot. The scale is created so that a perfect normal distribution would fall on

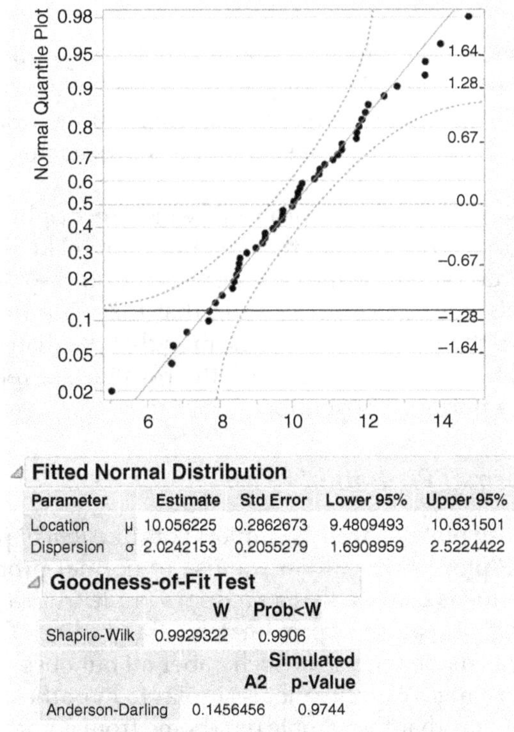

Fitted Normal Distribution

Parameter		Estimate	Std Error	Lower 95%	Upper 95%
Location	μ	10.056225	0.2862673	9.4809493	10.631501
Dispersion	σ	2.0242153	0.2055279	1.6908959	2.5224422

Goodness-of-Fit Test

	W	Prob<W
Shapiro-Wilk	0.9929322	0.9906

	A2	Simulated p-Value
Anderson-Darling	0.1456456	0.9744

Figure 17.7 Example of a normal probability plot.

the diagonal line drawn on the graph. The extent to which our actual data points follow this line tells us how well the normal distribution fits the data. Many texts tell analysts to apply a "fat pencil test": If we can cover up the data points by laying a fat pencil on the diagonal line, our data is most likely normal. Obviously, this method is rather subjective. Instead, we have a statistical test and p-value that we can rely on to determine non-normality. The probability plot in Figure 17.7 provides two different Goodness of Fit tests for the normal distribution. Both the Shapiro-Wilk and the Anderson-Darling statistics are displayed along with the p-values for the hypotheses:

H_0: Data follow a normal distribution

H_1: Data do not follow a normal distribution.

In hypothesis testing, we decide whether to reject the null hypothesis based on the *p-value*. The p-value and its use are discussed in detail in Chapter 21. For now, we will state that a p-value greater than 0.05 will indicate that there is no significant evidence against the null hypothesis. For the Shapiro-Wilk and Anderson-Darling tests specifically, a p-value greater than 0.05 means that we will fail to reject the assumption that the data are normally distributed. In Figure 17.7, the p-value is 0.9906 for the Shapiro-Wilk statistic and 0.9744 for the Anderson-Darling statistic, indicating that the normal assumption is not disputed by the data. This is much cleaner than the fat pencil test, and easier to justify in a meeting.

Figure 17.8 shows a normal probability plot for a symmetric but heavy-tailed, or leptokurtic, distribution. We see that there are data points farther out in the tails of the distribution than would be expected from a normal distribution. The p-value of the Anderson-Darling test, $p = 0.03$, shows us that we do not have a normal distribution.

Figure 17.9 shows the normal probability plot for a right-skewed, or positively skewed, distribution. We see that the data does not include any negative values, since the points do not start until the zero point on the x-axis. The cumulative probability builds very quickly, meaning that there are many data points near zero. The buildup then slows down, indicating that the distribution tails off as we move to the right. Once again, based on the p-value, we reject H_0 and claim the data is not from a normal distribution.

Constructing a Normal Probability Plot

Normal probability plots, as well as similar plots like *Rankit* plots, *QQ* plots, *Quantile* plots, and *PP* plots, originally made use of normal probability graph paper. This special paper was used so that a random sample from a normally distributed population would plot as an approximately straight line. Today, advanced computer software has made the use of such paper all but obsolete.

Using the normal probability plot is similar to hypothesis testing. In this case, the null hypothesis is that the sample data come from a normal population, while the alternate hypothesis is that the data come from a non-normal population.

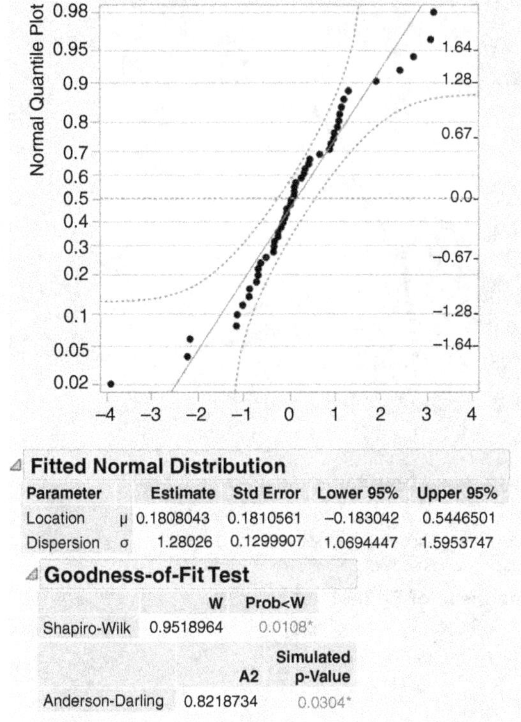

Fitted Normal Distribution

Parameter		Estimate	Std Error	Lower 95%	Upper 95%
Location	μ	0.1808043	0.1810561	−0.183042	0.5446501
Dispersion	σ	1.28026	0.1299907	1.0694447	1.5953747

Goodness-of-Fit Test

	W	Prob<W
Shapiro-Wilk	0.9518964	0.0108*

	A2	Simulated p-Value
Anderson-Darling	0.8218734	0.0304*

Figure 17.8 Normal probability plot, heavy-tailed distribution.

The process for constructing a normal probability plot is straightforward but can be tedious. There are several procedures that can be used to create a normal probability plot, such as the median rank method, the mean rank method, and the normal score method. We will present the normal score method here since it does not require any inverse normal score calculations or special grid paper.

The normal score method is as follows:

1. Collect and sort the data.
2. Based on the sample size n, record the normal scores found in Appendix H associated with each sorted observation in the data set.
3. Generate the normal plot with the observations on the x-axis and the normal scores on the y-axis.
4. Analyze the plot and draw a conclusion.

The above approach is best illustrated by example.

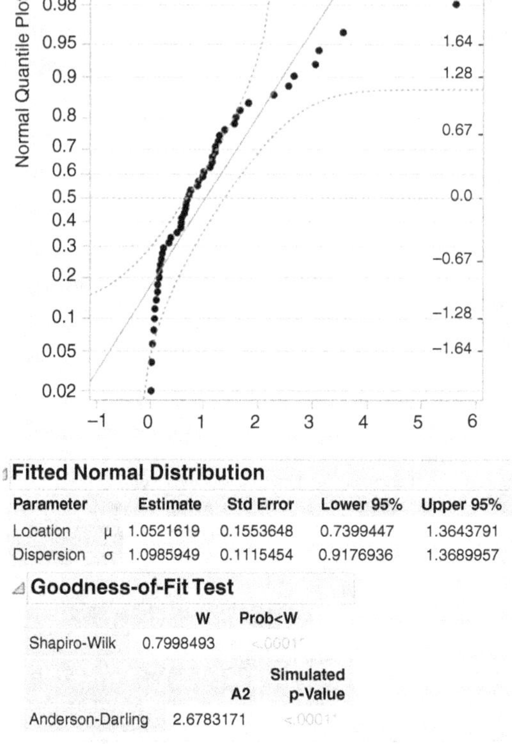

Fitted Normal Distribution

Parameter		Estimate	Std Error	Lower 95%	Upper 95%
Location	μ	1.0521619	0.1553648	0.7399447	1.3643791
Dispersion	σ	1.0985949	0.1115454	0.9176936	1.3689957

Goodness-of-Fit Test

	W	Prob<W
Shapiro-Wilk	0.7998493	<.0001*

	A2	Simulated p-Value
Anderson-Darling	2.6783171	<.0001*

Figure 17.9 Normal probability plot, right-skewed distribution.

EXAMPLE 17.7

Construct and interpret a normal plot using the data given in Table 17.2. Using the process described above, we sort the data and find the corresponding normal scores for n = 20 in Appendix H to create Table 17.6.

Continued

Continued

X	Normal scores for n = 20 from Appendix H
0.121	−1.824
0.121	−1.388
0.121	−1.118
0.122	−0.912
0.122	−0.739
0.122	−0.586
0.123	−0.445
0.123	−0.313
0.123	−0.186
0.123	−0.062

Table 17.6 Sorted data and normal scores for Example 17.7.

X	Normal scores for n = 20 from Appendix H
0.123	0.062
0.124	0.186
0.124	0.313
0.124	0.445
0.125	0.586
0.125	0.739
0.125	0.912
0.125	1.118
0.126	1.388
0.126	1.824

Table 17.6 *Continued*

We now can construct a plot as shown in Figure 17.10. Technically, this is a *normal plot,* since the *y*-axis shows normal scores, and not probabilities. However, the shape of the graph and interpretation is the same as with a normal probability plot, as shown in Figure 17.11. We see that in each, the points follow a straight line, indicating that the normal assumption is not disputed by the data.

The concept of the normal probability plots can be extended to testing hypotheses regarding populations other than the normal distribution. These situations usually involve data transformations and will not be discussed here. However, some statistical software packages will accommodate these situations.

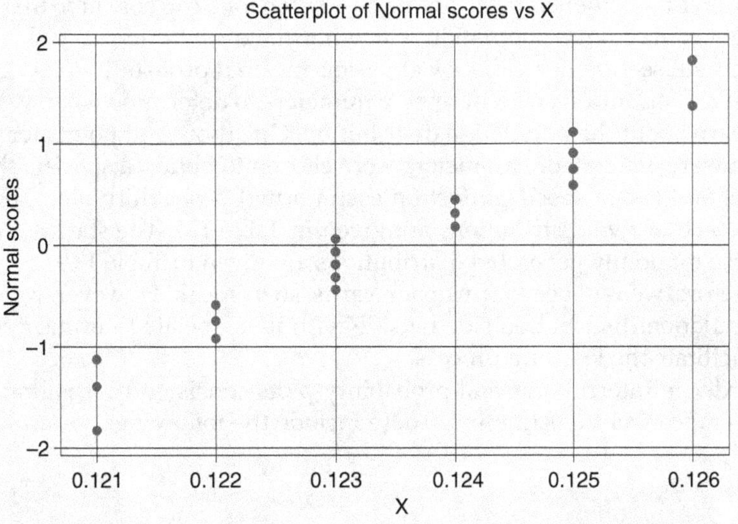

Figure 17.10 Normal plot for data in Example 17.7, normal score method.

Continued

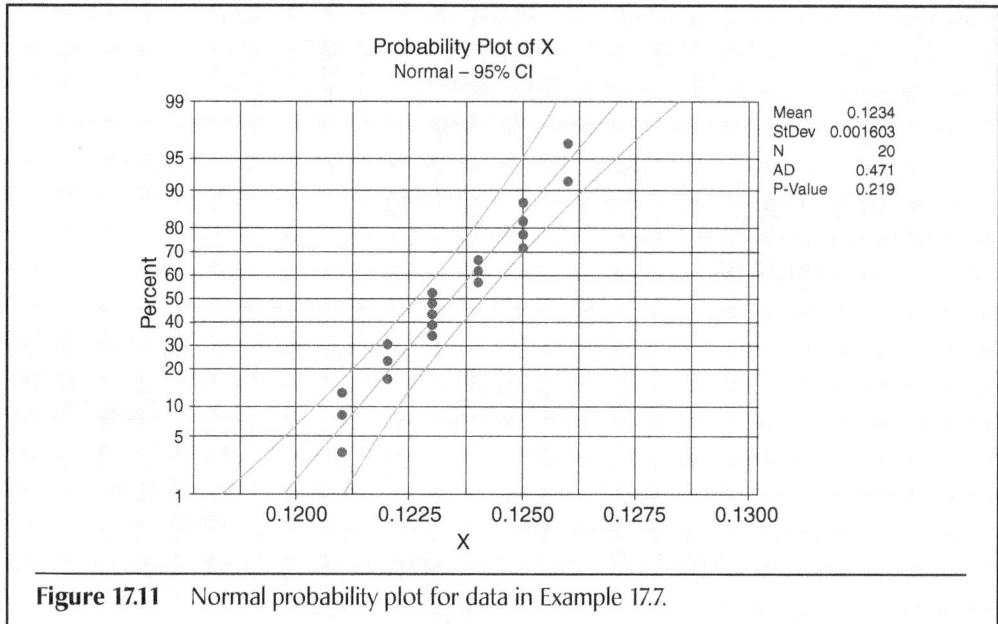

Figure 17.11 Normal probability plot for data in Example 17.7.

Interpreting Normal Probability Plots

Without the aid of a statistical test such as the Anderson-Darling test or something similar (such as the Shapiro-Wilk test or the Kolmogorov-Smirnov test, for example), the interpretation of the normal probability plot can be somewhat subjective. It would not be unusual for two highly experienced Black Belts to interpret the same plot and reach opposing conclusions regarding normality.

Usually, such disagreement occurs regarding how much departure from the distribution fit line there must be in the tails before one can conclude that the sample did not come from a population with a normal distribution.

In this subsection, we will look at various normal probability plots generated for specific distributions with defined parameters to determine what we might be able to learn about the population distribution. One thousand points for each distribution were generated. Parameters were chosen to obtain a specific shape and skewness and hence specific effect on each normal probability plot. The parameters for each of five distributions are given in Table 17.7. The statistics obtained from these randomly generated distributions are given in Table 17.8.

Therefore, we will be working backwards, so to speak. However, we will have each population distribution side by side with its associated normal probability plot to facilitate the learning process.

In order to interpret normal probability plots consistently, it is important to keep several conventions in mind. These include the following:

	Parameters						
Distribution	**Mean**	**Standard deviation**	**Shape**	**Location**	**Scale**	**Threshold**	**Degrees of freedom**
Standard normal	0	1					
Student's t							20
Exponential					1	0	
Lognormal				0	1	0	
Weibull			100		5	0	

Table 17.7 Parameters for Figures 17.13 through 17.17.

Distribution	**Mean**	**Standard deviation**	**N**	**Anderson-Darling**	***p*-value (α =0.05)**	**Skewness**	**Kurtosis**
Standard normal	−0.013	0.996	1000	0.17	0.9504	−0.0489	0.000592
Student's t	−0.0124	1.05	1000	0.339	0.5072	−0.0167	0.117
Exponential	0.981	0.991	1000	50.3	<0.0001	2.08	7.07
Lognormal	1.66	2.21	1000	99.7	<0.0001	4.47	32.2
Weibull	4.97	0.0614	1000	9.49	<0.0001	−0.864	1.03

Table 17.8 Statistics for Figures 17.13 through 17.17.

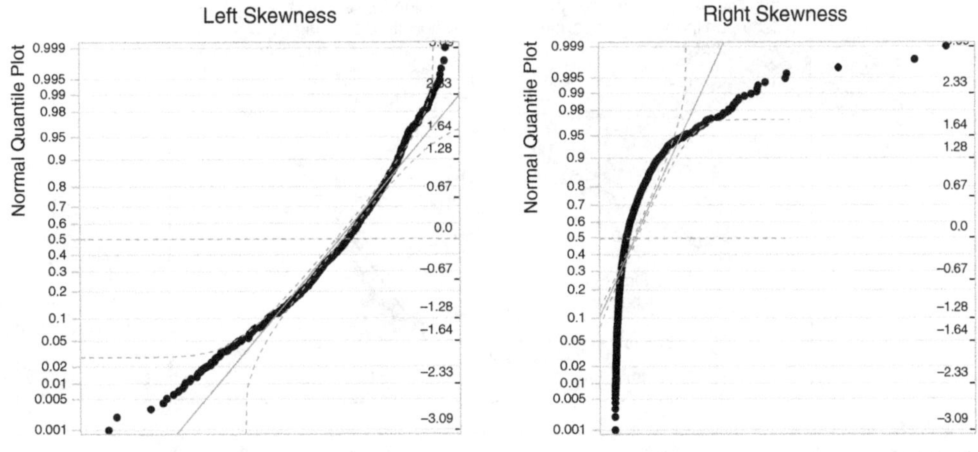

Figure 17.12 An illustration of left and right skewness in a normal probability plot.

- The definition of left and right skewness was given in Figure 17.2. Note that when we interpret distributions as skewed, left and right skewness is reflected in normal probability plots as shown in Figure 17.12.
- In order to maintain the conventions as noted in the first bullet above, the normal probability plots must be plotted with the percent, probability, or normal score on the y-axis. When normal probability plots are plotted in this manner, Figure 17.12 and Figure 17.13 hold.

Let's consider the following five distributions and their normal probability plots:

- *Standard normal distribution* ($\mu = 0$, $\sigma = 1$). Since this is the standard normal distribution, it should plot as a straight line, as shown in the top part of Figure 17.14. Since all the distributions were randomly generated, we expect to see some minor perturbations, especially toward the tails of the distributions. A visual review of this plot by an experienced Black Belt would likely confirm it as normal. The Anderson-Darling test for normality and associated p-value shown in Table 17.8 would lead one to conclude normality as well.
- *Student's* t *distribution (20 degrees of freedom).* From Figure 17.13, we might determine that the normal probability plot shown in Figure 17.15 is a normal distribution. In fact, the distribution is the Student's t distribution with 20 degrees of freedom. Although a Student's t distribution has positive excess kurtosis, or heavier tails than a normal distribution, when the sample size is sufficiently large, the difference from normal is small. From Table 17.8 we estimate that the data are slightly negatively (left) skewed and leptokurtic. Using the Anderson-Darling test at a = 0.05, we fail to reject the null hypothesis

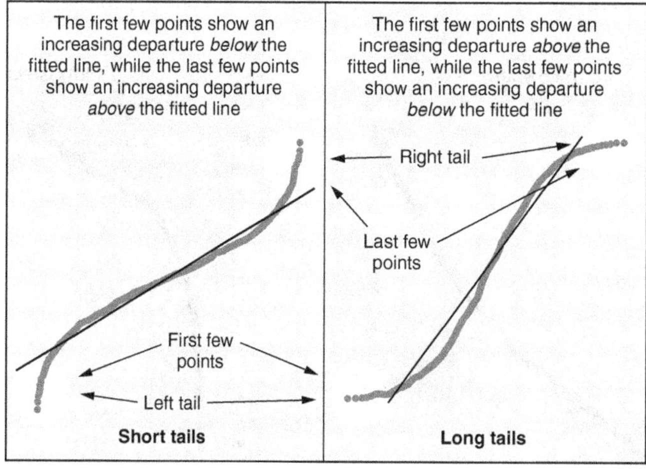

Figure 17.13 Direction of the tail bend on the normal probability plot tails for short- and long-tailed distributions.

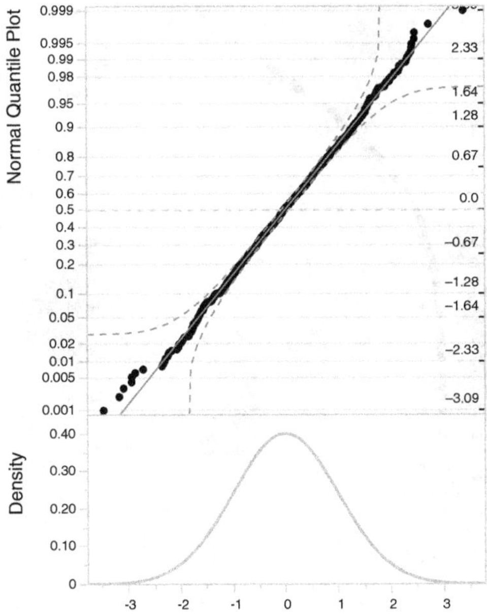

Figure 17.14 The standard normal distribution and its associated normal probability plot.

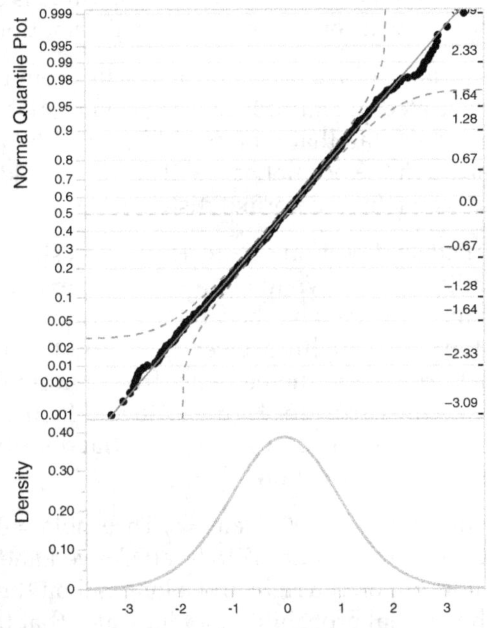

Figure 17.15 The Student's *t* distribution and its associated normal probability plot.

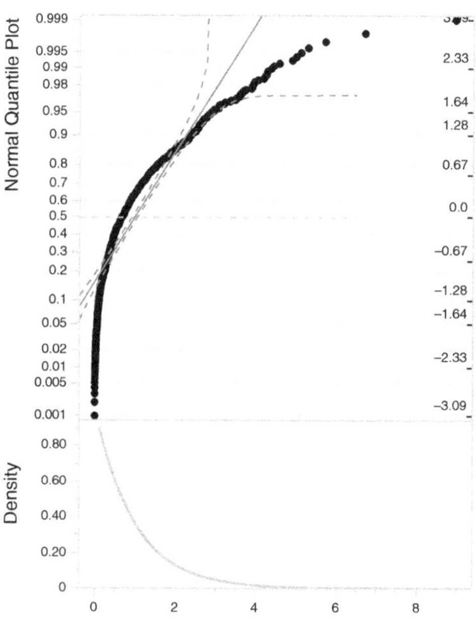

Figure 17.16 The exponential distribution and its associated normal probability plot.

of normally distributed data. Notice that the p-value is 0.5072. From a practical viewpoint, you could consider this distribution to be normal.

- *Exponential distribution* (Scale = 1, Threshold = 0). From Figure 17.12, the distribution illustrated in Figure 17.16 is skewed right, and from Figure 17.13, it has a short left tail that is bounded by zero and a long right tail. The curvature in the normal probability plot would indicate that the data did not come from a normal distribution.
- *Lognormal distribution* (Location = 0, Scale = 1, Threshold = 0). The normal probability plot shown in Figure 17.17 is very similar to Figure 17.16 and is bounded by zero on the left. The normal probability plot indicates that the data is highly skewed to the right and likely has a positive excess kurtosis and therefore not from a normal distribution. The normal probability plots for Figure 17.16 and Figure 17.17 look very similar, yet one was generated by an exponential distribution and the other by a lognormal distribution.
- *Weibull distribution* (Shape = 100, Scale = 5, Threshold = 0). The normal probability plot shown in Figure 17.18 is left skewed and bounded by 5.1 with a short tail on the right and a long tail on the left. The curvature to the normal probability plot indicates that the data did not come from a normal distribution and a positive excess kurtosis. From a practical viewpoint, Figure 17.18 is almost the mirror image of Figure 17.16 and Figure 17.17.

Normal probability plots aren't always easy to interpret. They require experience and occasionally statistical support via descriptive statistics and hypothesis

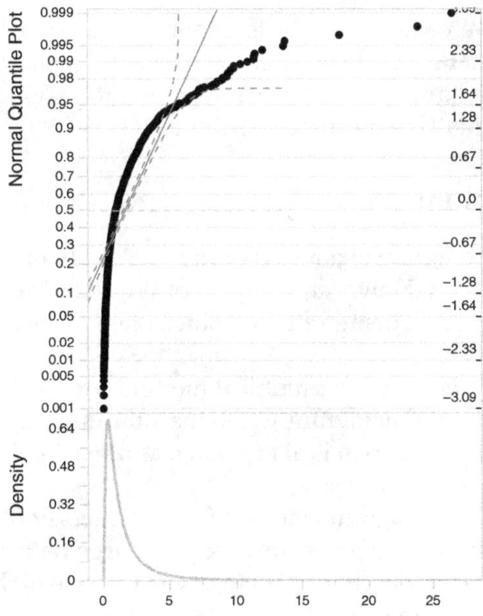

Figure 17.17 The lognormal distribution and its associated normal probability plot.

testing. We've seen how various distributions can be disguised as a normal distribution and how easy it is to draw a wrong conclusion. All it takes is a moment or two to complement the normal probability plot with additional graphics and statistics.

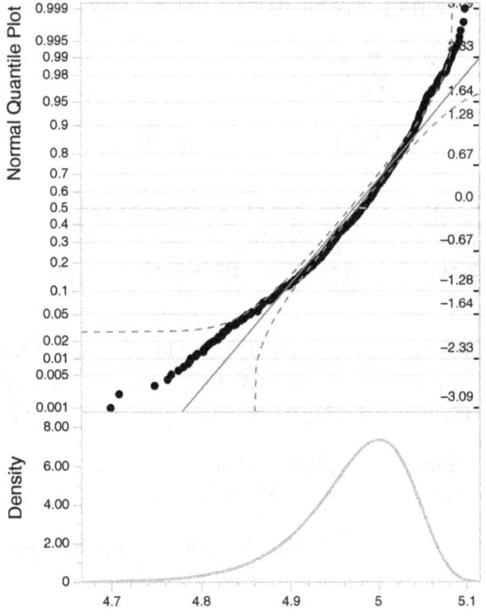

Figure 17.18 The Weibull distribution and its associated normal probability plot.

In addition, we've learned a little about interpreting the normal probability plot and about what type of distribution may have generated your data. If your data are not normal and your software supports it, you may be able to run probability plots for other than normal distributions.

Stem-and-Leaf Diagram

The stem-and-leaf diagram is not part of the 2022 Body of Knowledge and will not be on the examination. However, it is part of the 2022 Green Belt Body of Knowledge. Consequently, it is being retained since Black Belts are commonly expected to train Green Belts.

A *stem-and-leaf diagram* is a graphical method for displaying quantitative data in a format similar to a histogram while maintaining all or nearly all of the raw data. A stem-and-leaf diagram is also known as a *stem-and-leaf plot* or *stem-and-leaf display*.

The stem-and-leaf diagram is useful for small sets of data that are easy to sort manually, but it quickly becomes unwieldy for large data sets. Pyzdek (2003) recommends data sets smaller than 200. However, the size of the data set is irrelevant when computer software is involved.

The process for developing a stem-and-leaf diagram is quite straightforward:

1. Gather and sort the data in ascending order.
2. Determine the stem and the leaf. As described by Tague (2005),

   Decide which digits in the data are changing. Out of this group, choose the two or three digits on the left that are the most significant. Of these, the digit on the right will be the leaf, and the one or two on the left will be the stem.

   Note: It is possible that some stems will not have any leaves depending on the nature of the data set.
3. Round all data in accordance with your selection of stem and leaf above.
4. Draw a vertical line on a page.
5. On the left side of the line, write the stems in ascending order down the page.
6. On the right side of the line, match the leaves to each stem (regardless of duplicates) in ascending order from left to right across the page. Do not use any digits to the right of the leaf.
7. Add a key or legend to indicate how to read the stem-and-leaf diagram. A common example of the key or legend is "6|3 = 63."

It is often a convention in stem-and-leaf diagrams to create separate stems for leaf digits 0–4 and 5–9.

EXAMPLE 17.8

Using the data in Table 17.9, construct a stem-and-leaf diagram.

Number	Sorted Data	Number	Sorted Data	Number	Sorted Data
1	0.11	10	0.24	19	0.39
2	0.17	11	0.24	20	0.42
3	0.18	12	0.25	21	0.42
4	0.18	13	0.26	22	0.44
5	0.19	14	0.33	23	0.47
6	0.19	15	0.34	24	0.48
7	0.21	16	0.36	25	0.54
8	0.22	17	0.37	26	0.55
9	0.24	18	0.38	27	0.56

Table 17.9 Data for Example 17.8.

We will select the leaf to be the digit in the second decimal place and the stem will be everything in the first decimal place. The output is shown in Figure 17.19. The first column contains the stems in increments of 0.10, and the values following are the leaves in increments of 0.01. For example, the first row of the plot is made up of the data values 0.11, 0.17, 0.18, 0.18, 0.19, and 0.19.

Stem-and-Leaf Display: Data

```
Stem-and-leaf of Data N = 27
Leaf Unit = 0.010

      1   178899
      2   1244456
      3   346789
      4   22478
      5   456
```

Figure 17.19 Stem-and-leaf diagram for Example 17.8.

A stem-and-leaf plot can easily be constructed using paper and pencil and is an effective method for showing the distribution of the data while still preserving individual data values.

VALID STATISTICAL CONCLUSIONS

> Distinguish between descriptive and inferential statistical studies. Evaluate how the results of statistical studies are used to draw valid conclusions. (Evaluate)
>
> **Body of Knowledge V.D.5**

One of the results of current technology is that we're drowning in data and thirsting for information. Statistical studies provide tools for extracting information out of the data. The two principal types of statistical studies are usually called *descriptive (enumerative) and inferential (analytical).*

Descriptive studies use techniques such as those in the previous sections to present data in an understandable format. A long column of numbers is rendered more meaningful when the mean, the median, the mode, and the standard deviation are known. A histogram, scatter diagram, or other graphic provides additional information from the data.

Inferential studies analyze data from a sample to infer properties of the population from which the sample was drawn. This is especially important in those situations in which population data are unavailable or infeasible to obtain.

Suppose, for instance, that one needs to know the mean diameter produced by a particular tooling setup on a lathe. The population would consist of all the parts that could be produced by that setup, which could take weeks or might even be impossible to acquire since the population is infinite. Instead, a sample is selected, its properties studied, and a reasonable inference about the population mean diameter is obtained.

In this case, the mean of the sample would provide an approximation for the population mean. The amount of variation in the sample would provide information about how close that approximation is to the actual population mean.

Inferential studies allow us to make statements about populations with a certain degree of confidence. When conducted properly, these studies can help us draw meaningful and practical conclusions. We will explore inferential statistical procedures in Chapter 21.

Chapter 18
Probability

We must become more comfortable with probability and uncertainty.

—Nate Silver

This chapter will address the basic concepts of probability theory, as well as both the discrete and continuous statistical distributions commonly used in Lean Six Sigma. The material in this chapter is adapted from Mary McShane-Vaughn, *The Probability Handbook* (2015). Numerous examples are used to illustrate the concepts presented.

BASIC CONCEPTS

> Describe and apply probability concepts, e.g., independence, mutually exclusive events, addition and multiplication rules, conditional probability, complementary probability, and joint occurrence of events. (Understand)
>
> **Body of Knowledge V.E.1**

Events, Trials, and Outcomes

The basic building blocks of probability are events, trials, and outcomes. Each unique occurrence that is possible for a particular scenario is known as a *simple event*. These simple events have an equal probability of occurring and are collected into a *sample space* Ω (omega). The sample space contains all the possible simple events that can occur for a particular experiment or procedure. For example, if we toss a single die, the sample space for this procedure is composed of six simple events: {1, 2, 3, 4, 5, 6}. If we are tossing two coins, the sample space would contain the simple events {HH, HT, TH, TT}. *A compound event* can be any combination of simple events that are of interest. For example, we could define a compound event A as rolling a die and getting a number less than 3. Or, for our coin toss, we could define a compound event R as having at least one head in two tosses. We see that Event R is mapped to the simple events {HH, HT, and TH}.

By throwing the die, or tossing the coins, we are performing a *trial* of the experiment or procedure. The result of the trial is the *outcome*. Any outcome can be mapped to a simple event in the sample space. In summary, simple events are occurrences that are possible, and outcomes are actual occurrences, or results, of a trial. Compound events are a collection of two or more simple events.

Classical versus Empirical Probability

There is a *classical definition of probability* that is predicated on the fact that the probability of each event in the sample space is known and equal. This will be true for cases such as die or coin tosses or selecting cards from a standard poker deck. The classical definition of the probability of an event A, then, is shown in Equation 18.1.

Equation 18.1 Classical definition of probability

$$Pr(A) = \frac{\textit{number of ways A can occur}}{\textit{number of total simple events}} = \frac{a}{N}$$

By definition, probabilities are between 0 and 1, with a probability of 0 meaning that the outcome is impossible, and a probability of 1 meaning that the outcome is certain.

For situations in which the probabilities of the events are not known, we can perform an experiment with several trials, and then count the number of favorable outcomes and divide by the number of trials. This is referred to as *empirical probability*, or *relative frequency*. We can calculate the relative probability of Event A using Equation 18.2:

Equation 18.2 Empirical, or relative frequency, definition of probability

$$Pr(A) \cong \frac{\textit{number of times A occurred}}{\textit{total number of trials}} = \frac{a}{n}$$

Note that the empirical probability is an estimate of the true Pr(A). As the number of trials increases, this estimate will get closer and closer to the true probability of Event A due to the Law of Large Numbers. The empirical probability equation is more practical for most real-world situations in which all simple events or probabilities are not necessarily known *a priori* (ahead of time).

Unions and Intersections

We can calculate the probability of two or more events occurring by using the ideas of *union* and *intersection*. The union of two events A and B contains the total number of unique simple events that comprise each event. For example, for a single die toss, let Event A be defined as rolling either a 1 or a 3, and Event B as rolling either a 1 or a 5. The union of these two events is {1, 3, 5}. We can write this by using the symbol for a union, ∪:

$$A \cup B = \{1, 3\} \cup \{1, 5\} = \{1, 3, 5\}.$$

Note that A ∪ B is equivalent to B ∪ A. We can think of the union set as the numbers that will satisfy A OR B.

An intersection between two events A and B contains the simple events they have in common. The intersection of Events A and B, then, is {1}. We can use the symbol for intersection, ∩:

$$A \cap B = \{1, 3\} \cap \{1, 5\} = \{1\}.$$

Note that A ∩ B is equivalent to B ∩ A. The intersection is the set of simple events that satisfy A AND B. Events A and B can be represented in a Venn diagram, as shown in Figure 18.1.

Complement Rule

The *complement* of an Event A includes all the simple events in which A *does not* occur. The notation for the complement of A is $\bar{A}$, read as "not A." The probability of $\bar{A}$ is equal to 1 – Pr(A), as shown in Equation 18.3.

Equation 18.3 Complement rule

$$\Pr(\bar{A}) = 1 - \Pr(A)$$

In addition, Pr(A) can be found using $1 - \Pr(\bar{A})$. This complement rule comes in handy when we need to find the probability of Event A, but the calculation is laborious. We can instead find the probability of $\bar{A}$ and subtract the result from 1.

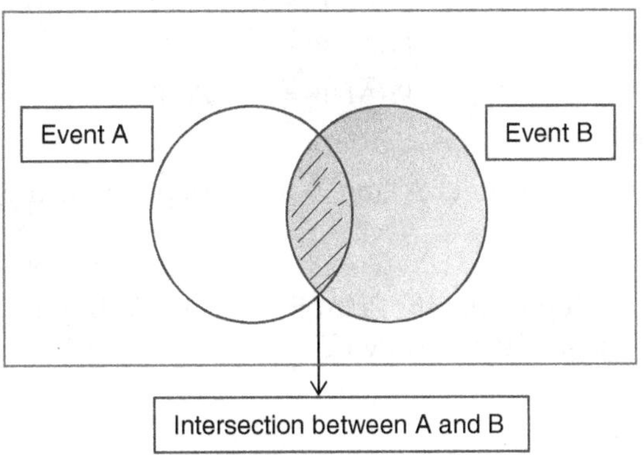

Figure 18.1 Venn diagram with intersection.

EXAMPLE 18.1

To find the probability of rolling a die and getting number greater than or equal to 2, we would need to solve:

$$Pr(X \geq 2) = Pr(X = 2) + Pr(X = 3) + Pr(X = 4) + Pr(X = 5) + Pr(X = 6)$$

Using the complement, we instead can calculate the simpler calculation to arrive at the same answer:

$$Pr(X \geq 2) = 1 - Pr(X = 1).$$

Independence

Two events A and B are said to be *independent* if the occurrence of one event does not influence the occurrence of the other. For example, let Event A be the outcome of a single toss of a coin, and Event B the outcome of a second coin toss. Events A and B are independent because the outcome of the first toss does not influence the outcome of the second. Regardless of what transpires on the first toss, the simple events for B are still {H, T}.

We can also think of independence as the transfer of information from trial to trial. If Events A and B are independent, knowing if Event A has occurred does not give us any additional information on the possible outcomes of Event B.

If Events A and B are independent, then the following statements are true:

$$\Pr(A \cap B) = \Pr(A)\Pr(B)$$
$$\Pr(A \cap \bar{B}) = \Pr(A)\Pr(\bar{B})$$
$$\Pr(\bar{A} \cap B) = \Pr(\bar{A})\Pr(B)$$
$$\Pr(\bar{A} \cap \bar{B}) = \Pr(\bar{A})\Pr(\bar{B})$$

To show that two events A and B are independent the following condition must be met:

A and B are independent iff $\Pr(A \cap B) = \Pr(A \text{ and } B) = \Pr(A)\Pr(B)$
where "iff" means "if and only if."

EXAMPLE 18.2

A company determines that 25% of its customers are located in-state, 68% of customers are members of the reward program, and 17% of customers are both in-state and reward members. We can prove that Event A = (in-state location) and Event B = (reward member) are independent by showing $Pr(A \cap B) = Pr(A)\,Pr(B)$:

$$Pr(\text{In-state and Reward member}) = 0.17$$

$$Pr(\text{In-state})Pr(\text{Reward member}) = (0.25)(0.68) = 0.17$$

In this example, independence of the events implies that customer location does not influence whether a customer joins the reward program, and vice versa. Knowing that a customer is in-state does not give us any information about whether they are a reward member.

However, if Events A and B are not independent, then knowing the status of Event A gives us information about the sample space for Event B. In fact, for cases in which A and B are not independent, the sample space of B cannot be fully determined until the status of Event A is known.

EXAMPLE 18.3

Let's imagine that we have ten socks in a drawer: six are white and four are black. If we select two socks from the drawer, one after the other, without looking, what is the probability that we will get two matching socks?

Let Event A be defined as the color of the sock on the first trial, and Event B be the color of the sock chosen on the second trial. When we first open the drawer, we have a probability of 6/10 of choosing a white sock and 4/10 of selecting a black sock.

What is the probability of choosing a particular color of sock on the second trial? It depends. If we choose a white sock on the first trial, then the drawer is left with five white socks and four black. If we choose a black sock first, we would be left with six white socks and three black socks. Since the sample space for Event B depends on the outcome of Event A, we say that Events A and B are not independent.

The probability of choosing a white sock on the first draw and a white sock on the second is $6/10 \times 5/9 = 1/3$. For a black match, we have $4/10 \times 3/9 = 2/15$. The probability of a matched pair is thus 7/15.

Mutually Exclusive Events

Two events A and B are said to be mutually exclusive if they cannot occur at the same time. For example, if we toss a coin one time, we cannot simultaneously flip a head (H) and a tail (T). As soon as the coin lands on heads, we know with surety

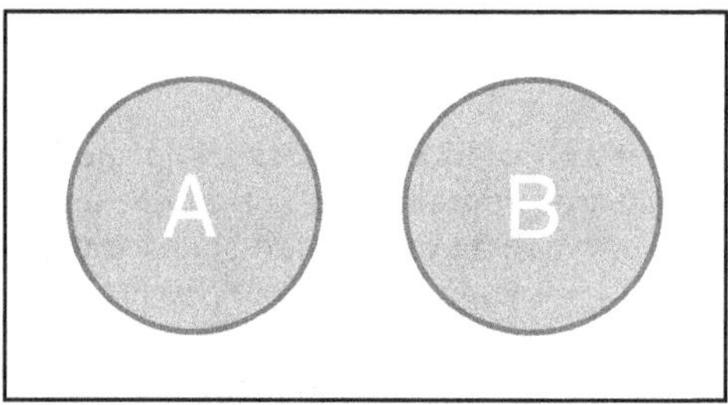

Figure 18.2 Venn diagram of mutually exclusive events.

that the coin has not landed on tails. In quality, when we check the dimensions of a part with a go/no-go gage, the part will either pass or fail, not both.

In terms of information transfer, mutually exclusive events are *completely dependent* since knowing that one event has occurred gives us perfect knowledge about the outcome of the second event.

A Venn diagram of two mutually exclusive events shows no overlap between the event circles, as shown in Figure 18.2.

Conditional Probability

For two events A and B, the probability of Event A *given that Event B has occurred* is denoted as Pr(A|B). Conditional probability can be explained graphically. Let Event A reside in a universe Ω that is divided into two parts, B and $\bar{B}$, as shown in Figure 18.3. By definition, the area of the universe is equal to one.

Once we are told that Event B has occurred, we can divide the universe to form Ω′ as shown in Figure 18.4. Here, the probability of Event A given Event B is the ratio of the area of Event A the area of Ω′, or Event B.

The conditional probability Pr(A|B) can be computed using Equation 18.4. Note that Pr(A and B) ≤ Pr(B).

Equation 18.4 Conditional probability

$$Pr(A \mid B) = \frac{Pr(A \cap B)}{Pr(B)} = \frac{Pr(A \text{ and } B)}{Pr(B)}$$

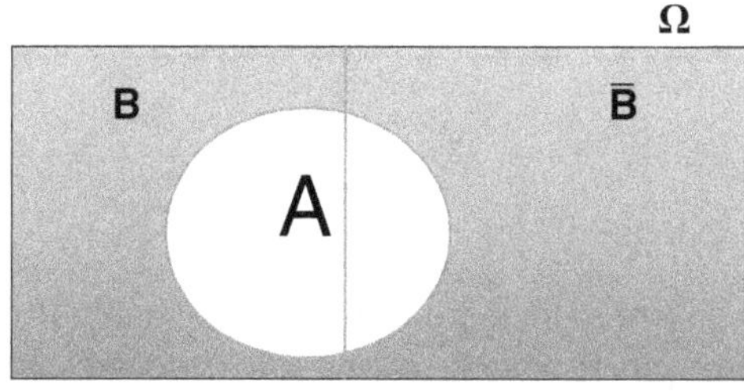

Figure 18.3 Universe with Events A and B.

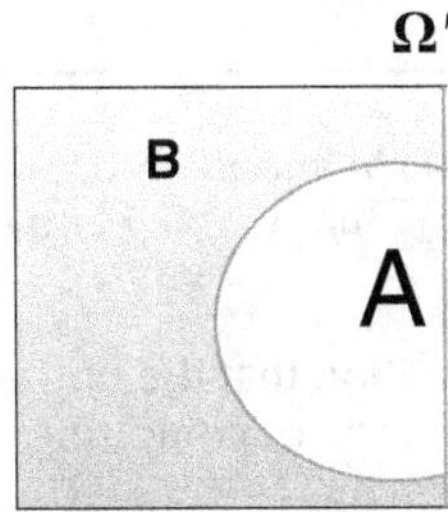

Figure 18.4 Universe with A given B.

EXAMPLE 18.4

If Pr(A and B) = 0.25 and Pr(B) = 0.40, find Pr(A|B).

$$Pr(A\,|\,B) = \frac{Pr(A\ and\ B)}{Pr(B)} = \frac{0.25}{0.40} = 0.625$$

EXAMPLE 18.5

The data in Table 18.1 shows the number of defects found in samples from different production lines.

	Defective	Non-defective	Total
Line 1	3	87	90
Line 2	10	75	85
Line 3	25	230	255
Line 4	7	63	70
Total	45	455	500

Table 18.1 Defects found per production line.

Using Table 18.1 we can find the probability that a unit came from Line 2, given that it is defective. Define Event A as Line 2, and Event B as a defective unit. From the table, the probability of a unit being defective and from Line 2 equals 10/500. The probability of a defective unit is 45/500. Putting the information into the conditional formula gives:

Continued

Continued

$$Pr(A \mid B) = \frac{Pr(A\ and\ B)}{Pr(B)} = \frac{10/500}{45/500} = 0.222$$

As soon as we are given the information that the unit is defective, we can also solve the problem by dividing the universe and concentrating only on the defective column as shown in Table 18.2.

	Defective
Line 1	3
Line 2	10
Line 3	25
Line 4	7
Total	45

Table 18.2 Reduced table, conditional on defectives.

The proportion of Line 2 units in the defective column is 10/45 = 0.222.

Now, given that a unit is from Line 2, what is the probability that unit is defective? Here, we define Event A as a defective unit and Event B as Line 2.

$$Pr(A \mid B) = \frac{Pr(A\ and\ B)}{Pr(B)} = \frac{10/500}{85/500} = 0.118$$

Note that this last example illustrates that Pr(A|B) is not equivalent to Pr(B|A). The numerators of both formulas are equal, but the denominators are not the same. Mistaking Pr(A|B) for Pr(B|A) is an error in logic referred to as *transposing the conditional.*

The conditional probability formula reduces to a simpler form when Events A and B are independent. Recall that if two events are independent, the occurrence of one event does not influence the occurrence of the other. If Events A and B are independent, the conditional probability is shown in Equation 18.5.

Equation 18.5 Conditional probability for independent events

$$\Pr(A \mid B) = \frac{\Pr(A\,and\,B)}{\Pr(B)} = \frac{\Pr(A)\Pr(B)}{\Pr(B)} = \Pr(A)$$

If two events A and B are *mutually exclusive,* then their conditional probability is equal to zero: Pr(A|B) = Pr(B|A) = 0 since Pr(A and B) = 0.

Multiplication Rule

To calculate the intersection of two or more events, we use the *multiplication rule* shown in Equation 18.6. For Events A and B, the multiplication rule states that the probability of Events A and B occurring is the probability of Event B given that Event A has occurred times the probability of Event A.

Equation 18.6 General multiplication rule for two events

$$Pr(A \cap B) = Pr(A \text{ and } B) = Pr(B \mid A)Pr(A)$$
$$Pr(A \cap B) = Pr(A \text{ and } B) = Pr(A \mid B)Pr(B)$$

If Events A and B are independent, then the conditional probability of Event A given Event B is equal to the probability of Event A, Pr(A|B) = Pr(A), so the multiplication rule simplifies to Equation 18.7.

Equation 18.7 Multiplication rule, two independent events

$$Pr(A \cap B) = Pr(A \text{ and } B) = Pr(A)Pr(B)$$

Addition Rule

The probability addition rule is used to calculate the probability of a union of two or more events. Because we won't always enumerate all the possible simple events for a scenario, we need a formula that will allow us to find probabilities for unions of events. This general addition rule is shown in Equation 18.8.

Equation 18.8 General addition rule

$$Pr(A \cup B) = Pr(A \text{ or } B) = Pr(A) + Pr(B) - Pr(A \text{ and } B)$$

Note that the multiplication rule is used in the addition rule, since we must calculate the intersection of Events A and B. We subtract off the intersection of Events A and B to avoid double counting the simple event that satisfies both conditions of A and B.

If Events A and B are independent, the addition rule can be written as Equation 18.9.

Equation 18.9 Addition rule, independent events

$$Pr(A \cup B) = Pr(A \text{ or } B) = Pr(A) + Pr(B) - Pr(A)Pr(B)$$

If Events A and B are mutually exclusive, their intersection is equal to zero. Therefore, the addition rule simplifies to Equation 18.10:

Equation 18.10 Addition rule, mutually exclusive events

$$Pr(A \cup B) = Pr(A \text{ or } B) = Pr(A) + Pr(B)$$

Counting Techniques

Factorial

A more convenient way to determine the number of possible orderings of items is to use a *factorial.* A factorial of a positive integer (meaning 1, 2, 3, etc.) is the product of all the positive integers from 1 up to that number. For example, the factorial of 3 is equal to $1 \times 2 \times 3 = 6$. Note that due to the commutative property of multiplication we can also write this as $6 = 3 \times 2 \times 1$. The mathematical operator for factorial is an exclamation point (!). The factorial of 3 is denoted as 3!, and is read as "three factorial."

EXAMPLE 18.6

An inspector selects four products and lines them up on a workbench for inspection. How many ways can the products A, B, C, and D be arranged on the bench? As shown in Figure 18.5, there are four choices for the first spot in the line. Once we have chosen a product for the first space, we have three products to choose from for the second spot, then two for the third spot, and then the remaining product will be in the last space. Hence, we have $4 \times 3 \times 2 \times 1 = 4!$ ways to arrange products A, B, C, and D. If product E is added to the sample, we now have $5! = 5 \times 4 \times 3 \times 2 \times 1 = 120$ arrangements. If product F is then added as well, we have $6! = 720$ unique orderings.

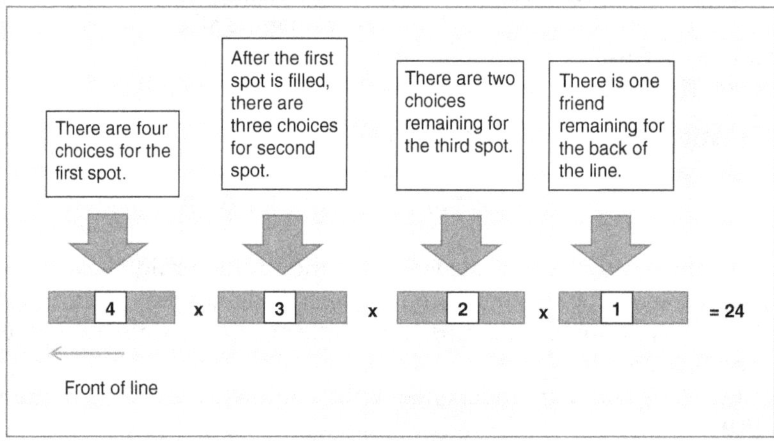

Figure 18.5 Ordering four products on a work bench.

Note here that 4! can be written as $4 \times 3!$, $5! = 5 \times 4!$, $6! = 6 \times 5!$ and $7! = 7 \times 6!$. We can say in general that n items can be arranged in $n \times (n-1)!$ ways, as shown in Equation 18.11.

Equation 18.11 Factorial

$$n! = n(n-1)!$$

We can also denote the factorial formula using a multiplication operator, the capital letter pi, Π, as in Equation 18.12.

Equation 18.12 Factorial, alternate version

$$\prod_{i=1}^{n} i = n!$$

Let's break down the meaning of Equation 18.12. The multiplication operator, denoted by the Greek capital letter pi (Π), tells us to multiply an integer variable i letting i equal 1, all the way up to some number n. For $n = 3$, we can find 3! by using the formula:

$$\prod_{i=1}^{3} i = 1 \times 2 \times 3 = 3!$$

This is an elegant way to succinctly represent the factorial formula.

There is exactly one way for zero things to be arranged in order. *Therefore, as a special case, zero factorial, or 0!, by definition, equals one.* This fact will become quite useful in the upcoming sections when we discuss permutations and combinations.

EXAMPLE 18.7

In our previous factorial examples, each product could be distinguished from the others. However, if we want to order n items, in which some items are identical to the others, we will need a slightly different strategy.

Say we are arranging five cubes in a row. Three of these cubes are red, and are identical to each other, and the remaining two cubes are green, and also indistinguishable from each other. How many ways can these five cubes be arranged? If all five cubes were different colors, we know we would have 5! = 120 ways to line them up. But in the current case, we can only tell red and green cubes apart. We are right to suspect that the red/green orderings will be less than 5!. The number of unique orderings in this situation is

$$\frac{5!}{3!2!} = 10$$

In general, if we have n items with r_1 identical items in one group, r_2 identical items in another group, and so on for a total of g groups, the number of ways that the items can be ordered is shown in Equation 18.13.

Equation 18.13 Orderings for groups of identical items

$$\frac{n!}{r_1!r_2!\ldots r_g!}$$

Note that the sum of the r's in Formula 2.3 must equal n.

A more mathematically tidy way to display the equation would be to use the pi multiplication operator, as shown in Equation 18.14.

Equation 18.14 Orderings for groups of identical items

$$\frac{n!}{\prod_{i=1}^{g} r_i!},\ with\ i = 1, 2, \ldots, g,\ and \sum_{i=1}^{g} r_i = n$$

Permutations

The number of *permutations* gives us the number of ways r items out of n items can be arranged in order. We illustrate this with an example.

EXAMPLE 18.8

For example, consider a focus group participant who is asked to review five versions of a new webpage design and rank their top three versions in order of preference. How many different ways could the five versions be ranked by the participant? We again could solve this using enumeration, or by using a diagram as shown in Figure 18.6. Here $n = 5$ and $r = 3$.

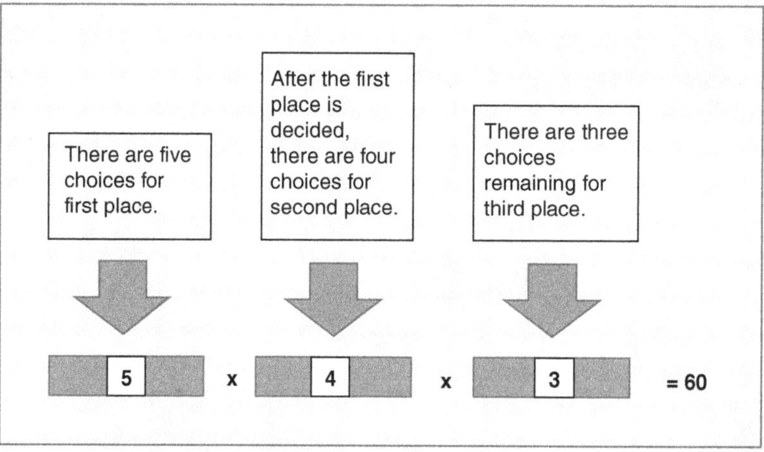

Figure 18.6 Number of ways five items can be ranked 1 to 3.

We notice in each of these cases that the number of ways the designs can be ranked first, second, and third places is equal to or less than the number of ways they can be lined up on the work bench. In the workbench example, each product had a specific spot to fill. Here, in the focus group example, we are only concerned with filling three spots.

In general, the number of ways n items can be arranged in r places, *in which order matters*, can be written using the *permutation formula* shown in Equation 18.15:

Equation 18.15 Permutation formula

$$nPr = \frac{n!}{(n-r)!}, r \leq n$$

We read this formula as "n permute r equals n factorial divided by the quantity n minus r factorial." Note that the number of positions we have, r, must be less than or equal to the number of items we have, n.

For n equal to 5 and r equal to 3, we have:

$$5P3 = \frac{5!}{(5-3)!} = \frac{5!}{2!} = \frac{5\times4\times3\times2\times1}{2\times1} = 5\times4\times3 = 60.$$

When n and r themselves are equal, the permutation formula reduces to the factorial. For example, if $n = 5$ and $r = 5$, we get

$$5P5 = \frac{5!}{(5-5)!} = \frac{5!}{0!} = \frac{5\times4\times3\times2\times1}{1} = 5!.$$

Recall that 0! equals 1 by definition.

Combinations

When we choose r items from a total of n items, there are times we aren't concerned with the order of the selections.

EXAMPLE 18.9

Suppose that five team members, Arnoldo, Beth, Cameron, Daniel, and Eve, needed to choose three people among themselves to be on a planning committee. How many ways can three people from a team of five members be chosen to serve on the committee? The possible configurations of the committee are enumerated in Table 18.3.

ABC	ABD	ABE	ACD	ACE
ADE	BCD	BCE	CED	BDE

Table 18.3 Ways for five team members to be chosen for a committee of three.

In contrast to Example 18.8 in which webpages were ranked, note here that the committee membership denoted by ABC in Table 18.3 would be exactly the same if we chose ABC, ACB, BAC, BCA, CAB, or CBA. Clearly, order of selection does not matter here. Instead of permutations, in our committee case we are calculating *combinations*. Because there are fewer configurations when order does not matter, *for given values of* n *and* r, *the number of combinations will always be smaller than or equal to the number of permutations.*

In general, the number of ways r items can be chosen from a total of n items, *in which order does not matter,* can be written using the *combination formula,* in Equation 18.16:

Equation 18.16 Combination formula

$$nCr = \frac{n!}{r!(n-r)!}, r \leq n$$

We read the term nCr as "n choose r." In many texts, the combination term is presented as $\binom{n}{r}$, as shown in Equation 18.17:

Equation 18.17 Combination formula, alternate notation

$$\binom{n}{r} = \frac{n!}{r!(n-r)!}, r \leq n$$

EXAMPLE 18.10

Let's solve our committee problem using the formula. We have $n = 5$ and $r = 3$.

$$5C3 = \binom{5}{3} = \frac{5!}{3!(5-3)!} = \frac{5!}{3!(2)!} = \frac{5 \times 4 \times 3 \times 2 \times 1}{3 \times 2 \times 1 \times (2 \times 1)} = \frac{5 \times 4}{2 \times 1} = 10$$

There are ten unique committees of three that can be chosen among the five team members.

If we compare the permutation calculation in Equation 18.15 and the combination calculation in Equation 18.16, we find that the combination has an extra term in the denominator, $r!$. *For a given* n *and* r, *the number of permutations will always be more than the number of combinations by a factor of* r!. It follows that, as a special case, the number of permutations will equal the number of combinations when $r = 1$. Contrasting the formulas for our example, we see

$$5P3 = \frac{5!}{(5-3)!} = \frac{5!}{2!} = \frac{5 \times 4 \times 3 \times 2 \times 1}{2 \times 1} = 5 \times 4 \times 3 = 60$$

$$5C3 = \binom{5}{3} = \frac{5!}{3!(5-3)!} = \frac{5!}{3!(2)!} = \frac{5 \times 4 \times 3 \times 2 \times 1}{3 \times 2 \times 1 \times (2 \times 1)} = \frac{5 \times 4}{2 \times 1} = 10$$

The number of permutations (60) is greater than the number of combinations (10) by a factor of $3! = 6$.

For a given number of items n, there is mirror symmetry in the number of combinations as we increase r from 0 to n. Table 18.4 shows us this phenomenon for the case of $n = 5$.

$\binom{5}{0} = \frac{5!}{0!(5-0!)} = 1$	$\binom{5}{5} = \frac{5!}{5!(5-5!)} = 1$
$\binom{5}{1} = \frac{5!}{1!(5-1!)} = 5$	$\binom{5}{4} = \frac{5!}{4!(5-4!)} = 5$
$\binom{5}{2} = \frac{5!}{2!(5-2!)} = 10$	$\binom{5}{3} = \frac{5!}{3!(5-3!)} = 10$

Table 18.4 Mirror symmetry for combinations, n = 5.

Note that for both $r = 0$ and $r = 5$, the denominators equal 5, resulting in the same number of combinations. Similarly, $r = 1$ and $r = 4$ result in 5 combinations, and $r = 2$ and $r = 3$ result in 10 combinations.

In practical terms, we can think about choosing a committee of, say, three from five friends by either choosing three people outright, or by choosing the two that will not be on the committee. Both approaches yield us the same result.

Configurations

We can also calculate the number of configurations that are possible given a set of options.

EXAMPLE 18.11

Imagine that a company offers a product that comes in a choice of three sizes, two colors, and three option packages. The number of configurations can be calculated outright as follows:

3 sizes × 2 colors × 3 option packages = 18 product configurations

In general, we multiply the number of choices for each option to determine the total number of possible configurations. More formally, we can say we have a number of options from $i = 1$ to g, and each option i has a number of choices defined as n_i. Then the total number of configurations is calculated as shown in Equation 18.18.

Equation 18.18 Total number of configurations

$$n_1 \times n_2 \times \ldots \times n_g = \prod_{i=1}^{g} n_i$$

COMMON DISTRIBUTIONS

> Common distributions: Describe, interpret, and use normal, Poisson, binomial, chi-square, Student's *t* and F distributions. (Evaluate)
>
> **Body of Knowledge V.E.2**

Binomial Distribution

The binomial distribution is used when counting the number of defective units in a sample and is the basis for the *np* and *p* statistical process control charts presented in Chapter 27. The distribution is built from a series of independent *Bernoulli trials*. In a Bernoulli trial, there are only two possible outcomes, such as heads or tails; pass or fail; success or failure; or defective or non-defective. The probability of the outcome of interest is equal to p, and by the complement rule, the probability of the second outcome is equal to $(1 - p)$.

The binomial random variable X is the sum of the outcomes of a series of independent Bernoulli trials, resulting in a discrete, finite set of possible outcomes. For example, if we toss a coin three times, each toss is a Bernoulli trial. We can count the number of heads in the three trials, and this count, X, will then follow a binomial distribution. Let the discrete random variable X equal the number of "successes" in n trials. Note that this definition of success is arbitrary and can be better described as the "outcome of interest." For example, we could just as well be counting the number of defectives in a sample as the number of good parts. The variable X will follow a binomial distribution if all the following conditions are satisfied:

1. There are a fixed number of trials, n.
2. There are only two possible, mutually exclusive, outcomes for each trial.
3. Trials are independent.
4. The probability of success p is constant from trial to trial.

Binomial Probability Mass Function

The probability mass function for the binomial variable X is shown in Equation 18.19:

Equation 18.19 Binomial probability mass function

$$\Pr(X = x) = \binom{n}{x} p^x (1 - p)^{n-x}, x = 0, 1, \ldots, n$$

In Equation 18.19, the number of trials is n, the probability of "success" is p, and the number of successes in n trials is the random variable X. Converting the formula into plain English: "The probability that the random variable X equals some value x is equal to n choose x, times the probability of success to the x power, times the probability of failure to the n minus x power."

Note that the random variable can take on whole number values from a minimum of 0 to a maximum of n successes. In other words, if you flip a coin 10 times, you can't get a negative number of heads, or 2.5 heads, or 11 heads.

EXAMPLE 18.12

Let's pull the formula apart to make sense of it using a coin toss with n = 3 trials as an illustrative example. These trials, or tosses, are independent, meaning that the outcome of one trial does not influence the outcome of the next. Define X as the number of heads in three tosses. The probability of success p equals ½, as does the probability of failure (tails). Let X = 2. What is the probability of getting exactly two head in three tosses? We can enumerate the possibilities, as shown in Table 18.5.

First trial	Second trial	Third trial	Probability of specific outcome
H	H	T	$p \times p \times (1-p)$
H	T	H	$p \times (1-p) \times p$
T	H	H	$(1-p) \times p \times p$

Table 18.5 Coin toss: ways that two heads in three trials can occur.

We can see from the table of enumerated outcomes that there are three ways that two heads can occur in three trials, which is 3C2, and each of these ways has a probability of occurrence equal to $p^2(1-p)$. Applying Equation 18.19, we can see the probability that X = 2 is equal to

$$\Pr(X=2)=\binom{n}{x}p^x(1-p)^{n-x}=\binom{3}{2}(0.5)^2(0.5)^1=\frac{3}{8}.$$

We can also use a table of binomial probabilities, provided in Appendix B.1. Based on n and p, we can find Pr(X = x) in the interior of the table.

Before evaluating the binomial probability equation, do these "sanity checks" to make sure you are not making an error:

1. The probability of success p and the probability of failure $(1-p)$ should equal 1.
2. The number of successes x should not exceed the number of trials n.
3. The exponents of p and $(1-p)$ should sum to n.

To find the cumulative probability using a binomial distribution, we use the summation operator, as shown in Equation 18.20. To find the probability that X will be equal to a value x or less, we sum the probabilities for the values 0 to x.

Equation 18.20 Binomial cumulative probability mass function

$$\Pr(X \le x) = \sum_{x=0}^{x} \binom{n}{x} p^x (1-p)^{n-x}$$

EXAMPLE 18.13

A sample of size six is randomly selected from a batch with 18.1% nonconforming units. Find the probability that the sample has one or fewer nonconforming units.

From the problem statement, we are given that $n = 6$, and $p = 0.181$. We want the probability that x = 0 or 1.

Using Equation 18.20, we have

$$\begin{aligned}\Pr(X \le 1) &= \sum_{x=0}^{1} \binom{6}{x} (0.181)^x (1-0.181)^{6-x} \\ &= \binom{6}{0} (0.181)^0 (1-0.181)^{6-0} + \binom{6}{1} (0.181)^1 (1-0.181)^{6-1} \\ &= (1-0.181)^6 + 6(0.181)(1-0.181)^5 \\ &= 0.702\end{aligned}$$

Thus, the probability that the sample contains one or fewer nonconforming units is 0.702.

We can solve the problem using the Excel function *=binom.dist*. This function takes four arguments: number of successes, trials, probability of success, and the cumulative flag, as shown in Figure 18.7. The cumulative argument can be turned on by entering TRUE or the value 1.

Continued

Continued

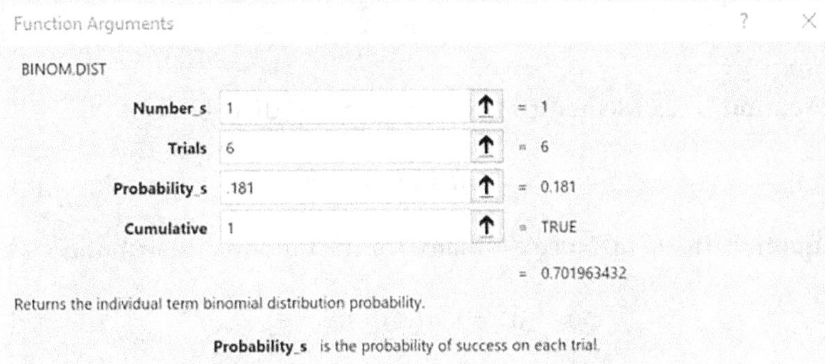

Function Arguments

BINOM.DIST

Number_s	1	= 1
Trials	6	= 6
Probability_s	.181	= 0.181
Cumulative	1	= TRUE

= 0.701963432

Returns the individual term binomial distribution probability.

Probability_s is the probability of success on each trial.

Figure 18.7 *Binom.dist* function in Excel.

Alternatively, we can also use a table of cumulative binomial probabilities, provided in Appendix B.2. Based on n and p, we can find $\Pr(X \leq x)$ in the interior of the table.

Binomial Parameters, Expected Value, and Variance

The binomial distribution can be described using two parameters: n and p. (Note that these parameters are not represented by Greek letters, an exception to the general rule.) The expected value, variance, and standard deviation of the binomial distribution are shown in Equation 18.21, Equation 18.22, and Equation 18.23.

Equation 18.21 Expected value of the binomial distribution

$$\mu = E(X) = np$$

Equation 18.22 Variance of the binomial distribution

$$\sigma^2 = Var(X) = np(1 - p)$$

Equation 18.23 Standard deviation of the binomial distribution

$$\sigma = \sqrt{np(1-p)}$$

If the parameter p is unknown, it can be estimated by dividing the number of successes by the number of trials, as shown in Equation 18.24. The quality of the estimate will improve as the number of trials increases. We read the term $\hat{p}$ as "p hat." Statisticians often use the hat symbol to signify that a parameter is estimated. The expected value, variance, and standard deviation of the binomial random variable X can be estimated using Equation 18.25, Equation 18.26, and Equation 18.27, respectively.

Equation 18.24 Estimator of p for binomial distribution

$$\hat{p} = \frac{x}{n}$$

Equation 18.25 Mean estimator for binomial distribution

$$\hat{\mu} = \hat{E}(X) = n\hat{p}$$

Equation 18.26 Variance estimator for the binomial distribution

$$\hat{\sigma}^2 = V\hat{a}r(X) = n\hat{p}(1-\hat{p})$$

Equation 18.27 Standard deviation estimator for the binomial distribution

$$\hat{\sigma} = \sqrt{n\hat{p}(1-\hat{p})}$$

Poisson Distribution

The Poisson distribution is used when counting the number of arrivals in a certain period of time, or when counting the number of defects found in a sampling unit of product. In the first case, the Poisson distribution is used in queuing applications. For example, we might want to determine the probability of X or more arrivals in a hospital emergency department during a certain period in order plan for adequate staffing.

The second application of the Poisson distribution allows quality practitioners to determine the probability of X defects per sampling unit. For example, an automobile manufacturer may sample three car hoods per hour and count the total number of paint defects found on those hoods. These defects could include any number of occurrences of dirt, runs, sags, overspray, underspray, or orange-peel defects. This type of data collection is in sharp contrast to that used for the binomial family of distributions, in which a unit is classified as either defective or nondefective or pass/fail.

The Poisson distribution has the following requirements:

1. The random variable X is defined as the number of occurrences of an event over some interval. This interval can be a time interval, or it can be interpreted as a sampling unit.
2. The occurrences are random.
3. The occurrences are independent of each other.
4. The probability of occurrence is constant across the interval of interest.

For the arrivals case, these requirements state that our random variable is the number of arrivals per period of time (hour, shift, week, and so on). The arrivals occur randomly, and each arrival is independent of the others, meaning that one arrival doesn't influence the occurrence of the next arrival, for example. Last, if we are measuring arrivals per hour, the probability of an arrival occurring in minute 15 is the same as the probability of an arrival in minute 59, for example.

For the defect count case, our random variable is the number of defects in the sampling unit, whether that is one car hood, or ten car hoods. The defects are assumed to occur at random and are independent of each other. In addition, the probability of a defect on the right corner of the hood is the same as the probability of a defect occurring in the center of the hood, etc.

Poisson Probability Mass Function

The probability mass function of the Poisson distribution is shown in Equation 18.28.

Equation 18.28 Poisson probability mass function

$$\Pr(X = x) = \frac{e^{-\mu}\mu^x}{x!}, \quad x = 0, 1, 2, \ldots$$

where μ is the sole parameter. Note that some texts use the Greek letter λ to denote the mean of the Poisson distribution. The range of the random variable X has no upper bound.

The term *e* is Euler's number, the result of the following infinite sum:

$$\sum_{i=0}^{\infty} \frac{1}{i!} = \frac{1}{0!} + \frac{1}{1!} + \frac{1}{2!} + \frac{1}{3!} + \frac{1}{4!} + \ldots = e \cong 2.71828$$

When performing calculations for the Poisson distribution on a calculator, it is important to use the "*e*" key instead of approximating by typing in just a few digits of the number, such as 2.72. If you don't use the "*e*" key, your result might have quite a bit of rounding error.

The Poisson probability that X exactly equals some value can be found in Appendix C.1. Based on μ we can find $\Pr(X = x)$ in the interior of the table.

The Poisson cumulative probability mass function is shown in Equation 18.29.

Equation 18.29 Poisson cumulative probability mass function

$$\Pr(X \le x) = \sum_{x=0}^{x} \frac{e^{-\mu}\mu^x}{x!}$$

EXAMPLE 18.14

The number of defects per shift has a Poisson distribution with $\mu = 4.2$. A plot of the probability mass function is shown in Figure 18.8. Find the probability that the second shift produces fewer than two defects.

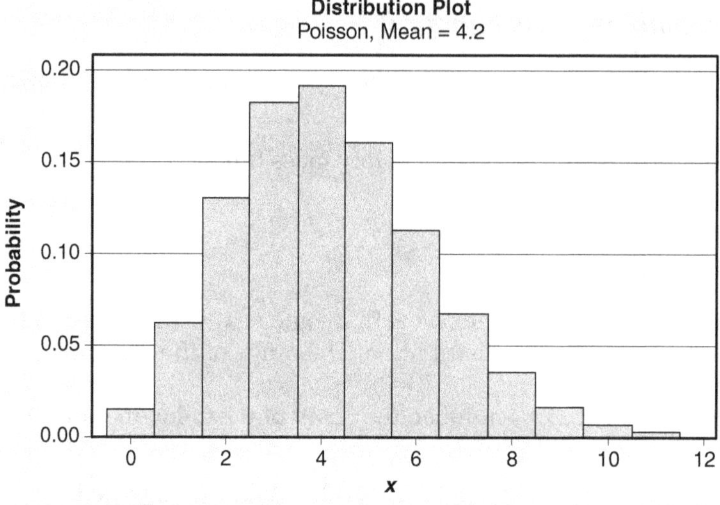

Figure 18.8 Poisson distribution with $\mu = 4.2$ for Example 18.14.

Here, X is a Poisson random variable with $\mu = 4.2$. We want the probability that we find fewer than two defects, which is the same as finding one or zero defects. Using Equation 18.29, we have:

$$\begin{aligned}
\Pr(X \le 1) &= \sum_{x=0}^{x} \frac{e^{-\mu}\mu^{x}}{x!} \\
&= \frac{e^{-4.2}4.2^{0}}{0!} + \frac{e^{-4.2}4.2^{1}}{1!} \\
&= e^{-4.2} + 4.2e^{-4.2} \\
&= 0.015 + 0.063 \\
&= 0.078
\end{aligned}$$

The probability that the second shift produces fewer than two defects is 0.0780.

We can also find the answer using a table of cumulative Poisson probabilities, provided in Appendix C.2. Based on the value of m we can find $\Pr(X \le x)$ in the interior of the table. In addition, we can solve the problem using the Excel function *=poisson.dist*. This function takes three arguments: X, mean, and the cumulative flag. The cumulative argument can be turned on by entering TRUE or the value 1. The function is shown in Figure 18.9.

Continued

Continued

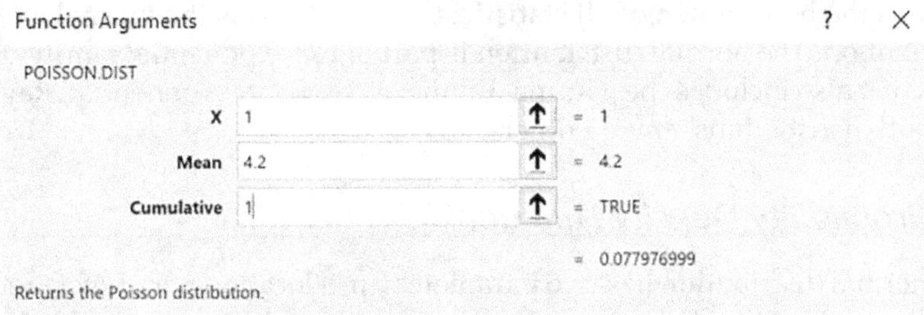

Function Arguments ? ×

POISSON.DIST

X	1	= 1
Mean	4.2	= 4.2
Cumulative	1	= TRUE

= 0.077976999

Returns the Poisson distribution.

Figure 18.9 *Poisson.dist* function in Excel.

Poisson Parameters, Expected Value, and Variance

The Poisson distribution is unusual in that only has one parameter, μ. Both the mean and the variance of the Poisson are equal to m. See Equation 18.30, Equation 18.31, and Equation 18.32.

Equation 18.30 Expected value of the Poisson distribution

$$\mu = E(X) = \mu$$

Equation 18.31 Variance of the Poisson distribution

$$\sigma^2 = Var(X) = \mu$$

Equation 18.32 Standard deviation of the Poisson distribution

$$\sigma = \sqrt{\mu}$$

If the parameter μ is not known, it can be estimated by calculating the average number of observed occurrences over several intervals. The estimators for the Poisson parameters are shown in Equation 18.33 through Equation 18.35.

Equation 18.33 Mean estimator for the Poisson distribution

$$\hat{\mu} = \hat{E}(X) = \overline{X}$$

Equation 18.34 Variance estimator for the Poisson distribution

$$\hat{\sigma}^2 = V\hat{a}r(X) = \overline{X}$$

Equation 18.35 Standard deviation estimator for the Poisson distribution

$$\hat{\sigma} = \sqrt{\overline{X}}$$

The Normal Distribution

Perhaps the best known of all statistical distributions is the normal, or Gaussian, distribution. The normal distribution is part of the exponential family of distributions that also includes the gamma, Erlang, chi-square, exponential, Rayleigh, and Weibull distributions, among others.

Normal Probability Density Function

The normal distribution has two parameters, μ, a location parameter, and s, a scale parameter. Notation for a normally distributed random variable X is X ~ N(μ,σ^2). The parameter μ can take on any value, but σ must be positive. The normal probability density function is shown in Equation 18.36.

Equation 18.36 Normal probability density function

$$f(x) = \frac{1}{\sqrt{2\pi\sigma^2}} e^{-\frac{(x-\mu)^2}{2\sigma^2}}, -\infty < x < \infty$$

This function produces the characteristic bell-shaped curve that we have all seen, an example of which is shown in Figure 18.10.

Figure 18.11 shows that changing μ moves the center of the distribution along the x-axis, while increasing σ makes the distribution more spread out. Note that the normal distribution is always symmetric. Its skewness is equal to zero, and its

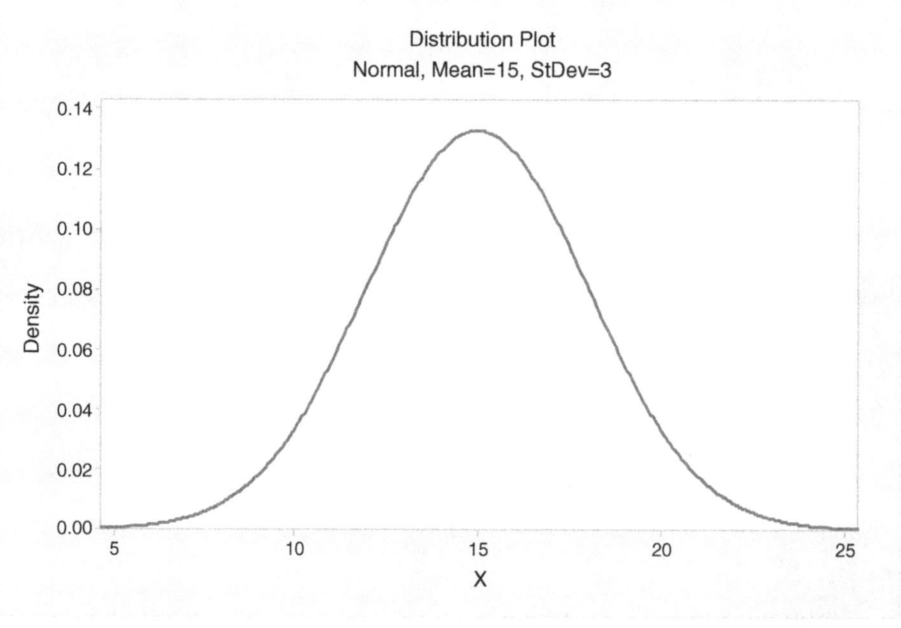

Figure 18.10 Normal distribution curve with μ = 15, σ = 3.

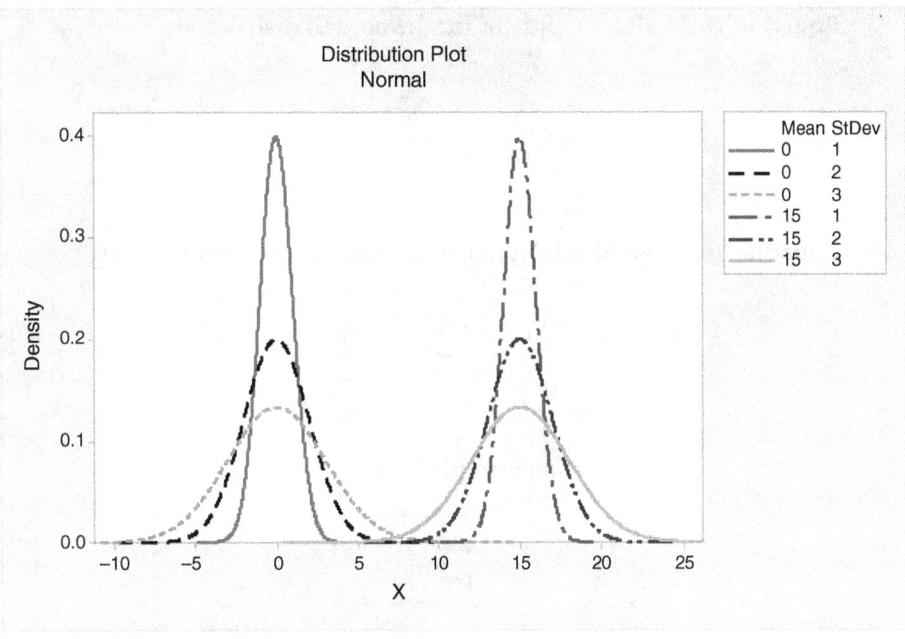

Figure 18.11 Normal distribution with various μ and σ.

kurtosis is equal to three. Often, the normal distribution is used as a standard for kurtosis, and many statistical software packages report excess kurtosis, which is the difference between a distribution's kurtosis and that of the normal distribution. It is calculated as (kurtosis – 3). It follows that the excess kurtosis for the normal distribution is equal to zero.

The expected value of a normally distributed variable X is equal to μ, and the variance is equal to σ^2, as shown in Equation 18.37 and Equation 18.38, respectively.

Equation 18.37 Expected value of normal distribution

$$E(X) = \mu$$

Equation 18.38 Variance of normal distribution

$$Var(X) = \sigma^2$$

Normal Distribution Parameter Estimators

Let $x_1, x_2, \ldots, x_n$ be a random sample from a normal distribution with mean μ and standard deviation σ. We can estimate the distribution parameters using the statistics $\bar{X}$ and s for μ and σ, respectively, as shown in Equation 18.39 and Equation 18.40. To estimate the variance σ^2, we would use the sample variance, s^2. An alternate form of the sample standard deviation equation is shown in Equation 18.41. This form is often used for manual calculations.

Equation 18.39 Mean estimator for the normal distribution

$$\bar{X} = \frac{\sum_{i=1}^{n} x_i}{n}$$

Equation 18.40 Standard deviation estimator for the normal distribution

$$s = \sqrt{\frac{\sum_{i=1}^{n} (x_i - \bar{x})^2}{n-1}}$$

Equation 18.41 Calculation formula for s

$$s = \sqrt{\frac{\sum_{i=1}^{n} x_i^2 - n\bar{x}^2}{n-1}}$$

Notice that the estimated standard deviation shown in Equation 18.40 and Equation 18.41 has $(n - 1)$ in its denominator. This quantity is called the *degrees of freedom,* and it reflects the size of the sample, less any restrictions placed on that sample. How is the restriction determined? In this instance, the restriction stems from using the mean estimator $\bar{x}$ in the calculation. Based on the formula for the sample mean, the quantity $n\bar{x}$ is equal to the sum of the n data points in the sample. Hence, the total has already been determined. For example, let the sum of the sample equal 10. If we have a sample of size of two, the sum would be

$$x_1 + x_2 = 10$$

How many choices would we have for x_1 in this equation? The data point x_1 could be equal to 3, or 17, or –324.6, etc. There is an infinite number of possibilities for x_1, meaning that we have complete freedom for this variable. However, as soon as we assign a number for x_1, x_2 is automatically determined since it must make the sum equal to 10. For two variables, then, we have one degree of freedom. For a sample size of three:

$$x_1 + x_2 + x_3 = 10$$

The points x_1 and x_2 can take on any values, but once these are chosen, x_3 is also automatically determined. Therefore, for a sample size of three, we have one restricted variable and two degrees of freedom.

In general, for a sum of n data points with a known total, there are (n – 1) degrees of freedom.

Uses and Applications

It is hard to underestimate the importance of the normal distribution in statistical analysis. The quality applications of the normal distribution are vast. Consider the following scenarios.

- A design engineer uses the normal distribution to develop tolerances for a new metal part.
- A Six Sigma Black Belt estimates the proportion of units that will fall out of specification if the current process mean shifts by 1.5 standard deviations.
- A quality engineer calculates the capability of a process to report to the customer.
- An R&D engineer tests whether a new design has significantly reduced the average weight of an aerospace component.
- A machine operator tracks the average and range of strength readings of a welded assembly using an X-bar and R chart.

Normal Distribution Connection to Statistical Process Control

Walter Shewhart drew the first statistical process control chart at the Westinghouse plant in Hawthorne, Illinois in 1924. His X chart was based on normal distribution theory and was a technique to monitor the distribution of a process variable. The chart signaled when the process mean or variance changed over time, indicating that a special cause of variation was acting on the process. The X-MR, $\bar{X}$-R, and $\bar{X}$-S charts all use the normal distribution as its basis for the control limits.

In broad terms, if a quality characteristic of a manufactured unit, such as weight, follows a normal distribution, then we can take a single sample at regular time intervals and plot the value of the weights on a control chart. The control limits will correspond to the +/– 3 sigma limits of the process weight distribution. In theory, 99.73% of all weights will fall with these limits. A point falling outside the control limits is most likely an outlier, indicating that the distribution has changed. We then investigate the cause of the outlier and make process adjustments to bring the process back into control. We cover this topic in more depth in Chapter 27.

The Standard Normal Distribution

If X is normally distributed with mean μ and variance σ^2, we can standardize X to have a mean equal to zero and a variance equal to one by computing what is known as a Z score, as shown Equation 18.42. By using the Z transformation, we are given a relative location of a data point x from a normal distribution: The point is $|z|$ standard deviations away from the mean. A negative Z indicates that the point is below the mean, while a positive Z tells us the point is above the mean. A Z equal to zero indicates that the data point is equal to the mean.

Equation 18.42 Z score

$$Z = \frac{(X - \mu)}{\sigma}$$

Standard Normal Probability Density Function

The random variable Z follows a standard normal distribution with E(Z) = 0 and Var(Z) = 1, written as Z ~ N(0,1). The probability density function is thus simplified as shown in Equation 18.43.

Equation 18.43 Probability density of the standard normal distribution

$$f(z) = \frac{1}{\sqrt{2\pi}} e^{-\frac{z^2}{2}}, -\infty < z < \infty$$

Areas Under the Curve

The graph of the standard normal probability density is shown in Figure 18.12. It is centered at the mean, which is equal to zero, and has a standard deviation equal to one.

For continuous distributions, probabilities are calculated as areas under the curve. The normal and standard normal distributions do not have a closed form solution for the area under the curve, so we rely on tabulated values that have

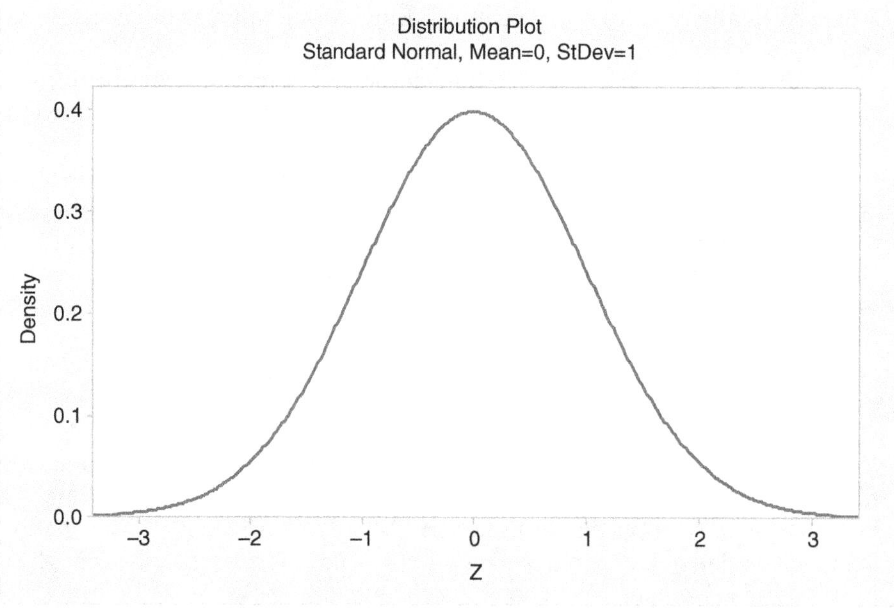

Figure 18.12 Standard normal probability density.

been integrated numerically to find probabilities. To determine a probability for a normal distribution with mean μ and variance σ^2, we first convert X to a standard normal distribution, $Z \sim N(0,1)$. Then we can use a cumulative standard normal table based on the Z scale to find probabilities. Why standardize X to Z? If we didn't, there would have to be a separate table of probabilities for every possible combination of μ and σ^2 (an infinite number of tables).

For all normal distributions, the probability of the random variable X lying with one standard deviation of the mean is 0.6827. The probability is 0.9545 that X is within two standard deviations of the mean, and 0.9973 that X is within three standard deviations of the mean. These probabilities are shown as areas under the curve in Figure 18.13, Figure 18.14, and Figure 18.15, respectively.

Using the Cumulative Standard Normal Table

The cumulative standard normal table in Appendix D gives the probability that the random variable Z is equal to or less than some value *a*. Note that for continuous distributions there is no probability associated with a single point. Therefore, the statements $\Pr(Z \leq a)$ and $\Pr(Z < a)$ are equivalent since $\Pr(Z = a) = 0$.

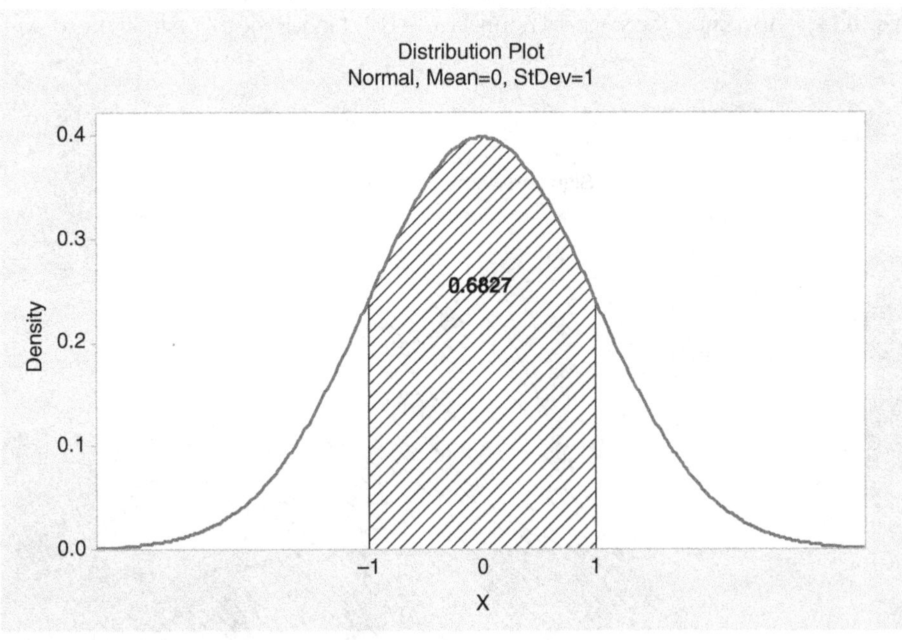

Figure 18.13 Area under the standard normal curve, ±1 standard deviation from the mean.

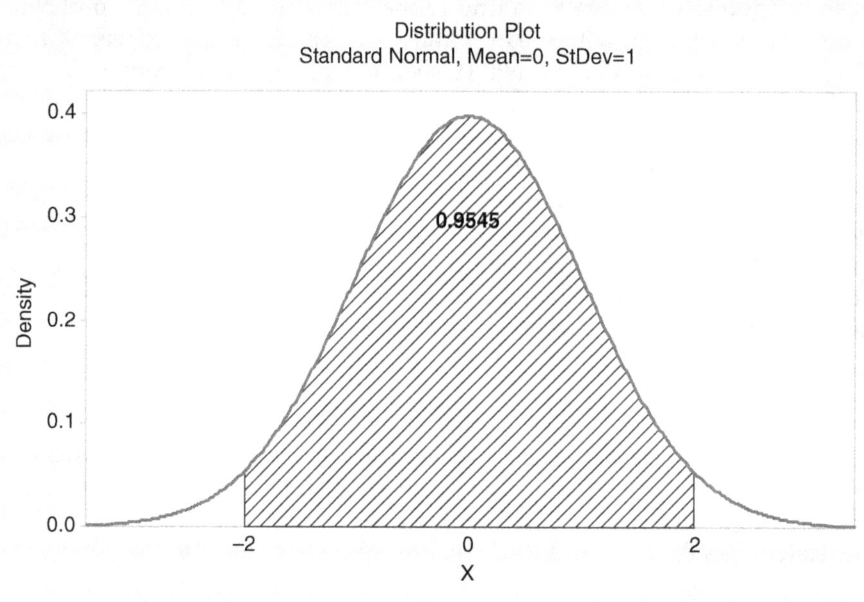

Figure 18.14 Area under the standard normal curve, ±2 standard deviation from the mean.

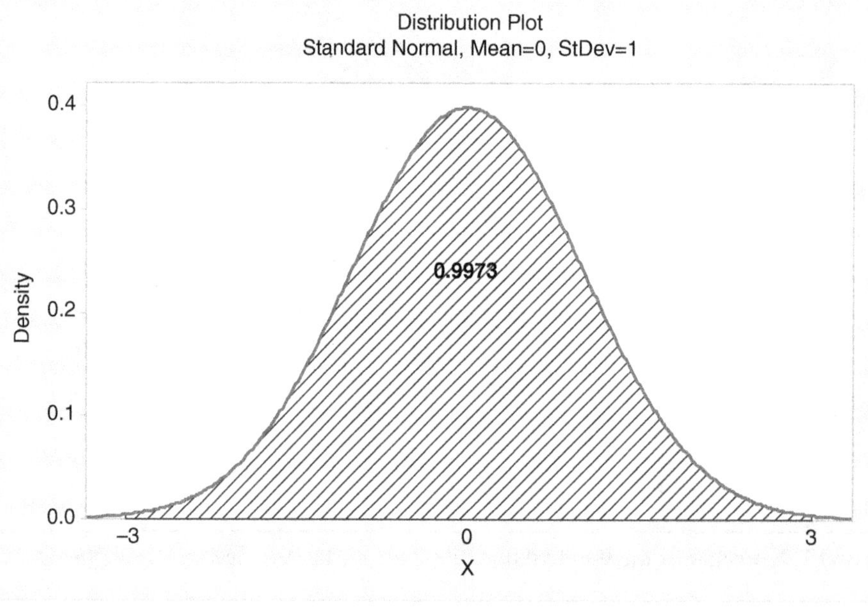

Figure 18.15 Area under the standard normal curve, ±3 standard deviations from the mean.

EXAMPLE 18.15

Let X ~ N(10, 4). If we want to know the probability that X is less than the value 12.1, we first convert to the Z scale:

$$Z = \frac{(X - \mu)}{\sigma} = \frac{(12.1 - 10)}{2} = 1.05$$

A portion of the cumulative standard normal table is shown in Table 18.6. To find Pr(Z ≤ 1.05), we look up the value 1.05 and read off the corresponding probability from the interior of the table. The value Z = 1.05 is found by using the first column to find 1.0 and then by looking across the top of the table to find the hundredths place 0.05. The corresponding value 0.85314 is the probability that Z is less than or equal to 1.05.

Standard Normal Z Table

Table values give $\phi(z) = \Pr(Z < z)$ for positive values of z

z	0.00	0.01	0.02	0.03	0.04	0.05	0.06	0.07	0.08	0.09
0.0	0.50000	0.50399	0.50798	0.51197	0.51595	0.51994	0.52392	0.52790	0.53188	0.53586
0.1	0.53983	0.54380	0.54776	0.55172	0.55567	0.55962	0.56356	0.56749	0.57142	0.57535
0.2	0.57926	0.58317	0.58706	0.59095	0.59483	0.59871	0.60257	0.60642	0.61026	0.61409
0.3	0.61791	0.62172	0.62552	0.62930	0.63307	0.63683	0.64058	0.64431	0.64803	0.65173
0.4	0.65542	0.65910	0.66276	0.66640	0.67003	0.67364	0.67724	0.68082	0.68439	0.68793
0.5	0.69146	0.69497	0.69847	0.70194	0.70540	0.70884	0.71226	0.71566	0.71904	0.72240
0.6	0.72575	0.72907	0.73237	0.73565	0.73891	0.74215	0.74537	0.74857	0.75175	0.75490
0.7	0.75804	0.76115	0.76424	0.76730	0.77035	0.77337	0.77637	0.77935	0.78230	0.78524
0.8	0.78814	0.79103	0.79389	0.79673	0.79955	0.80234	0.80511	0.80785	0.81057	0.81327
0.9	0.81594	0.81859	0.82121	0.82381	0.82639	0.82894	0.83147	0.83398	0.83646	0.83891
1.0	0.84134	0.84375	0.84614	0.84849	0.85083	0.85314	0.85543	0.85769	0.85993	0.86214
1.1	0.86433	0.86650	0.86864	0.87076	0.87286	0.87493	0.87698	0.87900	0.88100	0.88298

Table 18.6 Cumulative probabilities of the standard normal distribution, partial table.

We can also use the *=norm.dist* function in Excel. This function takes four arguments: X, mean, standard deviation, and the cumulative flag. The cumulative argument can be turned on by entering TRUE or 1. The function is shown in Figure 18.16.

Continued

Continued

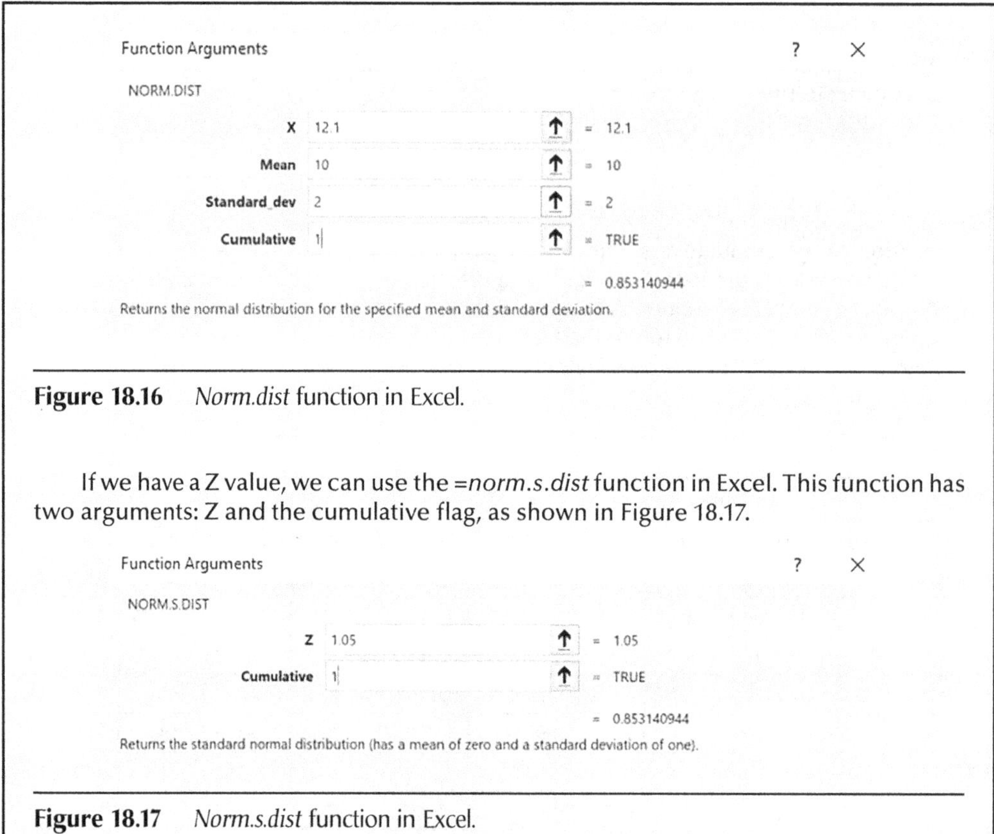

Figure 18.16 *Norm.dist* function in Excel.

If we have a Z value, we can use the *=norm.s.dist* function in Excel. This function has two arguments: Z and the cumulative flag, as shown in Figure 18.17.

Figure 18.17 *Norm.s.dist* function in Excel.

EXAMPLE 18.16

FINDING THE PROBABILITY THAT Z IS GREATER THAN THE VALUE a

If we want the probability that Z is *greater than* some value a, we can make use of the complement rule. Using the table, we can find the probability that Z is *less than* a, and then subtract the result from one. For example, to find $\Pr(Z > 1.05)$, we use the table and the complement to find $1 - \Pr(Z \le 1.05) = (1 - 0.8531) = 0.1469$, as shown in Figure 18.18.

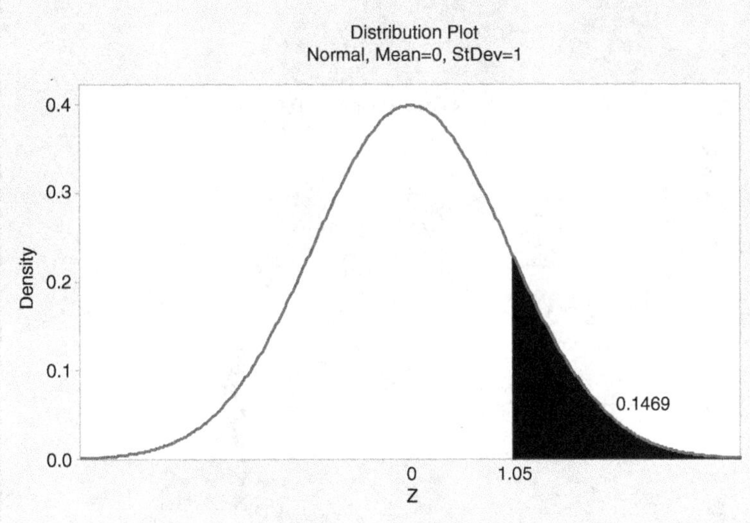

Figure 18.18 $\Pr(Z > 1.05)$.

EXAMPLE 18.17

FINDING THE PROBABILITY THAT Z IS BETWEEN TWO VALUES

The probability that Z is within an interval can be solved by first sketching the normal curve and shading in the area of interest. The sketch makes it clear what values need to be looked up and what needs to be done with them.

For example, to find Pr(1.20 < Z < 2.08), we can create the sketch found in Figure 18.19.

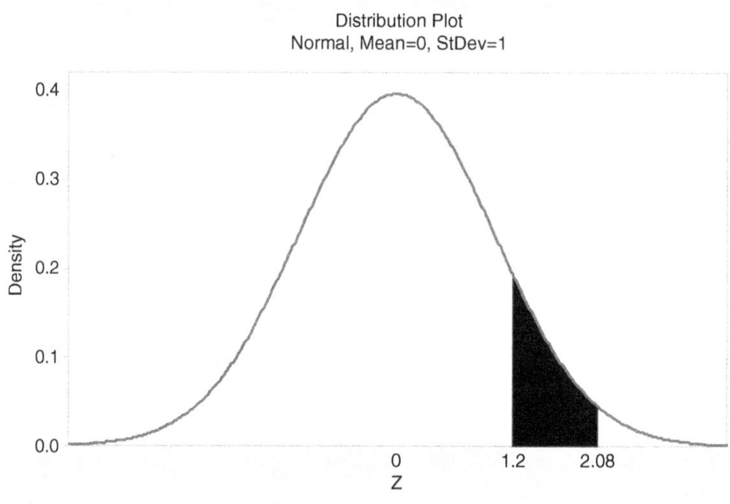

Figure 18.19 Pr(1.20 < Z < 2.08).

We see that we will need to find the area between the values 1.20 and 2.08. If we look up 2.08 in the standard normal table, that will give us the area from 2.08 all the way down to minus infinity. That area is more than we want. If we subtract off the area that is less than 1.20, we will be left with the shaded-in area between these two numbers, which is what we need to solve the problem.

$$Pr(1.20 < Z < 2.08) = Pr(Z < 2.08) - Pr(Z < 1.20) = 0.9812 - 0.8849 = 0.0963$$

EXAMPLE 18.18

FINDING THE PROBABILITY THAT Z IS LESS THAN A NEGATIVE VALUE

The standard normal distribution is centered on zero, which means half of its values are negative. Most cumulative standard normal tables do not include entries for negative Z values, but we have provided one in this handbook. We can find the probability of Z less than any negative value directly using the table in Appendix D. Once again, sketching is a vital step in understanding what area we are seeking. For example, if we need to find Pr(Z < –1.40), we can create a sketch similar to Figure 18.20.

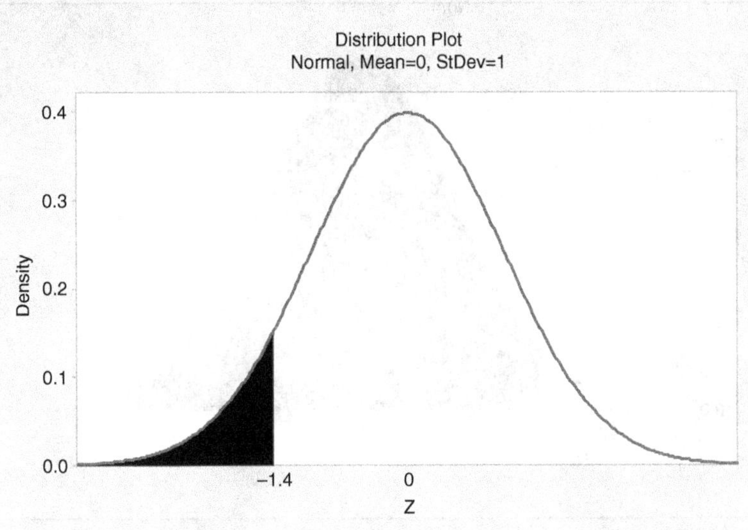

Figure 18.20 Pr(Z < –1.40).

We find Pr(Z < –1.40) = 0.0808 from Appendix D.

EXAMPLE 18.19

FINDING THE PROBABILITY THAT Z IS GREATER THAN A NEGATIVE VALUE

In order to find the probability that Z is greater than a negative value, we sketch and use the complement rule. For example, to find Pr(Z > –1.88), we first sketch as in Figure 18.21. Using Appendix D and the complement rule, we have Pr(Z > –1.88) = 1 – Pr(Z < –1.88) = 1 – 0.0301 = 0.9699.

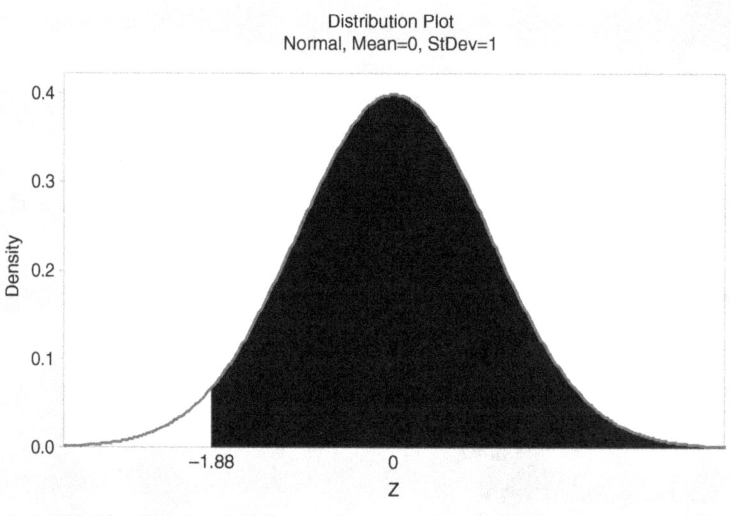

Figure 18.21 Pr(Z > –1.88).

EXAMPLE 18.20

FINDING THE PROBABILITY THAT Z IS BETWEEN TWO NEGATIVE VALUES

To find the probability that Z lies in an interval bounded by two negative values, we can sketch and use the table in Appendix D. For example, to find Pr(–2.34 < Z < –0.42), we use the sketch in Figure 18.22 and write:

$$\begin{aligned} Pr(-2.34 < Z < -0.42) &= Pr(Z < -0.42) - Pr(Z < -2.34) \\ &= 0.4904 - 0.1628 \\ &= 0.3276. \end{aligned}$$

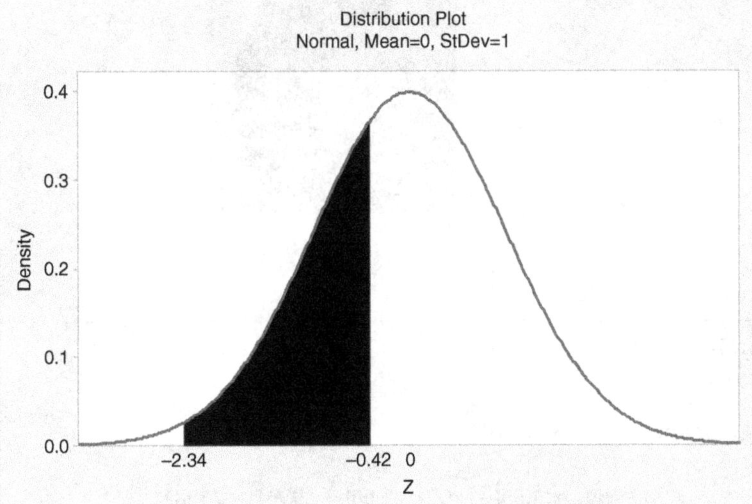

Figure 18.22 Pr(–2.34 < Z < –0.42).

EXAMPLE 18.21

FINDING THE PROBABILITY THAT Z IS BETWEEN A NEGATIVE AND A POSITIVE VALUE

To find Pr(–1.00 < Z < 1.55), we have the sketch in Figure 18.23:

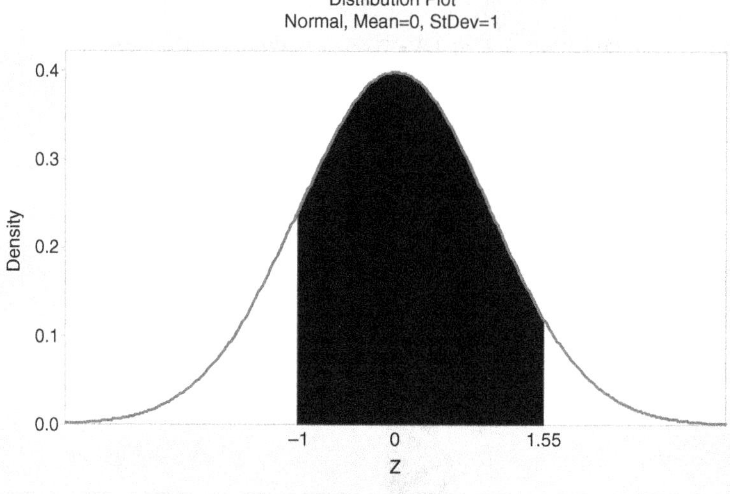

Figure 18.23 Pr(–1.00 < Z < 1.55).

Using Appendix D, we can solve:

$$\begin{aligned} Pr(Z < 1.55) - Pr(Z < -1.00) &= 0.9394 - (0.1587) \\ &= 0.7807. \end{aligned}$$

EXAMPLE 18.22

DETERMINING Z = a, GIVEN A PROBABILITY

In the examples and exercises in the last section, we were given a value *a*, and asked to find the probability that Z was less than *a*. What if we are given the probability, and asked to find *a*? We need to, in effect, read the Z table inside-out to find this answer. For example:

$$\text{If } \Pr(Z < a) = 0.9868, \text{ find } a.$$

The first thing we need to determine is if the value *a* is negative or positive. By sketching the normal curve, we see that the value *a* must be positive, since the probability that Z is less than the value *a* is more than 0.50. We can look directly in the table in Appendix D, find 0.9868 in the interior, then read over and up to find the *a* value. Here, *a* equals 2.22.

In Excel we can solve this problem by using the general *=norm.inv* function, or the *=norm.s.inv* function for the standard normal. The *norm.s.inv* function takes one argument, probability. The solution is shown in Figure 18.24.

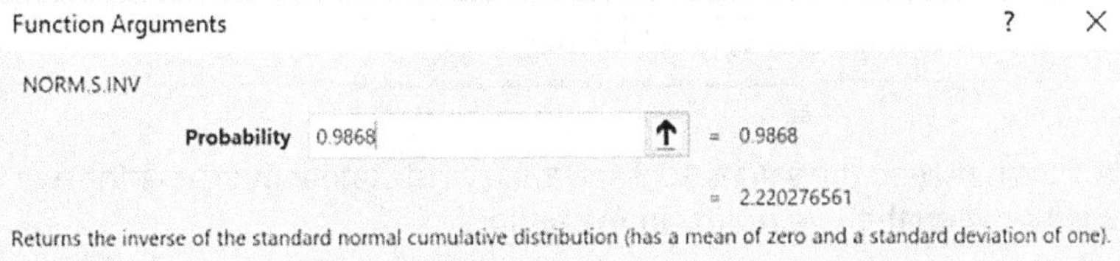

Function Arguments ? ×

NORM.S.INV

Probability 0.9868 ↑ = 0.9868

= 2.220276561

Returns the inverse of the standard normal cumulative distribution (has a mean of zero and a standard deviation of one).

Figure 18.24 *Norm.s.inv* function in Excel.

EXAMPLE 18.23

Next let's find $\Pr(Z < a) = .0708$. A quick sketch shows that *a* must be negative since the $\Pr(Z < a)$ is less than 0.50. To use the table, we first write the probability statement in terms of the positive *a* value:

$$\Pr(Z < -a) = 0.0708$$

We now find the value *a* corresponding to 0.0708, which is –1.47. Therefore, our solution is $\Pr(Z < -1.47) = 0.0708$.

EXAMPLE 18.24

LINEAR INTERPOLATION FOR PROBABILITY TABLES

What if, when solving for *a*, we can't find the exact probability in the interior of the table? In effect, the answer *a* is actually between two Z values. In these cases, we use *linear interpolation* to solve for *a*.

For example, say we need to solve the following statement for *a*:

$$\Pr(Z < a) = 0.9378$$

Since 0.9378 is greater than 0.50, we know that *a* is positive. Look for the value 0.9378 in the interior of the cumulative standard normal table. There is no exact match in the table, but two values are close:

a	Pr(Z < a) = p
1.53	0.9370
1.54	0.9382

The value *a* lies between the values 1.53 and 1.54. Using linear interpolation, we first find the slope m between the two points in the table:

$$m = \frac{\Delta y}{\Delta x} = \frac{\Delta a}{\Delta p} = \frac{a_2 - a_1}{p_2 - p_1} = \frac{(1.54 - 1.53)}{(0.9382 - 0.9370)} = \frac{0.01}{0.0012}$$

Next, we find how far the probability of interest is from the smaller probability value we have found in the table. Based on our problem, the probability of interest is 0.9378.

$$p - p_1 = (0.9378 - 0.9370) = 0.0008$$

Putting things together, we can find *a*:

$$\begin{aligned} a &= a_1 + (p - p_1)m \\ &= 1.53 + (0.0008)\frac{0.01}{0.0012} \\ &= 1.5367 \end{aligned}$$

Student's *t* Distribution

William Gossett was a brilliant mathematician who eventually became chief statistician at Guinness Brewing. In order to protect its trade secrets, Guinness prohibited employees from publishing research papers. Gossett was eventually allowed to publish his paper on the distribution of small samples, but only if he used a pseudonym. Hence, Gossett's paper appeared under the pseudonym of "Student" in Karl Pearson's journal *Biometrika* in 1908. Although Pearson did not appreciate the usefulness of the *t* distribution, R.A. Fisher recognized its merits and started using the *t* test for small samples and in regression analysis testing. Throughout his life, Gossett continued to publish under the pseudonym Student.

Student's t *Probability Density Function*

If we take *n* independent samples from a normal distribution with mean μ and standard deviation σ, then the random variable shown in Equation 18.44 follows a Student's *t* distribution with v degrees of freedom. The value of v is based on the sample size n, where $v = (n - 1)$. Note the random variable's similarity to the normal Z score for an average.

Equation 18.44 Student's *t* random variable

$$t = \frac{(\bar{X} - \mu)}{s/\sqrt{n}} \sim t(n-1)$$

The Student's *t* distribution has a single parameter, ν, or degrees of freedom. The distribution function is shown in Equation 18.45.

Equation 18.45 Probability density of Student's *t* distribution

$$f(x) = \frac{\Gamma\left(\frac{v+1}{2}\right)}{\sqrt{\pi v}\,\Gamma\left(\frac{v}{2}\right)\left(1+\frac{x^2}{v}\right)^{\frac{v+1}{2}}}, \quad -\infty < x < \infty$$

The term Γ is the *gamma function*. The gamma function is an integral, but for any positive integer n, the function simplifies to $\Gamma(n) = (n-1)!$.

The expected value and variance of the Student's *t* distribution are shown in Equation 18.46 and Equation 18.47, respectively.

Equation 18.46 Expected value of Student's *t* distribution

$$E(X) = 0$$

Equation 18.47 Variance of Student's *t* distribution

$$Var(X) = \frac{v}{v-2}, \quad v > 2$$

Distribution Shape

The Student's *t* distribution is centered at $\mu = 0$ and is symmetric around its mean. The distribution resembles the bell shape of the normal distribution, but with heavier tails, or leptokurtic. The distribution becomes more and more like a normal distribution as the degrees of freedom increase. Figure 18.25 shows the difference in shape for the Student's *t* distribution various degrees of freedom. As the degrees of freedom increase, the shape looks more and more like a normal distribution.

Using the Student's t Table

We use a Student's *t* table to find cumulative probabilities. An excerpt from the table found in Appendix E is shown in Table 18.7. In this table, the degrees of freedom are denoted by the Greek letter *v*, or nu. Each row corresponds to different value for degrees of freedom, which constitutes a separate distribution. The table columns map to different probabilities for the expression Pr(X < x). The interior of the table gives Student's *t* values associated with various values for degrees of freedom and cumulative probabilities.

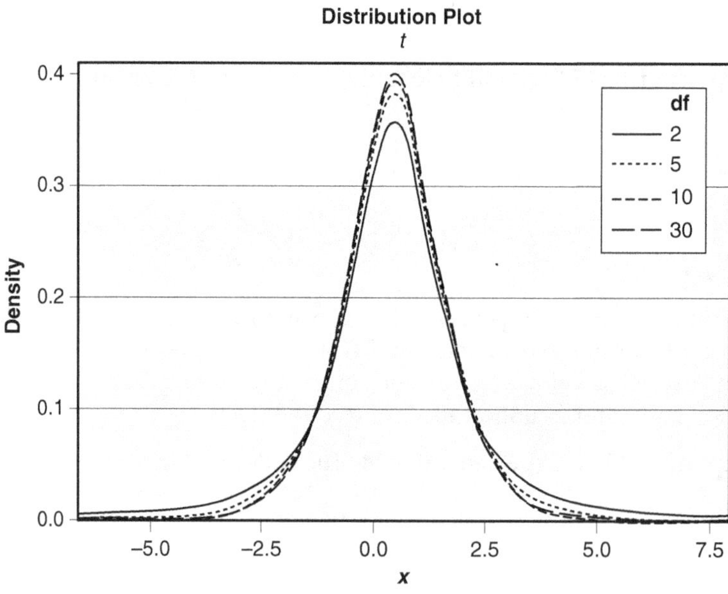

Figure 18.25 Example of a Student's *t* distribution with various degrees of freedom.

Student's *t* Cumulative Distribution Table					
Degrees of freedom, ν	α				
	0.1	**0.05**	**0.025**	**0.01**	**0.005**
1	3.078	6.314	12.706	31.821	63.657
2	1.886	2.92	4.303	6.965	9.925
3	1.638	2.353	3.182	4.541	5.841
4	1.533	2.132	2.776	3.747	4.604
5	1.476	2.015	2.571	3.365	4.032
6	1.44	1.943	2.447	3.143	3.707
7	1.415	1.895	2.365	2.998	3.499
8	1.397	1.86	2.306	2.896	3.355
9	1.383	1.833	2.262	2.821	3.25
10	1.372	1.812	2.228	2.764	3.169
11	1.363	1.796	2.201	2.718	3.106

Table 18.7 Excerpt from the Student's *t* table.

EXAMPLE 18.25

We will find the $(1-\alpha)$ critical value for a Student's *t* distribution with $(n - 1) = 9$ degrees of freedom for $\alpha = 0.05$.

Using the Student's *t* table in Appendix E we find the row with $v = 9$ degrees of freedom and read across to the 0.95 column. The critical value is 1.833, meaning that $Pr(t < 1.833) = 0.95$.

Uses and Applications

If the underlying distribution of a population being sampled is normal, but we do not know the value of the parameter σ, we can use the Student's *t* distribution to model the data. Since we are estimating σ (via s) from our sample of size n, the Student's *t* distribution takes this uncertainty into account by producing a bell-shaped distribution with more weight in the tails than a normal distribution. As our sample size increases, the tails increasingly resemble those of a standard normal distribution. Some statistics texts advise that an analyst can use the Z distribution in this situation if $n > 30$. However, since the critical values of the Student's *t* distribution are available in tables and easily accessible through software packages, an analyst would be better served to use the Student's *t* for large sample sizes as well.

Examples of the use of the Student's *t* distribution include:

- A quality manager uses the Student's *t* distribution to determine whether the mean burst strength of paper packages exceeds the minimum standard.
- A Six Sigma Green Belt uses the Student's *t* distribution to test whether there is a difference in mean porosity for two different membrane designs.
- A quality engineer uses a paired *t* test to evaluate the effectiveness of a new training program by analyzing the mean improvement in test scores before and after training.

Chi-square Distribution

The chi-square (pronounced *kai – square*) distribution is a workhorse in statistical analysis. It is used to perform parametric tests on the variance of a normal distribution, and in non-parametric tests of independence for contingency tables, Goodness of Fit tests, for example.

Chi-square Probability Density Function

The chi-square distribution is a special case of the gamma distribution with $\alpha = \nu/2$ and $\beta = 2$. The term ν is the degrees of freedom for the chi-square distribution. The chi-square random variable X is a function of the sample variance of the normal distribution, s^2. The random variable shown in Equation 18.48 follows a chi-square distribution with $\nu = (n - 1)$ degrees of freedom:

Equation 18.48 Chi-square random variable

$$\frac{(n-1)s^2}{\sigma^2} \sim \chi^2(n-1)$$

The pdf of the chi-square distribution is shown in Equation 18.49.

Equation 18.49 Probability density of chi-square distribution

$$f(x) = \frac{x^{\left(\frac{\nu}{2}-1\right)} e^{-x/2}}{\Gamma\left(\frac{\nu}{2}\right) 2^{\left(\frac{\nu}{2}\right)}}, x > 0$$

The term Γ is the *gamma function*. The gamma function is an integral, but for any positive integer n, the function simplifies to $\Gamma(n) = (n - 1)!$.

The expected value and variance of the chi-square distribution are displayed in Equation 18.50 and Equation 18.51, respectively.

Equation 18.50 Expected value of chi-square distribution

$$E(X) = \nu$$

Equation 18.51 Variance of chi-square distribution

$$Var(X) = 2\nu$$

Distribution Shape

The chi-square distribution becomes more symmetric as the degrees of freedom increase, as shown in Figure 18.26.

Using the Chi-square Distribution Table

The chi-square table in Appendix F gives the chi-square values x associated with Pr(X > x). To find a critical value, read down the first column to find the appropriate degrees of freedom and then read across to the desired alpha level. The intersection of the row and column will give the critical value.

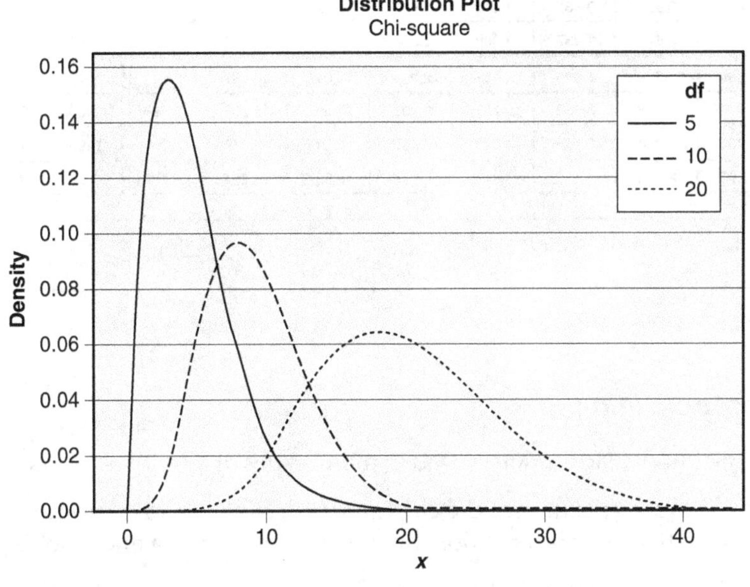

Figure 18.26 Example of chi-square distributions with various degrees of freedom.

EXAMPLE 18.26

We will find the critical value for a chi-square distribution with ν = 7 degrees of freedom and α = 0.025 using the partial table in Figure 18.27. (Note that the full table can be found in Appendix F.)

We read down the first column to find ν = 7, and then read across until we get to the column with α = 0.025. The intersection of the row and column gives us the critical value of 16.013.

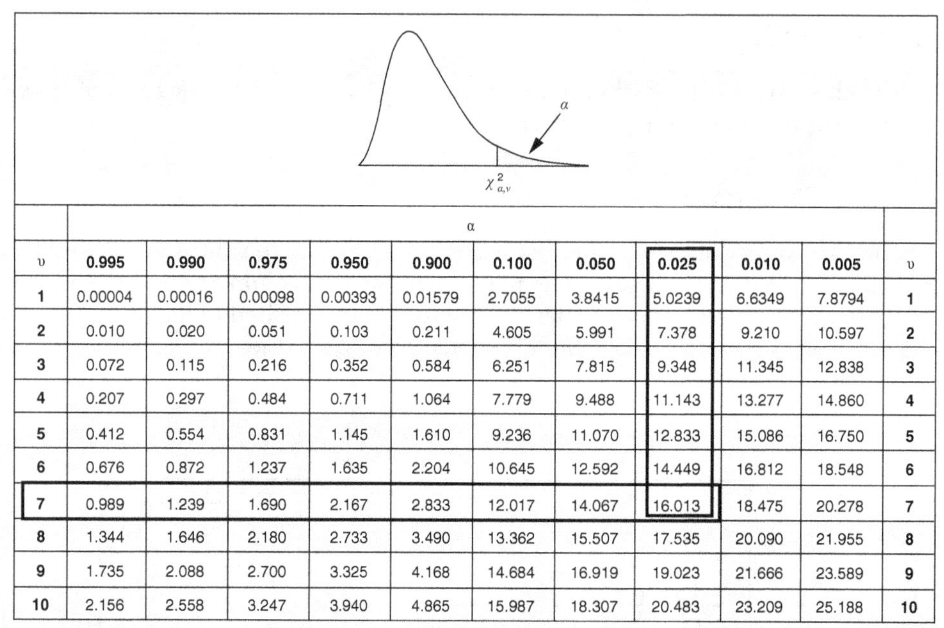

υ	α 0.995	0.990	0.975	0.950	0.900	0.100	0.050	0.025	0.010	0.005	υ
1	0.00004	0.00016	0.00098	0.00393	0.01579	2.7055	3.8415	5.0239	6.6349	7.8794	1
2	0.010	0.020	0.051	0.103	0.211	4.605	5.991	7.378	9.210	10.597	2
3	0.072	0.115	0.216	0.352	0.584	6.251	7.815	9.348	11.345	12.838	3
4	0.207	0.297	0.484	0.711	1.064	7.779	9.488	11.143	13.277	14.860	4
5	0.412	0.554	0.831	1.145	1.610	9.236	11.070	12.833	15.086	16.750	5
6	0.676	0.872	1.237	1.635	2.204	10.645	12.592	14.449	16.812	18.548	6
7	0.989	1.239	1.690	2.167	2.833	12.017	14.067	16.013	18.475	20.278	7
8	1.344	1.646	2.180	2.733	3.490	13.362	15.507	17.535	20.090	21.955	8
9	1.735	2.088	2.700	3.325	4.168	14.684	16.919	19.023	21.666	23.589	9
10	2.156	2.558	3.247	3.940	4.865	15.987	18.307	20.483	23.209	25.188	10

Figure 18.27 Partial chi-square table.

Uses and Applications

The chi-square distribution is used in many types of hypothesis tests. For example:

- A biostatistician uses the chi-square distribution to determine whether there is a relationship between melanoma and smoking.
- An engineer uses a chi-square distribution to test whether the variance in a part's dimension is less than a published industry standard.
- A quality engineer uses a chi-square test to determine whether a data set follows a uniform distribution.

The F Distribution

The F distribution was developed by George Snedecor who named it in honor of the statistician R.A. Fisher. It is used for testing the equality of two variances from normal populations. The F distribution is also used in the analysis of variance (ANOVA) to test the equality of means. In ANOVA, the F statistic compares the magnitude of the *between sample* variation to the *within sample* variation.

F Probability Density Function

Let the random variable X follow the form

$$X = \frac{U/a}{V/b}$$

where U and V are independent chi-square random variables with a and b degrees of freedom, respectively. Then, X follows an F(a, b) distribution. Recall from the previous section that the random variable $\frac{(n-1)s^2}{\sigma^2}$ follows a chi-square distribution with (n – 1) degrees of freedom. Therefore, we can rewrite the formula for the F random variable as:

$$X = \frac{\frac{(n_1-1)s_1^2}{\sigma^2} \Big/ (n_1-1)}{\frac{(n_2-1)s_2^2}{\sigma^2} \Big/ (n_2-1)} = \frac{s_1^2}{s_2^2}$$

Here, X follows an F distribution with $a = n_1 - 1$ and $b = n_2 - 1$.

It should be noted that if X ~ F(a, b), then the reciprocal $\frac{1}{X}$ will also follow an F distribution, but with degrees of freedom (b, a). This relationship is useful when finding cumulative probabilities of the F distribution, as we will see in Example 18.27.

The pdf of the F distribution is shown in Equation 18.52.

Equation 18.52 Probability density function of the F distribution

$$f(x) = \frac{\Gamma\left(\frac{a+b}{2}\right) a^{\frac{a}{2}} b^{\frac{b}{2}} x^{\left(\frac{a}{2}-1\right)}}{\Gamma\left(\frac{a}{2}\right)\Gamma\left(\frac{b}{2}\right)(a+bx)^{\frac{(a+b)}{2}}},\ x > 0,\ a,b > 0$$

The term Γ is the *gamma function*. The gamma function is an integral, but for any positive integer n, the function simplifies to $\Gamma(n) = (n-1)!$.

The expected value of the random variable F is calculated using Equation 18.53.

Equation 18.53 Expected value of F distribution

$$E(X) = \frac{b}{b-2}, \quad b > 2$$

The variance of F is undefined for $0 < b \leq 2$ and is infinite for $2 < b \leq 4$. For $b > 4$, the variance can be expressed using Equation 18.54.

Equation 18.54 Variance of F distribution

$$Var(X) = 2\left(\frac{b}{b-2}\right)^2 \frac{a+b-2}{a(b-4)}, \quad b > 4$$

Distribution Shape

The F distribution takes on various shapes depending on its degrees of freedom, as shown in Figure 18.28.

The F distribution is related to the Student's t distribution. If the random variable X follows a Student's t distribution with $(n - 1)$ degrees of freedom, then $Y = X^2$ follows an F distribution with $(1, (n - 1))$ degrees of freedom. This outcome is shown in Figure 20.19 in Chapter 20.

Using the F Distribution Table

The F distribution changes shape based on two sets of degrees of freedom. The F tables presented in statistics textbooks generally give separate tables for the often-used, right-tail probabilities $Pr(F > F_0)$ of 0.10, 0.05, 0.025, and 0.01, which map

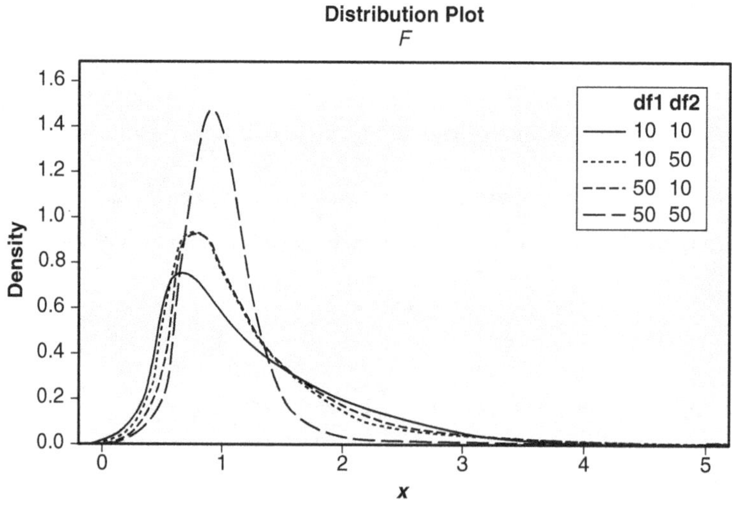

Figure 18.28 Example of F distributions with various degrees of freedom.

to the 90th, 95th, 97.5th, and 99th percentiles, respectively. For convenience, this handbook provides the cumulative F tables for the lower tails as well, which map to $Pr(F < F_0)$, or the right tail probabilities 0.90, 0.95, 0.975, and 0.99.

To use the F tables, match the percentile of interest, find the column and row associated with the numerator and denominator degrees of freedom, respectively, and read off the value of the F statistic. An excerpt of a 95th percentile table is shown in Table 18.8. The full set of F tables are found in Appendix G.

F distribution 95th percentile (5 percent in the right tail)									
	df numerator								
df denominator	**1**	**2**	**3**	**4**	**5**	**6**	**7**	**8**	**9**
1	161.448	199.500	215.707	224.583	230.162	233.986	236.768	238.883	240.543
2	18.513	19.000	19.164	19.247	19.296	19.330	19.353	19.371	19.385
3	10.128	9.552	9.277	9.117	9.013	8.941	8.887	8.845	8.812
4	7.709	6.944	6.591	6.388	6.256	6.163	6.094	6.041	5.999
5	6.608	5.786	5.409	5.192	5.050	4.950	4.876	4.818	4.772
6	5.987	5.143	4.757	4.534	4.387	4.284	4.207	4.147	4.099
7	5.591	4.737	4.347	4.120	3.972	3.866	3.787	3.726	3.677
8	5.318	4.459	4.066	3.838	3.687	3.581	3.500	3.438	3.388
9	5.117	4.256	3.863	3.633	3.482	3.374	3.293	3.230	3.179
10	4.965	4.103	3.708	3.478	3.326	3.217	3.135	3.072	3.020

Table 18.8 Excerpt of $\alpha = 0.05$, 95th percentile F table.

EXAMPLE 18.27

To find the value associated with the 95th percentile of an F(6,9) distribution, we can use Table 18.8 to find $x = 3.374$. This value would solve the statement $\Pr(F < x) = 0.95$, as shown in Figure 18.29.

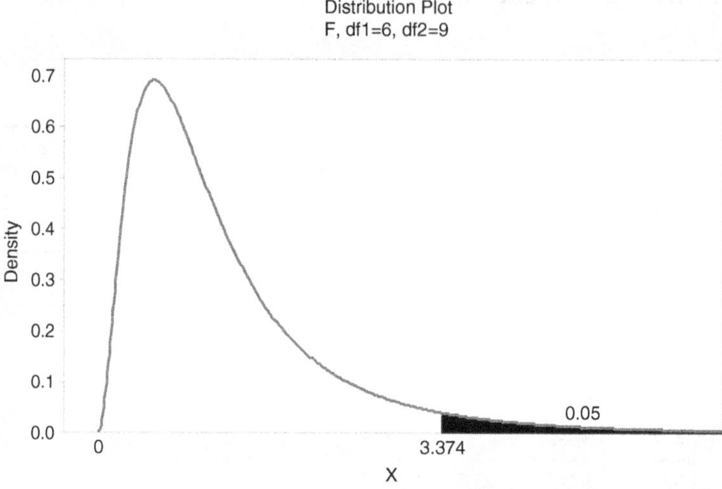

Figure 18.29 Distribution plot for F(6, 9).

EXAMPLE 18.28

This handbook provides cumulative F tables for left-tail and right-tail probabilities, but many textbooks do not. In those cases, to find the 0.05, 0.025, and 0.01 *left-tail* probability values that map to the 5th, 2.5th and 1st percentiles, respectively, we can use the relationship:

$$F_{0.05}(a,b) = \frac{1}{F_{0.95}(b,a)}$$

To find the value from an F(20, 7) distribution associated with the 5th percentile, we use the table to find the value from F(7, 20) associated with the 95th percentile. Then we take the reciprocal of this value, as shown in Figure 18.30.

$$F_{0.05}(20,7) = \frac{1}{F_{0.95}(7,20)} = \frac{1}{2.5140} = 0.3978$$

Note that we can find $F_{0.05,20,7}$ directly using the table in Appendix G.3.

Continued

Continued

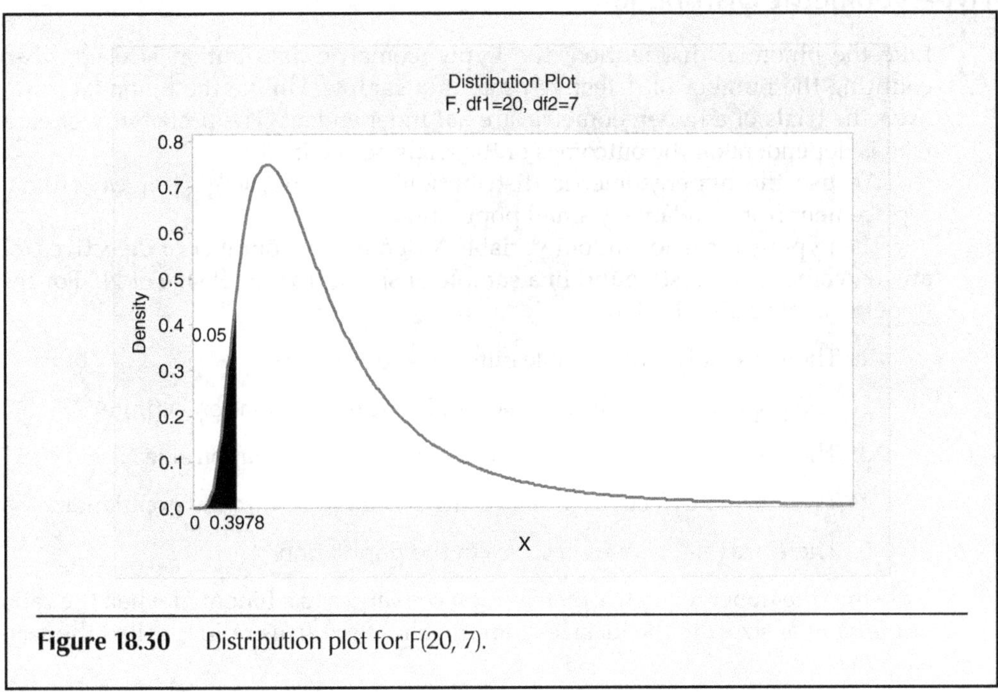

Figure 18.30 Distribution plot for F(20, 7).

Uses and Applications

The F distribution is used in several types of hypothesis tests. For example:

- A quality engineer tests whether the variability of two production lines is equivalent.
- A Six Sigma Black Belt tests whether the mean weights of injected molded parts made from four machines is equal.
- A statistician performs a Goodness of Fit test for a multiple regression analysis.

ADDITIONAL DISTRIBUTIONS

> Identify hypergeometric, bivariate normal, exponential, lognormal, and Weibull distributions. (Understand)
>
> **Body of Knowledge V.E.3**

Hypergeometric Distribution

Like the binomial distribution, the hypergeometric distribution is used when counting the number of defective units in a sample. Unlike the binomial, however, the trials of a hypergeometric are *not* independent. The probability of each trial is dependent on the outcomes of the trials before it.

We use the hypergeometric distribution when choosing samples without replacement from a relatively small population.

The hypergeometric random variable X denotes the number of defectives (or any outcome of interest) found in a sample of size n from a lot size of N. For the hypergeometric distribution,

1. There are only two possible outcomes for each trial.
2. The population size is denoted as N, and the population is finite.
3. The sample size *n* is less than or equal to the population size N.
4. There are D defectives (or any outcome of interest) in the population.
5. There are (N-D) non-defectives in the population.

Note that the hypergeometric distribution converges to a binomial when the ratio of the sample size *n* to the lot size N approaches zero. This ratio is called the *sampling fraction.*

Hypergeometric Probability Mass Function

The probability mass function for the hypergeometric variable X is shown in Equation 18.55:

Equation 18.55 Hypergeometric probability mass function

$$\Pr(X=x)=\frac{\binom{D}{x}\binom{N-D}{n-x}}{\binom{N}{n}},x\in\{\max(0,n-(N-D)),\ldots,\min(n,D)\}$$

In Equation 18.55, we find the probability of finding X = x defectives in a sample of size n. The population is finite and equal to N. Within that population, we have D defectives and N-D non-defectives. The numerator counts the number of ways we can choose x defectives and (n-x) non-defectives from the population. The denominator counts the number of ways a sample of *n* can be chosen from a population of size N.

The hypergeometric random variable has a discrete, finite number of possible outcomes. Based on Equation 18.55, the range of the random variable may look very confusing. The extra complication stems from the fact that the range of possible defectives in a hypergeometric sample is limited by both the sample size and the number of defectives in the population.

The minimum number of defectives possible in a sample n is either bounded by either 0, or the value of $n - (N - D)$, whichever is larger. Note that the expression $n - (N - D)$ is the difference between the sample size n and the number of non-defective items in the population or lot $(N - D)$. For example, if the lot size N = 10 and the number of defectives D = 8, a sample of n = 5 will always contain at least three defective parts, since there are only two non-defectives in the entire lot. Hence the minimum feasible X is calculated by $\max(0, n - (N - D)) = \max(0, 5 - (10 - 8))$ is equal to 3 in this case. If instead N = 10 and D = 2, then the sample of n = 5 could feasibly contain 0 defectives, since $\max(0, 5 - (10 - 2)) = 0$.

The maximum number of defectives in a sample is limited by the sample size n, or the number of defectives in the population D, whichever is smaller. For example, if a lot size is 10 units, and there are D = 6 defectives in the population, a sample of n = 3 units can return 0, 1, 2, or 3 defectives. Hence it is limited by the sample size. If the sample size is n = 8, then the sample can contain 0, 1, 2, 3, 4, 5, or 6 defectives, in this case limited by the number of defective units D in the population.

EXAMPLE 18.29

Find the following hypergeometric probabilities.

For N = 20, D = 5 and n = 7, find Pr(X = 4):

$$\Pr(X=4) = \frac{\binom{D}{x}\binom{N-D}{n-x}}{\binom{N}{n}} = \frac{\binom{5}{4}\binom{15}{3}}{\binom{20}{7}} = 0.029$$

Before evaluating the hypergeometric probability formula, it is helpful to do these "sanity checks" to prevent an error:

1. The values for D and N-D should equal the value of N in the denominator.
2. The values of x and n-x should equal the value of n in the denominator.

To find the cumulative probability using a hypergeometric distribution, we use the summation operator, as shown in Equation 18.56. To find the probability that X will be equal to a value x or less, we sum the probabilities for the values 0 to x.

Equation 18.56 Hypergeometric cumulative probability mass function

$$\Pr(X \le x) = \sum_{x=0}^{x} \frac{\binom{D}{x}\binom{N-D}{n-x}}{\binom{N}{n}}, x \in \{\max(0, n-(N-D)), \ldots, \min(n, D)\}$$

EXAMPLE 18.30

For the distribution described in Example 18.28, with For N = 20, D = 5 and n = 7, we can find the probability that we find two or fewer defects in the sample.

$$\Pr(X \le x) = \sum_{x=0}^{x} \frac{\binom{D}{x}\binom{N-D}{n-x}}{\binom{N}{n}}$$

$$= \sum_{x=0}^{2} \frac{\binom{5}{x}\binom{15}{7-x}}{\binom{20}{7}}$$

$$= \frac{\binom{5}{0}\binom{15}{7}}{\binom{20}{7}} + \frac{\binom{5}{1}\binom{15}{6}}{\binom{20}{7}} + \frac{\binom{5}{2}\binom{15}{5}}{\binom{20}{7}}$$

$$= 0.793$$

We can also use the Excel function =*hypgeom.dist*. This function takes five arguments: number of successes in the sample, sample size, number of successes in the population, population size, and the cumulative flag, as shown in Figure 18.31.

Function Arguments ? ×

HYPGEOM.DIST

Sample_s	2	= 2
Number_sample	7	= 7
Population_s	5	= 5
Number_pop	20	= 20
Cumulative	1	= TRUE

= 0.793214654

Returns the hypergeometric distribution.

Figure 18.31 *Hypgeom.dist* function in Excel.

Parameters, Expected Value, and Variance

The hypergeometric distribution can be described using three parameters: N, D, and n. (Note that these parameters are not represented by Greek letters, an exception to the general rule.) The expected value, variance, and standard deviation of the hypergeometric distribution are shown in Equation 18.57, Equation 18.58, and Equation 18.59, respectively.

Equation 18.57 Expected value of the hypergeometric distribution

$$\mu = E(X) = n\frac{D}{N}$$

Equation 18.58 Variance of the hypergeometric distribution

$$\sigma^2 = Var(X) = n\frac{D}{N}\left(1-\frac{D}{N}\right)\left(\frac{N-n}{N-1}\right)$$

Equation 18.59 Standard deviation of the hypergeometric distribution

$$\sigma = \sqrt{n\frac{D}{N}\left(1-\frac{D}{N}\right)\left(\frac{N-n}{N-1}\right)}$$

Distribution Shape

The shape of the hypergeometric distribution will change based on the number of trials n for any given N, also called the sampling proportion; the number of defectives in the population D. Figure 18.32 shows how the shape of the hypergeometric distribution with population size N = 100 and the number of defectives D = 20 changes as the sampling proportion increases.

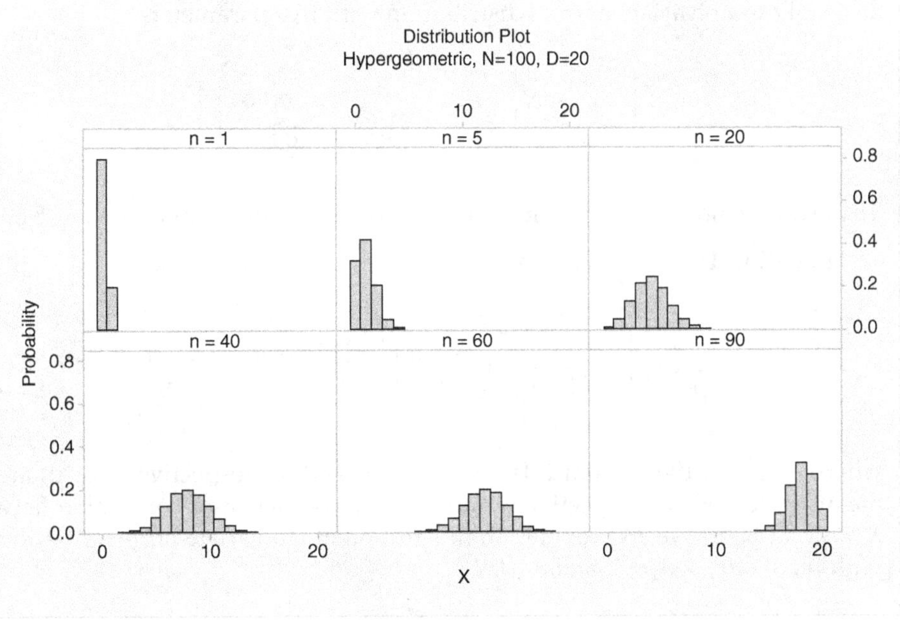

Figure 18.32 Hypergeometric distribution, n varied; N and D constant.

As shown in the first panel with n = 1 and N = 100, the only possible values for x are equal to 0 and 1. Here the sampling proportion is small, equal to 1%. As n increases, the sampling proportion also increases, meaning that sampling without replacement will increasingly affect the probability of success from trial to trial. Note the limiting factors in the range of x in play here as well. For n = 5, the only possible values for x are equal to 0, 1, 2, 3, 4, and 5. As n increases relative to the number of defectives, the minimum x will increase in value and top out at 20. For n = 90, the minimum number of defectives is 10.

Uses and Applications

The hypergeometric distribution has many applications in industry, as shown by the following example scenarios.

- A quality engineer uses the hypergeometric distribution to develop a sampling plan for small lots with an historic percent defective equal to 0.02.
- The hypergeometric distribution is used to design an incoming material inspection plan that rejects a lot based on the number of defectives found in the sample.

Bivariate Normal Distribution

If two random variables X_1 and X_2 are jointly normally distributed, then the variables follow a bivariate normal distribution with five parameters:

$$\begin{pmatrix} X_1 \\ X_2 \end{pmatrix} \sim N\left[\begin{pmatrix} \mu_1 \\ \mu_2 \end{pmatrix}, \begin{pmatrix} \sigma_1^2 & \rho\sigma_1\sigma_2 \\ \rho\sigma_1\sigma_2 & \sigma_2^2 \end{pmatrix}\right]$$

The bivariate normal probability density function is shown in Equation 18.60.

Equation 18.60 Bivariate normal probability density function

$$f(x_1, x_2) = \frac{1}{2\pi\sigma_1\sigma_2\sqrt{1-\rho^2}} \exp\left\{-\frac{1}{2(1-\rho^2)}\left[\left(\frac{x_1-\mu_1}{\sigma_1}\right)^2 - 2\rho\left(\frac{x_1-\mu_1}{\sigma_1}\right)\left(\frac{x_2-\mu_2}{\sigma_2}\right) + \left(\frac{x_2-\mu_2}{\sigma_2}\right)^2\right]\right\}$$

where σ_1, σ_2 are the standard deviations of X_1 and X_2, respectively; μ_1, μ_2 are the means of X_1 and X_2, respectively, and ρ is the coefficient of correlation between X_1 and X_2. Figure 18.33 provides an illustration of a bivariate normal distribution with $\mu_1, \mu_2 = 0$; $\sigma_1, \sigma_2 = 1$; and $\rho = 0.7$.

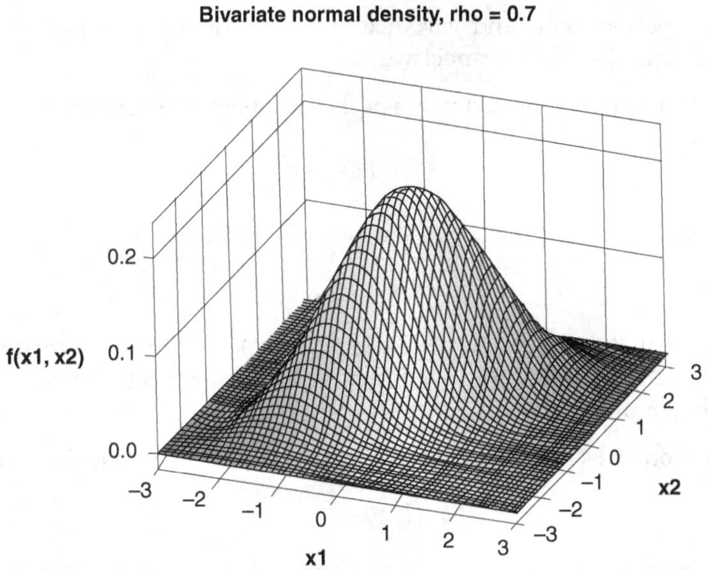

Bivariate normal density, rho = 0.7

f(x1, x2) 0.2 0.1 0.0

x1 −3 −2 −1 0 1 2 3

x2 −3 −2 −1 0 1 2 3

Figure 18.33 Bivariate normal distribution with $\mu_1, \mu_2 = 0$; $\sigma_1, \sigma_2 = 1$; and $\rho = 0.7$.

Uses and Applications

For an extruded plastic shaft, the critical dimensions X_1 and X_2 are jointly normally distributed. A Six Sigma Black Belt uses the bivariate normal distribution to calculate the percentage of parts that simultaneously meet the specifications for both dimensions.

Exponential Distribution

The exponential distribution is used extensively in simulation and in reliability. It is unusual in that it is the only continuous probability distribution that has the memoryless property.

Probability Density Function

Another special case of the gamma (α, β) distribution is the exponential distribution. The exponential distribution is a gamma with $\alpha = 1$. Therefore, the exponential distribution has only one parameter β, the scale parameter.

The exponential probability density function is shown in Equation 18.61.

Equation 18.61 Probability density function of exponential distribution

$$f(x) = \frac{1}{\beta} e^{-x/\beta}, \quad x > 0, \ \beta > 0$$

The expected value and variance of the distribution are shown in Equation 18.62 and Equation 18.63, respectively.

Equation 18.62 Expected value of the exponential distribution

$$E(X) = \beta$$

Equation 18.63 Variance of the exponential distribution

$$Var(X) = \beta^2$$

Note that the exponential distribution is sometimes parameterized using $\theta = 1/\beta$. This probability density function for the alternate form of the distribution is shown in Equation 18.64.

Equation 18.64 Alternate form for pdf of exponential distribution

$$f(x) = \theta e^{-\theta x,\, x} > 0,\ \theta > 0$$

The expectation and variance are denoted in Equation 18.65 and Equation 18.66, respectively:

Equation 18.65 Expected value of exponential, alternate form

$$E(X) = \frac{1}{\theta}$$

Equation 18.66 Variance of the expo nential distribution, alternate form

$$Var(X) = \frac{1}{\theta^2}$$

The cumulative distribution function of the exponential distribution is a closed form, as shown in Equation 18.67 and Equation 18.68.

Equation 18.67 Cumulative distribution function of exponential distribution

$$F(x) = 1 - e^{-x/\beta},\ x > 0$$

Equation 18.68 Cumulative distribution function of exponential distribution, alternate form

$$F(x) = 1 - e^{-\theta x},\ x > 0$$

Distribution Shape

The exponential distribution is right skewed. The slope of the distribution flattens as β increases. The y-intercept of the density function is equal to $1/\beta$. Figure 18.34 shows the shape of the exponential function for various values of β.

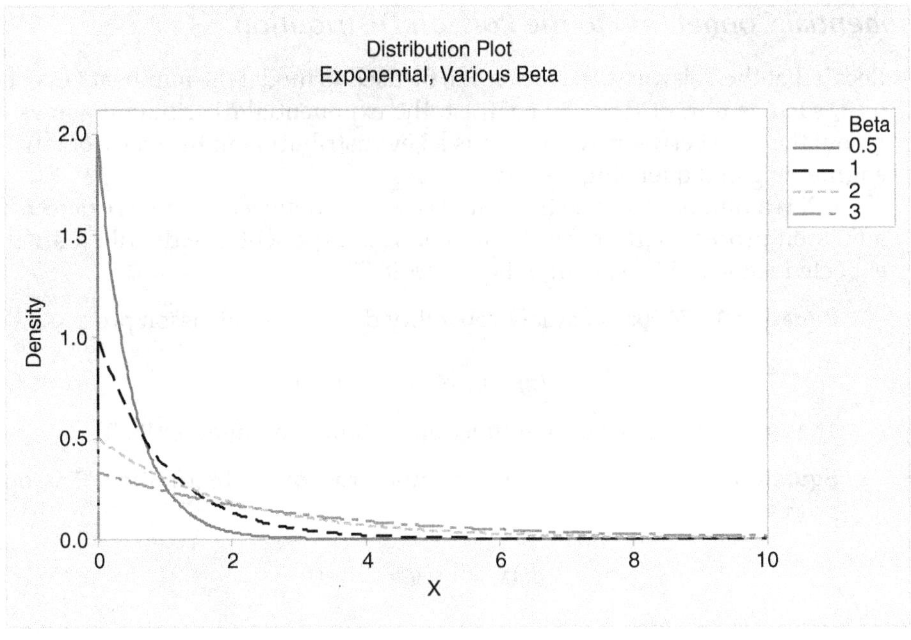

Figure 18.34 Shape of exponential function for various β.

Memoryless Property of the Exponential Distribution

The exponential distribution exhibits the *memoryless property*. The memoryless property states that the probability that X will be greater than to some value ($t + s$) given that it has already surpassed t is simply equal to the probability that X is greater than s, shown in Equation 18.69.

Equation 18.69 Memoryless property of the exponential distribution

$$\Pr(X > (t+s) \mid X > t) = \Pr(X > s)$$
$$= e^{-s/\beta}$$

For example, if the life of a light bulb is exponentially distributed, the probability that the light bulb will burn for at least 200 more hours (*s*), given that it has already burned for more than 50 hours (*t*) is simply equal to the probability that it will burn for at least 200 more hours.

Looked at another way, the probability that a unit will remain operational for an incremental time s is the same no matter how long it has been previously operational, expressed as *t*. It doesn't matter if a light bulb has been burning for 10 hours or 10,000 hours, the probability that it will burn for at least 200 more hours is the same.

Exponential Connection to the Poisson Distribution

Recall that the Poisson distribution can be used to model the number of events per unit, such as unit of time. By contrast, the exponential distribution allows us to model the time between events and is a key distribution in the study of reliability engineering and queueing theory.

If X is a random variable that equals the time between successive defects from a Poisson process with mean $\mu > 0$, then X is exponentially distributed with an expected value of $1/\mu$, shown in Equation 18.70.

Equation 18.70 Exponential probability distribution, Poisson process

$$f(x) = \mu e^{-\mu x},\ x > 0,\ \mu > 0$$

The cumulative distribution function is shown in Equation 18.71:

Equation 18.71 Cumulative exponential probability distribution, Poisson process

$$F(x) = 1 - e^{-\mu x},\ x > 0$$

EXAMPLE 18.31

Customers arrivals at the self-checkout counter at the supermarket follow a Poisson distribution with mean equal to 5 per hour. What is the probability that the next customer arrives in less than 15 minutes?

Before we can begin to solve this problem, we need to ensure that all time units are made consistent. Thus, we need to convert the 15-minute time interval to 0.25 hours.

From the cumulative exponential distribution in Equation 18.71, we can determine that

$$\begin{aligned} F(x) &= 1 - e^{-\mu x} \\ &= 1 - e^{-(5)(0.25)} \\ &= 1 - 0.2865 \\ &= 0.7135 \end{aligned}$$

Therefore, the probability that the next customer arrives in less than 15 minutes is 0.7135.

Alternatively, we can use the Excel function =*expon.dist*. This function takes three arguments: X, lambda, and the cumulative flag. The Excel function uses the alternate version of the exponential distribution shown in Equation 18.64 and Equation 18.70. The argument lambda is equivalent to $\theta = (1/\beta)$. To find $\Pr(X < x)$, we will enter a 1 in the cumulative flag argument as shown in Figure 18.35.

Continued

Continued

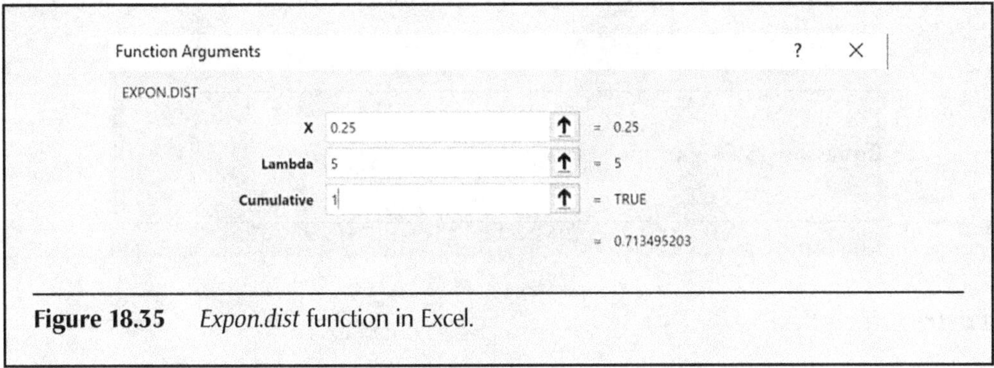

Figure 18.35 *Expon.dist* function in Excel.

Uses and Applications

The exponential distribution is widely used in simulation and reliability. For example:

- A Six Sigma Black Belt uses the exponential distribution to model wait times in a Monte Carlo simulation of patient flow through a hospital emergency department.
- A reliability engineer uses the exponential distribution to calculate the probability an electric component will function for more than 100 hours.

Lognormal Distribution

The lognormal distribution is useful when modeling random variables that are a product of many other random variables.

Probability Density Function

The lognormal distribution is a bit of a misnomer since it does not describe the distribution of the natural log of the normal. Instead, if X ~ N(μ,σ^2), then e^x will follow a lognormal distribution with parameters μ, σ^2. Therefore, we can say that X ~ LN(μ,σ^2) if and only if (ln X) ~ N(μ,σ^2). The lognormal probability density function is shown in Equation 18.72.

Equation 18.72 Probability density of lognormal distribution

$$f(x) = \frac{1}{x\sqrt{2\pi\sigma^2}} e^{\frac{-(\ln x-\mu)^2}{2\sigma^2}}, \quad x > 0$$

The expected value and variance of the log normal distribution are shown in Equation 18.73 and Equation 18.74, respectively.

Equation 18.73 Expected value of lognormal distribution

$$E(X) = e^{\mu+\frac{\sigma^2}{2}}$$

Equation 18.74 Variance of lognormal distribution

$$Var(X) = e^{2\mu+\sigma^2}\left(e^{\sigma^2} - 1\right)$$

Distribution Shape

Figure 18.36 shows the shape of the lognormal distribution for various values of σ. As the value of sigma nears zero, the log normal distribution has an increasingly higher peak near $e^{-\mu}$.

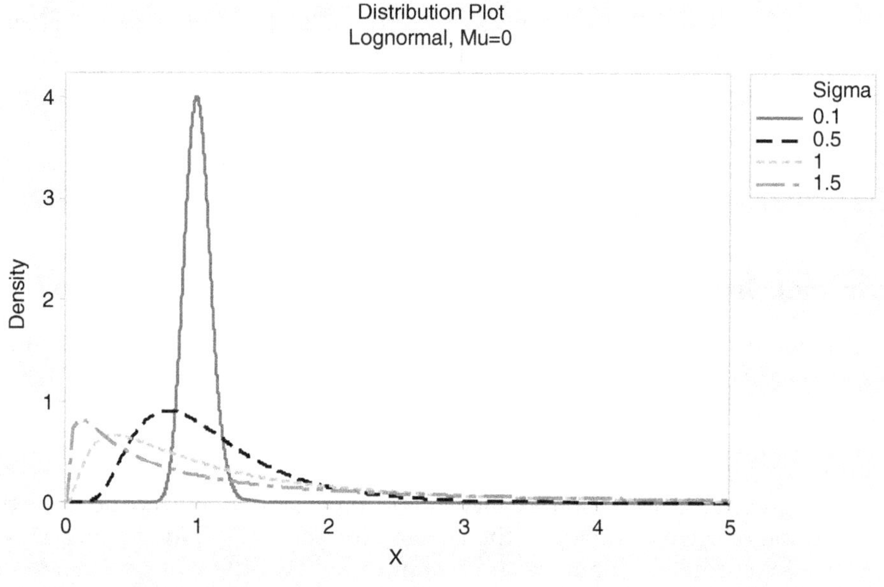

Figure 18.36 Shape of lognormal distribution, various σ.

EXAMPLE 18.32

Suppose that the random variable X, the lifetime of a plasma television in hours, is distributed as lognormal with parameters μ = 10 hours and σ = 2 hours. What is the probability that the lifetime of the plasma television exceeds 1000 hours?

Based on the information given, it follows that ln(X)~N(10, 4).

$$\begin{aligned}\Pr(X > 1000) &= 1 - \Pr(X < 1000)\\ &= 1 - \Pr(\ln X < \ln 1000)\\ &= 1 - \Pr\left(Z < \frac{(\ln 1000 - 10)}{2}\right)\\ &= 1 - \Pr\left(Z < \frac{6.9078 - 10}{2}\right)\\ &= 1 - \Pr(Z < -1.55)\\ &= 1 - 0.0606\\ &= 0.9394\end{aligned}$$

Therefore, the probability that the lifetime of the plasma television exceeds 1000 hours is 0.9394.

We can also solve this problem using the Excel function *=lognorm.dist*. This function takes four arguments: x, μ, σ, and the cumulative flag. (Note that μ and σ are the mean and standard deviation of the normally distributed variable ln(X), and not the mean and standard deviation of the lognormal distribution.) The function gives Pr(X < x) when 1 is entered into the cumulative argument, as shown in Figure 18.37. We subtract this result to get 0.9390. Note that the difference in the hand calculation and the Excel solution stems from rounding error.

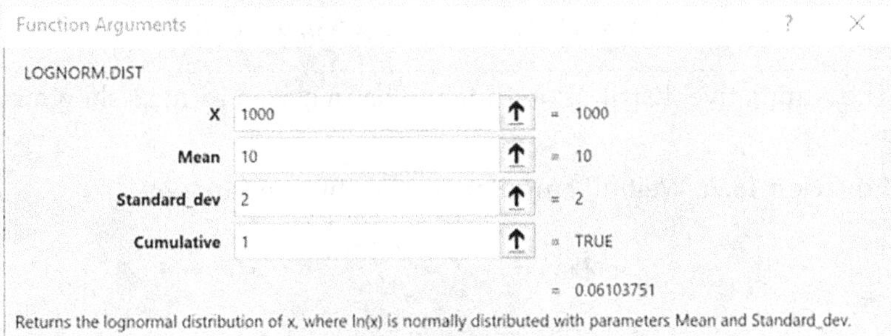

Figure 18.37 *Lognorm.dist* function in Excel.

Uses and Applications

The lognormal distribution is used when several independent variables are multiplied together. For example:

- A quality engineer uses the lognormal distribution to test whether a multiplicative quality index is significantly greater than a standard value.
- A scientist uses the lognormal distribution to model seismic activity on the Richter scale.

Weibull Distribution

The Weibull distribution was developed by a Swedish engineer, Waloddi Weibull, who popularized its use in modeling metallurgic failures. This distribution is most famously applied in the failure rate bathtub curve, in which three separate Weibull functions are plotted over time. The first is called the burn-in or infant mortality rate, in which failure rate is high and then falls off quickly over a short period of time. The middle segment is the constant failure rate, followed by the wear-out period of rapidly increasing failures.

Probability Density Function

Weibull distribution has a shape parameter, α, and a scale parameter, β. The parameter β is also known as the characteristic life. The probability density function is shown in Equation 18.75.

Equation 18.75 Weibull probability density function

$$f(x) = \alpha\beta^{-\alpha}x^{\alpha-1}e^{-\left(x/\beta\right)^{\alpha}}, \quad x > 0, \alpha > 0, \beta > 0$$

The cumulative distribution function has a closed form as shown in Equation 18.76.

Equation 18.76 Weibull cumulative distribution function

$$F(x) = 1 - e^{-(x/\beta)^{\alpha}}, \qquad x > 0$$

Distribution Shape

The elegance of the Weibull function is that it takes on many shapes depending on the value of α, as shown in Figure 18.38. For example, when:

- $0 < \alpha < 1$, the Weibull has a decreasing failure rate and can be used to model "infant mortality."
- $\alpha = 1$, the Weibull is reduced to the exponential distribution with a constant failure rate.

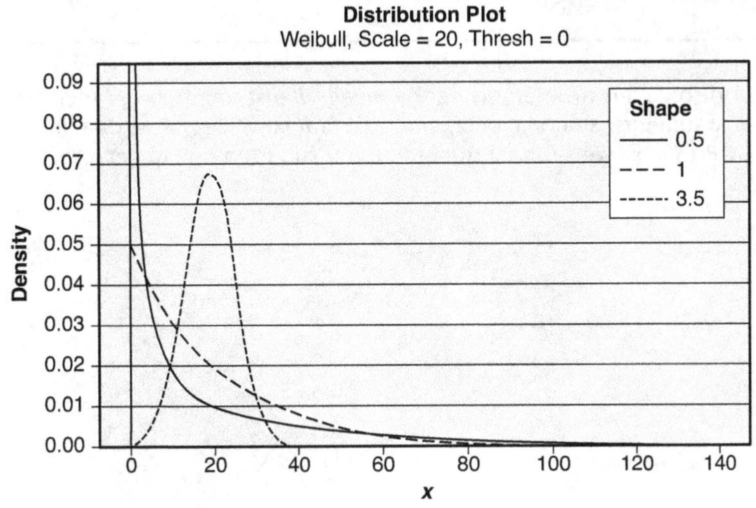

Figure 18.38 Example of a Weibull function for various values of the shape parameter.

- $\alpha > 1$, the Weibull has an increasing failure rate and can be used to model "wear-out."
- $\alpha = 3.5$, the Weibull is approximately the normal distribution, has an increasing failure rate, and can be used to model "wear-out."

As a result, the Weibull distribution is one of the fundamental distributions in the study of reliability engineering.

EXAMPLE 18.33

The time to failure of a belt on an engine is distributed as a Weibull random variable with $\alpha = 0.5$ and $\beta = 10{,}000$ hours. Determine the probability that the belt lasts at least 15,000 hours.

We can use the cumulative distribution function in Equation 18.76 to solve.

$$F(x) = \Pr(X < x) = 1 - e^{-\left(x/\beta\right)^{\alpha}}$$

$$\begin{aligned} \Pr(X > x) &= 1 - F(x) \\ &= e^{-\left(x/\beta\right)^{\alpha}} \\ &= e^{-\left(15000/10000\right)^{0.5}} \\ &= e^{-\left(1.5^{0.5}\right)} \\ &= 0.2938 \end{aligned}$$

Continued

Continued

We can also solve this problem using the =*weibull.dist* function in Excel. The function takes four arguments: X, alpha, beta, and the cumulative flag, as shown in Figure 18.39. To find the Pr(X > x), we subtract the function result from one to get 0.2938.

Figure 18.39 *Weibull.dist* function in Excel.

The expected value and variance of the Weibull distribution is shown in Equation 18.77 and Equation 18.78, respectively.

Equation 18.77 Expected value of Weibull distribution

$$E(x) = \beta\Gamma\left(1 + \frac{1}{\alpha}\right)$$

Equation 18.78 Variance of the Weibull distribution

$$Var(x) = \beta^2\left\{\Gamma\left(1 + \frac{2}{\alpha}\right) - \Gamma^2\left(1 + \frac{1}{\alpha}\right)\right\}$$

Recall that Γ(x) is the gamma function, which simplifies to $(x - 1)!$ if x is an integer.

Applications and Uses

The Weibull distribution is well suited for modeling the reliability of systems, since it can be used to model decreasing, constant, or increasing hazard rates depending on choice of parameters.

The reliability function for the Weibull distrbution takes the form shown in Equation 18.79.

Equation 18.79 Weibull reliability function

$$R(t) = e^{-\left(t/\beta\right)^{\alpha}}, \ t > 0$$

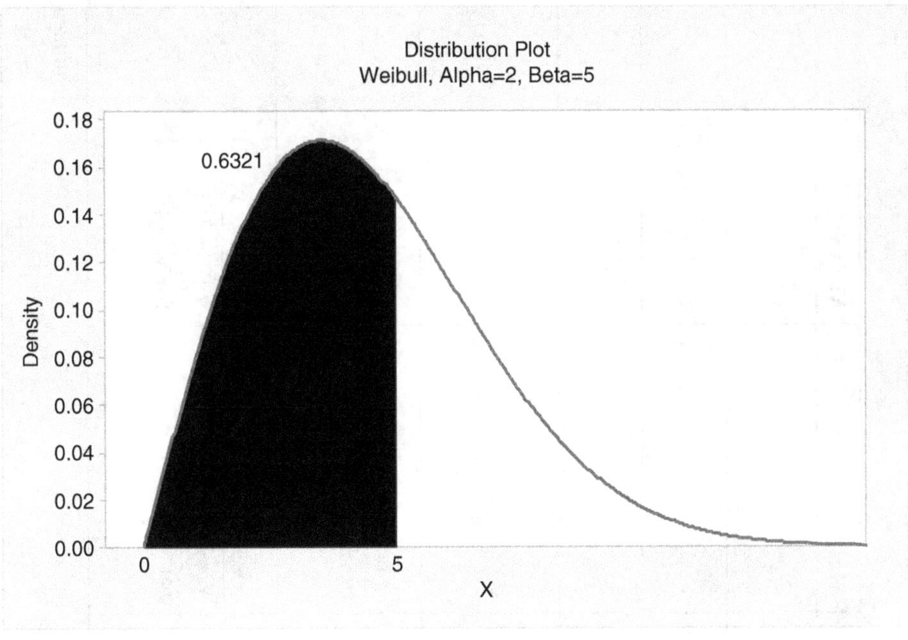

Figure 18.40 Weibull distribution Pr(T< t) at t = beta.

One important result of this equation is that when time to failure t = β, the cumulative time to failure function is equal to 0.632, regardless of the value of alpha. The probability of a component failing on or before time β is equal to 0.632. The relationship is illustrated in Figure 18.40.

$$F(X \leq \beta) = 1 - e^{-(1)^{\alpha}} = 0.632$$

Pertinent information about each distribution is summarized in Table 18.9.

Distribution	Formula	Mean	Variance
Normal	$f(x)=\frac{1}{\sigma\sqrt{2\pi}}e^{-\frac{(x-\ )^2}{2\sigma^2}}$ for $-\infty \le x \le \infty$		σ^2
Poisson	$f(x)=\frac{e^{-\lambda}\lambda^x}{x!}$ for $x = 0,1,2...$	λ	λ
Binomial	$f(x)=\frac{n!}{x!(n-x)!}p^x(1-p)^{n-x}$ for $x=0,1,\ldots n$	np	$np(1-p)$
Chi-square	$f(x)=\frac{e^{\frac{-x}{2}}x^{\left(\frac{\nu}{2}\right)-1}}{2^{\frac{\nu}{2}}\Gamma\left(\frac{\nu}{2}\right)}$ for $x\ge 0, \nu=$ degrees of freedom	ν	2ν
Student's t	$f(x)=\frac{1}{\sqrt{\pi\nu}}\frac{\Gamma\left(\frac{\nu+1}{2}\right)}{\Gamma\left(\frac{\nu}{2}\right)}\left(1+\frac{x^2}{\nu}\right)^{-(\nu+1)/2}$ for $-\infty\le x\le\infty$	0; for $\nu > 1$	$\frac{\nu}{\nu-2}$; for $\nu>2$
F	$f(x)=\frac{\Gamma\left(\frac{\nu_1+\nu_2}{2}\right)\left(\frac{\nu_1}{\nu_2}\right)^{\nu_1/2}x^{(\nu_1/2)-1}}{\Gamma\left(\frac{\nu_1}{2}\right)\Gamma\left(\frac{\nu_2}{2}\right)\left[\left(\frac{\nu_1}{\nu_2}\right)x+1\right]^{\frac{(\nu_1+\nu_2)}{2}}}$ for $0\le x\le\infty, \nu_1>0, \nu_2>0$	$\frac{\nu_2}{\nu_2-2}$ for $\nu_2>2$	$\frac{2\nu_2^2(\nu_1+\nu_2-2)}{\nu_1(\nu_2-2)^2(\nu_2-4)}$ for $\nu_2>4$

Table 18.9 Summary of distributions.

Continued

Distribution	Formula	Mean	Variance
Hypergeometric	$f(x)=\dfrac{\binom{S}{x}\binom{N-S}{n-x}}{\binom{N}{n}}$ for $x=\max\{0,n+S-N\}$ to $\min\{S,n\}$	np	$np(1-p)\left(\dfrac{N-n}{N-1}\right)$
Bivariate normal	$f_{XY}(x,y)=\dfrac{1}{2\pi\sigma_X\sigma_Y\sqrt{1-\rho^2}}e^{\left\{\frac{-1}{2(1-\rho^2)}\left[\frac{(x-\mu_X)^2}{\sigma_X^2}-\frac{2\rho(x-\mu_X)(y-\mu_Y)}{\sigma_X\sigma_Y}+\frac{(y-\mu_Y)^2}{\sigma_Y^2}\right]\right\}}$ for $\begin{Bmatrix}-\infty<x<\infty\\ -\infty<y<\infty\\ -\infty<\mu_X<\infty\\ -\infty<\mu_Y<\infty\\ \sigma_X>0\\ \sigma_Y>0\\ -1\le\rho\le1\end{Bmatrix}$	Conditional: $\mu_{x\mid y=y_0}=\mu_x+\rho\sigma_x\dfrac{(y-\mu_y)}{\sigma_y}$ $\mu_{y\mid x=x_0}=\mu_y+\rho\sigma_y\dfrac{(x-\mu_x)}{\sigma_x}$	Conditional: $\sigma_{x\mid y=y_0}=\sigma_x\sqrt{1-\rho^2}$ $\sigma_{y\mid x=x_0}=\sigma_y\sqrt{1-\rho^2}$
Exponential	$f(x)=\lambda e^{-\lambda x}$ for $0\le x\le\infty;\lambda>0$	$\dfrac{1}{\lambda}$	$\dfrac{1}{\lambda^2}$
Lognormal	$f(x)=\dfrac{1}{x\sigma\sqrt{2\pi}}e^{\left[\frac{-2}{2\sigma^2}(\ln(x)-\mu)^2\right]}$ for $x>0$	$e^{\mu+\frac{\sigma^2}{2}}$	$e^{2\mu+\sigma^2}\left(e^{\sigma^2}-1\right)$
Weibull	$f(x)=\dfrac{\beta}{\alpha}\left(\dfrac{x-\gamma}{\alpha}\right)^{\beta-1}e^{-\left(\frac{x-\gamma}{\alpha}\right)^{\beta}}$ for $x>0,\alpha>0,\beta>0,\gamma\ge0$	$\gamma+\alpha\Gamma\left(1+\dfrac{1}{\beta}\right)$	$\alpha^2\left[\Gamma\left(1+\dfrac{2}{\beta}\right)-\left[\Gamma\left(1+\dfrac{1}{\beta}\right)\right]^2\right]$

Table 18.9 *Continued*

Chapter 19

Process Capability

I should estimate that in my experience most troubles and most possibilities for improvement add up to the proportions something like this: 94% belongs to the system (responsibility of management), and 6% special.

—W. Edwards Deming

This chapter will address the area of process capability and its related concepts. Process capability is a means to characterize how well a process is meeting specifications, and by extension, customer requirements.

PROCESS CAPABILITY INDICES

> Define, select, and calculate C_p and C_{pk}. (Evaluate)
>
> Body of Knowledge V.F.1

Process capability can be defined as the inherent process performance. Specifically, it describes how well the measured output of a process compares to its specifications. This performance to specifications is measured over a period of stable operations. A process is said to be *capable* when the output conforms to the process specifications to a high degree.

In this section we will stray from the order of the Body of Knowledge to present four types of short-term capability measures that give an increasingly complete picture of the fitness of the process vis-à-vis its specifications: natural process variation (often called natural tolerance, NT), C_p, C_{pk}, and C_{pm}, shown in Figure 19.1. *For each of these measures, it is assumed that the process is in statistical control, meaning that it is predictable. In addition, for the formulas presented here, it is assumed the process output variable is normally distributed.* We cover methods for calculating capability measures for non-normal distributions later in the chapter.

Natural Process Variation, or Natural Tolerance (NT)

The *natural tolerance limits* of a process are based on the normal distribution of the process output variable in which:

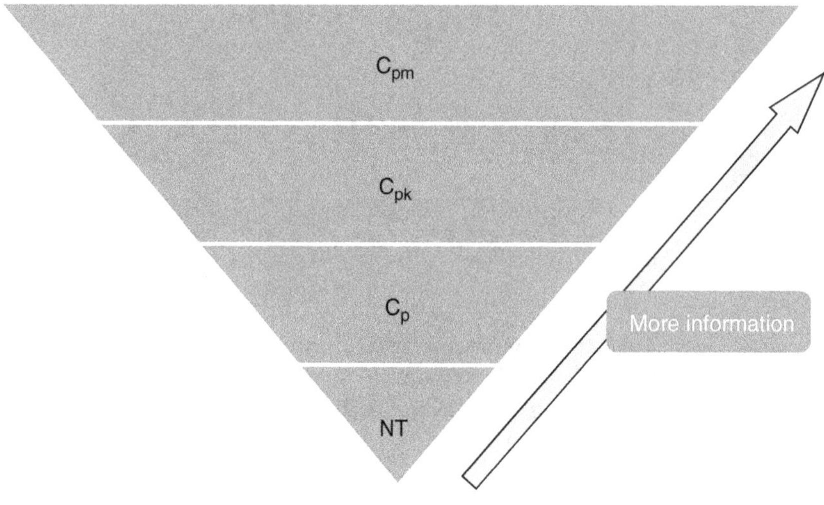

Figure 19.1 Capability measures for in-control processes with a normally distributed output variable.

$$\text{Lower natural tolerance limit} = LNTL = (\mu - 3\sigma)$$

$$\text{Upper natural tolerance limit} = UNTL = (\mu + 3\sigma)$$

The *natural tolerance,* also known as the *natural process variation,* is the difference between the upper and lower natural tolerance limits:

$$\begin{aligned} CAP &= (UNTL - LNTL) \\ &= (\mu + 3\sigma) - (\mu - 3\sigma) \\ &= 6\sigma \end{aligned}$$

For a normally distributed process variable, the value of the natural tolerance gives the width of the range that captures 99.73% of the distribution, as shown in Figure 19.2. As such it is often referred to as the *voice of the process.*

The natural tolerance (NT), or natural process variation, is a parameter. It can be estimated using an estimate for the standard deviation as shown in Equation 19.1:

Equation 19.1 Estimated NT

$$\widehat{NT} = 6\hat{\sigma}$$

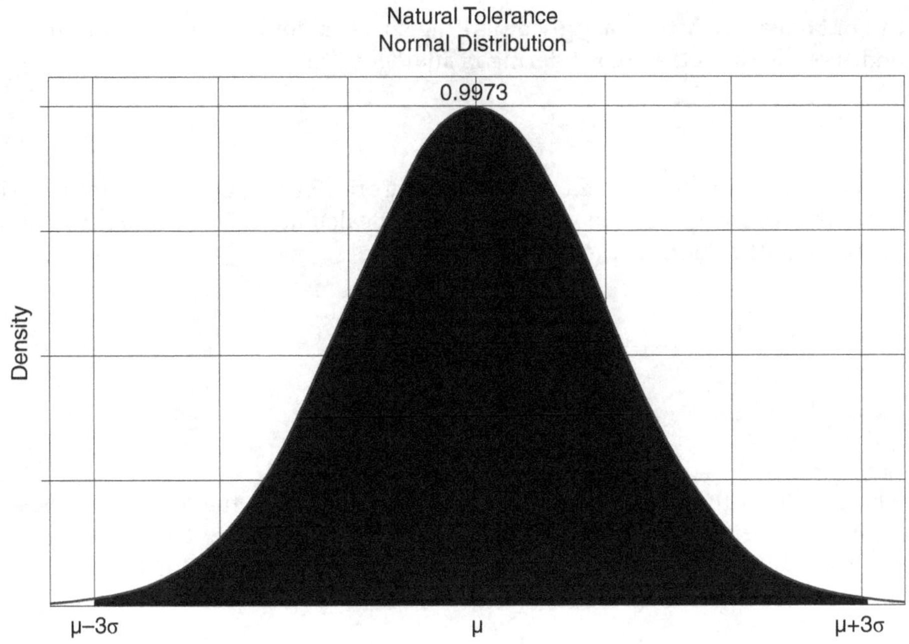

Natural Tolerance
Normal Distribution

0.9973

Density

μ−3σ μ μ+3σ

Figure 19.2 Natural tolerance for a normally distributed process variable.

Estimating σ from a Control Chart

The estimated standard deviation $\hat{\sigma}$ is the within-subgroup, or short-term, variability calculated from a control chart. For example, if we are using an $\bar{X}-R$ chart to monitor the process variable, we can calculate

$$\hat{\sigma}=\frac{\bar{R}}{d_2}$$

where $\bar{R}$ is the average from the range chart and d_2 is a table value based on subgroup size, found in Appendix K.5.

For an $\bar{X}-S$ chart, we can calculate

$$\hat{\sigma}=\frac{\bar{s}}{c_4}$$

where $\bar{s}$ is the average from the standard deviation chart and c_4 is a table value based on subgroup size, found in Appendix K.5.

For an $X-mR$ chart, with moving range of two, we can calculate

$$\hat{\sigma}=\frac{\overline{mR}}{1.128}$$

The natural tolerance gives us a measure of the dispersion of the process output. To use a popular analogy, imagine that you are considering buying a new car, but have a very tight assigned parking space in your apartment building. The width of the car you are considering is analogous to the NT.

C_p

We can move up the inverted pyramid in Figure 19.1 to gather more information about the performance of the process. We next calculate C_p to compare the natural tolerance to the width of the specifications.

$$C_p = \frac{(UCL - LCL)}{NT} = \frac{(UCL - LCL)}{6\sigma}$$

where UCL is the upper specification limit and LCL is the lower specification limit.

The C_p can also be thought of as comparing the voice of the customer (VOC) to the voice of the process (VOP):

$$C_p = \frac{(UCL - LCL)}{NT} = \frac{VOC}{VOP}$$

Like the estimated natural tolerance, the estimated C_p also uses $\hat{\sigma}$ calculated from a control chart, as shown in Equation 19.2:

Equation 19.2 Estimated C_p

$$\hat{C}_p = \frac{(UCL - LCL)}{6\hat{\sigma}}$$

The natural tolerance has the same units as the process variable, but C_p is a unitless measure or an index in which $C_p > 0$. Values of C_p and their meaning are presented in Table 19.1.

Returning to the car analogy, we can only increase C_p by buying a smaller vehicle; we cannot widen our assigned parking spot. In the same way, as much as we'd like to, we often cannot widen the process specifications, since they are chosen so that parts fit together into sub-assemblies, and sub-assemblies form a final product that meets customer expectations. The most common way to improve C_p is to shrink the variability in the process output.

Note that there are cases in which a capability analysis can bring attention to specifications that were set unnecessarily tight, and a better translation of customer requirements leads to wider specifications (analogously, a new, wider parking spot). Of course, if the specifications are set well, they should never be changed in order to improve the capability metric.

Value of C_p	Interpretation	Parking space analogy	Comment
$C_p < 1$	Width of process output is larger than the process specifications. For example, $C_p =$ 0.5 indicates that the process output is twice as wide as the specifications.	You choose a full-sized pickup that is too wide for the parking space.	This process will produce parts out of specifications.
$C_p = 1$	Width of process output is equal to the width of the specifications.	You choose a full-size sedan that could potentially fit in the parking space but takes up all the allowable room. You can't open the door to get out.	Assuming the process is centered at target, yield is 99.73%, but defectives will be produced if the mean moves any amount away from target.
$C_p > 1$	The width of the process is less than the width of the specifications.	You opt for a compact model that can fit into the parking space, and there is room for you to open the door to get out.	Process can be said to the "capable." Common goal values for C_p are 1.33 or 1.67.
$C_p = 2$	The width of the process is much smaller than the specifications.	You buy a motorcycle and have plenty of room to park and can even store items in your space.	This C_p value is comparable to a "6σ" level of quality.

Table 19.1 Interpretation of C_p values.

EXAMPLE 19.1

Note that natural tolerance and C_p measures both concentrate on the variability of the process output. However, the central tendency of the process output, in addition to its dispersion, can affect how well the output meets specifications. Consider the two process outputs shown in Figure 19.3, each with known short-term standard deviation equal to ½, and lower specification limit equal to –3 and upper specification limit equal to +3. The specification target, also known as specification nominal, is equal to 0.

Continued

Continued

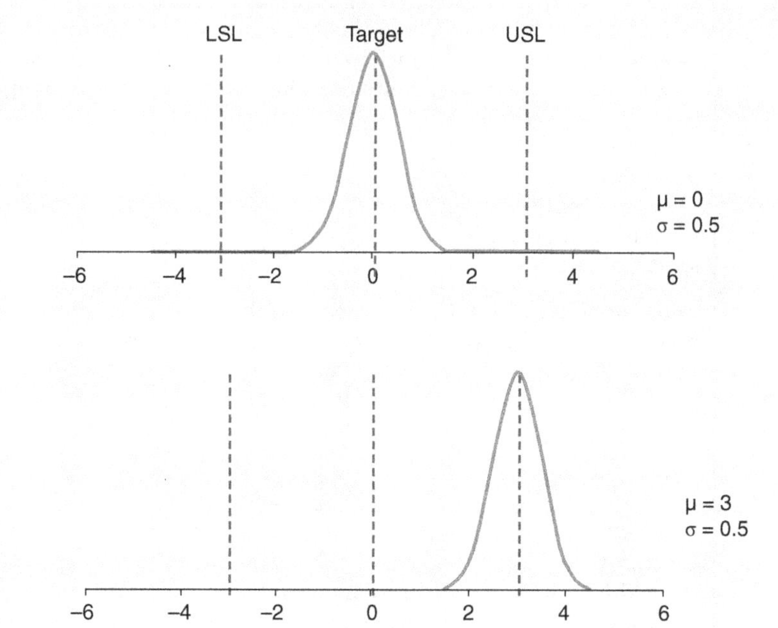

Figure 19.3 Two processes with equal C_p values.

Source: Used with permission. Mary McShane-Vaughn, *Statistics for Black Belts Slide Book* (Folsom, CA: University Training Partners Publishing, 2021), p. 256.

We can estimate the C_p value for the process shown in the first panel of Figure 19.3:

$$C_{p1} = \frac{(UCL - LCL)}{6\sigma} = \frac{(3-(-3))}{3} = 2.0$$

This process is comparable to a "6σ" level process in which it would produce only 1.9 parts-per-billion defective in the short term.

The C_p for the second process is calculated similarly:

$$\hat{C}_{p2} = \frac{(UCL - LCL)}{6\hat{\sigma}} = \frac{(6-(-6))}{6} = 2.0$$

From the diagram, we see that although the second process has a tight standard deviation relative to the specification width, the mean of the process is not centered between specification limits. Rather, it is centered on the upper specification limit, and 50% of its output is nonconforming. Clearly, both the mean and the variation in the process must be considered when assessing capability of a process.

C_{pk}

We now introduce the third capability measure, C_{pk}. The C_{pk} value is calculated using:

$$C_{pk} = \min\left(C_{pl}, C_{pu}\right) = \min\left(\frac{(\mu - LSL)}{3\sigma}, \frac{(USL - \mu)}{3\sigma}\right)$$

where $C_{pk} \leq C_p$ for a given process.

EXAMPLE 19.2

We can calculate the C_{pk} values for the two processes introduced in Example 19.1 and Figure 19.3:

$$\begin{aligned} C_{pk1} &= \min\left(C_{pl1}, C_{pu1}\right) \\ &= \min\left(\frac{(\mu_1 - LSL)}{3\sigma}, \frac{(USL - \mu_1)}{3\sigma}\right) \\ &= \min\left(\frac{(0 - (-3))}{1.5}, \frac{(3 - 0)}{1.5}\right) \\ &= \min(2.0, 2.0) \\ &= 2.0 \end{aligned}$$

For a process that is centered at the specification target, the C_{pk} value will be equal to the C_p.

For the second process, we have:

$$\begin{aligned} C_{pk2} &= \min\left(C_{pl2}, C_{pu2}\right) \\ &= \min\left(\frac{(\mu_2 - LSL)}{3\sigma}, \frac{(USL - \mu_2)}{3\sigma}\right) \\ &= \min\left(\frac{(3 - (-3))}{1.5}, \frac{(3 - 3)}{1.5}\right) \\ &= \min(2.0, 0) \\ &= 0 \end{aligned}$$

When the process mean is equal to one of the specification limits, the C_{pk} value will equal 0.

Note that C_{pk} will be negative if the process mean is outside the specification limits. The magnitude of the difference between C_{pk} and C_p indicates the extent to which the process is off-center. C_p is often referred to as the potential process capability, and C_{pk} as the actual capability.

C_{pk} value	Interpretation	Parking space analogy	Comment
$C_{pk} = C_p$	The process is centered at specification target.	You center the car in the parking space when pulling in.	The only way to further improve the process is to increase C_p (and C_{pk}) by shrinking process variation.
$C_{pk} < C_p$	The process is not centered at specification target.	You pull into the parking space but are not centered— you are too close to one of the lines.	If C_p is > 1, we can improve the process by first moving the mean to specification target. This will make $C_{pk} = C_p$. If $C_p < 1$, the variability should be addressed as well as the mean.
$C_{pk} = 0$	The process mean is centered on one of the specification limits. 50% of the output is nonconforming.	You are centered on one of the outside lines of the parking space; half of your vehicle will be outside the space.	The mean should be shifted to target to improve C_{pk}. Further improvement can be made by decreasing the variability.
$C_{pk} < 0$	The process mean is outside one of the specification limits. More than half of the output is out of specification.	You are parked off center and are more than halfway in the parking space next to you.	The mean should be moved to the target to improve C_{pk}. Further improvement can be made by decreasing the variability.

Table 19.2 Interpretation of C_{pk} values.

By comparing the C_p and C_{pk} values of each process in Figure 19.3, we can state that the first process is operating at a 6σ level. The second process has the *potential* of operating at the 6σ level, as evidenced by its C_p value, but because $C_{pk} < C_p$ we know that the process is not centered. In fact, the C_{pk} value equals zero, which is resulting in 50% defective product. To improve the second process, the mean should be moved to the specification target.

Values of C_{pk} and their meaning are presented in Table 19.2.

We can estimate C_{pk} by using information from a control chart using:

Equation 19.3 Estimate of C_{pk}

$$\hat{C}_{pk} = \min\left(\hat{C}_{pl}, \hat{C}_{pu}\right)$$

$$= \min\left(\frac{\left(\bar{\bar{X}} - LSL\right)}{3\hat{\sigma}}, \frac{\left(USL - \bar{\bar{X}}\right)}{3\hat{\sigma}}\right)$$

Here, $\bar{\bar{X}}$ is the average of the $\bar{X}$ chart and, as before, $\hat{\sigma}$ is calculated from using formulas earlier in this chapter.

The C_{pk} index does give a more complete picture of the performance of the process than the NT or C_p. However, its value increases as the variability of the process decreases, which can sometimes mask the fact that the process is off-center, as shown in Example 19.3.

EXAMPLE 19.3

Consider Processes 1 and 2 depicted in Figure 19.4. The lower specification limit is equal to 35 and the upper specification limit is equal to 65, with a specification nominal, or target T, equal to 50.

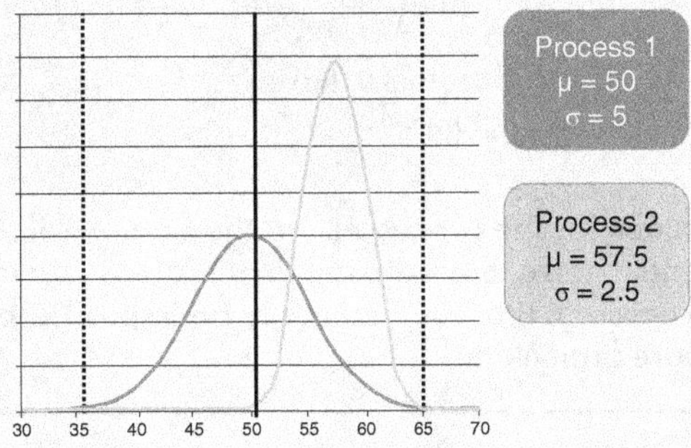

Figure 19.4 Two processes with equal C_{pk} values.

Source: Used with permission. Mary McShane-Vaughn, *Statistics for Black Belts Slide Book* (Folsom, CA: University Training Partners Publishing, 2021), p. 260.

The C_p and C_{pk} values for Process 1 are calculated:

$$
\begin{aligned}
C_{p1} &= \frac{USL - LSL}{6\sigma_1} \\
&= \frac{(65-35)}{30} \\
&= 1.0 \\
C_{pk1} &= \min\left(C_{pl1}, C_{pu1}\right) \\
&= \min\left(\frac{(\mu_1 - LSL)}{3\sigma_1}, \frac{(USL - \mu_1)}{3\sigma_1}\right) \\
&= \min\left(\frac{(50-35)}{15}, \frac{(65-50)}{15}\right) \\
&= \min(1.0, 1.0) \\
&= 1.0
\end{aligned}
$$

Continued

Continued

The C_p and C_{pk} for Process 2 are calculated:

$$\begin{aligned} C_{p2} &= \frac{(USL - LSL)}{6\sigma_2} \\ &= \frac{(65-35)}{15} \\ &= 2.0 \\ C_{pk2} &= \min\left(C_{pl2}, C_{pu2}\right) \\ &= \min\left(\frac{(\mu_2 - LSL)}{3\sigma_2}, \frac{(USL - \mu_2)}{3\sigma_2}\right) \\ &= \min\left(\frac{(57.5-35)}{7.5}, \frac{(65-57.5)}{7.5}\right) \\ &= \min(3.0, 1.0) \\ &= 1.0 \end{aligned}$$

Although the C_{pk} values for the processes are the same, Process 2 has a larger C_p and hence a larger potential. If we move the mean of Process 2 to target, the $C_p = C_{pk} = 2.0$. Since it is already centered, Process 1 can only be improved by reducing the process variation, often a more difficult task.

C_{pm}

A fourth capability measure, C_{pm}, allows us to better distinguish between processes that have different means and levels of variation. The calculation of the C_{pm} incorporates the width of the specifications, the variation of the process, as well as the distance between the mean and the specification target, T:

$$C_{pm} = \frac{(USL - LSL)}{6\sqrt{\sigma^2 + (\mu - T)^2}}$$

where $C_{pm} \leq C_{pk}$ for a given process.

The estimated C_{pm} is calculated using:

Equation 19.4 Estimate of C_{pm}

$$\hat{C}_{pm} = \frac{(USL - LSL)}{6\sqrt{\hat{\sigma}^2 + \left(\bar{\bar{X}} - T\right)^2}}$$

Where $\bar{\bar{X}}$ is the average of the $\bar{X}$ chart and $\hat{\sigma}$ is calculated from using the formulas presented earlier in this chapter.

EXAMPLE 19.4

We can compute the C_{pm} indices for Processes 1 and 2 from Example 19.3:

$$C_{pm1} = \frac{(USL - LSL)}{6\sqrt{\sigma_1^2 + (\mu_1 - T)^2}}$$
$$= \frac{(65 - 35)}{6\sqrt{5^2 + (50 - 50)^2}}$$
$$= 1.0$$

$$C_{pm2} = \frac{(USL - LSL)}{6\sqrt{\sigma_2^2 + (\mu_2 - T)^2}}$$
$$= \frac{(65 - 35)}{6\sqrt{2.5^2 + (57.5 - 50)^2}}$$
$$= 0.632$$

The capability results for Process 1 and Process 2 are summarized in Table 19.3. We see that Process 1 is analogous to centering a full-sized sedan that takes up the entire parking space, whereas Process 2 is akin to parking a motorcycle over on the edge of the parking space.

Process	NT	Cp	Cpk	Cpm	Interpretation
1	30.0	1.0	1.0	1.0	Your full-sized sedan is centered and fills the parking space.
2	15.0	1.0	1.0	0.632	Your motorcycle is parked over to one side of the parking space.

Table 19.3 Capability indices for Examples 19.3 and 19.4.

Note that when a process mean is equal to the specification target, $C_p = C_{pk} = C_{pm}$. The C_{pm} for Process 2 shows us that although the process has a high potential, it needs to be centered to achieve it. In general, when C_p is greater than or equal to 1.0, the C_{pm} applies a higher penalty to an uncentered process than when C_p is less than 1.0. It is good practice to calculate all the indices presented to create a complete picture of the process and its behavior.

PROCESS PERFORMANCE INDICES

> Define, select, and calculate P_p, P_{pk}, C_{pm} and process sigma. (Evaluate)
>
> **Body of Knowledge V.F.2**

Process performance is defined as a statistical measure of how well a process meets customer requirements based on its long-term variability. In this way, it differs from process capability, which is a measure of short-term process performance. In addition, process performance may be calculated for a process that *may not demonstrate a state of statistical control*. The process performance may therefore contain a component of variability from special causes of an unpredictable nature. This practice is not without its risks, however, with authors such as Montgomery (2005) and Kotz and Lovelace (1998) cautioning against the practice of making judgments or predictions about process performance if the process is not in control.

The *process performance index* is a dimensionless value that is used to represent the process's ability to meet specification limits on a characteristic of interest. The index compares the variability of the characteristic to the specification limits. Three basic process performance indices are P_p, P_{pk}, and P_{pm}. These indices are analogous to their process capability counterparts C_p, C_{pk}, and C_{pm} in that the process output variable is assumed to be normally distributed. However, the process performance indices use an overall estimate of variation rather than a within-subgroup estimate of variation. It can be argued that process performance indices provide an actual measure of capability, while the process capability indices provide a potential or optimistic measure of capability by ignoring the variation between subgroups. When the process is in control, then the values of the process capability and process performance indices are essentially the same.

Note: C_{pm} was moved to section V.F.1 above as it more comparable to C_p and C_{pk} than it is to P_p and P_{pk}. P_{pm} was also added in this subsection for completeness.

Pp

The P_p is calculated using:

$$P_p = \frac{(USL - LSL)}{6\sigma}$$

Its estimate $\hat{P}_p$ is computed by Equation 19.5:

Equation 19.5 Estimated P_p

$$\hat{P}_p = \frac{(USL - LSL)}{6s}$$

where USL is the upper specification limit, LSL is the lower specification limit, and s is the sample standard deviation calculated using

$$s = \sqrt{\frac{\sum_{i=1}^{n} (x_i - \bar{x})^2}{n-1}}$$

Ppk

The P_{pk} and its estimate are computed using:

$$\begin{aligned} P_{pk} &= \min\left(P_{pl}, P_{pu}\right) \\ &= \min\left(\frac{(\mu - LSL)}{3\sigma}, \frac{(USL - \mu)}{3\sigma}\right) \end{aligned}$$

The estimated P_{pk} is shown in Equation 19.6:

Equation 19.6 Estimated P_{pk}

$$\begin{aligned} \hat{P}_{pk} &= \min\left(\hat{P}_{pl}, \hat{P}_{pu}\right) \\ &= \min\left(\frac{(\bar{x} - LSL)}{3s}, \frac{(USL - \bar{x})}{3s}\right) \end{aligned}$$

where $\bar{x}$ is the sample mean of the data set and s is the sample standard deviation.

Notice that the P_{pk} determines the proximity of the process average to the nearest specification limit.

Ppm

Finally, the P_{pm} index and its estimate are calculated as:

$$P_{pm} = \frac{(USL - LSL)}{6\sqrt{\sigma^2 + (\mu - T)^2}}$$

Equation 19.7 Estimated P_{pm}

$$\hat{P}_{pm} = \frac{(USL - LSL)}{6\sqrt{s^2 + (\bar{x} - T)^2}}$$

where T = the specification target.

Process Sigma

In addition to capability ratios, *process sigma*, also known as *sigma level*, is a metric that can be used to indicate how well a process output is meeting specifications. Process sigma is defined as the number of standard deviations between the process mean and the nearest specification. The sigma level and its associated yield and defects per million opportunities are based on the normal distribution. A sigma level equal to three means that the output distribution is centered at the specification target and the lower and upper specifications map to at least $\mu \pm 3\sigma$ of the distribution. Based on normal distribution theory, a 3σ process has a yield equal to 99.73% with 2700 defects per million opportunities. A table relating C_p values with the corresponding process sigma level is shown in Table 19.4. Note that these process sigma values are considered *short-term levels* that do not incorporate any shift of the process mean. The 1.5σ shift is discussed at the end of this chapter.

C_p	Process sigma
0.25	0.75
0.50	1.50
0.75	2.25
1.00	3.00
1.25	3.75
1.50	4.50
1.75	5.25
2.00	6.00

Table 19.4 C_p and corresponding process sigma values.

GENERAL PROCESS CAPABILITY STUDIES

Describe and apply elements of designing and conducting process capability studies relative to characteristics, specifications, sampling plans, stability, and normality. (Evaluate)

Body of Knowledge V.F.3

Conducting a Process Capability Study

The purpose of a capability study is to determine whether a process is capable of meeting customer specifications and to devise a course of action if it cannot.

The general steps for any process capability study include the following:

1. Select a quality characteristic of a specific process for study. Ideally, a capability study should be performed for every critical quality characteristic. In practice, people familiar with the process are usually able to identify the few characteristics that merit a full capability study, typically characteristics that have shown to be difficult to hold to specification.

2. Confirm the measurement system used to acquire the process data. Large measurement system variation can obscure the "true" process variation and will produce an unreliable estimate of process capability.

3. Gather the data. Ideally, the data are readily available and are being tracked on a control chart. If not, collect data from the process—preferably randomly and with consideration given to rational subgrouping. Although the literature differs on the appropriate number of subgroups, approximately 25–30 uniformly sized subgroups are usually sufficient. Subgroup sizes typically range from three to five. The exact size of the subgroup varies because the underlying distribution may not be normal. The farther it departs from normality, the greater the subgroup size required.

4. Verify process stability and ensure that the process is in control. This can easily be accomplished using control charts. If the process is out of control, identify and eliminate special cause variation.

5. Verify that the individual data are normally distributed. Plot the data in a histogram and test for normality, which can be verified using a variety of statistical tests such as Anderson-Darling, Ryan-Joiner, Shapiro-Wilk, or Kolmogorov-Smirnov. If normality is not present and is required, it can be restored using the techniques described elsewhere in this chapter.

6. Obtain the process specifications. The process specifications may be either one- or two-sided specifications.

7. Determine process capability indices and interpret them. Apply the previously described methods. If the process is not capable, work to improve it.

8. Update the process control plan. Once the process has achieved a desired level of capability, update your control plan to ensure that the gains are maintained. If no control plan is present, create one.

Confidence Interval for C_{pk}

Process capability indices are *point estimates* and should be presented along with their confidence intervals. A two-sided confidence interval on C_{pk} can be calculated using Equation 19.8:

Equation 19.8 Two-sided confidence interval on C_{pk}

$$\hat{C}_{pk} - z_{\alpha/2}\sqrt{\frac{1}{9n} + \frac{\hat{C}_{pk}^2}{2n-2}} \le C_{pk} \le \hat{C}_{pk} + z_{\alpha/2}\sqrt{\frac{1}{9n} + \frac{\hat{C}_{pk}^2}{2n-2}}$$

We can also calculate a lower bound for a C_{pk} value using Equation 19.9:

Equation 19.9 Lower bound for C_{pk}

$$C_{pk} \ge \hat{C}_{pk} - z_{\alpha}\sqrt{\frac{1}{9n} + \frac{\hat{C}_{pk}^2}{2n-2}}$$

where n is the sample size used in the process capability study. It is usually this lower bound that is of interest. This is the minimum process capability level given the confidence level, sample size, and within-subgroup variation.

EXAMPLE 19.5

For $n = 45$, and $\hat{C}_{pk} = 1.75$, compute a 95% lower bound for C_{pk}. Here, $\alpha = 0.05$. Using Equation 19.9:

$$C_{pk} \ge \hat{C}_{pk} - z_{\alpha}\sqrt{\frac{1}{9n} + \frac{\hat{C}_{pk}^2}{2n-2}}$$

$$C_{pk} \ge 1.75 - 1.645\sqrt{\frac{1}{9(45)} + \frac{1.75^2}{2(45)-2}}$$

$$C_{pk} \ge 1.43$$

We can say that we are 95% confident that the true C_{pk} is at least 1.43.

PROCESS CAPABILITY FOR ATTRIBUTES DATA

> Calculate the process capability and process sigma level for attributes data. (Apply)
>
> **Body of Knowledge V.F.4**

In general, the process capability for attributes data can be reported as the centerline of the control chart monitoring the process. The chart must be in-control, indicating that the process is stable.

For example, if we are counting defectives and monitoring results using either an np or p chart, the process capability can be reported as $\overline{np}$ or $\overline{p}$. If we are monitoring defects using a c or u chart, the process capability can be reported as $\overline{c}$ or $\overline{u}$.

In addition, we can report a *process Z value* when we are monitoring defectives. For a p chart, we find the Z value such that $\Pr(Z < z) = 1 - \overline{p}$. For an np chart, this calculation would be $\Pr(Z > z) = \frac{\overline{np}}{n}$. A process Z value greater than 2.0 is considered desirable.

EXAMPLE 19.6

Consider a stable process monitored by a *p*-chart with centerline $\overline{p} = 0.01$. What is the estimated process capability and process Z value?

The process capability is $\overline{p} = 0.01$, and from Appendix D, we find the Z value associated with $\Pr(Z < z) = (1 - \overline{p}) = 0.99$ is 2.33.

EXAMPLE 19.7

Consider an in-control process monitored by an *np*-chart with a centerline $\overline{np} = 2.4$ and $n = 100$. What is the estimated process capability and process Z value?

The process capability is $\overline{np} = 2.4$, and from Appendix D, we find the Z value associated with $\Pr(Z > z) = \frac{\overline{np}}{n} = 0.024$ is 1.98. This Z value is less than the desired minimum of $Z = 2.0$.

PROCESS CAPABILITY FOR NON-NORMAL DATA

Identify non-normal data and determine when it is appropriate to use Box-Cox or other transformation techniques. (Apply)

Body of Knowledge V.F.5

To interpret the process capability and process performance indices presented earlier in this chapter, the basic assumption of a normally distributed process output must be met. Of course, not all process variables are normally distributed. We can determine if our data is non-normal by using the techniques in Chapter 17: creating a normal probability plot or running a statistical hypothesis test such as the Anderson-Darling test, or the Kolmogorov-Smirnov test for large samples or the Shapiro-Wilk test for smaller samples.

Once we establish that the process data is not normally distributed, we have three options, all of which are best performed using statistical software:

1. We might be able to transform the data to make it approximately normal using a Box-Cox transformation, and then calculate capability using the standard normal distribution method.
2. We might be able to transform the data to make it approximately normal using a Johnson transformation and then calculate capability using the standard normal distribution method.
3. We can run a distribution fitting algorithm, determine whether there is a distribution that fits our data well enough, and calculate the capability using that distribution. For example, if we have data on failure times or wait times, it may follow an exponential distribution.

For either the Box-Cox or Johnson transformations, the original data is transformed as well as the specifications. The Box-Cox method transforms the original data X into a new, more normally distributed variable $Y = X^{\lambda}$ with $-5 \leq \lambda \leq 5$. The Johnson transformation is often more complex, resulting in a linear equation that may involve the natural log or the inverse hyperbolic sine, or arcsinh, function. As you might imagine, these transformed values may be difficult to explain to a non-technical audience. Using the distribution identified by the fitting algorithm may be a more straightforward method, since the original data is not changed. Use of these three methods is shown in Example 19.8.

EXAMPLE 19.8

The source of this example is Bower (2001). The data included 120 temperature readings as shown in Table 19.5. The normal probability plot and Anderson-Darling test ($p < 0.005$) in Figure 19.5 show that the temperature data is not normally distributed.

13.81	13.05	13.29	22.33	4.40	10.70	3.42	10.04
17.64	8.19	14.48	4.95	6.19	15.37	11.37	7.79
10.41	3.35	5.82	5.82	10.01	3.78	13.93	6.14
11.31	1.87	13.07	8.04	8.85	5.30	10.87	4.65
9.81	4.58	2.52	15.20	4.59	8.73	9.57	16.15
12.09	21.21	7.29	10.44	15.22	5.57	4.67	17.95
8.46	4.41	10.33	6.18	2.36	2.97	7.95	7.15
9.69	3.79	9.75	4.34	8.60	6.13	4.20	17.19
6.26	15.43	6.28	8.37	13.64	4.09	6.03	7.12
2.39	7.70	6.60	12.66	7.58	9.39	4.14	9.60
9.72	7.93	2.44	9.54	8.25	11.32	11.67	7.61
10.05	8.07	6.38	5.99	12.99	7.25	4.97	5.43
8.20	5.16	6.87	9.74	17.37	12.93	8.58	4.00
9.59	4.53	15.25	9.38	13.00	4.91	8.14	4.48
8.47	8.05	3.02	10.38	7.02	18.20	8.97	11.62

Table 19.5 Temperature data for Example 19.8.
Source: Bower, 2001.

Continued

Continued

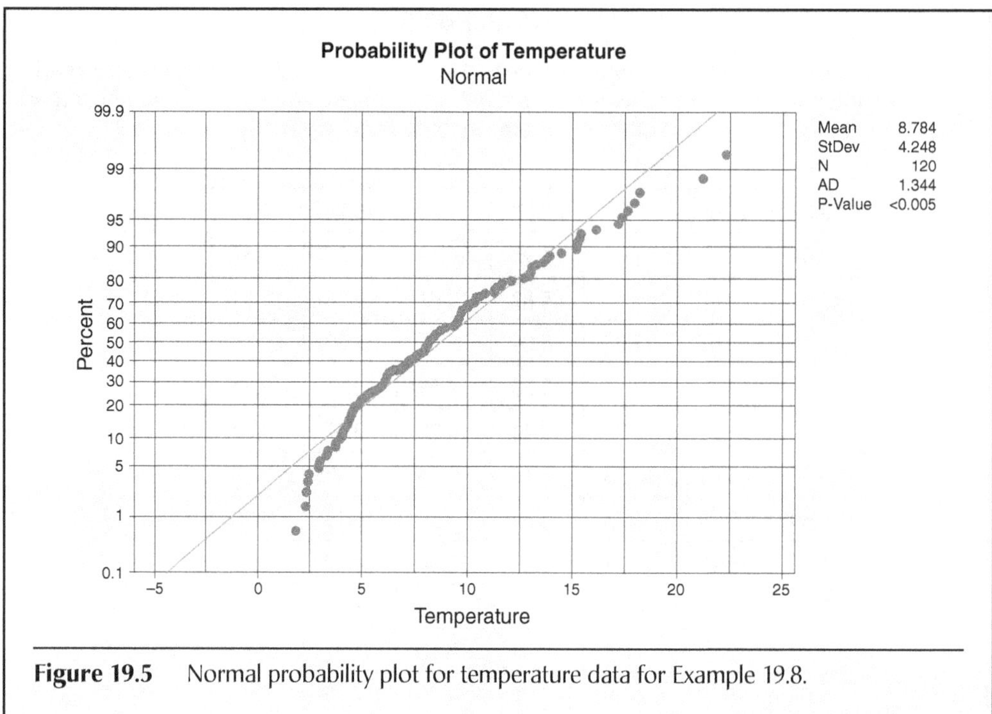

Figure 19.5 Normal probability plot for temperature data for Example 19.8.

We now will calculate the capability of the process, noting that there is a single specification limit, with LSL = 1.0.

1. The Box-Cox transformation results, shown in Figure 19.6, suggest that using a l value equal to 0.29 will render the original data more normal. Note though, that Minitab rounds this value up to 0.50, to yield a $Y = X^{0.50}$ transformation function. The exponent of 0.50 is equivalent to taking a square root, and is often used to "normalize" data taken from a Poisson distribution. The normal probability plot and Anderson-Darling test in Figure 19.7 show that the transformed data using $\lambda = 0.50$ does not indicate non-normality, which is a desired outcome.

2. The Johnson transformation results in a transformation equation of

$$Y = 1.61621 + 1.481170 ln\left[\left(\frac{X+0.181910}{32.2186-X}\right)\right]$$

   Figure 19.8 shows that the Anderson-Darling normality test for the Johnson-transformed data does not indicate non-normality.

   The first column of the original temperature data and the Box-Cox and Johnson transformed values is shown in Table 19.6.

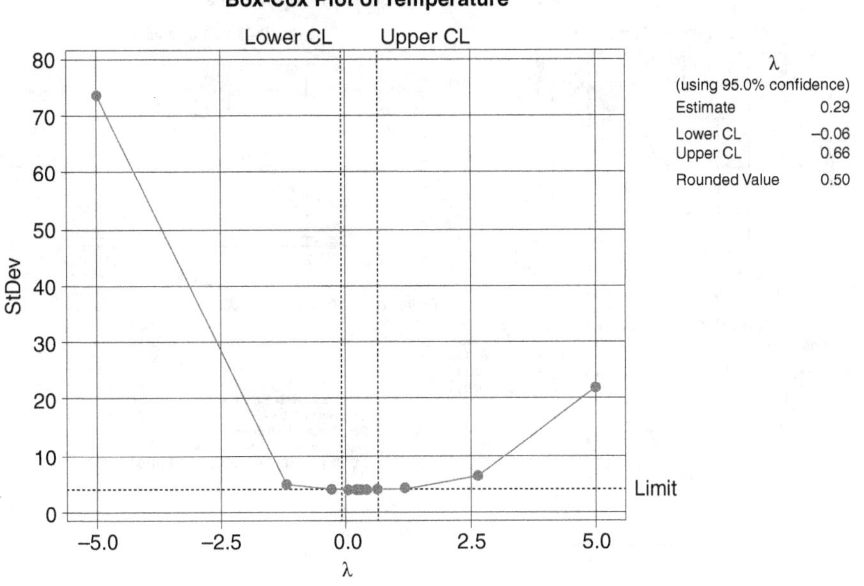

Figure 19.6 Box-Cox results for Example 19.8.

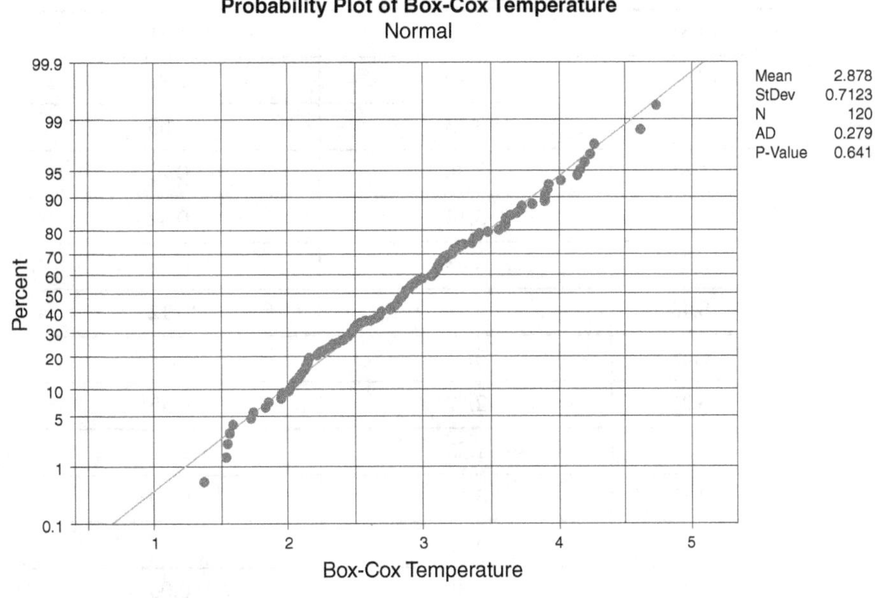

Figure 19.7 Normal probability plot for Box-Cox transformed data for Example 19.8.

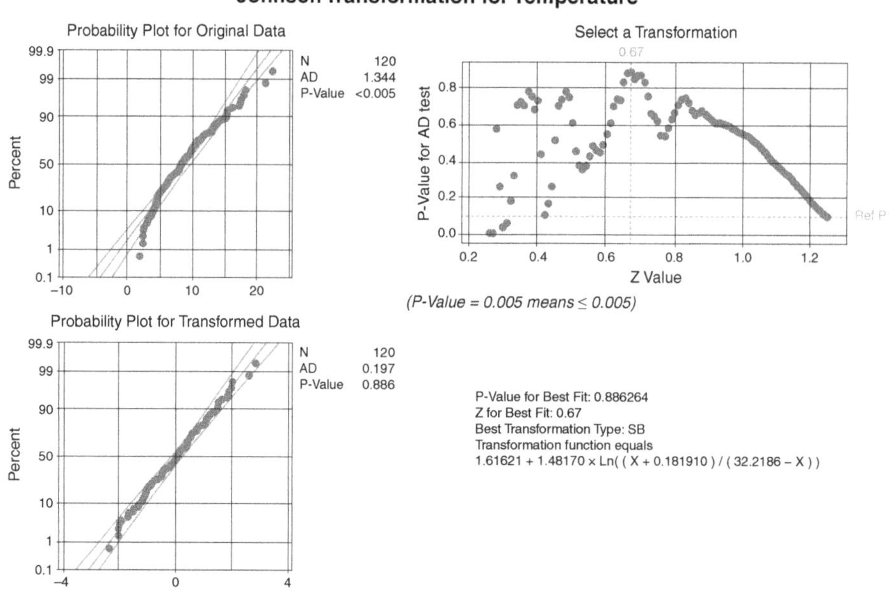

Figure 19.8 Johnson transformation results for Example 19.8.

Temperature	Box-Cox Transformation of Temperature	Johnson Transformation of Temperature
13.81	3.72	1.21
17.64	4.20	1.91
10.41	3.23	0.55
11.31	3.36	0.73
9.81	3.13	0.42
12.09	3.48	0.88
8.46	2.91	0.12
9.69	3.11	0.39
6.26	2.50	–0.45
2.39	1.55	–2.02
9.72	3.12	0.40
10.05	3.17	0.47
8.2	2.86	0.06
9.59	3.10	0.37
8.47	2.91	0.12

Table 19.6 Excerpt of temperature data showing original, Box-Cox, and Johnson transformed values for Example 19.8.

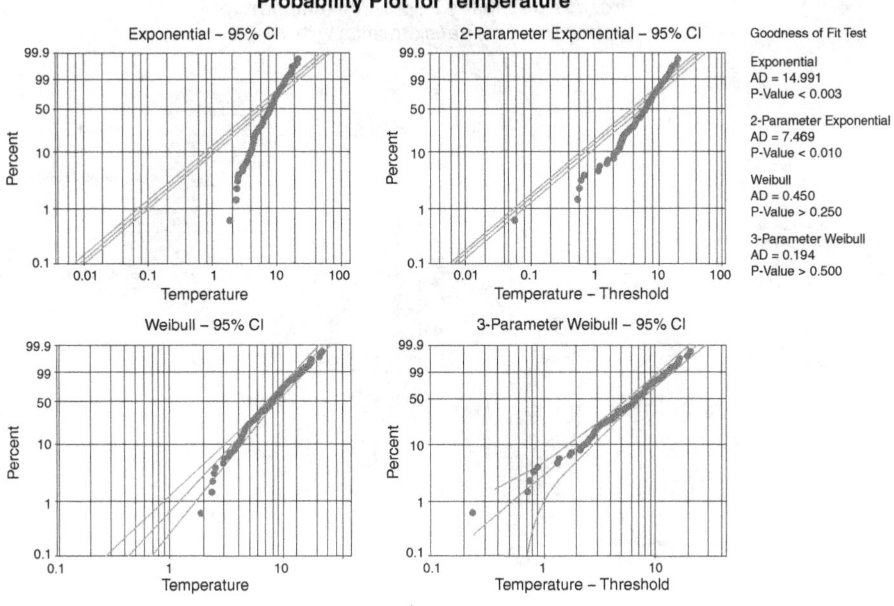

Figure 19.9 Distribution fitting results for Example 19.8.

Distribution	Location	Shape	Scale	Threshold
Weibull		2.21398	9.94772	
3-Parameter Weibull		1.73438	8.01749	1.63415

Table 19.7 Parameter estimates for Weibull distribution for Example 19.8.

3. The distribution fitting algorithm suggests either a 2-parameter or 3-parameter Weibull distribution might provide an appropriate distribution model for the data, based on the p values of the Anderson-Darling tests, as shown in Figure 19.9. For simplicity, we choose a 2-parameter Weibull with shape parameter $\beta = 2.214$ and scale parameter $\alpha = 9.948$, as shown in Table 19.7.

We now calculate the capability using the data from each of the three methods. Figure 19.10 shows the results using the Box-Cox transformed temperature data. Note that the transformed lower specification limit is also equal to 1 since the Box-Cox transformation applied a square root function to the original data. The P_{pk} is equal to 0.88, with an estimated ppm defective rate equal to 4194.0.

Figure 19.11 shows the results using the Johnson transformed temperature data. Note that the transformed lower specification limit is equal to –3.235, a value derived using the transformation equation:

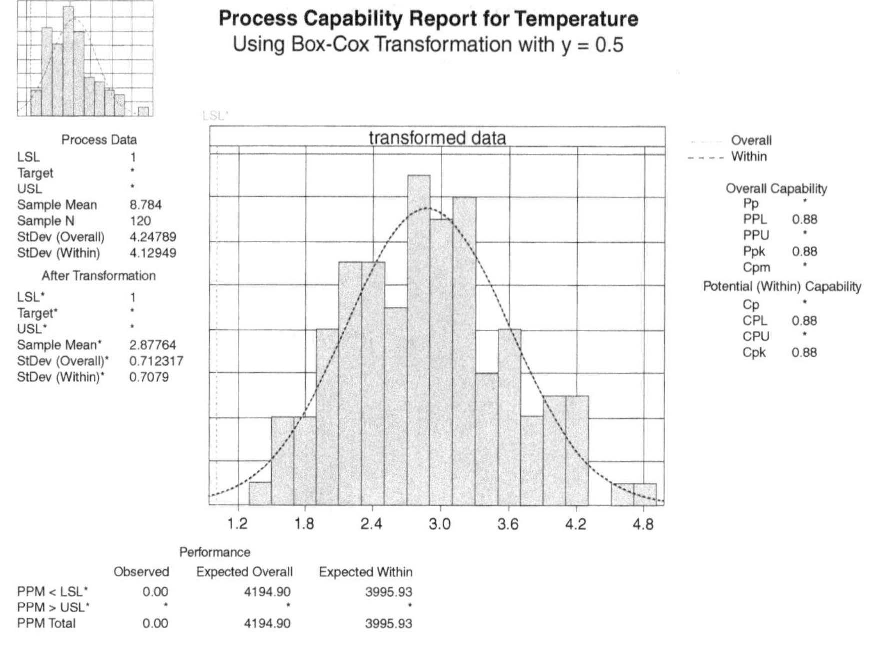

Figure 19.10 Process performance results using Box-Cox transformation for Example 19.8.

$$LSL = 1.61621 + 1.481170\, ln\left[\left(\frac{X + 0.181910}{32.2186 - X}\right)\right]$$

$$LSL = 1.61621 + 1.481170\, ln\left[\left(\frac{1.181910}{31.2186}\right)\right]$$

$$LSL = -3.235$$

The estimated P_{pk} is equal to 1.06, with an estimated ppm defective rate equal to 704.25, which is six times less than the estimate calculated using the data from the Box-Cox transformation.

Finally, Figure 19.12 shows the capability results using the Weibull distribution with shape parameter $\beta = 2.214$ and scale parameter $\alpha = 9.945$. Here, the estimated $P_{pk} = 0.83$ and the total ppm defective is estimated to be 6161.97.

The three methods used have resulted in estimated P_{pk} values equal to 0.88, 1.06, and 0.83. Which index should we report? We could opt for the higher $\widehat{P}_{pk} = 1.06$ or choose to be more conservative by reporting $\widehat{P}_{pk} = 0.83$. Practically speaking, there is a small difference between the values.

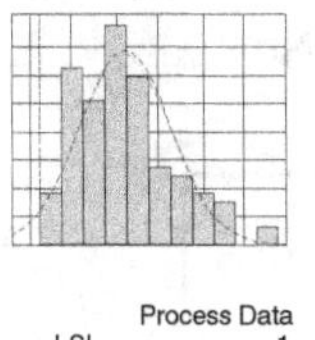

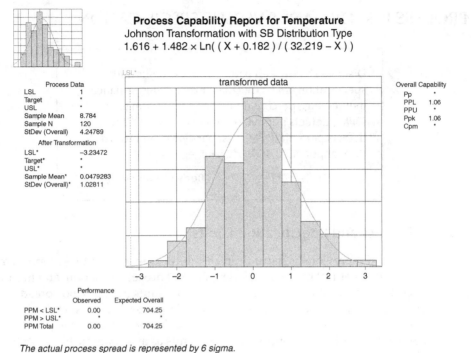

Process Capability Report for Temperature
Johnson Transformation with SB Distribution Type
1.616 + 1.482 × Ln((X + 0.182) / (32.219 − X))

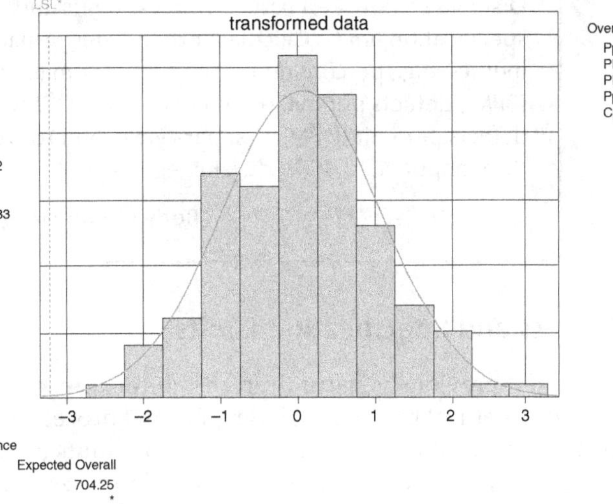

Process Data	
LSL	1
Target	*
USL	*
Sample Mean	8.784
Sample N	120
StDev (Overall)	4.24789
After Transformation	
LSL*	−3.23472
Target*	*
USL*	*
Sample Mean*	0.0479283
StDev (Overall)*	1.02811

Overall Capability	
Pp	*
PPL	1.06
PPU	*
Ppk	1.06
Cpm	*

Performance	Observed	Expected Overall
PPM < LSL*	0.00	704.25
PPM > USL*	*	*
PPM Total	0.00	704.25

The actual process spread is represented by 6 sigma.

Figure 19.11 Process performance results using Johnson transformation for Example 19.8.

Process Capability Report for Temperature
Calculations Based on Weibull Distribution Model

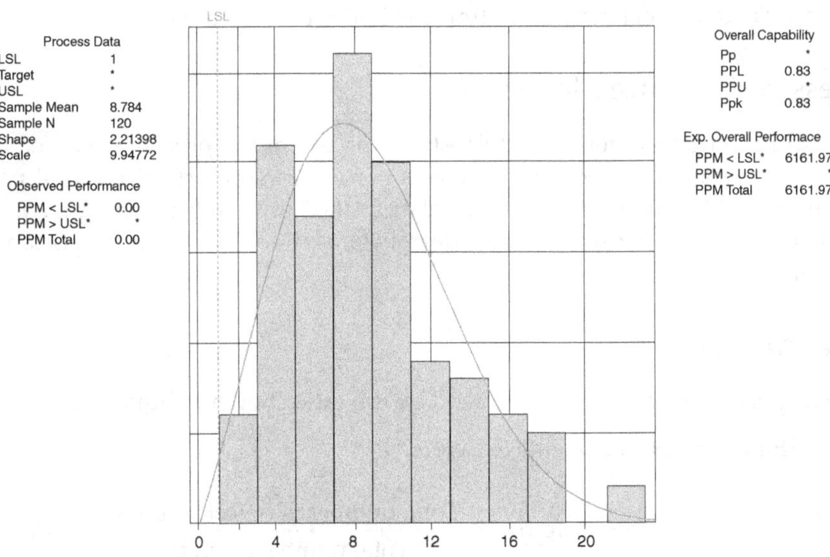

Process Data	
LSL	1
Target	*
USL	*
Sample Mean	8.784
Sample N	120
Shape	2.21398
Scale	9.94772

Observed Performance	
PPM < LSL*	0.00
PPM > USL*	*
PPM Total	0.00

Overall Capability	
Pp	*
PPL	0.83
PPU	*
Ppk	0.83

Exp. Overall Performace	
PPM < LSL*	6161.97
PPM > USL*	*
PPM Total	6161.97

The actual process spread is represented by 6 sigma.

Figure 19.12 Process performance results based on Weibull distribution for Example 19.8.

PROCESS PERFORMANCE VERSUS SPECIFICATION

> Distinguish between natural process limits and specification limits. Calculate process performance metrics, e.g., percent defective, parts per million (PPM), defects per million opportunities (DPMO), defects per unit (DPU), first pass yield, and rolled throughput yield (RTY). (Evaluate)
>
> **Body of Knowledge V.F.6**

Natural Process and Specification Limits

As mentioned previously, natural process limits are known by several names in the literature: natural process variation, normal process variation, and natural tolerance. In all cases, these terms refer to the $\pm 3\sigma$ limits (that is, a 6σ spread) around a process average. For a normally distributed process output, such limits include 99.73% of the process variation and are said to be the "voice of the process." Walter Shewhart originally proposed the $\pm 3\sigma$ limits as an economic trade-off between looking for special causes for points outside the control limits when no special causes existed and not looking for special causes when they did exist.

In contrast to natural process limits, *specification limits* are customer determined and used to define acceptable levels of process performance. Said to be the "voice of the customer," specification limits may be one-sided (that is, upper or lower) or two-sided (that is, both upper and lower). The difference between the upper and lower specification limits is known as the *tolerance.*

Process Performance Metrics

In this section we define and illustrate the use of the percentage defective, parts per million, defects per units, defects per million opportunities, first pass yield, and rolled throughput yield. The relationship between process sigma, percentage defective, parts per million, and defects per million opportunities is tabulated in Appendix I.

Percentage Defective

The percentage defective is defined by the ratio shown in Equation 19.10:

Equation 19.10 Percentage defective

$$\text{Percentage defective} = \frac{\text{Total number of defective units}}{\text{Total number of units}} \times 100\%$$

This percentage aligns with the binomial distribution and the p-chart in statistical process control. A defective unit is any unit containing one or more defects. Note that the term "fraction defective" is defined by Equation 19.11.

Equation 19.11 Fraction defective

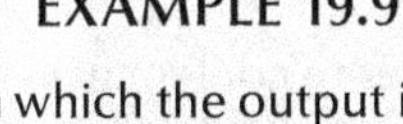

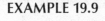

$$\text{Fraction defective} = \frac{\text{Total number of defective units}}{\text{Total number of units}}$$

We can also determine fraction defective by using the distribution of the process output and specifications. For example, if a process output is normally distributed, we can use the method shown in Example 19.9 to calculate the fraction and percentage defective rates.

EXAMPLE 19.9

We can also consider a process in which the output is normally distributed with a mean of 0 and a standard deviation of 1. Specifications are set at $\pm 3\sigma$. The fraction defective for the process is shown in the shaded areas beyond $\pm 3\sigma$ in Figure 19.13. The total fraction defective is the sum of the shaded areas, or 0.0027. Therefore, the percentage defective is 0.27%.

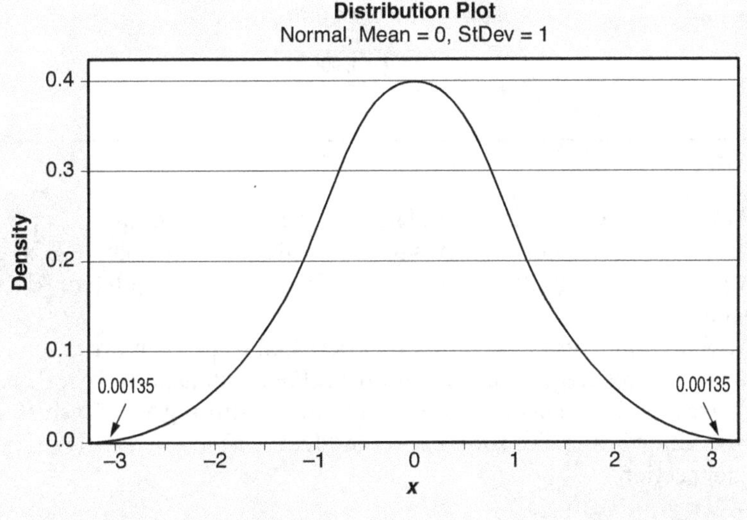

Figure 19.13 The fraction defective for the process given in Example 19.9.

Parts per Million (ppm)

In a typical quality setting, the *parts per million* (ppm) metric usually indicates the number of times a defective part will occur in a million parts produced. By contrast, the DPMO metric reflects the number of defects occurring in a million opportunities. At this point, it is important to note that some authors state that the ppm and DPMO metrics are identical. However, if we follow the definitions above, this would only be true when the number of opportunities for a defect per unit or part is 1.

In the Six Sigma context, ppm is also referred to as the ppm defect rate. Similarly, 3.4 ppm is often stated as 3.4 defects per million parts. However, in both examples, when we say *defects*, we are really referring to *defectives*.

Equation 19.12 Parts per million

$$\text{ppm} = \frac{\text{Total number of defective units}}{\text{Total number of units}} \times 1,000,000$$

EXAMPLE 19.10

Parts per million is also used to refer to contaminants. In a particular product, there are 0.23 grams of insect parts per 25 kilograms. What is the equivalent ppm? We can use Equation 19.12 to solve this problem, but first we must use dimensional analysis to convert to common units as follows:

$$\begin{aligned} \text{ppm} &= \frac{\text{Total number of defective units}}{\text{Total number of units}} \times 1,000,000 \\ &= \left(\frac{0.23g}{25kg}\right)\left(\frac{1kg}{1000g}\right) \times 1,000,000 = 9.2 \end{aligned}$$

Finally, in the more traditional scientific context, ppm may simply refer to the various ratios of components in, say, a mixture. For example, the oxygen component of air is approximately 209,000 ppm. In this case, the idea of "defective" isn't a consideration.

Appendix I illustrates the linkages between multiple metrics, including ppm, sigma level, percentage in specification, and percentage defective. The familiar 3.4 ppm corresponds to a 6-sigma level of quality, assuming a $\pm 1.5\sigma$ shift in the mean. Both the sigma level of a process and the $\pm 1.5\sigma$ shift in the mean will be addressed in a later section.

Defects per Unit (DPU)

The *defects per unit* (DPU) metric is a measure of capability for discrete (attributes) data that follows a Poisson distribution, and is defined by Equation 19.13:

Equation 19.13 Defects per unit (DPU)

$$\text{DPU} = \frac{\text{Total number of defects}}{\text{Total number of units}}$$

EXAMPLE 19.11

A process produces 40,000 pencils. Three types of defects occurred. The number of occurrences of each defect type is (1) blurred printing: 36; (2) too long: 118; and (3) rolled ends: 11. The total number of defects is 165.

Applying Equation 19.13 yields the following:

$$\begin{aligned} \text{DPU} &= \frac{\text{Total number of defects}}{\text{Total number of units}} \\ &= \frac{165}{40,000} \\ &= 0.004125 \end{aligned}$$

Defects per Million Opportunities (DPMO)

The *defects per million opportunities* (DPMO) metric is a measure of capability for discrete (attributes) data found in Equation 19.14:

Equation 19.14 Defects per million opportunities (DPMO)

$$\text{DPMO} = \frac{\text{Total number of defects}}{\text{Total number of opportunties}} \times 1,000,000$$

The DPMO metric is important because it allows you to compare different types of products. Developing a meaningful DPMO metric scheme across multiple product lines, however, can be very time-consuming because it is necessary to accurately determine the number of ways (or opportunities) a defect can occur per unit or part. This can be an enormous task, particularly when dealing with highly complex products and sub-assemblies, or even paperwork.

EXAMPLE 19.12

Continuing with the pencil example, let's calculate the number of opportunities. First, determine the number of ways each defect can occur on each item. For this product, blurred printing occurs in only one way (the pencil slips in the fixture), so there are 40,000 opportunities for this defect to occur.

There are three independent places where dimensions are checked, so there are (3) (40,000) = 120,000 opportunities for this dimensional defect. Rolled ends can occur at the top and the bottom of the pencil, so there are (2) (40,000) = 80,000 opportunities for this defect to occur. Thus, the total number of opportunities for defects is 40,000 + 120,000 + 80,000 = 240,000. Likewise, the total number of opportunities per unit is (1 + 3 + 2) = 6, for a total of 6 × 40,000 = 240,000.

Applying Equation 19.14, we can readily determine the DPMO metric:

Continued

Continued

$$\text{DPMO} = \frac{\text{Total number of defects}}{\text{Total number of opportunties}} \times 1{,}000{,}000$$
$$= \frac{165}{240{,}000} \times 1{,}000{,}000$$
$$= 687.5$$

First Pass Yield (FPY)

First pass yield (FPY), or throughput yield, is the percentage of conforming parts initially produced by a process. Thus, the number of conforming parts is net of any rework or scrap. It is calculated using Equation 19.15:

Equation 19.15 First pass yield (FPY)

$$\text{FPY} = \frac{\text{Total parts produced} - \text{rework} - \text{scrap}}{\text{Total parts produced}} \times 100\%$$

EXAMPLE 19.13

One hundred units enter a process. Three units are scrapped, and six units are reworked. Compute the first pass yield. Using Equation 19.15:

$$\text{FPY} = \frac{\text{Total parts produced} - \text{rework} - \text{scrap}}{\text{Total parts produced}} \times 100\%$$
$$= \frac{100 - 3 - 6}{100} \times 100\%$$
$$= 91\%$$

FPY using the DPU. Another method of determining the FPY is to calculate it by first determining the DPU of the process and then applying the Poisson distribution to find the probability of zero defects. Recall from Chapter 18 that the Poisson distribution with parameter μ is :

$$\Pr(X = x) = \frac{e^{-\mu}\mu^{x}}{x!}$$

It follows that the probability of x = 0 defects is

$$\Pr(X = 0) = e^{-\mu}$$

Using the defects per unit rate, we can calculate first past yield using Equation 19.16:

Equation 19.16 First pass yield using DPU

$$\text{FPY} = e^{-DPU}$$

EXAMPLE 19.14

Recall the pencil example from Example 19.11 above. The DPU from the example was 0.004125. Applying Equation 19.16, we have

$$\text{FPY} = e^{-0.004125} = 0.9959$$

On average, there will be slightly more than 4 defects in 1000 pencils.

Rolled Throughput Yield (RTY)

The *rolled throughput yield* (RTY) metric represents the percentage of units of product passing defect free through an entire process. It is determined by multiplying throughput yields from each subprocess of the total process using Equation 19.17:

Equation 19.17 Rolled throughput yield

$$\text{RTY} = \prod_{i=1}^{n} \text{FPY}_i$$

where

n = number of subprocesses and FPY_i = throughput yield of the ith subprocess.

It should be clear from the above formula that the multiplicative effect will work against the RTY. Consequently, it is advantageous to have the FPY of each subprocess as high as possible.

A significant advantage of using the RTY metric is that it provides a more complete view of the process. Subprocess yields that run high aren't likely to attract the attention necessary to drive improvement. Often, it is only when the total process yield becomes visible does real action occur.

EXAMPLE 19.15

The concept of the RTY is best illustrated by Figure 19.14, which depicts an overall process comprising four subprocesses. Suppose the FPY of the subprocesses are 0.95, 0.99, 0.98, and 0.90. Then the RTY is calculated using Equation 19.17:

$$\text{RTY} = \prod_{i=1}^{4} \text{FPY}_i = 0.95 \times 0.99 \times 0.98 \times 0.90 = 0.83$$

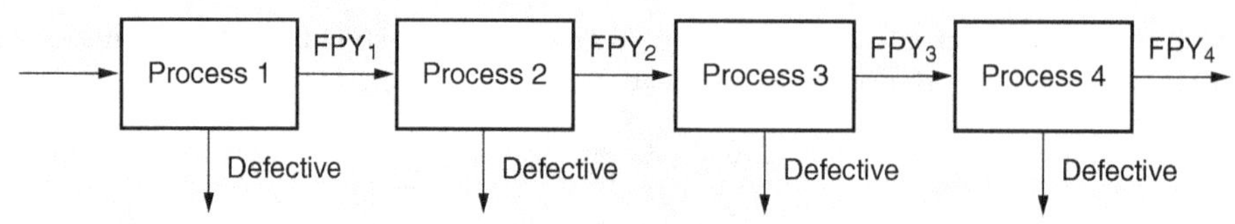

Figure 19.14 An illustration of the rolled throughput yield concept.

Because the value of the FPY is between 0 and 1, the RTY will always be less than the lowest FPY component in the calculation.

SHORT-TERM AND LONG-TERM CAPABILITY

Describe and use appropriate assumptions and conventions when only short-term data or only long-term data are available. Interpret the relationship between short-term and long-term capability. (Evaluate)

Body of Knowledge V.F.7

Short-Term Capability

Short-term capability encapsulates the following concepts:

- C_p, C_{pk}, and C_{pm} are short-term process capability indices. They are sometimes known as *within-subgroup, short-term,* or *potential* process capability indices.
- The process must be in statistical control for these indices to be used.
- These indices are derived using an estimate of short-term variation. Short-term variation is within-subgroups variation and is obtained from control charts.

- It is assumed that the individual process data elements are approximately normally distributed. When this assumption does not hold, an appropriate transformation or non-normal distribution model can be applied using the techniques described previously.
- The specification limits are based on customer requirements.

Long-Term Capability

P_p, P_{pk}, and P_{pm} fall into the long-term capability category and are known as *process performance indices*. The process does not need to be in statistical control for these indices to be used. However, if the process is not in statistical control, the indices are of limited value for predicting future performance.

These indices are derived using an estimate of long-term variation. Long-term variation is known as *total* or *overall variation* (which includes both within- and between-subgroup variation) and is obtained using the sample standard deviation formula:

$$s = \sqrt{\frac{\sum_{i=1}^{n}(x_i - \overline{X})^2}{n-1}}$$

It is assumed that the individual process data elements are approximately normally distributed. When this assumption does not hold, an appropriate transformation or non-normal distribution model can be applied using the techniques described previously. The specification limits are based on customer requirements.

The 1.5 Sigma Shift

The concept of the *1.5 sigma shift* was introduced by Motorola based on its observation that for most processes, the mean shifts up and down within a 1.5 sigma range over time. To account for a worst-case case scenario, then, we can subtract 1.5 from our process sigma, or subtract 0.5 from the calculated C_{pk} value.

Six Sigma practitioners should not blindly assume that this specific shift occurs unless it is applicable to their processes as well. In fact, their processes may shift, but in a range other than $\pm 1.5\sigma$. An organization can observe its own processes to determine if these shifts occur, and if they do, it can determine the magnitude of the shifts. Either way, the calculation is meant to capture a hypothetical, worst-case scenario that is not necessarily what the customer experiences. In fact, the quality level the customer sees is the estimated P_{pk}.

Table 19.8 shows the short-term percent yield and parts-per-million defective values for various process sigma levels with no mean shift applied.

Process Sigma (or Sigma Level)	Specification Limits Map to:	Percent Yield	Ppm Defective
1	$\mu \pm 1\sigma$	68.27%	317,300
2	$\mu \pm 2\sigma$	95.45%	45,500
3	$\mu \pm 3\sigma$	99.73%	2700
4	$\mu \pm 4\sigma$	99.9937%	63
5	$\mu \pm 5\sigma$	99.999943%	0.57
6	$\mu \pm 6\sigma$	99.9999998%	0.002

Table 19.8 Yield and ppm defective for short-term sigma levels (no mean shift).

Process Sigma (or Sigma Level)	Specification Limits Map to:	Percent Yield After a 1.5σ Shift Is Applied	Ppm Defective After a 1.5σ Shift Is Applied
1	$\mu \pm 1\sigma$	30.23%	317,300
2	$\mu \pm 2\sigma$	69.13%	608,700
3	$\mu \pm 3\sigma$	93.32%	66,810
4	$\mu \pm 4\sigma$	99.3790%	6210
5	$\mu \pm 5\sigma$	99.97670%	233
6	$\mu \pm 6\sigma$	99.999660%	3.4

Table 19.9 Yield and ppm defective after a 1.5 sigma shift is applied.

Table 19.9 displays the resulting yield and ppm defective values after a mean shift equal to 1.5 standard deviations is applied.

Relationship Between Long-Term and Short-Term Capability

Short-term capability measures such as C_p, C_{pk}, or C_{pm} can be thought of as snapshots of the process performance, whereas long-term capability can be thought of as more of a video. The short-term snapshot is taken under ideal conditions: when the process is in a state of control, and with variability calculated within homogeneous subgroups. Thus, by design, the estimated sigma for these measures is comparatively small, resulting in indices that are often larger than the corresponding long-term process performance values.

In contrast, the long-term process performance measures of P_p and P_{pk} are calculated using a measure of variability that captures both within- and between-subgroup variation. As well, these measures are often calculated when the process is not in control. Thus, it may be argued that the estimated sigma for these measures includes a longer, and perhaps more realistic, view of the process performance.

Part VI
Analyze

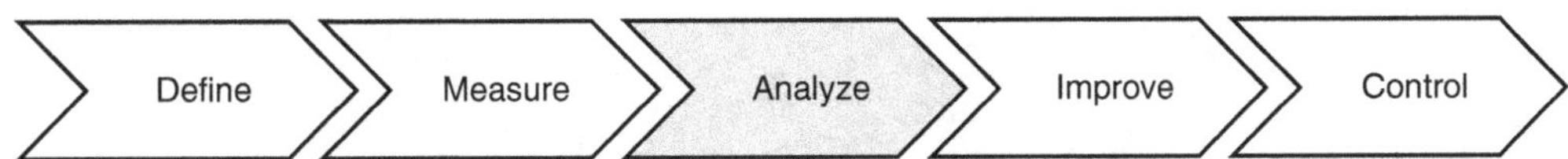

The purpose of this phase is to analyze and establish optimal performance settings for each X and verify root causes. Common tools used in this phase are shown in Table VI.1.

Affinity diagrams	*Histograms*	Regression
ANOVA	*Hpothesis testing*	Reliability modeling
Basic statistics	*Interrelationship diagraphs*	Root cause analysis
Box plot	Linear programming	*Run charts*
Brainstorming	Linear regression	*Scatter diagrams*
Cause-and-effect diagrams	Logistic regression	Shop audits
Components of variation	*Meeting minutes*	*Simulation*
Design of experiments (DOE)	*Multi-vari studies*	*Suppliers–inputs–process–outputs–customers (SIPOC)*
Exponentially weighted moving average charts	Multiple regression	
	Multivariate tools	*Tollgate reviews*
Failure mode and effects analysis (FMEA)	Nonparametric tests	*Tree diagrams*
Force-field analysis	Preventive maintenance	Waste analysis
Gap analysis	*Process capability analysis*	*Y=f(X)*
General linear models (GLMs)	*Project management*	
Geometric dimensioning and tolerancing (GD&T)	*Project tracking*	
	Qualitaive analysis	

Table VI.1 Common tools use in *analyze* phase.
Note: Tools shown in italic are used in more than one phase.

Chapter 20

Measuring and Modeling Relationships Between Variables

All models are wrong; some are useful.

—George E. P. Box

INTRODUCTION

We often find it useful to describe the relationship between two quantitative variables. For example, a production engineer may investigate the relationship between the diameter of a drilled hole and the age of the drill bit, or the strength of a package seal and the temperature of the sealing machine. A business analyst may want to study the relationship between the monthly revenue and the number of sales calls, or between production volume and supplier capacity. A scientist may want to study the relationship between the reaction time of a chemical process and the amount of catalyst used, or between the change in sea level and the level of atmospheric carbon dioxide. This chapter presents the correlation coefficient, simple linear regression, and multivariate tools that are useful in Six Sigma analysis.

LINEAR CORRELATION

> Calculate and interpret the correlation coefficient and its confidence interval and describe the difference between correlation and causation. (Evaluate)
>
> Body of Knowledge VI.A.1

Graphical Methods

When exploring relationships between variables, our first instinct should always be to graph the data on an X-Y plot, or scatter plot. In this type of plot, the variable that we want to predict is on the vertical or y-axis, and the input variable is placed on the x-axis. The Y variable is also called the *response variable*, or *dependent variable*.

The X variable is referred to variously as the *input variable*, the *predictor variable*, or the *independent variable*. Plotting the (x, y) pairs will show what type of relationship exists between the two variables, as well showing any unusual or outlying observations.

For example, consider the seal strength and temperature readings in Table 20.1. A production engineer tested the seal strength of paper packages produced at various temperatures. She would like to predict the seal strength of a paper package by using the temperature setting of the sealing machine. In this case, the seal strength will be plotted on the y-axis, and temperature will be plotted on the x-axis. The resulting scatter plot is shown in Figure 20.1.

Based on the pattern displayed in the scatter plot, the production engineer can characterize the association between the variables X and Y. Figure 20.1 shows that as temperature increases, the seal strength of the package also tends to increase. Since both variables are moving in the same direction, we call this a *positive association*, or, more precisely, a *positive correlation*. The term association is more generic

Temperature	Seal Strength
225	123.1
235	125.0
238	123.8
240	119.4
241	125.8
241	122.5
245	127.8
250	126.5
252	127.0
250	126.0
255	129.5
260	130.8
270	127.5
269	128.7
265	124.8
275	125.3
292	131.5
321	132.2
315	138.2
309	137.4

Table 20.1 Seal strength versus temperature.

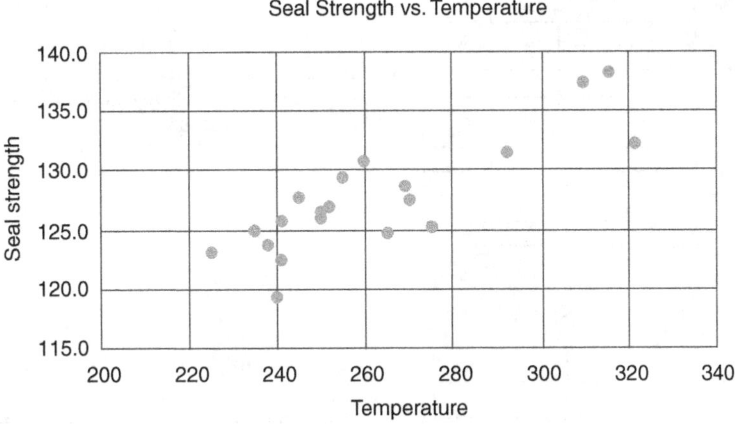

Figure 20.1 Scatter plot of seal strength versus temperature.

and can be used to describe the relationship between categorical variables. Correlation refers to the relationship between two quantitative variables. Figure 20.2 shows the types of linear patterns we may detect in a scatter plot.

As shown in Figure 20.2, if the variable Y tends to decrease as X increases, the correlation between the two variables is negative. If the points form a random cloud with no discernable pattern, this shows that the variables X and Y have no correlation: Knowing the change in X offers no insight into what the value of Y may be. If the variable Y tends to increase as X increases, the correlation between the two variables is positive.

Linear Correlation Coefficient

We can quantify the direction and strength of the linear relationship between the variables X and Y by calculating *Pearson's product-moment correlation coefficient*. The population correlation coefficient is denoted by the Greek letter ρ (rho), and the sample correlation coefficient is denoted by the lowercase letter r.

There are four assumptions behind Pearson's correlation coefficient:

1. *The level of measurement for the data is interval or ratio.* Both the X and Y variables should be at the interval or ratio level of measurement. Recall that at the interval level of measurement, the differences between data points are meaningful, but the zero point is arbitrary. Measures such as calendar years, or temperatures in Celsius or Fahrenheit, are interval level measures. For ratio level data, differences between data observations are meaningful and two data points can be compared in terms of ratios because a true zero exists. Examples of ratio level measures include money, weight, length, or counts. If the data are ordinal, such as ranks or results from a survey that uses a Likert scale, we can use nonparametric methods such as the *Spearman* or *Kendall rank correlation*. Readers are referred Montgomery and Runger (2020) to learn more.

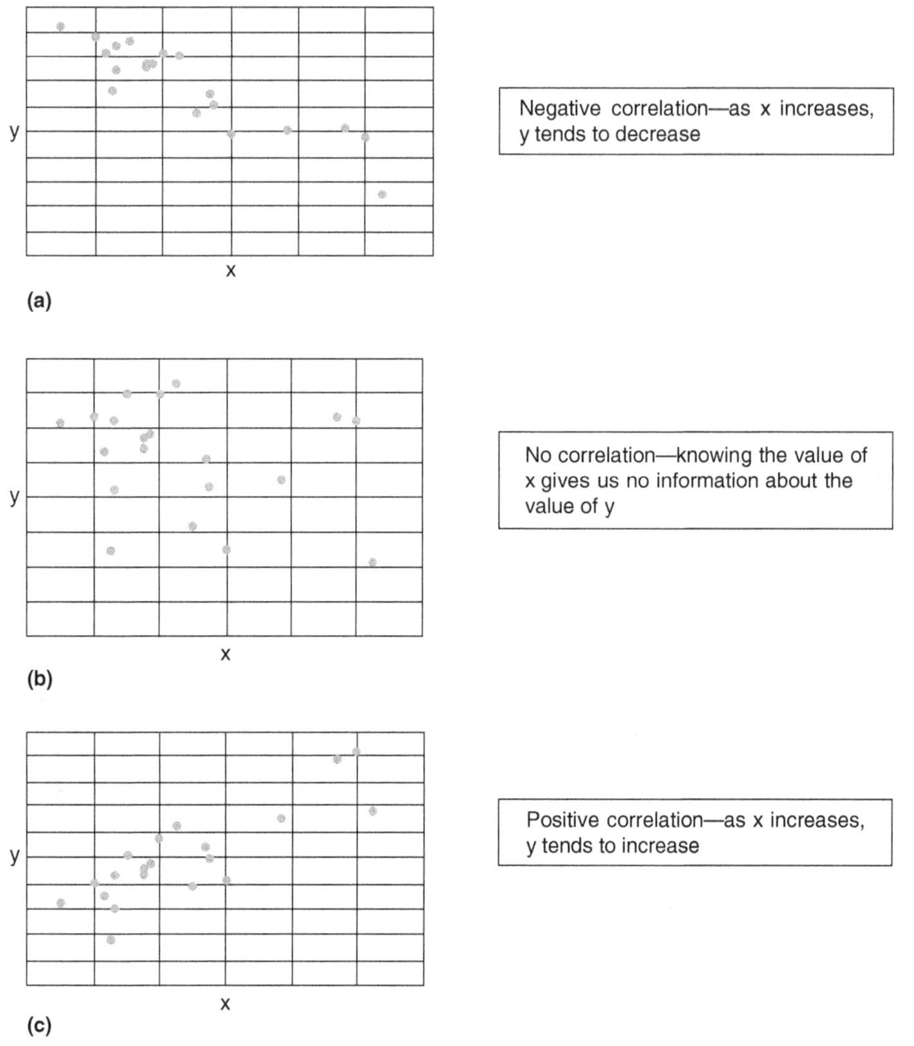
y
x
(a)
Negative correlation—as x increases, y tends to decrease
y
x
(b)
No correlation—knowing the value of x gives us no information about the value of y
y
x
(c)
Positive correlation—as x increases, y tends to increase

Figure 20.2 Types of linear patterns.

2. *The data are related pairs.* Each X value should have a corresponding value for Y. For example, in a medical study each subject may be measured on both X = (diastolic blood pressure) and Y = (weight).

3. *The relationship between X and Y is linear in nature.* The linearity assumption can be checked using a scatter plot. The points on the X-Y plot should suggest a straight line, and not any curvilinear relationship. This is a key assumption for linear correlation.

   There are many instances in which two variables are related, but in a curvilinear fashion. In these cases, calculating a correlation coefficient will provide misleading information. For example, the plots in

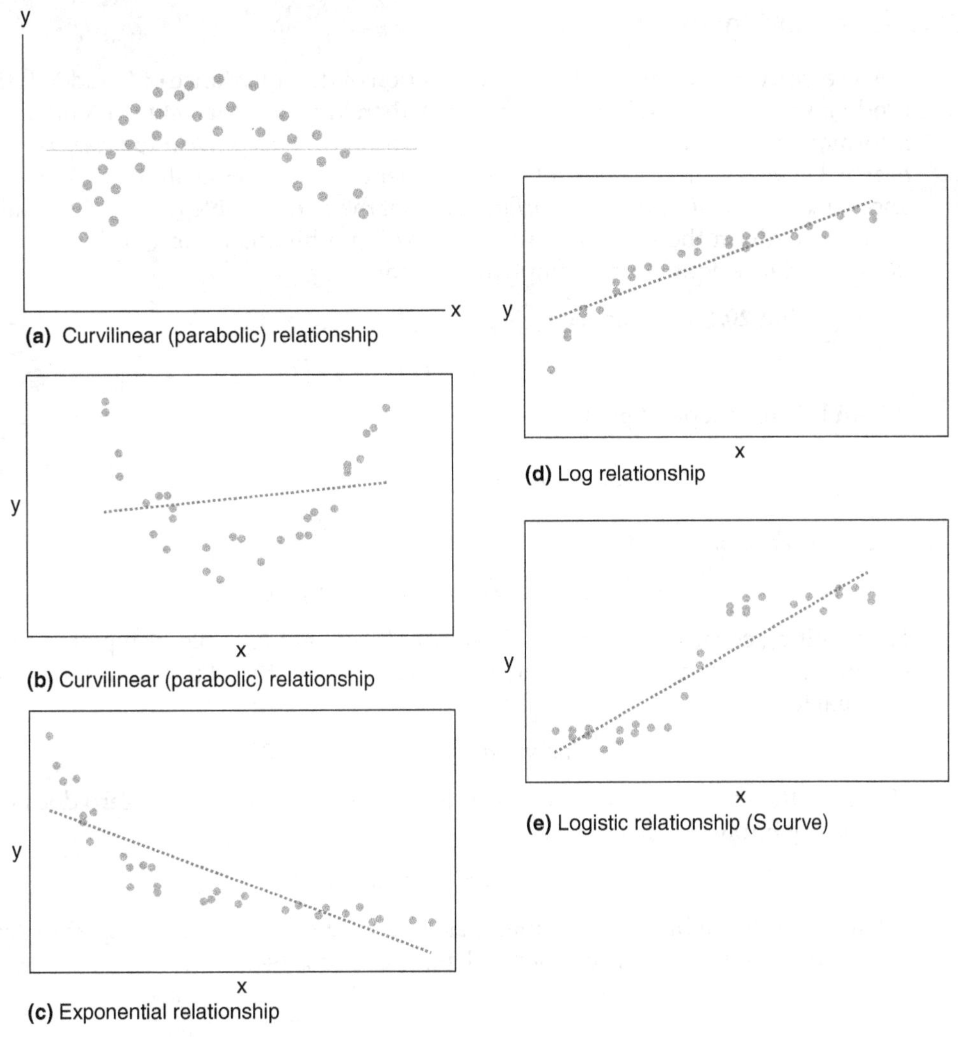

Figure 20.3 Types of curvilinear patterns.

Figure 20.3 display various curvilinear relationships. Among them include downward and upward facing parabolas; exponential relationships in which points decrease (or increase) very quickly; a log relationship in which the y variable increases at first, but then levels off; and a logistic relationship, in which the points follow an S-shaped curve.

4. *There are no outliers in the data.* This assumption can be graphically assessed using either visual inspection of a scatter plot, or by creating box-and-whisker plots for the X and Y variables. For example, an outlier for a normal distribution would be any point falling beyond the three-standard deviation limits.

Covariance and Independence

The Pearson correlation coefficient is a function of the covariance of X and Y. If the random variables X and Y are independent, then knowing the value of X offers no information about the value of Y. *The covariance of two independent variables is equal to zero.* However, the converse of this statement is not necessarily true: A covariance equal to zero *does not necessarily imply* that the two variables X and Y are independent. Only in the case of X and Y following a bivariate normal distribution does covariance equal to zero imply independence.

Equation 20.1 Covariance

$$Cov(X, Y) = E(XY) - E(X)\,E(Y)$$

If X and Y are independent, then

$$E(XY) = E(X)\,E(Y)$$

and covariance is calculated as

$$Cov(X, Y) = E(XY) - E(X)\,E(Y) = 0.$$

The resulting covariance between these two dependent variables is equal to zero. In summary, if two variables X and Y are independent, then their covariance will be equal to zero:

$$X, Y\ independent \Rightarrow Cov(X, Y) = 0$$

However, the inverse is not necessarily true: A covariance equal to zero does not necessarily imply independence:

$$Cov(X, Y) = 0 \not\Rightarrow X, Y\ independent$$

If X and Y follow a bivariate normal distribution, then a covariance equal to zero does imply that they are also independent, and vice versa.

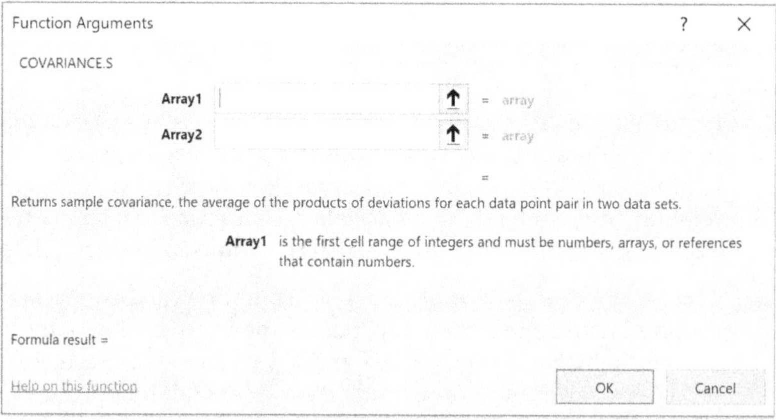

Figure 20.4 *Covariance.s* function in Excel.

$$Cov(X, Y) = 0 \Leftrightarrow X, Y \text{ independent}$$

The sample covariance of two variables X and Y can be calculated in Excel using the *=covariance.s* function as shown in Figure 20.4.

Note that using *Cauchy-Schwartz inequality* we can state that the squared covariance between any two variables X and Y will always be less than or equal to the product of the variances of X and Y:

$$[Cov(X,Y)]^2 \leq \sigma_X^2 \sigma_Y^2$$

Calculating Linear Correlation

The formula Pearson correlation parameter ρ is shown in Equation 20.2:

Equation 20.2 Pearson product-moment coefficient ρ

$$\rho = \frac{Cov(X,Y)}{\sigma_x \sigma_y}$$

Note in Equation 20.2 that the Pearson correlation is a function of the covariance of X and Y.

In almost all cases, we will not have access to values in the entire population, so we instead take a sample and estimate the correction coefficient. To estimate the Pearson correlation coefficient, we should first graphically check that the linear relationship assumption, at the very least, is met. Then, we can use Equation 20.3 to calculate the sample statistic r:

Equation 20.3 Pearson sample correlation coefficient r

$$\begin{aligned} r &= \frac{\widehat{Cov}(X,Y)}{s_x s_y} \\ &= \frac{\sum (x_i - \bar{x})(y_i - \bar{y})/(n-1)}{\sqrt{\frac{\sum (x_i - \bar{x})^2}{(n-1)}}\sqrt{\frac{\sum (y_i - \bar{y})^2}{(n-1)}}} \\ &= \frac{\sum x_i y_i - n\bar{x}\bar{y}}{\sqrt{\left(\sum x_i^2 - n\bar{x}^2\right)\left(\sum y_i^2 - n\bar{y}^2\right)}} \\ &= \frac{SS_{xy}}{\sqrt{SS_{xx} SS_{yy}}} \end{aligned}$$

The sample correlation coefficient can also be calculated in Excel using the *=correl* function as shown in Figure 20.5.

It is interesting to note that the correlation coefficient is scale invariant, remaining unchanged if a constant c is added to or multiplied by the values of one or both variables. For example, the correlation calculated between a group's height

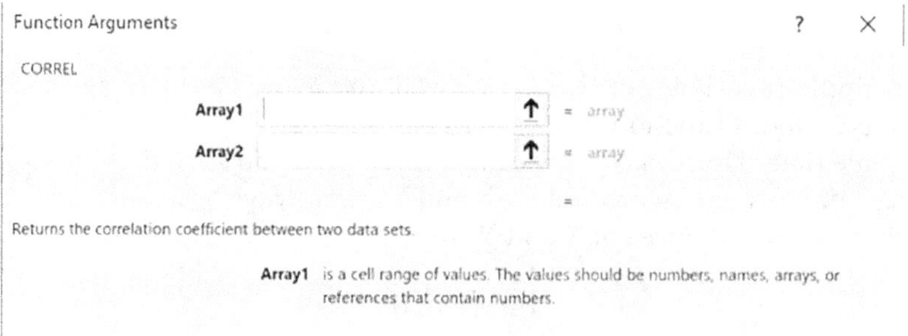

Figure 20.5 *Correl* function in Excel.

(a) Perfect negative correlation, $\rho = -1$	**(b)** Strong negative correlation, $\rho = -0.9$	**(c)** Moderate negative correlation, $\rho = -0.6$
(d) Weak negative correlation, $\rho = -0.30$	**(e)** Very weak correlation, ρ is near 0	**(f)** Weak positive correlation, $\rho = 0.30$
(g) Moderate positive correlation, $\rho = 0.6$	**(h)** Strong positive correlation, $\rho = 0.9$	**(i)** Perfect positive correlation, $\rho = +1$

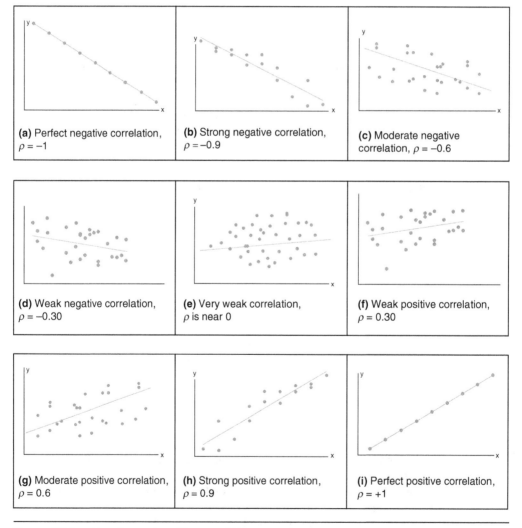

Figure 20.6 Negative and positive correlation examples.

and weight will remain constant whether the height is measured in inches or centimeters, or weight is measured in pounds or kilograms.

The Pearson correlation coefficient ρ and its estimate r, ranges from –1 to +1. A correlation coefficient equal to +1 maps to a perfect positive association between X and Y.

Graphically, the correlation coefficient of –1 has (x, y) pairs falling along a straight line with a negative slope, and the correlation coefficient $\rho = +1$ has pairs falling along a straight line with positive slope. Figure 20.6 shows examples of scatter plots with their corresponding correlation coefficients. Notice that as the plotted points become more scattered around the best fit line, the correlation coefficient gets closer to zero.

In general, a Pearson correlation coefficient in the range of [–1 to –0.7] and [0.7 to 1] indicates a strong association between X and Y. Recognize, though, that there is no crisp cut-off value to separate strong association from weak association. A correlation coefficient equal to zero indicates that X and Y are not linearly associated and are in fact independent if X and Y are bivariate normal.

We now illustrate the assumption checks and use of Equation 20.3 to calculate the value of r with the following example. The example has just a few data points so that readers can practice calculating r manually.

EXAMPLE 20.1

TESTING ASSUMPTIONS AND CALCULATING CORRELATION

Consider the chemical process data presented in Table 20.2, which shows the reaction times X in minutes, and the yield of a chemical Y in grams. We will check assumptions using Minitab statistical software, and manually calculate the sample correlation coefficient r between the reaction time and the yield of the chemical process. The number of data points in this example has been kept small by design so that the reader can practice performing the calculations manually.

X	7	8	9	11	12	14	16	17
Y	9	10	13	14	15	12	17	18

Table 20.2 Reaction time and yield data.

Solution: We first check to make sure all assumptions are met.

1. *The level of measurement for the data is interval or ratio.* The X variable, reaction time in minutes, is a ratio level of measurement, as is the Y variable, grams of yield.
2. *The data are related pairs.* There is a corresponding yield value for each reaction time; the data is paired.
3. *The relationship between X and Y is linear in nature.* A scatter plot of the data, shown in Figure 20.7, indicates a linear relationship between X and Y and does not display any curvilinear pattern.
4. *There are no outliers in the data.* By examining the scatter plot in Figure 20.7, we see that there are no outliers.

Continued

Continued

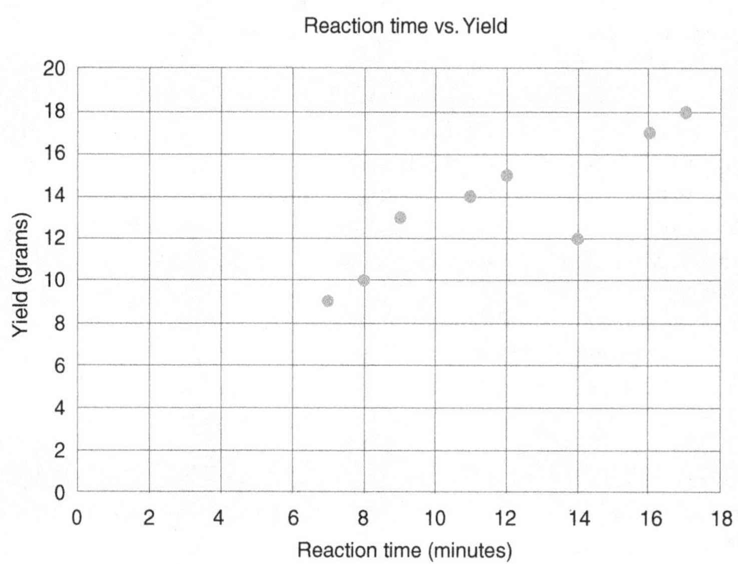

Figure 20.7 Scatter plot of yield versus reaction time.

Now that the assumptions have been successfully checked, we can move on to calculating the sample correlation coefficient *r*. Recall from Equation 20.3 that

$$r = \frac{\widehat{Cov}(X,Y)}{s_X s_Y} = \frac{\sum x_i y_i - n\bar{x}\bar{y}}{\sqrt{\left(\sum x_i^2 - n\bar{x}^2\right)\left(\sum y_i^2 - n\bar{y}^2\right)}} = \frac{SS_{xy}}{\sqrt{SS_{xx}SS_{yy}}}$$

We first determine the values of SS_{xx}, SS_{yy}, and SS_{xy}. Using the given values *x* and *y*, we obtain:

$$SS_{xy} = \sum x_i y_i - n\bar{x}\bar{y} = 1340 - 8(11.75)(13.5) = 71$$

$$SS_{xx} = \sum x_i^2 - n\bar{x}^2 = 1200 - 8(11.75)^2 = 95.5$$

$$SS_{yy} = \sum y_i^2 - n\bar{y}^2 = 1528 - 8(13.5)^2 = 70$$

Now, substituting in the values of SS_{xy}, SS_{xx}, and SS_{yy}, Equation 20.3 yields

$$r = \frac{SS_{xy}}{\sqrt{SS_{xx}}\sqrt{SS_{yy}}} = \frac{71}{\sqrt{95.5}\sqrt{70}} = 0.868$$

The scatter plots created for the assumption checks indicated that there was a strong positive correlation coefficient between the reaction time and the yield of the chemical, and this conclusion is supported by the value of the sample correlation coefficient $r = 0.868$.

Hypothesis Tests for the Correlation Coefficient ρ

To make a statement about the population correlation coefficient ρ based on sample data, we can use a hypothesis test. Often, we are interested in testing the null hypothesis

$$H_0 : \rho = 0$$

versus one of the three possible alternative hypotheses:

$$H_1 : \rho < 0$$
$$H_1 : \rho > 0$$
$$H_1 : \rho \neq 0$$

To perform this hypothesis test, we calculate the test statistic in Equation 20.4.

Equation 20.4 Test statistic for Pearson correlation

$$t = \frac{r}{\sqrt{1-r^2}}\sqrt{n-2}$$

Under the null hypothesis $H_0 : \rho = 0$, the test statistic in Equation 20.4 follows a Student's t distribution with $(n - 2)$ degrees of freedom, where n is the number of (x, y) pairs in our data set.

EXAMPLE 20.2
HYPOTHESIS TEST FOR ρ

We now illustrate the procedure to conduct a test of hypothesis for the population correlation coefficient ρ.

Using the reaction time and yield data in Table 20.1, test the hypotheses

$$H_0 : \rho = 0 \quad \text{versus} \quad H_1 : \rho > 0$$

at 5% level of significance.

Solution: We conduct this test of hypothesis using the six-step procedure presented in Chapter 21.

Step 1. *State the null hypothesis and the alternative hypothesis.*

$$H_0 : \rho = 0 \quad \text{versus} \quad H_1 : \rho > 0$$

Note that this is a one-sided hypothesis because H_1 is an inequality.

Continued

Continued

Step 2. *Assign an appropriate value to the level of significance.*
Here, we have chosen α.= 0.05. Since this is a one-sided hypothesis, we do not divide our α by two.

Step 3. *Calculate the appropriate test statistic.*
From the results of Example 20.1, we have r = 0.868. We then calculate:

$$t = \frac{r\sqrt{n-2}}{\sqrt{1-r^2}} = \frac{0.868\sqrt{8-2}}{\sqrt{1-(0.868)^2}} = 4.282$$

Step 4. *Determine the probability distribution of the test statistic designated in Step 3.*

$$t = \frac{r\sqrt{n-2}}{\sqrt{1-r^2}} \sim t_{n-2}$$

In this example, the test statistic follows the Student's t distribution with $(n - 2) = 6$ degrees of freedom.

Step 5. *Determine the rejection region(s) and locate the critical point(s) and compare these to the calculated test statistic. Alternatively, calculate the p-value for the test and compare it to alpha.*

The rejection region is determined by the value of α or the level of significance, and the form of the alternative hypothesis. The significance level in this example is 0.05, and the alternative hypothesis maps to a one-sided, right-tailed test.

From Step 4, we note that our test statistic follows a Student's t distribution with six degrees of freedom. Using the Student's t distribution table in Appendix E, the rejection region and the critical point can be found, as shown in Figure 20.8.

Since the observed value of the test statistic 4.282 is greater than the critical value of 1.943, the test statistic falls in the rejection region. Therefore, we reject the null hypothesis $H_0 : \rho = 0$ and conclude that at the 5% level of significance, there is a significant positive relationship between the reaction time and the yield of the chemical.

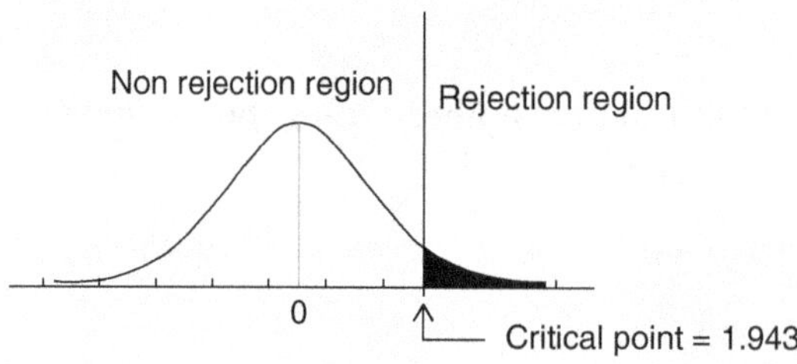

Figure 20.8 Rejection region under Student's t distribution in Example 20.2.

Continued

Continued

Function Arguments ? ×

T.DIST.RT

X = number

Deg_freedom = number

=

Returns the right-tailed Student's t-distribution.

X is the numeric value at which to evaluate the distribution.

Figure 20.9 *t.dist.rt* function in Excel.

Alternatively, we can be more precise with our level of confidence by calculating the p-value of the test using a statistical software package. The p-value is the probability of obtaining the value of test statistic, or something more extreme, under the assumption that the null hypothesis is true. This concept is discussed in greater detail in Chapter 21. For now, we will say that a p-value smaller than our chosen alpha from Step 2 results in our rejecting the null hypothesis.

We can also solve for the p-value directly by using the *=t.dist.rt()* function in Microsoft Excel to get the right-tailed probability of the Student's *t* distribution. The function takes two arguments: the value of the test statistic, and then the degrees of freedom, as shown in Figure 20.9.

For this example, the function =t.dist.rt(4.282,6) returns 0.0025.

Step 6. *State the conclusion in business terms.*
Using the p-value, we can state that we are $(1 - p)\%$, or 99.75%, confident that there is a significant positive relationship between the reaction time and the yield of the chemical. This is a much more precise conclusion than one derived from using a critical value from the Student's *t* table.

Confidence Interval for ρ

We can also construct a confidence interval around the parameter ρ. This calculation is performed in three steps.

Step 1
Fisher (1921) noted that under the assumption of bivariate normality, the statistic z_r follows an approximate normal distribution with variance equal to $1/(n - 3)$.

Equation 20.5 Z_r value of sample correlation statistic

$$z_r = \frac{1}{2}\ln\left(\frac{1+r}{1-r}\right)$$

Step 2
For a two-sided confidence interval, we compute the upper and lower limits on the z scale using Equation 20.6:

Equation 20.6 Upper and lower confidence interval bounds for correlation coefficient on the z scale

$$z_L = z_r - z_{1-\alpha/2}\sqrt{\frac{1}{n-3}}$$

$$z_U = z_r + z_{1-\alpha/2}\sqrt{\frac{1}{n-3}}$$

Step 3

We then transform the values of z_L and z_U back to the correlation scale using Equation 20.7:

Equation 20.7 Upper and lower confidence interval bounds of the correlation coefficient on the correlation scale

$$r_L = \frac{e^{2z_L} - 1}{e^{2z_L} + 1}$$

$$r_U = \frac{e^{2z_U} - 1}{e^{2z_U} + 1}$$

A one-sided confidence interval is calculated similarly using α instead of $\alpha/2$, as illustrated in Example 20.4.

EXAMPLE 20.3

TWO-SIDED CONFIDENCE INTERVAL ON ρ

Using the reaction time and yield data in Table 20.1, we will construct a 95% two-sided confidence interval on the correlation coefficient ρ.

Recall that we have calculated $r = 0.868$ and $n = 8$.

1. We first calculate the z score of the r statistic using Equation 20.5:

$$\begin{aligned} z_r &= \frac{1}{2}\ln\left(\frac{1+r}{1-r}\right) \\ &= \frac{1}{2}\ln\left(\frac{1+0.868}{1-0.868}\right) \\ &= 1.325 \end{aligned}$$

2. We now calculate z_L ad z_U using Equation 20.6, which will give us the 95% confidence interval on the z scale:

Continued

Continued

$$
\begin{aligned}
z_L &= z_r - z_{1-\alpha/2}\sqrt{\frac{1}{n-3}} \\
&= 1.325 - 1.96\sqrt{\frac{1}{8-3}} \\
&= 0.448 \\
z_U &= z_r - z_{1-\alpha/2}\sqrt{\frac{1}{n-3}} \\
&= 1.325 + 1.96\sqrt{\frac{1}{8-3}} \\
&= 2.202
\end{aligned}
$$

3. Finally, we convert this result back to the correlation scale using Equation 20.7:

$$
\begin{aligned}
r_L &= \frac{e^{2z_L} - 1}{e^{2z_L} + 1} \\
&= \frac{e^{2(0.448)} - 1}{e^{2(0.448)} + 1} \\
&= 0.420 \\
r_U &= \frac{e^{2z_U} - 1}{e^{2z_U} + 1} \\
&= \frac{e^{2(2.202)} - 1}{e^{2(2.202)} + 1} \\
&= 0.976
\end{aligned}
$$

We are 95% confident that the true parameter ρ is covered by the interval (0.420, 0.976).

EXAMPLE 20.4

ONE-SIDED CONFIDENCE INTERVAL ON ρ

Using the reaction time and yield data in Table 20.1, we will now construct a 95% one-sided lower bound on the correlation coefficient ρ. Recall that we have previously calculated r = 0.868, and n = 8.

1. We first calculate the z score of the r statistic using Equation 20.5:

$$
\begin{aligned}
z_r &= \frac{1}{2}\ln\left(\frac{1+r}{1-r}\right) \\
&= \frac{1}{2}\ln\left(\frac{1+0.868}{1-0.868}\right) \\
&= 1.325
\end{aligned}
$$

Continued

Continued

2. Next, we calculate the 95% lower bound on the z scale with Equation 20.6 using α instead of α/2:

$$z_L = z_r - z_{1-\alpha}\sqrt{\frac{1}{n-3}}$$
$$= 1.325 - 1.645\sqrt{\frac{1}{8-3}}$$
$$= 0.589$$

3. Then we convert this result back to the correlation scale using Equation 20.7:

$$r_L = \frac{e^{2z_L} - 1}{e^{2z_L} + 1}$$
$$= \frac{e^{2(0.589)} - 1}{e^{2(0.589)} + 1}$$
$$= 0.529$$

We are 95% confident that the true correlation coefficient ρ is no less than 0.529.

Correlation versus Causation

No discussion of correlation is complete without the requisite caution that *correlation does not imply causation.* If the variables X and Y are correlated, it is incorrect to then claim that X *causes* Y. For example, consider a study that shows that there is a significant positive correlation between the monthly amount of ice cream sold (X) and number of shark attacks that occur per month (Y). Will outlawing ice cream save swimmers from these dangerous attacks?

Clearly, there is something else afoot. But what? Each of the variables, ice cream sales and shark attacks, is itself correlated to another, *latent,* variable—in this case, season of the year, or temperature. Figure 20.10 shows a diagram of the relationship of the three variables. Shark attacks are correlated with ambient temperature because when it is hotter, more people go swimming in the ocean. Ice cream sales are also correlated with temperature because we eat ice cream to cool off from the heat. If we remove ambient temperature from the picture, shark attacks and ice cream sales are correlated themselves by means of their mutual relationship to temperature.

Nonetheless, the correlation between ice cream sales and shark attacks is useful, since it indicates that ice cream sales will be a good predictor of the number of shark attacks.

Now we present an example from the hospitality industry. A Six Sigma team collects data listing the number of guest complaints and the revenue per room generated for 24 consecutive months, as shown in Table 20.3 and displayed in the scatter plot in Figure 20.11. The two variables are highly positively correlated, with

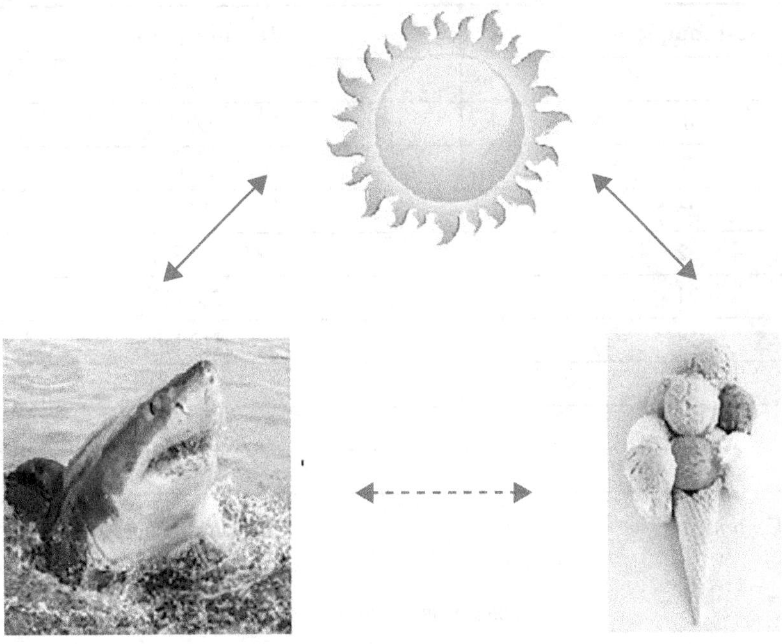

Figure 20.10 Relationship between temperature, shark attacks, and ice cream sales.

Guest complaints	Revenue per room
1	$1,100
0	$1,500
1	$4,000
3	$6,800
4	$8,400
18	$14,800
15	$15,200
15	$14,600
12	$9,800
10	$4,200
5	$2,500
9	$4,200
2	$1,395
2	$1,890

Table 20.3 Guest complaints and revenue per room.
Source: Mary McShane-Vaughn, *Statistics for Black Belts: Slide Book* (Folsom, CA: University Training Partners Publishing, 2021), p. 225. Used with permission.

Guest complaints	Revenue per room
4	$3,255
4	$7,628
5	$9,300
25	$17,438
22	$17,360
24	$16,120
18	$12,188
27	$12,000
15	$2,400
11	$4,883

Table 20.3 *Continued*

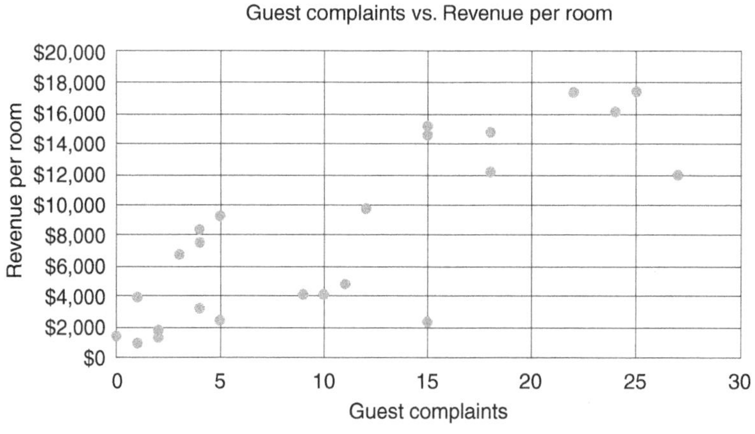

Figure 20.11 Scatter plot of guest complaints and revenue per room.

r = 0.81, meaning that the number of complaints is a good predictor of revenue per room.

If the team were to (incorrectly) subscribe to the "correlation implies causation" theory, it would conclude that average revenue per room can be increased by the generation of more customer complaints! It is likely that complaints and revenue per room are each also correlated with the latent variable *room occupancy*: higher occupancy rates bring in more revenue per room, and higher occupancy means there are more guests who can make a complaint.

Finding a strong correlation between variables can help us build a prediction equation, as discussed in the Linear Regression section of this chapter. Sometimes, however, two variables are correlated for no good reason, and the ability of one variable to predict the other in the future is highly suspect. For example,

Year	Number of people who drowned by falling into a swimming pool Deaths (US) (CDC)	Number of films Nicolas Cage appeared in Films (IMBD)
1999	109	2
2000	102	2
2001	102	2
2002	98	3
2003	85	1
2004	95	1
2005	96	2
2006	98	3
2007	123	4
2008	94	1
2009	102	4

Table 20.4 Drownings versus Nicolas Cage films.
Source: Adapted from www.tylervigen.com/spurious-correlations under Creative Commons license 4.0 https://creativecommons.org/licenses/by/4.0/.

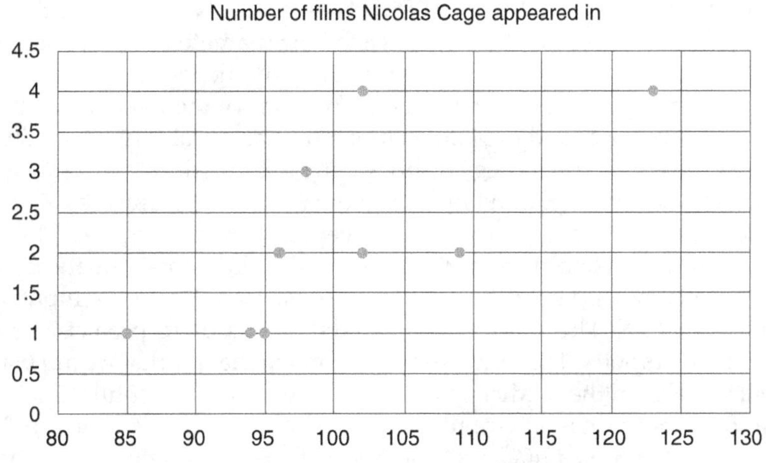

Figure 20.12 Drownings versus Nicolas Cage movies, r = 0.67.
Source: Adapted from www.tylervigen.com/spurious-correlations under Creative Commons license 4.0 https://creativecommons.org/licenses/by/4.0/.

Vigen (2015) has shown that the annual number of people who drowned by falling in a pool is positively correlated with the number of Nicolas Cage movies at the box office that year (r = 0.67), shown in Table 20.4 and Figure 20.12. These types of nonsensical correlations are often called *spurious correlations*.[1] It is quite unlikely that the number of pool drownings can be well predicted by the number of Cage's films in the future.

LINEAR REGRESSION

> Calculate and interpret regression analysis and apply and interpret hypothesis tests for regression parameters. Use the regression model for estimation and prediction, analyze the uncertainty in the estimate, and perform residual analysis to validate the model. (Evaluate)
>
> Body of Knowledge VI.A.2

Simple Linear Regression Motivation and Definition

Imagine that we are interested in predicting the diameter of a drilled hole. If the only data we had access to was historical diameter data, our best prediction of the diameter would be equal to the average diameter, or $\bar{y}$. Now imagine that we also have access to the age of the drill bit for each hole diameter. By incorporating this age data, we could potentially improve upon our prediction.

The goal in simple linear regression is to quantify the total variability of the response variable, or Y, and explain as much of that variability as possible using an input variable, X. In linear regression, we in effect partition the total variability of Y into two: the part explained by X, and the part not explained by X, which we call the residual, or random, error. This concept is shown in Figure 20.13.

We can use the concept of partitioning to develop a mathematical model to explain the relationship between the response variable Y and the input, or independent, variable X. The simple linear model allows us to predict an expected value y from an input x. The term "simple" refers to the fact that we are using only one input variable in the prediction equation, in contrast to multiple linear regression that uses more than one input variable. The term "linear" refers to how the slope is calculated (it is a linear combination of the observations of the response variable Y). This will become apparent later in this section when multiple linear regression models are introduced that include squared terms.

The general form of the simple linear regression model is shown in Equation 20.8:

Equation 20.8 General form of the simple linear regression model

$$y = \beta_0 + \beta_1 x + \varepsilon$$

[1]Tyler Vigen has compiled an amusing collection of nonsensical associations on his website www.tylervigen.com/spurious-correlations.

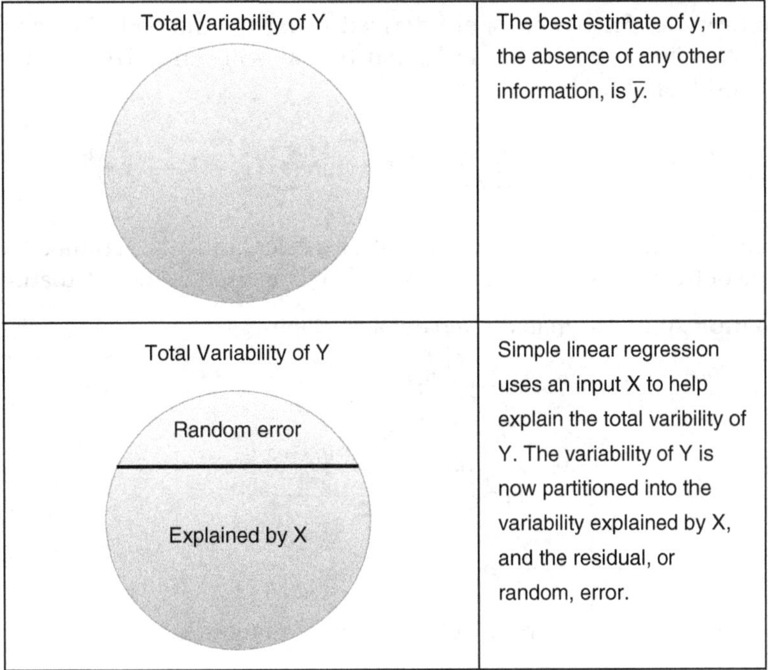

Figure 20.13 Concept of partitioning in simple linear regression.
Source: Adapted from Mary McShane-Vaughn, *Statistics for Black Belts: Slide Book* (Folsom, CA: University Training Partners Publishing, 2021), p. 235.

The variable Y is referred to as the *response, or dependent, variable.* The terms β_0 and β_1 are unknown parameters that represent the *y-intercept and slope,* respectively. The variable X is the *independent, or predictor, variable,* and the term ε is a random variable referred to as the *residual, or random, error.*

Because β_0 and β_1 are unknown parameters, they must be estimated from the data. We denote these estimates as b_0 and b_1, respectively. The random error term ε is also unknown, and we estimate its value by using its mean, where E(ε) = 0. Putting the estimates in for the parameters, we can write the *fitted regression equation or fitted trend line* shown in Equation 20.9.

Equation 20.9 Fitted regression equation

$$\hat{y} = b_0 + b_1 x$$

Note that the term $\hat{y}$ is pronounced "y hat." Statisticians often use the ^, or hat, symbol to denote an estimated value. The average value of the response variable y at a value of the predictor variable x can be estimated by Equation 20.9. The interpretation of the estimate b_0, or y intercept, is the value of y when it crosses the y-axis at x = 0. The term b_1 is the estimated slope of the line. To interpret the slope, we can say that as the variable x increases by one unit, the predicted y will change by b_1 units.

The formulas for b_0 and b_1 are derived using the method of ordinary least squares. We choose the values of b_0 and b_1 that will minimize the sum of the squared residuals (SS_E) from the model:

$$\min SS_E = \min \sum_{i=1}^{n} (y_i - \hat{y}_i)^2 = \min \sum_{i=1}^{n} (y_i - (b_0 + b_1 x_i))^2$$

With a bit of calculus, we arrive at formulas for calculating the estimated intercept and slope of the regression equation. Note that b_1 is used in the calculation of b_0.

Equation 20.10 Estimated intercept and slope

$$b_0 = \bar{y} - b_1\bar{x}$$

$$b_1 = \frac{SS_{xy}}{SS_{xx}} = \frac{\sum_{i=1}^{n} x_i y_i - n\bar{x}\bar{y}}{\sum_{i=1}^{n} x_i^2 - n\bar{x}^2}$$

The estimated residuals e_i are calculated using Equation 20.11

Equation 20.11 Estimated residuals

$$e_i = (y_i - \hat{y}_i)$$

A visual depiction of the intercept, slope, observed values y_i, and residuals is shown in Figure 20.14.

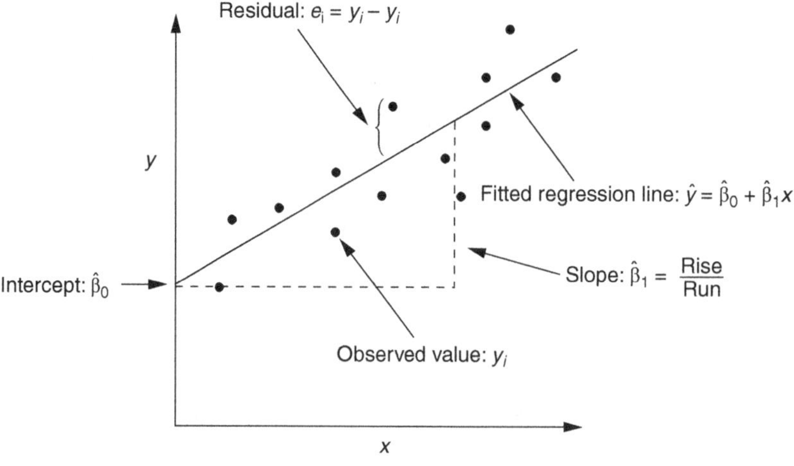

Figure 20.14 Graphical depiction of regression concepts.

EXAMPLE 20.5

CALCULATING b_0 AND b_1

We return to the data first introduced in Example 20.1 in which X is reaction time in minutes and Y is grams of yield for a chemical process. This is a small data set specifically used so that the reader can practice manual calculations.

X	7	8	9	11	12	14	16	17
Y	9	10	13	14	15	12	17	18

The previous calculations gave us:

$$\bar{x} = 11.75$$
$$\bar{y} = 13.5$$
$$SS_{xy} = \sum x_i y_i - n\bar{x}\bar{y} = 1340 - 8(11.75)(13.5) = 71$$
$$SS_{xx} = \sum x_i^2 - n\bar{x}^2 = 1200 - 8(11.75)^2 = 95.5$$
$$SS_{yy} = \sum y_i^2 - n\bar{y}^2 = 1528 - 8(13.5)^2 = 70$$

We will now calculate the slope and y-intercept of the simple linear regression equation that uses reaction time to predict grams of yield:

$$b_1 = \frac{SS_{xy}}{SS_{xx}} = \frac{71}{95.5} = 0.743$$
$$b_0 = \bar{y} - b_1\bar{x} = 13.5 - 0.743 \times 11.75 = 4.770$$

The resulting estimated regression model is

$$\hat{y} = 4.770 + 0.743x$$

To interpret the slope, we can say that if the reaction time increases by one minute, average yield will increase by 0.743 grams.

Connection Between Correlation Coefficient and Regression Slope

The correlation coefficient r is a unitless measure of association between two variables and is bounded by –1 and +1. The correlation coefficient is *scale invariant,* meaning that its value does not change when the scale of the data is changed. The slope of the simple linear regression line also measures the association between two variables, but it is based on the units of x: If the units of x change (say, from feet to miles), then the magnitude of the slope will change.

We can calculate the estimated slope b_1 from the correlation coefficient, and vice versa. Recall the formulas shown in Equation 20.3 and Equation 20.10:

$$r = \frac{SS_{xy}}{\sqrt{SS_{xx}SS_{yy}}}$$

$$b_1 = \frac{SS_{xy}}{SS_{xx}}$$

From here, we can write b_1 and r in terms of each other, as shown in Equation 20.12 and Equation 20.13.

Equation 20.12 Calculating b_1 from r

$$b_1 = \frac{r\sqrt{SS_{yy}}}{\sqrt{SS_{xx}}}$$

Equation 20.13 Calculating r from b_1

$$r = \frac{b_1\sqrt{SS_{xy}}}{\sqrt{SS_{yy}}}$$

where

$$SS_{xy} = \sum x_i y_i - n\bar{x}\bar{y}$$

$$SS_{xx} = \sum x_i^2 - n\bar{x}^2$$

$$SS_{yy} = \sum y_i^2 - n\bar{y}^2$$

EXAMPLE 20.6

CALCULATING b_1 FROM r

We now demonstrate the use of Equation 20.12 to calculate the slope of the linear regression model from the reaction time and yield data. Recall from Example 20.1 that the sample correlation was calculated to be 0.868, and

$$SS_{xx} = \sum x_i^2 - n\bar{x}^2 = 1200 - 8(11.75)^2 = 95.5$$

$$SS_{yy} = \sum y_i^2 - n\bar{y}^2 = 1528 - 8(13.5)^2 = 70$$

We now can use Equation 20.12 to calculate the estimated slope from the sample correlation coefficient:

$$b_1 = \frac{r\sqrt{SS_{yy}}}{\sqrt{SS_{xx}}} = \frac{0.868\sqrt{70}}{\sqrt{95.5}} = 0.743$$

Hypothesis Test for Regression Coefficients

Once we calculate the estimated slope of the simple linear regression, we next use this estimate to test whether the slope parameter β_1 is significantly different from zero. A slope that is equal to zero implies that there is no relationship between the input X and the response variable Y.

We test the following hypotheses:

$$H_0 : \beta_1 = 0$$
$$H_1 : \beta_1 \neq 0$$

This hypothesis tests whether X can be considered a meaningful predictor of Y. In other words, does a relationship exist between the two variables? The corresponding hypothesis test statistic is shown in Equation 20.14.

Equation 20.14 Test statistic for slope

$$t = \frac{b_1 - \beta_1}{s_{b_1}}$$

where s_{b_1} is the standard error of the estimated slope, calculated using Equation 20.15.

Equation 20.15 Standard error of the estimated slope

$$s_{b_1} = \frac{s_e}{\sqrt{SS_{xx}}}$$

where s_e is the sample standard deviation of the error, calculated using Equation 20.16:

Equation 20.16 Sample standard deviation of the error

$$s_e = \sqrt{\frac{\sum_{i=1}^{n}(y_i - \hat{y}_i)^2}{(n-2)}} = \sqrt{\frac{SS_E}{(n-2)}}$$

This test statistic follows a Student's t distribution with n – 2 degrees of freedom. For a two-sided hypothesis test, we use a critical value of $t_{\alpha/2,n-2}$ and reject H_0 if the absolute value of the test statistic is greater than the critical value found in the Student's t table.

The decision rule can be written:

$$\text{Reject } H_0 \text{ if } |t| > t_{\alpha/2, n-2}$$

EXAMPLE 20.7

HYPOTHESIS TEST FOR THE SLOPE

We will now conduct a hypothesis test on the slope of the yield regression model. We test whether the slope parameter is significantly different from zero. If the slope is zero, this implies that there is no association between X (reaction time) and grams of yield.

We conduct this test of hypothesis using the six-step procedure discussed in Chapter 21.

Step 1. *State the null hypothesis and the alternative hypothesis.*

$$H_0 : \beta_1 = 0 \text{ versus } H_1 : \beta_1 \neq 0$$

Note that this is a two-sided hypothesis.

Step 2. *Assign an appropriate value to the level of significance.*
Here, we have chosen $\alpha = 0.05$.

Step 3. *Calculate the appropriate test statistic.*
To calculate the test statistic t, we need the estimate of the standard error of b_1, denoted as s_{b_1}.

We first calculate the residuals of the regression equation to obtain SSE as shown in Table 20.5.

x	y	y-hat	y – y-hat	(y – y-hat)^2
7	9	9.971	–0.971	0.942841
8	10	10.714	–0.714	0.509796
9	13	11.457	1.543	2.380849
11	14	12.943	1.057	1.117249
12	15	13.686	1.314	1.726596
14	12	15.172	–3.172	10.061584
16	17	16.658	0.342	0.116964
17	18	17.401	0.599	0.358801
			SSE	17.21468

Table 20.5 Calculations for SSE for Example 20.7.

Recall from Example 20.1,

$$SS_{xx} = \sum x_i^2 - n\bar{x}^2 = 1200 - 8(11.75)^2 = 95.5$$

Now we calculate s_{b_1}, the standard error of the estimated slope using Equation 20.15:

$$s_{b_1} = \frac{s_e}{\sqrt{SS_{xx}}} = \frac{\sqrt{\dfrac{SS_E}{(n-2)}}}{\sqrt{SS_{xx}}} = \frac{\sqrt{\dfrac{17.215}{(8-2)}}}{\sqrt{95.5}} = 0.173$$

Continued

The test statistic t is then calculated using Equation 20.14:

$$t = \frac{b_1 - \beta_1}{s_{b_1}} = \frac{0.743 - 0}{0.173} = 4.29$$

Step 4. *Determine the probability distribution of the test statistic designated in Step 3.*

$$t = \frac{b_1 - \beta_1}{s_{b_1}} \sim t_{n-2}$$

In this example, the test statistic follows the Student's t distribution with $(n - 2) = 6$ degrees of freedom.

Step 5. *Determine the rejection region(s), locate the critical point(s), and compare these to the calculated test statistic. Alternatively, calculate the p-value for the test and compare it to alpha.*

The rejection region is determined by the value of α or the level of significance, and the form of the alternative hypothesis. The significance level in this example is 0.05, and the alternative hypothesis maps to a two-sided test, so we will divide use $\alpha/2 = 0.025$.

From Step 4, we note that our test statistic follows a Student's t distribution with six degrees of freedom. Using the Student's t distribution table in Appendix E, the critical value is 2.447.

Since the observed value of the test statistic $t = 4.29$ is greater than the critical value of 2.447, the test statistic lies in the rejection region.

Step 6. *State the conclusions in business terms.*

Based on Step 5, we reject the null hypothesis $H_0 : \beta_1 = 0$ and conclude that at the 5% level of significance, there is a significant linear relationship between the reaction time and the yield of the chemical.

Alternatively, we can be more precise with our level of confidence by calculating the p-value of the test using a statistical software package. The p-value is the probability of obtaining the value of test statistic, or something more extreme, under the assumption that the null hypothesis is true. This concept is discussed in greater detail in Chapter 21. A p-value smaller than our chosen α from Step 2 results in our rejecting the null hypothesis.

We can also solve for the p-value directly by using the *=t.dist.2t()* function in Microsoft Excel to get the two-tailed probability of the Student's t distribution. The function takes two arguments: the value of the test statistic, and then the degrees of freedom:

=t.dist.2t(4.29,6)

The function returns 0.005.

Using the p-value, we can state that we are $(1 - p)$%, or 99.5%, confident that there is a significant relationship between the reaction time and the yield of the chemical. This is a much stronger and more precise conclusion than the one derived from using the critical value from the Student's t table.

We previously noted that the sample correlation and slope are functions of each other. Therefore, the test statistics and p-values for the two-sided tests of correlation and slope will be identical.

While a hypothesis test for the y-intercept β_0 can be performed, as a rule we leave the intercept in the model even when it is not statistically significant. Intercepts should be set to zero only if there is a physical justification and the value $x = 0$ is contained in the range of data values. Otherwise, the confidence and prediction intervals for the x's of interest will be unnecessarily wide.

Interpreting Computer Output for Simple Linear Regression

We can also calculate an Analysis of Variance, or ANOVA table, for the regression model. Statistical software packages produce this table in addition to the hypothesis on the slope. In general, the ANOVA table for a regression model tests whether

Regression Equation

y = 4.77 + 0.743 x

Estimated regression model

Coefficients

Term	Coef	SE Coef	T-Value	P-Value
Constant	4.77	2.12	2.24	0.066
x	0.743	0.173	4.29	0.005

Student's *t* tests for the coefficients with H_0: $\beta_i = 0$ vs. H_1: $\beta_i \neq 0$
Note that the intercept is not significant at the 95% level, but as a practice, we leave it in the model.

Model Summary

S	R-sq
1.69384	75.41%

S is the estimated standard deviation of the error term, as well as the standard deviation of y at any given x. It is the square root of Adj MS of the error in the ANOVA table.
R-sq is the coefficient of determination and is the square of the sample correlation for a simple linear regression model. R-sq tells us the percentage of the variability in y that is explained by the model.

Analysis of Variance

Source	DF	SS	MS	F-Value	P-Value
Regression	1	52.79	52.785	18.40	0.005
x	1	52.79	52.785	18.40	0.005
Error	6	17.21	2.869		
Total	7	70.00			

The ANOVA table shows us the partition of the variability of Y. Of the total sum of squares (70.0), 52.79 is explained by the model, and 17.21 is left to random error. The MS Error of 2.869 is the variance of the error, and is also the variance of Y at any given value of x.

The hypotheses for the ANOVA F test are H_0: Model is not useful in predicting the response vs. H_1: Model is useful in predicting the response.

F is calculated as MS Regression divided by MS Error. For simple linear regression, F is the square of the t statistic associated with the slope (4.29). Note that the p-value for the slope and the ANOVA are equal (0.005).

Figure 20.15 Interpreting computer output for simple linear regression.

the model as a whole is significant in predicting y. For simple linear regression, this is the same as testing whether the slope β_1 is significantly different from zero.

H_o: Model is not useful in predicting Y

H_1: Model is useful in predicting Y

For the output displayed in Figure 20.15, we see that the p-value for the F test is the same as the value for the hypothesis test for the slope. And, in the case of *simple* linear regression, the F value is the square of the t statistic calculated for the slope (and correlation coefficient).

The R-squared (R^2) value given in the output is the *coefficient of determination.* This statistic is interpreted as the percentage of the variation in the response Y that is explained by the model. In the case of simple linear regression, R^2 is the square of the sample correlation coefficient r.

Linear Regression Assumptions

The assumptions for linear regression are less stringent than those for linear correlation: Unlike linear correlation, we do not assume X and Y are bivariate normal for the regression model. Instead, we treat the input values x_i as fixed constants.

The assumptions for linear regression are the same as those for the analysis of variance, or ANOVA; namely, the residuals ε_i are independently and identically normally distributed with mean zero and variance σ^2, summarized by $\varepsilon_i \sim iid\ N(0, \sigma^2)$. Note that these assumptions imply that the response variable y is normally distributed with mean $\beta_0 + \beta_1 x$ and variance σ^2; that is, $y \sim N(\beta_0 + \beta_1 x, \sigma^2)$. Before using the regression equation for prediction, we must assure that the underlying assumptions are not violated.

Normality Assumption

We can check the *normality assumption* of the residuals through a probability plot and/or an Anderson-Darling (AD) test. Recall that the hypotheses for the AD test are:

H_o: Data follows a normal distribution

H_1: Data does not follow a normal distribution

While we cannot prove the null hypothesis, a p-value of 0.05 or greater tells us that we have insufficient evidence to claim the data is non-normal.

Constant Variance Assumption

The *constant variance assumption* can be checked graphically using a plot of $\hat{y}$, the fitted value of y, versus the residuals. This graph should display no pattern. If a graph shows the values of the residuals steadily increasing or decreasing across the range of the fitted values, unequal variability (or *heteroskedasticity*) is likely. A variance stabilizing transformation is often used to mitigate heteroskedasticity.

If we see a curvilinear pattern in the residual plot, it suggests that a higher order term, such as an x^2, may be needed in the model. A new regression equation that includes x and x^2 would likely fit the data better.

In addition, if we plot the *standardized* residuals versus $\hat{y}$, we can immediately identify outliers in the data. Any standardized residual beyond –3 or +3 signals the presence of an outlier.

Independence Assumption

The next assumption is that of independence, meaning that the residuals are not correlated with each other (also called autocorrelation). We can check this *independence assumption* graphically by plotting the residuals in time order. If there is a pattern, then the assumption is violated. Of all the regression assumptions, violation of this independence assumption is the most serious. Autocorrelated errors will result in an estimated mean square error (MSE) that is inflated, which in turn reduces the power of the significance tests of the model and coefficients.

EXAMPLE 20.8

CHECKING MODEL ASSUMPTIONS

We'll now perform graphical checks of the normality, constant variance, and independence assumptions of the linear regression model predicting yield from reaction time.

The normal probability plot, augmented with an Anderson-Darling test, is shown in Figure 20.16. The residuals fall close to the 45-degree line of the plot, and the AD p-value is greater than 0.05, indicating no violation of the normality assumption.

We have kept this example data set small to allow the reader to manually calculate the regression coefficients and other statistics. Note that eight data points is the minimum required to perform an effective test of normality. ISO 5479:1997, "Statistical interpretation of data — Tests for departure from the normal distribution," provides guidance on methods and tests for use in deciding whether the hypothesis of a normal distribution is to be rejected, assuming that the observations are independent. The standard restricts the use of these tests to samples of eight or more because the tests are "very ineffective" for samples of size less than eight.

Continued

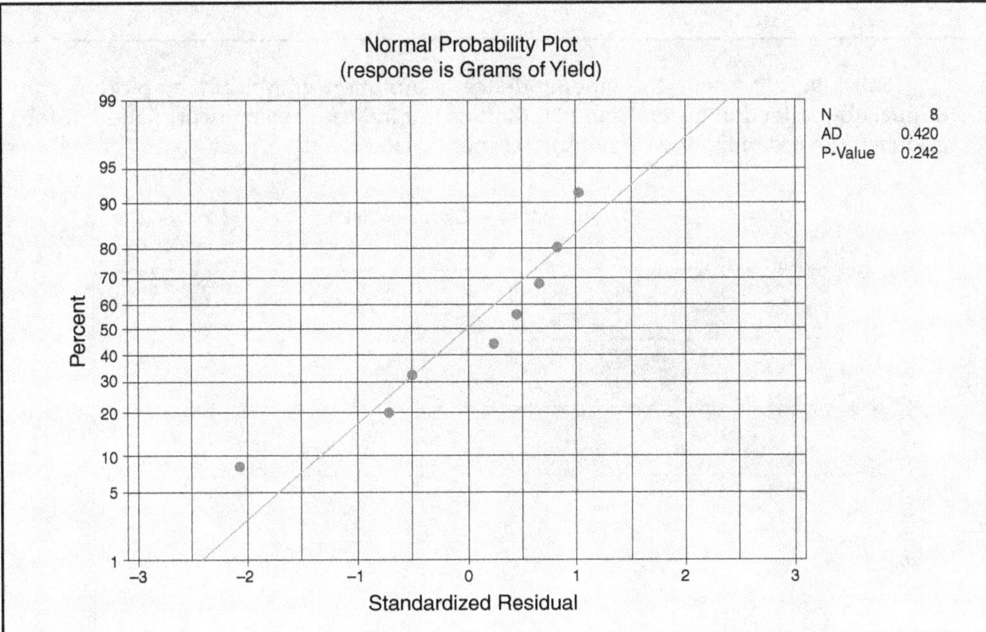

Figure 20.16 Normal probability plot of residuals for yield regression model.

The standardized residuals versus fitted response plot (Figure 20.17) shows no pattern that indicates that the variance of the residuals changes with the value of the estimated responses. As well, there are no standardized residuals that are outliers (less than –3 or greater than +3).

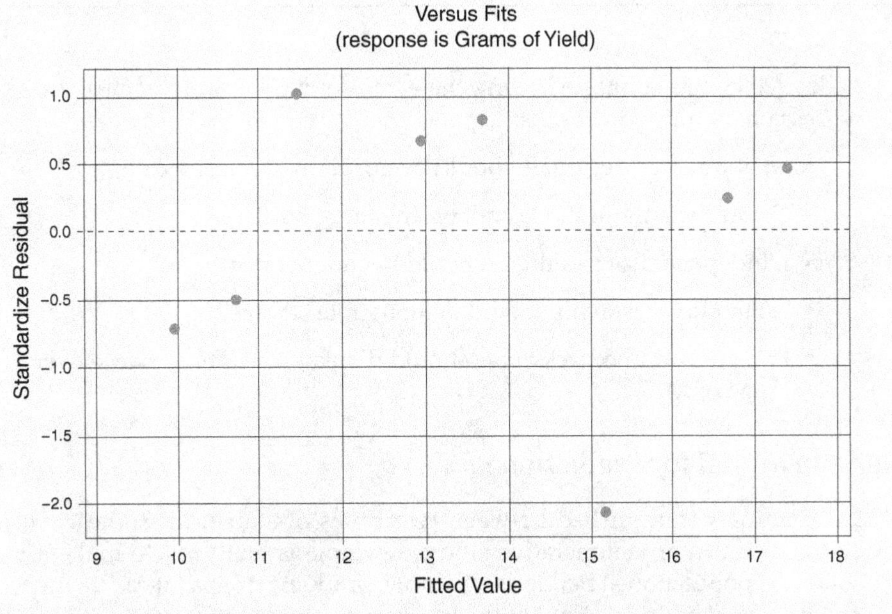

Figure 20.17 Standardized residuals versus fits for yield regression model.

Continued

Continued

Finally, we can check the independence assumption graphically by plotting the residuals by collection order. Figure 20.18 does not indicate any autocorrelation of the residuals. The independence assumption is not violated.

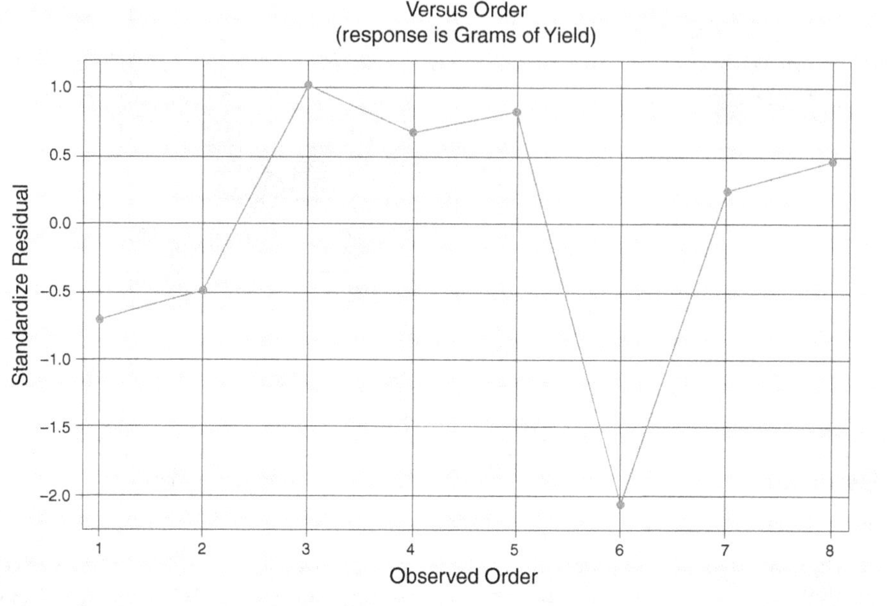

Figure 20.18 Standardized residuals versus collection order for yield regression model.

Bailey (2006) has suggested using the acronym NOISE to remember these linear regression assumption checks:

- N: Normality (residuals should be normally distributed)
- O: Outliers (there should not be any large outliers)
- I: Independence (residuals should be independent)
- S: Stability (residuals should demonstrate stability)
- E: Equal variance (residuals should display constant variance over the range of X)

Using the Model for Prediction

Dr. Deming distinguished between two types of statistical studies: *enumerative* and *analytic*. In an enumerative study, a sample is analyzed to make a decision about the population at hand. For example, products from a lot can be inspected to make a pass/fail decision about the lot itself. In an analytic study, data is analyzed to model the process or system to make decisions in the future.

Linear regression is an analytic study. The end purpose of estimating a linear regression model is not to fit the data at hand to a model. Rather, our aim is to estimate a model with our data to predict values of Y from the independent variable X in the future. Once we have estimated the model, tested its significance, and checked that assumptions are not violated, we can use the model to predict the mean response at a point x_0.

$$\hat{y}_0 = b_0 + b_1 x_0$$

We then calculate a (1-α)% two-sided confidence interval around this mean response using Equation 20.17:

Equation 20.17 Confidence interval for mean response

$$\hat{y}_0 \pm t_{\alpha/2,(n-2)}\, s_e \sqrt{\frac{1}{n} + \frac{(x_0 - \overline{x})^2}{SS_{xx}}}$$

Here, s_e is the standard deviation of the error. Recall from Equation 20.16:

$$s_e = \sqrt{\frac{\sum_{i=1}^{n}(y_i - \hat{y}_i)^2}{(n-2)}} = \sqrt{\frac{SS_E}{(n-2)}}$$

Note too that s_e is also the square root of the mean square error (MSE) entry in the regression ANOVA table.

Close examination of Equation 20.17 reveals that the confidence interval around the mean response is at its narrowest when $x_0 = \overline{x}$. The confidence interval widens as x_0 moves farther away from $\overline{x}$.

We can also create a prediction interval on a new, individual observation y_0. The formula for a (1 – α)% two-sided prediction interval is similar to the confidence interval, but with an additional term under the square root:

Equation 20.18 Prediction interval for a new observation y_0

$$\hat{y}_0 \pm t_{\alpha/2,(n-2)}\, s_e \sqrt{1 + \frac{1}{n} + \frac{(x_0 - \overline{x})^2}{SS_{xx}}}$$

Because individuals are more variable than averages, the prediction interval for a point y_0 will always be wider than the corresponding confidence interval. Again, the prediction interval is at its narrowest at $x_0 = \overline{x}$ and gets wider as x_0 moves away from $\overline{x}$.

EXAMPLE 20.9

CONFIDENCE AND PREDICTION INTERVALS

We will use our regression model to calculate a 95% two-sided confidence interval for the mean response and a prediction interval for an individual response at $x_0 = 13$ minutes.

First, we will gather all the inputs into the equation. Recall from previous examples, we have:

$$\bar{x} = 11.75$$

$$SS_{xx} = \sum x_i^2 - n\bar{x}^2 = 1200 - 8(11.75)^2 = 95.5$$

$$s_e = \sqrt{\frac{SS_E}{(n-2)}} = \sqrt{\frac{17.21}{(8-2)}} = 1.694$$

$$\hat{y}_0 = b_0 + b_1 x_0 = 4.770 + 0.743 \times 13 = 14.429$$

$$t_{0.025,6} = 2.447$$

Now, we use Equation 20.17:

$$\hat{y}_0 \pm t_{\alpha/2,(n-2)}\, s_e \sqrt{\frac{1}{n} + \frac{(x_0 - \bar{x})^2}{SS_{xx}}}$$

$$14.429 \pm 2.447(1.694)\sqrt{\frac{1}{8} + \frac{(13 - 11.75)^2}{95.5}}$$

$$[12.871, 15.988]$$

We are 95% confident that the true mean yield response at x = 13 minutes is covered by the interval [12.871, 15.998].

Now let's create a prediction interval for an individual response at $x_0 = 13$ using Equation 20.18:

$$\hat{y}_0 \pm t_{\alpha/2,(n-2)}\, s_e \sqrt{1 + \frac{1}{n} + \frac{(x_0 - \bar{x})^2}{SS_{xx}}}$$

$$14.429 \pm 2.447(1.694)\sqrt{1 + \frac{1}{8} + \frac{(13 - 11.75)^2}{95.5}}$$

$$[10.001, 18.857]$$

We are 95% confident that a new observation y0 at x0 = 13 will be covered by the interval [10.001, 18.857].

Extrapolation

It is important to note that the linear regression model can only be used to predict responses from x values that are within the original range of the data. For the yield example, the reaction times used are in the range [7, 17] minutes. We can only input x values within this range to predict expected yield in grams using our model. Using values outside this x range is called *extrapolation*. Since we have no information about the relationship between x and y outside the range of our original inputs, we should not predict responses for values outside this input range.

MULTIPLE LINEAR REGRESSION

A *multiple linear regression* model uses more than one input variable to predict the response. For example, a multiple linear regression model with $k > 2$ predictor variables can be expressed using Equation 20.19.

Equation 20.19 Multiple linear regression model

$$y = \beta_0 + \beta_1 x_1 + \beta_2 x_2 + \cdots + \beta_k x_k + \varepsilon$$

where
y is the response
$x_1, x_2, \ldots, x_k$ are the predictor variables
$\beta_0, \beta_1, \beta_2, \ldots, \beta_k$ are the regression coefficients
and ε is the random error term.

The predictor variables in a multiple linear regression can be stand-alone variables, or functions of the input variables, such as interaction terms $x_i x_j$, or squared terms x_i^2. Recall that the term "linear" in linear regression refers to the fact that the estimated coefficients b_i are linear combinations of the responses. The linear regression model itself can be a straight line (first-order), include interactions and/or squared terms (second-order), or third-order or higher.

The assumptions for multiple linear regression are the same as those for simple linear regression—that is, the residuals ε_i are independently and identically normally distributed with mean zero and variance σ^2, summarized by $\varepsilon_i \sim iid\ N(0, \sigma^2)$.

As we might expect, introducing multiple input variables in the modeling effort adds to the complexity of the development, computation, and interpretation of the regression model. The computational load can be handled easily by statistical software, but the model-building and interpretation are the responsibility of the analyst. We briefly discuss multicollinearity and model-building strategies.

Multicollinearity

Multicollinearity occurs when two or more input variables in a multiple linear regression model are correlated. When regression models are created using historical data, as opposed to data collected from a controlled environment such as a designed experiment, there will always be some degree of correlation among the input variables. Excessive multicollinearity among the inputs can result in some unusual results, however:

- The coefficients may appear to have the wrong sign or unexpected magnitude.
- The estimates of the coefficients change wildly when one variable is removed from the model.

- The ANOVA table shows that the model as a whole fits the data, but the t tests for the coefficients return high p-values. This phenomenon occurs because the estimated variability of the coefficients is inflated when there is severe multicollinearity.

To judge the degree of multicollinearity present in a model, we can look to the *variance inflation factor* (VIF), which is reported for each input variable by statistical software output. Generally, a VIF greater than five is considered a signal that a variable is highly correlated with other inputs in the model.

We can mitigate multicollinearity by removing a highly correlated input from the model, or by combining highly correlated variables into a new variable. To remove collinearity between a term (x) and its square (x^2), we can center and scale the data.

It is important to note that in even in the face of multicollinearity, the predictive capability of the model is not affected. However, the variability of the estimated responses will be inflated, resulting in wider confidence and prediction intervals.

Model-Building Strategies

There are many model-building algorithms available in software packages to help analysts sift through the many candidate variables (and functions of these variables) in the data. Best subsets and stepwise regression can give insights into which variables explain the variability in the responses.

Any final regression model should follow the *hierarchical modeling convention*. Using this convention, a model with a significant interaction term x_ix_j must include the individual main effects x_i and x_j in the model, regardless of their significance. Similarly, if there is a significant squared term in the model, the main effect must also be included. Using this convention standardizes the way interaction and squared terms are interpreted in the model.

MULTIVARIATE TOOLS

Understand sources of variation through multivariate tools (e.g., factor analysis, discriminant analysis, and multiple analysis of variance (MANOVA)). (Understand)

Body of Knowledge VI.A.3

Factor Analysis

Factor analysis is used quite often in the social sciences and education fields to reduce the dimensionality of a data set when performing a study that collects data on several variables that are correlated (e.g., income and educational attainment). Factor analysis groups correlated input variables with various weights, called factor loadings, to create factors. The researcher then considers the variables included in the factors and their relative weights to determine what overarching theme, or *latent variable,* it describes. For example, a researcher may define a factor that is the weighted sum of education level, job type, and income as "social status." Another researcher may combine scores on physical tests such as reaction time, grip strength, oxygen output, and sprint speed into a single factor labeled "athletic ability." The resulting factors are mutually independent and can be used in further analysis, such as a regression equation.

Principal Components Analysis

Principal components analysis, which is not in the Body of Knowledge, is a useful tool to reduce the dimensionality of a data set and to address multicollinearity. This technique calculates *principal components,* which are linear combinations of the input variables that aim to explain a maximal amount of the variance in the data. These principal components are orthogonal, or uncorrelated, which means that multicollinearity is eliminated. The subset of the principal components that explain the most variation is then used as input into the regression analysis.

Discriminant Analysis

The purpose of discriminant analysis is to develop a linear combination of the input variables that acts to separate the data into two or more classes. For example, a bank may use a loan applicant's income and credit rating to classify the potential loan as low, medium, or high risk. Here, the dependent variable, or category variable, is the risk class, and the independent variables are income and credit rating.

In discriminant analysis, the independent variables are assumed to be continuous and multivariate normal. In addition, variance is assumed to be constant across classes. In practice, these assumptions are rarely met. Classification can often be better achieved using a logistic regression model, or a classification and regression tree (CART), which is a non-parametric sorting algorithm.

Multiple Analysis of Variance (MANOVA)

A multiple analysis of variance is performed when we are interested in comparing the means of three of more groups that have more than one response of interest. For example, an engineer might run an experiment using $k = 3$ different machine settings and then measure both the strength and the weight ($j = 2$) of each of the resulting parts. The data would then be analyzed using MANOVA to determine if there were a difference in the means of strength and weight between machine settings.

For i = 1, 2, …, k groups, each with measurements of j responses, the hypotheses for MANOVA are:

$$H_0 : \boldsymbol{\mu}_1 = \boldsymbol{\mu}_2 = \cdots = \boldsymbol{\mu}_k$$

$$H_0 : \text{At least one } \boldsymbol{\mu}_i \text{ is not equal}$$

where μ_i is a vector containing the means of the j responses.

We assume that the j responses follow a multivariate normal distribution. It is advisable to run a MANOVA instead of separate ANOVAs since the former incorporates the correlation between the responses and will result in a more powerful test.

Chapter 21
Hypothesis Testing

In Chapter 17, mathematical and graphical techniques for describing a data set were presented. In this chapter, we introduce methods of inferential statistics, with which we use statistics calculated from random samples to make claims about population parameters. We start with an introduction to hypothesis testing, and then cover point estimation, and confidence, prediction, and tolerance intervals. We then present the procedures for hypothesis testing for one and two population means, variances, and proportions. Sample size calculations are covered, as well as the analysis of variance (ANOVA) and the chi-square Goodness of Fit test. Numerous examples are provided to illustrate hand calculations of the hypothesis tests and intervals. We acknowledge that Six Sigma professionals will likely use statistical software to perform these calculations in the workplace. For each example, the proper interpretation of the statistical results, whether computed by hand or by statistical software, is addressed.

TERMINOLOGY

> Define and interpret the significance level, power, type I, and type II errors of statistical tests. (Evaluate)
>
> **Body of Knowledge VI.B.1**

The purpose of a statistical hypothesis test is to make a claim about an unknown, and often unknowable, population parameter with a certain level of confidence. The hypotheses are presented in pairs: a null hypothesis (H_0) and an alternative hypothesis (H_1 or H_A). The term H_0 is often read as "H sub zero," or "H naught" and the alternative hypothesis is read as "H sub one," or "H sub A."

The null hypothesis can be thought of as the status quo condition, and the alternative hypothesis is the statement that the analyst would typically like to claim. These hypotheses are written in terms of the unknown population parameters. In classical hypothesis testing, the null hypothesis includes some form of equality sign, such as $\leq, =, \geq$, while the alternate hypothesis includes either a strict inequality (< or >) or a "not equal" ($\neq$) sign. Together, the hypotheses represent all the possible values for the parameter being tested.

Chapter 20 presented hypothesis tests for the population correlation coefficient ρ and the regression coefficient β. As we will see in this chapter, hypothesis tests can also be constructed for any other population parameter, such as μ, or σ.

Here is an example of a set of hypotheses for testing a population mean μ:

$$H_0 : \mu \leq 10$$
$$H_1 : \mu > 10$$

Because the alternative hypothesis involves a strict inequality, this set of hypotheses would be analyzed using a one-sided test. A two-sided test would be used to evaluate a set of hypotheses with H_1 including a "not equal" sign, as shown:

$$H_0 : \mu = 10$$
$$H_1 : \mu \neq 10$$

When conducting a statistical hypothesis test, we take random, representative samples from the population of interest and, using the information from the sample, we calculate a test statistic. We compare the value of the test statistic to a critical value in a corresponding distribution. Based on the value of the test statistic, we decide whether we have enough evidence to reject the null hypothesis. Alternatively, and more commonly, we can use the confidence interval method or *p*-value method to make the decision. Both methods are presented in detail later in this chapter.

Since the hypothesized parameters are unknown, we can never be certain that our decision is correct. There is a possibility that our decision causes us to commit either a Type I or a Type II error. Each error is dependent upon the decision we make about the null hypothesis.

- *Type I error.* This error occurs when we reject the null hypothesis when it is true. More formally, Pr(Type I error) = Pr(Rejecting $H_0 | H_0$ is true) = α. A Type I error is also known as a *false positive*, or an *α error.* One way to remember this connection is to note that α is the first letter of the Greek alphabet. Another is to remember that an *alpha* error is an error of *action*, in which we incorrectly reject H_0 and leap over to the alternative hypothesis. The Pr(Type I error) is also known as the *α-value*, *producer's risk*, and the *significance level.*

- *Type II error.* This error occurs when we fail to reject the null hypothesis when it is false. Here, Pr(Type II error) = Pr(not rejecting $H_0 | H_0$ is false) = β. The term β is the second letter of the Greek alphabet, which is a way to remember that it is used to represent Type II error. The Pr(Type II error) is also known as a *false negative*, *β-error,* or *consumer's risk.* The Type II error is also referred to as the "do-nothing error" since we stay with the null hypothesis, or the status quo, when we should have rejected it.

In many fields, such as healthcare and epidemiology, the types of correct decisions we can make based on the statistical test are also defined.

- The *specificity* of a test is the probability of a correct decision in which we do not reject H_0 when H_0 is true, or Pr(Do not reject $H_0 | H_0$ true).

Specificity can be calculated as $(1 - \alpha)$. This can be thought of as a medical screening test that returns a negative result for patients who do not have the disease, or a "true negative."

- The other type of correct decision is referred to is *sensitivity*, or $(1 - \beta)$, in which we reject H_0 when H_0 is false, or Pr(Reject $H_0 | H_0$ is false). This would be analogous to a medical screening test returning a positive result for patients who do in fact have the disease, or a "true positive."

These concepts can easily be extended to describe the ability of an automated inspection system to distinguish between conforming and nonconforming items. Table 21.1 illustrates the relationship between Type I and Type II errors, and sensitivity and specificity.

Other concepts related to Type I and Type II errors include the *p*-value and power. These terms are defined as:

- p-*value*. This is the probability of calculating the current test statistic or something more extreme assuming that the null hypothesis is true. Therefore, a *p*-value is a *conditional probability:*

  p = Pr(This test statistic value or one more extreme $| H_{0 \text{ is true}}$)

  A small *p*-value calls into question the validity of the null hypothesis assumption. If p is less than our chosen α value, we reject H_0. If the *p*-value is greater than the α value, we fail to reject H_0. Note that we do not "accept" the null hypothesis. Hypothesis tests are constructed in such a way that the null hypothesis cannot be proven to be true.

  Using the *p*-value method gives us more information about the confidence we have in our conclusion compared to the critical-value method. As Burke and Silvestrini (2017) point out, if the alpha value for a study is changed, a new critical value must be determined from the statistical tables compared to the test statistic. In contrast, the *p*-value method is designed to tell us the lowest level of alpha at which the null hypothesis will be rejected.

  The *p*-value method is not without controversy, however. McShane-Vaughn (2017) notes, "The *p*-value has undergone quite a bit of scrutiny in the past decade. The scientific literature is rife with misinterpretations and misuses of the p-value. In 2015, *The Journal of Basic and Applied Social Psychology* sent shock waves throughout the scientific community when it announced that it would no longer

		Decision based on statistical test	
		Reject H_0	**Do not reject H_0**
Truth	**H_0 is true**	Type I error (α)	Correct decision, Specificity $(1 - \alpha)$
	H_1 is true	Correct decision, Sensitivity $(1 - \beta)$	Type II error (β)

Table 21.1 Four outcomes associated with statistical hypothesis tests.

accept papers that use *p*-values. The American Statistical Association weighed in with a statement on the proper interpretation and use of p-values in 2016." In its statement, the Society laid out six principles:

1. *P*-values can indicate how incompatible the data are with a specified null hypothesis.
2. *P*-values do not measure the probability that the studied hypothesis is true, or the probability that the data were produced by random chance alone.
3. Scientific conclusions and business or policy decisions should not be based only on whether the *p*-value passes a specific threshold.
4. Proper inference requires full reporting and transparency.
5. A *p*-value, or statistical significance, does not measure the size of an effect or the importance of a result.
6. By itself, a *p*-value does not provide a good measure of evidence regarding a model or a hypothesis.

Goodman (2008) outlined a dozen common misinterpretations of the *p*-value, the four most common of which are noted here:

Misinterpretation #1: *If $p = 0.05$, the null hypothesis has only a 5% chance of being true.*

Why this is wrong: The *p*-value is calculated under the assumption that the null hypothesis is true, so it cannot give us information on the probability that the null hypothesis is false.

Misinterpretation #2: *If $p = 0.05$, we have a 5% probability of being wrong if we reject H_0.*

Why this is wrong: This is a variation of Misinterpretation #1. As explained by Nuzzo (2014), "All [the *p*-value] can do is summarize the data assuming a specific null hypothesis. It can't work backwards and make statements about the underlying reality." Doing so requires us to know the odds that the alternative hypothesis was true in the first place. In other words, to calculate the exact probability of making a Type I error, we would first need to know the probability of the alternative hypothesis being true.

Misinterpretation #3: *A nonsignificant difference (say, $p > 0.05$) means that the null hypothesis is true.*

Why this is wrong: The large *p*-value means that the data is consistent with the null hypothesis, but this in itself does not prove that the null hypothesis is true. This error in logic is referred to as the *transpose of the conditional* in which the $\Pr(A|B)$ is mistaken for $\Pr(B|A)$. In this case, the error would involve mistaking the *p*-value for the statement:

$$\Pr(H_0 \text{ is true} | \text{This test statistic value or one more extreme}).$$

Misinterpretation #4: *A* p-*value of 0.01 means that the effect is greater than if the* p-*value were 0.05.*

Why this is wrong: The numerical value of p does not refer to the size of the effect; it only gives us information about the probability of the calculating the current test statistic (or something more extreme) under the assumption that the null hypothesis is true.

A Black Belt should be able to state the interpretation correctly and precisely:

The p-*value is the probability of obtaining the current value of the test statistic, or one that is more extreme, assuming that the null hypothesis is correct.*

We should not rely solely on a single occurrence of a small *p*-value for making important decisions. Rather, the ability to replicate the study results will go far to assure that our original conclusion was correct.

- *Power.* The power of a statistical test is the probability of correctly rejecting H_0. More formally, it is the conditional probability of rejecting the null hypothesis given that the alternative hypothesis is true. We write this as Pr(Rejecting $H_0 \mid H_0$ is false) = $1 - \beta$. This can also be termed "sensitivity," or the ability to detect a true difference.

  The power of a test depends upon the variance of the data, the confidence level $(1 - \alpha)$, the size of the difference we are trying to detect E, and the sample size n. The higher the power of a hypothesis test, the more sensitive it is in detecting small differences in the values of parameters. For a given difference and alpha level, we can increase the power of a test by increasing the sample size. This concept will be explored further in the Sample Size section of this chapter.

STATISTICAL VERSUS PRACTICAL SIGNIFICANCE

> Define, compare, and interpret statistical and practical significance. (Evaluate)
>
> **Body of Knowledge VI.B.2**

Big data has given us access to extremely large sample sizes. When the sample size is very large, it is possible to detect a statistically significant difference between, say, two population parameters even when the size of the difference has no practical importance. Just because a *p*-value is less than our chosen α, it does not immediately follow that the result has any practical utility. Recall from the last section that the *p*-value does not indicate the size of the effect.

EXAMPLE 21.1

Suppose that a statistical test with n = 10,000 data points randomly drawn from a database has shown that adding an additional step in a chemical process results in a significant (p = 0.001) improvement of mean yield, from 560.40 g to 560.49 g. If the specifications for the yield are [550, 570], does this statistically significant result translate into practical significance? In this case, the large sample size increased the power of the test to a degree that was not necessary.

EXAMPLE 21.2

This phenomenon can also occur in smaller studies as well. In another case, suppose an experiment is conducted to determine whether there is a statistically significant difference in the mean surface finish when a lathe is operated at 400 rpm and at 700 rpm, with 50 samples processed at each speed. The hypothesis test detects a statistically significant difference in the mean surface finish. However, the difference in the means is equal to 0.001 microns, and the specifications are 0.01 microns wide. Here, the mean from the 400 rpm runs has a tiny but statistically significant improved surface. However, if both speeds produce surface finishes capable of meeting the specifications, it may be better to set the machine at the faster speed because of its associated increase in throughput. In this case, the difference in means may have statistical significance, but not practical significance.

POINT AND INTERVAL ESTIMATES

Define and distinguish between confidence and prediction intervals. Define and interpret the efficiency and bias of estimators. Calculate tolerance and confidence intervals. (Evaluate)

Body of Knowledge VI.B.4

Point Estimates

A *point estimate* is a statistic used to estimate a parameter of a population, a concept that was introduced in Chapter 17, Basic Statistics. Examples of point estimates include the sample mean, the sample variance, and sample proportion defective. The characteristics of a statistic can be described by various criteria such as unbiasedness, efficiency, sufficiency, and consistency.

Unbiased Estimators

An *unbiased estimator* is a point estimate of a parameter such that the expected value of the estimate equals the parameter. Let $\hat{\theta}$ be an estimator of the parameter θ. This estimator is said to be unbiased if

$$E(\hat{\theta}) = \theta.$$

We state, without providing a proof, that $\bar{X}$ and s^2 are an unbiased estimators of μ and σ^2, respectively, and the sample standard deviation s is a biased estimate of the population standard deviation σ. These proofs can be found in mathematical statistics textbooks such as Hogg, McKean, and Craig (2019).

Efficient Estimators

Statisticians characterize the "goodness" of estimators by using several mathematical criteria. Along with unbiasedness, the criteria can include efficiency, sufficiency, and consistency. The calculation of these criteria is beyond the scope of this handbook but can be found in a mathematical statistics textbook.

Efficiency is expressed as an index between 0 and 1, calculated by the dividing the minimum possible variance for an unbiased estimator by its actual variance. An efficiency of 1 means that the estimator is a minimum variance estimator.

We can compare competing estimators by calculating *relative efficiency*, which is the ratio of the variances of the respective parameter estimates.

An estimator is said to be *sufficient* if no other estimator calculated from the same sample provides any additional information about the population parameter.

A *consistent* estimator is one that becomes closer and closer to the true value of the parameter as sample size approaches infinity.

It is interesting to note that the statistic $\bar{X}$ is an unbiased, efficient, sufficient, and consistent estimator of the parameter μ.

Confidence Intervals

The point estimates presented in Chapter 17 are just that, single points on the number line. For example, consider a quality professional who calculates the average weight of cans coming off a particular assembly line and reports that $\bar{X} = 15.91$ oz. While it is highly unlikely that this value is equal to the true mean due to sampling error, we have no information on how close this point estimate is to μ. We can provide more information beyond the point estimate by calculating a *confidence interval* on the population parameter μ. A confidence interval is a range of values that combines information from a point estimate, the variability of the data, and the sample size to give a more complete estimate of a population parameter.

The general form of a $100(1 - \alpha)\%$ two-sided confidence interval for any population parameter (which we denote as θ) is

$$L \le \theta \le U$$

where
L = lower endpoint of the confidence interval
U = upper endpoint of the confidence interval

θ = parameter of interest, such as μ or σ
α = significance level

There are two general interpretations of the results from a confidence interval: the probabilistic interpretation and the practical interpretation. As Burke and Silvestrini (2017) explain:

> The probabilistic interpretation of the confidence level is the proportion of all confidence intervals constructed on that parameter (under repeated sampling and identical conditions) that would contain the true parameter. For example, a 95% confidence interval on μ would be interpreted as the percentage of all confidence intervals constructed (under repeated sampling and identical conditions) that would contain the population mean μ.

Consider a normal population with a mean $\mu = 25$ and variance $\sigma^2 = 9$ from which 20 samples of size $n = 40$ are selected. Twenty 95% confidence intervals on μ are constructed, as shown in Figure 21.1. We see that 19 of the 20 (or 95%) of the confidence intervals contain the true population mean $\mu = 25$. It follows that 5% of all intervals constructed do not contain the true population mean.

Burke and Silvestrini (2017) comment:

> Since the true parameter value, such as the population mean μ, is usually unknown (and unknowable) in practice, the probabilistic interpretation may not be very useful. Additionally, when we construct an interval, we have only one sample of data, not 20.

> The practical interpretation of a confidence interval constructed in this situation would be a statement of degree of belief that the confidence

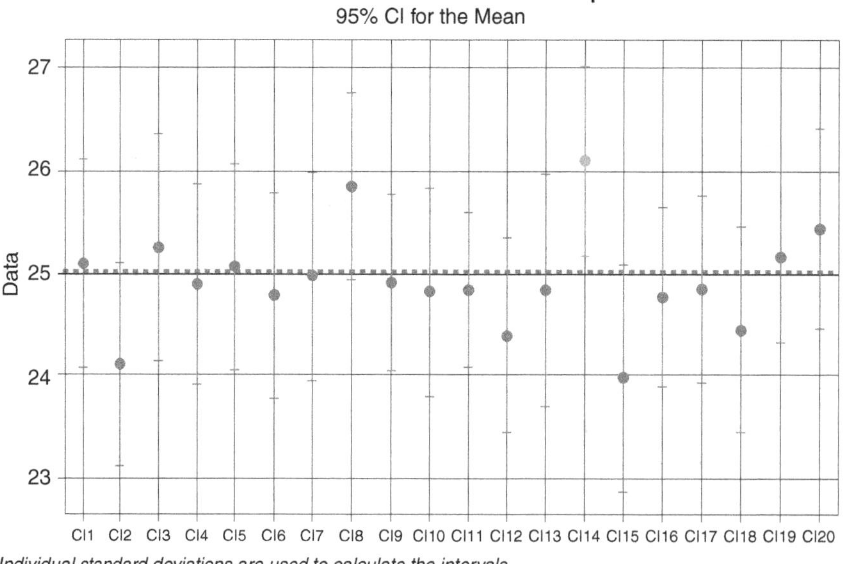

Figure 21.1 Plot of 95% confidence intervals on the mean from 20 samples.

> interval contains the true μ. For example, for a 95% confidence interval, we can say that we are 95% confident that the interval will contain the true population mean μ.
>
> It should be noted that the practical interpretation should never be misconstrued as saying that the "probability that the confidence interval contains the true value μ is 0.95." Remember, the true value of the population mean μ exists but is unknown. Therefore, when we construct a confidence interval on μ, either the interval contains the true value of μ, or it does not; there is no probability involved.

To add to this excellent advice, we note that, in the frequentist view, a population parameter is a fixed value. Therefore, we cannot interpret a 95% confidence interval on the mean by saying that "there is a 95% chance that the true mean will fall in the interval." The parameter is indifferent to the interval we calculate and will not try to fall into it. Where the uncertainty lies is in the interval's ability to cover the unknown (and unmoving) parameter.

In the following pages, we will present the assumptions, formulas, and examples for confidence intervals on population parameters including:

- one mean
- two means
- a mean difference for paired data
- one variance
- two variances
- one standard deviation
- two standard deviations
- one proportion
- two proportions

Confidence Intervals on One Population Mean

Table 21.2 displays the assumptions and formulas for one- and two-sided confidence intervals on a single population mean. These confidence intervals are calculated using a value from either the standard normal (Z) or Student's *t* table.

EXAMPLE 21.3

Suppose an estimate is needed for the average coating thickness for a population of 1000 circuit boards received from a supplier. Rather than measure the coating thickness on all 1000 boards, one might randomly select a sample of 25 for measurement. Assume that past experience has shown the coating thickness to follow a normal distribution. (Alternatively, we could conduct a formal test for normality, such as an Anderson-Darling test, or we could simply increase sample size to ensure that the average is

Continued

Continued

approximately normal via the Central Limit Theorem.) Suppose that the average coating thickness on these 25 boards is 0.003, and the standard deviation estimated from the sample is 0.005. Calculate a 95% confidence interval for the true mean.

We have $\bar{X} = 0.003$, s = 0.005, and n = 25. From Appendix E, we know that $t_{24,\,0.05/2} = 2.064$.

We use the following formula from Table 21.2 to calculate the confidence interval:

$$\bar{X} \pm t_{\alpha/2, n-1} \frac{s}{\sqrt{n}}$$

$$0.003 \pm 2.064 \frac{0.005}{\sqrt{25}}$$

$$0.003 \pm 0.00206$$

$$0.00094 \le \mu \le 0.00506$$

Thus, we are 95% confident that the true mean coating thickness is covered by the interval [0.00094, 0.00506].

Population Parameter	Assumptions	100(1 – α)% two-sided confidence interval on μ	100(1 – α)% one-sided confidence interval on μ
One population mean, μ	Random sample, independent observations, normal distribution, variance known	$\bar{X} \pm z_{\alpha/2} \frac{\sigma}{\sqrt{n}}$	Lower bound: $\bar{X} - z_\alpha \frac{\sigma}{\sqrt{n}}$ *or* Upper bound: $\bar{X} + z_\alpha \frac{\sigma}{\sqrt{n}}$ One-sided confidence intervals written as [LB, ∞) or (-∞, UB]
One population mean, μ	Random sample, independent observations, normal distribution or n > 30	$\bar{X} \pm t_{\alpha/2, n-1} \frac{s}{\sqrt{n}}$	LB: $\bar{X} - t_{\alpha,n-1} \frac{s}{\sqrt{n}}$ *or* UB: $\bar{X} + t_{\alpha,n-1} \frac{s}{\sqrt{n}}$ One-sided confidence intervals written as [LB, ∞) or (-∞, UB]

Table 21.2 Confidence interval formulas for one population mean, μ.

Confidence Intervals on Two Population Means

Table 21.3 gives the assumptions and formulas for one- and two-sided confidence intervals for the difference between two population means.

EXAMPLE 21.4

A quality engineer conducts a study to determine if there is a difference in the mean weight of packages being produced on two different assembly lines. The weights from each line have been shown to follow normal distributions with known variances of 85.5 and 69.2, respectively. Twenty samples are randomly selected from Line 1, yielding a sample mean equal to 105.2 oz. Fifteen samples are randomly selected from Line 2 resulting in a sample mean equal to 99.7 oz.
Construct a 95% confidence interval to determine if there is a significant difference in mean weights.

Here we have $\bar{X}_1 = 105.2, \bar{X}_2 = 99.7, \sigma_1^2 = 85.5, \sigma_2^2 = 69.2, n_1 = 20, n_2 = 15$, and $\alpha = 0.05$. Because we can assume normal distributions with known but unequal variances, we can use the following formula from Table 21.3. Using $\alpha/2 = 0.025$, we find $z_{0.025} = 1.96$ from Appendix D. Substituting in the values, we obtain:

$$(\bar{X}_1 - \bar{X}_2) \pm z_{\alpha/2}\sqrt{\frac{\sigma_1^2}{n_1} + \frac{\sigma_2^2}{n_2}}$$

$$(105.2 - 99.7) \pm 1.96\sqrt{\frac{85.5}{20} + \frac{69.2}{15}}$$

$$5.5 \pm 5.843$$

We are 95% confident that the true difference in mean weights is covered by the interval [−0.343, 11.343]. Because the interval includes the value zero, we can conclude there is insufficient evidence to claim that the mean package weights produced on the two lines are different. Remember that this does not imply that the null is true.

EXAMPLE 21.5

The training department at an insurance firm designed and delivered a new program to improve the technical skills of its customer service representatives. To determine the efficacy of the training, the department will test whether the mean wait time for customers calling in to the help line has decreased. Before the training program, sample data showed that customers waited an average of 10.9 minutes before being helped. After training, the customer mean wait time was 6.8 minutes. Details on the samples are shown in Table 21.4. Calculate a 95% one-sided confidence interval on the difference in the mean wait times to determine if the training was effective.

Continued

Population parameter of interest	Assumptions	$100(1 - \alpha)\%$ two-sided confidence interval on $\mu_1 - \mu_2$	$100(1 - \alpha)\%$ one-sided confidence interval on $\mu_1 - \mu_2$
Difference between two population means, $\mu_1 - \mu_2$	Random samples, independent groups, normal distribution, **variances known and equal**	$(\bar{X}_1 - \bar{X}_2) \pm z_{\alpha/2}\sigma\sqrt{\frac{1}{n_1} + \frac{1}{n_2}}$	LB: $(\bar{X}_1 - \bar{X}_2) - z_{\alpha}\sigma\sqrt{\frac{1}{n_1} + \frac{1}{n_2}}$ *or* UB: $(\bar{X}_1 - \bar{X}_2) + z_{\alpha}\sigma\sqrt{\frac{1}{n_1} + \frac{1}{n_2}}$ One-sided confidence intervals written as [LB, ∞) or (-∞, UB]
Difference between two population means, $\mu_1 - \mu_2$	Random samples, independent groups, normal distribution, **variances known and not equal**	$(\bar{X}_1 - \bar{X}_2) \pm z_{\alpha/2}\sqrt{\frac{\sigma_1^2}{n_1} + \frac{\sigma_2^2}{n_2}}$	LB: $(\bar{X}_1 - \bar{X}_2) - z_{\alpha}\sqrt{\frac{\sigma_1^2}{n_1} + \frac{\sigma_2^2}{n_2}}$ *or* UB: $(\bar{X}_1 - \bar{X}_2) + z_{\alpha}\sqrt{\frac{\sigma_1^2}{n_1} + \frac{\sigma_2^2}{n_2}}$ One-sided confidence intervals written as [LB, ∞) or (-∞, UB]

Table 21.3 Confidence interval formulas for the difference between two population means, μ1 - μ2.

Population parameter of interest	Assumptions	$100(1-\alpha)\%$ two-sided confidence interval on $\mu_1 - \mu_2$	$100(1-\alpha)\%$ one-sided confidence interval on $\mu_1 - \mu_2$
Difference between two population means, $\mu_1 - \mu_2$	Random samples, independent observations, independent groups, normal distributions or ($n_1 > 30$, $n_2 > 30$), **variances unknown but assumed equal**	$(\bar{X}_1 - \bar{X}_2) \pm t_{\alpha/2,(n_1+n_2-2)} s_p \sqrt{\frac{1}{n_1} + \frac{1}{n_2}}$ *where* $s_p = \sqrt{\frac{(n_1-1)s_1^2 + (n_2-1)s_2^2}{(n_1+n_2-2)}}$	$LB: (\bar{X}_1 - \bar{X}_2) - t_{\alpha,(n_1+n_2-2)} s_p \sqrt{\frac{1}{n_1} + \frac{1}{n_2}}$ *or* $UB: (\bar{X}_1 - \bar{X}_2) + t_{\alpha,(n_1+n_2-2)} s_p \sqrt{\frac{1}{n_1} + \frac{1}{n_2}}$ *where* $s_p = \sqrt{\frac{(n_1-1)s_1^2 + (n_2-1)s_2^2}{(n_1+n_2-2)}}$ One-sided confidence intervals written as $[LB, \infty)$ or $(-\infty, UB]$

Table 21.3 *Continued*

Population parameter of interest	Assumptions	100(1 – *α*)% two-sided confidence interval on $\mu_1 - \mu_2$	100(1 – *α*)% one-sided confidence interval on $\mu_1 - \mu_2$
Difference between two population means, $\mu_1 - \mu_2$	Random samples, independent observations, independent groups, normal distributions or ($n_1 > 30$, $n_2 > 30$), **variances unknown and not assumed equal**	$(\bar{X}_1 - \bar{X}_2) \pm t_{\alpha/2, v}\sqrt{\frac{s_1^2}{n_1} + \frac{s_2^2}{n_2}}$ with degrees of freedom v: $v = \dfrac{{\frac{s_1^2}{n_1} + \frac{s_2^2}{n_2}}^{2}}{\frac{\left(s_1^2/n_1\right)^2}{n_1 - 1} + \frac{\left(s_2^2/n_2\right)^2}{n_2 - 1}}$ Round v down to next lowest whole number	$LB: (\bar{X}_1 - \bar{X}_2) - t_{\alpha, v}\sqrt{\frac{s_1^2}{n_1} + \frac{s_2^2}{n_2}}$ *or* $UB: (\bar{X}_1 - \bar{X}_2) + t_{\alpha, v}\sqrt{\frac{s_1^2}{n_1} + \frac{s_2^2}{n_2}}$ with degrees of freedom v: $v = \dfrac{\left(\frac{s_1^2}{n_1} + \frac{s_2^2}{n_2}\right)^2}{\frac{\left(s_1^2/n_1\right)^2}{n_1 - 1} + \frac{\left(s_2^2/n_2\right)^2}{n_2 - 1}}$ Round v down to next lowest whole number One-sided confidence intervals written as as [LB, ∞) or (-∞, UB]

Table 21.3 *Continued*

	Baseline	After training
n	40	35
X-bar	10.9	6.8
S	10.5	6.4

Table 21.4 Wait time data for Example 21.5.

Even though wait times often follow a skewed distribution, such as an exponential, the sample sizes for each group allow us to use the Student's *t* test for the confidence interval on the difference in means.

Here, we will be calculating a one-sided confidence interval because the training department wants to know whether the mean wait time after the training is less than the mean time at baseline. We will calculate a lower bound on the difference, and if the confidence interval does not include the value 0, we will conclude that the training did significantly decrease the mean wait times.

For this problem, we will *not* assume that the population variances are equal. From Table 21.3 we will use the following formulas. We first calculate the degrees of freedom, v, for the *t* statistic:

$$LB: \left(\bar{X}_1 - \bar{X}_2\right) - t_{\alpha,v}\sqrt{\frac{s_1^2}{n_1} + \frac{s_2^2}{n_2}}$$

where

$$v = \frac{\left(\frac{s_1^2}{n_1} + \frac{s_2^2}{n_2}\right)^2}{\frac{\left(s_1^2/n_1\right)^2}{n_1 - 1} + \frac{\left(s_2^2/n_2\right)^2}{n_2 - 1}}$$

$$v = \frac{\left(\frac{10.5^2}{40} + \frac{6.4^2}{35}\right)^2}{\frac{\left(10.5^2/40\right)^2}{39} + \frac{\left(6.4^2/35\right)^2}{34}}$$

$$= \lfloor 65.59 \rfloor = 65$$

We use a floor function for the degrees of freedom, meaning that we round any non-integer result down to the next lowest integer. Here, we obtain v = 65.

The α value for our one-sided interval is 0.05. Using Appendix E, we find $t_{0.05,65}$ = 1.669. The one-sided confidence interval for the difference in means is calculated:

$$\left(\bar{X}_1 - \bar{X}_2\right) - t_{\alpha,v}\sqrt{\frac{s_1^2}{n_1} + \frac{s_2^2}{n_2}}$$

$$(10.9 - 6.8) - 1.669\sqrt{\frac{10.5^2}{40} + \frac{6.4^2}{35}}$$

$$[0.793, \infty)$$

Continued

Continued

We are 95% confident that the reduction in mean wait times is at least 0.793 minutes, or about 48 seconds. We conclude that the training program was effective in reducing mean wait times for customers.

Confidence Intervals on the Mean Difference from Paired Data

The previous examples showed procedures for calculating a confidence interval on means from two independent groups. If we have paired data, in which each item sampled has two observations associated with it, then we must use another technique. The formulas for constructing confidence intervals for paired data are shown in Table 21.5.

Situations in which paired data arises include two readings on the same item or subject at different points in time, such as:

- cholesterol readings for patients before and after beginning a new drug protocol
- test scores for learners before and after a training program
- hardness readings for metal parts before and after an annealing process.

Population parameter of interest	Assumptions	100(1 – α)% two-sided confidence interval on μ_d	100(1 – α)% one-sided confidence interval on μ_d
Mean difference, μ_d	Paired data, difference between pairs is normal, and/or n >30	$\bar{d} \pm t_{\alpha/2, n-1}\frac{s_d}{\sqrt{n}}$ *where* $s_d = \sqrt{\sum_{i=1}^{n}\frac{(d_i - \bar{d})^2}{n-1}}$	$LB: \bar{d} - t_{\alpha, n-1}\frac{s_d}{\sqrt{n}}$ *or* $UB: \bar{d} + t_{\alpha, n-1}\frac{s_d}{\sqrt{n}}$ *where* $s_d = \sqrt{\sum_{i=1}^{n}\frac{(d_i - \bar{d})^2}{n-1}}$ One-sided confidence intervals written as as [LB, ∞) or (-∞, UB]

Table 21.5 Confidence interval calculations for a mean difference using a paired sample.

In each of these examples, the two sets of data collected are not independent groups because they each measure the same items, just at different points in time. We calculate the difference within each item and then construct a confidence interval on the average difference.

EXAMPLE 21.6

The hand grip strength of 35 male patients was measured before and after a rehabilitation program involving weight training. The results are shown in Table 21.6.

Subject	Grip Strength Before	Grip Strength After	Difference (After-Before)
1	73	73	0
2	68	72	4
3	65	72	7
4	70	72	2
5	70	74	4
6	77	77	0
7	72	72	0
8	70	71	1
9	55	60	5
10	60	65	5
11	58	65	7
12	76	81	5
13	77	78	1
14	76	77	1
15	70	70	0
16	72	74	2
17	65	72	7
18	65	71	6
19	58	61	3
20	67	67	0
21	63	66	3
22	66	70	4
23	68	73	5
24	70	67	−3

Table 21.6 Grip strength (in lbs) for Example 21.6.

Continued

Subject	Grip Strength Before	Grip Strength After	Difference (After-Before)
25	73	73	0
26	74	72	–2
27	72	70	–2
28	70	70	0
29	69	72	3
30	55	58	3
31	78	76	–2
32	72	72	0
33	65	72	7
34	66	67	1
35	70	71	1

Table 21.6 *Continued*

A dot plot of the differences in grip strength is shown in Figure 21.2. The differences do not look especially normal in the dot plot; however, an Anderson-Darling test returns a *p*-value equal to 0.072. Even if we had rejected the Anderson-Daring test, our sample size of 35 offers protection against non-normality of the sample mean by way of the Central Limit Theorem.

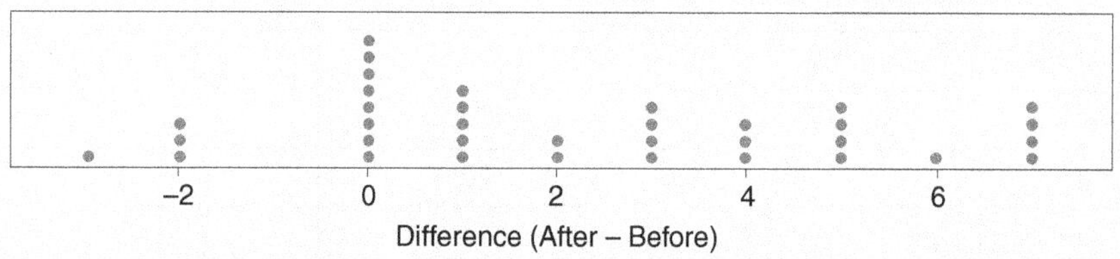

Figure 21.2 Dot plot of differences in grip strength for Example 21.6.

Here we will construct a 99% one-sided confidence interval on the mean difference in grip strength achieved through the rehabilitation program. The mean of the differences in the sample is equal to 2.229 and the sample standard deviation of the differences is 2.850. We will use the formula in Table 21.5 to calculate a lower bound on the mean difference. The α level is 0.01, and n = 35. We find $t_{0.01,34} = 2.441$ in Appendix E.

$$\bar{d} - t_{\alpha,n-1}\frac{s_d}{\sqrt{n}}$$

$$2.229 - 2.441\frac{2.850}{\sqrt{35}}$$

$$[1.05, \infty)$$

Continued

Continued

We are 99% confident that the mean increase in grip strength is at least 1.05 pounds. Note that we carried several digits in the intermediate calculations and then rounded the confidence interval result to two more digits than the original data at the end.

Confidence Intervals on One and Two Population Variances

Table 21.7 lists the assumptions and formulas for confidence intervals on one and two population variances. Note that the assumption of normality for these intervals is quite strict since both the chi-square and F distributions are sensitive to

Population parameter of interest	**Assumptions**	**100(1 – α)% two-sided confidence interval on σ²**	**100(1 – α)% one-sided confidence interval on σ²**
One population variance σ^2	Random sample, independent observations, normal distribution	$\frac{(n-1)s^2}{\chi^2_{\alpha/2,n-1}} \le \sigma^2 \le \frac{(n-1)s^2}{\chi^2_{1-\alpha/2,n-1}}$	$LB: \frac{(n-1)s^2}{\chi^2_{\alpha,n-1}}$ *or* $UB: \frac{(n-1)s^2}{\chi^2_{1-\alpha,n-1}}$ One-sided confidence interval: [LB, ∞) or (-∞, UB]
Population parameter of interest	**Assumptions**	**100(1 – α)% two-sided confidence interval on $\frac{\sigma_1^2}{\sigma_2^2}$**	**100(1 – α)% one-sided confidence interval on $\frac{\sigma_1^2}{\sigma_2^2}$**
Ratio of two population variances, $\frac{\sigma_1^2}{\sigma_2^2}$	Random samples, independent observations, normal distributions, independent groups	$\frac{s_1^2}{s_2^2}\frac{1}{F_{\alpha/2,\nu_1,\nu_2}} \le \frac{\sigma_1^2}{\sigma_2^2} \le \frac{s_1^2}{s_2^2}F_{\alpha/2,\nu_2,\nu_1}$ $\frac{s_1^2}{s_2^2}F_{1-\alpha/2,\nu_2,\nu_1} \le \frac{\sigma_1^2}{\sigma_2^2} \le \frac{s_1^2}{s_2^2}F_{\alpha/2,\nu_2,\nu_1}$ Note that the numerator and denominator degrees of freedom (ν_1 and ν_2) are switched.	$LB: \frac{s_1^2}{s_2^2}F_{1-\alpha,\nu_2,\nu_1}$ *or* $UB: \frac{s_1^2}{s_2^2}F_{\alpha,\nu_2,\nu_1}$ One-sided confidence interval: [LB, ∞) or (-∞, UB]

Table 21.7 Confidence interval formulas for one and two population variances.

departures from normality. There are nonparametric methods that can be used to calculate confidence intervals when the normal assumption is violated. Although beyond the scope of the Body of Knowledge, these methods are listed in the Nonparametric Tests section of this chapter.

EXAMPLE 21.7

Let's revisit the coating thickness data first introduced in Example 21.3. Past experience shows that these thickness reading are normally distributed. (Alternatively, we could conduct a formal test for normality, such as an Anderson-Darling test.) We would like to calculate a 95% confidence interval on the population variance. The α value is 0.05. Recall that $\bar{X} = 0.003$, $s = 0.005$, and $n = 25$.

We will use the formula from Table 21.7. From Appendix F, we find $\chi_{0.025,24} = 39.364$ and $\chi_{0.975,24} = 12.401$. Substituting the values, we obtain

$$\frac{(n-1)s^2}{\chi^2_{\alpha/2,n-1}} \le \sigma^2 \le \frac{(n-1)s^2}{\chi^2_{1-\alpha/2,n-1}}$$

$$\frac{(24)0.005^2}{39.364} \le \sigma^2 \le \frac{(24)0.005^2}{12.401}$$

$$0.00002 \le \sigma^2 \le 0.00005$$

Thus, the 95% confidence interval for the population variance is (0.00002, 0.00005). Note that the confidence interval is not symmetric around σ^2 because the chi-square distribution is not symmetric.

EXAMPLE 21.8

A Six Sigma team is considering installing a new fixture to reduce the cycle time for a drilling process. However, the team would like to test whether the new fixture also has more precision in locating the holes compared to the original fixture. The location readings are known to follow a normal distribution. A random sample of 20 parts produced using the original fixture was collected, and the sample standard deviation of the hole location was equal to 0.250 cm. A sample of 15 parts produced using the newly designed fixture had a standard deviation equal to 0.195. Construct a 90% one-sided confidence interval on the ratio of the two population variances to determine if the location variance of the new fixture is less than the original fixture.

Here the original fixture will be denoted as Sample 1, and the new fixture will be Sample 2. It follows that $s_1 = 0.250$, $s_2 = 0.195$, and $n_1 = 20$ and $n_2 = 15$. If the standard deviation from the new fixture is less than that of the original fixture, the ratio $\frac{\sigma_1^2}{\sigma_2^2}$ will be greater than one. We will use the formula from Table 21.7 to calculate a lower bound for the ratio of the population variance. Using $\alpha = 0.10$, from Appendix G.5, we find $F_{0.90,\,14,19} = 0.51$. *Note that when we look up the F value in the table for the confidence interval, we switch the degrees of freedom of the numerator and denominator.* Substituting the values, we obtain

Continued

Continued

$$\frac{s_1^2}{s_2^2} F_{1-\alpha,\nu_2,\nu_1} \le \frac{\sigma_1^2}{\sigma_2^2} < \infty$$

$$\frac{0.250^2}{0.195^2}(0.51) \le \frac{\sigma_1^2}{\sigma_2^2} < \infty$$

$$0.838 \le \frac{\sigma_1^2}{\sigma_2^2} < \infty$$

We are 90% confident that the ratio of the population variances is covered by the interval [0.838, ∞). Since the value of one is included in the interval, we do not have sufficient evidence to claim the variance of the new fixture is less than that of the original fixture.

Note that this handbook provides F table values for left-tail probabilities, but not all references do. If we do not have a table for the left-tail, we can use the following relationships to calculate it:

$$\text{One-sided: } F_{1-\alpha,\nu_2,\nu_1} = \frac{1}{F_{\alpha,\nu_1,\nu_2}}$$

$$\text{Two-sided: } F_{1-\alpha/2,\nu_2,\nu_1} = \frac{1}{F_{\alpha/2,\nu_1,\nu_2}}$$

For example, to find $F_{0.90,\,14,19}$ we can use

$$F_{0.90,14,19} = \frac{1}{F_{0.10,19,14}} = \frac{1}{1.97} = 0.51$$

Confidence Intervals on One or Two Population Standard Deviations

To calculate confidence intervals for population standard deviations, we can use the formulas in Table 21.8. Note that the same strict assumption of normality needed for the confidence intervals on variances holds here as well.

EXAMPLE 21.9

Let's revisit the coating thickness data first introduced in Example 21.3. Assume that past experience shows that these thickness readings are normally distributed. (Alternatively, we could conduct a formal test for normality, such as an Anderson-Darling test.) We would like to calculate a 95% confidence interval on the population standard deviation. The α value is 0.05. Recall that $\overline{X} = 0.003$, $s = 0.0005$, and $n = 25$.

We will use the formula from Table 21.8. From Appendix F, we find $\chi_{0.025,24} = 39.364$ and $\chi_{0.975,24} = 12.401$. Substituting the values, we obtain

Continued

Continued

$$s\sqrt{\frac{(n-1)}{\chi^2_{\alpha/2,n-1}}} \le \sigma \le s\sqrt{\frac{(n-1)}{\chi^2_{1-\alpha/2,n-1}}}$$

$$0.005\sqrt{\frac{(24)}{39.364}} \le \sigma \le 0.005\sqrt{\frac{(24)}{12.401}}$$

$$0.00390 \le \sigma \le 0.00696$$

Thus, the 95% confidence interval for the population standard deviation is (0.00390, 0.00696). Note that the confidence interval is not symmetric around σ because the chi-square distribution is not symmetric.

Population parameter of interest	Assumptions	100(1 – α)% two-sided confidence interval on σ	100(1 – α)% one-sided confidence interval on σ
One population standard deviation, σ	Random sample, independent observations, normal distribution	$\sqrt{\frac{(n-1)s^2}{\chi^2_{\alpha/2,n-1}}} \le \sigma \le \sqrt{\frac{(n-1)s^2}{\chi^2_{1-\alpha/2,n-1}}}$	$LB: \sqrt{\frac{(n-1)s^2}{\chi^2_{\alpha,n-1}}}$ *or* $UB: \sqrt{\frac{(n-1)s^2}{\chi^2_{1-\alpha,n-1}}}$ Confidence intervals: [LB, ∞) or (-∞, UB]
Population parameter of interest	**Assumptions**	**100(1 – α)% two-sided confidence interval on $\frac{\sigma_1}{\sigma_2}$**	**100(1 – α)% one-sided confidence interval on $\frac{\sigma_1}{\sigma_2}$**
Ratio of two population standard deviations $\frac{\sigma_1}{\sigma_2}$	Random sample, independent observations, normal distributions, independent groups	$\sqrt{\frac{s_1^2}{s_2^2}\frac{1}{F_{\alpha/2,v_1,v_2}}} \le \frac{\sigma_1}{\sigma_2} \le \sqrt{\frac{s_1^2}{s_2^2}F_{\alpha/2,v_2,v_1}}$ or $\sqrt{\frac{s_1^2}{s_2^2}F_{1-\alpha/2,v_2,v_1}} \le \frac{\sigma_1}{\sigma_2} \le \sqrt{\frac{s_1^2}{s_2^2}F_{\alpha/2,v_2,v_1}}$	$LB: \sqrt{\frac{s_1^2}{s_2^2}F_{1-\alpha,v_2,v_1}}$ *or* $UB: \sqrt{\frac{s_1^2}{s_2^2}F_{\alpha,v_2,v_1}}$ Confidence intervals: [LB, ∞) or (-∞, UB]

Table 21.8 Confidence interval calculations for one and two population standard deviations.

EXAMPLE 21.10

Here, we will use the data from Example 21.8 to construct a 90% one-sided confidence interval on the ratio of the two population standard deviations. Recall that $s_1 = 0.250$, $s_2 = 0.195$, and $n_1 = 20$ and $n_2 = 15$. We will use the formula from Table 21.8. Using $\alpha = 0.10$, from Appendix G.5 we find $F_{0.90,\,14,19} = 0.51$ as before. *Note that when we look up the F value in the table for the confidence interval, we switch the degrees of freedom of the numerator and denominator.* Substituting the values, we obtain

$$\frac{s_1}{s_2}\sqrt{F_{1-\alpha,v_2,v_1}} \le \frac{\sigma_1}{\sigma_2} < \infty$$

$$\frac{0.250}{0.195}\sqrt{0.51} \le \frac{\sigma_1}{\sigma_2} < \infty$$

$$0.916 \le \frac{\sigma_1}{\sigma_2} < \infty$$

We are 90% confident that the ratio of the population standard deviations is covered by the interval [0.916, ∞). Since the value of one is included in the interval, we cannot claim that the standard deviation of the new fixture is less than the standard deviation of the original fixture.

Confidence Intervals on Population Proportions

We can calculate confidence intervals on population proportions using the formulas in Table 21.9. For these confidence intervals, there is an assumption that we have a random sample and that the conditions of the binomial distribution are satisfied. In addition, if there are at least ten successes and ten failures, $X \ge 10$ and $(n - X) \ge 10$, we can apply the normal approximation and use a Z statistic in the calculations. This technique is especially convenient when we must calculate a confidence interval by hand.

Recall from Chapter 18 that the conditions of the binomial distribution include:

1. Fixed number of trials, n
2. Only two possible, mutually exclusive, outcomes of each trial
3. Trials are independent
4. Constant probability of success from trial to trial

Table 21.9 presents three methods for calculating a confidence for a single proportion: the normal approximation method, the *Wilson score method,* and the exact method.

1. The normal approximation method for a confidence on a single proportion is used most often. However, in some cases, the method can result in a lower limit less than 0 or an upper limit greater than 1.
2. As an alternative, the *Wilson score method* improves upon the normal approximation method. This method, recommended by Agresti and

Coull (1998), and Brown et al. (2001), assures that the end points of the confidence interval do not exceed the allowable range of p.

3. The exact method is based directly on the binomial distribution and can be used for any sample size and value of X and n – X. The formula is a bit cumbersome for manual calculation, but statistical software packages can be used to produce the interval.

Table 21.9 also present two methods for calculating confidence intervals on the difference between two proportions.

1. The normal approximation method, most often used when hand calculations are required
2. The *Agresti-Caffo method,* which improves the actual coverage probability regardless of sample size.

Note that the examples in this section will use the normal approximation method to calculate confidence interval since it is within the scope of the Body of Knowledge.

EXAMPLE 21.11

A quality inspector tests a random sample of 50 assemblies and finds that 10 are defective. Calculate a 95% confidence interval for the true proportion defective. Here, we have $\alpha = 0.05$, X = 10, and n = 50. The estimated proportion is calculated to be

$$\hat{p} = \frac{X}{n} = \frac{10}{50} = 0.20.$$

Checking assumptions, we note that we have a random sample, there is a fixed number of trials, each assembly is classified as defective or non-defective, the trials are independent and there is a constant probability of finding a defective on each trial. Furthermore, we see that both *X* and *n* – *X* are greater or equal to 10.

$$np = 50(0.20) = 10$$
$$n(1-p) = 50(0.80) = 40$$

We will thus use the normal approximation method formula from Table 21.9. From Appendix D, we find $z_{\alpha/2} = 1.96$.

$$\hat{p} \pm z_{\alpha/2}\sqrt{\frac{\hat{p}(1-\hat{p})}{n}}$$
$$0.20 \pm 1.96\sqrt{\frac{(0.20)(0.80)}{50}}$$
$$0.20 \pm 0.111$$
$$[0.089, 0.311]$$

Thus, we are 95% confident that the interval [0.089, 0.311] covers the true proportion defective.

Population parameter of interest	Assumptions	100(1 – α)% two-sided confidence interval on p	100(1 – α)% one-sided confidence interval on p
One Population proportion p	Simple random sample, independent observations, conditions of the binomial distribution are satisfied, X ≥ 10 and (n – X) ≥ 10	Normal approximation method: $\hat{p} \pm z_{\alpha/2}\sqrt{\frac{\hat{p}(1-\hat{p})}{n}}$ *where* $\hat{p} = \frac{X}{n}$ Wilson method $\frac{\hat{p} + \frac{z_{\alpha/2}^2}{2n} \pm z_{\alpha/2}\sqrt{\frac{\hat{p}(1-\hat{p})}{n} + \frac{z_{\alpha/2}^2}{4n^2}}}{1 + \frac{z_{\alpha/2}^2}{n}}$	Normal approximation method: $LB: \hat{p} - z_{\alpha}\sqrt{\frac{\hat{p}(1-\hat{p})}{n}}$ $UB: \hat{p} + z_{\alpha}\sqrt{\frac{\hat{p}(1-\hat{p})}{n}}$ *where* $\hat{p} = \frac{X}{n}$ Wilson method $LB: \frac{\hat{p} + \frac{z_{\alpha}^2}{2n} - z_{\alpha}\sqrt{\frac{\hat{p}(1-\hat{p})}{n} + \frac{z_{\alpha}^2}{4n^2}}}{1 + \frac{z_{\alpha}^2}{n}}$ $UB: \frac{\hat{p} + \frac{z_{\alpha}^2}{2n} + z_{\alpha}\sqrt{\frac{\hat{p}(1-\hat{p})}{n} + \frac{z_{\alpha}^2}{4n^2}}}{1 + \frac{z_{\alpha}^2}{n}}$ One-sided confidence intervals: [LB, ∞) or (-∞, UB]

Table 21.9 Confidence interval calculations for one and two population proportions.

Population parameter of interest	Assumptions	100(1 – α)% two-sided confidence interval on p	100(1 – α)% one-sided confidence interval on p
Exact Method	Simple random sample, independent observations, conditions of the binomial distribution are satisfied	Limits are not symmetric: $LL: \frac{v_1 F_{1-\alpha/2, v1, v2}}{v_2 + v_1 F_{1-\alpha/2, v1, v2}}$ $UL: \frac{v_1 F_{\alpha/2, v1, v2}}{v_2 + v_1 F_{\alpha/2, v1, v2}}$ *where* $v_1 = 2x$ $v_2 = 2(n - x + 1)$	$LB: \frac{v_1 F_{1-\alpha, v1, v2}}{v_2 + v_1 F_{1-\alpha, v1, v2}}$ $UB: \frac{v_1 F_{\alpha, v1, v2}}{v_2 + v_1 F_{\alpha, v1, v2}}$ *where* $v_1 = 2x$ $v_2 = 2(n - x + 1)$

Table 21.9 *Continued*

Population parameter of interest	Assumptions	100(1 – α)% two-sided confidence interval on $(p_1 - p_2)$	100(1 – α)% one-sided confidence interval on $(p_1 - p_2)$
Difference in two population proportions $(p_1\text{-}p_2)$	Simple random samples, independent observations, independent groups, conditions of the binomial distribution are satisfied for each, $X \geq 10$ and $(n - X) \geq 10$ for each sample	Normal approximation method: $(\hat{p}_1 - \hat{p}_2) \pm z_{\alpha/2}\sqrt{\frac{\hat{p}_1(1-\hat{p}_1)}{n_1} + \frac{\hat{p}_2(1-\hat{p}_2)}{n_2}}$ *where* $\hat{p}_1 = \frac{X_1}{n_1}, \hat{p}_2 = \frac{X_2}{n_2}$ Agresti-Caffo method: $(\tilde{p}_1 - \tilde{p}_2) \pm z_{\alpha/2}\sqrt{\frac{\tilde{p}_1(1-\tilde{p}_1)}{n_1+2} + \frac{\tilde{p}_2(1-\tilde{p}_2)}{n_2+2}}$ *where* $\tilde{p}_1 = \frac{X_1+1}{n_1+2}, \tilde{p}_2 = \frac{X_2+1}{n_2+2}$	Normal approximation method: $LB: (\hat{p}_1 - \hat{p}_2) - z_{\alpha}\sqrt{\frac{\hat{p}_1(1-\hat{p}_1)}{n_1} + \frac{\hat{p}_2(1-\hat{p}_2)}{n_2}}$ $UB: (\hat{p}_1 - \hat{p}_2) + z_{\alpha}\sqrt{\frac{\hat{p}_1(1-\hat{p}_1)}{n_1} + \frac{\hat{p}_2(1-\hat{p}_2)}{n_2}}$ *where* $\hat{p}_1 = \frac{X_1}{n_1}, \hat{p}_2 = \frac{X_2}{n_2}$ Agresti-Caffo method: $LB: (\tilde{p}_1 - \tilde{p}_2) - z_{\alpha}\sqrt{\frac{\tilde{p}_1(1-\tilde{p}_1)}{n_1+2} + \frac{\tilde{p}_2(1-\tilde{p}_2)}{n_2+2}}$ $UB: (\tilde{p}_1 - \tilde{p}_2) + z_{\alpha}\sqrt{\frac{\tilde{p}_1(1-\tilde{p}_1)}{n_1+2} + \frac{\tilde{p}_2(1-\tilde{p}_2)}{n_2+2}}$ *where* $\tilde{p}_1 = \frac{X_1+1}{n_1+2}, \tilde{p}_2 = \frac{X_2+1}{n_2+2}$ One-sided confidence intervals: [LB, ∞) or (-∞, UB]

Table 21.9 *Continued*

EXAMPLE 21.12

A hospital system tracks the percentage of readmissions for its community acquired pneumonia patients each quarter. Last quarter, a random sample of patient records showed that Hospital A readmitted 25 patients of the 255 discharged from the unit. Hospital B readmitted 10 of the 200 pneumonia patients discharged. Construct a 95% confidence interval to determine if there is significant difference in readmission rates between the two hospitals.

Here, we have $\alpha = 0.05$, $X_1 = 25$, $X_2 = 10$, $n_1 = 255$ and $n_2 = 200$. The estimated proportions are calculated to be

$$\hat{p}_1 = \frac{X_1}{n_1} = \frac{25}{255} = 0.098$$

$$\hat{p}_2 = \frac{X_2}{n_2} = \frac{10}{200} = 0.050.$$

Checking assumptions, we note that we have random samples, there is a fixed number of trials, and each patient is classified as readmitted or not readmitted. We assume the status of each patient is independent, and that there is a constant probability of readmission for each patient. Furthermore, we see that both X and $n - X$ are greater or equal to 10 for each hospital. Therefore, we can use the normal approximation method. From Appendix D, we know that $z_{0.025} = 1.96$.

We will use the following formula from Table 21.9:

$$(\hat{p}_1 - \hat{p}_2) \pm z_{\alpha/2}\sqrt{\frac{\hat{p}_1(1-\hat{p}_1)}{n_1} + \frac{\hat{p}_2(1-\hat{p}_2)}{n_2}}$$

$$(0.098 - 0.050) \pm 1.96\sqrt{\frac{0.098(0.902)}{255} + \frac{0.05(0.95)}{200}}$$

$$[0.00063, 0.09537]$$

We are 95% confident that the difference in the population proportions is covered by interval [0.00063, 0.09537]. Because this interval does not include the value 0, we conclude that Hospital A had a higher readmission rate for its pneumonia patients.

Prediction Intervals

A *prediction interval gives a range of values* that cover the value of a future observation with a stated level of confidence. Note that individual observations are more variable than averages. It follows that a prediction interval for a point $x = x_0$ will be wider than the corresponding confidence interval of the mean because it contains bounds on an individual observation rather than bounds on the mean. The $100(1 - \alpha)\%$ prediction interval for a single future observation from a normal distribution is given by

$$\bar{X} - t_{\alpha/2, n-1}\, s\sqrt{1+\frac{1}{n}} \leq X_{n+1} \leq \bar{X} + t_{\alpha/2, n-1}\, s\sqrt{1+\frac{1}{n}}$$

EXAMPLE 21.13

A Black Belt professional wants to calculate a 90% prediction interval on the 26th observation of a piece of fiberoptic cable. The n = 25 observations yielded $\bar{X} = 15.0$ and s = 2.07. The α level is 0.10. From Appendix E, we find $t_{0.05,24} = 1.711$.

Substituting in the values, we obtain

$$\bar{X} - t_{\alpha/2,n-1}\, s\sqrt{1+\frac{1}{n}} \le X_{n+1} \le \bar{X} + t_{\alpha/2,n-1}\, s\sqrt{1+\frac{1}{n}}$$

$$15 - 1.711(2.07)\sqrt{1+\frac{1}{25}} \le X_{n+1} \le 15 + 1.711(2.07)\sqrt{1+\frac{1}{25}}$$

$$11.388 \le X_{n+1} \le 18.612$$

We are 90% confident that a new observation will be covered by the interval [11.388, 18.612].

Tolerance Intervals

A *tolerance interval* (also known as a *statistical tolerance interval*) is an interval estimator determined from a random sample that provides a level of confidence that the interval covers at least a specified proportion of the sampled population. The lower tolerance limit (LTL) and the upper tolerance limit (UTL) are given by

$$LTL: \bar{X} - Ks$$

$$UTL: \bar{X} + Ks$$

where $\bar{X}$ = sample mean, s = sample standard deviation, and K = tolerance factor based on the confidence level, proportion, and sample size. Values of K can be found in Appendixes J.1 and J.2. Like confidence intervals, tolerance intervals may be one-sided or two-sided.

EXAMPLE 21.14

A 15-piece sample from a process has a mean equal to 10.821 and a standard deviation equal to 0.027. Find the tolerance interval so that there is 95% confidence that the interval will contain 99% of the population.

Here, $\bar{X} = 10.821$, s = 0.027, and n = 15. The confidence level is 0.95, and the proportion is 0.99. We find K = 3.867 based on the confidence level, proportion, and sample size from the two-sided tolerance factor table in Appendix J.2. Using the formulas given, we calculate:

Continued

Continued

$$
\begin{aligned}
LTL &= \bar{X} - Ks \\
&= 10.821 - 3.867(0.027) \\
&= 10.7166 \\
UTL &= \bar{X} - Ks \\
&= 10.821 + 3.867(0.027) \\
&= 10.9254
\end{aligned}
$$

We are 95% confident that the interval [10.7166, 10.9254] will cover 99% of the population.

TESTS FOR MEANS, VARIANCES, AND PROPORTIONS

Use and interpret the results of hypothesis tests for means, variances, and proportions. (Evaluate)

Body of Knowledge VI.B.5

Procedure for Hypothesis Testing

To ensure that hypothesis tests are carried out properly, it is useful to have a well-defined process for conducting them:

Step 1. *State the null hypothesis and the alternative hypothesis.*

Step 2. *Assign an appropriate value to the level of significance.*

Step 3. *Determine the probability distribution of the appropriate test statistic.*

Step 4. *Calculate the appropriate test statistic.*

Step 5. *Determine the rejection region(s) and locate the critical point(s) and compare these to the calculated test statistic. Alternatively, calculate the p-value for the test and compare it to alpha.*

Step 6. *State the statistical conclusion in business terms.*

Hypothesis Tests on One Population Mean

Choosing the appropriate hypothesis test for a population mean is dependent upon whether the population is normal, if the samples size is greater than 30, and if the population standard deviation is known. The flowchart in Figure 21.3 can be used to decide which test is appropriate.

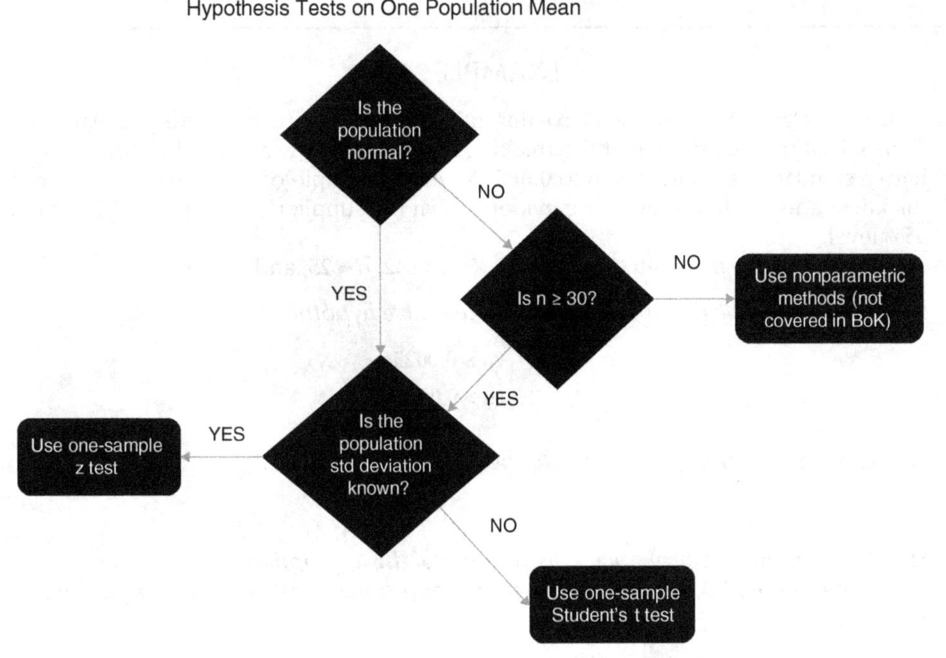

Figure 21.3 Flowchart for choosing a hypothesis test on one population mean.

Table 21.10 lists the assumptions, test statistic calculations, and decision rules for the hypothesis test on a single population mean. The distributions used are the standard normal (Z) and the Student's t. Note that in practice, the z-test is not often used since its assumption of a known population variance is rarely met.

Test name	Assumptions	Test statistic	Null hypothesis	Alternative hypotheses	Rejection criteria
Z-test for one population mean, μ	Random sample, independent observations, population normally distributed, population standard deviation known	$z_0 = \frac{(\bar{x} - \mu_0)}{\sigma/\sqrt{n}}$	$H_0 : \mu = \mu_0$	$H_1 : \mu \neq \mu_0$ $H_1 : \mu < \mu_0$ $H_1 : \mu > \mu_0$	$\lvert z_0 \rvert > z_{\alpha/2}$ $z_0 < -z_\alpha$ $z_0 > z_\alpha$
Student's t test for one population mean, μ	Random sample, independent observations, population normally distributed or sample size n ≥ 30	$t_0 = \frac{(\bar{x} - \mu_0)}{s/\sqrt{n}}$	$H_0 : \mu = \mu_0$	$H_1 : \mu \neq \mu_0$ $H_1 : \mu < \mu_0$ $H_1 : \mu > \mu_0$	$\lvert t_0 \rvert > t_{n-1,\alpha/2}$ $t_0 < -t_{n-1,\alpha}$ $t_0 > t_{n-1,\alpha}$

Table 21.10 Hypothesis tests for one population mean.

EXAMPLE 21.15

A supplier claims that the mean coating thickness of its circuit boards is greater than 0.0025. Past records show that the thickness readings follow a normal distribution and have a standard deviation equal to 0.005. A random sample of 25 boards yields a mean thickness equal to 0.0042. Is there evidence that the supplier's claim is true? Test at the 95% level.

Here, we have $\mu_0 = 0.0025$, $\sigma = 0.005$, $\bar{X} = 0.0042$, $n = 25$, and $\alpha = 0.05$.

Step 1. *State the null hypothesis and the alternative hypothesis.*

$$H_0 : \mu \leq 0.0025$$
$$H_1 : \mu > 0.0025$$

Step 2. *Assign an appropriate value to the level of significance.*

$$\alpha = 0.05$$

Step 3. *Determine the probability distribution of the appropriate test statistic.*

Using Figure 21.3, we determine that the appropriate test is a one-sample z-test on the mean.

Step 4. *Calculate the test statistic.*

Using the formula from Table 21.10, we calculate:

$$z_0 = \frac{(\bar{x} - \mu_0)}{\sigma / \sqrt{n}}$$

$$z_0 = \frac{(0.0042 - 0.0025)}{0.005 / \sqrt{25}}$$

$$z_0 = 1.70$$

Step 5. *Determine the rejection region(s) and locate the critical point(s) and compare these to the calculated test statistic. Alternatively, calculate the* p*-value for the test and compare it to alpha.*

This is a one-sided test. From Appendix D, we find $z_{0.05} = 1.645$. Table 21.10 gives the rejection criterion for this test:

Reject H_0 if $z_0 > z_\alpha$.

Step 6. *State the statistical conclusion in business terms.*

Since the test statistic $z_0 = 1.70$ is greater than the critical value $z = 1.645$, we reject H_0. At the 95% confidence level, we state that the supplier's claim that the mean thickness is greater than 0.0025 is supported.

Alternatively, we can use the *p*-value method to be able to give a more precise statement. Statistical software calculates $p = 0.045$ for this test. Since this value is less than our chosen $\alpha = 0.05$, we reject H_0.

EXAMPLE 21.16

Let's revisit the scenario in Example 21.15, but this time assume that the population standard deviation is not known but, rather, is calculated from the sample. We now have $\mu_0 = 0.0025$, $s = 0.005$, $\bar{X} = 0.0042$, $n = 25$, and $\alpha = 0.05$.

Step 1. *State the null hypothesis and the alternative hypothesis.*

$$H_0 : \mu \leq 0.0025$$
$$H_1 : \mu > 0.0025$$

Step 2. *Assign an appropriate value to the level of significance.*

$$\alpha = 0.05$$

Step 3. *Determine the probability distribution of the appropriate test statistic.*

Using Figure 21.3, we determine that the appropriate test is a one-sample Student's t test on the mean.

Step 4. *Calculate the appropriate test statistic.*

Using the formula from Table 21.10, we calculate:

$$t_0 = \frac{(\bar{x} - \mu_0)}{s/\sqrt{n}}$$

$$t_0 = \frac{(0.0042 - 0.0025)}{0.005/\sqrt{25}}$$

$$t_0 = 1.70$$

Step 5. *Determine the rejection region(s) and locate the critical point(s) and compare these to the calculated test statistic. Alternatively, calculate the* p-value *for the test and compare it to alpha.*

This is a one-sided test. From Appendix E, we find the critical value t 24, 0.05 = 1.711. Table 21.10 gives the rejection criterion for this test:

$$\text{Reject } H_0 \text{ if } t_0 > t_{n-1,\alpha}$$

Step 6. *State the statistical conclusion in business terms.*

Since the test statistic $t_0 = 1.70$ is less than the critical value $t_{24,\,0.05} = 1.711$, we fail to reject H_0. At the 95% confidence level, we state that the supplier's claim about the mean thickness is not supported.

Alternatively, we can use the *p*-value method to be able to give a more precise statement. Statistical software calculates $p = 0.051$ for this test. Since this value is greater than our chosen $\alpha = 0.05$, we fail to reject H_0.

Hypothesis Tests on Two Population Means

Choosing the appropriate hypothesis test for two population means is dependent upon whether the population is normal, if the samples sizes for each group are greater than 30, if the population standard deviations are known, and if the

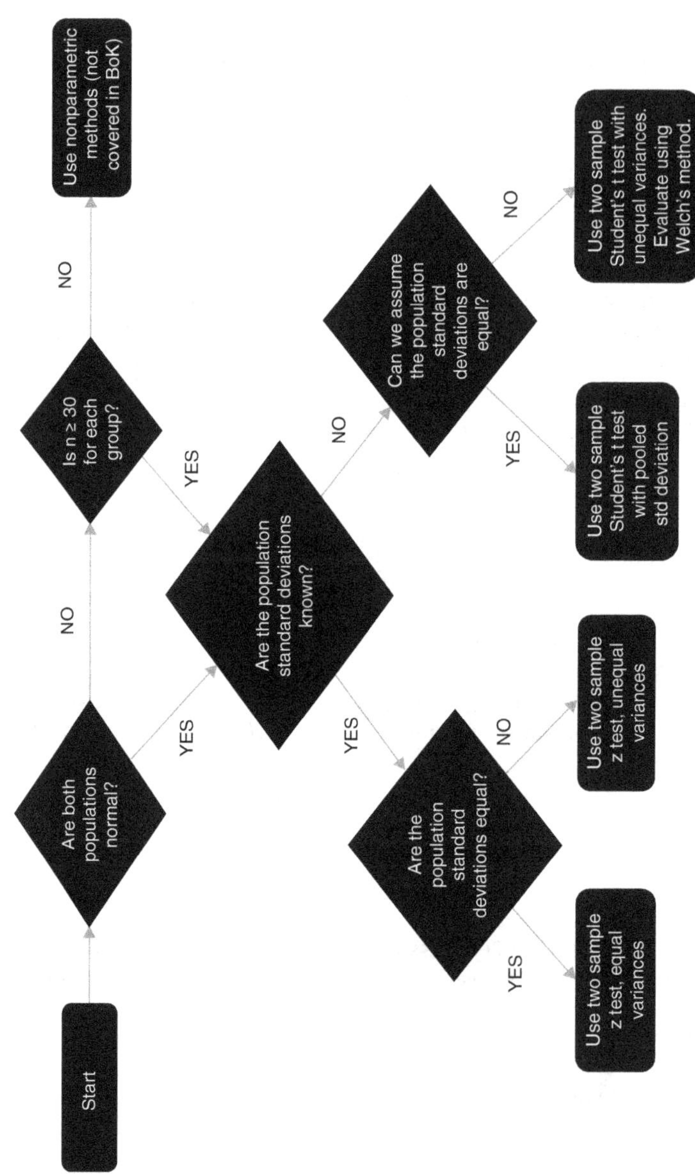

Figure 21.4 Flowchart for choosing a hypothesis test for two population means.

Test name	Assumptions	Test statistic	Null hypothesis	Alternative hypotheses	Rejection criteria
Z-test for difference in two population means, $\mu_1 - \mu_2$	Random samples, independent observations, independent groups, normal distribution, population **variances known and equal**	$z_0 = \dfrac{(\bar{X}_1 - \bar{X}_2) - \delta}{\sigma\sqrt{\dfrac{1}{n_1} + \dfrac{1}{n_2}}}$	$H_0 : \mu_1 - \mu_2 = \delta$	$H_1 : \mu_1 - \mu_2 = \delta$ $H_1 : \mu_1 - \mu_2 < \delta$ $H_1 : \mu_1 - \mu_2 > \delta$	$\lvert z_0 \rvert > z_{\alpha/2}$ $z_0 < -z_\alpha$ $z_0 > z_\alpha$
Z-test for difference in two population means, $\mu_1 - \mu_2$	Random samples, independent observations, independent groups, normal distribution, population **variances known and not equal**	$z_0 = \dfrac{(\bar{X}_1 - \bar{X}_2) - \delta}{\sqrt{\dfrac{\sigma_1^2}{n_1} + \dfrac{\sigma_2^2}{n_2}}}$	$H_0 : \mu_1 - \mu_2 = \delta$	$H_1 : \mu_1 - \mu_2 = \delta$ $H_1 : \mu_1 - \mu_2 < \delta$ $H_1 : \mu_1 - \mu_2 > \delta$	$\lvert z_0 \rvert > z_{\alpha/2}$ $z_0 < -z_\alpha$ $z_0 > z_\alpha$
Student's t test for difference in two population means, $\mu_1 - \mu_2$	Random samples, independent observations, independent groups, normal distributions or ($n_1 > 30$, $n_2 > 30$), **variances unknown but assumed equal**	$t_0 = \dfrac{(\bar{X}_1 - \bar{X}_2) - \delta}{s_p\sqrt{\dfrac{1}{n_1} + \dfrac{1}{n_2}}}$ *where* $s_p = \sqrt{\dfrac{(n_1 - 1)s_1^2 + (n_2 - 1)s_2^2}{(n_1 + n_2 - 2)}}$	$H_0 : \mu_1 - \mu_2 = \delta$	$H_1 : \mu_1 - \mu_2 = \delta$ $H_1 : \mu_1 - \mu_2 < \delta$ $H_1 : \mu_1 - \mu_2 > \delta$	$\lvert t_0 \rvert > t_{\alpha/2, n_1+n_2-2}$ $t_0 < -t_{\alpha, n_1+n_2-2}$ $t_0 > t_{\alpha, n_1+n_2-2}$

Table 21.11 Hypothesis tests on two population means.

Test name	Assumptions	Test statistic	Null hypothesis	Alternative hypotheses	Rejection criteria
Student's t test for difference in two population means, $\mu_1 - \mu_2$	Random samples, independent observations, independent groups, normal distributions or ($n_1 > 30$ and $n_2 > 30$), **variances unknown and not assumed equal**	Welch's method $t_0 = \frac{(\bar{X}_1 - \bar{X}_2) - \delta}{\sqrt{\frac{s_1^2}{n_1} + \frac{s_2^2}{n_2}}}$ $(\bar{X}_1 - \bar{X}_2) \pm t_{\alpha/2,v}\sqrt{\frac{s_1^2}{n_1} + \frac{s_2^2}{n_2}}$ with degrees of freedom v: $v = \frac{\left(\frac{s_1^2}{n_1} + \frac{s_2^2}{n_2}\right)^2}{\frac{\left(s_1^2/n_1\right)^2}{n_1 - 1} + \frac{\left(s_2^2/n_2\right)^2}{n_2 - 1}}$ Round v down to the next lowest integer	$H_0: \mu_1 - \mu_2 = \delta$	$H_1: \mu_1 - \mu_2 = \delta$ $H_1: \mu_1 - \mu_2 < \delta$ $H_1: \mu_1 - \mu_2 > \delta$	$\lvert t_0 \rvert > t_{\alpha/2,v}$ $t_0 < -t_{\alpha,v}$ $t_0 > t_{\alpha,v}$

Table 21.11 *Continued*

population standard deviations can be assumed to be equal. The flowchart in Figure 21.4 can be used to decide which test is appropriate.

Table 21.11 lists the assumptions, test statistic calculations, and decision rules for hypothesis tests on two population means. The distributions used are the standard normal (Z) and the Student's *t*. Note that in practice, the z-test is not often used since its assumption of known population variances is rarely met.

EXAMPLE 21.17

We will revisit the data presented in Example 21.4, in which a quality engineer conducts a study to determine if there is a difference in the mean weight of packages being produced on two different assembly lines. The weights from each line have been shown to follow normal distributions with known variances of 85.5 and 69.2, respectively. Twenty samples are randomly selected from Line 1, yielding a sample mean equal to 105.2 oz. Fifteen samples are randomly selected from Line 2 resulting in a sample mean equal to 99.7 oz. Perform a hypothesis test at the 95% confidence level to determine if there is a significant difference in mean weights.

Here we have $\bar{X}_1 = 105.2, \bar{X}_2 = 99.7, \sigma_1^2 = 85.5, \sigma_2^2 = 69.2, n_1 = 20, n_2 = 15,$ and $\alpha = 0.05$.

Step 1. *State the null hypothesis and the alternative hypothesis.*

$$H_0 : \mu_1 - \mu_2 = 0$$
$$H_1 : \mu_1 - \mu_2 \neq 0$$

Note that this set of hypotheses is equivalent to testing

$$H_0 : \mu_1 = \mu_2$$
$$H_1 : \mu_1 \neq \mu_2$$

Step 2. *Assign an appropriate value to the level of significance.*

$$\alpha = 0.05$$

Step 3. *Determine the probability distribution of the appropriate test statistic.*

Using Figure 21.4, we determine that the appropriate test is a two-sample z-test on the mean, unequal variances.

Step 4. *Calculate the appropriate test statistic.*

Using the formula from Table 21.11, we calculate:

$$Z_0 = \frac{(\bar{X}_1 - \bar{X}_2) - \delta}{\sqrt{\frac{\sigma_1^2}{n_1} + \frac{\sigma_2^2}{n_2}}}$$

$$Z_0 = \frac{(105.2 - 99.7) - 0}{\sqrt{\frac{85.5}{20} + \frac{69.2}{15}}}$$

$$Z_0 = 1.84$$

Step 5. *Determine the rejection region(s) and locate the critical point(s) and compare these to the calculated test statistic. Alternatively, calculate the p-value for the test and compare it to alpha.*

Continued

Continued

This is a two-sided test. From Appendix D, we find the critical value $z_{0.025} = 1.96$. Table 21.10 gives the rejection criterion for this test:

$$\text{Reject } H_0 \text{ if } |z_0| > z_{\alpha/2}$$

Step 6. *State the statistical conclusion in business terms.*

Since the test statistic $z_0 = 1.84$ is less than the critical value $z_{0.025} = 1.96$, we fail to reject H_0. There is insufficient evidence to claim that the mean weights of the packages produced on the two lines are significantly different.

Alternatively, we can use the *p*-value method to be able to give a more precise statement. Statistical software calculates $p = 0.066$ for this test. Since this value is greater than our chosen α of 0.05, we fail to reject H_0.

EXAMPLE 21.18

A pilot study was conducted to determine whether a new catalyst resulted in increased yields, measuring in ounces. Yields have historically followed a normal distribution. Test batches were produced in the lab using both catalysts with the results shown in Table 21.12. Perform a test at the 99% confidence level to determine if the new catalyst results in an increase in mean yield.

	Yield study	
	Current catalyst	**New catalyst**
Average	28.6 oz	31.9 oz
Std. deviation	3.5 oz	3.6 oz
Sample size	15	20

Table 21.12 Yield study results for Example 21.18.

Step 1. *State the null hypothesis and the alternative hypothesis.*

Here, we will be performing a one-sided test on two means because we want to show that the new catalyst produced a higher mean yield. Let μ_1 be the mean yield using the current catalyst, and μ_2 be the mean yield using the new catalyst. Then we have:

$$H_0: \mu_1 - \mu_2 \geq 0$$
$$H_1: \mu_1 - \mu_2 < 0$$

Note that this set of hypotheses is equivalent to testing

$$H_0: \mu_1 \geq \mu_2$$
$$H_1: \mu_1 < \mu_2$$

Step 2. *Assign an appropriate value to the level of significance.*

Here, we have chosen $\alpha = 0.01$.

Continued

Continued

Step 3. *Determine the probability distribution of the appropriate test statistic.*

The lab technician has decided to assume that the population variances are unknown but equal. Using Figure 21.7 we determine that the appropriate test is a two-sample t-test on two means using a pooled standard deviation calculation.

Step 4. *Calculate the test statistic.*

Using the formula from Table 21.11, we first calculate the pooled standard deviation:

$$s_p = \sqrt{\frac{(n_1-1)s_1^2+(n_2-1)s_2^2}{(n_1+n_2-2)}}$$

$$= \sqrt{\frac{(15-1)(3.5)^2+(20-1)(3.6)^2}{(15+20-2)}}.$$

$$= 3.558$$

Next, we calculate the value of the test statistic:

$$t_0 = \frac{(\bar{X}_1-\bar{X}_2)-\delta}{s_p\sqrt{\frac{1}{n_1}+\frac{1}{n_2}}}$$

$$= \frac{(28.6-31.9)-0}{3.558\sqrt{\frac{1}{15}+\frac{1}{20}}}$$

$$= -2.715$$

Step 5. *Determine the rejection region(s) and locate the critical point(s) and compare these to the calculated test statistic. Alternatively, calculate the* p*-value for the test and compare it to alpha.*

This is a one-sided test with $\alpha = 0.01$. The degrees of freedom for the Student's t critical value are equal to $(n_1 + n_2 - 2) = (15 + 20 - 2) = 33$. We find the critical value from the Student's t table in Appendix E, $t_{0.01,33} = 2.445$. From Table 21.11, we see that we will reject H_0 if $t_0 < -t_{\alpha,n_1+n_2-2}$.

Step 6. *State the statistical conclusion in business terms.*

Since the test statistic $t_0 = -2.715$ is less than the critical value $-t_{0.01,33} = -2.445$, we reject H_0. We conclude that the new catalyst increases mean yield in the lab.

Alternatively, we can use the p-value method to be able to give a more precise statement. Statistical software calculates $p = 0.005$ for this test. Since this value is less than our chosen $\alpha = 0.01$, we reject H_0.

The practice of assuming that unknown variances are equal and calculating the pooled standard deviation for the Student's t test has fallen out of favor. Moser and Stevens (1992) note that we rarely known that $\sigma_1 = \sigma_2$, and instead, we should calculate the Student's t test statistic using Welch's method, which does not require the equal variance assumption.

Calculations using Welch's method are illustrated in Example 21.19. The hand calculations are more onerous than those for the pooled standard deviation method, but this is not an issue when using statistical software. In fact, the unequal variance assumption and Welch's method is the default setting for two-sample t-tests in many statistical packages.

EXAMPLE 21.19

We will revisit the data in Example 21.5 involving a new training program for customer service representatives at an insurance firm. Before the training program, a sample of 40 randomly chosen calls showed that customers waited an average of 10.9 minutes before being helped, with a sample standard deviation equal to 10.5 minutes. After training, a sample of 35 calls showed the customer mean wait time was 6.8 minutes with a standard deviation of 6.4 minutes. To determine whether the training was effective, test whether the mean wait time for customers has decreased. Use $\alpha = 0.05$.

Step 1. *State the null hypothesis and the alternative hypothesis.*

Here, we will be performing a one-sided test on two means because the training department wants to know whether the mean wait time has decreased.

$$H_0 : \mu_1 - \mu_2 \leq 0$$
$$H_1 : \mu_1 - \mu_2 > 0$$

Note that this set of hypotheses is equivalent to testing

$$H_0 : \mu_1 \leq \mu_2$$
$$H_1 : \mu_1 > \mu_2$$

Step 2. *Assign an appropriate value to the level of significance.*

$$\alpha = 0.05$$

Step 3. *Determine the probability distribution of the appropriate test statistic.*

Using Figure 21.4, we determine that the appropriate test is a two-sample *t*-test on two means with variances unknown and assumed unequal. We will use Welch's method to evaluate the test statistic for this test.

Step 4. *Calculate the test statistic.*

Using the formula from Table 21.11, we calculate:

$$t_0 = \frac{(\bar{X}_1 - \bar{X}_2) - \delta}{\sqrt{\frac{s_1^2}{n_1} + \frac{s_2^2}{n_2}}}$$

$$t_0 = \frac{(10.9 - 6.8) - 0}{\sqrt{\frac{10.5^2}{40} + \frac{6.4^2}{35}}}$$

$$t_0 = 2.069$$

Step 5. *Determine the rejection region(s) and locate the critical point(s) and compare these to the calculated test statistic. Alternatively, calculate the* p*-value for the test and compare it to alpha.*

Using Welch's method, we must first calculate the degrees of freedom for the Student's *t* distribution critical value. We use a floor function for the degrees of freedom, rounding down any non-integer result to the next lowest integer.

Continued

Continued

$$v = \frac{\left(\frac{s_1^2}{n_1} + \frac{s_2^2}{n_2}\right)^2}{\frac{\left(s_1^2/n_1\right)^2}{n_1 - 1} + \frac{\left(s_2^2/n_2\right)^2}{n_2 - 1}}$$

$$v = \frac{\left(\frac{10.5^2}{40} + \frac{6.4^2}{35}\right)^2}{\frac{\left(10.5^2/40\right)^2}{39} + \frac{\left(6.4^2/35\right)^2}{34}}$$

$$= \lfloor 65.59 = 65$$

This is a one-sided test with $\alpha = 0.05$. We find the critical value from the Student's t table in Appendix E, $t_{0.05,65} = 1.669$. From Table 21.11, we see that we will reject H_0 if $t_0 > t_{\alpha,v}$.

Step 6. *State the statistical conclusion in business terms.*

Since the test statistic $t_0 = 2.069$ is greater than the critical value $t_{0.05,65} = 1.669$, we reject H_0. We conclude that the training program was effective in reducing mean wait times for customers.

Alternatively, we can use the *p*-value method to be able to give a more precise statement. Statistical software calculates $p = 0.021$ for this test. Since this value is less than our chosen $\alpha = 0.05$, we reject H_0.

Hypothesis Test for the Population Mean Difference from Paired Data

A hypothesis test for the mean difference is used when we have paired observations. These observations are not independent since they are measurements on the same subject at different points in time. The flowchart in Figure 21.5 shows the decision process for this choosing this type of test.

EXAMPLE 21.20

We will revisit Example 21.6, in which the grip strength of 35 male patients was measured before and after a rehabilitation program that included a weight training protocol. Because each patient was sampled before and after the protocol, this is a paired-data scenario. Summary statistics on the (After-Before) readings are shown in Table 21.14. Test whether the weight training program significantly increased mean grip strength.

Continued

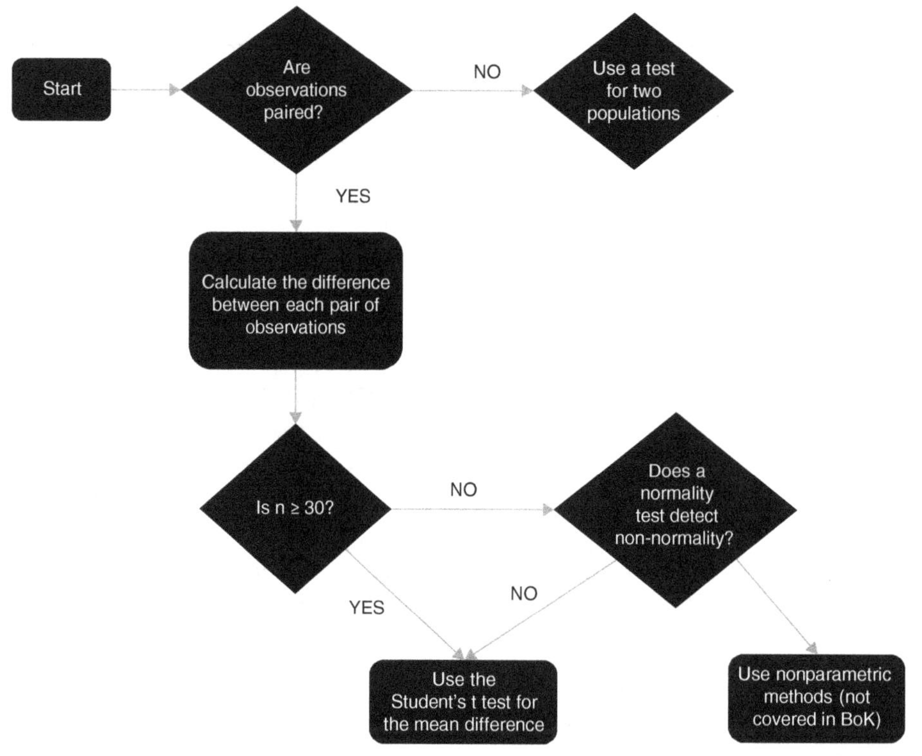

Figure 21.5 Flowchart for choosing a hypothesis test for the mean difference.

Test name	Assumptions	Test statistic	Null hypothesis	Alternative hypotheses	Rejection criteria
Student's t test for mean difference, μ_d	Paired data, difference between pairs is normal, or n ≥30	$t_0 = \frac{(\bar{d} - \mu_{d0})}{s_d / \sqrt{n}}$ *where* $s_d = \sqrt{\sum_{i=1}^{n} \frac{(d_i - \bar{d})^2}{n-1}}$	$H_0 : \mu_d = \mu_{d0}$	$H_1 : \mu \neq \mu_{d0}$ $H_1 : \mu < \mu_{d0}$ $H_1 : \mu > \mu_{d0}$	$\lvert t_0 \rvert > t_{n-1,\alpha/2}$ $t_0 < -t_{n-1,\alpha}$ $t_0 > t_{n-1,\alpha}$

Table 21.13 Hypothesis test for the mean difference from paired data.

Continued

Grip strength results for weight training protocol	
Average difference in grip strength (After-Before)	2.229 lbs
Sample standard deviation of the difference	2.850 lbs
Sample size	35

Table 21.14 Grip strength study summarized results for Example 21.20.

Step 1. *State the null hypothesis and the alternative hypothesis.*

Here, we will be performing a test on the mean difference. The difference was calculated as (After-Before), so if the weight training protocol had been successful, the mean difference would be significantly greater than zero.

$$H_0 : \mu_d \leq 0$$
$$H_1 : \mu_d > 0$$

Step 2. *Assign an appropriate value to the level of significance.*

We are running the test at a 95% confidence level, so $\alpha = 0.05$.

Step 3. *Determine the probability distribution of the appropriate test statistic.*

We determine that the appropriate test is a Student's *t* test on the mean difference.

Step 4. *Calculate the test statistic.*

Using the formula from Table 21.13, we calculate:

$$t_0 = \frac{(\bar{d} - \mu_{d0})}{s_d / \sqrt{n}} = \frac{(2.229 - 0)}{2.850 / \sqrt{35}} = 4.627$$

Step 5. *Determine the rejection region(s) and locate the critical point(s) and compare these to the calculated test statistic. Alternatively, calculate the* p-value *for the test and compare it to alpha.*

This is a one-sided test with $\alpha = 0.05$. We find the critical value from the Student's *t* table in Appendix E, $t_{0.05,34} = 1.691$. From Table 21.13, we see that we will reject H_0 if $t_0 > t_{\alpha,n-1}$.

Step 6. *State the statistical conclusion in business terms.*

Since the test statistic $t_0 = 4.627$ is greater than the critical value $t_{0.05,34} = 1.691$, we reject H_0 and conclude that the weight training was effective in increasing mean grip strength.

Alternatively, we can use the *p*-value method to be able to give a more precise statement. Statistical software calculates $p = 0.000$ for this test. Since this value is less than our chosen $\alpha = 0.05$, we reject H_0.

Hypothesis Tests on One and Two Population Variances or Standard Deviations

Choosing the appropriate hypothesis test for a variance or standard deviation depends on whether we are considering one or two populations, and if those populations are normal. The flowchart in Figure 21.6 can be used to decide which test is appropriate.

Table 21.15 shows assumptions, test statistics, hypotheses, and decision criteria for the tests of one or two population standard deviations or variances. Note that all the test statistics are calculated using the population variance.

If the normality assumption is not met, a Black Belt can use a nonparametric test such as Bonett's or Levene's test. Although quite useful, these tests are beyond the scope of the current Body of Knowledge. The reader is referred to Montgomery and Runger (2010) to learn more.

EXAMPLE 21.21

Let's revisit the coating thickness data first introduced in Example 21.15. We assume the thickness readings are normally distributed. (Alternatively, we could conduct a formal test for normality, such as an Anderson-Darling test.) We would like to test whether the population standard deviation is significantly different from 0.004 at a 95% confidence interval. Recall that s = 0.005 and n = 25.

Step 1. *State the null hypothesis and the alternative hypothesis.*

Here, we will be performing a test on whether the population standard deviation is significantly different from a certain value.

$$H_0: \sigma = 0.004$$
$$H_1: \sigma \neq 0.004$$

Step 2. *Assign an appropriate value to the level of significance.*

We are running the test at a 95% confidence level, so $\alpha = 0.05$.

Step 3. *Determine the probability distribution of the appropriate test statistic.*

We determine that the appropriate test is a chi-square test on the population variance.

Step 4. *Calculate the test statistic.*

Using the formula from Table 21.15, we calculate:

$$\begin{aligned}\chi_0^2 &= \frac{(n-1)s^2}{\sigma_0^2} \\ &= \frac{(25-1)0.005^2}{0.004^2} \\ &= 37.5\end{aligned}$$

Step 5. *Determine the rejection region(s) and locate the critical point(s) and compare these to the calculated test statistic. Alternatively, calculate the* p*-value for the test and compare it to alpha.*

This is a two-sided test with $\alpha = 0.05$. We must find two critical values from the chi-square table in Appendix F. We find $\chi^2_{0.025,24} = 39.364$ and $\chi^2_{0.975,24} = 12.401$. From Table

Continued

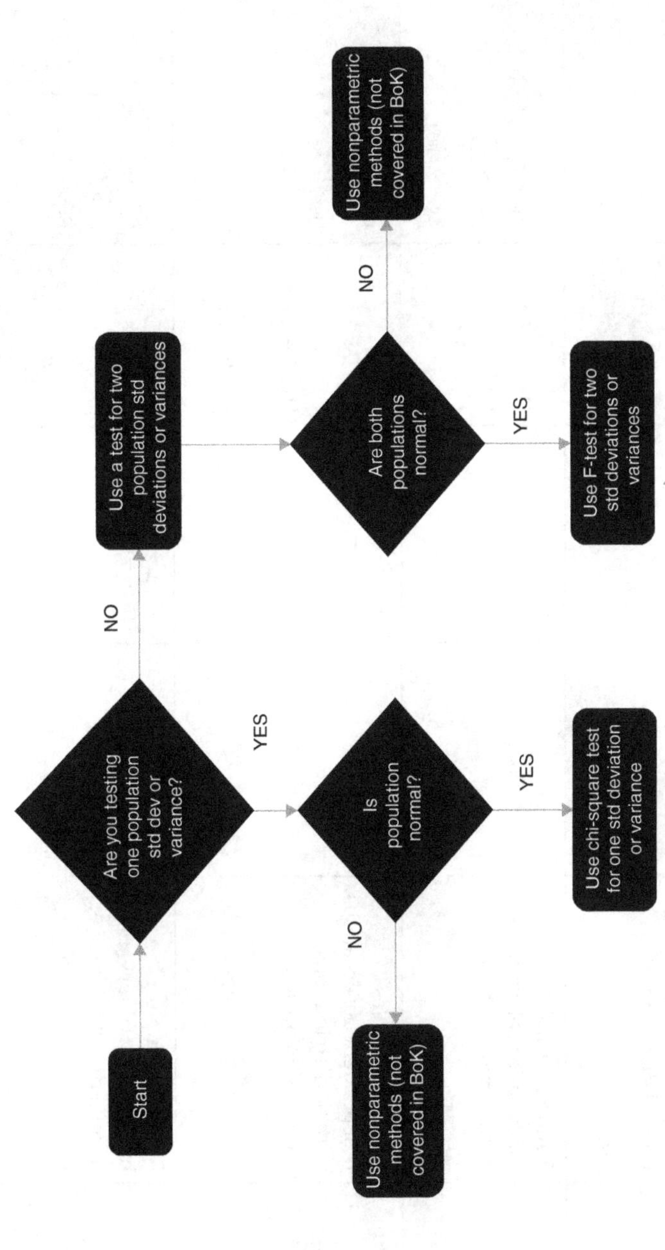

Figure 21.6 Flowchart for hypothesis tests for one or two population standard deviations or variances.

Test name	Assumptions	Test statistic	Null hypothesis	Alternative hypotheses	Rejection criteria
Chi-square test for one population variance, σ^2	Random sample, independent observations, normal distribution	$\chi_0^2 = \frac{(n-1)s^2}{\sigma_0^2}$	$H_0 : \sigma^2 = \sigma_0^2$	$H_1 : \sigma^2 \neq \sigma_0^2$ $H_1 : \sigma^2 < \sigma_0^2$ $H_1 : \sigma^2 > \sigma_0^2$	$\chi_0^2 > \chi^2_{\alpha/2,n-1}$ or $\chi_0^2 < \chi^2_{1-\alpha/2,n-1}$ $\chi_0^2 < \chi^2_{1-\alpha,n-1}$ $\chi_0^2 > \chi^2_{\alpha,n-1}$
Chi-square test for one population standard deviation, σ	Random sample, independent observations, normal distribution	$\chi_0^2 = \frac{(n-1)s^2}{\sigma_0^2}$	$H_0 : \sigma = \sigma_0$	$H_1 : \sigma \neq \sigma_0$ $H_1 : \sigma < \sigma_0$ $H_1 : \sigma > \sigma_0$	$\chi_0^2 > \chi^2_{\alpha/2,n-1}$ or $\chi_0^2 < \chi^2_{1-\alpha/2,n-1}$ $\chi_0^2 < \chi^2_{1-\alpha,n-1}$ $\chi_0^2 > \chi^2_{\alpha,n-1}$
F test for two population variances, $\frac{\sigma_1^2}{\sigma_2^2}$	Random samples, independent observations, normal distributions, independent groups	$F_0 = \frac{s_1^2}{s_2^2}$	$H_0 : \frac{\sigma_1^2}{\sigma_2^2} = 1$	$H_1 : \frac{\sigma_1^2}{\sigma_2^2} \neq 1$ $H_1 : \frac{\sigma_1^2}{\sigma_2^2} < 1$ $H_1 : \frac{\sigma_1^2}{\sigma_2^2} > 1$	$F_0 > F_{\alpha/2,n_1-1,n_2-1}$ or $F_0 < F_{1-\alpha/2,n_1-1,n_2-1}$ $F_0 > F_{\alpha,n_1-1,n_2-1}$ $F_0 > F_{\alpha,n_1-1,n_2-1}$
F test for two population standard deviations, $\frac{\sigma_1}{\sigma_2}$	Random samples, independent observations, normal distributions, independent groups	$F_0 = \frac{s_1^2}{s_2^2}$	$H_0 : \frac{\sigma_1}{\sigma_2} = 1$	$H_1 : \frac{\sigma_1}{\sigma_2} \neq 1$ $H_1 : \frac{\sigma_1}{\sigma_2} < 1$ $H_1 : \frac{\sigma_1}{\sigma_2} > 1$	$F_0 > F_{\alpha/2,n_1-1,n_2-1}$ $F_0 > F_{\alpha,n_1-1,n_2-1}$ $F_0 > F_{\alpha,n_1-1,n_2-1}$

Table 21.15 Hypothesis tests on one and two population variances and standard deviations.

Continued

21.15, we see that we will reject H_0 if $\chi_0^2 > \chi^2_{\alpha/2,n-1}$ or $\chi_0^2 < \chi^2_{1-\alpha/2,n-1}$.

Step 6. *State the statistical conclusion in business terms.*

Since the test statistic $\chi_0^2 = 37.5$ is not greater than the critical value $\chi^2_{0.025,24} = 39.364$, nor is it less than the critical value $\chi^2_{0.975,24} = 12.401$, we fail to reject H_0 and conclude that there is insufficient evidence to claim the population standard deviation is significantly different from 0.004.

Alternatively, we can use the *p*-value method to be able to give a more precise statement. Statistical software calculates p = 0.078 for this test. Since this value is greater than our chosen $\alpha = 0.05$, we fail to reject H_{0e}.

EXAMPLE 21.22

Here we will revisit the scenario presented in Example 21.8. A Six Sigma team would like to test whether a new fixture has more precision in locating drilled holes compared to the original fixture. The location readings are known to follow a normal distribution. The original fixture will be denoted as Sample 1, and the new fixture will be Sample 2. Sample data gives $s_1 = 0.250$, $s_2 = 0.195$, and $n_1 = 20$ and $n_2 = 15$. We will test at the $\alpha = 0.10$ level.

Step 1. *State the null hypothesis and the alternative hypothesis.*

Here, we will be performing a test on whether the new fixture has a smaller variance than the original fixture. This will occur if the ratio

$$\frac{\sigma_1^2}{\sigma_2^2}$$

is greater than one.

We set up the one-sided hypotheses:

$$H_0 : \frac{\sigma_1^2}{\sigma_2^2} \le 1$$

$$H_1 : \frac{\sigma_1^2}{\sigma_2^2} > 1$$

Step 2. *Assign an appropriate value to the level of significance.*

We are running the test at $\alpha = 0.10$, which maps to a 90% confidence level.

Step 3. *Determine the probability distribution of the appropriate test statistic.*

Since we are told that the location readings for each fixture are normally distributed, we determine that the appropriate test is an F test on the ratio of two population variances.

Step 4. *Calculate the test statistic.*

Using the formula from Table 21.15, we calculate:

Continued

Continued

$$
\begin{aligned}
F_0 &= \frac{s_1^2}{s_2^2} \\
&= \frac{0.250^2}{0.195^2} \\
&= 1.644
\end{aligned}
$$

Step 5. *Determine the rejection region(s) and locate the critical point(s) and compare these to the calculated test statistic. Alternatively, calculate the* p*-value for the test and compare it to alpha.*

This is a one-sided test with $\alpha = 0.10$. We must find the critical values from the F table in Appendix G.4. We find $F_{19,14,0.10} = 1.97$. From Table 21.15, we see that we will reject H_0 if $F_0 > F_{\alpha,n_1-1,n_2-1}$.

Step 6. *State the statistical conclusion in business terms.*

Since the test statistic $F_0 = 1.644$ is not greater than the critical value $F_{19,14,0.10} = 1.97$, we fail to reject H_0 and conclude that there is insufficient evidence to claim the variance of the new fixture is less than that of the original fixture.

Alternatively, we can use the *p*-value method to be able to give a more precise statement. Statistical software calculates $p = 0.173$ for this test. Since this value is greater than our chosen $\alpha = 0.10$, we fail to reject H_0.

Note that a hypothesis test on the ratio of the standard deviations would yield the same test statistic and the same conclusion.

Hypothesis Test on Population Proportions

Choosing the appropriate hypothesis test for a proportion depends on whether we are considering one or two populations, if assumptions concerning the number of successes and failures are satisfied, and if the samples satisfy the conditions of the binomial distribution. Recall from Chapter 18 that the requirements for a binomial distribution include the following:

1. Fixed number of trials, n
2. Only two possible, mutually exclusive, outcomes of each trial
3. Trials are independent
4. Constant probability of success from trial to trial

The flowchart in Figure 21.7 can be used to decide which test is appropriate. In all cases, we assume that we have a random sample and that the conditions of the binomial distribution are met. Note that the variances used in calculating the test statistics for the hypothesis tests of one or two proportions are different from those used for the confidence interval calculations in Table 21.9.

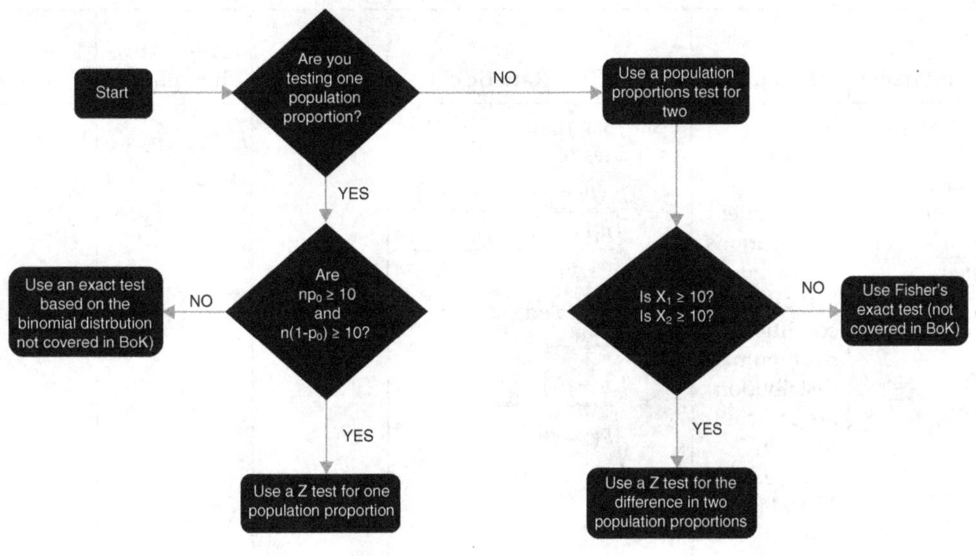

Figure 21.7 Flowchart for hypothesis tests for one and two population proportions.

Test name	Assumptions	Test statistic	Null hypothesis	Alternative hypotheses	Rejection criteria
Z-test for one population proportion, p	Simple random sample, independent observations, conditions of the binomial distribution are satisfied, $np_0 \ge 10$ and $n(1-p_0) \ge 10$	$z_0 = \dfrac{(\hat{p}-p_0)}{\sqrt{\dfrac{p_0(1-p_0)}{n}}}$ Variance is based on hypothesized value of p.	$H_0: p = p_0$	$H_1: p \ne p_0$ $H_1: p < p_0$ $H_1: p > p_0$	$\lvert z_0 \rvert > z_{\alpha/2}$ $z_0 < -z_\alpha$ $z_0 > z_\alpha$

Table 21.16 Hypothesis tests for one and two population proportions

Test name	Assumptions	Test statistic	Null hypothesis	Alternative hypotheses	Rejection criteria
Z-test for difference in two population proportions, p_1-p_2	Simple random samples, independent observations, independent samples, conditions of the binomial distribution are satisfied for each sample, $X \geq 10$ and $(n - X) \geq 10$ for each sample	Using separate estimates of p $z_0 = \dfrac{(\hat{p}_1-\hat{p}_2)-(p_1-p_2)}{\sqrt{\dfrac{\hat{p}_1(1-\hat{p}_1)}{n_1}+\dfrac{\hat{p}_2(1-\hat{p}_2)}{n_2}}}$ Using a pooled estimate of p $z_0 = \dfrac{(\hat{p}_1-\hat{p}_2)-(p_1-p_2)}{\sqrt{P(1-P)\ \dfrac{1}{n_1}+\dfrac{1}{n_2}}}$ *where* $P = \dfrac{n_1\hat{p}_1+n_2\hat{p}_2}{n_1+n_2}$ is the pooled proportion	$H_0: p_1-p_2 = 0$	$H_1: p_1-p_2 \neq 0$ $H_1: p_1-p_2 < 0$ $H_1: p_1-p_2 > 0$	$\lvert z_0 \rvert > z_{\alpha/2}$ $z_0 < -z_\alpha$ $z_0 > z_\alpha$

Table 21.16 *Continued.*

EXAMPLE 21.23

A webpage designer wants to determine whether the click rate on a call-to-action button on a newly designed web page is greater than 20%. A random sample of 150 unique visitors to the site shows 33 click-throughs. Test the designer's hypothesis at the 95% confidence level.

Checking assumptions, we note that we have a random sample, there is a fixed number of trials, and each visit is classified as a click-through or not a click-through. The visits are independent and there is a constant probability of clicking through on each visit. Furthermore, we see that both np_0 and $n(1 - p_0)$ are greater or equal to 10:

$$np_0 = 150(0.20) = 30$$
$$n(1-p_0) = 150(0.80) = 120$$

Note that p_0 is the proportion claimed in the hypothesis, not the sample proportion. From Figure 21.7 we see that a z-test for one population proportion is an appropriate choice.

Step 1. *State the null hypothesis and the alternative hypothesis.*

$$H_0: p \leq 0.20$$
$$H_1: p > 0.20$$

Step 2. *Assign an appropriate value to the level of significance.*

$$\alpha = 0.05$$

Continued

Continued

Step 3. *Determine the probability distribution of the appropriate test statistic.*

Using Figure 21.3, we determine that the appropriate test is a z-test on one population proportion.

Step 4. *Calculate the test statistic.*

Using the formula from Table 21.16, we calculate:

$$z_0 = \frac{(\hat{p} - p_0)}{\sqrt{\frac{p_0(1-p_0)}{n}}}$$

$$z_0 = \frac{(0.22 - 0.20)}{\sqrt{\frac{0.20(1-0.20)}{150}}}$$

$$z_0 = 0.612$$

Step 5. *Determine the rejection region(s) and locate the critical point(s) and compare these to the calculated test statistic. Alternatively, calculate the* p-*value for the test and compare it to alpha.*

This is a one-sided test. From Appendix D, we find $z_{0.05} = 1.645$. Table 21.16 gives the rejection criterion for this test:

Reject H_0 if $z_0 > z_\alpha$.

Step 6. *State the statistical conclusion in business terms.*

Since the test statistic $z_0 = 0.612$ is less than the critical value $z = 1.645$, we fail to reject H_0. At the 95% confidence level, we state that there insufficient evidence to claim the click-through rate is greater than 20%.

Alternatively, we can use the *p*-value method to be able to give a more precise statement. Statistical software calculates $p = 0.270$ for this test. Since this value is greater than our chosen $\alpha = 0.05$, we fail to reject H_0.

Note that we can also use an exact test using the binomial distribution, which is not covered in the Body of Knowledge. The calculations are a bit more cumbersome; however, the exact test can easily be performed using a statistical package and is actually the preferred analysis method.

EXAMPLE 21.24

We will revisit the hospital readmissions data in Example 21.12. A hospital system tracks the percentage of readmissions for its community acquired pneumonia patients each quarter. Last quarter, a random sample of patients showed that Hospital A readmitted 25 patients of the 255 discharged from the unit. Hospital B readmitted 10 of the 200 pneumonia patients discharged. Test whether there is a significant difference in readmission rates between the two hospitals at the 95% confidence level.

Here, we have $\alpha = 0.05$, $X_1 = 25$, $X_2 = 10$, $n_1 = 255$ and $n_2 = 200$. The estimated proportions are calculated to be

Continued

$$\hat{p}_1 = \frac{X_1}{n_1} = \frac{25}{255} = 0.098$$
$$\hat{p}_2 = \frac{X_2}{n_2} = \frac{10}{200} = 0.050.$$

Checking assumptions, we note that we have a random sample, there is a fixed number of trials, and each patient is classified as readmitted or not readmitted. We assume the status of each patient is independent, and that there is a constant probability of readmission for each patient. Furthermore, we see that both X and (n – X) are greater than or equal to 10 for each hospital. We will evaluate this hypothesis using a pooled estimate of p.

Step 1. *State the null hypothesis and the alternative hypothesis.*

$$H_0: p_1 - p_2 = 0$$
$$H_1: p_1 - p_2 \neq 0$$

Step 2. *Assign an appropriate value to the level of significance.*

$$\alpha = 0.05$$

Step 3. *Determine the probability distribution of the appropriate test statistic.*

Using Figure 21.3, we determine that the appropriate test is a z-test on two population proportions.

Step 4. *Calculate the test statistic.*

Using the formula from Table 21.16, we calculate z_0 using the pooled proportion:

$$z_0 = \frac{(\hat{p}_1 - \hat{p}_2) - (p_1 - p_2)}{\sqrt{P(1-P)\left(\frac{1}{n_1} + \frac{1}{n_2}\right)}}$$

where

$$P = \frac{n_1\hat{p}_1 + n_2\hat{p}_2}{n_1 + n_2}$$

$$P = \frac{n_1\hat{p}_1 + n_2\hat{p}_2}{n_1 + n_2} = \frac{255(0.098) + 200(0.05)}{255 + 200} = 0.0769$$

$$z_0 = \frac{(0.098 - 0.05) - (0)}{\sqrt{0.0769(1 - 0.0769)\left(\frac{1}{255} + \frac{1}{200}\right)}}$$
$$= 1.91$$

Step 5. *Determine the rejection region(s) and locate the critical point(s) and compare these to the calculated test statistic. Alternatively, calculate the* p-*value for the test and compare it to alpha.*

This is a two-sided test. From Appendix D, we find $z_{0.025} = 1.96$. Table 21.16 gives the rejection criterion for this test:

Reject H_0 if $|z_0| > z_\alpha$.

Continued

Continued

Step 6. *State the statistical conclusion in business terms.*

Since the test statistic $z_0 = 1.91$ is less than the critical value $z = 1.96$, we fail to reject H_0. At the 95% confidence level, we state that there is insufficient evidence to claim the hospital readmission rates are different.

Alternatively, we can use the *p*-value method to be able to give a more precise statement. Statistical software calculates $p = 0.056$ for this test. Since this value is greater than our chosen $\alpha = 0.05$, we fail to reject H_0.

If we were performing this hypothesis test using a statistical software package, the preferred analysis method would be to use Fisher's exact test, which is not covered in the Body of Knowledge.

Equivalence Tests

Recall that the standard set of hypotheses for testing two population means follows the form

$$H_0: \mu_1 - \mu_2 = 0$$

$$H_1: \mu_1 - \mu_2 \neq 0$$

We have stressed in the previous sections that failure to reject H_o does not prove that the means are equal. In fact, we can never prove the null hypothesis; we can only prove the alternative hypothesis.

Consider an analysis situation in which our purpose is to prove the equivalence of two means. How can this be accomplished? We can use a different format for the hypotheses and perform two one-sided tests (TOST) (Schuirmann, 1987). First, the analyst must define a *margin of equivalence,* denoted by θ, which is the limit beyond which the difference in mean values should be considered practically and statistically significant (Limentani et al., 2005). Conversely, we will deem any difference in means between $(-\theta, \theta)$ as demonstrating equivalence. Equivalence is different than equality: Equivalence implies that for the situation at hand, the means are close enough that there is no effect of any small difference within the range of $\{-\theta , \theta\}$. (Note that defining a value for θ is a non-trivial task and must be derived on the basis of prior experience or expert knowledge.)

Once θ is defined, we set up the two one-sided hypotheses and evaluate them using Student's t tests.

$$H_0: \mu_1 - \mu_2 \leq -\theta$$

$$H_1: \mu_1 - \mu_2 > -\theta$$

$$H_0: \mu_1 - \mu_2 \geq \theta$$

$$H_1: \mu_1 - \mu_2 < \theta$$

If both sets of hypotheses are rejected, we conclude that the means are equivalent. The *p*-value for the equivalence test is equal to the larger of the two *p*-values for the individual one-sided tests.

Although useful, this topic is beyond the scope of the Body of Knowledge. Readers wanting to learn more can refer to Limentani et al. (2005) for a straightforward introduction to the topic.

Nonparametric Tests

The flowcharts in the previous sections show that if the assumptions for the hypothesis tests are not satisfied, we must use an alternative, nonparametric test. Although these tests are not in the Body of Knowledge, we list parametric tests and their nonparametric analogs in Table 21.16. Readers can refer to a statistics text such as Montgomery and Runger (2010) for more information on nonparametric testing.

Parametric test	**Nonparametric alternative(s)**
Z-test or Student's *t*-test for one mean	Sign test Wilcoxon signed-ranks test
Z-test or Student's *t*-test for two means	Wilcoxon rank-sum test (also known as the Mann-Whitney U test) Kruskal-Wallis test Mood's median test
Student's *t*-test for mean difference, paired data	Sign test Wilcoxon signed-ranks test
Chi-square test for one standard deviation or variance	Bonett's test
F-test for two standard deviations or variances	Bonett's test Levene's test
Bartlett's test for three or more standard deviations or variances	Levene's test
Z-test for one population proportion	Exact test (assumes binomial conditions hold)
Z-test for two population proportions	Fisher's exact test (assumes binomial conditions hold)
Analysis of variance (three or more means)	Kruskal-Wallis test Mood's median test

Table 21.17 Parametric tests with nonparametric analogs.

SAMPLE SIZE

> Calculate sample size for common hypothesis tests: equality of means and equality of proportions. (Apply)
>
> Body of Knowledge VI.B.3

If we perform a hypothesis test and fail to reject the null hypothesis, it does not mean that the null hypothesis is necessarily true. It might be the case that the null hypothesis is false, but we do not have enough evidence to reject it. By increasing the sample size of a given test, we can increase the probability of rejecting H_0 when it is false, thus increasing the power of the test. With a little algebra we can determine *a priori* what sample size will be necessary to be able to achieve a margin of error E or detect a difference δ in a population parameter with a certain level of confidence (1 – α).

In this section we present sample size calculations for achieving a specific margin of error E in a confidence interval, and for detecting a difference δ in a hypothesis test.

Sample Size to Achieve a Specified Margin of Error

Table 21.18 presents sample size formulas for assuring a certain margin of error E in a confidence interval on a mean or proportion.

Population parameter	Purpose	Sample size formula for (1 – α)% two-sided confidence interval	Sample size formula for (1 – α)% one-sided confidence interval
Population mean, μ	Assuring a (1 – α)% confidence interval on μ has a margin of error of at most E.	$n=\left(\frac{z_{\alpha/2}\sigma}{E}\right)^2$	$n=\left(\frac{z_{\alpha}\sigma}{E}\right)^2$
Difference between two population means, $\mu_1-\mu_2$	Assuring a (1 – α)% confidence interval on $\mu_1-\mu_2$ has a margin of error of at most E.	$n=n_1=n_2=\frac{(z_{\alpha/2})^2(\sigma_1^2+\sigma_2^2)}{E^2}$	$n=n_1=n_2=\frac{(z_{\alpha})^2(\sigma_1^2+\sigma_2^2)}{E^2}$
Population proportion, p	Assuring a (1 – α)% confidence interval on p has a margin of error of at most E.	$n=\left(\frac{z_{\alpha/2}}{E}\right)^2\hat{p}(1-\hat{p})$	$n=\left(\frac{z_{\alpha}}{E}\right)^2\hat{p}(1-\hat{p})$

Table 21.18 Sample size calculations to assure a margin of error of E in a confidence interval.

EXAMPLE 21.25

A Six Sigma professional wants to estimate the mean diameter of fiberoptic cable. How many samples must be randomly selected if they want 95% confidence that the sample mean is within 0.5 mm of the population mean? From past experience it is known that the population standard deviation, σ, is equal to 2 mm.

Here, $\alpha = 0.05$, and from Appendix D, we find that $z_{0.025} = 1.96$. The population standard deviation is $\sigma = 2$ and the desired margin of error is $E = 0.5$.

We will use the following formula from Table 21.17 for our problem:

$$n = \left(\frac{Z_{\alpha/2}\sigma}{E} \right)^2$$

Substituting in the values, we obtain

$$n = \left(\frac{Z_{\alpha/2}\sigma}{E} \right)^2 = \left(\frac{1.96 \times 2}{0.5} \right)^2 = 61.47$$

$$\lceil n = 62$$

Based on our confidence level and the inherent variation in the data, we will need a sample size of at least n = 62 to obtain a 95% confidence with a margin of error of at most 0.5 mm.

Note that the calculation of the sample size n is a *ceiling function*, denoted by the symbol $\lceil$, in which any non-integer result is rounded up to the next whole number. For example, if the result of the calculation were 61.07, we would round this up to 62 as well.

EXAMPLE 21.26

A polling firm would like to report the estimated proportion of respondents who are in favor of a proposed sales tax increase that would benefit the local public schools. How many respondents must be randomly selected to assure a margin of error equal to three percentage points with a 95% confidence?

Here, $\alpha = 0.05$, and from Appendix D, we find that $z_{0.025} = 1.96$. The desired margin of error is $E = 0.03$. We do not have an estimate of the proportion in favor at this time, so we will use the most conservative value of $\hat{p} = 0.50$. Using this value for the estimated proportion will maximize the estimate of n.

$$n = \left(\frac{Z_{\alpha/2}}{E} \right)^2 \hat{p}(1 - \hat{p})$$

$$n = \left(\frac{1.96}{0.03} \right)^2 0.50(1 - 0.50)$$

$$n = 1067.11$$

$$\lceil n = 1068$$

To achieve a margin of error of +/–3 percentage points, the polling firm will need to randomly sample 1068 respondents for the survey.

Sample Size to Detect a Difference with a Specified Probability

Table 21.19 presents sample size formulas for detecting a difference δ for hypothesis tests on population means and proportions.

EXAMPLE 21.27

A Six Sigma Black Belt plans a test at the 95% confidence level to determine whether a new drilling station has resulted in a change in the mean diameter of a metal flange. How many samples should be randomly collected to be able to detect a change of 1 mm in the mean diameter with a probability of 90%? The standard deviation of the diameters is known and equal to 1.7 mm, and the chosen α is equal to 0.05.

Here, α = 0.05, and from Appendix D, we find that $z_{\alpha/2} = z_{0.025} = 1.96$ and $z_\beta = z_{0.10} = 1.28$. (Note that even for a two-sided test, the β error is never split.) The desired detectable change is $\delta = 1$. Substituting the values into the equation in Table 21.19 we have:

$$n = \frac{\left(z_{\alpha/2} + z_\beta\right)^2 \sigma^2}{\delta^2}$$

$$n = \frac{(1.96 + 1.28)^2 1.7^2}{1^2}$$

$$n = 30.34$$

$$\lceil n = 31$$

Using computer software, we can also generate a power curve that gives the probability of detection at a = 0.05 and n = 31 for various differences in the mean, shown in Figure 21.8. From this curve, we can see that the sample size equal to 31 achieves the required power for a one-millimeter change in the mean. If the change were 0.5 mm, the probability of detection with this sample size is approximately 0.37.

Continued

Population parameter	Purpose	Sample size formula for two-sided hypothesis	Sample size formula for one-sided hypothesis
Population mean, μ	Detecting a difference of δ with a probability (1 – β)	$n = \frac{(z_{\alpha/2} + z_\beta)^2 \sigma^2}{\delta^2}$	$n = \frac{(z_\alpha + z_\beta)^2 \sigma^2}{\delta^2}$
Difference between two population means, **μ₁ – μ₂**	Detecting a difference of δ with a probability (1 – β).	$n = n_1 = n_2 = \frac{(z_{\alpha/2} + z_\beta)^2 (\sigma_1^2 + \sigma_2^2)}{\delta^2}$	$n = n_1 = n_2 = \frac{(z_\alpha + z_\beta)^2 (\sigma_1^2 + \sigma_2^2)}{\delta^2}$
Population proportion, p	Detecting a difference of δ with a probability (1 – β).	$n = \left(\frac{z_{\alpha/2}\sqrt{\hat{p}_0(1-\hat{p}_0)} + z_\beta\sqrt{\hat{p}(1-\hat{p})}}{\delta} \right)^2$	$n = \left(\frac{z_\alpha\sqrt{\hat{p}_0(1-\hat{p}_0)} + z_\beta\sqrt{\hat{p}(1-\hat{p})}}{\delta} \right)^2$
Difference in population proportions, p1 – p2	Detecting a difference of δ with a probability (1 – β).	$n = \left(\frac{z_{\alpha/2}\sqrt{(p_1 + p_2)(q_1 + q_2)/2} + z_\beta\sqrt{p_1 q_1 + p_2 q_2}}{\delta} \right)^2$ *where* $q_1 = (1 - p_1),\ q_2 = (1 - p_2)$	$n = \left(\frac{z_\alpha\sqrt{(p_1 + p_2)(q_1 + q_2)/2} + z_\beta\sqrt{p_1 q_1 + p_2 q_2}}{\delta} \right)^2$ *where* $q_1 = (1 - p_1),\ q_2 = (1 - p_2)$

Table 21.19 Sample size calculations for detecting a difference with a specified probability.

Continued

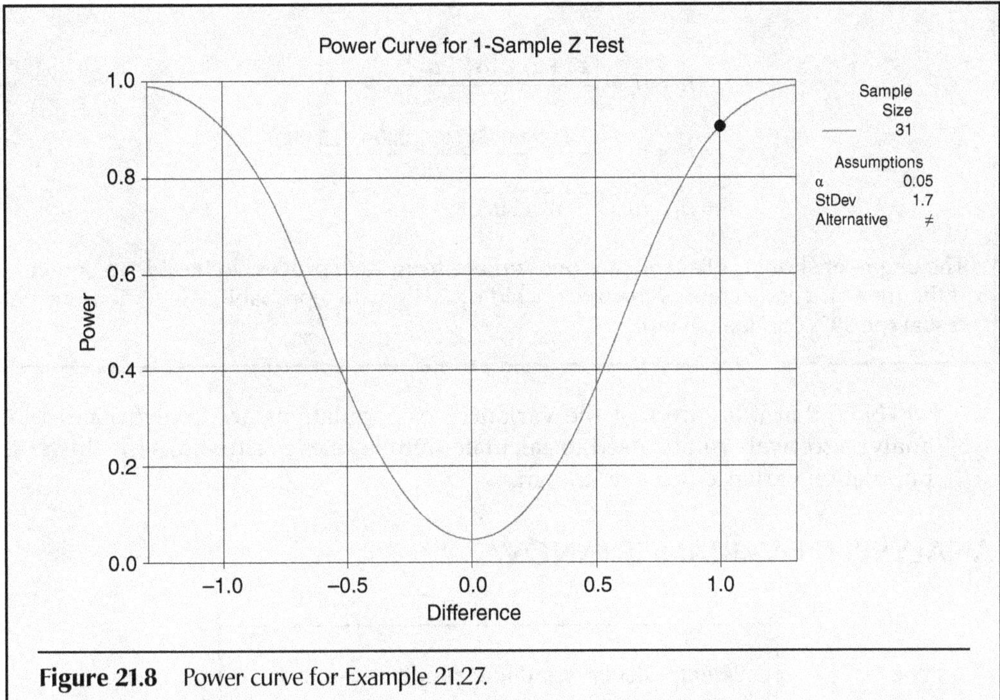

Figure 21.8 Power curve for Example 21.27.

EXAMPLE 21.28

A chemical engineer is studying the yields of an existing process and a newly designed process that produce the same product. They plan to conduct a test on the difference between means at the 99% confidence level. They would like to be able to detect whether the newly designed process increases the mean yield by at least 275 grams with a probability of 95%. What sample sizes should be used to collect yield data from the existing process (μ_1) and the new process (μ_2)? The variance of the new process is equal to 110,000 g and the variance of the existing process is 125,000 g.

Here we have a one-sided test on the difference between means. We are trying to show that the new process mean yield is at least 275 g larger than the existing process mean. The corresponding hypotheses can be written as:

$$H_0 : \mu_2 - \mu_1 \leq 275$$
$$H_1 : \mu_2 - \mu_1 > 275$$

Here, we have $\alpha = 0.01$, and from Appendix D, we find that $z_\alpha = z_{0.01} = 2.33$ and $z_\beta = z_{0.05} = 1.645$. The desired detectable change is $\delta = 275$. Substituting in the values from the equation in Table 21.18, we have:

Continued

Continued

$$n = n_1 = n_2 = \frac{(z_\alpha + z_\beta)^2(\sigma_1^2 + \sigma_2^2)}{\delta^2}$$

$$= n_1 = n_2 = \frac{(2.33 + 1.645)^2(110{,}000 + 125{,}000)}{275^2}$$

$$= n_1 = n_2 = \lceil 49.10 \rceil = 50$$

The engineer should collect 50 random samples from each process to be able to detect if the new process increases the mean yield by 275 g with a probability of 95% using a test at the 99% confidence level.

Note that it is rare that the variances of populations are known. Statistical analysis software can be used to calculate sample sizes in situations in which the population variances are not known.

ANALYSIS OF VARIANCE (ANOVA)

Select, calculate, and interpret the results of ANOVAs. (Evaluate)

Body of Knowledge VI.B.6

The ANOVA procedures extend the hypothesis tests for means discussed in the previous section to a test of means of more than two populations.

One-Way ANOVA

If we were testing the equality of three population means, we might be tempted to conduct a series of Student's t tests on each pair of means. For example, if we want to test the equality of μ_1, μ_2, and μ_3, we could set up ${}_3C_2 = 3$ sets of hypotheses:

$$H_0 : \mu_1 = \mu_2$$
$$H_1 : \mu_1 \neq \mu_2$$

$$H_0 : \mu_1 = \mu_3$$
$$H_1 : \mu_1 \neq \mu_3$$

$$H_0 : \mu_2 = \mu_3$$
$$H_1 : \mu_2 \neq \mu_3$$

If each test were conducted at an alpha level of 0.05, then the probability of the conclusions for all three hypotheses being correct simultaneously would be $(0.95)^3 = 0.86$. If we extend the example out to five means, in which ${}_5C_2 = 10$ Student's t tests would need to be conducted, the resulting overall confidence level would be a disheartening $(0.95)^{10} = 0.60$. This reduction of confidence due to sequential tests is often called the "expanding alpha" problem.

R.A. Fisher addressed the problem of multiple sequential tests by developing the analysis of variance, or ANOVA procedure that allows us to test the equality of the means of three or more groups.

In a one-way ANOVA we have one factor that has k > 2 levels. These levels are also called treatments. The terminology of treatments is a nod to the technique's agricultural origins in which yields from several fertilizer treatments were compared. Using ANOVA, we can compare the average costs for five different suppliers; the average lengths of metal flanges made on four production lines; or the average number of clicks from three different versions of a web ad.

The hypotheses for one-way ANOVA are

$$\begin{aligned} &H_0 : \mu_1 = \mu_2 = \cdots = \mu_k \\ &H_1 : \text{At least one mean not equal} \end{aligned}$$

It should be noted that although this set of hypotheses is written in terms of the means, the F test statistic used for ANOVA compares the equality of variances. We calculate the variability within each of the k groups (the noise) and compare this to the variability between the k group means (the signal). If the variability between group means is sufficiently large compared to the random variability within each group, we reject H_0 and state that at least one mean is different from the rest.

Figure 21.9 illustrates the idea of partitioning the total variation in the data into the variation due to the treatments and variation due to the experimental error (that is, within-treatment variation). We see that the points within each group represent the "within" variation, or noise, and the differences in the three group means (shown connected by a line) represent the "between" variation, or the signal.

The one-way analysis of variance involves calculating the element of a source table, shown in Table 21.20. The first column lists the sources of variation: between treatments (signal), within treatments (noise, or error), and the total. The second column includes the corresponding sum of squares of the variation, calculated using the formulas:

$$\begin{aligned} SS_T &= \sum_{i=1}^{k}\sum_{j=1}^{n_i}\left(y_{ij} - \frac{y_{\bullet\bullet}}{N}\right)^2 = \sum_{i=1}^{k}\sum_{j=1}^{n_i} y_{ij}^2 - \frac{y_{\bullet\bullet}^2}{N} \\ SS_B &= \sum_{i=1}^{k}\frac{y_{i\bullet}^2}{n_i} - \frac{y_{\bullet\bullet}^2}{N} \\ SS_E &= SS_T - SS_B \end{aligned}$$

where

SS_T is the total sum of squares

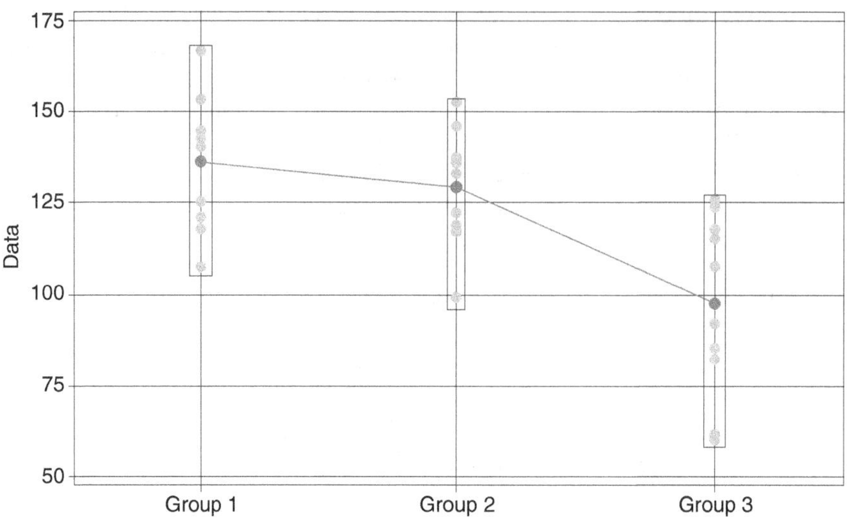

Figure 21.9 Between variation versus within variation for ANOVA.

SS_B is the sum of squares between treatments

SS_E is the sum of squares of the error, or within treatment

i is the index for the treatments, $i = 1, \ldots, k$

j is the index for the data values in each of the k treatments, $j = 1, \ldots, n_k$

y_{ij} is the jth measurement of the ith treatment

$y_{\circ\circ}$ is the sum of all measurements in the data set

$y_{i\circ}$ is the sum of the measurements of the ith treatment

n_i is the number of data points in the ith treatment

N is the total sample size:

$$N = \sum_{i=1}^{k} n_i$$

The third column displays the degrees of freedom for each source of variation.

The fourth column presents the mean squares, or variance, between treatments and the error.

These values are calculated by dividing the sums of squares by the respective degrees of freedom:

Source of variation	Sum of squares	Degrees of freedom	Mean squares	F-statistic
Between treatments	SS_B	$k-1$	$MS_B = \frac{SS_B}{k-1}$	$F_0 = \frac{MS_B}{MS_E}$
Within treatments (error)	SS_E	$N-k$	$MS_E = \frac{SS_E}{N-k}$	
Total	SS_T	$N-1$		

Table 21.20 Example of one-way ANOVA source table.

$$MS_B = \frac{SS_B}{k-1}$$

$$MS_E = \frac{SS_E}{N-k}$$

The last column is the test statistic for the F distribution where

$$F_0 = \frac{MS_B}{MS_E}$$

The value of this test statistic is compared to the critical value $F_{\alpha, k-1, N-k}$. We will reject the hypothesis if $F_0 > F_{\alpha,k-1,N-k}$ and conclude that at least one mean is different from the rest.

The underlying assumptions of ANOVA are that the data are independent, that each group is normally distributed, and that each group has an equal variance. Alternatively, these assumptions can be stated in terms of the residuals, or errors: The errors are independent, identically normally distributed with mean zero and constant variance σ^2.

EXAMPLE 21.29

A study is conducted to measure the mean moisture content of an industrial additive processed at three different temperatures: 180°F, 200°F, and 220°F. Four batches of additives were processed at each temperature, and the moisture content of each batch was measured. Use the data in Table 21.21 to determine whether temperature significantly affects moisture content. Use a 95% confidence level.

Continued

Moisture Content by Temperature		
180°F	**200°F**	**220°F**
10.8	11.4	14.3
10.4	11.9	12.6
11.2	11.6	13.0
9.9	12.0	14.2

Table 21.21 Moisture content by temperature for Example 21.29.

Step 1. *State the null hypothesis and the alternative hypothesis.*

$$H_0: \mu_1 = \mu_2 = \mu_3$$
$$H_1: \text{At least one mean not equal}$$

Step 2. *Assign an appropriate value to the level of significance.*

$$\alpha = 0.05$$

Step 3. *Determine the probability distribution of the appropriate test statistic.*

Since we are testing more than two population variances, we will using one-way ANOVA and the F distribution for the test.

Step 4. *Calculate the test statistic.*

Here we will calculate all the elements of the ANOVA table.

We have $k = 3$, $n_1 = n_2 = n_3 = 4$.

The sum of all the data:

$$y_{\infty} = \sum_{i=1}^{3}\sum_{j=1}^{4} y_{ij} = 143.3$$

The sum of the squares of all data values:

$$\sum_{i=1}^{k}\sum_{j=1}^{n_i} y_{ij}^2 = 10.8^2 + 10.4^2 + \cdots + 14.2^2 = 1732.27$$

The sum of moisture content readings at each temperature setting:

$$y_{1\bullet} = \sum_{j=1}^{4} y_{1j} = 42.3$$

$$y_{2\bullet} = \sum_{j=1}^{4} y_{2j} = 46.9$$

$$y_{3\bullet} = \sum_{j=1}^{4} y_{3j} = 54.1$$

Continued

Calculating sums of squares:

$$SS_T = \sum_{i=1}^{k}\sum_{j=1}^{n_i} y_{ij}^2 - \frac{y_{\bullet\bullet}^2}{N} = 1732.27 - \frac{143.3^2}{12} = 21.03$$

$$SS_B = \sum_{i=1}^{k} \frac{y_{i\bullet}^2}{n_i} - \frac{y_{\bullet\bullet}^2}{N} = \frac{(42.3^2 + 46.9^2 + 54.1^2)}{4} - \frac{143.3^2}{12} = 17.69$$

$$SS_E = SS_T - SS_B = 21.03 - 17.69 = 3.34$$

A time-saving tip for calcuting SST by hand is to recognize that SST is equal to (N – 1) times the sample variance of the data set:

$$SS_T = (N-1)s^2 = 11(1.912) = 21.03$$

The degrees of freedom for between treatments are (k – 1) = 2 and the total degrees of freedom are (N – 1) = 11. We get the degrees of freedom for the error by subtraction, (11 – 2) = 9.

We now calculate the mean squares for between treatments and the error:

$$MS_B = \frac{SS_B}{k-1} = \frac{17.69}{2} = 8.85$$

$$MS_E = \frac{SS_E}{N-k} = \frac{3.34}{9} = 0.37$$

Finally, the test statistic F_0 can be calculated:

$$F_0 = \frac{MS_B}{MS_E} = \frac{8.85}{0.37} = 23.92$$

We now have enough information to fill in all the cells in the source table, shown in Table 21.22:

Source of variation	Sum of Squares	Degrees of Freedom	Mean Square	F_0
Between treatments	17.69	2	8.85	23.92
Within treatments (Error)	3.34	9	0.37	
Total	21.03	11		

Table 21.22 ANOVA source table for Example 21.29.

Step 5. *Determine the rejection region(s) and locate the critical point(s) and compare these to the calculated test statistic. Alternatively, calculate the* p-value *for the test and compare it to alpha.*

From Appendix G.3 we find $F_{0.05,2,9} = 4.26$. The rejection criterion for this test is:

Continued

$$\text{Reject } H_0 \text{ if } F_0 > F_{\alpha,k-1,N-k}.$$

Since 23.92 > 4.26, we reject H_0. At least one treatment mean is different from the rest.

Step 6. *State the statistical conclusion in business terms.*
Since we reject H_0, we conclude that there is a significant effect between temperature and moisture content, and that at least one of the moisture content means is different from the others.

Alternatively, we can use the *p*-value method to be able to give a more precise statement. Statistical software calculates p = 0.0003 for this test. Since this value is less than our chosen $\alpha = 0.05$, we reject H_0.

We can easily check the validity of the ANOVA assumptions using statistical software. Recall that assumptions are that errors are independent, identically normally distributed with mean zero and constant variance σ^2. The normal probability plot and Anderson-Darling test in Figure 21.10 does not show a significant departure from normality, and the residual plot in Figure 21.11 does not show any outliers or unequal variances across temperature settings. To check independence, we would plot the residuals in observation order to determine if there were any patterns, or autocorrelation.

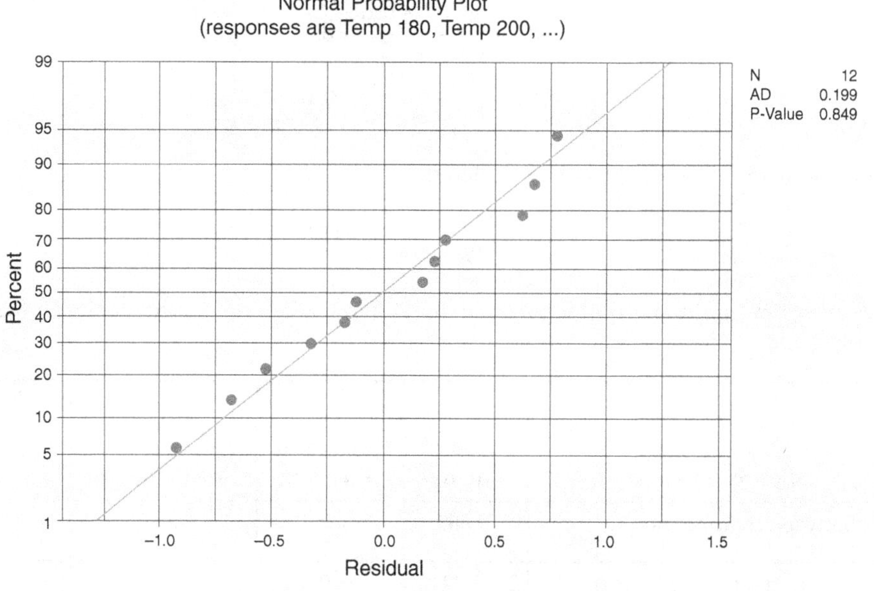

Figure 21.10 Normal probability plot and Anderson-Darling test for Example 21.29.

Continued

Continued

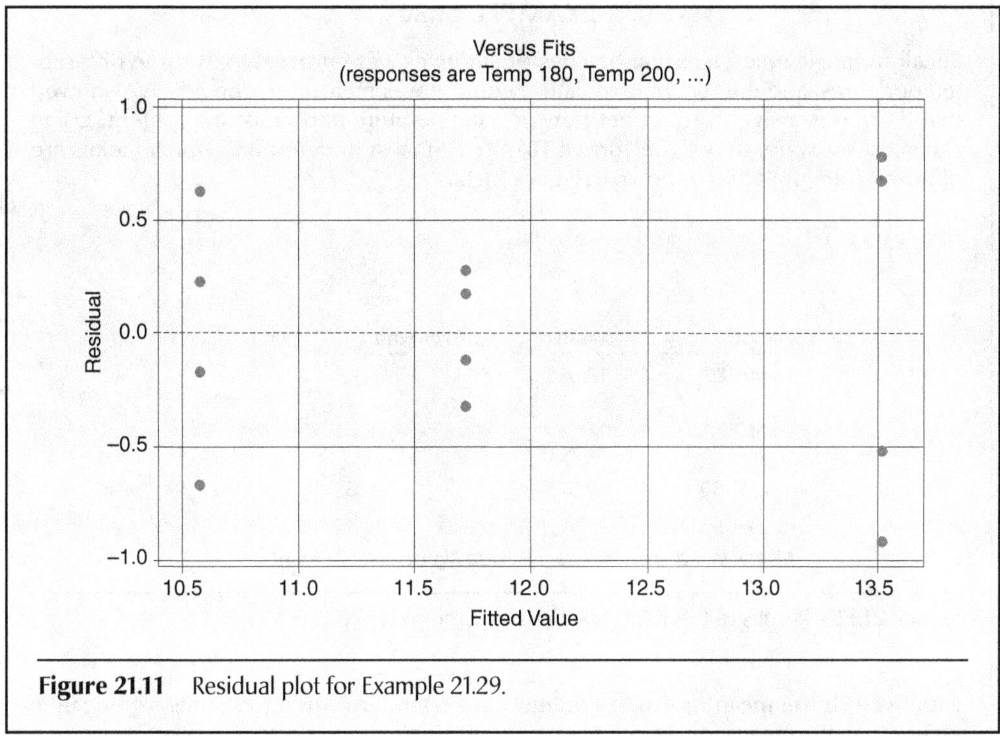

Figure 21.11 Residual plot for Example 21.29.

Tests After ANOVA

Of course, if a Black Belt were to state in a meeting that they were 95% confident that at least one treatment mean were different from the rest, the logical follow-up question would be, "Which means are different from which?" Alas, the analysis of variance does not tell us which means are different, only that at least one of them is.

If we reject the ANOVA hypothesis, we must then do a *test after ANOVA,* also called a *post-hoc test,* to determine which means are significantly different from each other. Here, we are presented with the same problem of "expanding alphas" when doing multiple hypothesis tests. Several specialized tests have been developed that allow us to determine which means are different from the rest, contingent upon rejecting the ANOVA null hypothesis. Each of these tests uses a different method to control the overall, or family, error rate. One of the most popular tests after ANOVA is Tukey's *Honest Significant Difference* (HSD) test. Although the test statistics can be calculated by hand, in practice, these tests are conducted using statistical software.

EXAMPLE 21.30

Recall from Example 21.29 that batches of additives were processed at three different temperatures, and the resulting moisture content was measured. The ANOVA showed that there was a significant effect between temperature and moisture content. Using statistical software, we will perform a Tukey's HSD test to determine which means are different from the others, shown in Figure 21.12.

Tukey Pairwise Comparisons
Grouping Information Using the Tukey Method and 95% Confidence

Factor	N	Mean	Grouping	
Temp 220	4	13.525	A	
Temp 200	4	11.725		B
Temp 180	4	10.575		B

Means that do not share a letter are significantly different.

Figure 21.12 Results of the Tukey HSD test for Example 21.30.

Here we see the mean moisture content at temperature setting 220°F is significantly higher than the means for the other settings. If the aim is to minimize moisture content, we could choose to run the process at either 180°F or 200°F degrees since there is no significant difference in means for these two settings. It is likely that we would choose the lower temperature to save energy costs.

Two-Way ANOVA

In *two-way ANOVA*, we are interested in investigating two factors, A and B, each set at a and b levels, respectively. For example, a Black Belt may run a full-factorial experiment to study the seal strength of packages produced at three temperature levels and two levels of pressure. Here, A = Temperature, $a = 3$, B = Pressure, and $b = 2$. Using two-way ANOVA, she can determine which factors significantly affect the seal strength. Two-way ANOVA would also allow her to detect an interaction effect of the experimental factors.

Table 21.23 shows the structure of a two-way ANOVA table with two factors A and B each set at a and b levels, respectively. The structure of the table is similar to the one-way ANOVA table. The F-statistics in the last column are compared with the critical values from the F table to determine whether there is a statistically significant effect due to factor A, factor B, or the interaction between them.

Although the formulas for the sum of squares values are similar to those for one-way ANOVA, the equations for the two-way ANOVA are not provided. The additional factors make computation tedious, and as a result, most two-way ANOVA tables are computed using readily available statistical software. The

Source of variation	Sum of squares	Degrees of freedom	Mean squares	*F*-statistic
Factor A	SS_A	$a-1$	$MS_A = \dfrac{SS_A}{a-1}$	$F_0 = \dfrac{MS_A}{MS_E}$
Factor B	SS_B	$b-1$	$MS_B = \dfrac{SS_B}{b-1}$	$F_0 = \dfrac{MS_B}{MS_E}$
Interaction of factors A and B	SS_{AB}	$(a-1)(b-1)$	$MS_{AB} = \dfrac{SS_{AB}}{(a-1)(b-1)}$	$F_0 = \dfrac{MS_{AB}}{MS_E}$
Error	SS_E	$(N-ab)$	$MS_E = \dfrac{SS_E}{N-ab}$	
Total	SS_T	$N-1$		

Table 21.23 Example of a two-way ANOVA source table.

analysis and interpretation of two-way ANOVA is explained in more detail in Chapter 24.

The concepts behind two-way ANOVA can be extended to include any number of factors and their interactions. We can refer to this type of analysis as N-way ANOVA.

GOODNESS OF FIT (CHI-SQUARE) TEST

> Define, select, and interpret the results of these tests. (Evaluate)
>
> **Body of Knowledge VI.B.7**

We can use the chi-square Goodness of Fit test to determine whether our observed data follows a reference distribution. This test can be used to determine if our data follows a specific named distribution, such as a Poisson or normal, or it can be used to determine if data follows a historical pattern. For example, the chi-square Goodness of Fit test can be used to determine if the sales mix of products has changed from last year; if the proportions of customers from various regions has changed over the past quarter; or if the actual production mix differs from the planned production schedule.

The hypotheses for the χ^2 Goodness of Fit test take on the form:

H_0: The data follow a specified distribution

H_1: The data do not follow a specified distribution

For this type of study, a data set of size n is arranged into a frequency table of *k* class intervals. Then these observed frequencies are compared to the frequencies expected if the null hypothesis were true. A chi-squared statistic is calculated, and if the observed values vary significantly from what is expected, we will conclude that the observed data does not follow the distribution assumed under the null hypothesis.

The chi-square test statistic is calculated as:

$$\chi_0^2 = \sum_{i=1}^{k} \frac{(O_i - E_i)^2}{E_i}$$

This test statistic approximately follows a chi-square distribution with $(k - p - 1)$ degrees of freedom in which k is the number of categories in the frequency table and p is the number of parameters of the hypothesized distribution that are estimated. The approximation improves as the sample size n increases. The chi-square test will be valid if the observations are independent and no more than 20% of the expected counts are less than five. If this last assumption does not hold, categories can be combined to meet this requirement.

If $\chi_0^2 > \chi_{\alpha,k-p-1}^2$ then we reject H_0 and conclude the observed distribution does not follow the distribution in the null hypothesis.

EXAMPLE 21.31

Table 21.24 provides historical data for IT helpline requests. Percentages of each request type have been computed from the previous year's data. Additionally, the total number of calls last month have been categorized by request type. Is the distribution of last month's calls the same as last year's distribution? Use $\alpha = 0.05$.

IT Helpline request type	Last year's percentage of requests	Observed number of calls last month
File recovery	16%	40
Log-in issue	28%	35
Slow Internet	42%	80
Printer issue	14%	28
Total	**100%**	**183**

Table 21.24 IT Helpline request data for Example 21.31.

Step 1. *State the null hypothesis and the alternative hypothesis.*

H_0: The data follow last year's distribution

H_1: The data do not follow last year's distribution

Alternatively, we could state

Continued

H_0: The distribution of request types has not changed

H_1: The distribution of request types has changed

Step 2. *Assign an appropriate value to the level of significance.*

$$\alpha = 0.05$$

Step 3. *Determine the probability distribution of the appropriate test statistic.*
We determine that the appropriate test is a chi-square Goodness of Fit test.

Step 4. *Calculate the test statistic.*
We can calculate the expected number of calls last month using the last year's percentage. There are k = 4 request types. Because the reference distribution is fully specified, p = 0. Here, we take the total number of observed calls for the month and multiply it by last year's percentage for each category. Once these expected values are calculated, we calculate the chi-square component for each request type and sum the values to find the chi-square test statistics. These calculations are shown in Table 21.25.

IT Helpline request type	Observed number of calls last month	Last year's percentage of requests	Expected number of calls last month	Chi-square = $(O-E)^2/E$
File recovery	40	16%	183 × 0.16 = 29.28	$\frac{(O_1-E_1)^2}{E_1} = \frac{(40-29.28)^2}{29.28} = 3.925$
Log-in issue	35	28%	183 × 0.28 = 51.24	$\frac{(O_2-E_2)^2}{E_2} = \frac{(35-51.24)^2}{51.24} = 5.147$
Slow Internet	80	42%	183 × 0.42 = 76.86	$\frac{(O_3-E_3)^2}{E_3} = \frac{(80-76.86)^2}{76.86} = 0.128$
Printer issue	28	14%	183 × 0.14 = 25.62	$\frac{(O_4-E_4)^2}{E_4} = \frac{(28-25.62)^2}{25.62} = 0.221$
Total	**183**	100%	183	$\chi_0^2 = 9.421$

Table 21.25 Observed and expected numbers of calls per month and chi-square contribution.

Step 5. *Determine the rejection region(s) and locate the critical point(s) and compare these to the calculated test statistic. Alternatively, calculate the* p*-value for the test and compare it to alpha.*

The degrees of freedom for the critical value are equal to $k - p - 1 = (4-0-1) = 3$. From Appendix F, we find the critical value $\chi^2_{0.05,3} = 7.815$. The rejection criterion for this test is:

$$\text{Reject } H_0 \text{ if } \chi_0^2 > \chi^2_{\alpha,k-p-1}$$

Continued

Step 6. *State the statistical conclusion in business terms.*

Since the test statistic $\chi_0^2 = 9.421$ is greater than the critical value $\chi_{0.05,3}^2 = 7.815$, we reject H_0. The distribution of the IT helpline requests last month do not follow the historical distribution.

Alternatively, we can use the *p*-value method to be able to give a more precise statement. Statistical software calculates $p = 0.024$ for this test. Since this value is smaller than our chosen α of 0.05, we reject H_0.

Some additional analysis can give us more insight into what is driving the change in the call types. Figure 21.13 shows the differences between the expected and observed call counts for each category. We see that file recovery calls were more frequent than expected, and log-in issues were less frequent. Figure 21.14 is a Pareto chart of contributions to the chi-square test statistic. We see that the changes in log-in issues and file recovery were the top contributing categories to the change in the call mix.

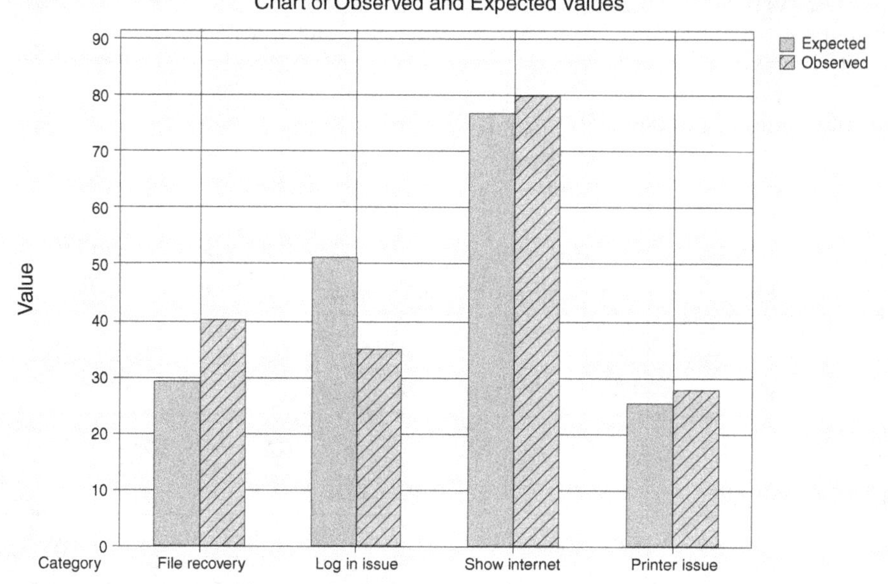

Figure 21.13 Expected versus observed requests for Example 21.31.

Continued

Continued

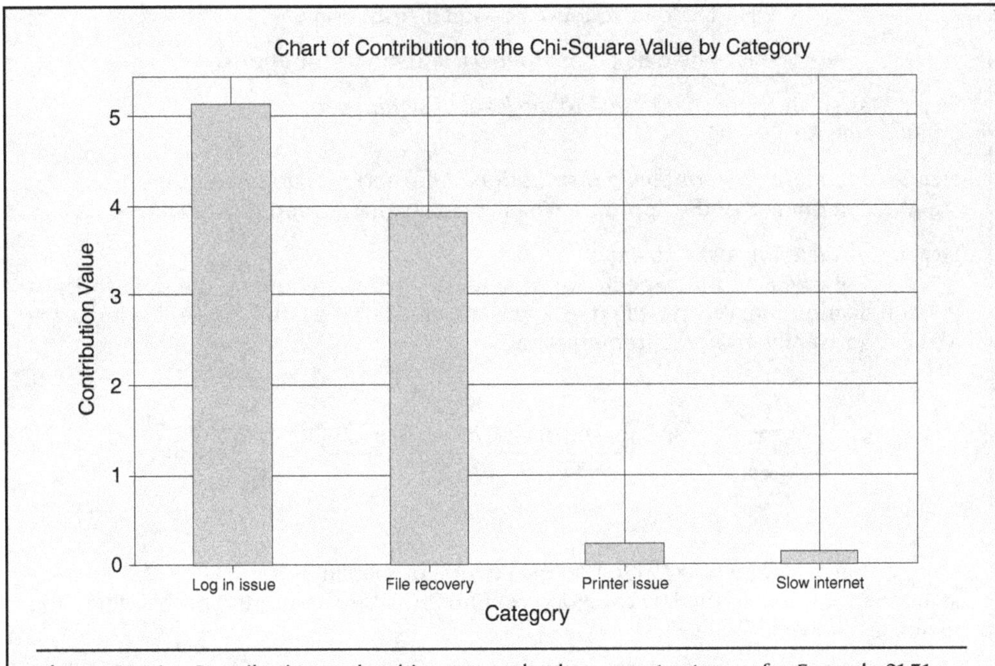

Figure 21.14 Contribution to the chi-square value by request category for Example 21.31.

EXAMPLE 21.32

An inspection process counts the number of surface defects on stainless steel panels each day. A Six Sigma professional has tabulated the defect data from 100 samples, as shown in Table 21.26, and wants to test whether the defect counts follow a Poisson distribution at the $\alpha = 0.05$ significance level.

Number of surface defects (X)	Frequency (f)
0	33
1	29
2	20
3	11
4	7

Table 21.26 Frequency table for surface defects for Example 21.32.

Step 1. *State the null hypothesis and the alternative hypothesis.*

Continued

H_0: The data follow a Poisson distribution

H_1: The data do not follow a Poisson distribution

Step 2. *Assign an appropriate value to the level of significance.*
We will use α = 0.05.

Step 3. *Determine the probability distribution of the appropriate test statistic.*
We determine that the appropriate test is a chi-square Goodness of Fit test.

Step 4. *Calculate the test statistic.*
We will calculate the expected frequency of defects, assuming the data follow a Poisson distribution. We must first estimate the mean of the Poisson distribution using a weighted average from the frequency table.

$$\bar{X} = \frac{\sum_{i=1}^{k} x_i f_i}{\sum_{i=1}^{k} f_i} = \frac{(0)(33)+(1)(29)+(2)(20)+(3)(11)+(4)(7)}{33+29+20+11+7} = \frac{130}{100} = 1.30$$

Next, we can use Appendix C.1 to find the Poisson probabilities for X = {0, 1, 2, 3} defects assuming μ = 1.16. For the last category, we find Pr(X≥4) to assure the probabilities add to one, as shown in Table 21.27.

Number of defects	Observed frequency of defects	Poisson Pr(X = x) With μ = 1.3	Expected frequency of defects (np)
0	33	Pr(X = 0) = 0.2725	100 × 0.2725 = 27.25
1	29	Pr(X = 1) = 0.3543	35.43
2	20	Pr(X = 2) = 0.2303	23.03
3	11	Pr(X = 3) = 0.0998	9.98
≥4	7	$\Pr(X \geq 4) = 1 - \Pr(X \leq 3) = 1 - 0.9569 = 0.0431$	4.31
Total	100	1.0	100

Table 21.27 Expected value calculations for Example 21.32.

Of the five defect categories, one has an expected frequency less than five. This is in line with the requirement that no more than 20% of the expected values can be less than five, so we can proceed with the chi-square calculations, shown in Table 21.28.

Continued

Number of defects (x)	Observed frequency	Expected frequency	Chi-square = (O–E)²/E
0	33	27.25	$\frac{(O_1-E_1)^2}{E_1}=\frac{(33-27.25)^2}{27.25}=1.212$
1	29	35.43	$\frac{(O_2-E_2)^2}{E_2}=\frac{(29-35.43)^2}{35.43}=1.167$
2	20	23.03	$\frac{(O_3-E_3)^2}{E_3}=\frac{(20-23.03)^2}{23.03}=0.398$
3	11	9.98	$\frac{(O_4-E_4)^2}{E_4}=\frac{(11-9.98)^2}{9.98}=0.104$
≥4	7	4.31	$\frac{(O_5-E_5)^2}{E_5}=\frac{(7-4.31)^2}{4.31}=1.680$
Total	100	100	$\chi_0^2=4.561$

Table 21.28 Chi-square calculations for Example 21.32.

Step 5. *Determine the rejection region(s) and locate the critical point(s) and compare these to the calculated test statistic. Alternatively, calculate the* p*-value for the test and compare it to alpha.*

There are k = 5 defect categories, and we estimated the Poisson parameter μ, so p = 1. The degrees of freedom for the chi-square critical value are then $k-p-1=3$. From Appendix F, we find the critical value $\chi^2_{0.05,3}=7.81$. The rejection criterion for this test is:

$$\text{Reject } H_0 \text{ if } \chi_0^2 > \chi^2_{\alpha,k-p-1}$$

Step 6. *State the statistical conclusion in business terms.*

Since the test statistic $\chi_0^2=4.561$ is less than the critical value $\chi^2_{0.05,3}=7.815$, we fail to reject H_0. The assumption that the defect counts follow a Poisson distribution is not disputed by the data.

Alternatively, we can use the *p*-value method to be able to give a more precise statement. Statistical software calculates p = 0.207 for this test. Since this value is greater than our chosen α of 0.05, we fail to reject H_0. This is shown in the computer output in Figure 21.15.

Continued

Continued

Poisson Goodness of Fit Test: Defect Count

Descriptive Statistics

N	Mean
100	1.3

Observed and Expected Counts for Defect Count

Defect Count	Poisson Probability	Observed Count	Expected Count	Contribution to Chi-Square
0	0.272532	33	27.2532	1.21182
1	0.354291	29	35.4291	1.16666
2	0.230289	20	23.0289	0.39839
3	0.099792	11	9.9792	0.10442
>=4	0.043095	7	4.3095	1.67965

1 (20.00%) of the expected counts are less than 5.

Chi-Square Test

Null hypothesis	H_0: Data follow a Poisson distribution
Alternative hypothesis	H_1: Data do not follow a Poisson distribution

DF	Chi-Square	P-Value
3	4.56094	0.207

Figure 21.15 Computer output for Example 21.32.

CHI-SQUARE TEST OF ASSOCIATION

The chi-square test of association is not included in the current Body of Knowledge, but we will mention it briefly here for completeness. For this test scenario, we have two categorical variables with r and c levels, respectively. We construct a contingency table that lists the levels of the first variable in rows, and the second in columns. The interior of the table contains the counts for each resulting cell. We test whether the two variables have an association. The hypotheses for this test are:

H_0: Variables are independent

H_1: Variables are dependent (associated)

We illustrate this test with a short example.

EXAMPLE 21.33

A training company offers courses in Leadership and Quality Principles. The marketing department would like to determine whether one course is more attractive to participants based on their undergraduate majors. Enrollment data by course and participants' undergraduate major were summarized using a contingency table with two rows and four columns, as shown in Table 21.29.

	Undergraduate Major				
Training Course	**Business**	**Liberal Arts**	**Engineeering**	**Other**	**Total**
Leadership	39	45	17	12	113
Quality Principles	12	15	17	9	53
Total	51	60	34	21	166

Table 21.29 Contingency table for Example 21.33.

The hypotheses for this test of association are:

H_0: Training course and undergraduate major are independent

H_1: Training course and undergraduate major are dependent (associated)

A chi-square test of association was conducted using Minitab. The results are shown in Figure 21.16.

Course	**Business**	**Liberal Arts**	**Engineering**	**Other**	**Total**
Leadership					
Actual Count	39	45	17	12	113
Expected Count	34.72	40.84	23.14	14.30	
Contribution to chi-square	0.5284	0.4230	1.6313	0.3685	
Quality Principles					
ActualCount	12	15	17	9	53
Expected Count	16.28	19.16	10.86	6.70	
Contribution to chi-square	1.1266	0.9019	3.4781	0.7857	
Total	51	60	34	21	166

Chi-Square Test

	Chi-Square	**DF**	**P-Value**
Pearson	9.244	3	0.026
Likelihood Ratio	8.992	3	0.029

Figure 21.16 Expected versus observed requests for Example 21.31.

Here we see that the *p*-value for the chi-square test is equal to 0.026. We will reject H_0 and conclude that there is a significant association between participants' undergraduate majors and the courses they take.

Continued

The Pareto chart of percent contribution to the chi-square value shown in Figure 21.17 reveals that the engineering majors contributed to more than half of the chi-square test statistic. Figure 21.18 gives a fuller picture, showing that fewer engineering majors registered for the Leadership course than expected, and more registered for Quality Principles. In addition, fewer Business and Liberal Arts majors registered for Quality Principles than expected.

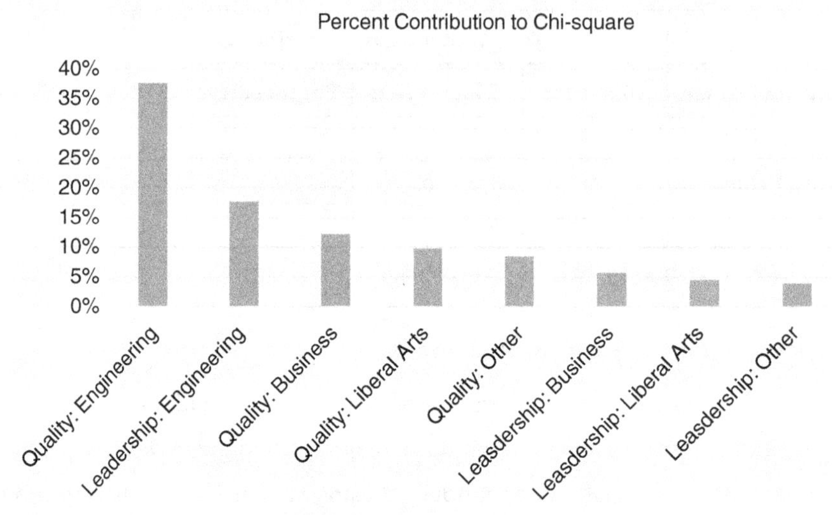

Figure 21.17 Pareto chart of contribution to the chi-square test statistic for Example 21.33.

Continued

Continued

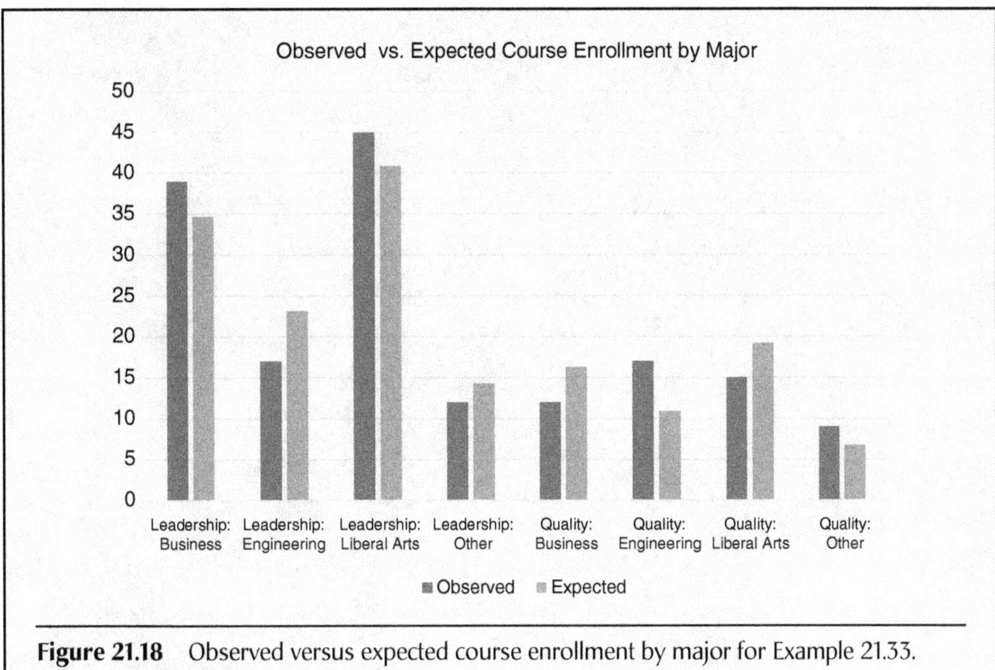

Figure 21.18 Observed versus expected course enrollment by major for Example 21.33.

Chapter 22

Risk Analysis and Management

The first step in the risk management process is to acknowledge the reality of risk. Denial is a common tactic that substitutes deliberate ignorance for thoughtful planning.

—Charles Tremper

TYPES OF RISK

> Identify, assess, and prioritize various types of risk such as enterprise, operational, supplier, security, product, and cybersecurity. (Analyze)
>
> **Body of Knowledge V1.C.1**

ISO 31000:2018 defines risk as "the effect of uncertainty on objectives," focusing on the effect that incomplete knowledge of events or circumstances has on an organization's decision making. It is designed to help organizations:

- Increase the likelihood of achieving objectives
- Encourage proactive management
- Be aware of the need to identify and trace risk throughout the organization
- Improve identification of opportunities and threats
- Comply with relevant legal and regulatory requirements and international norms
- Improve financial reporting
- Improve governance
- Improve stakeholder confidence and trust
- Establish a reliable basis for decision making and planning
- Improve controls

- Effectively allocate and use resources for risk treatment
- Improve operational effectiveness and efficiency
- Enhance health and safety performance, as well as environmental protection
- Improve loss prevention and incident management
- Minimize losses
- Improve organizational learning
- Improve organizational resilience

Risk Management

Risk management is focused on evaluating events that may impact any objective within an organization. A typical risk management process can be thought of as following a DMAIC cycle:

1. *Define.* In this phase risk events are identified.
2. *Measure.* The impact of these risks is assessed in terms of probability of occurrence, and their consequences such as cost, schedule, performance impact, or functionality impact.
3. *Analyze.* Techniques such as FMEA are used to prioritize the risks from most- to least-critical.
4. *Improve.* A risk mitigation plan is created and implemented.
5. *Control.* Success of the mitigation plan is monitored, current risks are reassessed, and new risks identified.

According to Moon (2020), *enterprise risk management* is the coordinated approach for centralized management of risks and their cascade from the strategic mission level.

Operational risk management is the coordination and control of all risky activities of the system at the operational business unit or functional level to successfully achieve the predefined expected operational outputs and objectives.

Product, process, or service-level risk management focuses on managing the day-to-day ground-level risks in terms of the specific end deliverables of the organization to its customers.

ISO 31000:2018 presents 11 principles to consider when creating a risk management plan:

1. *Create and protect value.* The risk management plan should help the organization achieve its objectives by continuous review of processes and systems.
2. *Be integral to the organization's processes.* Risk management needs to be integrated with the governance framework and be a part of the planning process at both the strategic and operational levels.

3. *Be part of decision making.* Risk management should help the organization identify priorities and select the most appropriate actions.
4. *Explicitly address uncertainty.* Risk management helps the organization identify potential problems and perform risk assessments that address uncertainty.
5. *Be systematic, structured, and timely.* The process of managing risk should be consistent across the organization, ensuring reliability and consistency of results.
6. *Be based on the best available information.* All available and relevant information should be considered.
7. *Be tailored.* The risk management plan needs to fit the organization in terms of risk profile, and internal and external operating environments.
8. *Take into account human and cultural factors.* Risk management needs to recognize the contributions that people and culture have made toward achieving objectives.
9. *Be transparent and inclusive.* The organization needs to identify and engage internal and external stakeholders through the planning process to be able to identify, analyze, and monitor risk.
10. *Be dynamic, iterative, and responsive to change.* The risk management process needs to be flexible so that the organization can respond to changing situations and identify new risks.
11. *Facilitates the continual improvement of the organization.* The risk management plan will help the organization demonstrate continual achievement of its objectives.

Identifying Risk

We can state a risk using the syntax:

> Because of <defined cause>, <an uncertain event> may occur, which would lead to <effect on objective>.

There are a number of techniques that can be used to identify risks and their causes. For example, a team may use brainstorming methods, fishbone diagrams, the Delphi method, the SWIFT method, or hazard and operability analysis (HAZOP). A SWOT analysis, presented in Chapter 1, can also be useful in identifying internal weaknesses and outside threats to an organization. In addition, organizations can use fault tree analysis (FTA) or failure mode and effects analysis (FMEA) to identify, analyze, and prioritize risks. FMEA is covered later in this chapter.

A useful framework for brainstorming to identify risks and their causes is the concept of volatility, uncertainty, complexity, and ambiguity (VUCA), first used by the U.S. Army War College. Causes of risk can then be brainstormed using a fishbone diagram. In addition, the team can use the following sources to uncover potential risks (Moon, 2020):

1. Design and development plan/project plan/action plan
2. Specifications and constraints
3. Human resources management plan
4. Cost and schedule documentation
5. Assumptions
6. Stakeholder list
7. Quality management plan
8. Technical documentation
9. Supplier quality and procurement documentation
10. Academic and published studies
11. Quality checklists and forms
12. Standard operating procedures
13. Historical similar activities and their risk management plans

Using the Delphi method, a questionnaire is sent to experts in the field to collect feedback on risk, one at time. After each survey response, the results are anonymized and summarized and sent out to the next expert until a consensus is achieved. This technique can be time consuming, but it allows the experts time to think through the problem. In addition, this method avoids team pitfalls such as groupthink, or having a few dominant personalities steer the conversation.

The structured what-if technique (SWIFT) technique was originally used in the chemical process industry. In a SWIFT exercise, the team brainstorms using guide words to address two major questions:

1. Risk identification by asking *What if?*
2. Cause identification by asking *How could?*

For example, if a healthcare team is brainstorming patient safety risks, the facilitator could use the guide word "dosage," and ask *What if a patient was given the wrong dosage?* to identify risks. The team would then respond to the second question *How could a patient be given the wrong dosage?* to identify causes.

Burke and Silvestrini (2017) present the following on HAZOP:

> Hazard and operability analysis (HAZOP) can be used to identify operability issues and potential hazards that may lead to unacceptable products, processes, or services. The method is based on the assumption that risks occur due to deviations from the intended design or operating plan. The goal of HAZOP is to identify potential risks from these deviations.

Much like the SWIFT technique, HAZOP analysis uses guide words to systematically identify potential deviations from expected design or operating conditions. However, the HAZOP guide words describe deviation conditions, as shown in Table 22.1, whereas SWIFT guide words are nouns. When used as part of a

Guide Word	Meaning	Examples
No (no, none)	None of the design intent is achieved	• Preventive maintenance was not performed • No sterilization process was performed
More (more of, higher)	Quantitative increase in a parameter	• Overconcentration of drug • Infusion pump delivering more dosage than needed
Less (less of, lower)	Quantitative decrease in a parameter	• Customer receiving less product than expected (lower pill count or fill volume) • Drug product under-concentrated
Other than (other)	Complete substitution — another activity takes place	• Product mix-ups • Product sterilized with an incorrect method
Part of	Only some of the design intention is achieved	• Device kit missing one component • No detergent used for cleaning, only water
As well as (more than)	An additional activity occurs	• An additional component was added to the formulation of the batch
Reserve	Logical opposite of the design intention occurs	• Sterile injectable drug with bacterial contamination
Early/late	Timing is different from the intention	• Detergent added too early (prior to pre-rinse of soiled equipment)
Before/after	Step (or part of it) performed out of order	• Components added to the batch in incorrect order

Table 22.1 HAZOP guide words.
Source: Burke and Silvestrini (2017).

cross-functional team, the guide works in a HAZOP analysis can generate ideas as well as discussion of potential risks.

Assessing and Prioritizing Risk

Tools such FMEA, presented later in this chapter, and FTA, found in Chapter 23, are excellent ways to identify, assess, and prioritize risk. A team can also use a *risk matrix* that defines levels of risk based on their probability of occurrence and severity using a qualitative scale. Table 22.2 shows an example of a risk assessment matrix. Events can then be placed in the risk matrix according to their likelihood and impact, as shown in Table 22.3.

	Severity				
Probability	**Negligible**	**Minor**	**Major**	**Critical**	**Catastrophic**
Certain	Medium	High	High	High	High
Likely	Medium	Medium	Medium	High	High
Possible	Low	Medium	Medium	High	High
Unlikely	Low	Low	Medium	High	High
Rare	Low	Low	Medium	Medium	High

Table 22.2 Risk matrix.

	Impact				
Likelihood	**Negligible**	**Minor**	**Major**	**Critical**	**Catastrophic**
Certain					
Likely		Device surface scratched	Device overheats		
Possible				Device gets wet	
Unlikely					Device develops electrical short
Rare					

Table 22.3 Events placed on the risk matrix.

Mitigating Risk

Once a risk is identified, analyzed, and prioritized, an organization can choose one of four actions, known as the 4Ts, to address it:

1. *Tolerate the risk.* For low-priority risks, the organization accepts the risk, allowing it to direct resources to higher priority issues.
2. *Terminate the risk.* This action completely removes the risk by redesigning the product, changing suppliers, or mistake-proofing the system, for example.
3. *Treat the risk.* Actions are taken to reduce the risk based on feasibility and cost.
4. *Transfer the risk.* Here, the organization shifts the risk to a different entity, for example, by outsourcing.

Supplier Risk

Kraljic (1983) suggests that supplier items can be mapped against two dimensions: risk and profit impact. Webb (2017) states that supplier risk can depend upon geographic location, unreliable transportation routes, changing legislation, natural disasters, political upheaval, and the length of the supply chain. By plotting each supplied item on the grid shown in Figure 22.1, an organization can classify the item and take certain actions.

Items that are in the low supply risk and low profitability quadrant are classified as *Non-critical*. There is an abundant supply of these items, and organizations should work to standardize the products and make the ordering process as efficient as possible.

Items that have a low supply risk but a high profitability to the organization also have an abundant supply and are classified as *Leverage* items. The organization should exploit its purchasing power and negotiate for the best price.

Items that have a high supply risk but low profitability are classified as *Bottleneck* items. There is a production-based scarcity to these items, and the organization has low control over the suppliers. Effort should be made to innovate and find substitutes for these items.

Finally, items that are both high supplier risk and high profit impact are classified as *Strategic* items. There is a natural scarcity to these items, with perhaps only

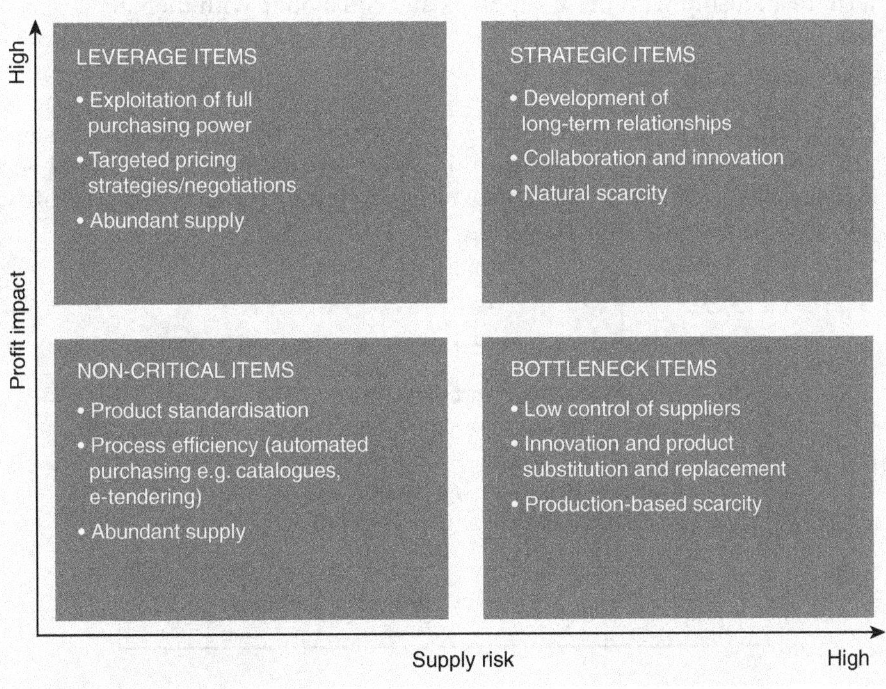

Figure 22.1 Kraljic supplier risk matrix.
Source: Peter Kraljic, HBR, 1993.

Strategy	Identify	Protect	Detect	Respond	Recover
1. Update and upgrade software immediately	x	x			
2. Defend privileges and accounts	x	x			
3. Enforce signed software execution policies		x	x		
4. Exercise a system recovery plan	x			x	x
5. Actively manage systems and configurations	x	x			
6. Continuously hunt for network intrusions	x			x	x
7. Leverage modern hardware security features	x	x			
8. Segregate networks using application-aware defenses		x	x		
9. Integrate threat reputation services		x	x		
10. Transition to multi-factor authentication	x	x			

Table 22.4 Cybersecurity risk mitigation strategies.
Source: U.S. National Security Agency (2018).

a few suppliers who can provide them. An organization should develop a long-term relationship with these suppliers and collaborate with them.

Cybersecurity Risk

Organizations face ever increasing cybersecurity threat through ransomware, phishing, data leakage, hacking, and insider threats. The U.S. National Security Agency (2018) lists ten cybersecurity mitigation strategies that aim to identify, protect, detect, respond, and recover.

THE FMEA TOOL

Describe the purpose and elements of FMEA, including risk priority number (RPN), and evaluate FMEA results for processes, products, and services. Distinguish between design FMEA (DFMEA) and process FMEA (PFMEA) and interpret their results. (Evaluate)

Body of Knowledge VI.C.2

A *failure mode and effects analysis* (FMEA) is a prevention-based risk management tool that focuses the user or team on systematically:

- Identifying and anticipating potential failures
- Identifying potential causes for the failures
- Prioritizing failures
- Taking action to reduce, mitigate, or eliminate failures

The real value of the FMEA is reflected in its use as a long-term living document. It is essential that the document is owned and updated as changes are made to the design or the process.

FMEA was first developed and used by reliability engineers in the 1950s to study malfunctions of military systems and has proven to be a worthy and valuable technique. Subsequently, it has become commonplace in about every Lean Six Sigma practitioner's tool kit. As common as the tool is, however, it is often used incorrectly. Users who invest considerable time and effort in the tool often do not reap all it has to offer.

Types of FMEAs

According to Stamatis (2003), there are four types of FMEAs: system, design, process, and service. A brief overview of each type follows:

1. *System FMEA.* An analysis process used to identify and evaluate the relative risk associated with a system, subsystem, or component usually associated with a particular system hardware design. The focus is on minimizing costs and failure effects on the system while maximizing the system reliability and maintainability.

2. *Design FMEA (DFMEA).* An analysis process used to identify and evaluate the relative risk associated with a particular hardware design. The focus is on minimizing costs and failure effects on the design while maximizing the design reliability and maintainability.

   A specific variation of DFMEA is the *machine failure mode and effects analysis* (MFMEA). This analysis follows a specific hierarchical model that, according to Stamatis (2003), "divides the machine into subsystems, assemblies, and lowest replaceable units." Stamatis provides the following bullet breakdown:

   - System level—generic machine
   - Subsystem level—electrical, mechanical, controls
   - Assembly level—fixtures and tools, material handling, drives
   - Component level

   For a more detailed discussion regarding MFMEAs, see Stamatis (2003).

3. *Process FMEA (PFMEA).* An analysis process used to identify and evaluate the relative risks associated with a particular process design. Keeping the 7 M's (machine, methods, manpower, mother nature, materials, measurement, and management) in mind when conducting

the PFMEA is an excellent way of capturing failures at each process step. The focus is on minimizing process failures and cost while maximizing process performance and productivity.

4. *Service FMEA.* An analysis process used to identify and evaluate the relative risks associated with a particular service. Since "service" is nothing more than a process in a nonmanufacturing environment, using the 7 M's when conducting the service FMEA is an excellent way of capturing failures. The focus of the service FMEA is to minimize process failures and cost while maximizing process performance and productivity. Consequently, it will be conducted like a PFMEA.

Figure 22.2 provides an example of an FMEA document format. All FMEAs are similar—except for the first column.

The first column of the system and design FMEA uses a system, subsystem, product, assembly, sub-assembly, or part. By contrast, the process and service FMEAs use a process. Therefore, the first column contains the process steps. Thus, a process map, cause-and-effect matrix, suppliers, inputs, process, outputs, and customers (SIPOC) diagram, value stream map, cause-and-effect diagram, or something similar usually feeds these types.

The PFMEA Document

Of the primary types of FMEA documents, the Lean Six Sigma practitioner will deal with the PFMEA the most. The PFMEA document's columns include:

May be a product, assembly, subassembly, or part

Initial development of the FMEA									Improvement activities		Post-improvement activities				
Process step/ input	Potential failure mode	Potential failure effects	SEV	Potential causes	OCC	Current controls	DET	RPN	Actions recom-mended	Resp	Actions taken	SEV	OCC	DET	RPN
1	2	3	4	5	6	7	8	9	10	11	12	13			

DET = Detection
OCC = Occurence
PFMEA = Process failure mode and effects analysis
Resp = Responsible
RPN = Risk priority number
SEV = Severity

Figure 22.2 FMEA document general format.

1. *Process step.* Identify the process step and input under investigation. Each step is identified sequentially. If the PFMEA is fed from a cause-and-effect matrix, only high-value steps might be listed.
2. *Potential failure mode.* Identify all the ways a failure can occur at this process step.

Process step/input	Potential failure mode	Potential failure effects	Potential causes	Current controls
n	1	1	1	1
				2
				3
			2	4
				5
				6
		2	3	7
				8
				9
			4	10
				11
				12
	2	3	5	13
				14
				15
			6	16
				17
				18
		4	7	19
				20
				21
			8	22
				23
				24
	3	5	9	25
$n + 1$	4	6	10	26

Table 22.5 Many-to-many relationships between key columns in a PFMEA document.

3. *Potential failure effects.* Identify all the effects each failure mode produces, including the effects on the customer. Use a new line for each failure effect. Table 22.5 demonstrates the many-to-many relationships that exist across the document columns for any given step.

   Stamatis (2003) introduces a column in his general FMEA format document between columns 3 and 4 for the use of "critical characteristics" and denotes it by the inverted delta symbol. This additional column accommodates the needs of the automotive industry. See Stamatis (2003) for details.

4. *Severity.* Quantify the severity of the impact of the failure effect. The scale for severity ranges from "no effect" on the low end to "safety hazard"—up to and including "loss of life without warning"—on the high end. Also, the effect can be expressed in monetary damages, as well as destruction and delays. All scales must be described in the context of the FMEA situation (see Table 22.6).

5. *Potential causes.* Identify all root causes leading to the failure. If root causes are unknown at the time the FMEA is conducted, it may be necessary to divert from the FMEA temporarily and conduct a root cause analysis using the variety of quality tools available.

6. *Occurrence.* Quantify the frequency of occurrence of the failure mode. The scale for occurrence ranges from "highly unlikely" on the low end to "highly likely" on the high end. Some users, teams, and organizations will go to great lengths to provide absolute definitions for the frequency of occurrence. For example, the Automotive Industry Action Group (1995b), *Potential Failure Mode and Effects Analysis (FMEA) Reference Manual,* stated that an occurrence entry value of 1 designates a potential failure rate ≤ 0.01 per thousand vehicles/items, and an entry value of 10 designates a potential failure rate ≥ 100 per thousand vehicles/items. The occurrence scale will translate to a rate or even a probability (see Table 22.7).

7. *Current controls.* Identify all the existing controls and procedures, including inspections and tests, that prevent the cause of the failure mode. Include a standard operating procedure number, if available.

Severity value	Descriptor	Description
1	None	No effect
3	Minimal	Greater than $1000 and up to $100,000 in damages
7	Moderate	Greater than $100,000, but less than $1 million in damages
10	Extreme	Loss of life without warning or greater than $1 million in damages

Table 22.6 Severity scale example.

Occurrence value	Descriptor	Description
1	Highly unlikely	1 in 10,000
3	Unlikely	1 in 1000
7	Likely	1 in 100
10	Highly likely	1 in 10

Table 22.7 Occurrence scale example.

8. *Detection.* Quantify the ability to detect the failure at a specific process step (that is, not at a previous or subsequent step, but at the step under consideration). The scale for detection ranges from "almost certain" on the low end to "not possible" on the high end (see Table 22.8).

9. *Risk priority number (RPN).* Determine the multiplicative effect (that is, *RPN = Severity value × Occurrence value × Detection value*) of values assigned to columns 4, 6, and 8, respectively. Although teams often work the highest RPN values first, they may set additional prioritization criteria, such as working any line item on the FMEA where the severity value is at the highest level, the detection value is at its highest, or any value is at its highest.

10. *Actions recommended.* Recommend actions for reducing the severity of the impact, frequency of occurrence, or the ability to improve detection.

11. *Responsible.* Identify who is responsible for the actions recommended. If more than one individual is identified, a lead should be specified as responsible.

12. *Actions taken.* List the actions taken and completed and include the completion date.

13. *Severity, occurrence, detection, and RPN.* Identify new severity, occurrence, and detection values, and compute the new RPN value. These have the same meaning as items 4, 6, 8, and 9, respectively. However, these values reflect the actions taken in item 12. Ideally, one or more of these values

Detection value	Descriptor	Description
1	Almost certain	P(detection) 0.95
3	Likely	0.50 ≤ P(detection) < 0.95
7	Possible	0 < P(detection) < 0.50
10	Not possible	P(detection) = 0

Table 22.8 Detection scale example.

will be reduced by the actions taken, resulting in a lower RPN value. If the value is not reduced, the actions taken were ineffective.

Developing FMEA Scales

For FMEAs to be successful, a team must seriously consider the scales it will use to assign values to each component of the RPN.

Some authors advocate using a ten-point scale. One issue with this is that it tends to promote debate as to whether to assign an item a 2 versus a 3, or a 5 versus a 6. In such instances, the overall influence on the RPN value may be minimal, yet the team wastes considerable time and energy debating values that are close together.

In contrast, other authors advocate using scales skewed and sparse in terms of assignable values. For example, instead of selecting a 1-to-10 scale, some teams will choose 1, 3, 7, and 10 scales, or something similar. The benefit of this type of scale is that it minimizes meaningless debate on close values and forces the team to discuss how to assign values. Furthermore, it bounds the RPN values between 1 and 1000 (inclusive), which is convenient and easy to understand. Regardless of the scales used, they should be well defined, consistent, and clearly understood by each team member.

EXAMPLE 22.1

Figure 22.3 provides an example of a PFMEA for two failure modes for the first step of a process. Notice that the severity and detection values are high in the first row. The detection control is ineffective, and the recommended actions attempt to address both issues. The recommended actions were taken, but only affected the detection value. After applying the revised values, the new RPN value is 10. This represents a significant drop from the previous RPN value of 300.

Although the severity value remains at a value of 10, the occurrence value dropped from a 3 to a 1. Therefore, the team felt that because the failure is "highly unlikely" to occur, it will "almost certainly" be detected when it does. Consequently, the team decided not to pursue any additional improvements. Of course, this might be debatable.

In the second row, no current detection control mechanism exists. Therefore, the team must default to the highest value on the scale, which is a 10 in this case. This results in an RPN value of 490.

Thus, a simple action recommended is to separate the parts. This makes the revised detection value equal to 3 and the resulting RPN value equal to 21.

Continued

Process step/ input	Potential failure mode	Potential failure effects	SEV	Potential causes	OCC	Current controls	DET	RPN	Actions recom-mended	Resp.	Actions taken	SEV	OCC	DET	RPN
1	Part not installed	Device does not work	10	Process step skipped	3	SOP 123: process routing sheet	10	300	Modify program to halt production	T. Kubiak 06/17/14	Program modified to detect missing parts	10	1	1	10
1	Wrong part installed	Device overheats	7	Parts commingled in bin	7	None	10	490	Place different parts in different bins	T. Kubiak 06/17/14	Parts sorted and new bins added	7	1	3	21

DET = Detection
OCC = Occurence
PFMEA = Process failure mode and effects analysis
Resp = Responsible
RPN = Risk priority number
SEV = Severity
SOP = Standard operating procedure

Figure 22.3 FMEA for Example 22.1.

Action Priority Table

The *AIAG & VDA FMEA Handbook* (2019) presents an alternative to the RPN method for assessing and prioritizing risk. An *action priority (AP) table* lists failure effects sorted first by severity, then occurrence, and then detection. An example of an AP table for severity levels 9-10 is shown in Table 22.9.

Useful Tips

Often, conducting an FMEA work session can be time-consuming, tiresome for all, and, in many cases, less than productive. Here are tips to make the sessions more meaningful:

1. *Establish team norms.* Team norms keep teams moving forward. Use them to the fullest.

2. *Keep work sessions to a reasonable length of time.* Though this might be included in the team norms, it requires special consideration. The FMEA work sessions can be quite intense and focused, and draining on the participants. Thus, this must be taken into consideration when setting the duration of the session. A work session of two or three hours is reasonable.

3. *Establish an FMEA owner.* "No owner, no FMEA." An FMEA without an owner has no support and, consequently, either is done once, haphazardly, or not done at all.

Effect	Severity	Occurrence	Probability of failure cause occurring	Detection	Ability to Detect	Action Priority
Effects with very high severity rankings of 9-10 go in this column	9-10	8-10	Very high	7-10	Low - Very Low	H
				5-6	Moderate	H
				2-4	High	H
				1	Very High	H
		6-7	High	7-10	Low - Very Low	H
				5-6	Moderate	H
				2-4	High	H
				1	Very High	H
		4-5	Moderate	7-10	Low - Very Low	H
				5-6	Moderate	H
				2-4	High	H
				1	Very High	M
		2-3	Low	7-10	Low - Very Low	H
				5-6	Moderate	M
				2-4	High	L
				1	Very High	L
		1	Very Low	1-10	Very High to Very Low	L

Table 22.9 Action priority table for severity ratings of 9-10.

4. *Use subject matter experts (SMEs).* Some organizations use the "who's available method" (WAM). This is nonsense. SMEs understand the process or the component. Use them. Doing anything else is foolish.

5. *Use a professional facilitator.* Although team norms are helpful, a professional facilitator or individual who is exceptionally skilled in facilitation is occasionally necessary to keep the team moving forward. Using a facilitator should not be viewed as a negative by the team or a negative trait of the team leader. A team leader who recognizes the need for a facilitator demonstrates the ability to build a strong, cohesive team capable of producing results. Such an individual shows their leadership abilities.

6. *Create meaningful scales.* Meaningful scales, in conjunction with proper facilitation, can keep the team moving forward. If thoughtful consideration is given to the development of the scales before beginning the FMEA, it is unlikely there will be a need to change the scales during the development of the FMEA. Unforeseen circumstances do arise,

however, so there may be those rare times when it is necessary. An example of a scale that sometimes requires changing during the FMEA is the *occurrence* scale. Usually, the need to do so arises because the scale was insufficient in the first place, and a situation arose that the scale could not accommodate.

7. *Establish a trigger.* Triggers should be used to initiate an update to an FMEA or the creation of a new one. When no trigger exists, FMEAs are at the mercy of someone's thought or memory, and that's a shame.
8. *Limit the ability of participants to review past decisions for current steps.* When columns 2 and 3, and/or 5, and 7 are identical, teams have a propensity to want to carry previous scores forward to the current step, based on the rationale that the current step wording is the same. Teams want to do this without regard to what has transpired between steps. This is usually done for convenience and is not necessarily supported by logic. For example, there is no reason to believe that identical failure modes and failure effects occurring in process steps 2 and 22 should have the same severity scores. If the scores are the same, the sameness should be supported by logic, not convenience.
9. *Remember that all decisions reflect the current step.* This is an important aspect of the FMEA and must be constantly reinforced to all team members. It is especially important when it comes to scoring the detection value because team members have a propensity to look ahead for detection potential.
10. *Write modes, effects, controls, and causes in clear and meaningful ways.* These should be written in clear, succinct, and unambiguous language. Otherwise, thoughts are lost from work session to work session. Try to avoid using adjectives and adverbs.
11. *Complete each step during a given work session to the extent possible.* Although this requires the participants to be flexible in the termination time of the work session, this helps maintain continuity of thought. If the termination time of the work session is unreasonable (for example, strays too far from tip number 2), seek to find a reasonable stopping point and make appropriate notes that will help the team pick up quickly at the next work session.
12. *Minimize the duration between work sessions.* If the duration between work sessions is too long, momentum is lost, and team members begin to forget their discussion points. This tip is particularly important when the FMEA is being developed for the first time.
13. *Identify root causes.* Ideally, root causes should be identified. Otherwise, the actions taken to reduce the high-value RPNs will be ineffective because they will be addressing symptoms.
14. *Score appropriately.* It is important to score as the situation dictates. Some individuals and teams are reluctant to score at the extreme values of the scales. For example, if it's not possible to detect a failure at a given step,

a score of 10 should be given. Some individuals and teams resist scoring a 10 and fight to score a 7. It's unclear whether this is human nature or something else. Regardless, if the situation calls for a 10, a 10 must be given. Such situations should be addressed up front and included in the team norms, if necessary.

15. *Support FMEAs with additional quality tools.* It should be evident from this list of tips that additional quality tools can be beneficial when conducting FMEAs. For example, cause-and-effect diagrams, root cause analysis, and brainstorming can all play valuable roles in completing an FMEA.

Up-Front Work

FMEAs should be owned, considered living documents, and updated appropriately. They require intensive work up front on the part of the team, but their value is almost immeasurable in terms of providing a positive impact on quality. The tips provided are born from experience and, if applied, will ensure the effectiveness of your FMEA.

Chapter 23

Additional Analysis Methods

Most people spend more time and energy going around problems than trying to solve them.

—Henry Ford

GAP ANALYSIS

> Analyze scenarios to identify performance gaps and compare current and future states using predefined metrics. (Analyze)
>
> Body of Knowledge VI.D.1

A *gap analysis* is a tool used to identify a performance difference between a current state and a desired or future state using metrics implied by the states. The desired or future state may be set by recognizing potential performance determined through activities such as benchmarking. Gap analyses are performed at multiple levels:

- *Business level.* A business may compare its performance directly with that of competitors or the general average industry performance. Gaps at this level are usually financial in nature.

  These gaps often cascade down to subordinate entities of an enterprise. For example, a $10M profit gap might be allocated as a gap of $2M to each of five business units.

EXAMPLE 23.1

Current state: Profit for FY 2022 = $4.26M
Future state: Profit for FY 2023 = $5M

Continued

Continued

EXAMPLE 23.2

Current state: Sales for FY 2022 = $18.1M
Future state: Sales for FY 2023 = $21.5M

EXAMPLE 23.3

Current state: Representatives in 11 cities
Future state: Representatives in 16 cities by 3Q 2023

EXAMPLE 23.4

Current state: 20K books circulated in academic year 2022
Future state: 22K books circulated in academic year 2023

EXAMPLE 23.5

Current state: Utility cost: $975K in calendar year 2022
Future state: Utility cost: $850K in calendar year 2023

EXAMPLE 23.6

Current state: FY 2022 square feet leased 100K
Future state: FY 2023 square feet leased 0

- *Process level.* The current performance of a process might be compared with the cost, cycle time, and quality characteristics of other processes or at performance levels required to remain competitive. These gaps may also cascade to lower entities. For instance, parts of a process cycle time reduction may be allocated to various subprocesses.

EXAMPLE 23.7

Current state: June volume 253 units
Future state: July volume 270 units

EXAMPLE 23.8

Current state: Standard deviation 0.006
Future state: Standard deviation 0.004 by 2Q 2023

EXAMPLE 23.9

Current state: Leaking packages 0.2% in August 2022
Future state: Leaking packages 0.05% in December 2022

Continued

Continued

EXAMPLE 23.10

Current state: Labor content: 0.13 hours per unit
Future state: Labor content: 0.10 hours per unit by 3Q 2023

EXAMPLE 23.11

Current state: External failures FY 2022 = 6
Future state: External failures FY 2023 = 0

- *Product level.* Gaps at this level are usually identified through differences in features and capabilities, cost, quality, or by critical-to-X perspectives.

EXAMPLE 23.12

Current state: Switch has 99% reliability @ 10K cycles
Future state: Switch has 99% reliability @ 20K cycles by 2/17

EXAMPLE 23.13

Current state: Invoice register doesn't show credit status
Future state: Invoice register shows credit status by 1Q 2023

EXAMPLE 23.14

Current state: Fleet mpg for model year 2022 = 22 mpg
Future state: Fleet mpg for model year 2023 = 35 mpg

If the gap between the current state and the future state is sufficiently large, a series of intermediate steps or milestones may be required, with more achievable gaps between each one. However, it is important to recognize that gaps are seldom stationary. Therefore, it may be necessary to account for an increasing gap over time, particularly when future states are set relative to competitor performance. Gap analysis may be stated in terms of external conditions.

EXAMPLE 23.15

Current state: FY 2022 Profit = $18.6M
Future state: FY 2023 Profit = $21.5M (If customer A builds 100,000 units)
FY 2023 Profit = $23M (If customer A builds 150,000 units)
FY 2023 Profit = $25M (If customer A builds 200,000 units)

Continued

Continued

EXAMPLE 23.16

Current state: Market share FY 2022 = 31%
Future State: Market share FY 2023 = 35% (If there are 100K housing starts)
Market share FY 2023 = 38% (If there are 140K housing starts)
Market share FY 2023 = 40% (If there are 160K housing starts)

EXAMPLE 23.17

Current state: Phosphates in effluent = 2.1 ppm June 2022
Future state: Phosphates in effluent < 1.6 ppm in June 2023 (If rain total < 2″)
Phosphates in effluent < 1.8 ppm in June 2023 (If 2″ < rain < 3″)
Phosphates in effluent < 2.0 ppm in June 2023 (If rain > 3″)

ROOT CAUSE ANALYSIS

Define and describe the purpose of root cause analysis, recognize the issues involved in identifying a root cause, and use various tools (e.g., 5 whys, Pareto charts, fault tree analysis, cause and effect diagrams, and A3) to resolve chronic problems. (Analyze)

Body of Knowledge VI.D.2

Solving a process problem means identifying the root cause and eliminating it. The ultimate test of whether the root cause has been eliminated is the ability to toggle the problem on and off by removing and reintroducing the root cause. Several tools for identifying root causes are discussed in the following paragraphs.

5 Whys

The *5 whys* is a technique used to drill down through the layers of cause and effect to the root cause. It consists of looking at an undesired result and asking, Why did this occur? When the question is answered, the next question is, And why did that occur? and so on. The number five is, of course, arbitrary.

When the root cause is identified, then the logic can be checked by simply reading back up from the cause with the word "therefore." Example 23.18 shows how this logic checking process works.

There is not one single root cause for every problem. Sometimes it is necessary to look at several causes and work on them one at a time, as Example 23.19 illustrates.

EXAMPLE 23.18

Undesired result: A customer is not satisfied.

Asking Why

"Why is the customer not satisfied?" *Because the order arrived late.*

"Why did the order arrive late?" *Because it was shipped late.*

"Why was it shipped late?" *Because final assembly wasn't completed on time.*

"Why wasn't final assembly completed on time?" *Because a part was received from the paint line late.*

"Why was the part from the paint line late?" *Because it arrived late from the fabrication department.*

"Why was it late from the fabrication department?" *Because the fabrication machine was running another part for the same order.*

"Why was the fabrication machine running another part for the same order?" *Because that machine always runs these two parts.*

Confirming Therefore: Always start with the root cause and work back to the problem or issue.

Root Cause: *"The machine was running another part for the same order."*

Therefore: *"This prevented timely production of the needed part."*

Therefore: *"The part arrived late from the fabrication department."*

Therefore: *"The part was received from the paint line late."*

Therefore: *"The final assembly wasn't completed on time."*

Therefore: *"The assembly was shipped late."*

Therefore: *"The order arrived late."*

Therefore: *"The customer was not satisfied."*

Consider Solution(s)

"Could they be on separate machines simultaneously when a delivery date is imminent?" *Yes.*

EXAMPLE 23.19

A problem-solving team at a trucking company is given the following gap analysis:

Current state: Number of customer complaints, FY 2022 = 238

Future state: Reduce the number by 25% for FY 2024

The team asks the first *why*: Why did the customers complain?

They decide to look at the complaint data for the 2022 FY, as shown in Figure 23.1.

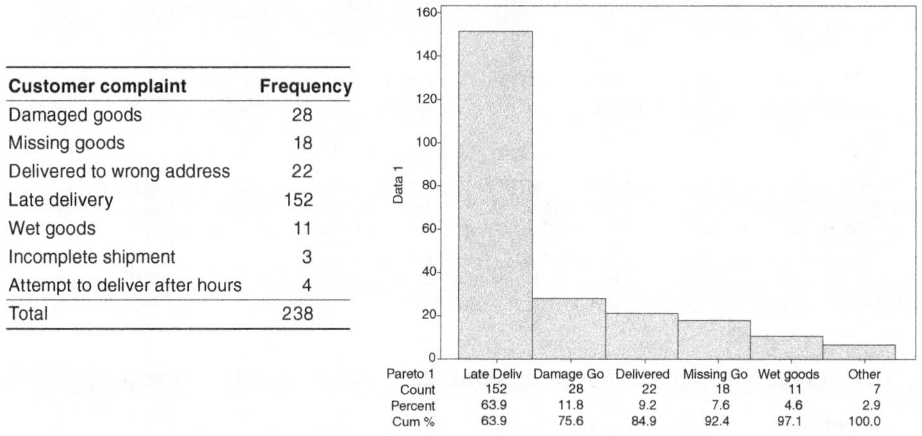

Customer complaint	Frequency
Damaged goods	28
Missing goods	18
Delivered to wrong address	22
Late delivery	152
Wet goods	11
Incomplete shipment	3
Attempt to deliver after hours	4
Total	238

Figure 23.1 Complaint data for Example 23.19.

Since late delivery is the most frequent cause, the team asks the second *why*: Why did we have so many late deliveries?

They study the 152 late delivery events, as shown in Figure 23.2.

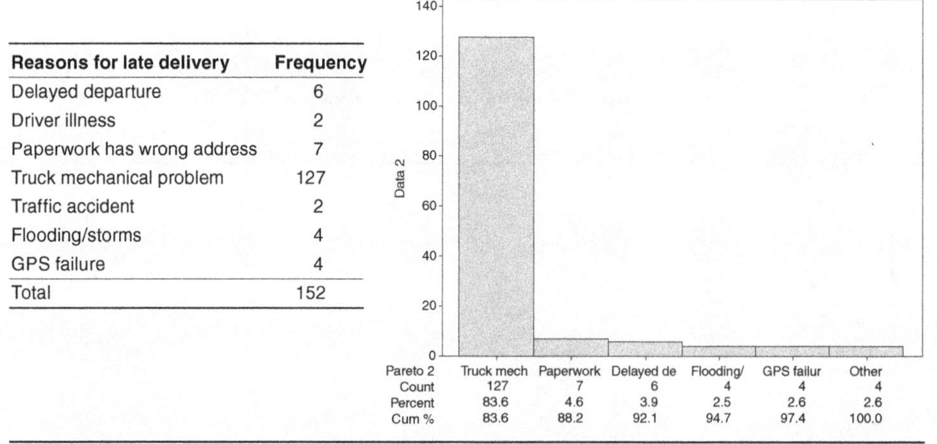

Reasons for late delivery	Frequency
Delayed departure	6
Driver illness	2
Paperwork has wrong address	7
Truck mechanical problem	127
Traffic accident	2
Flooding/storms	4
GPS failure	4
Total	152

Figure 23.2 Reason for late delivery for Example 23.19.

Continued

The third *why*: Why did we have so many trucks with mechanical problems?

The team looks further at the "mechanical problem" events and produces the following list, shown in Figure 23.3.

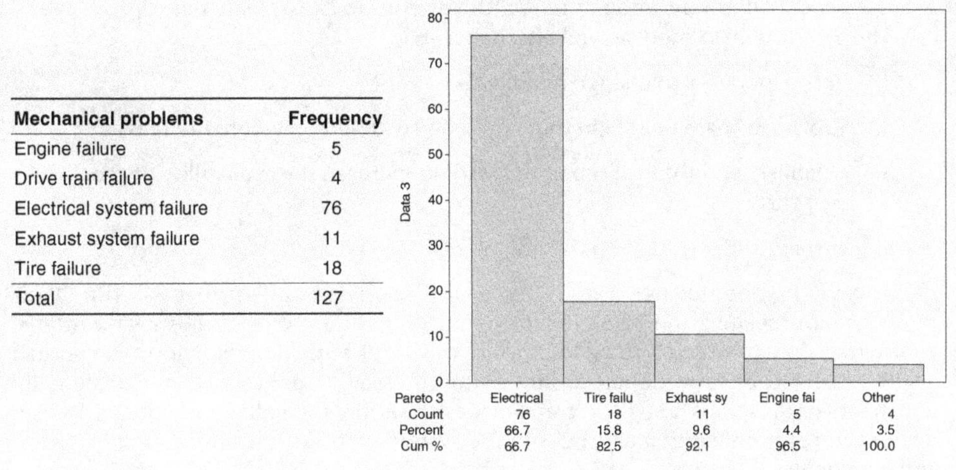

Mechanical problems	Frequency
Engine failure	5
Drive train failure	4
Electrical system failure	76
Exhaust system failure	11
Tire failure	18
Total	127

Figure 23.3 Mechanical problems for Example 23.19.

Fourth *why*: Why did we have so many electrical system failures?

Further analysis of the electrical systems failures is shown in Figure 23.4.

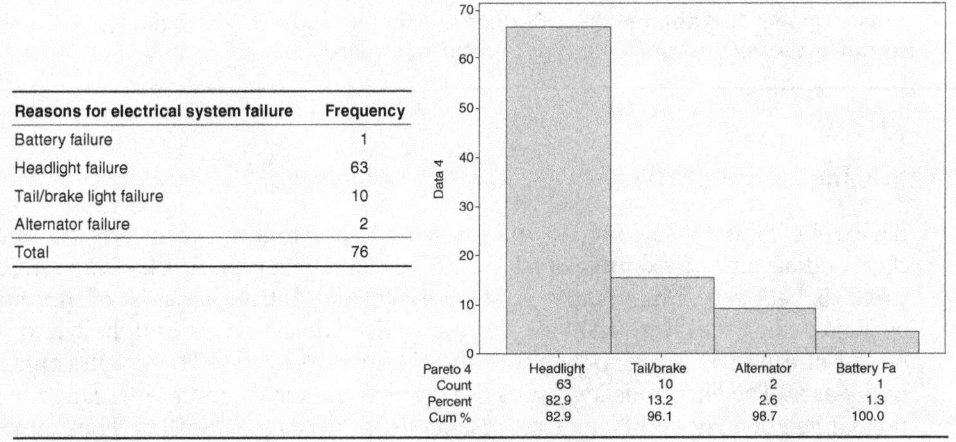

Reasons for electrical system failure	Frequency
Battery failure	1
Headlight failure	63
Tail/brake light failure	10
Alternator failure	2
Total	76

Figure 23.4 Reasons for electrical system failure for Example 23.19.

Based on the analysis, 41% of late deliveries are caused by a failed headlight.

Why do we have so many headlight failures?

The team studies the current headlight's life cycle. They find that after 1800 hours of service, there is a 50/50 chance that the bulb will fail. They also discover that the

Continued

Continued

headlight repair procedure consists of having the driver pull off the road, call the nearest company depot, and wait for a mechanic to arrive. Depending on the weather, location, and so on, the headlight may be repaired on site, or the truck may be towed to the nearest depot. Either way, enough time often elapses to cause a late delivery.

The team brainstormed several alternatives:

1. Train operators to change headlights
2. Provide a spare headlight that could be switched on when one fails
3. Establish a non-depot repair network to increase the availability of repair people
4. Install a different type of headlight

A team member locates a more expensive headlight system that will run 20,000 hours before reaching the 50/50 failure point. In addition, these bulbs cast a reddish light when they have fewer than 200 hours of useful remaining life, so they can usually be changed prior to departure and without delaying delivery. Unfortunately, the new headlight requires a step-up transformer to supply the voltage needed. The team decides to recommend that all trucks in the system be fitted with the new transformer and headlights.

Management agrees to retrofit 100 vehicles (10% of the fleet) with the new system for a one-year trial. At the end of the year, none of the 100 vehicles had a failed headlight. Management then decided to retrofit the entire fleet and to specify to their tractor supplier that all new units be equipped with the new headlight system. Customer complaints decreased by 22% during the following year. The team had a restrained celebration because they had not met the 25% decrease that had been their original goal. They set about analyzing the complaint types for further improvement.

Pareto Chart

An excellent tool for seeking out and prioritizing potential root causes is the *Pareto chart* or diagram. An example of a Pareto chart for defect types is illustrated in Figure 23.5. Let's take a moment to analyze this chart. Notice that a list of mutually exclusive categories is given along the *x*-axis. Each defect type is graphed, and the height of each bar is proportional to the number of defects. The graph contains two *y*-axes. The left *y*-axis identifies the number of defects and is associated with the bar heights. The right *y*-axis represents the percentage of defects. The cumulative percentage of each defect type is graphed above the bars. The purpose of the Pareto chart is to separate the "vital few" causes from the "trivial many." This is often reflected in what is called the 80/20 rule. Figure 23.5 illustrates that the first two bars (that is, *bridging* and *voids*) represent 80% of the defects. The remaining 20% is spread across the three subsequent bars. Notice that the last bar is identified as "other." Because there are many types of minor defects that are few in quantity, they are collected in this category. There is no real need to identify them by specific type since they make up the trivial many and will not be investigated.

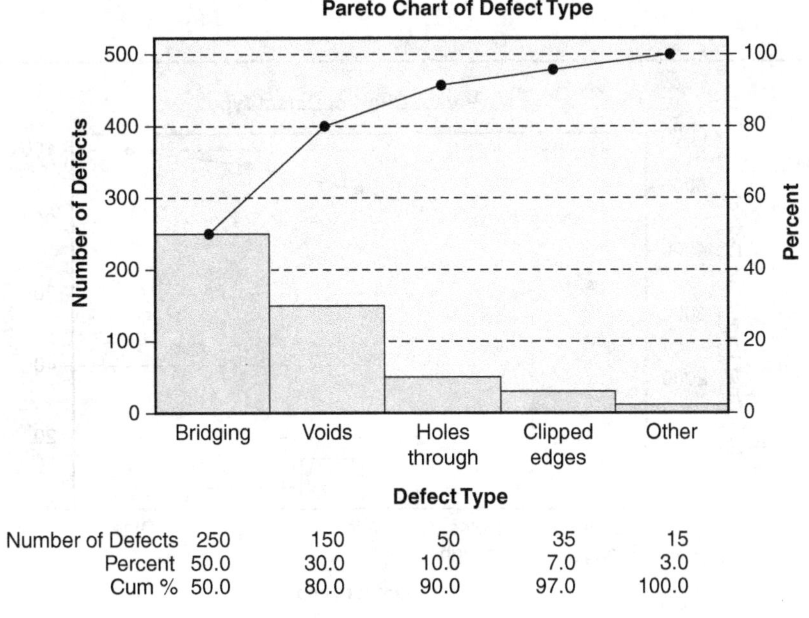

Figure 23.5 Example of a Pareto chart for defects.

Pareto charts can be and often are decomposed into lower-level charts. For example, an investigation into the *bridging* bar in Figure 23.5 may determine that bridging can be further subdivided into additional meaningful categories.

One drawback of Figure 23.5 is that it assumes all defects have an equal impact. However, if we quantify the cost of correcting each defect, we can weight each quantity of defect type by the cost of correction. This weight could very well yield a Pareto chart completely different from Figure 23.5.

EXAMPLE 23.20

Let's consider the data given in Table 23.1. Applying the cost data in this table to Figure 23.5 yields the revised Pareto chart depicted in Figure 23.6, which illustrates a completely different picture and dictates a different course of investigation and action.

Defect type	Cost to correct ($)
Bridging	1.00
Voids	5.00
Holes through	25.00
Clipped edges	100.00
Other	10.00

Table 23.1 Cost to correct each defect type.

Continued

Continued

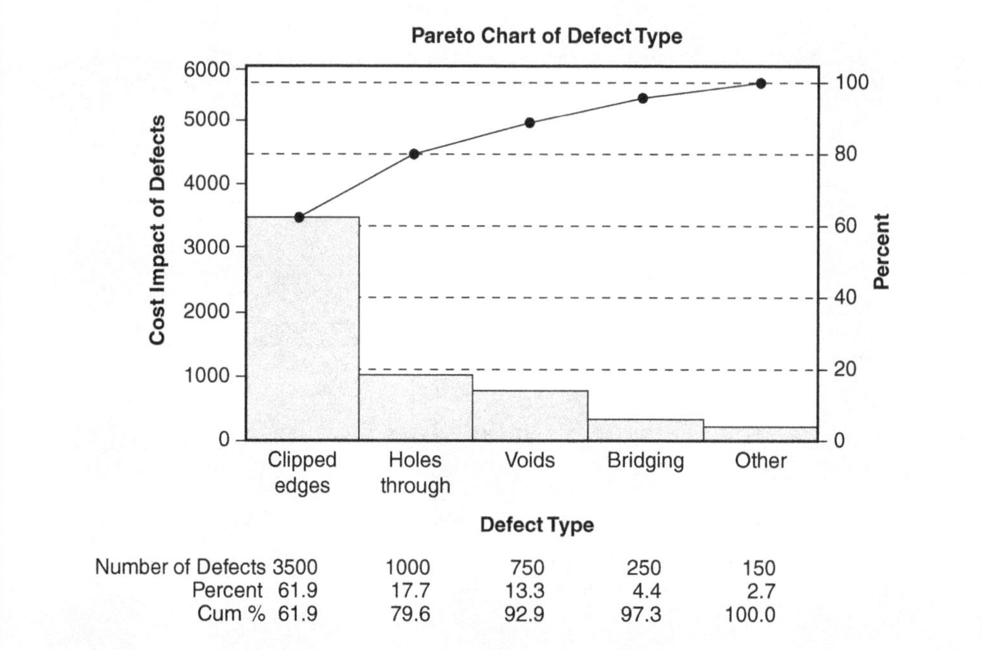

Number of Defects	3500	1000	750	250	150
Percent	61.9	17.7	13.3	4.4	2.7
Cum %	61.9	79.6	92.9	97.3	100.0

Figure 23.6 Example of a Pareto chart for defects weighted by the cost to correct.

The Pareto principle says that the most important things should be treated differently than the least important things. To put it another way, the Pareto principle requires that most of our resources should be expended on the critical few rather than the trivial many.

Consider the case of stockroom management. The basic requirements are

1. Always have material on hand when it is needed
2. Don't maintain excess inventory.

An elaborate software system with predictive capability, alarm messages, sensors on all bins, automatic ordering, and careful monitoring may be established for all stock items. Another alternative is to use this elaborate, resource-intensive system for the few important items, in this case the most expensive and critical items. The inventories of the trivial many less expensive items can be allowed to be larger in number because they have less impact on the bottom line. The stockroom for an appliance manufacturer may have a month's supply of fasteners but only a calculated three-day supply of electric motors. The medical community has long taught this principle for situations when a limited staff confronts a large group of people with injuries. They don't treat everyone equally nor do they say, "The vast majority of injuries are sprained ankles, so we'll treat those first." Instead, they use *triage*, dividing the group into three subgroups based on the severity of their injuries. They use most of their resources on the group that will survive only if they receive immediate care. The Pareto principle provides guidance in many areas.

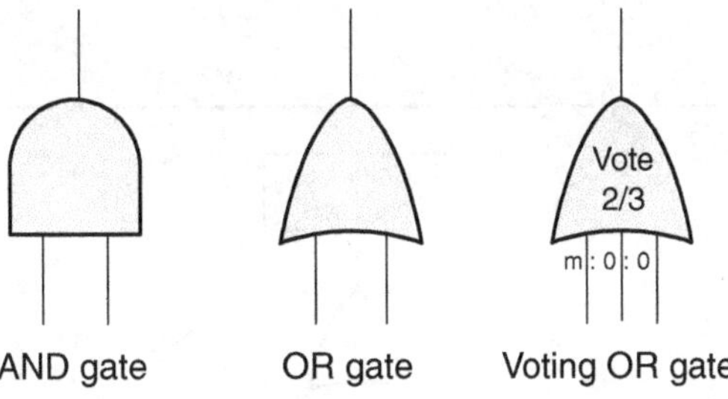

Figure 23.7 Basic fault tree analysis symbols.

Fault Tree Analysis

Once a failure has been identified as requiring additional study, a *fault tree analysis* (FTA) can be performed. Basic symbols used in FTA are borrowed from the electronics and logic fields. The fundamental symbols are the AND gate and the OR gate. Each of these has at least two inputs and a single output. Another key gate is the voting OR gate. In this gate, the output occurs if and only if k or more of the input events occur, where *k* is specified, usually on the gate symbol. Common FTA gate symbols are depicted in Figure 23.7.

The output for the AND gate occurs if and only if all inputs occur. The output for the OR gate occurs if and only if at least one input occurs. Rectangles are typically used for labeling inputs and outputs. The failure mode being studied is sometimes referred to as the "top" or "head" event. An FTA helps the user consider underlying causes for a failure mode and study relationships between various failures.

EXAMPLE 23.21

The failure being studied is the stoppage of agitation in a tank before mixing is complete. This becomes the top event. Further team study indicates this will happen if any of the following occurs:

- Power loss due to both the external power source and the backup generator failing.
- Timer shuts off too soon because it is set incorrectly or has a mechanical failure.
- Agitator motor fails because it is overheated, or a fuse or capacitor fails.
- Agitator power train fails because both belts A and B break, or the clutch fails, or the transmission fails.

This test is symbolized by the FTA diagram shown in Figure 23.8.

Continued

Continued

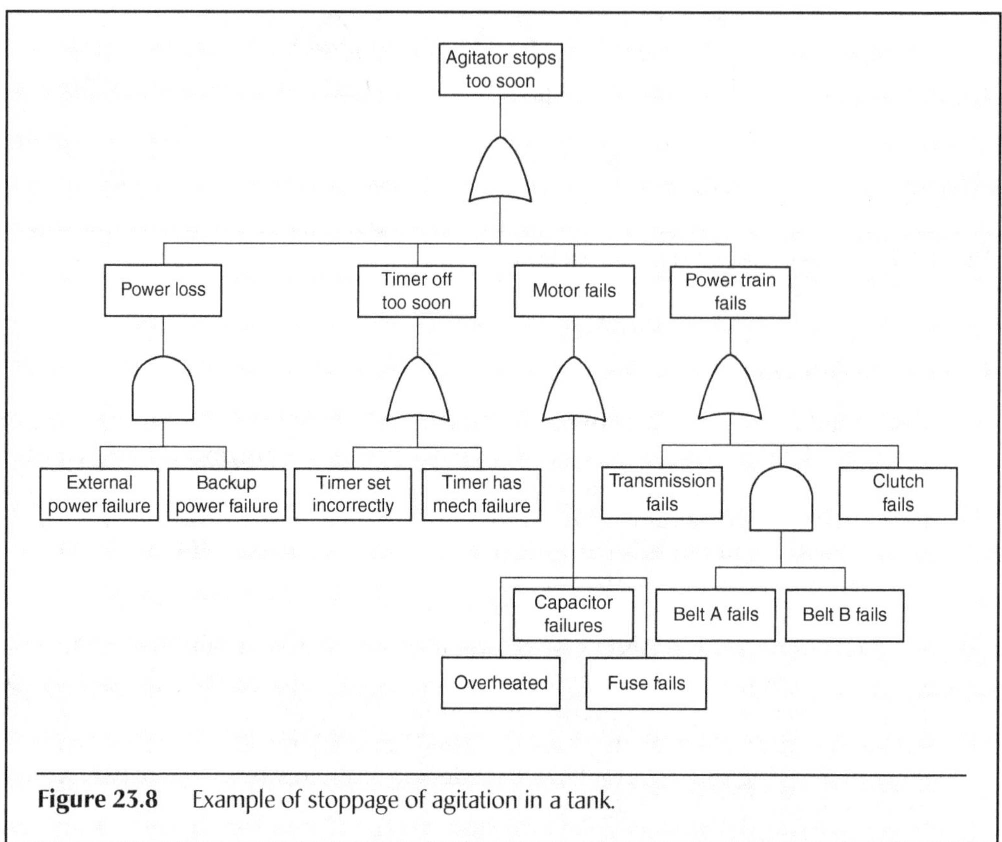

Figure 23.8 Example of stoppage of agitation in a tank.

Cause-and-Effect Diagram

A *cause-and-effect diagram* (also called the *Ishikawa diagram* or *fishbone diagram*) traditionally divides potential causes into several generic categories. In use, a large empty diagram is often drawn on a whiteboard or flip chart, as shown in Figure 23.9. Notice that the main branches of the diagram are the 7 M's, which were discussed in Chapter 14. An undesirable end effect is specified, and a brainstorming session is usually held to identify potential causes, sub-causes, and so on. The participants in the session should include people with a working knowledge of the process as well as subject matter experts. For example, suppose a circuit board plating operation is producing defects. After a few steps of brainstorming, the diagram might look like Figure 23.10. The beauty of a team-built cause-and-effect diagram is that the thought process of an individual is stimulated by others. A group will usually be much more creative than the same people working independently. Sometimes an idea from one person causes others to think along a new track. This may result in putting branches on branches as Figure 23.10 illustrates.

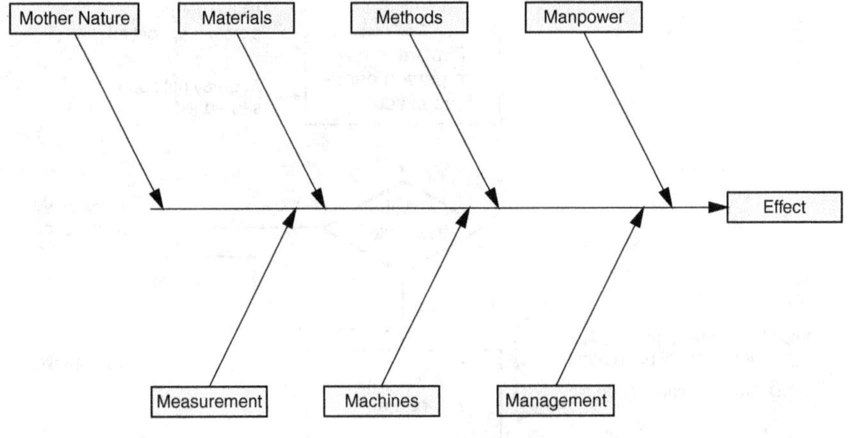

Figure 23.9 Example of a blank cause-and-effect diagram.

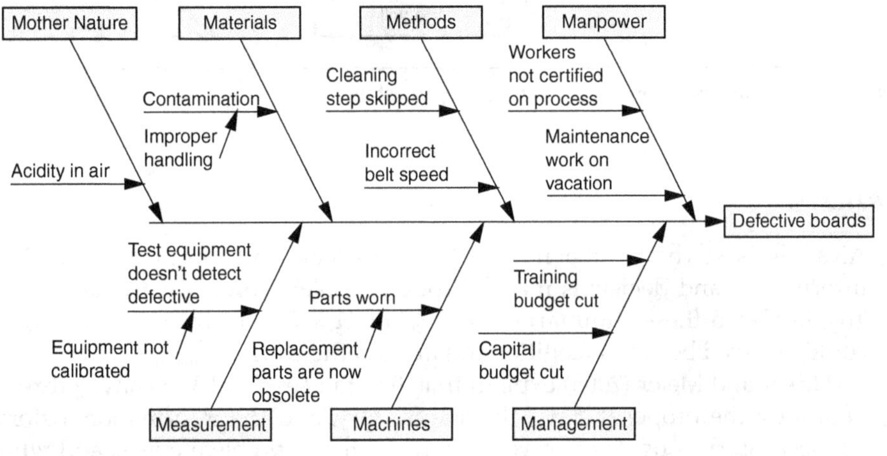

Figure 23.10 Example of a cause-and-effect diagram after a few brainstorming steps.

Alternative methods for naming the bones of the fish are as follows:

- Brainstorming and Affinity Diagramming: Use the resultant categories
- Macro Process Map: Use these major process steps as labels
- 4M's, 1P, and 1E: Materials, Methods, Measurement, Machines, People, Environment

Some teams have found it useful to use a *flowchart* as a starting point rather than the traditional fishbone diagram, as shown in Figure 23.11.

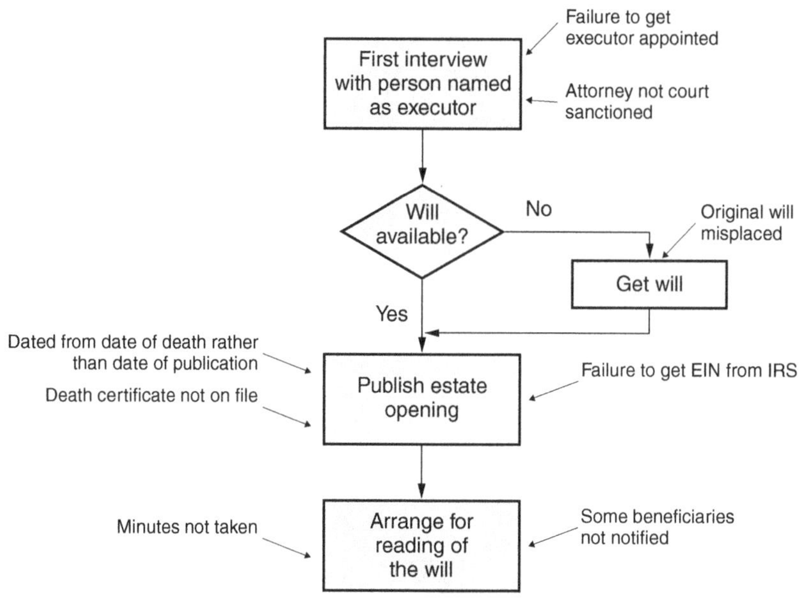

Figure 23.11 Causes for errors when opening an estate.

A3 Analysis

A3 analysis was born out of need at Toyota to document and share with others key information and decisions made through problem-solving activities. Originally Toyota placed these summaries on "A3," or 11 × 7 inch sized, paper so that they could be faxed between facilities and around the world.

Liker and Meier (2005) explain that Toyota uses the A3 to convey three types of stories: the proposal story, the status story, and the informational story. The proposal story is used when you are aware that a problem exists, and when you are developing the proposal to work on the problem. Once work is started on the problem, the status story provides updates on progress. The informational story is used to share knowledge you have gained with others who will find it useful.

A3 has now become synonymous with a way of thinking through problems. Although varying in exact format and content, A3's follow these categories: Problem Definition and Description, Problem Analysis, Implementation Plan, Results, and Future Steps. The A3 process uses at its core the PDCA process (Plan, Do, Check, and Act).

Figure 23.12 shows an example of an A3.

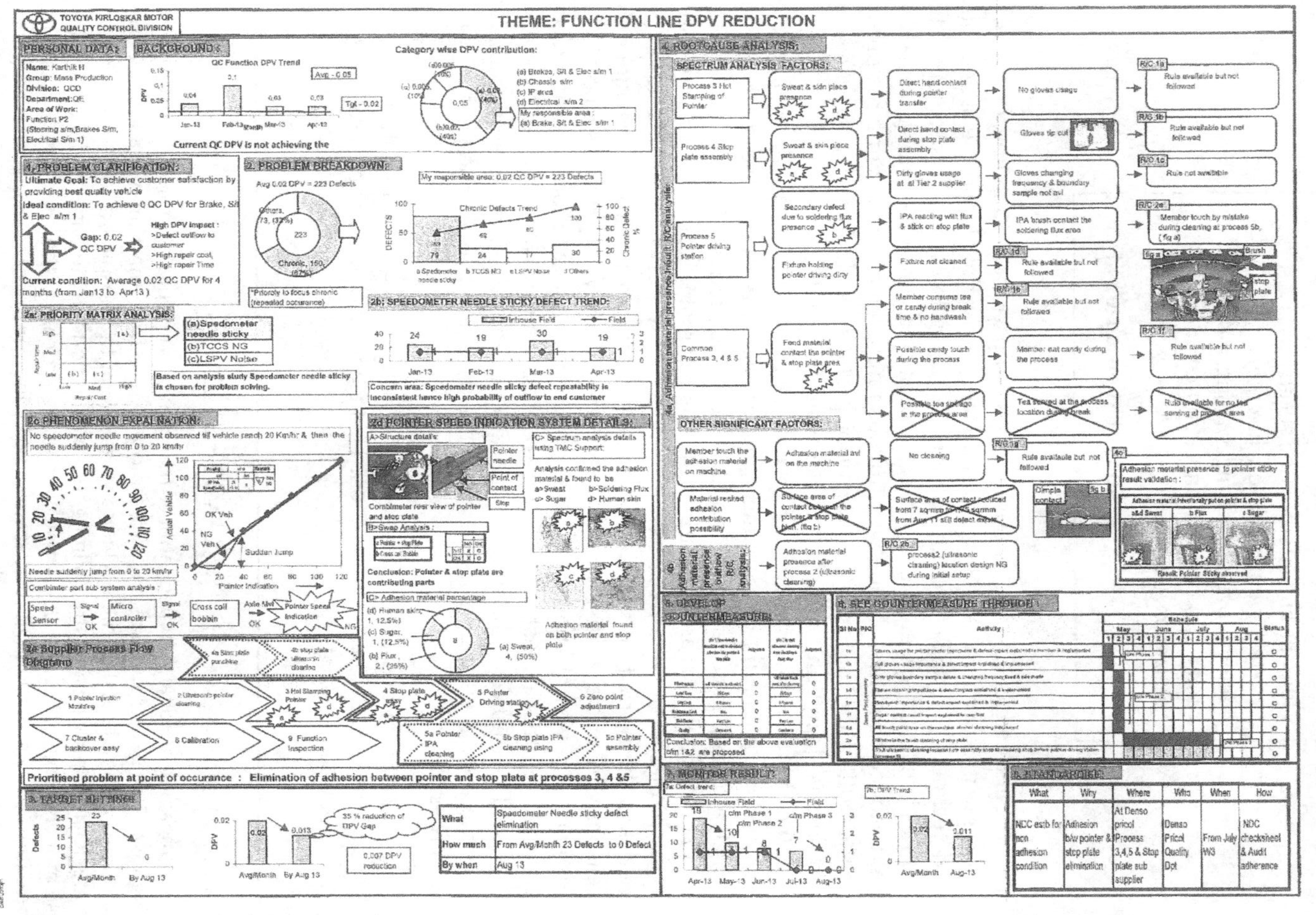

Figure 23.12 Example A3.

WASTE ANALYSIS

> Identify and interpret the seven classic wastes (overproduction, inventory, defects, overprocessing, waiting, motion, and transportation) and resource under-utilization. (Analyze)
>
> **Body of Knowledge VI.D.3**

Finding and reducing waste can significantly impact the bottom line. Lean proponents put great emphasis on this effort. In fact, the National Institute of Standards and Technology (NIST) through its Manufacturing Extension Partnership (MEP) defines *lean* as "[a] systematic approach to identifying and eliminating waste (non-value-added activities) through continuous improvement by flowing the product at the pull of the customer in pursuit of perfection." It defines *non-value-added activities* as "[a]nything a final customer wouldn't want to pay for."

Shoichiro Toyoda, president of Toyota, says that waste is "anything other than the minimum amount of equipment, materials, parts, space, and worker's time which are absolutely necessary to add value to the product."

The difficult part about eliminating waste is that it is so often hidden. Identifying hidden waste requires careful study of all aspects of an organization's processes. Utilizing root cause analysis techniques helps in identifying the underlying reasons why waste occurs. In fact, considering not only why the waste occurs, but also how did we not know that it was occurring and even more what in our culture allowed this to exist in the first place are great ways to understand why.

NIST identifies eight sources of waste: overproduction, inventory, defects, overprocessing, waiting, motion, transportation, and people. Each of the wastes is defined below:

- *Overproduction.* Producing sooner or faster or in greater quantity than is needed by the next operation. This feeds *Inventory,* the next category of waste (muda).

EXAMPLE 23.22

A well-meaning hospital volunteer notices that the welcome packets for patients are running low. They gather supplies and order more copies from the administration department and assemble 300 packets. Unknown to them, the hospital is in the process of strategically improving and streamlining the information flow to patients, including the use of technology. They roll out a new welcoming process at the check-in desk and in the patient rooms utilizing QR code scanning. The improvement team even has a limited number of brochures printed with the new QR code to equip the volunteers to share with people coming to the hospital to ease the transition. Unfortunately, the prepared welcome packets are now out of date and must be thrown away.

- *Inventory*. Excessive supply of parts or materials. Some accounting systems consider inventory an asset, but considering the need to store, protect, locate, handle, and retrieve it, it may be considered a liability by lean professionals.

EXAMPLE 23.23

Organizations with assembly lines sometimes arrange with vendors of standard parts to go through their assembly line before a shift starts and stock it with the number of parts needed for that shift. This obviates the necessity of running the parts through the stockroom with the associated picking and moving operations.

- *Defects*. When defects occur, additional material, labor, and machine time may be required in addition to a possible increase in warranty costs and the potential for product recalls.
- *Overprocessing*. This waste represents effort that does not add value as seen from the customer's point of view.

EXAMPLE 23.24

A company found that parts waiting to be painted were rusting. An oil dip tank was installed to prevent rust. Of course, a de-oiling dip tank was also needed because oily parts don't paint well. The oil/degrease steps were processing waste. Processing waste (some call it *overprocessing*) is one of the most difficult types of waste to detect.

- *Waiting*. Most workers can identify with this issue. Waiting for equipment, instructions, materials, and so on does not add value to a product or service.
- *Motion*. Movement by persons or equipment that does not add value. This can usually be improved by altering workplace layout, whether behind a receptionist desk or on a production floor.
- *Transportation*. Movement of anything a process produces (goods, parts, patients). In supply chain, this may be complex paths and handoffs to move goods across the globe. In some plants the decision as to where to place a newly arrived machine is based on where room can be found, not on optimized flow. In hospitals, it may be due to physical constraints of the building and additions requiring long circuitous routes for patients to navigate.
- *Resource underutilization*. Failing to make use of all an employee has to offer in terms of ideas and creativity in making continuous improvement. This is often considered the eighth waste.

Helpful Mnemonics

To help practitioners remember the Eight Wastes, a few helpful mnemonics have been devised:

1. DOWNTIME

   This stands for defects, overproduction, waiting, non-utilized talent, transportation, inventory, motion, and extra-processing.

2. TIM WOODS

   This is a way to remember transportation, inventory, motion, waiting, overproduction, overprocessing, defects, and skills.

3. MEDICINE

   For healthcare settings, McShane-Vaughn (2018) suggests using this version to remember motion, excess processing, defects, inventory, conveyance (i.e., transportation), idling (i.e., waiting), non-utilized talent, and excess production.

Part VII
Improve

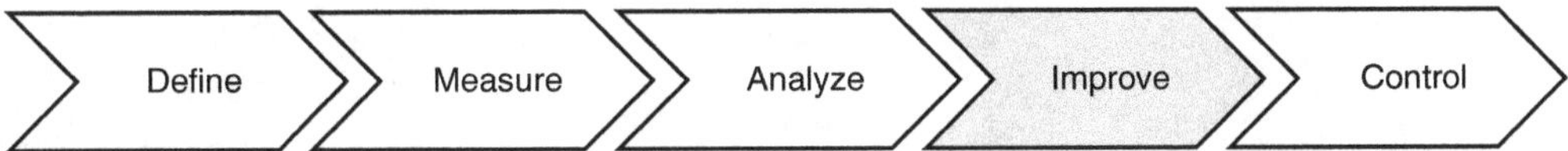

The purpose of this phase is to identify, select, pilot, if necessary, and implement process improvement solutions. Common tools used in this phase are shown in Table VII.1.

- *Activity Network Diagram*
- Analysis of Variance (ANOVA)
- *Brainstorming*
- *Control Charts*
- *Design of Experiments*
- *Failure Mode and Effects Analysis* (FMEA)
- Fault Tree Analysis (FTA)
- *Flowchart/Process Mapping*
- *Gantt Charts*
- *Histograms*
- *Hypothesis Testing*
- *Measurement Systems Analysis (MSA)*
- *Meeting Minutes*
- *Mistake-proofing*
- *Multi-voting*
- *Nominal Group Technique*
- *Pareto Charts*
- Project Evaluation and Review Technique (PERT)
- Pilot
- *Prioritization Matrix*
- *Process Capability Analysis*
- *Process Sigma*
- *Project Management*
- *Project Tracking*
- *Quick Changeover*
- Reliability Analysis
- Risk Analysis
- *Simulation*
- Statistical Tolerancing
- Taguchi Robustness Concepts
- *Tollgate Review*
- *Value Stream Maps*
- Work Breakdown Structure
- $y = f(X)$

Table VII.1 Common tools used in improve phase.
(Note: Tools shown in italic are used in more than one phase.)

Chapter 24

Design of Experiments (DOE)

Statistical design of experiments refers to the process of planning the experiment so that appropriate data will be collected and analyzed by statistical methods, resulting in valid and objective conclusions. The statistical approach to experimental design is necessary if we wish to draw meaningful conclusions from the data.

—Douglas C. Montgomery

This chapter will address the concepts, principles, strategy, and a significant amount of terminology behind design of experiments. Numerous detailed examples are provided to help the reader understand the mechanics of the experiments. The design and analysis of some experiments can be done manually but statistical software provides many features that specifically support this work and it enables the use of designs that are not possible with manual computation.

An alternative approach to designing an experiment is to start with some initial condition and vary inputs through "trial and error" in the hope of improving the output. The choice of the starting point and the decisions about new conditions in this search do not guarantee that the optimal condition will be found, that any understanding of how the inputs affect the output will be gained, or that the number of samples provide sufficient information for a confident decision. The best that we can hope for is a chance to "pick the winner" from among the samples obtained.

In contrast, design of experiments (DOE) offers many important benefits over *ad hoc* methods of data collection that might be important to Six Sigma improvement projects.

- Predictable expectations of the experimental outcomes.
- The designed experiment encompasses the reasonable range of input values that might contain the optimal settings. It can be modified, when necessary, when new information indicates that the optimum escaped the original range, but without losing information or wasting data.
- The relationship between the simultaneous changes in multiple inputs and the resulting change in the outcome can be studied and modeled by using a design experiment.
- A designed experiment guarantees that the parameters of the chosen model can be estimated and tested for statistical significance.

- The probability that a real change in the outcome will be found to be significant can be determined before any resources or time have been spent.
- The number of samples necessary to achieve a given level of confidence can be determined while planning the experiment.
- The number of samples can be much less for a designed experiment than the total number of samples for independent tests of each input that achieve the same confidence.
- A designed experiment can establish causality by changes in the inputs under controlled conditions.
- The often-important effect of interacting inputs may be accounted for and used to achieve the desired output.

The principles of designing experiments were established in the 1920s. They remain as relevant today as ever before. Over the same period, though, myriad methods of design have been developed. In fact, methods of design remain a very active and important area of development in statistics. This chapter will review the principles, which do not depend on the methods. At the same time, several methods, but by no means all methods, will be presented that have proven useful to Six Sigma improvement projects. Some situations might require more advanced techniques than those presented in this chapter.

TERMINOLOGY

> Define basic DOE terms, e.g., independent and dependent variables, factors and levels, response, treatment, error, nested. (Understand)
>
> **Body of Knowledge VII.A.1**

Design of experiments (DOE) is a statistical approach to gaining empirical knowledge. Design of experiments provides the most efficient and economical methods of determining the effect of a set of independent variables, or factors, on a response variable. Knowledge of this relationship permits the experimenter to optimize a process and predict a response variable by setting the factors at specific levels. In other words, the objective of a designed experiment is to generate knowledge about a product or process and establish the mathematical relationship $Y = f(X)$, or empirical model, where X is a list of independent variables and Y is the dependent variable.

Suppose that there is a process for etching the surface of a silicon wafer and there are three factors that determine the rate of etching. Each of the three factors can be set at either a low or high level. The question is, "What level should each factor be set to in order to provide the desired rate of etching?"

To better understand the concept of DOE, we will first provide a few fundamental definitions:

- An *experimental design* is a formal plan that details the specifics for conducting an experiment, such as which responses, factors, levels, blocks, treatments, and tools are to be used.
- An *effect* is a change in the response when the level of one or more factors changes. A model typically represents the relationship between a factor and a response variable. Note that there can be many factors and response variables. The model includes any terms that are necessary to account for the effect. Specific types of terms include main effect (first-order or additive change); dispersion effect (change in variation); interaction effect (the effect of one factor depends on the level of another factor); and quadratic effect (second-order change). We will deal specifically with main and interaction effects.
- The *response variable* is the observed result or value of an experimental treatment. It is sometimes known as the *output variable, dependent variable,* or y *variable.* There may be multiple response variables in an experimental design.
- The *observed value* is a particular value of a response variable determined as a result of a test or measurement.
- A *factor* is an independent variable or assignable cause that might affect the responses, and of which different levels are included in the experiment. There are different kinds of factors. Each kind of factor determines the levels that may be set and the way its effects may be modeled. Factors are also known as *explanatory variables, predictor variables, input variables,* or *x variables.*
- A *continuous factor* may take on any value over a given range. A temperature between 20°C and 35°C is an example of a continuous factor. A continuous factor effect is modeled as a coefficient of change, or a slope. A discrete numeric factor is also a continuous factor that can be set to a predetermined set of three or more values. A temperature that must be tested at 20°C, 25°C, 30°C, and 35°C is an example of a discrete numeric factor. A discrete numeric effect is modeled as coefficients for all the polynomial terms required.
- A *categorical factor* may take on only one of a given set of values. A choice of suppliers (Supplier A, B, or C) is an example of a categorical factor.
- A factor might be the proportion of an ingredient in a formulation. Such factors are known as *mixture components.* Flour present in a recipe as a proportion between 0.6 (60%) and 0.7 (70%) is an example of a

mixture component. The proportion of all the mixture components in a formulation are constrained to add to one (100%) or some constant proportion less than one for a sub-mixture. For example, flour might range from 0.6 to 0.7 among the dry ingredients, which total 0.8 (80%) of the entire recipe, while the wet ingredients are not varied, but always make up the remaining 0.2 (20%).

- A *noise factor* is an independent variable that is difficult or too expensive to control as part of standard experimental conditions. In general, it is not desirable to make inferences on noise factors, but they are included in an experiment to broaden the conclusions regarding control factors.
- A *level* is the setting or assignment of a factor at a specific value. Factor levels generally change independently of one another. Some situations put constraints on changes or combinations of factor levels. For example, the levels of mixture components do not change independently because they must sum to one.
- The *design space* is the multidimensional region of possible treatment combinations formed by the selected factors and their levels. We can think of each factor as adding another dimension to the space. For their "Quality by Design" (QbD) requirements, the U.S. Food and Drug Administration (FDA) defines design space as the range for each process factor that will produce consistently acceptable results for manufacture of the products they regulate.
- *Experimental error* is the variation that occurs in the response variable beyond that which is accounted for by changes in the factors, blocks, or other assignable source when conducting an experiment. This unexplained variation is included in the statistical model as a random term or effect and estimated as a variance. This variance is used to estimate the standard error of the estimated model coefficients. In practice, this term is truncated to just "error."
- A *treatment* is the specific setting or combination of factor levels for an experimental unit.
- An *experimental unit* is the smallest entity receiving a particular treatment that yields a value of the response variable.
- An *optimal design* is one in which the set of all treatments maximizes an optimization criterion. These designs are discovered using numerical search algorithms instead of being generated by rules about combining factor levels. Optimal designs often reproduce designs generated by the older methods. Optimal designs can accommodate real-world requirements and constraints more easily than factorial methods.
- An *optimization criterion* is a mathematical function of the treatments that represents a useful characteristic of a design. The *D-optimality* criterion represents the amount of information available to estimate

the parameters in the model. The D-optimal design generally provides higher power and smaller confidence intervals for the parameters. Factorial designs, which are described below, are D-optimal. The *I-optimality* criterion represents the amount of information available in the estimate of the response from the model. The I-optimal design generally provides smaller confidence intervals of the predicted response. The response surface designs, described below, are nearly I-optimal. Many other criteria have been developed for more specialized characteristics of a design, but D-optimality and I-optimality are the most common choices.

- An *experimental run* results from applying a specific treatment combination in the design to an experimental unit.
- The *number of runs, n,* represents the total number of treatment combinations and replicates that will be conducted. The number of runs in a full-factorial design, if all factors have the same number of levels, is

$$n = rL^k$$

where

n = Number of runs

r = Number of replicates

L = Number of levels

k = Number of factors

For a two-level factorial experiment, the number of runs is written:

$$n = r2^k$$

- According to Montgomery (2019), "by a *factorial design,* we mean that in each complete trial or replicate of the experiment all possible combinations of the levels of the factors are investigated."

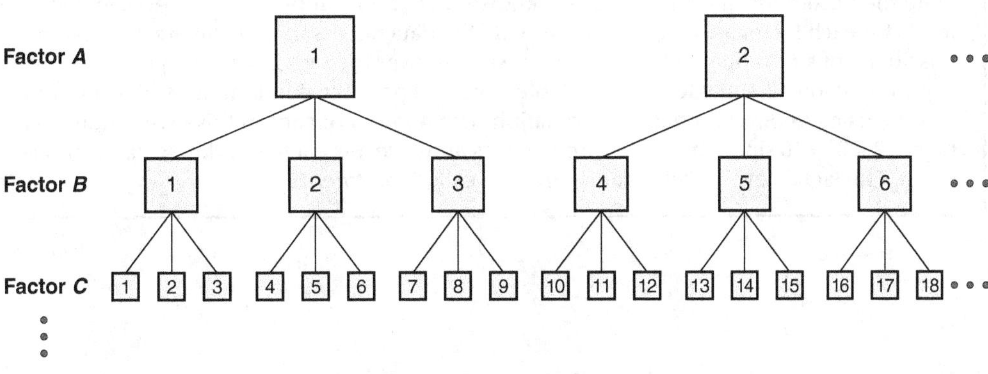

Figure 24.1 A typical structure of a nested design.

- A *nested design* is one in which the levels of one factor, say factor B, are nested under the levels of another factor, say factor A, and the levels of B are different for every level of A. These designs can be especially useful in the collection of data for a measurement system analysis from which the components of variance are to be estimated. This concept is best illustrated graphically as shown in Figure 24.1. Note the uniqueness of the numbering in Figure 24.1. In this figure, each subordinate level box is assigned to one unique higher-level box. To further illustrate, let's assume factor A is suppliers, factor B is ovens, and factor C is batches. Supplier 1 owns oven 1, which produced batches 1, 2, and 3, whereas supplier 2 owns oven 4, which produced batches 10, 11, and 12.

We will now illustrate the design of a full-factorial experiment with three factors varied at two levels each.

EXAMPLE 24.1

Suppose an operator can adjust the electrode gap, C_2F6 gas flow rate, and cathode RF power of a silicon wafer nitride etching process. See Montgomery (2019). Furthermore, she wishes to find the settings that will produce the desired etch rate. The gap, gas flow, and power are called the *factors*, or *independent variables*. The silicon nitride etch rate of (Å/m) is called the *response*, or *dependent variable*, because its value depends on the values of the independent variables through the mathematical relationship that will be determined by the experiment. There might be additional independent variables, such as the batch of the etching agent, which influence the dependent variable, but these variables will be controlled.

The experimenter has decided that three continuous factors will be tested at two levels each:

- Gap (*G*): 0.8 and 1.2 (cm)
- Gas Flow (*GF*): 125 and 200 (SCCM)
- Power (*P*): 275 and 325 (W)

The experimenter has decided to conduct a replicated full-factorial experiment to generate the maximum amount of process knowledge. (Replication is described later.) Two levels for each factor, though, do not provide the data necessary to estimate and test the possibility of a non-linear change in the response over the factor ranges. A full-factorial experiment (discussed later in this chapter) tests all possible combinations of levels and factors, using one run for each combination. The number of runs in this experiment will be $n = 2 \times 2^3 = 16$ since there are three factors at two levels each and the design is replicated. The factor level combinations are also called *treatments*.

Continued

Continued

Gap	Gas Flow	Power	Etch Rate Rep. 1	Etch Rate Rep. 2
0.8	125	275	550	604
0.12	125	275	669	650
0.8	200	275	633	601
0.12	200	275	642	635
0.8	125	325	1037	1052
1.2	125	325	749	868
0.8	200	325	1075	1063
1.2	200	325	729	860

Table 24.1 A 2^3 full-factorial experimental design for Example 24.1.

DESIGN PRINCIPLES

> Define and apply DOE principles, e.g., power, sample size, balance, repetition, replication, order, efficiency, randomization, blocking, interaction, confounding, resolution. (Apply)
>
> **Body of Knowledge VII.A.2**

DOE is an effective tool for determining causal relationships between independent and response variables. However, considerable attention must be given to planning and conducting an experiment. Therefore, it is important to identify and define critical concepts underlying experimental designs:

- Coded factor levels
- Power and sample size
- Repeated measures (repetition)
- Replication
- Confounding
- Order
- Randomization
- Blocking
- Main effect

- Interaction effect
- Balanced design
- Resolution
- Source table

Each of these concepts will be discussed in detail in the following subsections.

Coded Factor Levels

The estimates of the model parameters depend on the measurement scale of the factor. This dependence makes interpretation difficult and unnecessarily introduces correlation among the parameter estimates. For example, a change in temperature of 1 degree is different if the scale is in degrees Celsius, Fahrenheit, or Kelvin. A scale-invariant estimate may be based on *coded factor levels*. The low setting is replaced by a coded value of –1 and the high setting is replaced by +1. The middle of the factor range, or center point, is replaced by 0. The new settings are often represented simply as – and + as seen in the examples that follow.

Using the coded factor levels, the resulting parameter estimates represent the change of one unit on the coded scale, which is now half the range for all factors. Twice the estimate is the change over the entire range, or the full effect of the factor. Now one can compare the relative importance of each effect. The intercept in the model is now the mean response at the origin of the design space.

Coding the factor levels provides additional statistical benefits as well, especially when the model contains higher-order terms for interaction and non-linear effects.

Statistical software for the analysis of a design experiments automatically codes the factor levels during a linear regression analysis, so it is not necessary to manually perform this coding. The parameter estimates may then be doubled to obtain the same effects that are manually calculated here.

Power and Sample Size

The concepts of power and sample size were discussed in Chapter 21. Recall that the more power a test has, the greater the sensitivity of that test to detect small differences. More power also conveys more confidence in conclusions and indicates greater reproducibility of findings. Power increases as the sample size increases, the response variance decreases, or the effect size increases. Power should be determined before conducting an experiment. Also, as the power of the test increases, the probability of a Type II error, β, decreases.

Repeated Measures (Repetition)

A *repeated measure*, also known as a *repetition*, is the measurement of a response variable more than once for the same run. Repetition occurs when the responses from each run are measured *n* times in a row, or measured over time, as with stability studies. Repetition allows one to determine the variation of the measurements. Table 24.2 provides an example of repetitions.

Replication

Replication occurs when the same treatment is applied to a new experimental unit. Replication of the entire experiment is often performed for a factorial design. Each new run is called a *replicate.* Replication allows one to determine the variation of response, or the experimental error. Replication increases the precision of the estimated effects in an experiment. Replication differs from repeated measures because it repeats the entire factorial experiment, not just the measurements for the same run. It is more effective when all elements contributing to the experimental error are included. Replication reflects the sources of variability both within and between runs and adds degrees of freedom to the experiment.

In some cases, replication may be limited to repeated measures under essentially the same conditions. In this case, we would use the average when analyzing the experiment. For example, a food is assessed on a 1 to 9 scale by a panel of tasters. Putting these results in as if they were true replicates will generate false-positive results due to underestimating the true variation of re-making each food product from scratch.

Table 24.3 provides an example of an experiment that uses replication (different runs). (Note that the actual low and high factor levels have been replaced by their coded levels –1 and +1, respectively, or simply – and +, to be described below.)

Confounding

Confounding means that the effects of factors cannot be distinguished from one another. Confounding occurs when the column of levels in the model matrix that is used to estimate an effect is the same as the column to estimate another effect. In other words, these effects are all *aliases* for the same analysis column. Confounding occurs with fractional factorial designs because such designs do not include every possible combination of factor levels. However, some of the effects of confounding are mitigated because higher-order interactions are generally assumed to not be statistically significant. Domain expertise is valuable in assessing the likelihood of higher-order effects. We can choose which effects are confounded to

Run	Gap	Gas Flow	Power	Responses	
1	–	–	–	550	604
2	+	–	–	669	650
3	–	+	–	633	601
4	+	+	–	642	635
5	–	–	+	1037	1052
6	+	–	+	749	868
7	–	+	+	1075	1063
8	+	+	+	729	860

Table 24.2 Repetition (16 measurements, 2 from each of 8 runs).

Run	Gap	Gas Flow	Power	Responses
1	–	–	–	550
2	+	–	–	669
3	–	+	–	633
4	+	+	–	642
5	–	–	+	1037
6	+	–	+	749
7	–	+	+	1075
8	+	+	+	729
9	–	–	–	604
10	+	–	–	650
11	–	+	–	601
12	+	+	–	635
13	–	–	+	1052
14	+	–	+	868
15	–	+	+	1063
16	+	+	+	860

Table 24.3 Replication (16 measurements, 1 from each of 16 runs).

some extent to permit the estimation of these higher-order terms, but this choice often requires knowledge that is not available when designing the experiment.

Order

Order refers to the sequence in which the runs of an experiment will be conducted. Generally, we talk about two types of order:

- *Standard order* is also referred to as Yate's order, in which the first factor varies the fastest while the last factor varies the slowest. To understand the Yate's pattern, examine the second, third, and fourth columns of Table 24.3. Notice the pattern of the low and high levels. The first factor changes the most frequently, and the last factor the least. Note that some statistical software packages display a catalog of design choices that are not written in Yate's order.
- *Run order* shows what the order of the runs in an experiment would be if the experiment were run in random order. Random order works to spread the effects of noise variables and to help the data meet some of the important assumptions of regression analysis: independent observations and normally distributed errors.

Randomization

Randomization is used to assign treatments to experimental units so that each unit has an equal chance of being assigned a particular treatment, thus minimizing the effect of variation from uncontrolled noise factors. A completely randomized design is one in which the treatments are assigned at random to the full set of experimental units and all the factors are reset before each run. For example, when using the design shown in Table 24.3 the power factor must be set 16 times, not just four times, to benefit from randomization. Randomization might be impractical or impossible, in which case the experiment requires a split-plot design, but such a design and its analysis is beyond the scope of this handbook. No blocks are involved in a completely randomized design.

Blocking

A *block* is a group of experimental units. Blocks are usually selected to allow for special causes that are part of the experiment but are not from a factor of interest. These special causes may be avoided within blocks, thus providing a more homogeneous response. *Blocking* refers to the method of grouping runs in an experiment to minimize the impact of selected assignable causes. Randomization of the experiment is now restricted because it only occurs within blocks. The *block effect* is the result of changing the block in an experimental design. Existence of a block effect generally means that the method of blocking was appropriate. The regression model may treat the block effect as either a fixed effect or as a random effect. The regression model also does not allow the block effect to interact with factor effects.

An experimental design consisting of b blocks with t treatments assigned via randomization to the experimental units within each block is known as a *randomized block design* and is used to control the variability of experimental units. For completely randomized designs, no stratification of the experimental units is made. In the randomized block design, the treatments are randomly allotted within each block; that is, the randomization is restricted. Like the randomized block design, a *randomized block factorial design* is a design where each block includes a complete set of factorial combinations.

EXAMPLE 24.2

Table 24.3 depicts eight treatments, and each treatment is replicated, thus producing 16 tests. If it is not possible to run all 16 treatments under the same conditions, the experimenter might decide to use blocking. For example, if the 16 runs must be spread over two shifts, the experimenter would be concerned about the impact the shift difference could have on the results. This concern could benefit from blocking by shift. That is, the runs would be randomized in one of the replicates of the entire design (eight runs) for each shift. The two replicates for each treatment are thus split between the two blocks (shifts). The result is formally known as a randomized complete block design. On the other hand, the electrode gap is likely the most difficult to adjust, so the experimenter might be tempted to perform all the runs with Gap = 0.8 cm during the first shift and all the runs with Gap = 1.2 cm during the second shift. This approach is no longer a blocked design or a randomized design. The problem here is that the impact of the change in

Continued

Continued

the electrode gap is confounded with the impact of the change in shift. Another problem is that the electrode gap is not reset in every run, so the experiment is not randomized. The regression model is no longer appropriate because it uses a single term for the random effect of the statistical errors. Another term for the random effect (variance) of resetting the electrode gap is required.

Main Effect

A *main effect* is the impact or influence of a single factor on the mean of the response variable. A *main effects plot* is a visualization of the average responses at the various levels of individual factors.

EXAMPLE 24.3

Refer to the data given in Table 24.3. This experiment is replicated but not blocked. The first step in calculating the main effects, sometimes called the *average main effects,* is to average the results for each level of each factor. For example, the mean response when the Gap = 0.8 cm is calculated by averaging the result of the eight runs in which electrode was set to 0.8 cm. Note that this method of calculating the main effect is only valid for a balanced design, such as this full-factorial design. Linear regression is required to estimate the effects when the design is not balanced.

Table 24.4 shows the calculations for the mean response at each level of each factor. Figure 24.2 plots the three main effects.

Condition	Calculation	Mean Response
Gap = 0.8 cm	$\frac{550+604+663+601+1037+1052+1075+1063}{8}$	826.875
Gap = 1.2 cm	$\frac{669+650+642+635+749+868+729+860}{8}$	725.25
Gas Flow = 125 SCCM	$\frac{550+604+669+650+1037+1052+749+868}{8}$	772.375
Gas Flow = 250 SCCM	$\frac{633+601+642+635+1075+1063+729+860}{8}$	779.75
Power = 275 W	$\frac{550+604+669+650+633+601+642+645}{8}$	623.00
Power = 325 W	$\frac{1037+1052+749+868+1075+1063+729+860}{8}$	929.125

Table 24.4 Mean response for each factor level for Example 24.3.

Continued

Continued

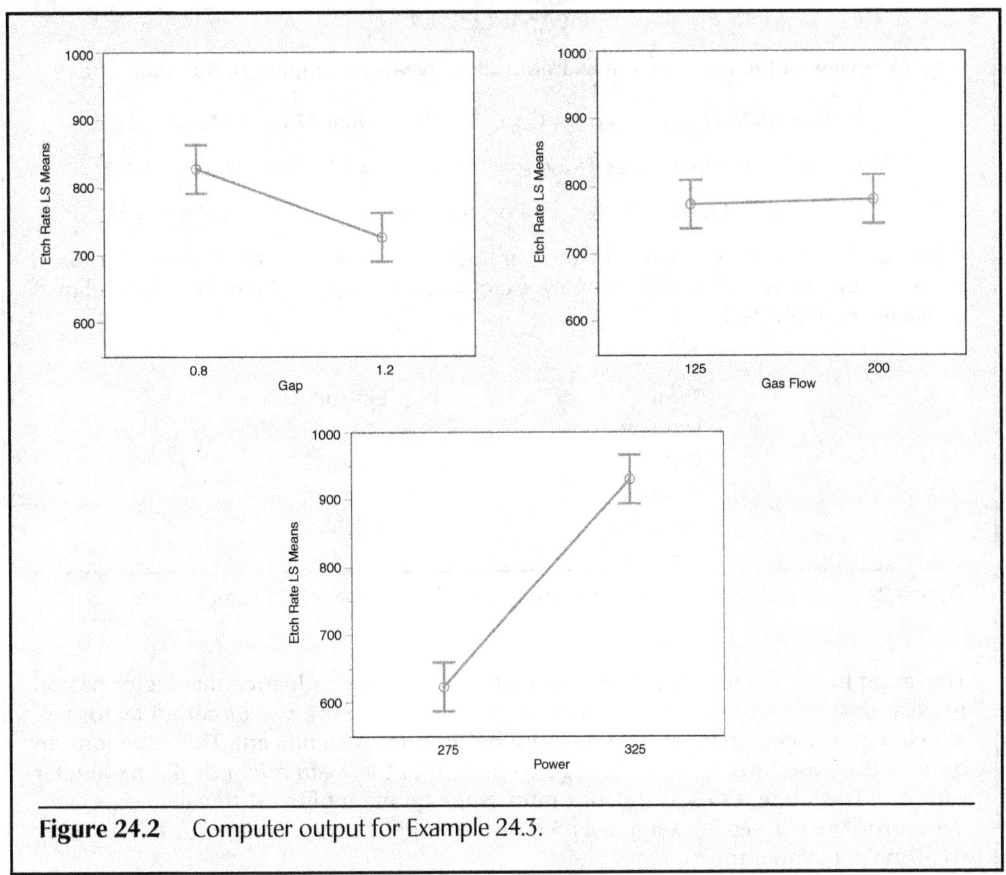

Figure 24.2 Computer output for Example 24.3.

EXAMPLE 24.4

A quick review of the results from Example 24.3 reveals the impact of the main effects:

$$Gap\ Main\ Effect = Gap_{1.2} - Gap_{0.8} = 725.25 - 826.875 = -101.635$$

$$Gas\ Flow\ Main\ Effect = Gas\ Flow_{200} - Gas\ Flow_{125} = 779.75 - 772.375 = 7.375$$

$$Power\ Main\ Effect = Power_{325} - Power_{275} = 929.125 - 623.00 = 306.125$$

Figure 24.3 shows the estimates of the parameters from statistical software that used coded factor levels, so the estimates are exactly half the size of the main effects shown above for Example 24.4.

Term	Estimate
Intercept	776.0625
Gap	-50.8125
Gas Flow	3.6875
Power	153.0625

Figure 24.3 Estimates of main effects using coded factor levels for Example 24.4.

The larger the absolute value of the main effect, the more influence that factor has on the response variable. This comparison is facilitated with the use of coded factor levels. However large, a main effect might not be statistically significant. This situation can occur if the experimental error is large compared to the main effect or the parameter estimate. The Student's *t* statistic, or *t*-ratio, is the quotient of the estimate and its standard error. We will see in Example 24.5 how the *t*-ratio can be assessed by determining its probability under the null hypothesis.

Interaction Effect

An *interaction effect* occurs when the effect of one factor depends on the level of one or more other factors. The existence of an interaction effect means that the effect of changing factors is more than the sum of the main effects. An *interaction plot* is a graphical depiction that gives the average responses at the combinations of levels of two distinct factors.

Interaction effects are important for two reasons. The first reason is that interaction effects lead to unexpected results when they are unknown, or when they are ignored. That is, you cannot predict the change in the response without knowing the level of both factors. The second reason is that they represent an opportunity to mitigate the impact of a hard-to-control factor. We can use the other factor that is involved in the interaction to reduce the effect of the hard-to-control factor. This approach is known as *robust design*.

EXAMPLE 24.5

Interaction effects may be determined by multiplying the coded factor levels as shown in Table 24.5. The corresponding parameters estimates (half the effect size when using coded factor levels) are shown along with the interaction plot in Figure 24.4.

Run	G	GF	P	G × GF	G × P	GF × P	G × GF × P	Average Etch Rate
1	–	–	–	+	+	+	–	577.0
2	+	–	–	–	–	+	+	659.5
3	–	+	–	–	+	–	+	617.0
4	+	+	–	+	–	–	–	638.5
5	–	–	+	+	–	–	+	1044.5
6	+	–	+	–	+	–	–	808.5
7	–	+	+	–	–	+	–	1069.0
8	+	+	+	+	+	+	+	794.5

Table 24.5 The columns for calculation of the interaction effects for Example 24.5.

For analysis of data from an experiment, the null hypothesis is that changing the factor level makes no difference in the response. The α risk is the probability that the analysis will show that there is a significant difference when there is no difference (i.e., the null hypothesis is true). This conclusion is called a *Type I error* or a "false positive." The β risk is the probability that the analysis will show that there is no significant difference when there is a difference (i.e., the null hypothesis is false). This conclusion is called a *Type II error* or a "false negative." The power of the experiment is defined as $(1 - \beta)$, so the higher the power of the experiment, the lower the β risk. In general, a higher number of runs or replicates provides a more precise estimate of experimental error, which in turn reduces the β risk.

The standard error is the estimated variation in the parameter estimate. It is interpreted much like the standard deviation of the data that informs you about typical variation or deviation from the mean value. The standard error informs you of the typical variation or deviation of the estimate from the mean parameter. Note that the standard error for all the estimates is the same because the design is balanced.

Based on the *p*-values for the Student's t test, we conclude that the (Gap × Power) interaction is statistically significant, as are the Gas and Power main effects.

Continued

Continued

Term	Estimate	Std Error	t Ratio	Prob>|t|
Intercept	776.0625	11.2259	69.13	<.0001*
Gap	-50.8125	11.2259	-4.53	0.0014*
Gas Flow	3.6875	11.2259	0.33	0.7501
Power	153.0625	11.2259	13.63	<.0001*
Gap * Gas Flow	-12.4375	11.2259	-1.11	0.2966
Gap * Power	-76.8125	11.2259	-6.84	<.0001*
Gas Flow * Power	-1.0625	11.2259	-0.09	0.9267

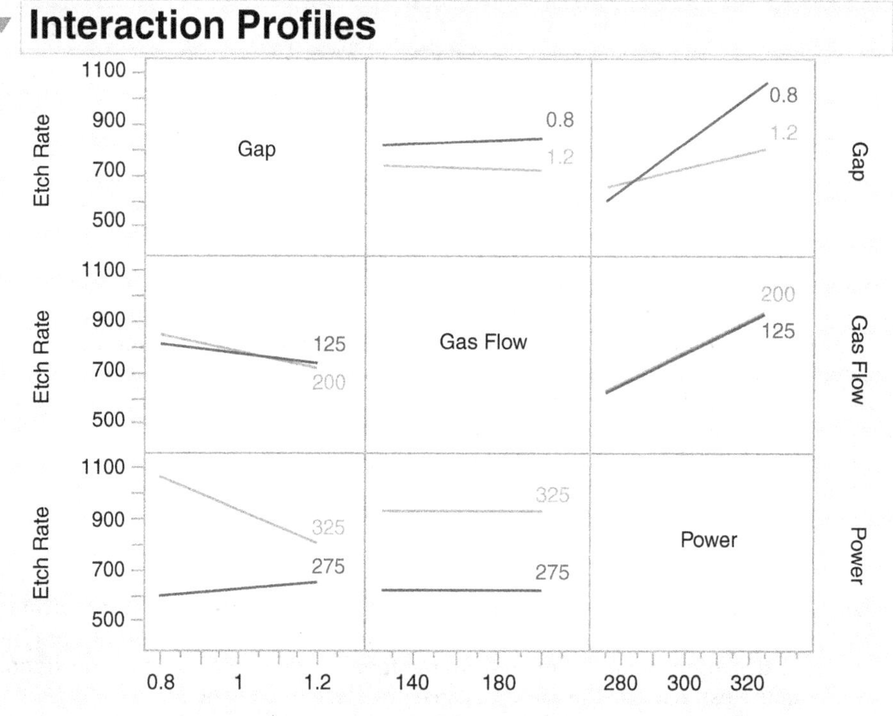

Figure 24.4 Estimated interaction effects and plots using coded factor levels for Example 24.5.

We notice the following in Figure 24.4:

- The parameter estimates are half the size of the effects calculated above due to the coded factor levels.
- The Gas Flow and Power curves are parallel, indicating that no interaction is present.
- The Gap and Gas Flow curves are not parallel, but the interaction effect is small.
- The Gap and Power curves are not parallel and indicate a large interaction effect. We cannot predict the etch rate at a power setting equal to 325 unless we know the level of the gap.

Balanced Design

The number of runs associated with each factor level is the same in a balanced design. For example, in Table 24.1, there are four runs with a low Gap and four runs with a high Gap. Moreover, the number of runs associated with each factor level is balanced over all the levels of the other factors. For example, the four runs with a low Gap are balanced over low and high levels of Gas Flow and Power. Notice that the number of runs for the low level is the same as the number of runs for the high level for all three factors. Moreover, the runs for the low level are balanced over the low and high levels of the other factors.

A balanced design benefits the analysis in several ways. First, all the parameter estimates are uncorrelated. As a result, the estimates do not change when terms are added or removed from the model. Second, the lack of correlation means that the standard errors of the estimates are the smallest possible. (Correlation inflates the standard errors of the estimates, which in turn decreases the *t*-ratios and, therefore, the power of the hypothesis tests.) Third, the calculation of the effects simplifies to the difference between mean responses for each level.

Resolution

Resolution in the context of experimental design refers to the level of confounding in a fractional factorial design. Resolution is important when choosing a fractional factorial design. The amount and kind of information available from the experiment must be weighed against the number of runs. Higher resolution yields more information and is generally achieved by using a larger design, but it is less economical. Black Belts must consider this information/cost trade-off when planning an experiment.

The resolution of a design is generally one more than the smallest order of any term with which a main effect is confounded. It is also the smallest sum of the order of the effects on both sides of the confounding equations. For example, if the first order term for factor A in a three-factor design is confounded with the second order interaction effect B × C, then the confounding equation is A = B × C, and the resolution is 1 + 2 = III. Resolution is numbered with Roman numerals. Common resolution designs follow:

- Resolution III
  - No main effects are confounded with another main effect
  - One or more main effects are confounded with two-factor interactions
  - Some two-factor interactions may be confounded with other two-factor interactions
- Resolution IV
  - No main effects are confounded with another main effect
  - No main effects are confounded with two-factor interactions
  - Main effects are confounded with three-factor interactions
  - Some two-factor interactions are confounded with other two-factor interactions

- Resolution V
  - No main effects are confounded with another main effect
  - No main effects are confounded with two-factor interactions
  - No main effects are confounded with three-factor interactions
  - Main effects are confounded with four-factor interactions
  - No two-factor interactions are confounded with other two-factor interactions
  - Two-factor interactions may be confounded with three-factor interactions

Higher levels of resolution can also be achieved depending on the specific fractional factorial design. However, the matter of resolution is based on addressing the issue of confounding. Confounded effects cannot be simultaneously estimated. The terms with aliases may not appear together in the same model. If both effects are active, then leaving one of them out of the model will lead to biased estimates for the term that remains in the model.

Some questions an experimenter must ask when choosing a fractional factorial design regarding confounding include:

- Which terms, if any, are confounded?
- Can I live with the confounding? Is the confounding in higher-order interactions that can be assumed to be negligible? (See key screening principles later.)
- Does the confounding exist in lower-order interactions that have an impact?
- Can I remove or minimize the confounding through a carefully designed fractional factorial? This change requires prior knowledge that might not be available.

Thoughtful consideration along with subject matter expertise is required before designing fractional factorial designs.

EXAMPLE 24.6

Table 24.6 shows a 2^4 (two levels for four factors) full-factorial design. Table 24.7 illustrates confounding with interaction columns in the model matrix based on one of the half fractions of the 2^4 full-factorial design. It is a resolution IV design. Note that there are six two-factor interactions, four three-factor interactions, and one four-factor interaction. Also note that factor A is confounded with the BCD interaction because they have the same pattern in the column from the model matrix. All the confounded pairs are shown in Table 24.7. Different terms that have identical columns are called aliases of that column.

Continued

The big advantage of this fractional factorial is that, although there is confounding, main effects are confounded with three-factor interactions only. Since three-factor interactions are often small, the aliasing of main effects is usually minor. If there is a significant three-factor interaction, though, it will be missed with this design. Another downside of this design is that two-factor interactions are confounded with each other (for example, AB with CD). This means that an accurate picture of two-factor interactions is not possible.

Table 24.8 depicts an alternate or complementary one-half fraction of the same 2^4 factorial design given in Table 24.6. The alternate might include treatments that are more practical to run. In fact, the confounded (or aliased) pairs are the same as Table 24.7. However, notice that the header row is a bit different. A negative sign precedes some of the interactions, and the signs in corresponding columns are reversed from Table 24.7. This change is because the *defining relation* for this design is negative. The discussion of the defining relation is beyond the scope of this book. Readers interesting in pursuing this topic further are referred to Montgomery (2019).

Run	*A*	*B*	*C*	*D*
1	–	–	–	–
2	+	–	–	–
3	–	+	–	–
4	+	+	–	–
5	–	–	+	–
6	+	–	+	–
7	–	+	+	–
8	+	+	+	–
9	–	–	–	+
10	+	–	–	+
11	–	+	–	+
12	+	+	–	+
13	–	–	+	+
14	+	–	+	+
15	–	+	+	+
16	+	+	+	+

Table 24.6 2^4 full-factorial design without interactions shown for Example 24.6.

Continued

Continued

Confounded (aliased) pairs

Runs	*A*	*B*	*C*	*D*	*AB*	*AC*	*AD*	*BC*	*BD*	*CD*	*ABC*	*ABD*	*ACD*	*BCD*	*ABCD*
1	–	–	–	–	+	+	+	+	+	+	–	–	–	–	+
4	+	+	–	–	+	–	–	–	–	+	–	–	+	+	+
6	+	–	+	–	–	+	–	–	+	–	–	+	–	+	+
7	–	+	+	–	–	–	+	+	–	–	–	+	+	–	+
10	+	–	–	+	–	–	+	+	–	–	+	–	–	+	+
11	–	+	–	+	–	+	–	–	+	–	+	–	+	–	+
13	–	–	+	+	+	–	–	–	–	+	+	+	–	–	+
16	+	+	+	+	+	+	+	+	+	+	+	+	+	+	+

Table 24.7 One-half fraction of a 2^4 factorial design given in Table 24.6.

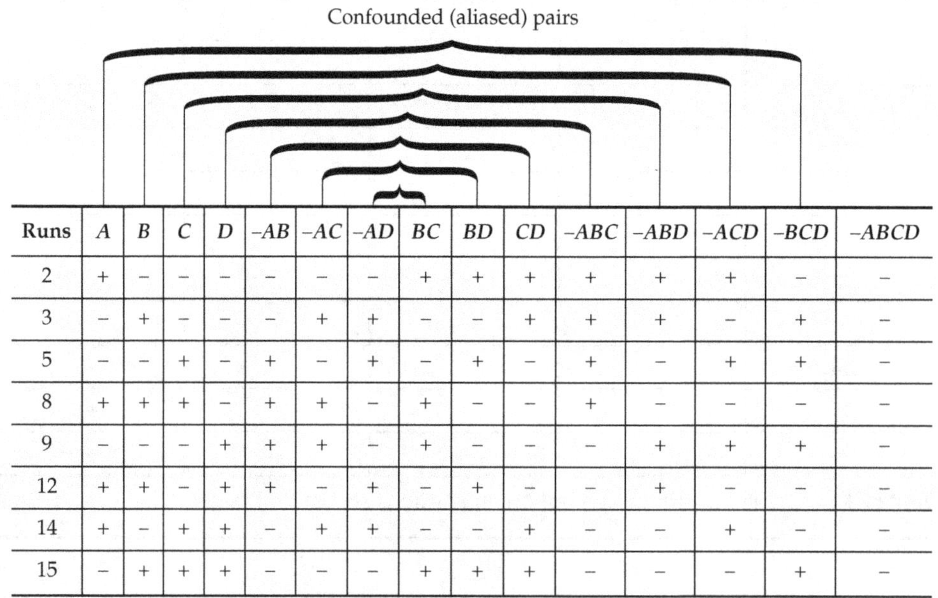

Confounded (aliased) pairs

Runs	*A*	*B*	*C*	*D*	–*AB*	–*AC*	–*AD*	*BC*	*BD*	*CD*	–*ABC*	–*ABD*	–*ACD*	–*BCD*	–*ABCD*
2	+	–	–	–	–	–	–	+	+	+	+	+	+	–	–
3	–	+	–	–	–	+	+	–	–	+	+	+	–	+	–
5	–	–	+	–	+	–	+	–	+	–	+	–	+	+	–
8	+	+	+	–	+	+	–	+	–	–	+	–	–	–	–
9	–	–	–	+	+	+	–	+	–	–	–	+	+	+	–
12	+	+	–	+	+	–	+	–	+	–	–	+	–	–	–
14	+	–	+	+	–	+	+	–	–	+	–	–	+	–	–
15	–	+	+	+	–	–	–	+	+	+	–	–	–	+	–

Table 24.8 Alternative (complementary) one-half fraction of a 2^4 factorial design given in Table 24.6.

Experimental designs are frequently generated today using computer software. Such software presents candidate designs and detailed information, including resolution, to help you decide which design is the best for your situation. A more detailed coverage of the topic of resolution is beyond the scope of this book. Readers interested in pursuing the topic in more depth should consult Montgomery (2019) or Box et al. (2005).

Source Table

A *source table* is a computational table used to analyze an experimental design. The analysis with this table is based on the mean sum of squares, or variances, so this method is more generally known as an *analysis of variance* (ANOVA). The typical structure of a source table is illustrated with two factors *A* and *B* in Table 24.9. These tables are five columns wide and the length depends on the number of factors. The table is built moving from left to right. Column 1 identifies the terms for the main effects, interactions, blocks, and so on. Column 2 lists the sums of squares, which convey the variation in the response that is associated with each term. Formulas for sums of squares for common designs are provided later in this chapter. Column 3 is the degrees of freedom, which account for how much independent information was contributed to each corresponding sum of squares in Column 2. The formulas for the degrees of freedom are provided for common designs later in the chapter. Column 4 is the quotient of the sum of squares and the degrees of freedom, or the mean sum of squares, which is an estimate of the variance associated with each term or the errors. Column 5 is the quotient of the mean sum of squares for a term and the mean sum of squares error, which is an

	1 Sources of variation	2 Sum of squares	3 Degrees of freedom	4 Mean squares	5 F_0 statistic
List of factors	Factor *A*	SS_A	$a-1$	$MS_A = \frac{SS_A}{a-1}$	$F_0 = \frac{MS_A}{MS_E}$
	Factor *B*	SS_B	$b-1$	$MS_B = \frac{SS_B}{b-1}$	$F_0 = \frac{MS_B}{MS_E}$
List of interactions	Interaction *AB*	SS_{AB}	$(a-1)(b-1)$	$MS_{AB} = \frac{SS_{AB}}{(a-1)(b-1)}$	$F_0 = \frac{MS_{AB}}{MS_E}$
Error term	Error	SS_E	$ab(n-1)$	$MS_E = \frac{SS_E}{ab(n-1)}$	
Total term	Total	SS_T	$abn-1$		

Table 24.9 The typical structure of a source table.

F statistic. The variance in the numerator depends on a true effect (alternative hypothesis) but the variance in the denominator does not. Ultimately, the F statistics in Column 5 will be evaluated with an F distribution under the null hypothesis as to whether each term is significant.

Typically, terms related to error, such as *sums of squares* and *degrees of freedom,* are calculated by subtraction. More specifically, for Table 24.9:

$$SS_E = SS_T - SS_A - SS_B - SS_{AB}$$

$$DF_E = DF_T - DF_A - DF_B - DF_{AB}$$

Of course, the above equations can be generalized to account for multiple factors and their effects. This generalization is represented by additional terms in the linear regression model and performed by the statistical software.

Another common source table splits the computations above into two tables. The first table evaluates the whole model (all terms combined), and the second table evaluates the individual terms (effects) as shown in Figure 24.5. The Model Sum of Squares in the Analysis of Variance is equal to the total of the sum of squares for each effect in the Effect Tests. The Model DF in the Analysis of Variance is the total of the DF for each effect in the Effect Tests. The term Nparm refers to the number of parameters associated with the effect, which for a two-level factor, is equal to one.

Analysis of Variance

Source	DF	Sum of Squares	Mean Square	F Ratio
Model	6	42.000000	7.00000	3.5000
Error	1	2.000000	2.00000	**Prob > F**
C. Total	7	44.000000		0.3878

Effect Tests

Source	Nparm	DF	Sum of Squares	F Ratio	Prob > F
Feed(0.01, 0.04)	1	1	0.000000	0.0000	1.0000
Speed (1300, 1800)	1	1	12.500000	6.2500	0.2422
Temperature (100, 140)	1	1	24.500000	12.2500	0.1772
Feed*Speed	1	1	0.500000	0.2500	0.7048
Feed*Temperature	1	1	4.500000	2.2500	0.3743
Speed*Temperature	1	1	0.000000	0.0000	1.0000

Figure 24.5 Computer output using coded factor levels for Example 24.1.

PLANNING EXPERIMENTS

> Plan and evaluate DOEs by determining the objective; selecting appropriate factors, responses, and measurement methods; and choosing the appropriate design. (Evaluate)
>
> **Body of Knowledge VII.A.3**

When preparing to conduct an experiment, the first consideration is, "What question are we seeking to answer?" For example, in Example 24.1, the objective was to find the combination of process settings that produce the target etch rate. Examples of other experimental objectives might be:

- Find the combination of mail and media ads that produces the most sales
- Find the cake recipe that produces the most consistent taste in the presence of oven temperature variation
- Find the combination of valve dimensions that produces the greatest linear output

Sometimes the objective derives from a question. For example, "What's causing the excess variation in hardness at the rolling mill?" could generate the objective "Identify the factors responsible for the hardness variation and find the settings that minimize it." The objective must be related to the goals and objectives of the enterprise. It must also be measurable, so the next step is to establish an appropriate measurement system. The measurement system must be reasonably simple and easy to operate.

In simpler terms, the primary objective of an experimental design is to:

- Identify which independent variables explain the most variation in the response variable
- Determine what levels of the independent variables minimize or maximize the response variable

Once the objective and a measurement system have been determined, the factors and levels are selected. People with the most experience and knowledge about the product or process should be consulted to determine what factors and what levels of each factor are important to achieve the objective. The list of factors and the levels for each factor should flow from their input. But be careful to rule out potential factors based on expert advice in the absence of reproducible and tested data.

Choosing the Appropriate Design: Sequential Experimentation

The next step is to choose the appropriate design. The selection of the design may be constrained by such things as affordability and time available. At this stage, some experimenters establish a budget of time, cost, and other resources that may be used to reach the objective. If production equipment and personnel must be used, how much time is available? How much product and other consumables are available? The choice might also depend on the available prior knowledge and the number of factors involved (complexity). A sequence of experiments is planned to answer all the questions with sufficient detail and accuracy. This strategy is called the *sequential design of experiments.* The initial experiment might only provide the most basic information. For example, the initial experiment may help decide which factors of the many candidates indeed affect the response, separating the "vital few" factors from the "trivial many" factors. The next experiment is run to provide additional data that give new information and improve the accuracy of the information. For example, it is possible to add new runs to the initial experiment in what is called an *augmented design,* for more information and with some economy. Typically, 20 to 25% of the available budget should be allocated to the first experiment because it seldom meets all the objectives and, in fact, often raises as many questions as it answers. Examples of such new questions include:

- What if an additional level had been used for factor A?
- What if a different factor had been included instead of factor B?
- What if the change in the response is not linear?

Therefore, in the absence of much prior knowledge, rather than designing a large initial experiment involving many variables and levels, it is usually best to begin with more a modest screening design. A *screening design* is an experiment intended as a first step to identify a subset of the potential factors for subsequent study. A screening design is not intended to identify all the possible effects to estimate an unbiased model. Examples of screening designs are regular or minimum-run Resolution IV two-level fractional factorial designs, *Plackett-Burman designs,* and *Definitive Screening designs.* All these designs rely on several key screening principles that generally hold when there is little prior knowledge and there are many factors to study. It should be noted that Plackett-Burman designs are Resolution III designs, and are more appropriate for ruggedness testing (based on ASTM's E1169 Standard). If intended for screening, the designs work best if folded over. To learn more about screening designs, readers can refer to Montgomery (2019).

The principle of the *sparsity of effects* states that while there are many factors and potentially many effects of each factor, most factors will be inactive. Screening designs provide only enough data to fit a model with a minority of the potential factors.

The principle of the *hierarchy of effects* states that contribution of effects decreases as the order of the term in the model increases. So main effects tend to be the largest effects, two-factor interaction effects and quadratic effects tend to be the next largest effects, and so on. Screening designs tend to focus on the main effects, but some also consider active second-order effects, but none address third-order effects or higher.

The *hierarchical modeling convention* requires that the individual effects used in higher-order terms be included in the model, regardless of their significance, to prevent ill-formulated polynomials. For example, a model with a significant interaction term involving factors *A* and *B* must also include the main effects of A and B. This convention allows for a standard interpretation of interaction effects.

The principle of the *heredity of effects* states that higher-order terms tend to include the same factors that exhibit main effects. *Strong heredity* implies that all the factors included in the interaction effect are also main effects. *Weak heredity* implies that some of the factors included in the interaction effect are also main effects. For example, if the A × B interaction effect is important, then both A and B are important as main effects under strong heredity but only A or B is important under weak heredity. Heredity often guides the choice of terms in the model.

The principle of *projection* states that the design matrix for a low-resolution screening experiment will exhibit higher resolution and support the estimation of more terms of higher order when only a minority of the factors are active. This property relies on the previous three properties. For example, a resolution III design for 9 factors in 16 runs *projects* into a replicated full factorial (full resolution) for any 3 factors. A definitive screening design may also support the estimation of the full quadratic model when many of the potential factors have been eliminated.

Screening experiments are intended to eliminate the inactive factors from further consideration, so the risk of a Type II error (ruling out) is more important than a Type I error (ruling in). There are two considerations that can help reduce the risk of a false negative outcome. The first approach is to accept a higher Type I error rate. This approach leads to more significant factors that are false positives, but fewer active factors will be determined to be insignificant (false negatives).

The second approach is more quantitative: a power analysis. The analysis of power requires the specification (prior knowledge) of four quantities that control the Type II error rate (β): the level of significance (α), the size of the effect (δ), the sample size (n), and the response variance (σ). The relationship between power and these four experimental variables depends on the statistical hypothesis test that is used to decide significance, but in general, power increases when the level for significance increases, the size of the effect increases, the sample size increases, or the variance decreases. High power is desirable, but it should be at least 80% for screening experiments. It is best to use statistical software for the power analysis. Consult the software documentation for the proper setup of this analysis.

Screening designs may then be augmented after determining which factors and effects might be active to resolve questions about bias in the model from confounding.

The activities outlined in the earlier discussion should not be left to happenstance. Instead, they should result from the development of an experimental plan. An *experimental plan* is the assignment of treatments to each experimental unit and the time order in which the treatments are to be applied. Planning an experiment requires several design considerations:

- Factors that are not varied in the design (held constant)
- Noise factors (discussed previously)
- Confounding and resolution (discussed previously)

- Blocking and randomization (discussed previously)
- The cost to run the experiment
- Time considerations—limited time might be available to conduct the experiment

Montgomery (2019) offers guidelines for conducting experiments:

1. *Recognition and statement of the problem.* As discussed earlier, this step might start with a question, but it must eventually be translated into a statistical problem.
2. *Selection of the response variable.* People most familiar with the process should be consulted.
3. *Choice of factors, levels, and range.* As with guideline #2, the subject matter experts who are familiar with the process should be consulted. Experiments might fail to find significant effects or estimate the effects of continuous factors well because the factor range is too narrow to produce a large enough effect. Do not shrink the range because you think you know where the best setting occurs. Keep the range wide so that the model parameters are estimated well and then use the model to find the best setting.
4. *Choice of experimental design.* Choosing an experimental design requires consideration of an experimental plan (discussed previously).
5. *Performing the experiment.* It is critical that the experimenter understand the conditions under which the experiment was conducted. Ideally, these conditions should match those conditions under which the process is routinely performed.
6. *Statistical analysis of the data.* The data must be carefully analyzed to ensure statistical validity.
7. *Conclusions and recommendations.* Statistical conclusions and recommendations must be translated into terms that management and operations people can understand, particularly if they are expected to support and/or fund process changes.

The next few sections discuss various common designs.

ONE-FACTOR EXPERIMENTS

Understand when to use completely randomized, randomized block, and Latin square designs, and evaluate their results. (Understand)

Body of Knowledge VII.A.4

This section addresses the following designs:

- One-way ANOVA completely randomized
- Randomized complete block design (RCBD)
- Latin square design

For the reader's convenience, the statistical models, source tables, and definitions for the sums of squares have been summarized in three tables. This summary allows the reader to compare each model more readily.

In addition, a *dot notation* is introduced that is commonly used in many formulas. For readers who may be unfamiliar with this notation, see Table 24.10. This table illustrates how the notation is simply a shorthand notation that uses subscripts to show completed summations. This notation is particularly convenient when multiple subscripts are being used concurrently.

The subscript *i* denotes rows and the subscript *j* denotes columns. Replace the subscript *i* with the index value and replace the subscript *j* with the dot (all columns) when summing across the columns. Replace the subscript *i* with the dot (all rows) and replace the subscript *j* with the index value when summing across the rows.

Completely Randomized Design

A *one-factor analysis* is known as a one-way analysis of variance (ANOVA) if the factor is categorical, or as a linear regression if the factor is continuous. The

Sum across "j"

Sum across "i"

y_{11}	y_{12}	.	.	.	y_{1n}	$\sum_{j=1}^{n} y_{ij} = y_{1.}$
y_{21}	y_{22}				y_{2n}	$\sum_{j=1}^{n} y_{ij} = y_{2.}$
.	.				.	.
.	.				.	.
.	.				.	.
y_{n1}	y_{n2}	.	.	.	y_{nn}	
$\sum_{i=1}^{n} y_{ij} = y_{.1}$	$\sum_{i=1}^{n} y_{ij} = y_{.2}$					$\sum_{j=1}^{n} y_{.j} = \sum_{i=1}^{n} y_{i.} =$ $\sum_{i=1}^{n}\sum_{j=1}^{n} y_{ij} = y_{..}$

Table 24.10 Using the "dot" notation in matrices and summations.

categorical factor might include only two levels, in which case it is also known as an "A-B comparison." The categorical factor might have any number of levels greater than two. It is still a one-way ANOVA. The treatments are the levels of only a single factor. The design is replicated to increase power and maintain balance.

The top portions of Tables 24.11-24.13 provide the statistical model, the source table, and the definition of the sums of squares for the one-way ANOVA, respectively. See Example 21.12.

Randomized Complete Block Design

There might be one or two blocking variables in the design. The block effect is also estimated separately from the factor effect. This separation improves the precision of the estimates of the factor effects because the block effects are additional and undesirable variation in the response. In a *randomized complete block design* (RCBD), each block contains all the treatments, and randomization is restricted within blocks.

The middle portions of Table 24.13 provide the statistical model, the source table, and the definition of the sums of squares for the RCBD. Typically, such designs are analyzed using statistical software. However, the following example will be analyzed manually.

EXAMPLE 24.7

This example is taken from Montgomery (2019). A medical device manufacturer produces vascular grafts. These grafts are produced by extruding resin along with a lubricant into tubes. The engineer suspects batch-to-batch variation. Consequently, the developer investigates the effects of four different levels of extrusion pressure using an RCBD design with the batches considered as blocks. The data for this example are shown in Table 24.14. Table 24.16 is like Table 24.15, but column and row totals have been added for treatment and block totals, respectively. In addition, the computations for the sum of squares for both blocks and treatments are shown. Table 24.16 is used for computing the sum of squares for the total. Each cell that held an original data element is now replaced by the square of that original data element. The bottom right corner shown in bold is $y^2 = 193999.3$. The computation for the sum of squares for the total is shown.

At this point, we transfer our sums of squares to the source table shown in Table 24.17 and begin to complete the table. There are four treatments. Therefore, there are three degrees of freedom for the factor. Similarly, there are six blocks. Therefore, there are five degrees of freedom for the block. There are $4 \times 6 - 1$ or 23 degrees of freedom for the total. The degrees of freedom for the error term are obtained by subtraction. The remainder of the table is completed using the procedure described previously.

Assuming $\alpha = 0.05$, we must compare our F_0 value for the treatments to $F_{0.05,3,15}$. From Appendix G.3, the F-value is 3.29. Since $8.1 > 3.29$, we reject the null hypothesis and conclude there is a difference in the mean extrusion pressure. Note that a modern approach to blocks for such sources as batches treat their effect as random. The six batches are just a sample from a population of the batches. Estimating the mean effect of each batch is not useful but estimating the variance across batches is useful. This approach requires the use of a *linear mixed effects regression model*, or simply *mixed model*, which is beyond the scope of this handbook.

Continued

Name	Model	Hypotheses	Assumptions
One-way ANOVA (completely randomized design with fixed effects)	$y_{ij} = \mu + \tau_i + \varepsilon_{ij} \begin{cases} i = 1,2,\ldots,a \\ j = 1,2,\ldots,n \end{cases}$ y_{ij} = jth observation of the ith treatment μ = overall mean τ_i = effect of the ith treatment ε_{ij} = error term	$H_0 : \mu_1 = \mu_2 = \ldots = \mu_a$ $H_A : \mu_i \neq \mu_j$ for at least one pair (i, j) or $H_0 : \tau_1 = \tau_2 = \ldots = \tau_a = 0$ $H_A : \tau_i \neq 0$ for at least one i	$\varepsilon_{ij} : NID(0, \sigma^2)$ and the variance, σ^2, of each factor is constant for all levels
Randomized complete block design (RCBD)	$y_{ij} = \mu + \tau_i + \beta_j + \varepsilon_{ij} \begin{cases} i = 1,2,\ldots,a \\ j = 1,2,\ldots,b \end{cases}$ y_{ij} = jth observation of the ith treatment jth block μ = overall mean τ_i = effect of the ith treatment β_j = effect of the jth block ε_{ij} = error term	$H_0 : \mu_1 = \mu_2 = \ldots = \mu_a$ $H_A : \mu_i \neq \mu_j$ for at least one pair (i, j) or $H_0 : \tau_1 = \tau_2 = \ldots = \tau_a = 0$ $H_A : \tau_i \neq 0$ for at least one i	$\varepsilon_{ij} : NID(0, \sigma^2)$

Table 24.11 Statistical models for common experimental designs.

Note: NID(0, σ^2) means normal and independently distributed with mean 0 and variance σ^2.

Source: Montgomery (2009).

Name	Model	Hypotheses	Assumptions
Latin square design ($p \times p$)	$y_{ijk} = \mu + \alpha_i + \tau_j + \beta_k + \varepsilon_{ijk} \begin{cases} i = 1,2,\ldots,p \\ j = 1,2,\ldots,p \\ k = 1,2,\ldots,p \end{cases}$ y_{ijk} = observation of the ith row, kth column for the jth treatment μ = overall mean α_i = effect of the ith row τ_j = effect of the jth treatment β_k = effect of the kth column ε_{ij} = error term	$H_0 : \mu_1 = \mu_2 = \ldots = \mu_p$ $H_A : \mu_i \neq \mu_j$ for at least one pair (i, j) or $H_0 : \tau_1 = \tau_2 = \ldots = \tau_p = 0$ $H_A : \tau_j \neq 0$ for at least one j	$\varepsilon_{ij} : NID(0, \sigma^2)$

Table 24.11 *Continued.*

Sources of variation	Sum of squares	Degrees of freedom	Mean squares	F_0 statistic
Between treatments	$SS_{\text{Treatments}}$	$a-1$	$MS_B = \frac{SS_B}{a-1}$	$F_0 = \frac{MS_B}{MS_E}$
Error (within treatments)	SS_E (By subtraction	$N-a$	$MS_E = \frac{SS_E}{N-a}$	
Total	SS_T	$N-1$		

One-way ANOVA source table (completed randomized design with fixed effects)

Sources of variation	Sum of squares	Degrees of freedom	Mean squares	*F* statistic
Treatments	$SS_{\text{Treatments}}$	$a-1$	$MS_{\text{Treatments}} = \frac{SS_{\text{Treatments}}}{a-1}$	$F_0 = \frac{MS_{\text{Treatments}}}{MS_E}$
Blocks	SS_{Blocks}	$b-1$	$MS_{\text{Blocks}} = \frac{SS_{\text{Blocks}}}{b-1}$	
Error	SS_E	$(a-1)(b-1)$	$MS_E = \frac{SS_E}{(a-1)(b-1)}$	
Total	SS_T	$N-1$		

Randomized complete block design (RCBD) source table

Sources of variation	Sum of squares	Degrees of freedom	Mean squares	*F* statistic
Treatments	$SS_{\text{Treatments}}$	$p-1$	$MS_{\text{Treatments}} = \frac{SS_{\text{Treatments}}}{p-1}$	$F_0 = \frac{MS_{\text{Treatments}}}{MS_E}$
Rows	SS_{Rows}	$p-1$	$MS_{\text{Rows}} = \frac{SS_{\text{Rows}}}{p-1}$	
Columns	SS_{Columns}	$p-1$	$MS_{\text{Columns}} = \frac{SS_{\text{Columns}}}{p-1}$	
Error	SS_E (By subtraction)	$(p-2)(p-1)$	$MS_E = \frac{SS_E}{(p-2)(p-1)}$	
Total	SS_T	(p^2-1)		

Latin square design source table

Table 24.12 Source tables for the models in Table 24.11.
Source: Montgomery (2009).

Statistical model	Sums of squares (SS)
One-way ANOVA (completely randomized design with fixed effects)	$SS_T = \sum_{i=1}^{a}\sum_{j=1}^{n} y_{ij}^2 - \frac{y_{..}^2}{N}$ $SS_{\text{Treatments}} = \sum_{i=1}^{a} \frac{y_{i.}^2}{n} - \frac{y_{..}^2}{N}$ $SS_E = SS_T - SS_{\text{Treatments}}$
Randomized complete block design (RCBD)	$SS_T = \sum_{i=1}^{a}\sum_{j=1}^{b} y_{ij}^2 - \frac{y_{..}^2}{N}$ $SS_{\text{Treatments}} = \sum_{i=1}^{a} \frac{y_{i.}^2}{b} - \frac{y_{..}^2}{N}$ $SS_{\text{Blocks}} = \sum_{j=1}^{b} \frac{y_{.j}^2}{a} - \frac{y_{..}^2}{N}$ $SS_E = SS_T - SS_{\text{Treatments}} - SS_{\text{Blocks}}$
Latin square design ($p \times p$)	$SS_T = \sum_{i=1}^{p}\sum_{j=1}^{p}\sum_{k=1}^{p} y_{ijk}^2 - \frac{y_{...}^2}{N}$ $SS_{\text{Treatments}} = \sum_{i=1}^{p} \frac{y_{.j.}^2}{p} - \frac{y_{...}^2}{N}$ $SS_{\text{Rows}} = \sum_{i=1}^{p} \frac{y_{i..}^2}{p} - \frac{y_{...}^2}{N}$ $SS_{\text{Columns}} = \sum_{k=1}^{p} \frac{y_{..k}^2}{p} - \frac{y_{...}^2}{N}$ $SS_E = SS_T - SS_{\text{Treatments}} - SS_{\text{Rows}} - SS_{\text{Columns}}$

Table 24.13 Sums of squares for the models given in Table 24.11.
Source: Montgomery (2009).

Pressure	1	2	3	4	5	6
8500	90.3	89.2	98.2	93.9	87.4	97.9
8700	92.5	89.5	90.6	94.7	87.0	95.8
8900	85.5	90.8	89.6	86.2	88.0	93.4
9100	82.5	89.5	85.6	87.4	78.9	90.7

Table 24.14 Data for Example 24.7.

Continued

	Block (Batch)						
Pressure	**1**	**2**	**3**	**4**	**5**	**6**	**Treatment totals**
8500	90.3	89.2	98.2	93.9	87.4	97.9	556.9
8700	92.5	89.5	90.6	94.7	87.0	95.8	550.1
8900	85.5	90.8	89.6	86.2	88.0	93.4	533.5
9100	82.5	89.5	85.6	87.4	78.9	90.7	514.6
Block totals	350.8	359.0	364.0	362.2	341.3	377.8	2155.1

$$SS_{\text{Treatment}} = \frac{(556.9)^2 + (550.1)^2 + (533.5)^2 + (514.6)^2}{4} - \frac{(2155.1)^2}{24} = 178.2$$

$$SS_{\text{Block}} = \frac{(350.8)^2 + (359.0)^2 + (364.0)^2 + (362.2)^2 + (341.3)^2 + (377.8)^2}{6} - \frac{(2155.1)^2}{24} = 192.3$$

Table 24.15 Computation of $SS_{\text{Treatment}}$ and SS_{Block}.

	Block (Batch)						
Pressure	**1**	**2**	**3**	**4**	**5**	**6**	**Total**
8500	8154.1	7956.6	9643.2	8817.2	7638.8	9584.4	51794.4
8700	8556.3	8010.3	8208.4	8968.1	7569.0	9177.6	50489.6
8900	7310.3	8244.6	8028.2	7430.4	7744.0	8723.6	47481.1
9100	6806.3	8010.3	7327.4	7638.8	6225.2	8226.5	44234.3
Total	30826.8	32221.8	33207.1	32854.5	29177.0	35712.1	193999.3

$$SS_T = 193999.3 - \frac{(2155.1)^2}{24} = 193999.3 - 193519.0 = 480.3$$

$$SS_{Error} = SS_T - SS_{Treatment} - SS_{Block} = 480.3 - 178.2 - 192.3 = 109.8$$

Table 24.16 Computation of SS_T.

Continued

Continued

Source	Sum of Squares	Degrees of Freedom	Mean Squares	F Ratio
Treatment	178.2	3	59.4	8.1
Block	192.3	5	38.5	
Error	109.8	15	7.3	
Total	480.3	23		

Table 24.17 Source table for Example 24.7.

Note that the F statistic for the block effect is not presented in the ANOVA table. The F statistic for blocks is often calculated by statistical software, but it should not be reported or assessed. The restriction on the randomization (only within blocks) produces an F statistic that does not follow the F distribution, so critical F values or associated p-values cannot be determined. Recall that the block itself is not a factor of experimental interest, and it may not be actionable. We leave the blocking variable in the model since it acts as a sponge to absorb any additional variation introduced by the block. Note also that extrusion pressure is a continuous variable, so it could be analyzed as a continuous factor using a linear regression model instead of the one-way ANOVA.

Continued

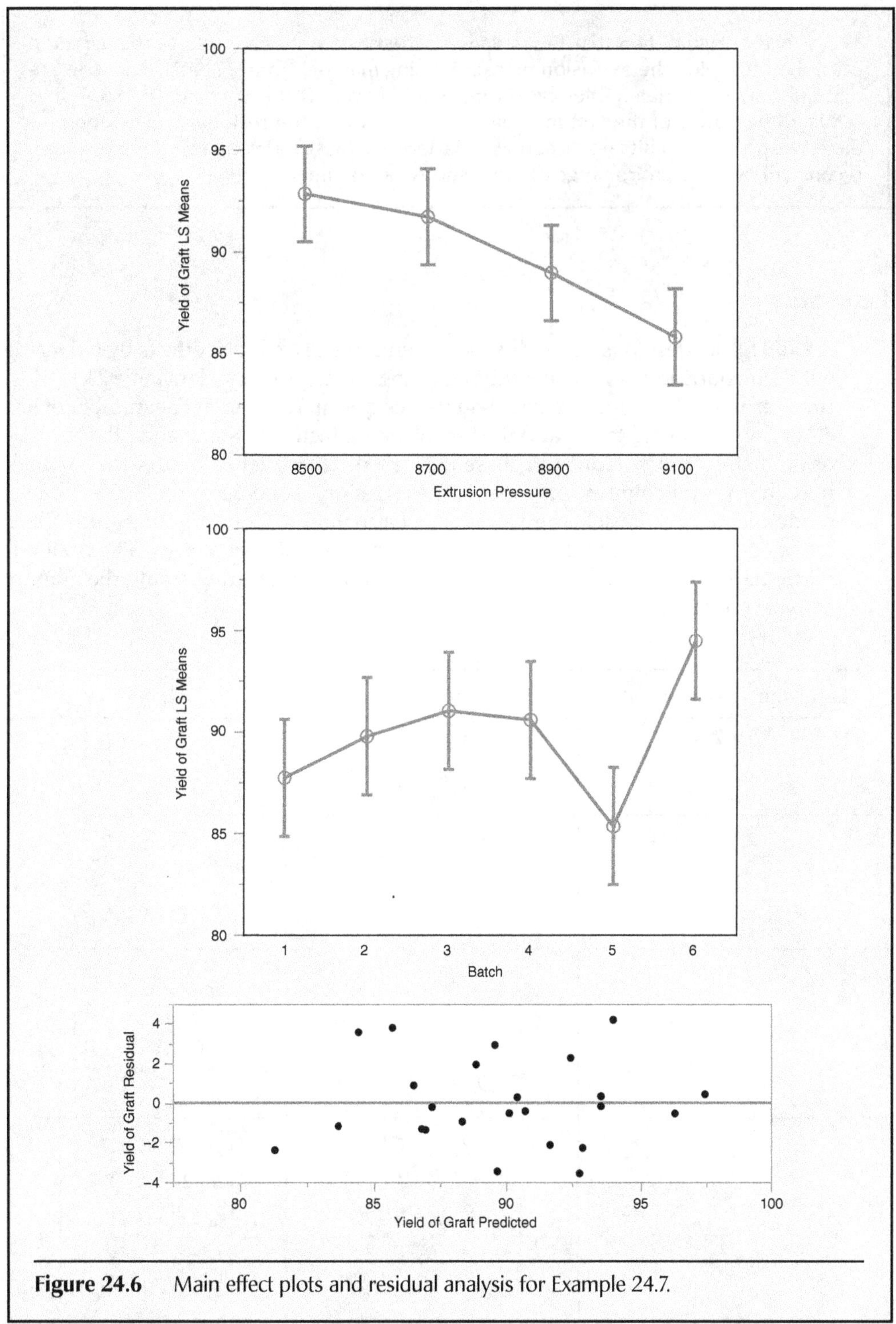

Figure 24.6 Main effect plots and residual analysis for Example 24.7.

Continued

Notice in Figure 24.6 that the variation across lots is comparable to the variation caused by changing the extrusion pressure. Using material from six batches in a design that did not appropriately block the runs would have left the SS_{Block} in the SS_{Error} and reduced the power of the test for treatment. The plot of the residuals versus the predicted responses exhibits no discernable pattern (no bias) and variance of the residuals is constant over the entire range of the response as assumed.

Latin Square

A *Latin square* design is generally used to eliminate two block effects by balancing out their contributions when studying a single categorical factor. Table 24.18 illustrates examples of common Latin square designs up to order 5. The number of levels of the categorical factor and the two blocking factors is matched with the order of the Latin square. Notice in these designs that each letter occurs exactly once in each row and column. As a result, these designs are balanced but they restrict randomization. A basic assumption of a Latin square design is that these block factors do not interact with the factor of interest or with each other. The design is particularly useful (when the assumptions are valid) for minimizing the amount of experimentation.

Latin square size ($n \times n$)	Example 1	Example 2
2 × 2	$\begin{bmatrix} A & B \\ B & A \end{bmatrix}$	$\begin{bmatrix} B & A \\ A & B \end{bmatrix}$
3 × 3	$\begin{bmatrix} A & B & C \\ B & C & A \\ C & A & B \end{bmatrix}$	$\begin{bmatrix} A & C & B \\ B & A & C \\ C & B & A \end{bmatrix}$
4 × 4	$\begin{bmatrix} A & B & C & D \\ B & A & D & C \\ C & D & A & B \\ D & C & B & A \end{bmatrix}$	$\begin{bmatrix} A & B & C & D \\ B & D & A & C \\ C & A & D & B \\ D & C & B & A \end{bmatrix}$
5 × 5	$\begin{bmatrix} A & B & C & D & E \\ B & C & E & A & D \\ C & E & D & B & A \\ D & A & B & E & C \\ E & D & A & C & B \end{bmatrix}$	$\begin{bmatrix} A & B & C & D & E \\ B & D & A & E & C \\ C & E & D & B & A \\ D & A & E & C & B \\ E & C & B & A & D \end{bmatrix}$

Table 24.18 Examples of Latin square designs from each main class up to order 5.

EXAMPLE 24.8

A process can be run at 180°F, 200°F, or 220°F. What might an experimenter do to determine whether temperature significantly affects the moisture content? The treatments are blocked by Day (1, 2, and 3) and by Machine (A, B, and C).

Table 24.19 shows a 3 × 3 Latin square design that will be used as the basis for this example.

Table 24.20 depicts the design from Table 24.19 with the response data included. Note the linkage of the data to the Latin letters. This linkage will be become important later as we determine the sum of squares of the moisture content.

	Temperature		
Day	**180 °F**	**200 °F**	**220 °F**
1	A	B	C
2	B	C	A
3	C	A	B

Table 24.19 The chosen design and the Latin letter assignments for Example 24.8.

	Temperature		
Day	**180 °F**	**200 °F**	**220 °F**
1	A = 10.8	B = 11.4	C = 14.3
2	B = 10.4	C = 11.9	A = 12.6
3	C = 11.2	A = 11.6	B = 13.0

Table 24.20 The moisture content linked to the Latin letter assignments.

	Temperature					
Day	**180 °F**	**200 °F**	**220 °F**	**Total**	**Total squared**	**Average total squared**
1	10.8	11.4	14.3	36.5	1332.25	
2	10.4	11.9	12.6	34.9	1218.01	
3	11.2	11.6	13.0	35.8	1281.64	
Total	32.4	34.9	39.9	**107.2**	3831.90	
Total squared	1049.76	1218.01	1592.01	3859.78		**1286.59 (columns)**
Average total squared					**1277.30 (rows)**	

$$SS_{\text{Rows}} = \frac{1332.25+1218.01+1281.64}{3} - \frac{(107.2)^2}{9} = 1277.30 - 1276.87 = 0.43$$

$$SS_{\text{Columns}} = \frac{1049.76+1218.01+1592.01}{3} - \frac{(107.2)^2}{9} = 1286.59 - 1276.87 = 9.72$$

Table 24.21 Computation of SS_{Rows} (day) and SS_{Columns} (temperature = treatment).

Continued

Continued

Table 24.21 through Table 24.23 have the original data matrix as their basis but have been expanded to allow for additional column and/or row computations. Furthermore, the computations for sum of squares have been added to these tables for completeness purposes. All that is required is to transfer the sum of squares to the source table shown in Table 24.24.

Table 24.24 is then completed using the procedure described previously.

Machine/ Latin Letter	180°F	200°F	220°F	Total	Total Squared
A	10.8	11.6	12.6	35.0	1225.00
B	10.4	11.4	13.0	34.8	1211.04
C	11.2	11.9	14.3	37.4	1398.76
Total	32.4	34.9	29.9	1079.2	3834.80
				Average	1278.27

$$SS_{\text{Temperature}} = \frac{1225.00+1211.04+1398.76}{3} - \frac{(107.2)^2}{9} = 1278.27 - 1276.87 = 1.40$$

Table 24.22 Computation of SS_{Machine} (Latin letters).

Day	180°F	200°F	220°F	Total Squared
1	$10.8^2 = 116.64$	129.96	204.49	451.09
2	108.16	1451.61	158.76	408.53
3	125.44	134.56	169.00	429.00
Total	350.24	406.13	532.25	1288.62

$$SS_T = (116.64+129.96+\ldots+169.00) - \frac{(107.2)^2}{9} = 1288.62 - 1276.87 = 11.75$$

$$SS_{Error} = SS_T - SS_{Treatment} - SS_{Machine} - SS_{Day} = 11.75 - 9.72 - 1.40 - 0.43 - 0.02$$

Table 24.23 Computation of SS_T.

Continued

Source	Sum of Squares	Degrees of Freedom	Mean Squares	*F* Statistic
Temperature	9.72	2	4.86	48.60
Day (Block)	0.43	2	0.22	
Machine (Block)	1.40	2	0.70	
Error	0.2	2	0.10	
Total	11.75	8		

Table 24.24 Source table for Example 24.8.

Assuming $\alpha = 0.05$, we must compare our F_0 value to $F_{0.05, 2, 2}$. From Appendix G.3 the *F* critical value is 19.00 since the degrees of freedom are 2 and 2. Remember that the *F* statistic for the block effects should not be used to evaluate the significance of the blocking. Temperature is significant since 48.60 > 19.00. Thus, we can conclude that temperature affects moisture content.

The analysis using software, shown in Figure 24.7, is based on *p*-values instead of comparing the *F* statistic to the critical *F* value, but the conclusion is the same using the same $\alpha = 0.05$ level of significance. Note that the software output calculates *F* statistics for the blocks, but these should be ignored, as explained in the block section earlier in this chapter.

Continued

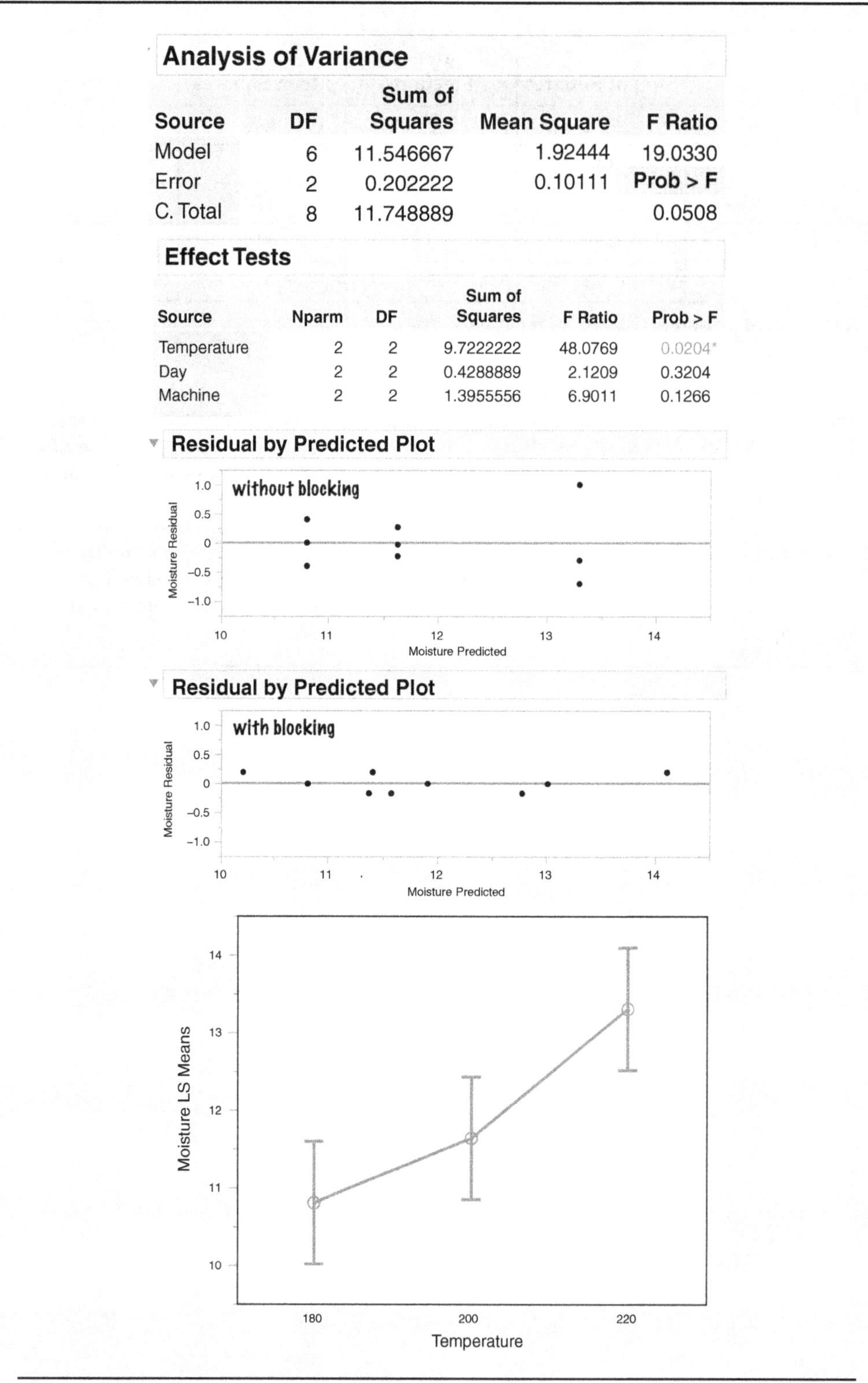

Analysis of Variance

Source	DF	Sum of Squares	Mean Square	F Ratio
Model	6	11.546667	1.92444	19.0330
Error	2	0.202222	0.10111	Prob > F
C. Total	8	11.748889		0.0508

Effect Tests

Source	Nparm	DF	Sum of Squares	F Ratio	Prob > F
Temperature	2	2	9.7222222	48.0769	0.0204*
Day	2	2	0.4288889	2.1209	0.3204
Machine	2	2	1.3955556	6.9011	0.1266

Figure 24.7 Computer output for Example 24.8.

FULL-FACTORIAL EXPERIMENTS

Understand these types of experiments. (Understand)

Body of Knowledge VII.A.6

The analysis of variance can be used for any number of factors and can accommodate all interaction terms that are estimable by the factorial design. For example, a Black Belt may run an experiment that varies temperature at two levels and pressure at three levels and uses material from four different suppliers. One replicate of the experiment would be comprised of 2×3×4 = 24 runs, and the three main effects, three two-factor interactions, and one three-factor interaction would be estimable. This type of experiment is referred to as a *general factorial design.*

Table 24.25 provides the model, hypothesis, and assumptions for a completely randomized, full-factorial experiment with two factors A and B tested at i and j levels, respectively, with k replicates.

Table 24.26 presents the formulas for the ANOVA table calculations and sums of squares for the model in Table 24.25.

The formula for number of runs in a full-factorial experiment in which all the factors have the same number of levels is shown in Equation 24.1.

Equation 24.1 Minimum number of runs for a full factorial, all factors having same number of levels

$$n = L^k$$

where

n = Number of runs

L = Number of levels

k = Number of factors

2^k Full-Factorial Designs

A particularly useful class of full-factorial designs is one in which each of the k factors is varied at two levels. These are referred to as 2^k *designs*. The 2^k designs are orthogonal, which simplifies their analysis and interpretation. The minimum number of runs for various 2^k designs is shown in Table 24.27. Note that we can use Equation 24.1 with $L = 2$ to calculate the minimum number of runs for each selected 2^k design.

We can represent the 2^2 and 2^3 experiments geometrically, shown in Figure 24.8. Each run occurs at a corner point.

Name	Model	Hypotheses	Assumptions
Two-way ANOVA (completely randomizes design with fixed effects)	$y_{ijk} = \mu + \tau_i + \beta_j + (\tau\beta)_{ij} + \varepsilon_{ijk} \left\{ \begin{array}{c} i = 1,2,\ldots,a \\ j = 1,2,\ldots,b \\ k = 1,2,\ldots,n \end{array} \right\}$ y_{ijk} = kth observation in the *i*th row, *j*th column μ = Overal mean τ_i = Effect of the *i*th level of row factor *A* β_j = Effect of the *j*th level of column factor *B* $(\tau\beta)_{ij}$ = Effect of the interaction of the *i*th level of row factor A and the *j*th level of column factor B ε_{ijk} = residual for the *ijk*th observation	$H_0 : \tau_1 = \tau_2 = \ldots = \tau_a = 0$ $H_1 : \tau_i \neq 0$ for at least one i $H_0 : \beta_1 = \beta_2 = \ldots = \beta_b = 0$ $H_1 : \beta_j \neq 0$ for at least one j $H_0 : (\tau\beta)_{ij} = 0$ for all i, j $H_1 : (\tau\beta)_{ij} \neq 0$ for at least one i, j	$\varepsilon_{ijk} \sim NID\ (0, \sigma^2)$

Table 24.25 Statistical model for the two-way ANOVA.
Adapted from Montgomery (2019).

Source of variation	Sum of squares	Degrees of freedom	Mean squares	F_0 statistic
Factor A	SS_A	$a-1$	$MS_A = \frac{SS_A}{a-1}$	$F_0 = \frac{MS_A}{MS_E}$
Factor B	SS_B	$b-1$	$MS_B = \frac{SS_B}{b-1}$	$F_0 = \frac{MS_B}{MS_E}$
Interaction AB	SS_{AB}	$(a-1)(b-1)$	$MS_{AB} = \frac{SS_{AB}}{(a-1)(b-1)}$	$F_0 = \frac{MS_{AB}}{MS_E}$
Error	SS_E By subtraction	By subtraction	$MS_E = \frac{SS_E}{ab(n-1)}$	
Total	SS_T	$abn-1$		

Two-way ANOVA source table

Statistical model	Sums of squares (SS)
Two-way ANOVA (completely randomized design with fixed effects)	$SS_T = \sum_{i=1}^{a}\sum_{j=1}^{b}\sum_{k=1}^{n} y_{ijk}^2 - \frac{y_{...}^2}{abn}$ $SS_A = \frac{1}{bn}\sum_{i=1}^{a} y_{i..}^2 - \frac{y_{...}^2}{abn}$ $SS_B = \frac{1}{an}\sum_{j=1}^{b} y_{.j.}^2 - \frac{y_{...}^2}{abn}$ $SS_{AB} = \frac{1}{n}\sum_{i=1}^{a}\sum_{j=1}^{b} y_{ij.}^2 - \frac{y_{...}^2}{abn} - SS_A - SS_B$ $SS_E = SS_T - SS_A - SS_B - SS_{AB}$

Sums of squares for the two-way ANOVA

Table 24.26 ANOVA table calculations for a two-factor full-factorial design.
Source: Montgomery (2019).

Type of design	Number of factors	Number of factor levels	Minimum number of runs = 2^k
2^2	2	2	4
2^3	3	2	8
2^4	4	2	16
2^5	5	2	32
2^6	6	2	64

Table 24.27 Minimum number of runs for selected 2^k designs.

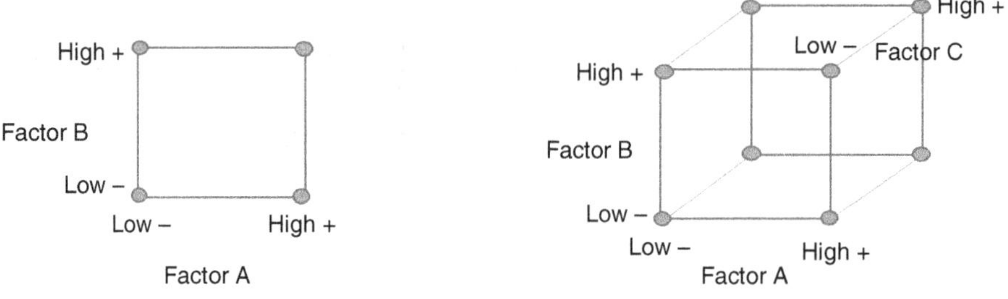

Figure 24.8 Geometric representation of 2^2 and 2^3 designs.

EXAMPLE 24.9

Here we present the analysis of a 2^2 full-factorial experiment with two replicates. Such an analysis is typically performed by statistical software, but we will hand calculate the effects, and the ANOVA table using the formulas in Table 24.26.

A quality engineer is interested in learning how the temperature and pressure settings on a sealing machine affect the burst strength of a paper package. She designs a 2^2 experiment with two replicates and performs the experimental runs in random order. The low and high settings for temperature are 250°F and 300°F, and 35 psi and 45 psi for pressure. Burst strength will be measured in kPa. The experimental results have been tabulated using the standard run order in Table 24.28, and the randomized run order is also indicated.

Standard Order	Randomized Run Order	Temperature	Pressure	Burst strength, kPa
1	7	250	35	54
2	4	300	35	60
3	2	250	45	60
4	6	300	45	74
5	5	250	35	58
6	1	300	35	54
7	8	250	45	60
8	3	300	45	73

Table 24.28 Burst strength experiment results for Example 24.9.

The average responses for each run are shown in what Minitab labels as a "cube plot" shown in Figure 24.9.

Continued

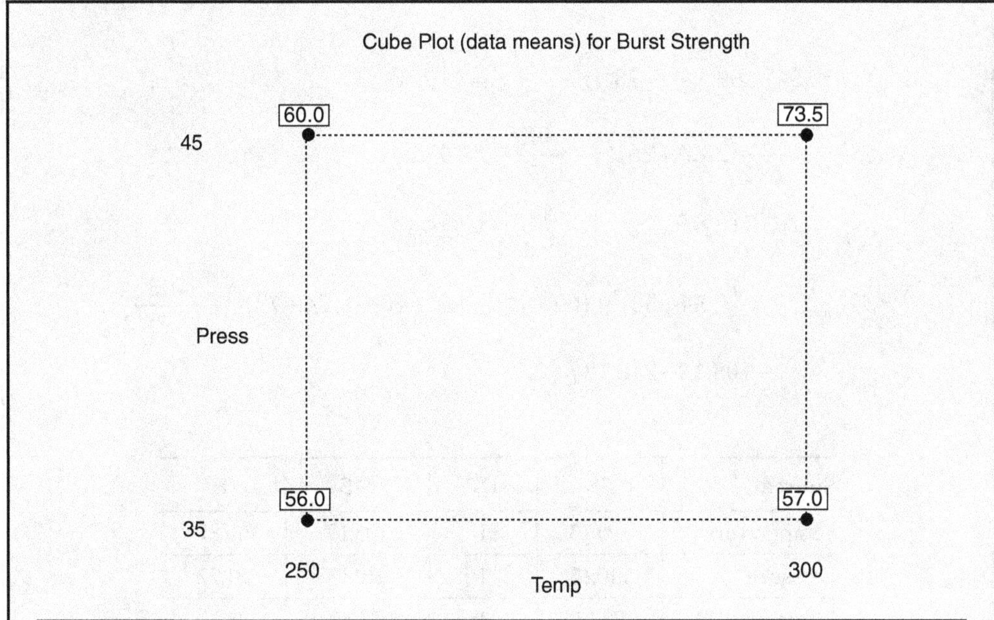

Figure 24.9 "Cube plot" for burst strength experiment results for Example 24.9.

Figure 24.10 shows the ANOVA table calculations using the formulas in Table 24.26 with $a = b = n = 2$. An ANOVA table generated using Minitab corroborates the results. Based on the p-values, we see that there is a significant interaction between temperature and pressure, and that the two main effects are significant as well.

	Pressure		
Temperature	**35**	**45**	**Total**
250	54	60	232
250	58	60	
300	60	74	261
300	54	73	
Total	226	267	493

Continued

$$SST = \left(54^2 + 60^2 + \cdots + 73^2\right) - \frac{493^2}{2\times2\times2} = 419.88$$

$$SS_{Temp} = \frac{1}{2\times2}\left(232^2 + 261^2\right) - \frac{493^2}{2\times2\times2} = 105.13$$

$$SS_{Press} = \frac{1}{2\times2}\left(226^2 + 267^2\right) - \frac{493^2}{2\times2\times2} = 210.13$$

$$SS_{Temp\times Press} = \frac{1}{2}\left((54+58)^2 + (60+54)^2 + (60+60)^2 + (74+73)^2\right) - \frac{493^2}{2\times2\times2}$$

$$-105.13 - 210.13 = 78.13$$

Source	SS	DF	MS	F
Temperature	105.13	1	105.13	15.87
Pressure	210.13	1	210.13	31.72
Interaction	78.13	1	78.13	11.79
Error	26.50	4		
Total	419.88	7		

Analysis of Variance

Source	DF	Adj SS	Adj MS	F-Value	P-Value
Model	3	393.38	131.125	19.79	0.007
Temp	1	105.13	105.125	15.87	0.016
Press	1	210.13	210.125	31.72	0.005
Temp*Press	1	78.13	78.125	11.79	0.026
Error	4	26.50	6.625		
Total	7	419.88			

Figure 24.10 ANOVA calculations for Example 24.9.

The coded coefficients table calculated by Minitab® statistical software as well as the manual calculations are shown in Figure 24.11. We can use the coded effects and coefficients table to determine which factor has the most influence on burst strength. For example, the pressure effect tells us that moving the pressure settings from the low to the high level increases the burst strength by an average of 10.25 kPa. The *p*-value column indicates that the interaction between temperature and pressure is significant, as are the temperature and pressure main effects. This result was also shown in the previous ANOVA table. The prediction equation in the original, uncoded units is also given. Note that, based on the hierarchical model convention, we would include the Temperature and Pressure main effects in the model even if they were not significant because the Temperature × Pressure interaction is significant.

Continued

Coded Coefficients

Term	Effect	Coef	SE Coef	T-Value	P-Value
Constant		61.625	0.910	67.72	0.000
Temp	7.250	3.625	0.910	3.98	0.016
Press	10.250	5.125	0.910	5.63	0.005
Temp*Press	6.250	3.125	0.910	3.43	0.026

$$\text{Effect Temp} = \frac{(60+54+74+73)-(54+58+60+60)}{4} = 7.25$$

$$\text{Coeff Temp} = \frac{7.25}{2} = 3.625$$

$$\text{Effect Press} = \frac{(60+60+74+73)-(54+58+60+54)}{4} = 10.25$$

$$\text{Coeff Temp} = \frac{10.25}{2} = 5.125$$

$$\text{Effect Temp*Press} = \frac{(74+73+54+58)-(60+60+60+54)}{4} = 6.25$$

$$\text{Coeff Temp*Press} = \frac{6.25}{2} = 3.125$$

Regression Equation in Uncoded Units

Burst Strength = 255.7 – 0.855 Temp – 5.85 Press + 0.02500 Temp*Press

Figure 24.11 Calculations of effects and coefficients for Example 24.9.

We can check the assumptions behind the ANOVA model: Residuals are independent, identically normally distributed with mean zero and constant variance as shown graphically in Figure 24.12.

The *p*-value for the Anderson-Darling test displayed on the normal probability plot of residuals indicated that there is not a significant departure from normality. The standardized residual plot versus the fits indicates that there are no outliers, and no major concerns about heterogeneity of the variance. The histogram reflects the normal probability plot, and the residuals-versus-run-order plot does not indicate any autocorrelation in the errors. Hence, the independence assumption is met.

Continued

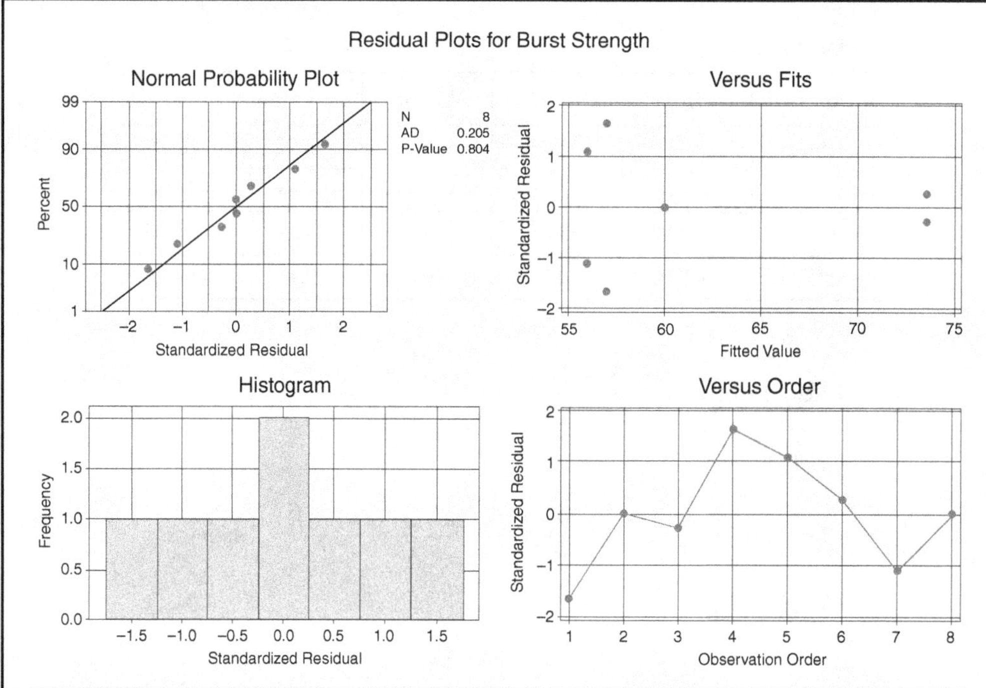

Figure 24.12 Graphical assumption checks for Example 24.9.

The main effects and interaction plots are shown in Figure 24.13. We see from the interaction plot that when pressure is set at the high level of 45 psi, increasing temperature from 250°F to 300°F has a significant positive impact on the burst strength. On the other hand, when the pressure is set to 35 psi, increasing temperature has minimal effect on the burst strength.

Continued

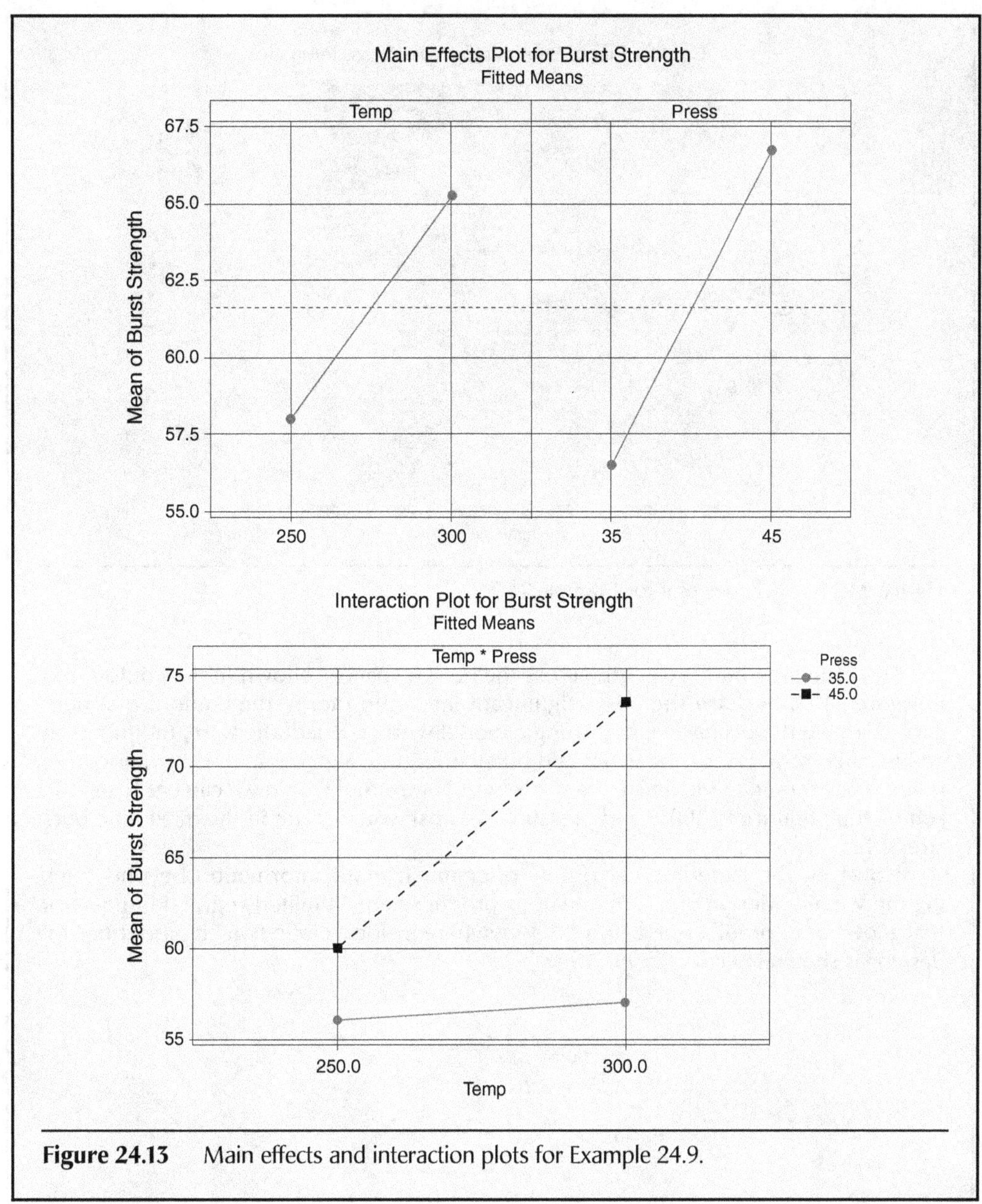

Figure 24.13 Main effects and interaction plots for Example 24.9.

Continued

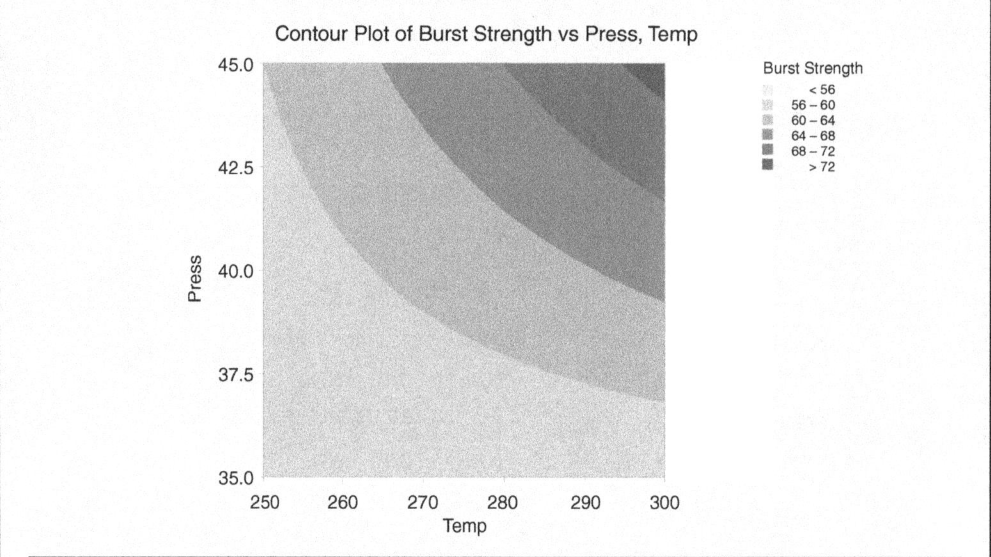

Figure 24.14 Contour plot for Example 24.9.

The estimated burst strength across the design space is shown in the contour plot in Figure 24.14. Because there is a significant interaction term, the contour plot has a curved gradient. Because we are fitting a model with no quadratic term, the minimum and maximum values for the estimated burst strength will occur at a design, or corner, point. If we wanted to maximize burst strength, for example, then we can easily see that setting temperature to 300°F and pressure at 45 psi would result in the maximum burst strength.

However, the experimental results offer much more information beyond "picking the winning design run." The analysis produces an estimated regression equation that allows us to predict burst strengths anywhere inside a circle that circumscribes the design, as shown in Figure 24.15.

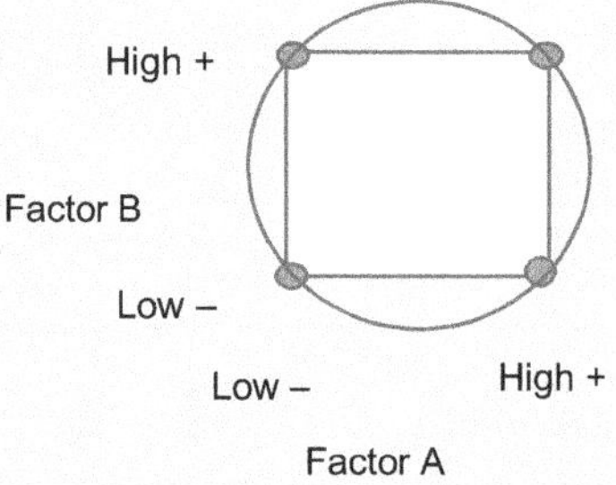

Figure 24.15 Prediction area for the regression equation in Example 24.9.

Continued

Continued

For example, if the required burst strength for individual packages is greater than or equal to 59 kPa, the engineer may not need to run the machine at 300°F to satisfy the specification. Instead, she can use the equation in Figure 24.11 to determine if running the machine at, say, 275°F would meet the standard. The estimated burst strength at a temperature setting of 275°F and 45 psi results in

$$255.7 - 0.855 \times 275 - 5.85 \times 45 + 0.025 \times 275 \times 45 = 66.75\text{kPa}$$

The one-sided prediction interval, shown in Figure 24.16 for the individual burst strength at 275°F and 45 psi, has a lower bound equal to 60.6152, which satisfies the requirement.

Temp	Press	Fit	SE Fit	95% Lower Confidence Bound	95% Lower Prediction Bound
275	45	66.75	1.28695	64.0064	60.6152

Figure 24.16 One-sided confidence and prediction intervals for Example 24.9.

Center Points

Any factorial experiment with continuous factors can be augmented by center points. For example, the experimental design in Example 24.9 could have been run using four center points, shown in Table 24.29. Center points are set at the

Temperature	Pressure
250	35
300	35
275	40
250	45
300	45
275	40
250	35
300	35
275	40
250	45
300	45
275	40

Table 24.29 Burst strength experiment with center points.

midpoint between the low and high levels of the continuous factors and are coded with zeroes in the design matrix. Here, the center point runs map to 275°F and 40 psi.

Adding center points to an experiment has many advantages. First, these points allow us to test whether there is any curvature in the model, something that cannot be done with an experiment run at only two levels for each factor. If the ANOVA table indicates that there is significant curvature, and it is of practical importance, we can run a follow-up experiment to determine which factor or factors have a quadratic effect on the response. If there is no indication of significant curvature, we still benefit from the center point runs since we have more degrees of freedom to estimate the error term, which is particularly helpful when we are running an unreplicated experiment. And, if the center points are randomized along with the other runs, we have a way to detect if the experimental environment has changed over time, which would introduce bias into our results. There is much to gain by adding a few center points into any experiment.

TWO-LEVEL FRACTIONAL FACTORIAL EXPERIMENTS

> Understand these types of experiments, and describe how confounding can affect their use. (Understand)
>
> Body of Knowledge VII.A.5

A *factorial design* is an experimental design consisting of all possible combinations of the factor levels of two or more factors, with each factor being studied at two or more levels. When all combinations are run, the interaction effects as well as the main effects can be estimated. By contrast, a *fractional factorial design* is an experimental design consisting of a subset (fraction) of the factorial design. Typically, the fraction is a simple proportion of the full set of possible treatment combinations. For example, half-fractions, quarter-fractions, and so forth, are common. While fractional factorial designs require fewer runs, some degree of confounding occurs.

Full-factorial experiments might require many runs, especially if several factors or several levels are involved. Recall Equation 24.1 introduced in the last section. The minimum number of runs in a full-factorial experiment in which all the factors have the same number of levels is

$$n = L^k$$

where

n = Number of runs

L = Number of levels

k = Number of factors

For example, an experiment with eight two-level factors has $2^8 = 256$ runs, and an experiment with five three-level factors has $3^5 = 243$ runs. As you can see, full-factorial experiments require a significant number of runs, which can be very costly and time-consuming.

Furthermore, if the experiment tests the effect of various factors on product quality in a manufacturing process, the tests typically must be run sequentially rather than simultaneously, so a large full-factorial experiment with several factors or levels might require that a piece of production equipment be taken out of production for a considerable amount of time. Fractional factorial experimental designs were developed because of the extensive resource requirements of full-factorial experiments. Typically, only one replicate of a fractional factorial experiment is run.

For the $2^8 = 256$ run experiment we can choose to run only one-eighth of the treatment combinations. These treatment combinations are chosen using an algorithm that minimizes the confounding structure of the design. Noting that one-eighth equals $\frac{1}{2^3}$, the resulting fractional factorial experiment would thus have 32 runs:

$$\frac{2^8}{2^3} = 2^{8-3} = 2^5$$

A one-eighth fraction of a two-level experiment is denoted as 2^{k-3}. Table 24.30 lists the notation for other two-level fractional factorial experiments.

Fraction	Fractional-Factorial Notation
1/2	2^{k-1}
1/4	2^{k-2}
1/8	2^{k-3}
1/16	2^{k-4}

Table 24.30 Fractional factorial notation for two-level experiments.

EXAMPLE 24.10

Consider the 2^{4-1} fractional factorial design and data given in Table 24.31. This is an eight-run, resolution IV design in which main effects are confounded with three-factor interactions, and two-factor interactions are confounded with other two-factor interactions. Analyze this design to determine which factors are significant. Assume $\alpha = 0.05$.

Continued

Std Order	Run #	Temp	Pressure	Time	Matl Type	Y
1	5	–1	–1	–1	–1	10
2	3	+1	–1	–1	+1	83
3	1	–1	+1	–1	+1	45
4	6	+1	+1	–1	–1	205
5	8	–1	–1	+1	+1	12
6	4	+1	–1	+1	–1	57
7	7	–1	+1	+1	–1	65
8	2	+1	+1	+1	+1	187

Table 24.31 A one-half 2^{4-1} fractional factorial design for Example 24.10.

The following results illustrate the analysis of this design using Design-Expert® software (Stat-Ease, Inc.):

- Figure 24.17 lays out the alias structure from the design evaluation in which A = Temperature, B = Pressure, C = Time, and D = Material Type. All main effects (MEs) are aliased with a three-factor interaction (3fi); e.g., A = BCD. The two-factor interactions (2fi's) are aliased with each other; e.g., AB = CD.

Intercept	= Intercept
A	= A + BCD
B	= B + ACD
C	= C + ABD
D	= D + ABC
AB	= AB + CD
AC	= AC + BD
AD	= AD + BC

Figure 24.17 Alias structure for Example 24.10.

- Figure 24.18 shows the half-normal plot with three selected effects labeled—the three largest one (those falling off to the right). Per general DOE practice, the aliasing of the chosen MEs (A and B) is disregarded due to 3FI's (BCD and ABD, respectively) being very unlikely, that is, negligible. Given the emergence of A and B, the AB interaction is chosen over its alias CD per the principle of effect heredity—AB being the "child" of "parents" A and B. The other (unlabeled) effects (C, D, AC, AD and their aliases) fall in a straight line emanating from the origin at zero effect—presumably due to them exhibiting normal variation, that is, not creating any significant change in the measured response. They will be used to estimate error.

Continued

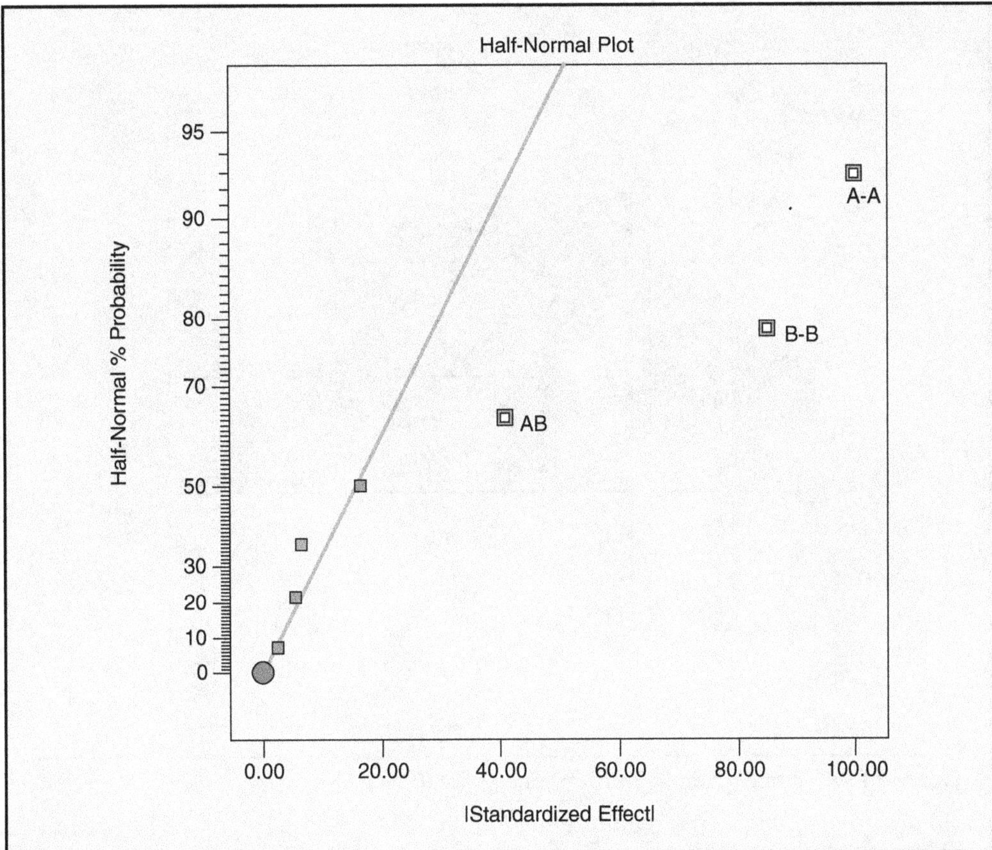

Figure 24.18 Half-normal plot of effects for Example 24.10.

- Figure 24.19 displays the resulting Pareto plot of effects. All four of the unchosen (unlabeled) effects fall below the basic t-value limit (lower line). The two main effects (A = Temperature and B = Pressure) exceed the more conservative upper line set with a "Bonferroni" correction for multiple pairwise comparisons. The AB = (Temperature × Pressure) interaction falls between the two limit-lines but merits being chosen, at least on provisional basis.

Continued

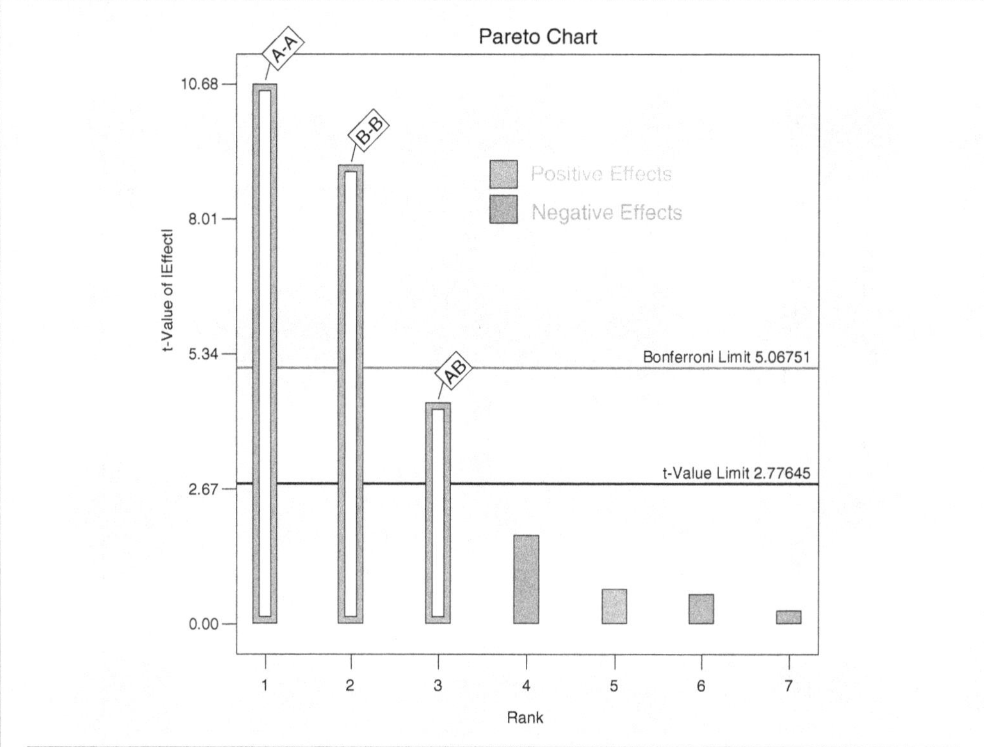

Figure 24.19 Pareto plot of effects for Example 24.10.

- Figure 24.20 provides the analysis of variance (ANOVA) for the selected factorial model. It comes out highly significant overall ($p < 0.05$). The individual model terms are also statistically significant, particularly the two main effects (A and B).

Source	Sum of Squares	df	Mean Square	F-value	p-value	
Model	37812.00	3	12604.00	71.82	0.0006	significant
Temp	20000.00	1	20000.00	113.96	0.0004	
Press	14450.00	1	14450.00	82.34	0.0008	
Temp × Press	3362.00	1	3362.00	19.16	0.0119	
Residual	702.00	4	175.50			
Corrected Total	38514.00	7				

Figure 24.20 Analysis of variance table for Example 24.10.

The ANOVA statistics depend on several key assumptions about the *statistical errors*—the difference between the actual and the predicted responses (referred to as *residuals*):

- Independent or uncorrelated statistical errors

Continued

- Identically normally distributed statistical errors with a mean = 0 and a constant variance, σ^2. That is, the variance does not depend on the level of response.

Various plots of residuals can be used diagnose appreciable deviations from these assumptions, including:

1. *Normal probability plot* or *normal quantile plot.* This chart plots the residuals versus their predicted probability or predicted quantile, respectively, from a fitted normal distribution. A quantile is a data value equal to a given proportion of the distribution. For example, the median is a quantile that is located at the middle of the distribution or where 50% of the data are less. The chart also plots the graph of the cumulative distribution function for the normal distribution for reference. The chart uses a transformation of the y-axis such that the residuals and the graph of the normal cumulative distribution function are straight line with a slope equal to σ. Evaluate normality by comparing the pattern residuals to the straight reference line, known as the "fat pencil test." A small departure from normality such as that exhibited in Figure 24.21 does not create any cause for alarm—a fat pencil covers up all the points.

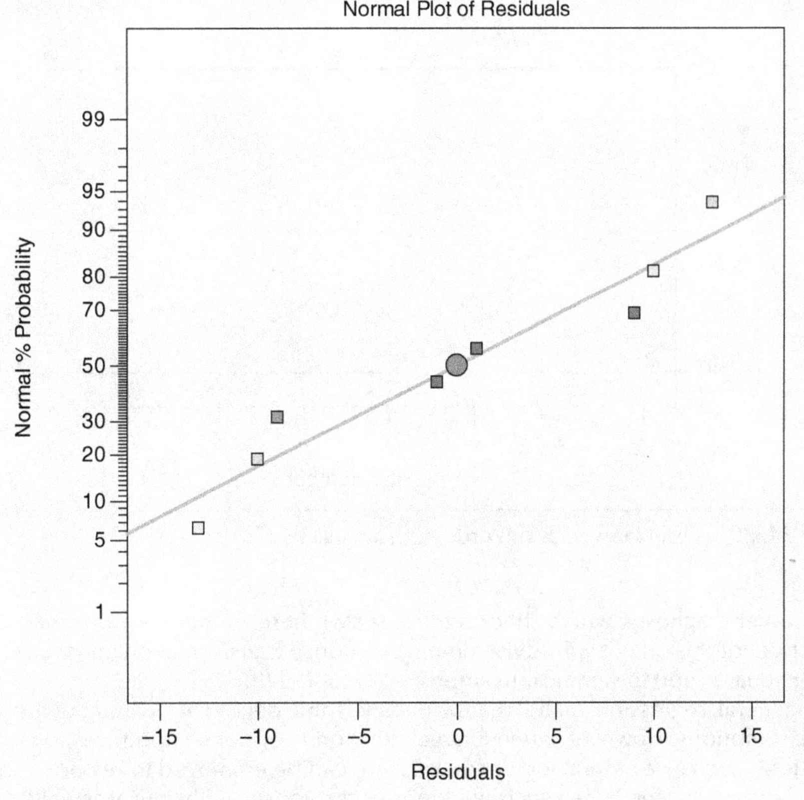

Figure 24.21 Normal plot of residuals for Example 24.10.

Continued

2. *Residuals versus run.* If the model accounts for all factor influences, the residuals should be random. Thus, this chart should not exhibit a discernable pattern. Figure 24.22, with the residuals scaled by their standard deviation (referred to as "internally Studentized"), shows no noticeable shifts or trends; thus, it creates no concerns. This chart is also useful for detecting outliers—individual points falling outside of the upper or lower limits (set at p = 0.05). This set of residuals stays well within the normal zone.

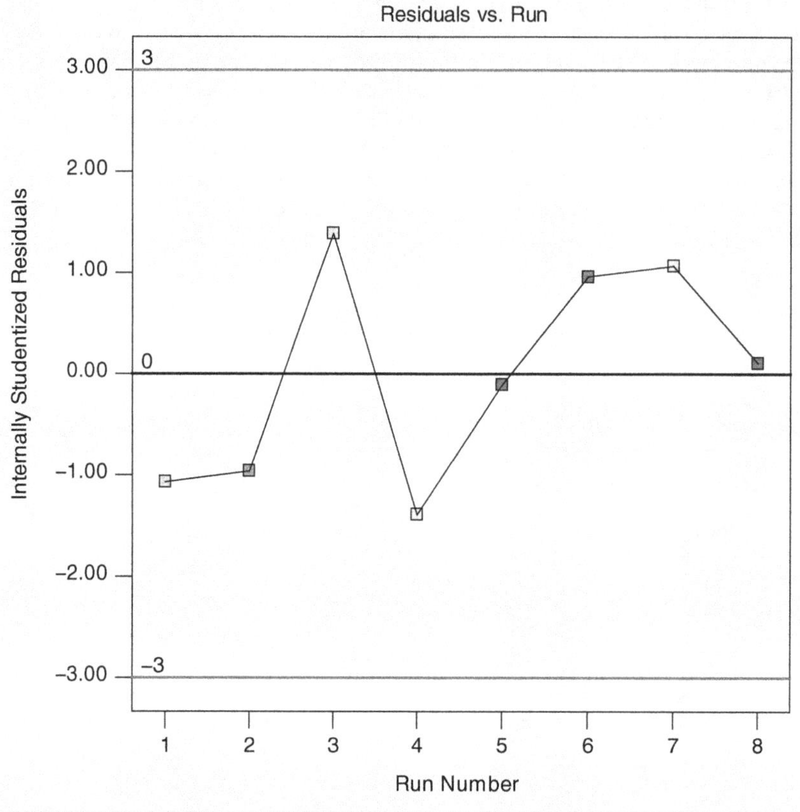

Figure 24.22 Residuals versus run order for Example 24.10.

Another diagnostic worth checking (not shown here) is the *Box-Cox plot.* In some cases (but not this one) it will advise doing a response transformation (most commonly a log or square root) to significantly improve the model fit.

In general, regression analysis can withstand some degree of violation of the underlying assumptions. However, when a large violation is evident, various response transformations, such as a natural log or square root, can be employed to restore normality and equalize variances. When such situations occur, consult with your Master Black Belt.

Continued

Continued

Seeing nothing abnormal in the diagnosis of residuals, the results from this fractional two-level factorial experiment can be interpreted graphically. Only factors A = Temperature and B = Pressure remain in play—the other two factors (C and D) are not creating any significant effects. However, due to the interaction of Temperature and Pressure, it would be misleading to show their main effects. The interaction plot in Figure 24.23 tells the complete story.

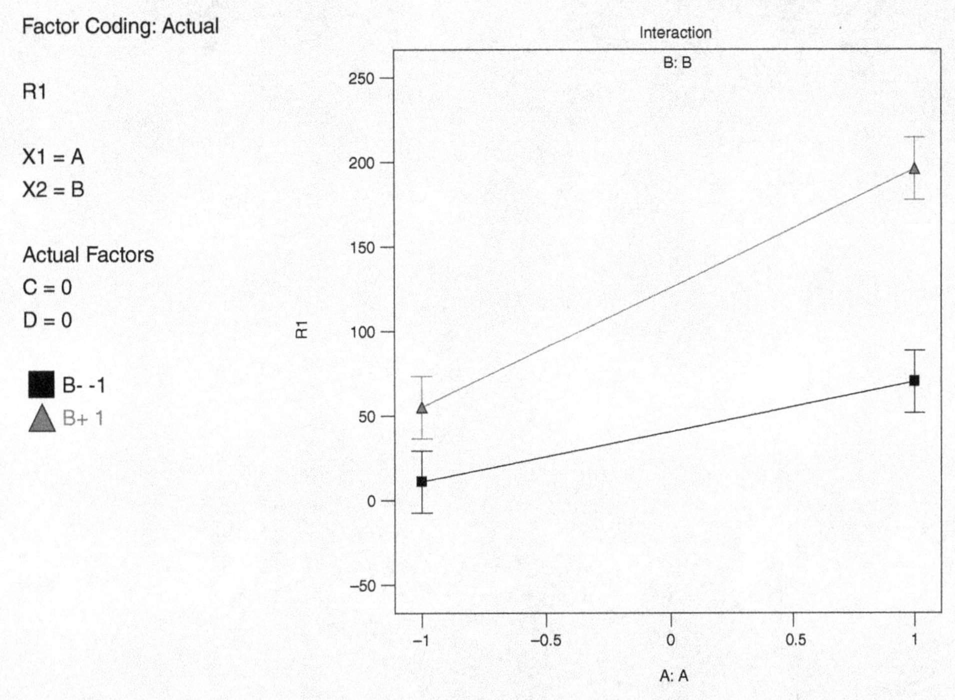

Figure 24.23 Interaction plot for Example 24.10.

In this case, the effect of A depends on the level of B. When Pressure is at its low (minus) level, increasing Temperature creates a significantly lesser increase in the response than it does with Pressure set high (plus). Only by taking the multifactor approach of DOE can interactions like this be revealed.

Chapter 25

Lean Methods

The most dangerous kind of waste is the waste we do not recognize.

– Shigeo Shingo

WASTE ELIMINATION

> Select and apply tools and techniques for eliminating or preventing waste, e.g., pull systems, kanban, 5S, standard work, poka-yoke. (Analyze)
>
> Body of Knowledge VII.B.1

Over the years a great deal of effort has gone into improving *value-added* activities—those activities that impact the form or function of the product. For instance, improvements in machine operations, communications, and technology enhance the final product the customer receives. Lean thinking focuses on *non-value-added* activities—those activities that occur in every enterprise but do not add value for the customer. Some of these activities can be eliminated, and some can be simplified, improved, combined, and so forth. Tools for identifying and eliminating or reducing waste of all kinds are the topic of this section.

Kanban

A *kanban* is a system that signals the need to replenish stock or materials or to produce more of an item. Kanban is also known as a "pull" approach. Kanban systems need not be elaborate, sophisticated, or even computerized to be effective. Toyota's Taiichi Ohno developed the concept of a kanban system after visiting a U.S. supermarket. He observed that there were two boxes of each type of canned goods, one box placed behind the other on the shelf. When the front box was emptied and the rear box was pulled forward to replace it, that signaled them to bring in a full box and place it behind the box that was currently on the front of the shelf.

A system is best controlled when material and information flow into and out of the process in a smooth and rational manner. If process inputs arrive before they are needed, unnecessary confusion, inventory, and costs occur. If process outputs are not synchronized with downstream processes, the result is often delays, disappointed customers, and associated costs. A kanban system may be used to simplify and improve resupply procedure.

EXAMPLE 25.1

In a typical two-bin kanban arrangement on an assembly line, as the first bin is emptied, the user signals resupply personnel. The signal is usually visual and may involve displaying a card that came with the bin, turning on a light, or just showing the empty bin. The resupply employee gathers the information on supplies needed and replenishes the bins.

Sometimes, the bins are resupplied from a stockroom, although often it is from a closer supply point, sometimes referred to as a *supermarket*. In some cases, bins are replenished directly by an outside vendor. The entire string of events occurs routinely, often with no paperwork. The result is a smoother flow requiring less inventory. A properly administered kanban system improves system control by ensuring timely movement of products and information. It reduces waste involved with ordering, waiting for parts, and paperwork.

Pull Systems

In a *pull system*, the customer order process withdraws the needed items from a supermarket, and the supplying process produces product to replenish what was withdrawn. Also known as a *kanban* system, a pull system is the opposite of the traditional push system.

From the definition of the pull system, it can be seen that many manufacturing enterprises traditionally operate in a push system. This refers to the fact that raw materials and sub-assemblies are pushed through the production process with the anticipation that they will be needed by customers.

The main question is how large should the kanbans be? When the kanbans are too small, purchase orders are placed more often, and stock-outs occur with greater frequency. When the kanbans are too large, work-in-progress inventory (one of the waste categories) builds up and incurs carrying costs that may include a tax burden as well.

A kanban can be a designated area on the floor, space on a shelf, a rack, a bin, or any place that is convenient to draw from and resupply. In some situations, a card is placed below or behind the last item in a container. This kanban card is used by the resupply person as a reminder of the item to be restocked. The word *kanban* is translated as "cardboard," so the phrase *kanban card* is a little redundant.

It should be noted that some products do not fit the kanban pull system well. This is particularly true of seasonal products. An air conditioner manufacturer may sell 95% of its products in a three-month span. If it were to operate on a strict pull system, it would be necessary to expand manufacturing capacity—capacity that would not be needed the other nine months of the year. Instead, the company will spend most of the year building inventory that it hopes to sell during the rush months.

EXAMPLE 25.2

An appliance manufacturer receives an order for 50 model XYZs. The warehouse ships the appliances to the customer, which leaves a blank space "open kanban" in the warehouse. This signals the assembly department to assemble 50 appliances to replenish those that have been sold. As the assembly department draws down the inventory of various sub-assemblies and purchased parts, the empty kanbans signal primary operations and purchasing agents to replenish those items.

5S

5S, or *five S*, derives its name from the five Japanese terms beginning with "s" utilized to create a workplace suited for visual control and lean production. Collectively, 5S is about how to create a workplace that is visibly organized, free of clutter, neatly arranged, and sparkling clean. English-speaking authors have tried to come up with five words that begin with the letter "s" that roughly translate as the Japanese words. Each "s" of 5S is defined as follows:

1. *Seiri (sort* or *sifting).* To separate needed tools, parts, and instructions from unneeded materials and to remove the latter
2. *Seiton (set in order).* To neatly arrange and identify parts and tools for ease of use
3. *Seiso (shine,* also *sanitize* or *scrub).* To conduct a cleanup campaign
4. *Seiketsu (standardize).* To conduct seiri, seiton, and seiso at frequent, indeed daily, intervals to maintain a workplace in perfect condition
5. *Shitsuke (sustain* or *self-discipline).* To form the habit of always following the first four Ss

A process is impacted by its environment, as is the ability of personnel to respond to process change. Improvements in the general state of the work area, including access to hand tools, aid in process control. Especially critical is the cleanliness, lighting, and general housekeeping status for any area where measurements are conducted since process control data are filtered through the measurement system.

The 5S system is often a starting place for implementing lean operations, so it is important that it be done properly and periodically. Remember shitsuke, the fifth "s," which calls for performing the first four Ss on an ongoing basis. The weak point of a 5S event is thinking of it as an event, like spring cleaning. It is instead to be thought of as part of daily activities. An effective way to make this happen is to have the workers in an area draw up a schedule with rotating 5S responsibilities, such as "On Monday, Bill sweeps the entryway."

Some organizations have taken 5S further, adding a sixth step, Safety. Safety is an important outcome of 5S done well, and some companies have prioritized their focus on safety as naming their sixth "S" for Safety. This addition did not originate with Toyota, so it has not historically been referenced by its Japanese name.

Standard Work

Standard work is a concept whereby each work activity is organized around human motion to minimize waste. Each work activity is precisely described, including specifying cycle time, takt time, task sequence, and the minimum inventory of parts on hand required to conduct the activity. Standard work is also known as *standardized work*.

Finding better ways of producing an ever more consistent product (or delivering an ever more consistent service) is the essence of process control. Standard work contributes to this effort by ensuring that product or services flowing into a process have minimal variation and that there is a reduction in the variation caused by the process. In addition, work is performed the same way every time. One of the problems with producing standard work documentation is that people are constantly finding better ways to do things, and the standard work document must be constantly updated.

Some organizations have found that rotating jobs helps everyone become acquainted with additional standard work opportunities.

EXAMPLE 25.3

An assembly line worker installs a wiring harness that is connected to various components at subsequent stations. Through conversations with fellow assemblers, it was discovered that if the wiring harness was always placed in a certain configuration, downstream work was simplified. Subsequently, a change was made to the product routing sheets to incorporate the wiring harness change to ensure that all assembly line workers install wiring harnesses in the same configuration. This change to the product routing sheets was supplemented with training.

Poka-Yoke

Poka-yoke is a term that means to mistake-proof a process by building safeguards into the system that avoid or immediately find errors. A poka-yoke device is one that prevents incorrect parts from being made, assembled, or stored, or that easily identifies a flaw or error. The term comes from the Japanese terms *poka*, which means "error," and *yokeru*, which means "to avoid." Poka-yoke is also known as *error-proofing*, *fool-proofing*, and *mistake-proofing*. Poka-yoke activities enable process control by automatically eliminating a source of variation. Poka-yoke methods are also helpful in reducing the occurrence of rare events. With the increase in flexible work assignments and cross-trained personnel, poka-yoke becomes even more important.

EXAMPLE 25.4

A customer is ready to complete their purchase for the items in their online shopping cart. After they click on the Purchase button, a form pops up for the customer to enter in address and payment information. As the address is entered, the system automatically checks the address in the database and both auto-fills and suggests the enhanced four-digit "adder" to the zip code. With the payment information, the system checks the credit card entry field and the three-digit security code against the registered customer information maintained by the credit card company. The purchase will not proceed if an incorrect number of digits, or incorrect digits, is entered.

EXAMPLE 25.5

A manufacturer found that about 1 in 2000 of its assemblies shipped was missing one of its 165 components. A poka-yoke technique was used to eliminate this defect. The manufacturer now uses a bar code on each component and scans the serial number and bar code of each component as it is added to the assembly. The software is written so that the printer at the shipping department will not print a shipping label if any component is missing or otherwise incorrect.

EXAMPLE 25.6

Another poka-yoke solution involves the selection of the correct part from a rack of bins with similar contents. As the product reaches the workstation, its bar code is read. Light beams crisscross the front of the bins. If the operator reaches into the wrong bin, the conveyor stops until appropriate corrections have been made.

EXAMPLE 25.7

A newly assigned press operator placed finished parts on a pallet in the incorrect orientation. The next operator didn't notice the error; thus, several hundred products were spoiled. A fixture for the pallet now makes it impossible to stack the parts in an incorrect orientation.

CYCLE-TIME REDUCTION

Use various tools and techniques for reducing cycle time, e.g., continuous flow, single-minute exchange of die (SMED), and heijunka (production leveling). (Analyze)

Body of Knowledge VII.B.2

Cycle time is the time required to complete one cycle of an operation. It is useful to find ways to reduce cycle time and cycle time variation. Reducing variation in cycle time makes a system more predictable. Sometimes, the cycle time variation can be analyzed by studying the cycle times of sub-activities instead. For example, suppose the activity consists of using a word processor to modify a standard bid form. Sub-activities might include inserting client information, listing the proposed budget, or detailing alternatives. The total time to prepare the bid might vary a great deal, while the time required to accomplish each sub-activity should show less variation. The activities performed should be continually studied to eliminate non-value-added components and find better and faster ways to complete the value-added components. One successful technique for accomplishing these goals goes by many names: *kaizen methods, kaizen blitz, rapid continuous improvement* (RCI), and similar titles. The usual procedure is to form a small team that is given a process to improve and a limited time frame, often only a few days. The team should include the people who perform the targeted activity, outsiders who can provide a fresh perspective, and people authorized to approve changes. The team observes the process and raises questions about its various parts, including:

- Why is that stored there? Is there a better place to put it?
- Why do things in that order?
- Would a different table height work better?
- Could your supplier (internal or external) provide a better service?
- Does your supplier know what you need?
- Do you know what your customer needs?
- Are you providing your customer (internal or external) with the best possible service?
- Should parts of this activity be performed by the customer or the supplier?
- Are there steps that can be eliminated?
- Is there enough light, fresh air, etc., to do the job efficiently?
- Would another tool, software package, and so on, be more helpful?
- Are tools conveniently and consistently stored?
- Can the distance the person and/or product moves be reduced?
- Should this activity be moved closer to the supplier or customer?
- How many of these items should be kept on hand?
- Would it help to do this activity in less space?

In other words, the team questions everything about the process and its environment. Kaizen activity usually results in making several small improvements. In many situations the team implements a change and studies the result before making a recommendation.

Another useful time-based measure is *takt time,* which is sometimes confused with cycle time. However, the discussion immediately following should alleviate any confusion. Takt time is determined by customer demand. It is defined in Equation 25.1:

Equation 25.1 Takt time

$$\text{Takt time} = \frac{\text{Available Time}}{\text{Average Daily Demand}}$$

Takt time is defined as an expression of rate of customer pull calculated by comparing our available time to the average daily demand. Available time is defined further below but can best be described by expressing the scheduled process's uptime for a given portion of the day. Similarly, average daily demand is simply establishing the quantity the customers will pull in a given day. Both measures need to be adjusted to cover the same duration before computing takt time.

One final note about the average daily demand: Think of it as defining the rate of customer pull for a given scenario. For instance, the rate of Internet purchase deliveries needed leading up to the holiday season will of course be more than, say, the rate leading up to the non-holiday season. In this case, we may need to establish an average daily demand for the "busy" season and one for the "slow" season. As a result, we would have two takt times that we would aim to match depending on the time of the year.

In Example 25.8 the system must average one unit approximately every 95 seconds. To meet this demand rate, the drop-off rate for each process must be less than or equal to 95 seconds. So, to meet demand, the basic relationship between drop-off rate and takt time is

$$\text{Drop-off Rate} \leq \text{Takt time}$$

Drop-off Rate is simply the rate (expressed in seconds) at which the process completes an item, one at a time.

EXAMPLE 25.8

Let's calculate takt time if 285 units is our average demand across a shift consisting of 28,800 seconds with 30 minutes of a lunch break and two 15-minute breaks (15-minute breaks are covered, i.e., the process does not stop),

First, we need to calculate the available time. Each shift is on-site for 8 hours, the production line runs for 7.5 hours (the line is down for 30 minutes each shift for lunch). Ideally, takt time is reported in seconds per unit, so we need to convert the times to units of seconds.

Time shift is on-site: 8 hours = 28,800 seconds

Available Time: 7.5 hours = 27,000 seconds (with 30-minute break subtracted)

Note: When calculating available time, we aim to reflect the scheduled uptime for the process.

Continued

Continued

Next, we need to define average daily demand (adjusted for the time of reference for our available time, in this case 8 hours, or 1/3 of the day). Using Equation 25.1, takt time is calculated as follows:

$$\text{Takt time} = \frac{27{,}000}{285} \approx 94.7\,\text{seconds/unit}$$

Takt time is recalculated whenever the average daily demand changes significantly due to factors such as seasonality or promotions, as shown in Example 25.9.

EXAMPLE 25.9

If the number of units needed is increased to 312 from 285, the takt time is reduced to 86.5 from 94.7 seconds. Adjustments to drop-off rates, by adding people or equipment, may be necessary. In lean, this is often captured in multiple playbooks for different demand patterns.

Example 25.9 illustrates the traditional approach of using takt time for manufacturing products that aim to meet customer demand. However, takt concepts can also apply to other processes. Consider the rate of guests checking in at a hotel. This rate could be measured in seconds between people appearing to check in, which is the takt of needed check-ins. The rate of completion of user stories in an Agile software development framework can be used for takt time calculations. In each case, we could build our processes to satisfy the needed rate of completions as expressed by the customers.

It is important to note that if cycle time for every operation in a complete process can be reduced to equal or less than the takt time, products can be made in single-piece flow, or simply a batch size of one. Achieving a batch size of one is the basis for continuous flow manufacturing, discussed in the next section.

Continuous Flow Manufacturing

Continuous flow manufacturing (CFM) is a method in which items are produced and moved from one processing step to the next, one piece at a time. Each process makes only the one piece that the next process needs, and the transfer batch size is one. CFM is sometimes known as *one-piece flow* or *single-piece flow.*

The traditional manufacturing wisdom, however, has been to study the marketplace to obtain a forecast of sales of various products. This forecast is used as a basis for orders that are issued to suppliers and to departments responsible for fabrication and assembly. This is referred to as a "push" system. One major problem with this strategy is that if the forecast is imperfect, products are produced that customers don't want, and/or products that customers want are not available. A second major problem with the forecast-based strategy is the increasing expectation by customers for exactly the product they want, exactly when they want it. These two problems have led to a response by the manufacturing community that is sometimes called *mass customization.* As illustrated by the automotive industry, a vehicle ordered by a customer with a choice between dozens of options, with perhaps hundreds of combinations, cannot be accurately forecast. Instead, the customer order initiates the authorization to build the product. This is referred to as a "pull" system, because the pull of the customer instead of the push of the forecast activates the system.

Rather than producing batches of identical products, a pull-oriented organization produces a mix of products with the mix of features that customers order. In the ideal pull system, the receipt of the customer order initiates orders for the component parts to be delivered to the assembly line at scheduled times. The mixture of features of the components as they continuously flow to and through the line results in exactly the product the customer needs. Making this happen in a reasonable amount of time would have been unthinkable only a few years ago.

If a system were to achieve the state of perfection, each activity would move a component through the value stream so that it arrives at the next activity at the time it is needed. Achieving and maintaining this state may require a great deal of flexibility in allocating resources to various activities. Cross-training of personnel is essential. The resulting flexibility and system nimbleness would permit reduction of work-in-progress. Excessive cycle times are a barrier to CFM.

Reducing Changeover Time

Lean thinking is built on timely satisfaction of customer demand. This means there must be a system for quickly responding to changes in customer requirements. In metal-forming industries, for example, it was customary practice to produce hundreds or even thousands of a particular part before changing the machine's dies and then producing hundreds of another part. This often led to vast inventories of work-in-progress and the associated waste. These procedures were "justified" because changeover time of dies took several hours. *Changeover time* is the time between the last good piece off the current run and the first good piece off the next run. This includes the time required to modify a system or workstation, which involves both teardown time for the existing condition and setup time for the new condition.

Single-minute exchange of die (SMED), pioneered by Shigeo Shingo, is a system used to reduce changeover time and improve timely response to demand. SMED is a series of techniques that facilitate changeovers of production machinery in less than ten minutes (hence, "single-minute"). The long-term objective is always zero setup, in which changeovers are instantaneous and do not interfere in any way with continuous flow. Setup in a single minute is not required but used as a reference. Shingo (1985) gives greater detail.

The initial application of SMED often requires considerable resources in special staging tables, die storage areas, etc. SMED defines activities performed while the machine is down as *internal activities,* whereas *external activities* are performed in preparation or follow-up to the die change. Shingo's method is to move as many activities from internal to external as possible. A cornerstone to this entire process is to reduce the time required to "change over" to within the cycle time of one action, i.e., no extra time needed to change to the next.

A useful technique is to make a video recording of a typical changeover and have the user identify internal activities that can be converted to external activities. Positioning correct tooling, equipment, and labor should all be done in external time.

The Shingo methodology can be summarized as follows:

- Identify and classify internal and external activities
- Make a video of the changeover process
- Evaluate video and establish logical steps for changeover
- Assess which steps are no longer required and eliminate them
- Separate internal and external activities
- Convert internal to external activities
- Assess which steps include waste and identify mitigation strategies
- Apply engineering changes to convert any remaining internal activities to external activities as appropriate
- Minimize external activity time

As can be imagined, sometimes SMED requires a significant and costly process redesign. Cost–benefit analyses are required to ensure that the ROI exists for the needed improvements. When justifying expenses for the improvements, consider the amount of wasted time getting ready to do the next operation, the amount of overtime expense required because of lengthy changeovers, holding excess inventory because of the "batch mentality" still holding on, and the lack of flexibility to meet customers' changes in demands and needs.

EXAMPLE 25.10

A procedure for changing cameras requires several steps:

1. Shoot last good picture with camera A.
2. Remove camera A and its power supply and place in storage cupboard.
3. Remove type A tripod.
4. Remove type A lighting and reflectors.
5. Install type B lighting and reflectors.
6. Install type B tripod. Measure distance to subject with tape measure.
7. Locate camera B in cupboard and install it and its power supply.
8. Shoot first good picture with camera B.

Continued

Continued

A team working to reduce changeover time designed a fitting so both cameras could use the same tripod. By purchasing extra cables, the team was able to avoid moving power supplies. More-flexible lighting reflectors were designed so that one set would work for both cameras. Tape was placed on the floor to mark the location of the tripod feet, thus avoiding the use of a tape measure. Of course, another alternative would be to obtain a more versatile camera that would not need to be changed. However, such an approach might be cost prohibitive.

EXAMPLE 25.11

A procedure for changing from approving a personal bank loan to approving a business bank loan requires the following steps:

1. Evaluate personal loan application.
2. Assess risk given personal financial statement and credit score.
3. Approve or reject loan application.
4. Close personal loan approval software.
5. Open business loan approval software.
6. Evaluate business loan application.
7. Assess risk given business loan financial statement, the P&L, and the business credit score.
8. Approve or reject loan application.

A team working to reduce changeover time looked at the activities and systems required to complete both loan reviews. They worked to eliminate searching time by making Icon groups for each type of loan, grouping personal loan approval applications in one group and the business loan approval applications in another group. They also reviewed the applications for both personal and business loans and standardized the forms where they could, making them match to reduce chances for confusion during review. Lastly, they worked with the software vendor to make the interfaces for personal loan and the business loan approvals the same. All these changes worked together to reduce the time necessary to swing from one type of approval to another.

Heijunka (Production Leveling)

Reducing variation is always a desirable goal. Variation in production scheduling can be a source of problems, so leveling production is a valid goal. Another goal is the satisfaction of the customer, that is, providing the customer what is needed when it is needed. These two goals can be contradictory because the customer's needs may be quite variable, and variation in production causes problems. *Heijunka* is a technique for meeting variable customer requirements while reducing variation in the production schedule. It has two forms, volume leveling and product leveling.

Volume Leveling

A customer needs 100 units per week, so the supplier decides to produce 20 units per day. On Monday, the customer orders 15. The supplier ships 15 and puts the remaining 5 in heijunka storage (labeled H). On Tuesday, the customer orders 25 and the supplier ships the 20 produced that day plus the 5 in storage. On Wednesday, the customer orders 18, so the supplier ships 18 and puts 2 units in storage. On Thursday, the customer orders 19 and the supplier ships 19 and puts one additional unit in storage. On Friday, the customer orders 23 units. The supplier ships the 20 produced that day plus the 3 that are in storage. Thus, although the customer's orders varied, the supplier was able to maintain a constant 20 units per week. The week's activity is summarized in Table 25.1. In this example, no parts are in storage at the beginning of the week.

The alert reader will ask, "What if the customer orders 23 on Monday?" The solution is to have a certain amount of heijunka storage before the week starts. The amount required will depend on experience, projections, and so on, but will not be more than one week's customer requirements, in this case 100 units. This would cover the case where the Monday order is 100. A heijunka storage amount of 80 would be sufficient because Monday's production of 20 units would bring the total to 100.

The first reaction to this arrangement is that it increases inventory, and of course it does. So, the heijunka technique presents a trade-off between leveling production and maintaining a low inventory. Table 25.2 illustrates the situation in which the customer front-loads the orders during the week. Again, daily production rates are 20 per day, and we started with 80 in heijunka storage before the week began.

Product Leveling

In a mixed model scenario, the supplier ships more than one product type to the customer. If the customer needs 38 of part A and 62 of part B each week, the supplier might decide to produce 8 part-A units and 12 part-B units on Monday, Wednesday, and Friday, and produce 7 part-A units and 13 part-B units on Tuesday and Thursday. Table 25.3 depicts a theoretical week, again recognizing that daily total production rates are 20 per day. Also, the week started with 30 parts of A and 50 parts of B in stock in the heijunka storage.

Customer order		Supplier reaction	Heijunka storage
Monday	15	Ship 15, put 5 in H storage	5
Tuesday	25	Ship 25 by drawing 5 from H	0
Wednesday	18	Ship 18, put 2 in H storage	2
Thursday	19	Ship 19, put 1 in H storage	3
Friday	23	Ship 23 by drawing 3 from H	0

Table 25.1 Heijunka volume leveling example.

Customer order		Supplier reaction	Heijunka storage
Monday	50	Ship 50 by drawing 30 from H	50
Tuesday	50	Ship 50 by drawing 30 from H	20
Wednesday	0	Ship 0, put 20 in H storage	40
Thursday	0	Ship 0, put 20 in H storage	60
Friday	0	Ship 0, put 20 in H storage	80
Initial heijunka storage = 80			

Table 25.2 Another heijunka volume leveling example.

Customer order			Supplier reaction				Heijunka storage	
	A	B		A		B	A	B
Monday	5	13	Store	3	Draw	1	33	49
Tuesday	8	10	Draw	1	Store	3	32	52
Wednesday	15	25	Draw	7	Draw	13	25	39
Thursday	10	12	Draw	3	Store	1	22	40
Friday	0	2	Store	8	Store	10	30	50
Heijunka storage at start of week: A = 30, B = 50								

Table 25.3 Heijunka product leveling example.

In the real world the exact number of each product that a customer will order is usually not known, but the general approach has been shown to reduce variability in day-to-day production. The daily schedules are often displayed in a *heijunka box,* which may be a matrix drawn on a display board as shown in Figure 25.1.

Mon	Tue	Wed	Thur	Fri
A	A	A	A	A
A	A	A	A	A
A	A	A	B	A
B	B	B	B	B
B	C	B	C	C
C	C	C	C	C
C	D	C	D	C
	E		E	

Figure 25.1 A heijunka box displaying daily schedules.

KAIZEN

> Define and distinguish between kaizen and kaizen blitz and describe when to use each method. (Apply)
>
> Body of Knowledge VII.B.3

Kaizen is a Japanese term made famous by Masaaki Imai in his book *Kaizen: The Key to Japan's Competitive Success* (1986). It refers to a mindset in which all employees are responsible for making continuous incremental improvements to the functions they perform. The aggregate effect of this approach is cost-effective and practical improvements that have instant buy-in by those who use them.

Kaizen is a term that has come to mean gradual unending improvement by doing little things better and setting and achieving increasingly higher standards. A *kaizen event or kaizen blitz* is usually implemented as a small, intensive event or project over a short duration, such as a week. It is advantageous to use the kaizen approach in the following situations:

- The responsibility for implementation of change because of the kaizen activity lies mostly within the team, and the risk of failure is small.
- Projects are time-bound, and results must be demonstrated quickly.
- Projects are clearly defined.
- Improvement opportunities are readily identifiable, such as excess waste.

EXAMPLE 25.11

A kaizen team observed that fan blades were retrieved from large boxes that the operator was required to move around to accommodate model changes. A kaizen team designed a "Christmas tree" with arms holding the appropriate fan blades, which the assemblers could easily reach from their workstation. The assembly line supplier was responsible for assuring that the next blade on the tree was the right one for the next product on the line.

EXAMPLE 25.12

An overhead chain assembly line is populated by 35 workers. Each person can stop the line when they see an opportunity for improvement. A clock that is visible to everyone is set at 12:00 at the start of each shift and runs only when the line is stopped for these improvements.

Management policy is that the clock should run about 30 to 40 minutes each shift because, "Only when the clock is running are we solving problems and making things better. . . . We need around 30 to 40 minutes of improvements each shift."

Process control can be enhanced through kaizen events that reduce non-value-added activities. The resulting work is more productive and permits a closer process focus by all involved.

Kaizen, then, is really an approach to process and enterprise management that recognizes the importance of each employee's creative ability and interest in continuous improvement. This approach may be difficult to instill in organizations with a history of top-down management. Barriers include an adversarial attitude and the feeling that "It's not my job to make my job better." In some situations, this may be overcome by demonstrating successful kaizen blitz events.

A *kaizen blitz* is performed by a team in a short amount of time, usually a few days. The team focuses on a specific work area with the intent of making low-cost improvements that are easy to implement and are often installed during the blitz. The team should consist of people from the work area plus others from similar work areas, technical support, supervisory personnel with decision-making responsibilities, and outsiders who can see with "fresh eyes." The blitz begins with training and team-building activities and quickly proceeds to the work area, where each function is observed and explained in detail. Teams may split into sub-teams assigned to specific tasks. At some point the entire team hears reports and recommendations from the sub-teams and reaches a consensus on changes to be implemented. In some cases, these changes can be carried out immediately, and in others a schedule of future implementation efforts is prepared. This schedule should include deadlines and persons responsible. The team sometimes makes a report to the next higher level of management, which provides recognition. Some organizations have found these reports and the time spent to prepare for them to be unnecessary as blitz events become routine and a part of the standard way of operating. A side benefit of blitz events is that employees begin to see that their input is valuable and valued, which may lead to more support for the incremental kaizen mindset.

EXAMPLE 25.13

A team is assigned to perform a blitz event on an assembly line for an appliance manufacturer. The team consists of the departmental foreman, a group leader, three line-workers (including one from a similar line elsewhere in the plant), one engineer with assembly line responsibilities, a technician, and a guest from a nearby factory. After introductory training, communication of the ground rules and expectations, and a discussion of previous kaizen events, the team proceeds to the observation phase, which takes about three hours. Special attention is given to material handling and resupply, availability of tools, and motion by individual workers. The team then splits into sub-teams. Two of the sub-teams will work on specific resupply problems, one will work with workplace organization and clutter, and a fourth will examine the need for better flow of sub-assemblies to the line.

The results of this blitz event included better design and positioning of material racks, with the stockroom responsible for making sure that the next item on the rack is the next item needed on the line. (Note: This is especially important when the schedule calls for a model change.) New routes for the resupply personnel were defined. Designated areas for sub-assemblies were signed and painted. Standard work issues were resolved and documented so that some assemblers now had slightly modified jobs that will make downstream functions more efficient. Material storage racks were redesigned.

Toyota Kata has recently emerged as an extension of *kaizen*. The *kaizen* philosophy and development and practice by leaders has in recent years been captured in a routine called Toyota Kata. According to Mike Rother (2009) and his team, a unique success factor in Toyota's management system is that Toyota practices and teaches a method of scientific thinking every day, with managers and supervisors as coaches. Different than a *kaizen* event, Kata aims to capture and deploy the *kaizen* philosophy, teaching people how to think and conduct experiments to make incremental change and improvement.

In summary, the term *kaizen* is used to describe the gradual but continuous improvement process that extends over time. It has been found to improve processes, products, and morale, and is a philosophy for how to think about processes and incremental improvement. *Kaizen blitz*, on the other hand, describes a short-term event designed to make quick and easy improvements and set the stage for the mindset required for the long-term kaizen approach. And Toyota Kata aims to teach the philosophy and practice of the mindset of *kaizen*.

OTHER IMPROVEMENT TOOLS AND TECHNIQUES

> Identify and describe how other process improvement methodologies are used, e.g., theory of constraints (TOC), overall equipment effectiveness (OEE). (Understand)
>
> **Body of Knowledge VII.B.4**

The *theory of constraints* (TOC) is a problem-solving methodology that focuses on the weakest link in a chain of processes (Goldratt, 1999). Usually, the *constraint* is the slowest process. Flow rate through the system cannot increase unless the rate at the constraint increases. The TOC lists five steps to system improvement:

1. *Identify*. Find the process that limits the effectiveness of the system. If throughput is the concern, the constraint will often have work-in-progress (WIP) awaiting action.
2. *Exploit*. Use kaizen or other methods to improve the throughput of the constraining process, such as:
   - Enlarge kanban size so there is plenty of WIP ahead of the constraint, so it never has to wait on upstream processes.
   - Ensure that no defective parts are in this WIP, so the constraint only processes good parts.
   - Adjust the schedule so the constraint always runs, even during breaks and lunch. Use overtime.
   - Reduce changeover time.

    - Keep maintenance interruptions to a minimum.
    - Send some work through other processes.
3. *Subordinate.* Adjust (or subordinate) the rates of other processes in the chain to match that of the constraining process.
    - If the constraint equipment needs maintenance, it should have highest priority—maintenance of other units should be subordinated to that of the constraint.
4. *Elevate.* If the system rate needs further improvement, the constraining process may require extensive revision (or elevation). This could mean investment in additional equipment or new technology.
5. *Repeat.* If these steps have improved the process to the point where it is no longer the constraint, the system rate can be further improved by repeating these steps with a new constraint.

The strength of the TOC is that it employs a systems approach, emphasizing that improvements to individual processes will not improve the rate of the system unless they improve the performance of the constraining process.

Drum-Buffer-Rope

The "subordinate" step requires further explanation. To illustrate how to manage operations, Goldratt (1997) uses a group of people walking in single file as an analogy for a string of production processes (see Figure 25.2). As the first person moves forward, that person receives unprocessed material, the fresh ground. Each succeeding person performs another process by walking on that same ground. As the last person passes over the ground, it becomes finished goods. Thus, the individual processes are moving over fixed material rather than the other way around. *Lead time* is the time it takes for the group to pass a certain point. If each person moves as fast as possible, the lead time tends to lengthen, with the slower people falling behind and holding up those behind them, since passing is not permitted.

The system constraint is the slowest person. The ground can't be processed faster than this person can move. This person sets the drumbeat for the entire system. To avoid lengthening the lead time, a rope connects the lead person to the slowest person.

The length of the rope is the size of the *buffer.* When the lead person, walking faster than the constraint, gets far enough ahead, the rope becomes taut and signals the lead person to stop. In this way, maximum lead time and WIP are fixed.

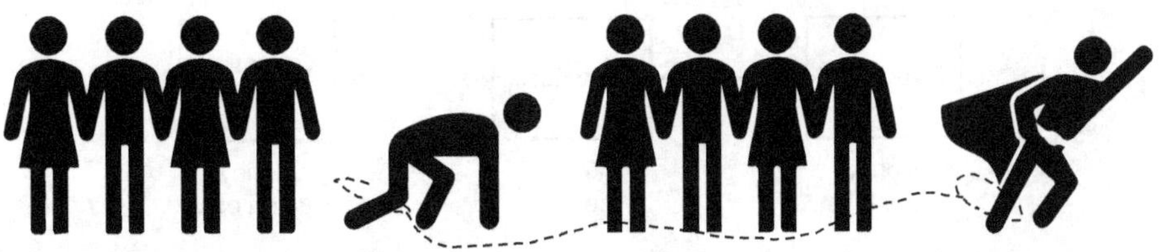

Figure 25.2 The drum-buffer-rope subordinate step analogy—with rope.

If a person behind the slowest person happens to drop something, they will fall behind a little but will be able to catch up since they are not the slowest person. This is analogous to a minor process problem at one station. If a person in front of the slowest person drops something, the group will not have to stop unless the slowest person catches up with the one in front of them. So, if the group has a high tendency to drop things, the rope must be longer. The length of the rope is the size of the buffer. In summary, to avoid long lead times and excess WIP, all system processes should be slowed down (via the rope) to the speed of the slowest process (the drum), and the amount of WIP (or buffer) is determined by the dependability of the individual processes.

The TOC as described by Goldratt has significant impact on three key interdependent operating measures of a business. Dettmer (2007) describes these as:

- Throughput (designated as T)—the rate at which the entire system generates money through sales
- Investment (designated as I)—the money the system invests in things it intends to sell
- Operating expense (designated as OE)—the money the system spends turning inventory into throughput

Figure 25.3 illustrates the relationships between these operating measures. Notice that as throughput increases, the other two measures decrease. This makes sense because as constraints are removed, throughput increases. Increased throughput means less investment tied up in the system. Less investment, along with a higher throughput, means that less money (that is, operating expense) is required to turn inventory into throughput (or output as the case may be).

Overall Equipment Effectiveness (OEE)

OEE provides a metric for evaluating processes and process improvement efforts. The basic formulas are:

Equation 25.2 OEE

$$\text{OEE} = \text{Availability} \times \text{Performance} \times \text{Quality}$$

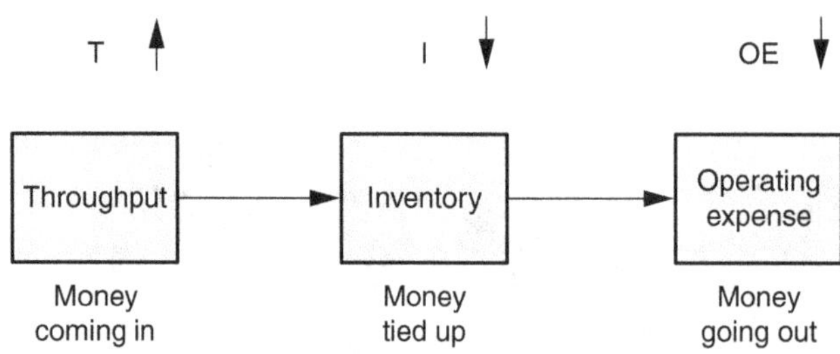

Figure 25.3 The interdependence of throughput, inventory, and operating expense measures.

where availability, performance, and quality are calculated by:

Equation 25.3 Availability

$$\text{Availability} = \frac{\text{Actual operating time}}{\text{Planned production time}}$$

Equation 25.4 Performance

$$\text{Performance} = \frac{\text{Total pieces / Actual operating time}}{\text{Ideal run time}}$$

Equation 25.5 Quality

$$\text{Quality} = \frac{\text{Number of good pieces}}{\text{Total number of pieces}}$$

In addition, we have the following definitions:

Planned production time = Shift length – Breaks, lunch and so on

Actual operating time = Planned production time – Downtime for setup, maintenance, and so on

Ideal run rate = Designed maximum cycle time

Note: Availability is also referred to as Percent Uptime, Performance is also referred to as Percent of Published Rate, and Quality is also referred to as Percent Yield.

EXAMPLE 25.14

A machine scheduled for a 10-hour shift minus 80 minutes for breaks and a meal is down for 70 minutes for maintenance. It is designed to process 300 pieces per hour. During the shift, it makes 1783 good parts and 91 bad parts. The OEE calculation follows (all times in minutes):

Planned production time (min.) = 600 (10-hour shift) – 80 (breaks) = 520 minutes

Actual operating time = 520 – 70 (maintenance) = 450 minutes

Total pieces = 1783 (good parts) + 91 (bad parts) = 1874 parts

Ideal run time = 5 parts/min

Number of good pieces = 1783 parts

Total number of pieces = 1874 parts

Continued

Continued

Using Equations 25.2 through 25.5, we have:

$$\text{Availability} = \frac{450}{520} = 0.865$$

$$\text{Performance} = \frac{\left(\frac{1874}{450}\right)}{5} = 0.833$$

$$\text{Quality} = \frac{1783}{1874} = 0.951$$

$$\text{OEE} = 0.865 \times 0.833 \times 0.951 = 0.685$$

The OEE number is a good metric for making comparisons between two identical machines making identical parts. It can also be used to compare a machine or process before and after implementation of a quality improvement. Care must be used in comparing machines or processes that aren't very similar because the factors that are multiplied together can be influenced by maintenance differences, which may not be comparable. In addition, the "ideal run time" is not always calculated the same way.

Six Big Losses

The best place to do an initial OEE calculation is at the constraint step in a process, as defined in the previous section on theory of constraints. This is because improvements at a constraint improve the whole process. When seeking to improve the OEE value, examine the values of the three factors of availability, performance, and quality, and determine which one(s) can be raised cost-effectively. We can conduct root cause analysis on the reasons for downtime in the *availability* factor, reduced cycle time in the *performance* factor, and defect level in the case of the *quality* factor.

We can also concentrate on reducing the *Six Big Losses* to maximize OEE. As shown in Figure 25.4, the first two losses are equipment breakdowns and setup and changeover time. Together, these two losses affect Availability.

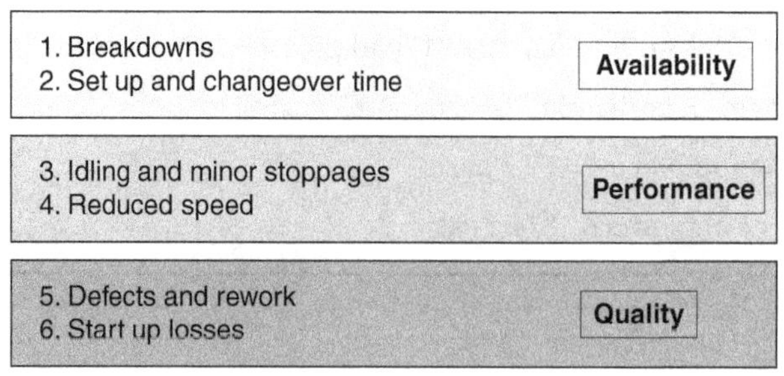

Figure 25.4 The Six Big Losses and their relation to OEE.

Next, we have the losses due to minor stoppage and idling machines, as well as reduced machine speed. These losses adversely affect the Performance metric. Finally, the fifth and sixth losses are defects and rework, and scrap due to machine startup. These losses affect the Quality metric. If we concentrate on reducing the Six Big Losses, improvement in OEE will follow.

Chapter 26
Implementation

Almost all quality improvement comes via simplification of design, manufacturing, . . . , layout, processes, and procedures.

—Tom Peters

> Develop plans for implementing proposed improvements, including conducting pilot tests or simulations, and evaluate results to select the optimum solution. (Evaluate)
>
> **Body of Knowledge VII.C**

Once the root causes have been identified, the next step should be to identify a potential set of solutions. These should be considered tentative until they are evaluated. When evaluating a set of solutions, it is important that specific criteria be established. Examples of such criteria include cost of implementation, ease of implementation, maintainability, reliability, organizational acceptance, customer impact, impact to the bottom line, and so forth. Whatever criteria are chosen, they should be relevant, well defined, and a result of team consensus.

Figure 26.1 depicts a prioritization matrix, first introduced in Chapter 13, of potential solutions and the associated evaluation criteria. Also depicted are weights associated with each criterion. For each criterion, a rank is assigned to each potential solution, with the best being the highest number and the worst being the lowest number. Decimal values indicate ties between two rank values. For instance, if multiple criteria are tied for a specific rank, each would be assigned the average rank value. An easy way to check if ties are handled correctly is to assure that each criterion column adds to $\sum_{i=1}^{n} i$, in which n is the number of potential solutions. Figure 26.1 shows that there are five potential solutions, so the ranks for each criterion columns should add to

$$\sum_{i=1}^{5} i = 1+2+3+4+5 = 15.$$

Criteria	Percent process improvement	Cost of implementation	Reliability	Maintainability	Installation resources required	Adverse impact	Total
Relative Importance (%)	25%	20%	15%	10%	10%	20%	100%
Potential solutions							
A	5	2	5	4	2	3	3.60
B	1	3	3.5	5	5	2	2.78
C	2.5	5	2	1.5	4	4	3.28
D	2.5	4	1	1.5	1	5	2.83
E	4	1	3.5	3	3	1	2.53
Rank cross-check	15	15	15	15	15	15	

Figure 26.1 Example of a prioritization matrix for selection of solutions.

Once each cell has been assigned a value, the corresponding weight value is multiplied by each of the assigned values and totaled. The potential solution with the highest weighted value becomes the solution of focus for implementation.

Using ranks and handling ties can become cumbersome: It is recommended that the team use a scale of 1 to 5 or 1 to 10 to rate the potential solutions for each criterion. With the rating method, two or more projects can be assigned the same value for a criterion, with no need to handle ties.

Following is a list of other common and useful approaches that yield highly actionable insight:

- *Pilot run.* A short, limited production run usually terminated by elapsed time or quantity produced. A pilot run provides the team with valuable information regarding how an improved process will run since the pilot represents actual production. It also provides significant insight into issues or problems that were overlooked. Hence, an additional opportunity is available to correct outstanding problems prior to full-scale implementation.

- *Simulation.* Simulation is performed with computer software and is either deterministic or probabilistic in design. A *deterministic* simulation provides little information other than to ensure that process flows are correct and that the general design of the simulation matches the operational environment. A *probabilistic,* or *stochastic,* simulation provides insight into the statistical and operational measures associated with the process being simulated. However, careful attention must be given to interpreting the statistical output to ensure that parameters are being estimated properly. Overall, simulation provides the ability to "implement" solutions off-line but to draw conclusions regarding how the process improvement will operate online. When conducting simulations, the team should both verify and validate them before use. However, many transactional process improvement activities can benefit from trying out the process in a simulation, to determine the best course of action prior to physical implementation.

- *Physical model.* A smaller physical representation developed on a specified scale. Unlike simulations, models simply provide a three-dimensional miniature version of whatever is being modeled and are a highly effective means of communicating an improvement alternative since they play to the visual sense.
- *Prototype.* A representation of the actual product in terms of form, fit, and functionality, with perhaps some limitations on functions and/or features. Prototypes provide the team with the ability to experiment with a product by adjusting a wide range of both product and process parameters, usually at a lower cost.

Once the team settles on a particular solution, it must then establish an implementation strategy. A first step in this approach might be the development of a force-field analysis. Recall that a force-field analysis is useful for identifying those forces that both support and oppose the process implementation. These forces can be integrated into the implementation strategy to ensure that those forces that support the implementation are retained or strengthened, and those that oppose it are eliminated or mitigated.

EXAMPLE 26.1

A plastic recycling process grinds plastic waste, heats it to a liquid state, and pours it into rectangular molds approximately 2 × 8 × 84 inches. The material is allowed to solidify in the molds. Then the molds containing the material are submerged in a water bath for cooling. The resulting product is unstable, tending to warp out of spec. The improvement team believes that the water bath develops hot spots around portions of the material that are denser, thus retaining more heat. This results in different cooling rates and different final temperatures, which causes warping. The team believes that a flow of cool water should be passed through the bath container to provide a more stable cooling process. Before they implement this belief, they consider each of the four testing techniques listed above.

Pilot run: The team could construct a set of troughs with water pumps and chillers and run several days of production through the new system. The resultant material could be checked for warp.

Simulation: The team would use heat transfer equations for various plastic densities and various water temperatures. They would use these formulas to predict the water temperature rise at the hot spots and the associated cooling rates. By executing the resulting software, they could predict final temperature at various locations on the finished product by knowing the density of the material in that neighborhood. They could then check the predicted temperatures against measured values to validate the simulation. The next step would be to run the software under the assumption of flowing chilled water to predict final temperatures at various density points. This simulation could also be used to predict the best chiller output temperature, flow rate, and time in bath. Such predictions must be viewed with caution, but they can help when deciding whether to embark on extensive capital investment.

Continued

Continued

Model: The team could build a 1/8-scale model of the proposed system and run water at various temperatures over miniature slabs in miniature molds. They could collect warpage data for comparison.

Prototype: The team could rig up a special trough with a water pump and chiller and measure the amount of warp in the finished product. Various water temperatures could be tried. The amount of warp in the finished product could be measured. If the prototype is constructed in a lab environment, consideration must be given to differences between lab conditions and the production environment.

Although many authors propose various improvement implementation strategies and methodologies, they are usually offered in a one-size-fits-all approach. Implementation of any initiative or process improvement must be performed with care and due consideration of the organization's culture. With respect to this idea, consider the following framework, which can be tailored to a specific organization's needs during an improvement implementation:

Infrastructure. This includes everything necessary to ensure a successful implementation. Examples include changes to hardware or software, training, acquisition of talent, organizational changes, facilities, and so forth. The infrastructure requirements will vary from project to project.

Example 26.2 shows a force-field analysis completed to assess both the driving forces as well as the resisting forces an improvement is likely to encounter.

EXAMPLE 26.2

The board of directors of a hospital has decided to build a new building on the south side of town rather than continue to update the current building, parts of which are 100 years old. It is the only hospital in a town of 30,000, and they begin their implementation plan with a force-field analysis (see Chapter 8) as shown in Figure 26.2.

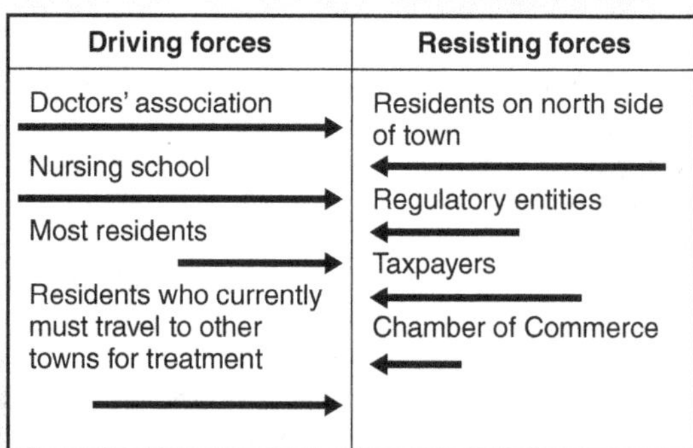

Figure 26.2 Example of a force-field analysis.

Continued

Continued

The team forms a plan based on the force-field analysis with the following elements:

1. Request that the medical association make its support known by providing speakers at service clubs and publishing a letter of support in the local newspaper.
2. Assure the north side residents that the ambulance service will continue to be housed in the fire station on the north side.
3. Request that the nursing school inform the public of the advantages to student nurses of having access to the latest in facilities and equipment.
4. Request that residents send letters of support for the move. These letters will be combined, summarized, and provided to the regulatory entities.
5. Request that residents who must travel elsewhere for treatment provide testimonies of support to be used by hospital staff as they communicate with various stakeholders.
6. Assure the members of the Chamber of Commerce that the move will be incremental over a period of eight years, which will allow businesses to adjust plans accordingly.

COMMUNICATION PLAN

Communication is one aspect of implementation whose importance is frequently underestimated. The team must effectively communicate its solution to the organization to reduce fear and resistance to change. Developing a communication plan can help address these concerns. A communication plan should be specific regarding:

- *Who communicates it.* It is important that communication start at the top; however, the message needs to cascade down through all levels of management until it reaches those who need to know. This cascading of communication cannot be emphasized enough as it creates and reinforces a sense of urgency. Furthermore, it reinforces the message that management believes it is important to implement the process improvement.
- *What is communicated.* What should be communicated is the "who," "what," "when," "where," and "why." If each of these questions is addressed, then a clear and concise message will be delivered. No communication should raise more questions than it answers. And it should not assume an existing knowledge of the improvement implementation on the part of the recipient of the communication. What is to be communicated must remain consistent throughout. Thus, the development of "canned" presentations, a script, and so forth, are beneficial in maintaining that consistency.
- *When it is communicated.* The timeliness of a communication is, at best, tricky, and often more than one communication is required.

Communications may be timed for release just prior to the phases of the implementation schedule. Occasionally, it is prudent to issue an overarching, up-front communication and support it with phased communications throughout the implementation. Regardless of the approach chosen, there are three important considerations:

1. Multiple communications may be necessary
2. Communications should reinforce and progress logically
3. Timely communications should occur before a phase is executed, not after

- *Where it is communicated.* This speaks to the geographic, demographic, and organizational areas of the communication. For example, the communication may be intended for the engineering function located in North Carolina.
- *How it is communicated.* All communication media are not created equal. An effective communication plan should recognize that most organizations have a variety of communication media available to them. Choosing the right medium for the right audience is essential. Examples of media include newsletters, e-mail, recorded videos, staff meetings, town halls, Internet meetings, telephone broadcasts, and so forth. It is important to keep in mind that for any given audience, multiple delivery media may be appropriate. Social media (both internal and external) can be effective modes of communication.
- *To whom it is communicated.* Without a doubt, it is critical to communicate to all who might be impacted by the improvement implementation. This includes not only those responsible for carrying out the process, but also upstream suppliers and downstream customers.
- *Competition for time, energy, and resources.* As with most organizations, the team's improvement initiative is not the only critical activity in the organization that demands resources. Therefore, it is essential to outline the requirements for implementation in advance and to secure approval by management. An actual document requiring "sign-off" is helpful in this regard.

Communication Plan					
Who Do We Communicate To	**Team Members**	**How To Communicate**	**What's The Message**	**When**	**Where**
Tymer Road Production	D. Beamers	Onsite visit	Question about the new process	Each Thursday	Transportation Office
Tymer Road Quality	B. Frankin	Email report	Weeks overdue inspections	Monday by 10AM	Inbox
Corporate	N. Flowers	Conference Call	Status update for project improve	Monthly, in week 1	Zoom call

Figure 26.3 Example communication plan.

- *Management commitment*. By now, "management commitment" has become cliché. In terms of the framework, this item is pivotal. Nothing will be accomplished without it. Management must be visible, active, and engaged to ensure a successful implementation. Lip service won't cut it. If there is no management commitment, the only assurance the team has is that it will fail.

Part VIII

Control

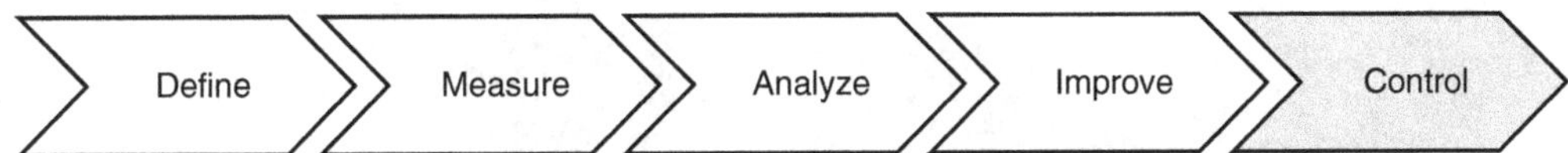

The purpose of this phase is to transition the improved process back to the process owner and to establish and deploy a control plan to ensure that gains in performance are maintained. Common tools used in this phase are shown in Table VIII.1.

5S	Kanban	Six Sigma storyboard
Basic statistics	Lessons learned	Standard operating procedures (SOPs)
Communication plan	Measurement systems analysis (MSA)	Standard work
Continuing process measurements	Meeting minutes	*Statistical process control (SPC)*
Control charts	Mistake-proofing/poka-yoke	Tollgate review
Control plan	Pre-control	Total productive maintenance
Data collection	*Project management*	Training plan deployment
Data collection plan	*Project tracking*	Visual factory
Kaizen	*Run charts*	Work instructions

Table VIII.1 Common tools used in *control* phase.
Note: Tools shown in *italic* are used in more than one phase.

Chapter 27

Statistical Process Control

Effective statistical process control is 10% statistics and 90% management action.

–John Hradesky

This chapter will address the basic concepts of statistical process control (SPC), including the objectives of SPC, the selection of critical process characteristics for control chart monitoring, the ever-important aspect of rational subgrouping, the selection and use of variables and attributes control charts, and the recognition and interpretation of out-of-control conditions. Numerous examples and control charts are presented, as well as several flowcharts to aid in the selection of control charts. In addition, several summary tables have been provided to assist the reader for examination and desktop reference purposes.

OBJECTIVES

> Explain the objectives of SPC, including monitoring and controlling process performance, tracking trends, runs, and reducing variation within a process. (Understand)
>
> Body of Knowledge VIII.A.1

Control charts are statistically based graphical tools used to monitor the behavior of a process. Walter A. Shewhart developed them in the 1920s while working at Bell Laboratories. More than 100 years later, control charts continue to serve as the foundation for statistical process control.

Broadly speaking, the objectives of a statistical process control (SPC) chart are to first establish the distribution of the process output and to then monitor that process to determine if the initial output distribution has changed in some way. More specifically, SPC consists of the following set of tools and activities:

- *Quantifying the variation of a process.* Calculating the process variation is a fundamental step in developing a control chart. Control chart limits, traditionally set at $\pm 3\sigma$ from the mean, are statistically derived from the process output. This is in contrast to product specifications, which are derived from the customer requirements and engineering design.

- *Centering a process.* Calculating the mean of the process output is another fundamental step in control charting. It is important to note that the process average may not be equal to the nominal value defined by the specifications.
- *Improving product and process design.* SPC is beneficial for improving the process design because it provides quantitative feedback regarding the process average and process variation. However, additional tools and methodologies are often required, such as Lean Six Sigma, Design for Six Sigma (DFSS), process capability studies, and machine capabilities, among others.
- *Tracking trends and runs in the process.* Rules have been developed to recognize statistically out-of-control conditions on control charts. Such conditions include trends and runs, which often occur due to "special," or assignable, causes.
- *Determining when or when not to take action on a process.* Control charts illustrate two types of variation: common cause and special, or assignable, cause. We take action on special cause variation when we are trying to maintain control on a process. We do not take action on common cause variation unless we are trying to improve the process.
- *Making statistically valid decisions.* Control charts are created to help us make statistically valid decisions about the behavior of a process.

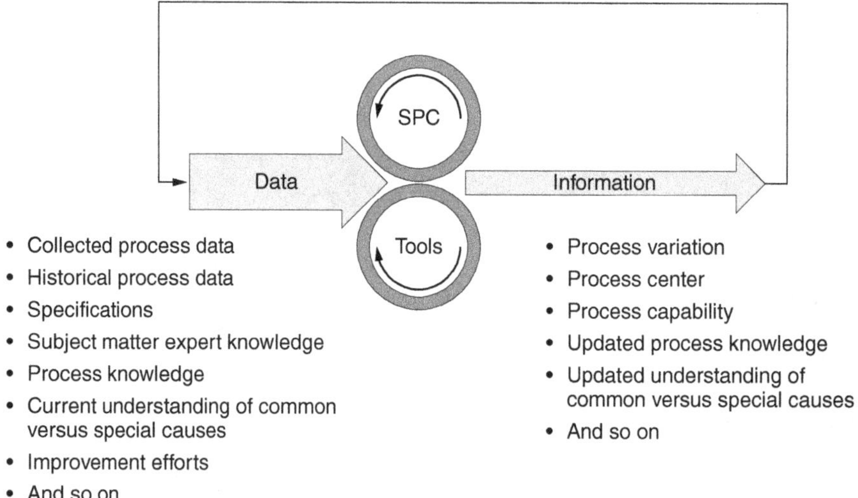

Figure 27.1 Function of SPC and related tools.

Figure 27.1 depicts SPC as a machine that uses data as input and produces information as its output. The SPC tools squeeze the information out of the raw data both graphically and statistically.

A wide variety of control charts have been developed over the years. However, we will focus on those that are the most popular in both manufacturing and transactional environments. These include the $\bar{X}$ and R chart, $\bar{X}$ and S chart, ImR chart, p-chart, np-chart, c-chart, u-chart, and several short-run charts. These and other SPC tools are available in various statistical software packages.

Special Cause versus Common Cause Variation

Every process has variation. The sources of process variation can be divided into two categories: special and common.

Common causes are those that are inherent to the process and generally are not controllable by process operators. Examples of common causes include variation in raw materials, variation in ambient temperature and humidity, variation in electrical or pneumatic sources, and variation within equipment, such as worn bearings.

In the case of service processes, common causes typically include variation in the input data, variations in customer load, and variation in computer operations. Some authors refer to common cause variation as *natural variation.*

Special, or assignable, causes of variation include unusual events that the operator (or if needed, the maintenance crew or process engineer), when properly alerted, can usually remove or adjust. Examples include large changes in raw materials and broken equipment.

A principal problem in process management is the separation of special and common causes. If the process operator tries to adjust a process in response to common cause variation, the result is usually more variation rather than less. This is sometimes called *overadjustment* or *overcontrol.* If a process operator fails to respond to the presence of a special cause of variation, this cause is likely to produce additional process variation. This is referred to as *under adjustment* or *under control.*

One of the main objectives of control charts is to help the process operator recognize the presence of special causes so that appropriate action can be taken in a timely manner. Control charts are discussed in detail in the following paragraphs.

Basic Structure of a Control Chart

Constructing control charts is straightforward and, more often than not, aided by computer software designed specifically for this purpose.

Figure 27.2 illustrates the general form for a control chart. Its critical components are:

1. *X-axis.* This axis represents the time order of subgroups. Subgroups represent samples of data taken from a process. It is critical that the integrity of the time dimension be maintained when plotting control charts.

2. *Y-axis.* This axis represents the measured value of the quality characteristic under consideration when using variables charts. When attributes charts are used, this axis is used to quantify defectives or defects.

3. *Centerline.* The centerline represents the process average.

4. *Control limits.* Control limits typically appear at ±3 standard deviations from the process average. The width of the control limits is sometimes referred to as the *voice of the process (VOP).*

5. *Zones.* The zones represent the distance between each standard deviation and are useful when discussing specific out-of-control rules.

6. *Rational subgroups.* The variation within subgroups should be as small as possible so it's easier to detect subgroup-to-subgroup variation. It follows that units in a subgroup should be as similar as possible.

Notice that there are no specification limits present on the control chart in Figure 27.2. This is by design, not by accident. The presence of specification limits on control charts could easily lead to inaction, particularly when a process is out of control but within specification. In addition, specifications are meant to be applied to individuals, and in the case of the $\bar{X}$ chart, we are plotting averages.

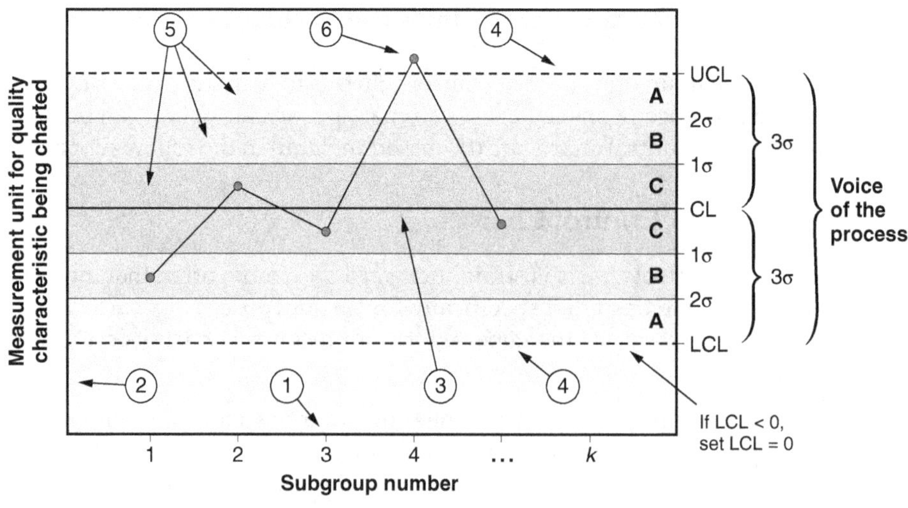

Figure 27.2 Structure of a typical control chart.

SELECTION OF VARIABLES

> Identify and select critical process characteristics for control chart monitoring. (Apply)
>
> **Body of Knowledge VIII.A.2**

When a control chart is to be used, a variable must be selected for monitoring. Sometimes that variable is the most critical dimension on the product. In some cases, the variable of choice is a "leading indicator" of special causes—one that detects special causes before others do. Contractual requirements with a customer sometimes specify the variable(s) to be monitored via control charts. If the root cause of the special variation is known, an input variable may be monitored. Often, the variable to be monitored is the one that is the most difficult to hold, as determined by capability analyses. It is possible to monitor several variables on separate control charts, especially if computerized charting is employed. In the end, the selection of the variable to be charted depends on experience and judgment.

RATIONAL SUBGROUPING

> Define and apply the principle of rational subgrouping. (Apply)
>
> **Body of Knowledge VIII.A.3**

The method used to select samples for a control chart must be logical, or "rational." In the case of the $\bar{X}$ and R chart, it is desirable that the $\bar{X}$ chart detects a process shift, while the R chart should quantify only common cause variation. That means there should be a high probability of variation between successive samples while the variation within the sample is kept low. Therefore, to minimize the within-sample variation, samples frequently consist of parts that are produced successively by the same process. The next sample is chosen somewhat later so that any process shifts that have occurred will be displayed on the chart as between-sample variation.

Choosing the rational subgroup requires care to make sure the same process is producing each item. For example, suppose a candy-making process uses 40 pistons to deposit 40 gobs of chocolate on a moving sheet of waxed paper in a 5 × 8 array, as shown in Figure 27.3. How should rational subgroups of size five be selected? Choosing the first five chocolates in each row, as indicated in Figure 27.3, would have the five elements of the sample being produced by five different

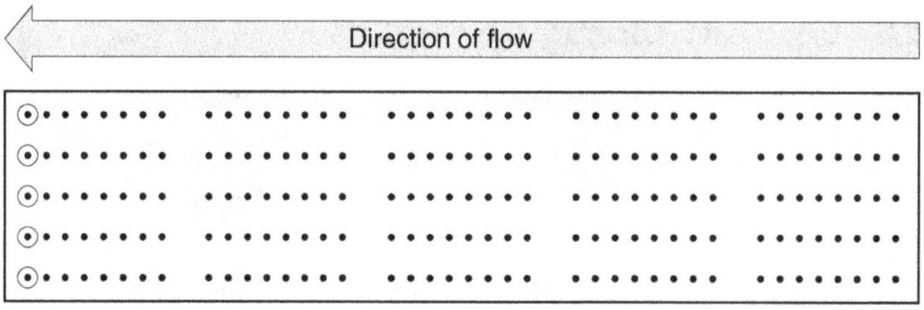

Direction of flow

Figure 27.3 Conveyor belt in chocolate-making process.

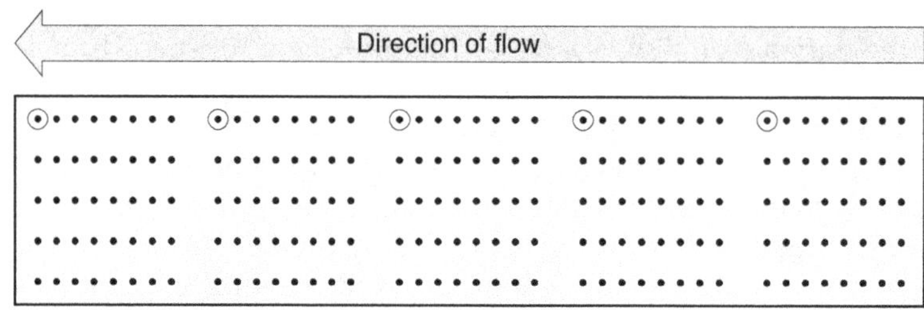

Figure 27.4 Conveyor belt in chocolate-making process with rational subgroup choice.

processes (the five different pistons). A better choice would be to select the upper left-hand chocolate in five consecutive arrays, as shown in Figure 27.4, because the same piston forms them all. This rational subgrouping scheme minimizes the within-subgroup variation, thus allowing subgroup-to-subgroup variation to become more prominent.

The choice of sample size can also depend on the resources available to do the measuring. However, the larger the sample size, the more sensitive the chart.

CONTROL CHART SELECTION

> Select and use control charts in various situations: $\bar{X}$-R, $\bar{X}$-S, individual and moving range (ImR), p, np, c, u, short-run SPC, and moving average. (Apply)
>
> **Body of Knowledge VIII.A.4**

Types of Control Charts

Control charts can be categorized into two types: variables and attributes. Charts fall into the *variables* category when the data to be plotted result from measurement on a continuous scale. *Attributes* charts are used for discrete, count data in which each data element is classified in one of two categories, such as good or bad.

Variables charts are preferred over attributes charts because the data contain more information and are typically more sensitive to detecting process shifts than attributes charts. It should be noted that measurement data collected for a variables control chart can be categorized and applied to an attributes control chart. For example, consider five temperature readings in which each reading can be classified as being within specification (for example, good) or out of specification (for example, bad). Had each reading been classified as attribute data (for example, either within or out of specification) at the time of collection and the actual measurement value not recorded, the attribute data could not be transformed for use in a variables control chart.

Variables Charts

Three common charts used to track the output of continuous, or measurement, data are the $\bar{X}$ and R, $\bar{X}$ and S, and individuals and moving range (ImR) charts. Figure 27.5 provides a flowchart for selecting the proper control chart based on the subgroup size. The formulas for the control limits for each chart are summarized in Appendix K.1, and all necessary control chart constants are listed in Appendix K.4.

Control Limits

When first calculating control limits, it is prudent to collect as much data as practical. Many authors suggest at least 25-30 subgroups. The data are plotted, and the charts are reviewed for out-of-control conditions. If out-of-control conditions are found, root causes should be investigated, and the associated data removed.

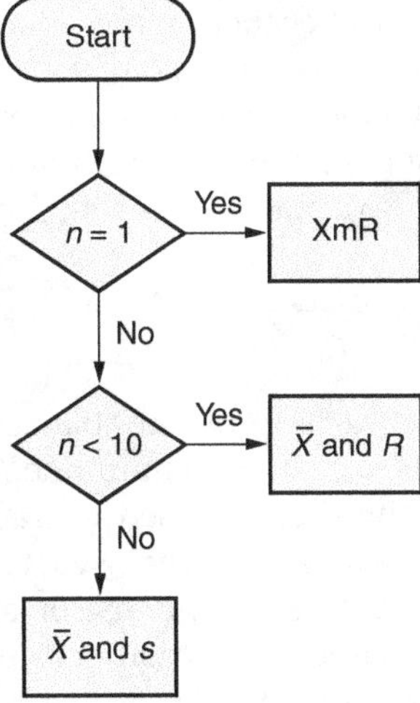

Figure 27.5 Selecting a variables control chart based on the subgroup size.

Consequently, a revised set of control limits should be computed. If it is not possible to determine root causes, the associated data should remain in the calculation for the limits. In this situation, it is likely the out-of-control condition was a statistical anomaly and actually due to common cause variation.

Because control limits are calculated based on data from the process, they represent the *voice of the process* (VOP). Typically, they are set at ±3σ. The upper control limit is designated as *UCL* while the lower control limit is designated as *LCL*. The difference between the UCL and the LCL constitutes a 6σ spread. This spread is known as the VOP and is a necessary value when determining process capability representing the natural process variation (see Chapter 19).

Remember, if the data are normally distributed, ±3σ represents 99.73% of the distribution. When the process is stable, the probability of a point falling outside the limits is only 0.27%. This occurrence is referred to as a false alarm, or an α, or Type I, error. The Type I error rate of 0.27% translates into an average run length (ARL) of 370, meaning that on average, 370 points will be plotted for the stable process before a false alarm occurs:

$$
\begin{aligned}
ARL &= \frac{1}{\alpha} \\
&= \frac{1}{0.0027} = 370
\end{aligned}
$$

Shewhart felt the ±3σ limits represented an economical trade-off between the consequences of looking for a special cause that doesn't exist and failing to look for one when it does exist. That being said, users are free to set limits at values other than ±3σ. However, caution is recommended since the out-of-control rules given later in this chapter would no longer apply.

It is important to note that calculating the lower control limit on the process variation chart could result in a negative value. If this should occur, the LCL is artificially set to zero because it is not possible to have negative ranges or standard deviations. Likewise, when an LCL computes to a negative value on attributes charts, the LCL is set to zero because, again, it is not possible to have a negative percentage defective or negative defect counts.

The examples in the following sections use fewer samples for simplicity. Subgroup sizes are generally held constant with variables control charts. However, subgroup sizes may vary with specific attributes control charts, or with an $\bar{X}$ and S chart.

The $\bar{X}$ and R Chart

The $\bar{X}$ and *R* chart is the flagship of variables control charts. It comprises two charts that are plotted and monitored simultaneously: the $\bar{X}$ chart, used to track the process average, and the *R* chart, used to track process variation using subgroup ranges. The range was originally used to monitor variation since these charts were implemented before computers, or even calculators, were available on the shop floor. An operator could easily calculate the range of five readings with just pencil and paper. An underlying assumption for the $\bar{X}$ and *R* chart is that the process metric is normally distributed. However, with subgroup sizes even as small as four, the $\overline{X}$ chart is fairly robust against all but the most extreme departures from normality. However, the range chart is more sensitive to these departures.

$\overline{X}$ and R Chart Control Limits

The $\overline{X}$ and R chart is typically used when the sample size of each subgroup is less than ten since the range loses efficiency in estimating dispersion as sample size increases. Control limits for the $\overline{X}$ and R chart are given by Equation 27.1 and Equation 27.2:

Equation 27.1 Control limits for the $\overline{X}$ chart

$$LCL_{\overline{X}} = \overline{\overline{X}} - A_2\overline{R}$$
$$UCL_{\overline{X}} = \overline{\overline{X}} + A_2\overline{R}$$

Equation 27.2 Control limits for the R chart

$$LCL_R = D_3\overline{R}$$
$$UCL_R = D_4\overline{R}$$

Note that

$$\overline{X}_i = \frac{\sum_{j=1}^{n} x_{ij}}{n} = \text{Average of the } i\text{th subgroup; plot points}$$

$$\overline{\overline{X}} = \frac{\sum_{i=1}^{k} \overline{X}_i}{k} = \text{Centerline of the } \overline{X} \text{ chart}$$

R_i = Range of the ith subgroup; plot points

$$\overline{R} = \frac{\sum_{i=1}^{k} R_i}{k} = \text{Centerline of the } R \text{ chart}$$

x_{ij} = jth individual data measurement within the ith subgroup
k = Number of subgroups
n = Constant sample size of each subgroup
The values of A_2, D_3, and D_4 are found in Appendix K.4 for various values of n.

EXAMPLE 27.1

Data are collected in a face-and-plunge operation done on a lathe. The dimension being measured is the groove inside diameter (ID). Four parts are measured every hour, as shown in Table 27.1. Determine the centerlines and control limits for the $\bar{X}$ and R chart.

Using Equation 27.1 and Equation 27.2, we have

$$\bar{\bar{X}} = 7.12565$$
$$\bar{R} = 0.0037$$

$$LCL_{\bar{X}} = \bar{\bar{X}} - A_2\bar{R}$$
$$= 7.12565 - (0.729)(0.0037) = 7.1230$$

$$UCL_{\bar{X}} = \bar{\bar{X}} + A_2\bar{R}$$
$$= 7.12565 + (0.729)(0.0037) = 7.1283$$

$$LCL_R = D_3\bar{R} = (0)(0.0037) = 0$$
$$UCL_R = D_4\bar{R} = (2.282)(0.0037) = 0.0084$$

The values of A_2, D_3, and D_4 were found in Appendix K.4 for the value of $n = 4$.

The completed $\bar{X}$ and R chart is given in Figure 27.6. Both charts are in statistical control.

7:00 a.m.	8:00 a.m.	9:00 a.m.	10:00 a.m.	11:00 a.m.	12:00 p.m.	1:00 p.m.	2:00 p.m.	3:00 p.m.	4:00 p.m.
7.127	7.125	7.123	7.127	7.128	7.125	7.126	7.126	7.127	7.128
7.123	7.126	7.129	7.127	7.125	7.125	7.123	7.126	7.129	7.123
7.123	7.121	7.129	7.124	7.126	7.127	7.123	7.127	7.128	7.122
7.126	7.122	7.124	7.125	7.127	7.128	7.125	7.128	7.129	7.124

Table 27.1 Data for Example 27.1 and Example 27.2.

Continued

Continued

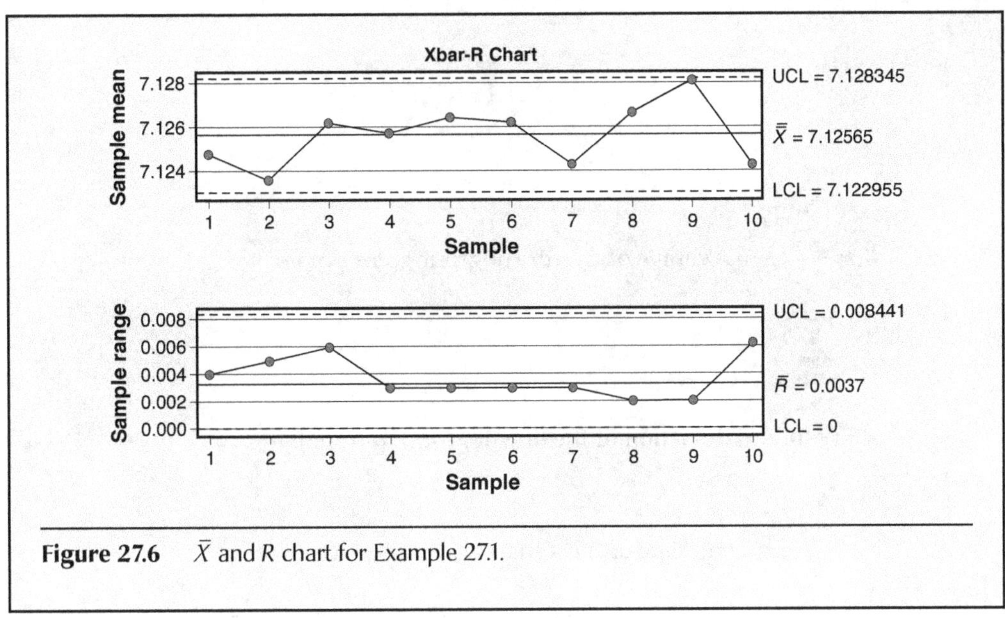

Figure 27.6 $\bar{X}$ and R chart for Example 27.1.

The $\bar{X}$ and S Chart

The $\bar{X}$ and S chart is another variables control chart. With this chart, the sample standard deviation, s_i, for each subgroup is used to track process variation instead of the range. The standard deviation is a better measure of variation when the sample size is large (approximately ten or larger). Montgomery (2021) points out that the range method of estimating the variation loses efficiency for samples sized ten or greater, since it ignores the information in the sample between the extremes. Note that unlike the $\bar{X}$ and R chart, the $\bar{X}$ and S chart can be used when the subgroup size varies.

As with the $\bar{X}$ and R chart, an underlying assumption for this chart is that the process metric is normally distributed. However, with subgroup sizes as small as four, the $\bar{X}$ chart is fairly robust against all but the most extreme departures from normality. However, the S chart is more sensitive to these departures.

$\bar{X}$ and S Chart Control Limits

The $\bar{X}$ and S chart is typically used when the sample size of each subgroup is greater than or equal to ten since the standard deviation is a better estimate of dispersion for larger sample sizes.

Control limits for an $\bar{X}$ and S chart are given by:

Equation 27.3 Control limits for the $\bar{X}$ chart

$$LCL_{\bar{X}} = \bar{\bar{X}} - A_s\bar{s}$$

$$UCL_{\bar{X}} = \bar{\bar{X}} + A_3\bar{s}$$

Equation 27.4 Control limits for the *S* chart

$$LCL_S = B_3\overline{s}$$
$$UCL_S = B_4\overline{s}$$

where

$$\overline{X}_i = \frac{\sum_{j=1}^{n} x_{ij}}{n} = \text{Average of the } i\text{th subgroup; plot points}$$

$$\overline{\overline{X}} = \frac{\sum_{i=1}^{k} \overline{X}_i}{k} = \text{Centerline of the } \overline{X} \text{ chart}$$

s_i = Standard deviation of the *i*th subgroup; plot points

$$\overline{s} = \frac{\sum_{i=1}^{k} s_i}{k} = \text{Centerline of the } s \text{ chart}$$

x_{ij} = *j*th individual data measurement within the *i*th subgroup
k = Number of subgroups
n = Constant sample size of each subgroup

The values of A_3, B_3, and B_4 are found in Appendix K.4 for various values of n.

EXAMPLE 27.2

Using the same data provided in Table 27.1, construct an $\overline{X}$ and *S* chart. Using Equation 27.3 and Equation 27.4, we have

$$\overline{\overline{X}} = 7.12565$$
$$\overline{s} = 0.001798$$

$$LCL_{\overline{X}} = \overline{\overline{X}} - A_s\overline{s}$$
$$= 7.12565 - (1.6278)(0.001798) = 7.1227$$

$$UCL_{\overline{X}} = \overline{\overline{X}} + A_3\overline{s}$$
$$= 7.12565 + (1.6278)(0.001798) = 7.1286$$

$$LCL_S = B_3\overline{s} = (0)(0.001798) = 0$$
$$UCL_{\overline{S}} = B_4\overline{s} = (2.266)(0.001798) = 0.0041$$

Continued

Continued

The values of A_3, B_3, and B_4 were found in Appendix K.4 for the value of $n = 4$. The completed $\bar{X}$ and S chart is given in Figure 27.7. Both charts are in statistical control.

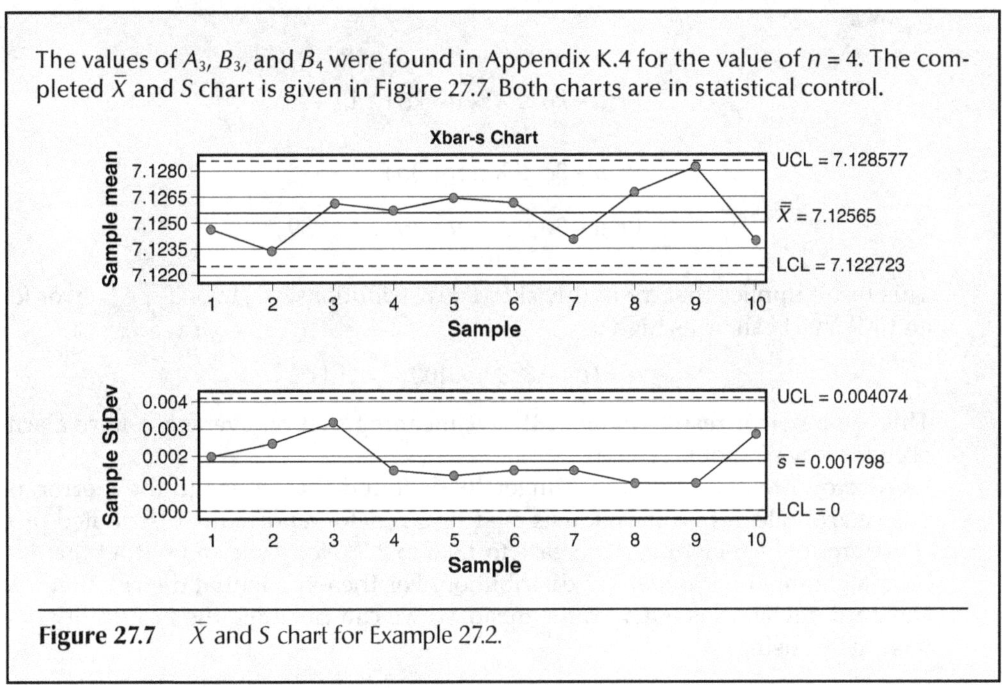

Figure 27.7 $\bar{X}$ and S chart for Example 27.2.

The Individual and Moving Range (ImR) Chart

Montgomery (2005) states that the individual and moving range chart, or ImR, is a useful chart when rational subgrouping is difficult, as described in the following scenarios:

- Automated inspection and measurement technology are used to sample every unit produced.
- The production rate is very slow and waiting to accumulate a subgroup would be inefficient.
- Repeated measurements on the process output vary only due to laboratory error, such as in chemical processing industry.

In addition, if the measurement involves a destructive test of an expensive product, an ImR chart may be desirable.

As the name implies, individual data points are plotted on one chart while the moving range (for example, the absolute value of the difference between successive data points) is plotted on the moving range chart. However, if the data are not normally distributed, these charts can produce false alarms, signaling special cause variation when only common cause variation is present.

Using Chebyshev's inequality, we can calculate a lower bound on the proportion of a distribution that lies within three standard deviations of the mean. The lower bound applies to all distributions with a defined mean and variance, as follows:

$$\Pr(\mu - k\sigma \le X \le \mu + k\sigma) \ge 1 - \frac{1}{k^2}$$

$$\Pr(\mu - 3\sigma \le X \le \mu + 3\sigma) \ge 1 - \frac{1}{3^2}$$

$$\Pr(\mu - 3\sigma \le X \le \mu + 3\sigma) \ge 0.8889$$

This result implies that for highly skewed distributions, the α, or Type I, error for an ImR chart can be as high as

$$\alpha = (1 - 0.8889) \times 100\% = 11.11\%$$

This Type I error results in an ARL = 9, meaning that on average, a false alarm occurs every nine observations.

Borror, Montgomery, and Runger (1999) found that although the α-error, or false alarm rate, for an individuals chart is 0.27% for a normally distributed process output, the α-error can increase to 1.0% to 2.2% for a skewed output that follows a gamma or exponential distribution. For the exponential distribution, the standard deviation is equal to the mean, so we can calculate the probability of a false alarm using:

$$\Pr(X > \mu + k\sigma) = e^{-\frac{(\mu + k\mu)}{\mu}}$$

$$\begin{aligned}\Pr(X > \mu + 3\sigma) &= e^{-\frac{(4\mu)}{\mu}} \\ &= e^{-4} \\ &= 0.01832\end{aligned}$$

The corresponding ARL for the exponential distribution is 54.6. Depending on the application, this increase in Type I error may be nontrivial.

Borror et al. (1999) also found that for a Student's *t* distribution, Type I errors decrease as the degrees of freedom increase. For example, the false alarm rate decreases from 1.3% to 0.35% as the Student's *t* degrees of freedom increase from 4 to 50, respectively.

A normal probability plot and/or Anderson-Darling test on the process output data can be easily run before an ImR chart is created. If we conclude that the data is non-normal, there are two possible reasons:

1. The underlying process output is normally distributed, but it is affected by special cause variation.

2. The process follows a non-normal distribution that is affected only by common cause variation.

It is worth noting that wait times, or time between failures, often follow an exponential distribution. In these cases, we can plot the individuals chart using control limits mapped to the percentiles of the source distribution, or we can use individuals charts that are robust against normality, such as the moving-average/

moving-range (MAMR), the exponentially weighted moving average (EWMA), or the cumulative sum (CUSUM) chart. The latter two charts are quite useful but are not included the Body of Knowledge. We refer readers to Montgomery (2005) to learn more.

ImR Chart Control Limits

The moving range is calculated by taking the absolute value of the difference between each measurement and the previous one. For this reason, the moving range chart has one fewer point plotted than the corresponding individuals chart.

Control limits for the individuals and moving range chart are given by Equation 27.5 and Equation 27.6:
where

Equation 27.5 Control limits for the I chart

$$LCL_I = \overline{X} - E_2\overline{mR}$$
$$UCL_I = \overline{X} + E_2\overline{mR}$$

Equation 27.6 Control limits for the mR chart

$$LCL_{mR} = D_3\overline{mR}$$
$$UCL_{mR} = D_4\overline{mR}$$

where

$$\overline{X} = \frac{\sum_{i=1}^{k} x_i}{k} = \text{Average of the individual data measurements; centerline of I chart}$$

$$\text{mR}_i = |x_i - x_{i-(n-1)}|, i = 1,2,\ldots,k; n = \text{period for moving range; plot points}$$

$$m\overline{R} = \frac{\sum_{i=1}^{k} mR_i}{k-1} = \text{Centerline for the mR chart}$$

where

x_i = Individual data measurements; plot points for I chart
n = The period for the moving range. Usually, $n = 2$
k = Number of individual data measurements

The values of E_2, D_3, and D_4 are found in Appendix K.4 for various values of n.

EXAMPLE 27.3

Using the data provided in Table 27.2, construct an ImR chart.

Reading	Individual data element
1	290
2	288
3	285
4	290
5	291
6	287
7	284
8	290
9	290
10	288

Table 27.2 Data for Example 27.3–individuals and moving range chart.

Several of the intermediate calculations for this example are shown in Table 27.3. The values of E_2, D_3, and D_4 are found in Appendix K.4 for $n = 2$.

Reading	Individual data element	Difference	Absolute value of the difference
1	290		
2	288	–2	2
3	285	–3	3
4	290	5	5
5	291	1	1
6	287	–4	4
7	284	–3	3
8	290	6	6
9	290	0	0
10	288	–2	2
Average	**288.3**	**Moving range**	**2.89**

Table 27.3 Calculations for Example 27.3–individuals and moving range chart.

Continued

Continued

Using Equation 27.5 and Equation 27.6, we have

$$\bar{X} = 288.3$$
$$m\bar{R} = 2.89$$

$$LCL_I = \bar{X} - E_2 m\bar{R}$$
$$= 288.3 - (2.660)(2.89) = 280.62$$

$$UCL_I = \bar{X} + E_2 m\bar{R}$$
$$= 288.3 + (2.660)(2.89) = 295.99$$

$$LCL_{mR} = (0)(2.89) = 0$$
$$UCL_{mR} = (0)(2.89) = 9.44$$

The completed individuals and moving range chart is given in Figure 27.8. Both charts demonstrate statistical control.

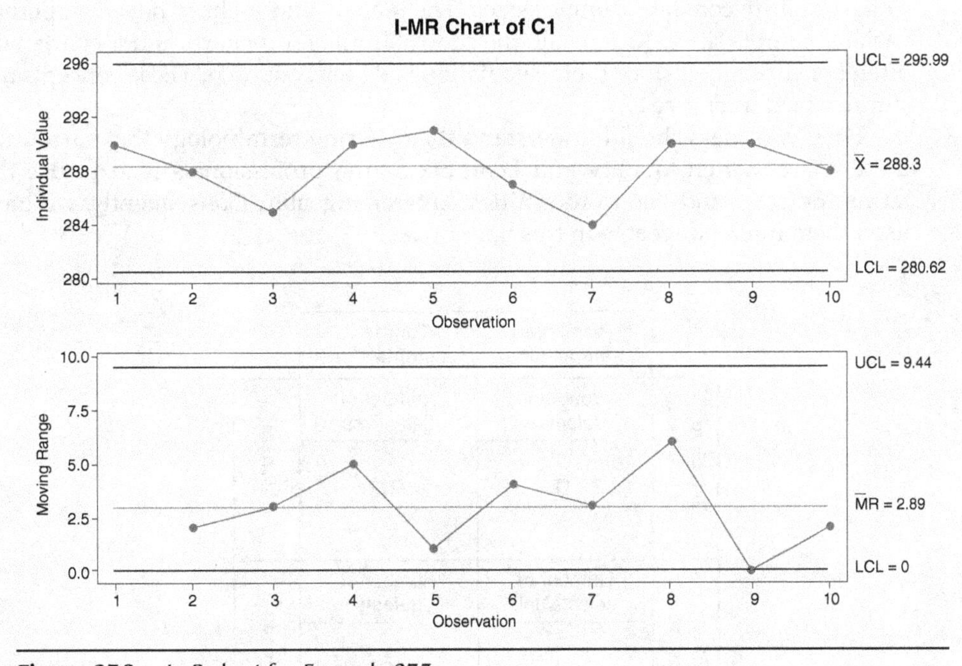

Figure 27.8 ImR chart for Example 27.3.

A summary of the formulas used for constructing the variables control charts is provided in Table 27.4.

Attributes Charts

Attributes charts are used for count data in which each data element is classified in one of two categories, such as good or bad. The *p*-charts and *np*-charts are used to plot proportion defective and number of defectives, respectively. The *c*-charts and *u*-charts are used to plot counts of defects and defects per unit, respectively.

Both *p*-charts and *np*-charts are based on the binomial distribution. Thus, it is assumed that items are categorized using two outcomes (defective/non-defective, success/failure, pass/fail, go/no go), and the probability of a defective remains constant from subgroup to subgroup. The number of defectives found in a subgroup is also bounded by the sample size *n*.

The *c*-charts and *u*-charts are based on the Poisson distribution. Therefore, the probability of the occurrence of a defect is assumed constant from subgroup to subgroup. There is also no upper limit to the number of occurrences that can be found in a sample size of *n*. When constructing attributes charts, it is important to keep these assumptions in mind to ensure statistical validity of the results.

Additionally, users of attributes charts should note that the *np*-chart and the *c*-chart require constant samples sizes. The *p*-chart and *u*-chart, however, permit variable sample sizes. As a result, the control limits for *p*-charts and *u*-charts will often appear ragged since their calculation is dependent on n. These concepts are summarized in Figure 27.9.

Finally, readers should understand the differing terminology that surrounds these charts. Often, quality and Lean Six Sigma professionals tend to use the terms "defects" and "nonconformities" interchangeably. Consequently, we have used them interchangeably in this handbook.

	Variable sample size	**Constant sample size**	
Defective (Nonconformance)	Proportion defective	Number of defectives	**Binomial**
	p	***np***	
Defect (Nonconformity)	Number of defects/unit	Number of defects	**Poisson**
	u	***c***	
	Ragged limits	**Fixed limits**	

Figure 27.9 Characteristics of attributes charts.

Average chart				Individuals chart			
Chart	Centerline	LCL	UCL	Chart	Centerline	LCL	UCL
$\overline{X}$	$\overline{\overline{X}}$	$LCL_{\overline{X}} = \overline{\overline{X}} - A_2\overline{R}$	$UCL_{\overline{X}} = \overline{\overline{X}} + A_2\overline{R}$	X	$\overline{X}$	$LCL_X = \overline{X} - E_2\,\overline{mR}$	$UCL_X = \overline{X} + E_2\,\overline{mR}$
R	$\overline{R}$	$LCL_R = D_3\overline{R}$	$UCL_R = D_4\overline{R}$	mR	$\overline{mR}$	$LCL_{mR} = D_3\,\overline{mR}$	$UCL_{mR} = D_4\,\overline{mR}$
$\overline{X}$	$\overline{\overline{X}}$	$LCL_{\overline{X}} = \overline{\overline{X}} - A_3\overline{s}$	$UCL_{\overline{X}} = \overline{\overline{X}} + A_3\overline{s}$				
s	$\overline{s}$	$LCL_s = B_3\overline{s}$	$UCL_s = B_4\overline{s}$				

$$\overline{X}_i = \frac{\sum_{j=1}^{n} x_{ij}}{n} = \text{Average of the } i\text{th subgroup; plot points}$$

$$\overline{\overline{X}} = \frac{\sum_{i=1}^{k} \overline{X}_i}{k} = \text{Centerline of the } \overline{X} \text{ chart}$$

R_i = Range of the ith subgroup; plot points

$$\overline{R} = \frac{\sum_{i=1}^{k} R_i}{k} = \text{Centerline of the } R \text{ chart}$$

s_i = Standard deviation of the ith subgroup; plot points

$$\overline{s} = \frac{\sum_{i=1}^{k} s_i}{k} = \text{Centerline of the } s \text{ chart}$$

$x_{ij} = j$ individual data measurements within i subgroups

k = Number of subgroups

n = Sample size of each subgroup

$$\overline{X} = \frac{\sum_{i=1}^{n} x_i}{k} = \text{Center of the } X \text{ chart}$$

$mR_i = |x_i - x_{i-1}|$ for $i = 2, 3, \ldots, k$; plot points

$$\overline{mR} = \frac{\sum_{i=2}^{n} mR_i}{k-1} = \text{Centerline for the } mR \text{ chart}$$

x_i = Individual data measurements; plot points

k = Number of individual data measurements

Table 27.4 Formulas for calculating the centerline and control limits for variables charts. Constants can be found in Appendix K.4.

However, there is a technical distinction between these two terms that is worth noting. ANSI Z1.4-2003 (R2013), which is in accordance with ISO 3534-2:2006(E), provides the following definitions:

- *Defect.* A departure of a quality characteristic from its intended level or state that occurs with a severity sufficient to cause an associated product or service not to satisfy intended normal, or foreseeable, usage requirements.
- *Nonconformity.* A departure of a quality characteristic from its intended level or state that occurs with severity sufficient to cause an associated product or service not to meet a specification requirement.

ISO 3534-2:2006(E) adds two important notes to the definition of defects:

- *Note 1.* The distinction between the concepts *defect* and *nonconformity* is important as it has legal connotations, particularly those associated with product liability issues. Consequently, the term "defect" should be used with extreme caution.
- *Note 2.* The intended use by the customer can be affected by the nature of the information, such as operating or maintenance instructions, provided by the customer.

Based on the above definitions and supporting notes, one might argue that we can generally align a nonconformity to occurring within the organization and a defect to occurring outside the organization (that is, external customer).

Note: All the examples presented in the attributes charts section that follows use the same count data. However, they are presented in different contexts. Only the sample sizes and types of counts change as necessary to fit the particular type of chart being studied. This is done to help the reader grasp the underlying concepts of each chart more readily and to simultaneously compare and contrast the charts. We think this approach will be more beneficial to our readers than presenting each chart with entirely different data.

p-*Chart and Control Limits*

The p-chart is used when tracking defective units when sample sizes vary. We use this chart to plot the proportion or percentage of defectives. Note: The control limits on this chart appear ragged because they reflect each subgroup's individual sample size.

The formulas for the centerline and the upper and lower control limits for the p-chart are shown in Equation 27.7.

Equation 27.7 Control limits for p-chart

$$LCL_p = \overline{p} - 3\sqrt{\frac{\overline{p}(1-\overline{p})}{n_i}}$$

$$UCL_p = \overline{p} + 3\sqrt{\frac{\overline{p}(1-\overline{p})}{n_i}}$$

where

$$p_i = \frac{D_i}{n_i} = \text{Plot points}$$

$$\overline{p} = \frac{\sum_{i=1}^{k} D_i}{\sum_{i=1}^{k} n_i} = \text{Centerline of p chart}$$

D_i = the number of defective items in the ith subgroup
K = number of subgroups
n_i = sample size of the ith subgroup

EXAMPLE 27.4

A test was conducted to determine the presence of the Rh factor in 13 samples of donated blood. The results of the test are given in Table 27.5. Construct a p-chart.

Date	Number of defectives (D_i)	Sample size (n_i)
8-Sep	12	116
9-Sep	14	126
10-Sep	18	112
11-Sep	13	134
12-Sep	17	121
13-Sep	15	119
14-Sep	15	138
15-Sep	16	109
16-Sep	11	111
17-Sep	14	125
18-Sep	13	129
19-Sep	14	144
20-Sep	17	141

Table 27.5 Data for Example 27.4–p-chart.

We obtain the results shown in Table 27.6 using Equation 27.7. Note that the control limits will change for each value of n_i.

Continued

$$\bar{p} = \frac{189}{1625} = 0.1163$$

$$LCL_p = \bar{p} - 3\sqrt{\frac{\bar{p}(1-\bar{p})}{n_i}}$$

$$= 0.1163 - 3\sqrt{\frac{0.1163(0.8837)}{n_i}}$$

$$UCL_p = \bar{p} + 3\sqrt{\frac{\bar{p}(1-\bar{p})}{n_i}}$$

$$= 0.1163 + 3\sqrt{\frac{0.1163(0.8837)}{n_i}}$$

Date	Number of defectives (D_i)	Sample size (n_i)	Plot points (p_i)	Centerline ($\bar{p}$)	LCL	UCL
8-Sep	12	116	0.1034	0.1163	0.0270	0.2056
9-Sep	14	126	0.1111	0.1163	0.0306	0.2020
10-Sep	18	112	0.1607	0.1163	0.0254	0.2072
11-Sep	13	134	0.0970	0.1163	0.0332	0.1994
12-Sep	17	121	0.1405	0.1163	0.0289	0.2037
13-Sep	15	119	0.1261	0.1163	0.0281	0.2045
14-Sep	15	138	0.1087	0.1163	0.0344	0.1982
15-Sep	16	109	0.1468	0.1163	0.0242	0.2084
16-Sep	11	111	0.0991	0.1163	0.0250	0.2076
17-Sep	14	125	0.1120	0.1163	0.0303	0.2023
18-Sep	13	129	0.1008	0.1163	0.0316	0.2010
19-Sep	14	144	0.0972	0.1163	0.0362	0.1964
20-Sep	17	141	0.1206	0.1163	**0.0353**	**0.1973**
Total	**189**	**1625**				
***p*-bar**	**0.1163**					

Table 27.6 Calculations for Example 27.4–*p*-chart.

The completed *p*-chart is given in Figure 27.10 and demonstrates statistical control.

Continued

Continued

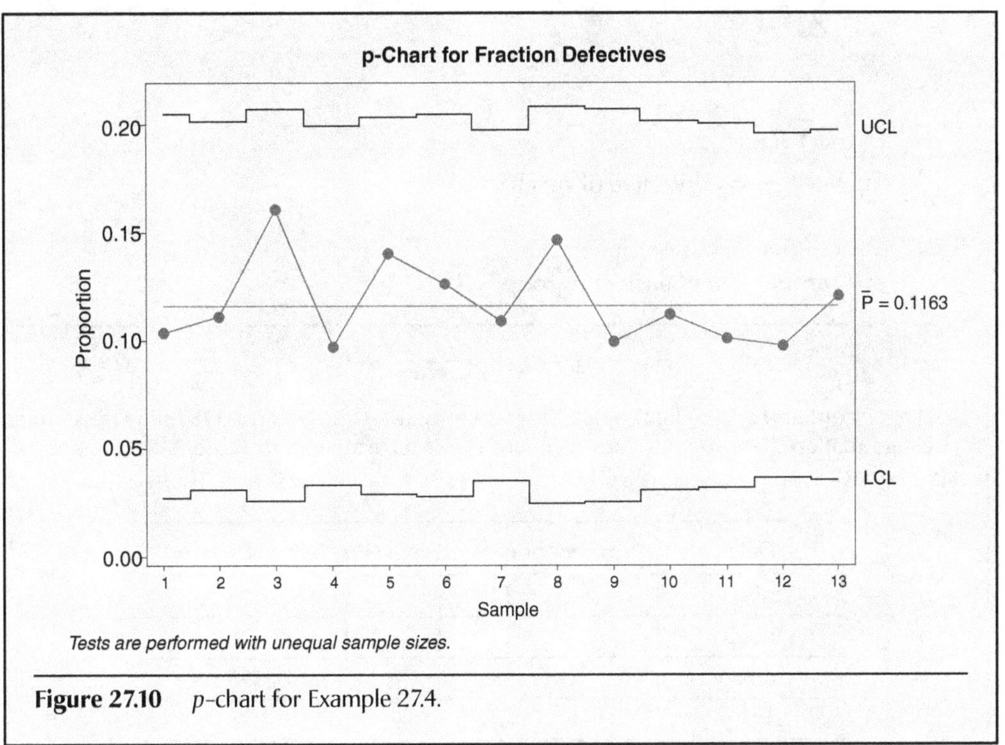

Figure 27.10 *p*-chart for Example 27.4.

np-*Chart Control Limits*

Recall that the *np*-chart is used when the sample size is constant. We use this chart to plot the number of defectives.

Equation 27.8 gives the upper and lower control limits for the *np*-chart:

Equation 27.8 Control limits for *np*-chart

$$LCL_{np} = n\bar{p} - 3\sqrt{n\bar{p}(1-\bar{p})}$$

$$UCL_{np} = n\bar{p} + 3\sqrt{n\bar{p}(1-\bar{p})}$$

where

D_i = the number of defective items in the *i*th subgroup; plot points

$$\bar{p} = \frac{\sum_{i=1}^{k} D_i}{nk}$$

$$n\bar{p} = \frac{\sum_{i=1}^{k} D_i}{k} = \text{Centerline of np chart}$$

k = number of subgroups
n = sample size of each subgroup

EXAMPLE 27.5

Packages containing 1000 light bulbs are randomly selected, and n = 125 bulbs from the package that are light-tested. The results of the tests are given in Table 27.7. Construct an *np*-chart.

Date	Number of defectives (D_i)	Sample size (n)
8-Sep	12	125
9-Sep	14	125
10-Sep	18	125
11-Sep	13	125
12-Sep	17	125
13-Sep	15	125
14-Sep	15	125
15-Sep	16	125
16-Sep	11	125
17-Sep	14	125
18-Sep	13	125
19-Sep	14	125
20-Sep	17	125

Table 27.7 Data for Example 27.5–*np*-chart.

Using Equation 27.8 we obtain the results shown in Table 27.8 and immediately below:

Continued

$$\bar{p} = \frac{\sum_{i=1}^{k} D_i}{nk} = \frac{189}{1625} = 0.1163$$

$$n\bar{p} = \frac{\sum_{i=1}^{k} D_i}{k} = \frac{189}{13} = 14.54$$

$$LCL_{np} = n\bar{p} - 3\sqrt{n\bar{p}(1-\bar{p})}$$
$$= 14.54 - 3\sqrt{14.54(0.8837)} = 3.78$$
$$UCL_{np} = n\bar{p} + 3\sqrt{n\bar{p}(1-\bar{p})}$$
$$= 14.54 + 3\sqrt{14.54(0.8837)} = 25.29$$

Date	Number of defectives (D_i)	Sample size (n)	Centerline ($n\bar{p}$)	LCL	UCL
8-Sep	12	125	14.54	3.78	25.29
9-Sep	14	125	14.54	3.78	25.29
10-Sep	18	125	14.54	3.78	25.29
11-Sep	13	125	14.54	3.78	25.29
12-Sep	17	125	14.54	3.78	25.29
13-Sep	15	125	14.54	3.78	25.29
14-Sep	15	125	14.54	3.78	25.29
15-Sep	16	125	14.54	3.78	25.29
16-Sep	11	125	14.54	3.78	25.29
17-Sep	14	125	14.54	3.78	25.29
18-Sep	13	125	14.54	3.78	25.29
19-Sep	14	125	14.54	3.78	25.29
20-Sep	17	125	14.54	3.78	25.29
Total	**189**	**1625**			
$\bar{p}$	**0.1163**				
$n\bar{p}$	**14.54**				

Table 27.8 Calculations for Example 27.5–*np*-chart.

The completed *np*-chart is given in Figure 27.11 and demonstrates statistical control.

Continued

Continued

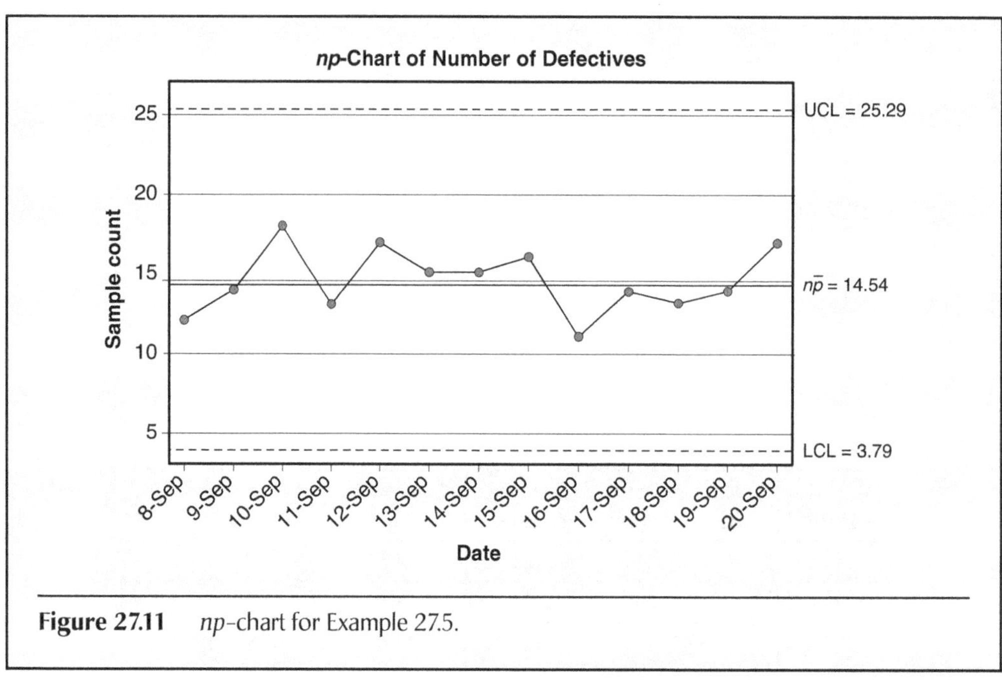

Figure 27.11 *np*-chart for Example 27.5.

c-*Chart Control Limits*

Recall that the *c*-chart is used when the sample size *n* is constant. We use this chart to plot the number of defects. There can be any number of defects in a sampled item.

Equation 27.9 gives the upper and lower control limits for the *c*-chart:

Equation 27.9 Control limits for *c*-chart

$$LCL_c = \bar{c} - 3\sqrt{\bar{c}}$$
$$UCL_c = \bar{c} + 3\sqrt{\bar{c}}$$

where

$$\bar{c} = \frac{\sum_{i=1}^{k} c_i}{k}$$

c_i = Number of defects found in the *ith* subgroup; plot points
k = Number of subgroups

EXAMPLE 27.6

Panes of glass of uniform area are inspected for defects such as bubbles, scratches, chips, inclusions, waves, and dips with a constant sample size equal to 125. The results of the inspection are given in Table 27.9. Construct a c-chart.

Date	Number of defects (c_i)	Sample size (n)
8-Sep	12	125
9-Sep	14	125
10-Sep	18	125
11-Sep	13	125
12-Sep	17	125
13-Sep	15	125
14-Sep	15	125
15-Sep	16	125
16-Sep	11	125
17-Sep	14	125
18-Sep	13	125
19-Sep	14	125
20-Sep	17	125

Table 27.9 Data for Example 27.6 *c*-chart.

Using Equation 27.9, we obtain the results shown in Table 27.10 and immediately below:

$$\bar{c} = \frac{\sum_{i=1}^{k} c_i}{k} = \frac{189}{13} = 14.54$$

$$\begin{aligned} LCL_c &= \bar{c} - 3\sqrt{\bar{c}} \\ &= 14.54 - 3\sqrt{14.54} = 3.10 \\ UCL_c &= \bar{c} + 3\sqrt{\bar{c}} \\ &= 14.54 + 3\sqrt{14.54} = 25.98 \end{aligned}$$

Continued

Continued

Date	Number of defects—plot points (c_i)	Sample size (n)	Centerline ($\bar{c}$)	LCL	UCL
8-Sep	12	125	14.54	3.10	25.98
9-Sep	14	125	14.54	3.10	25.98
10-Sep	18	125	14.54	3.10	25.98
11-Sep	13	125	14.54	3.10	25.98
12-Sep	17	125	14.54	3.10	25.98
13-Sep	15	125	14.54	3.10	25.98
14-Sep	15	125	14.54	3.10	25.98
15-Sep	16	125	14.54	3.10	25.98
16-Sep	11	125	14.54	3.10	25.98
17-Sep	14	125	14.54	3.10	25.98
18-Sep	13	125	14.54	3.10	25.98
19-Sep	14	125	14.54	3.10	25.98
20-Sep	17	125	14.54	3.10	25.98
Total	**189**				
$\bar{c}$	**14.54**				

Table 27.10 Calculations for Example 27.6–*c*-chart.

The completed *c*-chart is given in Figure 27.12 and demonstrates statistical control.

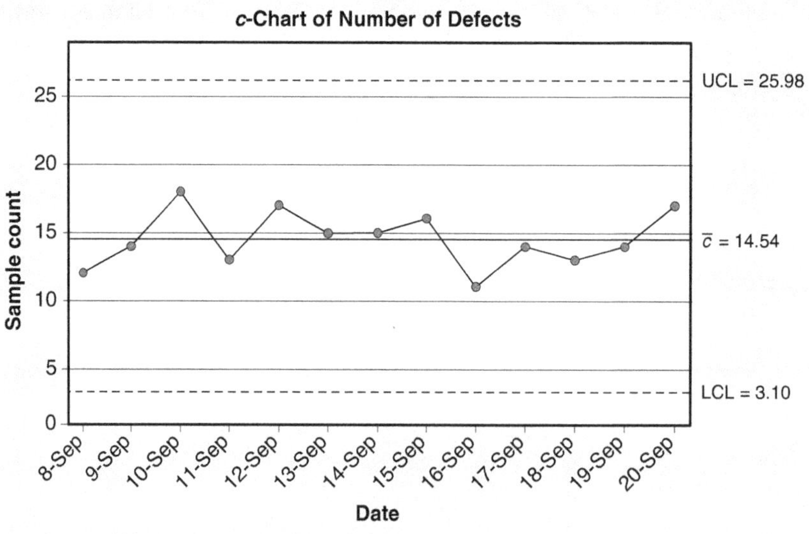

Figure 27.12 *c*-chart for Example 27.6.

u-*Chart Control Limits*

Recall that the *u*-chart is used when the sample size varies. We use this chart to plot the number of defects per unit. Note: The control limits on the chart appear ragged because they reflect each subgroup's individual sample size.

Equation 27.10 gives the upper and lower control limits for the *u*-chart:

Equation 27.10 Control limits for *u*-chart

$$LCL_u = \bar{u} - 3\sqrt{\frac{\bar{u}}{n_i}}$$

$$UCL_u = \bar{u} + 3\sqrt{\frac{\bar{u}}{n_i}}$$

where

$$\bar{u} = \frac{\sum_{i=1}^{k} c_i}{\sum_{i=1}^{k} n_i} = \text{Centerline for u chart}$$

$$\mathrm{u}_i = \frac{c_i}{n_i} = \text{Number of defects per unit in the } ith \text{ subgroup; plot point}$$

c_i = Number of defects found in the *ith* subgroup
k = Number of subgroups
n_i = Sample size of the *ith* subgroup

> **EXAMPLE 27.7**
>
> Panes of glass of uniform area are inspected for defects such as bubbles, scratches, chips, inclusions, waves, and dips with sample size varying with the production count. The results of the inspection are given in Table 27.11. Construct a *u*-chart.

Continued

Date	Number of defects (c_i)	Sample size (n_i)
8-Sep	12	116
9-Sep	14	126
10-Sep	18	112
11-Sep	13	134
12-Sep	17	121
13-Sep	15	119
14-Sep	15	138
15-Sep	16	109
16-Sep	11	111
17-Sep	14	125
18-Sep	13	129
19-Sep	14	144
20-Sep	17	141

Table 27.11 Data for Example 27.7–u-chart.

Using Equation 27.10, we obtain the results shown in Table 27.12 and immediately below:

$$\bar{u} = \frac{\sum_{i=1}^{k} c_i}{\sum_{i=1}^{k} n_i} = \frac{189}{1625} = 0.1163$$

$$LCL_u = \bar{u} - 3\sqrt{\frac{\bar{u}}{n_i}} = 0.1163 - 3\sqrt{\frac{0.1163}{n_i}}$$

$$UCL_u = \bar{u} = 3\sqrt{\frac{\bar{u}}{n_i}} = 0.1163 + 3\sqrt{\frac{0.1163}{n_i}}$$

Continued

Date	Number of defects (c_i)	Sample size (n_i)	Plot points (c_i/n_i)	Centerline ($\bar{u}$)	LCL	UCL
8-Sep	12	116	0.1034	0.1163	0.0213	0.2113
9-Sep	14	126	0.1111	0.1163	0.0252	0.2074
10-Sep	18	112	0.1607	0.1163	0.0196	0.2130
11-Sep	13	134	0.0970	0.1163	0.0279	0.2047
12-Sep	17	121	0.1405	0.1163	0.0233	0.2093
13-Sep	15	119	0.1261	0.1163	0.0225	0.2101
14-Sep	15	138	0.1087	0.1163	0.0292	0.2034
15-Sep	16	109	0.1468	0.1163	0.0183	0.2143
16-Sep	11	111	0.0991	0.1163	0.0192	0.2134
17-Sep	14	125	0.1120	0.1163	0.0248	0.2078
18-Sep	13	129	0.1008	0.1163	0.0262	0.2064
19-Sep	14	144	0.0972	0.1163	0.0310	0.2016
20-Sep	17	141	0.1206	0.1163	**0.0301**	**0.2025**
Total	**189**	**1625**				
$\bar{u}$	**0.1163**					

Table 27.12 Calculations for Example 27.7–*u*-chart.

The completed *u*-chart is given in Figure 27.13 and demonstrates statistical control.

Continued

Continued

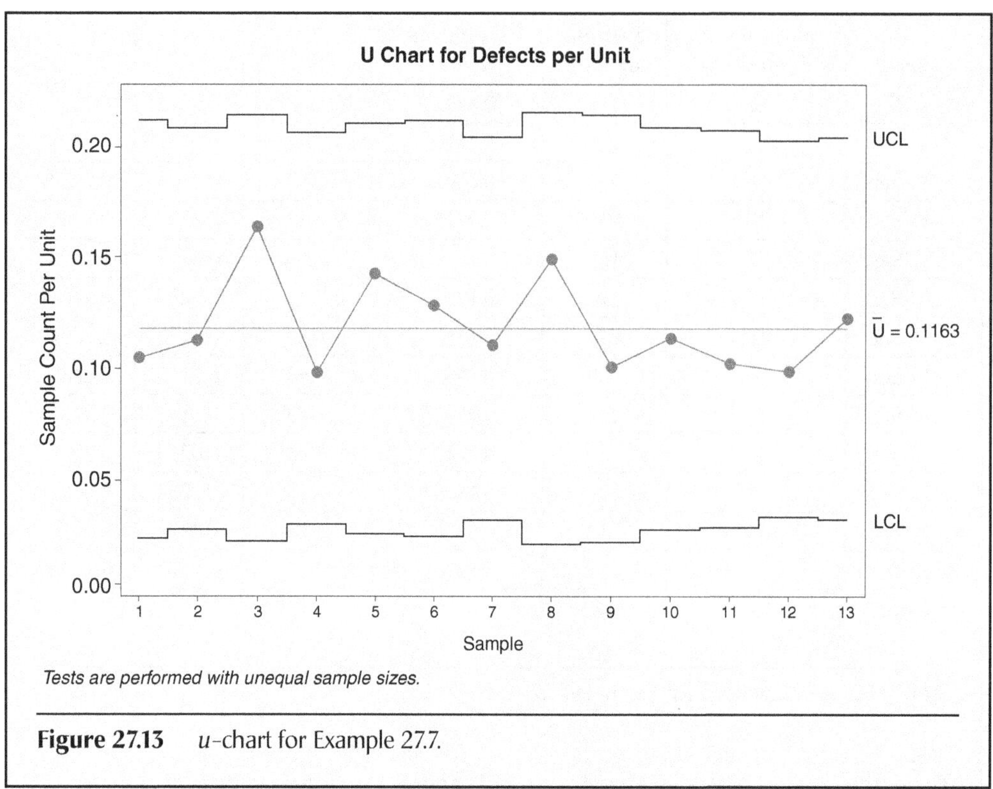

Figure 27.13 *u*-chart for Example 27.7.

The *u*-chart can also be used if single samples are inspected but are of differing sizes. For example, a *u*-chart can be used to track the number of defects found on pipes of varying length, or fabric samples of varying areas.

A summary of the formulas used for constructing the attributes control charts is provided in Table 27.13.

Short-Run Control Charts

Short-run control charts should be considered when data are collected infrequently or aperiodically. They may be used with historical target or target values, attributes or variables data, and individual or subgroup averages.

While the subject of short-run control charts is not overly difficult, it can be particularly confusing due to the various nomenclatures and terminologies used by authors. Figure 27.14 is a flowchart to aid the reader in determining what type of chart is most appropriate and will link to a comprehensive set of examples.

Table 27.14 contains all the formulas needed to construct the short-run charts discussed in this subsection. Furthermore, an attempt has been made to provide

Chart	Centerline	LCL	UCL	Plot point
p	$\bar{p} = \frac{\sum_{i=1}^{k} D_i}{\sum_{i=1}^{k} n_i}$	$\mathrm{LCL}_p = \bar{p} - 3\sqrt{\frac{\bar{p}(1-\bar{p})}{n_i}}$	$\mathrm{UCL}_p = \bar{p} + 3\sqrt{\frac{\bar{p}(1-\bar{p})}{n_i}}$	$p_i = \frac{D_i}{n_i}$
np	$n\bar{p} = n\frac{\sum_{i=1}^{k} D_i}{\sum_{i=1}^{k} n_i}$	$\mathrm{LCL}_{np} = n\bar{p} - 3\sqrt{n\bar{p}(1-\bar{p})}$	$\mathrm{UCL}_{np} = n\bar{p} + 3\sqrt{n\bar{p}(1-\bar{p})}$	D_i
c	$\bar{c} = \frac{\sum_{i=1}^{k} c_i}{k}$	$\mathrm{LCL}_c = \bar{c} - 3\sqrt{\bar{c}}$	$\mathrm{UCL}_c = \bar{c} + 3\sqrt{\bar{c}}$	c_i
u	$\bar{u} = \frac{\sum_{i=1}^{k} c_i}{\sum_{i=1}^{k} n_i}$	$\mathrm{LCL}_u = \bar{u} - 3\sqrt{\frac{\bar{u}}{n_i}}$	$\mathrm{UCL}_u = \bar{u} + 3\sqrt{\frac{\bar{u}}{n_i}}$	$u_i = \frac{c_i}{n_i}$

Table 27.13 Formulas for calculating the centerline and control limits for attributes charts.

Note:

1. n = Constant sample size of each subgroup
2. n_i = Sample size of the ith subgroup
3. k = Number of subgroups
4. D_i = Number of *defective* units in the ith subgroup
5. c_i = Number of *defects* in the ith subgroup
6. u_i = Number of *defects*/unit in the *i*th subgroup

the reader with alternate names of charts so that recognition is possible among the various sources and references.

The focus of the next subsection will be on selecting the appropriate chart or pair of charts and computing the corresponding statistics to be plotted. Since formulas are provided and the construction of most tables and charts is fundamentally similar, an example table will be developed for plotting the $\bar{Z}$, W, $\bar{Z}^*$, and W^* charts only. Little attention will be given to the actual plotting of the data.

Key Considerations When Using a Short-Run Chart

Griffith (1996) recommends the following rules when dealing with short-run control charts:

- Focus on the process, not the parts. Traditional (or product) control charts should be used to monitor parts.

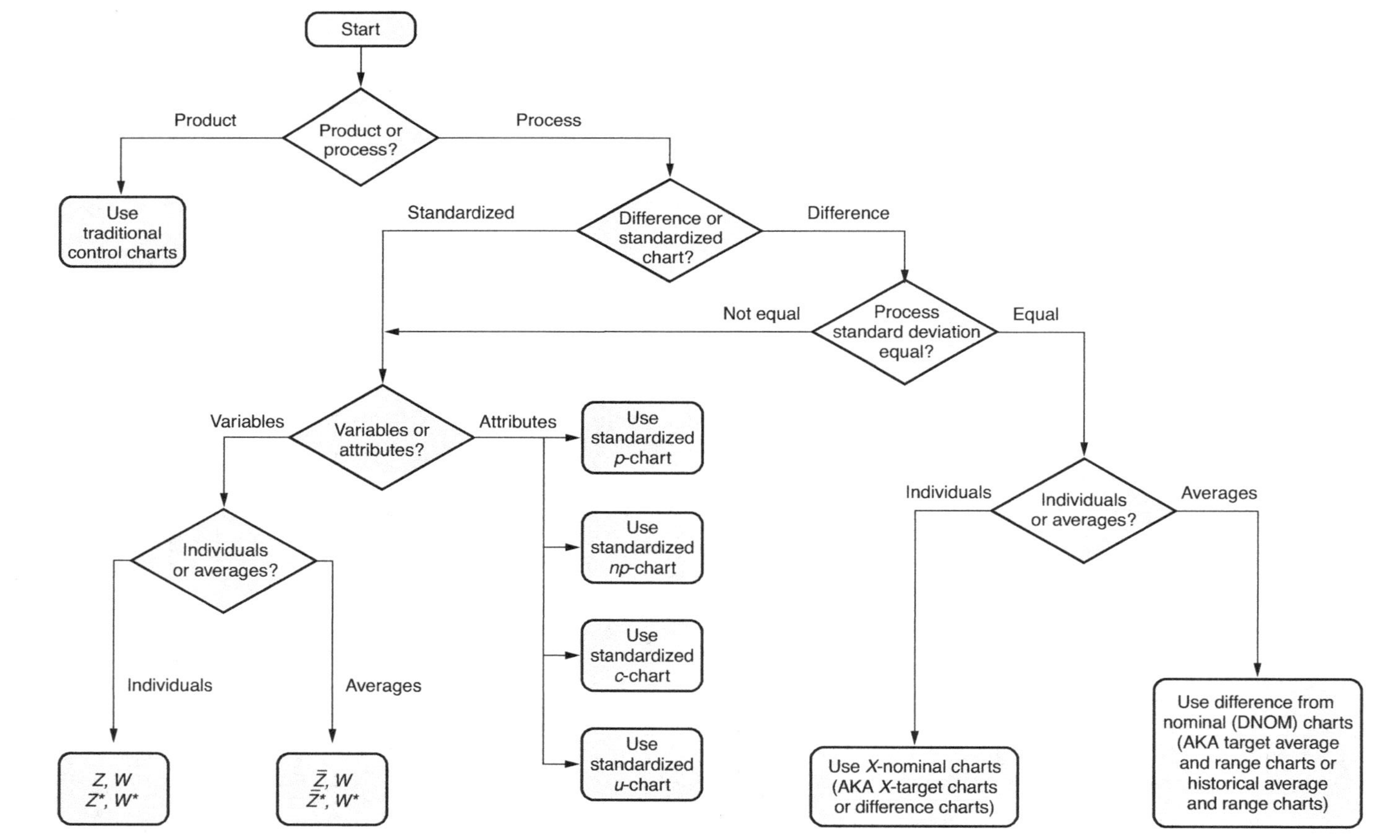

Figure 27.14 Short-run SPC control charts decision flowchart.

Charts for non-subgrouped data						
	Paired charts		Paired charts		Paired charts	
Chart type	Difference (X-nominal, X-target)	mR	Z	W	Z^*	W^*
Plot points	$X - Nom$	mR	$Z = \frac{X - Nom}{Sigma(X)}$	$W = mR_W$	$Z^* = \frac{X - Nom}{\overline{R}}$	$W^* = mR_W$
CL	0.0	$\overline{mR}$	0.0	d_2	0.0	1.0
UCL	$+A_3\overline{mR}$	$D_4\overline{mR}$	+3.0	$d_2 + 3d_3$	$+A_3$	D_4
LCL	$-A_3\overline{mR}$	$D_3\overline{mR}$	–3.0	0	$-A_3$	D_3

Where *Nom* = *Nominal* or *Target* and *Sigma* $(X) = \frac{\overline{R}}{d_2}$ and $n = 2$.

See Appendix 4 for A_3, D_3, and D_4 values.

See Appendix 6 for d_2 and d_3 values.

Table 27.14 Summary of formulas for short-run SPC charts.

Charts for subgrouped data						
	Paired charts		Paired charts		Paired charts	
Chart type	Difference	R	$\bar{Z}$	W	$\bar{Z}^*$	W^*
Plot points	$\bar{X} - Nom$	R	$\bar{Z} = \frac{\bar{X} - Nom}{Sigma(\bar{X})}$	$W = \frac{R}{Sigma(X)}$	$\bar{Z}^* = \frac{\bar{X} - Nom}{\bar{R}}$	$W^* = \frac{R}{\bar{R}}$
CL	0.0	$\bar{\bar{R}}$	0.0	d_2	0.0	1.0
UCL	$+A_2\bar{\bar{R}}$	$D_4\bar{\bar{R}}$	+3.0	$d_2 + 3d_3$	$+A_2$	D_4
LCL	$-A_2\bar{\bar{R}}$	$D_3\bar{\bar{R}}$	–3.0	$d_2 - 3d_3$	$-A_2$	D_3

Where Nom = *Nominal* or *Target* and $Sigma\,(\bar{X}) = \frac{\bar{R}}{d_2\sqrt{n}}$ and $n = 2$.
See Appendix 4 for A_3, D_3, and D_4 values.

See Appendix 6 for d_2 and d_3 values.

Standardized attributes charts				
Chart type	p	np	c	u
Plot points	$Z_i = \frac{p_i - \bar{p}}{\sqrt{\bar{p}(1-\bar{p})/n}}$	$Z_i = \frac{np_i - n\bar{p}}{\sqrt{n\bar{p}(1-\bar{p})/n}}$	$Z_i = \frac{c_i - \bar{c}}{\sqrt{\bar{c}}}$	$Z_i = \frac{u_i - \bar{u}}{\sqrt{\bar{u}/u}}$
CL	0.0	0.0	0.0	0.0
UCL	+3.0	+3.0	+3.0	+3.0
LCL	–3.0	–3.0	–3.0	–3.0

Table 27.14 *Continued.*

- Be sure the process stream is the same. For example, parts may vary in size, shape, and material, but the process remains the same.
- Look for generic families of product made by the process.
- Use coded data. This permits different parts, dimensions, tolerances, and so on, to be used together.
- Use the 20 subgroups minimum rule. The immediately preceding bullets all work to help meet this requirement.
- Variation between different parts aggregated on a chart must be the same. Statistically, we call this *homogeneity of variance*. Various tests are available to determine homogeneity of variance. When homogeneity of variance is not present in the data, the reader will note from Figure 27.14 that standardized charts must be used.

Also, it is important to point out that the measurement system should be sufficiently granular to detect variation. This is a particularly important consideration when dealing with parts of varying size, shape, and other measured characteristics.

A special word of caution is in order when interpreting short-run charts. Remember, these types of charts reflect multiple part numbers. Subsequently, the short-run chart may be in control but not the specific part numbers that comprise it. Undoubtedly, the reader will notice we are frequently working with coded data (that is, differences from target or historical target for averages and ranges). Therefore, it is critical that the data for each part be coded with its own target or historical target. This point cannot be emphasized enough.

Constructing a Short-Run Chart

1. Determine the historical average and historical range for each product. The historical average may also be a target or nominal value.
2. Collect a set of data—$x_1, x_2, \ldots, x_n$—for a number of different products that follow the same process.
3. Compute the average and range for each subgroup.
4. Compute $\hat{\sigma}_X$ or $\hat{\sigma}_{\bar{X}}$ depending on the set of charts to be developed.
5. Compute $\bar{Z}$, W, $\bar{Z}^*$, and W^* depending on the set of charts to be developed.
6. Compute the centerline for the $\bar{Z}$ moving average chart using the appropriate formulas given in the "Charts for Subgrouped Data" section of Table 27.14.
7. Compute the LCL and the UCL for the W chart, using the appropriate formulas given in the "Charts for Subgrouped Data" section of Table 27.14.
8. Compute the centerline for the $\bar{Z}^*$ chart using the appropriate formulas given in the "Charts for Subgrouped Data" section of Table 27.14.

9. Compute the LCL and the UCL for the W^* chart, using the appropriate formulas given in the "Charts for Subgrouped Data" section of Table 27.14.
10. Plot the data, centerline, LCL, and UCL for both of the chosen pairs of charts (that is, steps 6 and 7, or 8 and 9).
11. Interpret results and take action accordingly.

EXAMPLE 27.8

The data shown in Table 27.15 are taken from Wheeler (1991). Three different products from the same processes are included in the data. The data collected by product in time order by subgroup are given in columns E–I, respectively. A subgroup size of five has been used. The product, historical average, and historical range are given in columns B–D, respectively. Using the procedure given above, compute the plot points for a $\bar{Z}$–W chart and a $\bar{Z}^*$–W^* chart. Also provide the centerlines and LCL and UCL limits for each pair of charts. Table 27.16 has been developed using Excel, Table 27.15, and the formulas given in Table 27.14.

If we review Table 27.16, we will see that the average and range for each subgroup have been computed and are given in columns J and K, respectively.

The term σ_X is given in column L, and $\sigma_{\bar{X}}$ is given in column M. These values were computed using $d_2 = 2.326$ for $n = 5$. Note: The historical average range given in column D has been used to compute these values for each product.

Again, using the formulas given in Table 27.14, the values for $\bar{Z}$, W, $\bar{Z}^*$, and W^* are computed as reflected in columns N–Q, respectively.

Let's review the $\bar{Z}$ chart. From Table 27.14, the centerline is 0, the LCL = –3.0, and the UCL = 3.0.

Using the same table for the W chart, we know that the centerline is $d_2 = 2.326$ and $d_3 = 0.8641$ for $n = 5$ from Appendix K.5. This makes the LCL = –0.2663, which we set to 0.0, and the UCL = 4.9183.

Continuing with the $\bar{Z}^*$ chart, the centerline is 0 with the LCL at $-A_2$ and the UCL at $+A_2$. For $n = 5$, we have $A_2 = 0.577$ from Appendix K.4. Therefore, the LCL = –0.577 and UCL = 0.577.

The centerline for the W^* chart is 1.0, while the LCL = D_3 and the UCL = D_4. For $n = 5$, $D_3 = 0$ and $D_4 = 2.114$. Therefore, the LCL = 0 and the UCL = 2.114.

The centerlines and control limits are summarized in Table 27.16.

Continued

Column A	Column B	Column C	Column D	Column E	Column F	Column G	Column H	Column I
Date	Product	Historical average/ Target/ Nominal value	Historical average range for 10 previous subgroups	X_1	X_2	X_3	X_4	X_5
11–Jul	1407	9.5	10.50	16	11	13	7	10
12–Jul	1407	9.5	10.50	14	15	15	10	16
15–Jul	1404	4.5	4.10	4	0	6	4	4
16–Jul	1404	4.5	4.10	2	4	5	8	5
17–Jul	1404	4.5	4.10	5	8	3	5	3
18–Jul	1404	4.5	4.10	6	6	5	3	5
19–Jul	1404	4.5	4.10	4	5	4	2	8
22–Jul	1407	9.5	10.50	5	7	7	8	15
23–Jul	1408	8.5	7.90	0	9	9	7	0
24–Jul	1408	8.5	7.90	5	7	7	12	8
25–Jul	1404	4.5	4.10	4	2	7	2	2
26–Jul	1404	4.5	4.10	3	6	4	2	6
29–Jul	1407	9.5	10.50	3	10	16	6	10
30–Jul	1408	8.5	7.90	9	7	8	8	13
31–Jul	1407	9.5	10.50	5	15	9	5	10
1–Aug	1408	8.5	7.90	8	8	8	10	10
2–Aug	1407	9.5	10.50	11	15	12	8	14
5–Aug	1404	4.5	4.10	3	2	5	4	4
6–Aug	1404	4.5	4.10	4	5	5	4	8
7–Aug	1404	4.5	4.10	2	3	1	4	1

Table 27.15 Data for Example 27.8–short-run chart.

Continued

Column A	Column B	Column C	Column D	Column E	Column F	Column G	Column H	Column I	Column J	Column K	Column L	Column M	Column N	Column O	Collumn P	Column Q
Date	Product	Historical average/ Target/ Nominal value	Historical average range for 10 previous subgroups	X_1	X_2	X_3	X_4	X_5	$\bar{X}$	R	σ_X	$\sigma_{\bar{X}}$	$\bar{Z}$	W	$\bar{Z}^*$	W^*
11–Jul	1407	9.5	10.50	16	11	13	7	10	11.4	9	4.51	2.02	0.94	2.0	0.18	0.9
12–Jul	1407	9.5	10.50	14	15	15	10	16	14.0	6	4.51	2.02	2.23	1.3	0.43	0.6
15–Jul	1404	4.5	4.10	4	0	6	4	4	3.6	6	1.76	0.79	–1.14	3.4	–0.22	1.5
16–Jul	1404	4.5	4.10	2	4	5	8	5	4.8	6	1.76	0.79	0.38	3.4	0.07	1.5
17–Jul	1404	4.5	4.10	5	8	3	5	3	4.8	5	1.76	0.79	0.38	2.8	0.07	1.2
18–Jul	1404	4.5	4.10	6	6	5	3	5	5.0	3	1.76	0.79	0.63	1.7	0.12	0.7
19–Jul	1404	4.5	4.10	4	5	4	2	8	4.6	6	1.76	0.79	0.13	3.4	0.02	1.5
22–Jul	1407	9.5	10.50	5	7	7	8	15	8.4	10	4.51	2.02	–0.54	2.2	–0.10	1.0
23–Jul	1408	8.5	7.90	0	9	9	7	0	5.0	9	3.40	1.52	–2.30	2.6	–0.44	1.1
24–Jul	1408	8.5	7.90	5	7	7	12	8	7.8	7	3.40	1.52	–0.46	2.1	–0.09	0.9
25–Jul	1404	4.5	4.10	4	2	7	2	2	3.4	5	1.76	0.79	–1.40	2.8	–0.27	1.2
26–Jul	1404	4.5	4.10	3	6	4	2	6	4.2	4	1.76	0.79	–0.38	2.3	–0.07	1.0
29–Jul	1407	9.5	10.50	3	10	16	6	10	9.0	13	4.51	2.02	–0.25	2.9	–0.05	1.2
30–Jul	1408	8.5	7.90	9	7	8	8	13	9.0	6	3.40	1.52	0.33	1.8	0.06	0.8
31–Jul	1407	9.5	10.50	5	15	9	5	10	8.8	10	4.51	2.02	–0.35	2.2	–0.07	1.0
1–Aug	1408	8.5	7.90	8	8	8	10	10	8.8	2	3.40	1.52	0.20	0.6	0.04	0.3
2–Aug	1407	9.5	10.50	11	15	12	8	14	12.0	7	4.51	2.02	1.24	1.6	0.24	0.7
5–Aug	1404	4.5	4.10	3	2	5	4	4	3.6	3	1.76	0.79	–1.14	1.7	–0.22	0.7
6–Aug	1404	4.5	4.10	4	5	5	4	8	5.2	4	1.76	0.79	0.89	2.3	0.17	1.0
7–Aug	1404	4.5	4.10	2	3	1	4	1	2.2	3	1.76	0.79	–2.92	1.7	–0.56	0.7
d_2 =	2.326															
d_3 =	0.8641											**UCL**	3.0	4.9183	0.557	2.114
A_2 =	0.577											**Centerline**	0.0	2.326	0.0	1.0
D_3 =	0											**LCL**	–3.0	0.0	–0.557	0.0
D_4 =	2.114															

Table 27.16 Calculations for Example 27.8–short-run chart.

Moving Average and Moving Range (MAMR) Chart

The moving average and moving range (MAMR) chart may be suitable in the following situations:

- When data are collected periodically or when it takes time to produce a single item
- When it may be desirable to dampen the effects of overcontrol
- When it may be necessary to detect smaller shifts in the process than with a comparable Shewhart chart

Key Considerations When Using an MAMR Chart. The user of an MAMR chart must address the following:

- *Selection of a moving average length.* The overall sensitivity of the chart in detecting process shifts is affected by the selection of the moving average length. Generally, the longer the length, the less sensitive the chart is to detecting shifts. However, specific selection of the length should be made with consideration of the out-of-control detection rules being used. Wheeler (1995) presents and compares a series of power function curves (that is, probability of detecting a shift in the process average) for n-point moving averages to various "chart for individuals" detection rules. When the moving average length becomes a practical consideration, the reader is encouraged to consult a more rigorous source on this topic. Note: Minitab allows the user to set the size of the moving average length.
- *Selection of a method for estimating σ.* Wheeler (1995) suggests two methods:
  - Average moving range ($\bar{R}$)
  - Median moving range ($\tilde{R}$)

  Although the use of the average moving range is more popular, variability present in the data may suggest the use of the dispersion statistics. However, Wheeler (1995) computes control limits by using a variety of dispersion statistics (for example, range, median moving range, standard deviation) and concludes that "there is no practical difference between any of the sets of limits."

The following two considerations are particularly important when using moving average charts:

- *Rational subgrouping.* As with any control chart, consideration of rational subgrouping remains paramount. Example 27.9 assumes a rational subgroup of one with a moving average length of three. If statistical and technical considerations were appropriate for a rational subgroup of five, the average of each subgroup would constitute a point in the moving average of length five. Note: Minitab allows the user to set the subgroup size.

- *Interpretation of the charts.* By nature of their construction, points on moving average charts and moving range charts do not represent independent subgroups. Hence, these points are correlated. While single points exceeding the control limits may still be used as out of control, other tests such as zone run tests may lead to false conclusions. Some software packages recognize this and limit the out-of-control tests on the moving range charts to the following:
  - One point more than three sigma from the centerline
  - Nine points in a row on the same side of the centerline
  - Six points in a row, all increasing or all decreasing
  - Fourteen points in a row, alternating up and down

Constructing an MAMR Chart. Use the following steps when constructing an MAMR chart:

1. Collect a set of data: $x_1, x_2, \ldots, x_n$.
2. Specify the length of the moving average (for example, 2, 3, . . .).
3. Calculate the moving averages.
4. Calculate the moving ranges.
5. Calculate the centerline of the moving average chart where the centerline equals $\overline{X}_{MA}$.
6. Calculate the centerline of the moving range chart where the centerline equals $\overline{mR}$.
7. Compute the LCL and the UCL for the moving range chart using $LCL = D_3\overline{mR}$ and $UCL = D_4\overline{mR}$, where D_3 and D_4 are constants found in Appendix K.4.
8. Compute the LCL and the UCL for the moving average chart, using $\overline{X}_{MA} \pm A_2\overline{mR}$, where A_2 is a constant found in Appendix K.4.
9. Plot the data, centerline, LCL, and UCL for both the moving average and moving range charts.
10. Interpret the results and take action accordingly.

EXAMPLE 27.9

The data shown in Table 27.17 are taken from Griffith (1996). Develop an MAMR chart with a moving average length of three.

Continued

Column A	Column B
Number	X_i
1	8.0
2	8.5
3	7.4
4	10.5
5	9.3
6	11.1
7	10.4
8	10.4
9	9.0
10	10.0
11	11.7
12	10.3
13	16.2
14	11.6
15	11.5
16	11.0
17	12.0
18	11.0
19	10.2
20	10.1
21	10.5
22	10.3
23	11.5
24	11.1
	Average

Table 27.17 Data for Example 27.9–MAMR chart.

Using the procedure given above, the results are shown in Table 27.18. Since a moving average length of three was specified in the problem statement, Table 27.18 shows two fewer plot points. The completed charts are given in Figures 27.15 and 27.16.

Continued

Column A	Column B	Column C	Column D	Column E	Column F	Column G	Column H	Column I	Column J	Column K	Column L	Column M
Number	X_i	Moving average	Moving range	A_2	D_3	D_4	Average moving average	Average moving range	LCL_{MA}	UCL_{MA}	LCL_{MR}	UCL_{MR}
1	8.0											
2	8.5											
3	7.4	7.97	1.10	1.023	0.000	2.574	10.65	1.99	8.61	12.68	0.00	5.12
4	10.5	8.80	3.10	1.023	0.000	2.574	10.65	1.99	8.61	12.68	0.00	5.12
5	9.3	9.07	3.10	1.023	0.000	2.574	10.65	1.99	8.61	12.68	0.00	5.12
6	11.1	10.30	1.80	1.023	0.000	2.574	10.65	1.99	8.61	12.68	0.00	5.12
7	10.4	10.27	1.80	1.023	0.000	2.574	10.65	1.99	8.61	12.68	0.00	5.12
8	10.4	10.63	0.70	1.023	0.000	2.574	10.65	1.99	8.61	12.68	0.00	5.12
9	9.0	9.93	1.40	1.023	0.000	2.574	10.65	1.99	8.61	12.68	0.00	5.12
10	10.0	9.80	1.40	1.023	0.000	2.574	10.65	1.99	8.61	12.68	0.00	5.12
11	11.7	10.23	2.70	1.023	0.000	2.574	10.65	1.99	8.61	12.68	0.00	5.12
12	10.3	10.67	1.70	1.023	0.000	2.574	10.65	1.99	8.61	12.68	0.00	5.12
13	16.2	12.73	5.90	1.023	0.000	2.574	10.65	1.99	8.61	12.68	0.00	5.12
14	11.6	12.70	5.90	1.023	0.000	2.574	10.65	1.99	8.61	12.68	0.00	5.12
15	11.5	13.10	4.70	1.023	0.000	2.574	10.65	1.99	8.61	12.68	0.00	5.12
16	11.0	11.37	0.60	1.023	0.000	2.574	10.65	1.99	8.61	12.68	0.00	5.12
17	12.0	11.50	1.00	1.023	0.000	2.574	10.65	1.99	8.61	12.68	0.00	5.12
18	11.0	11.33	1.00	1.023	0.000	2.574	10.65	1.99	8.61	12.68	0.00	5.12
19	10.2	11.07	1.80	1.023	0.000	2.574	10.65	1.99	8.61	12.68	0.00	5.12
20	10.1	10.43	0.90	1.023	0.000	2.574	10.65	1.99	8.61	12.68	0.00	5.12
21	10.5	10.27	0.40	1.023	0.000	2.574	10.65	1.99	8.61	12.68	0.00	5.12
22	10.3	10.30	0.40	1.023	0.000	2.574	10.65	1.99	8.61	12.68	0.00	5.12
23	11.5	10.77	1.20	1.023	0.000	2.574	10.65	1.99	8.61	12.68	0.00	5.12
24	11.1	10.97	1.20	1.023	0.000	2.574	10.65	1.99	8.61	12.68	0.00	5.12
	Average	**10.65**	**1.99**									

Table 27.18 Calculations for Example 27.9–MAMR chart.

Continued

Continued

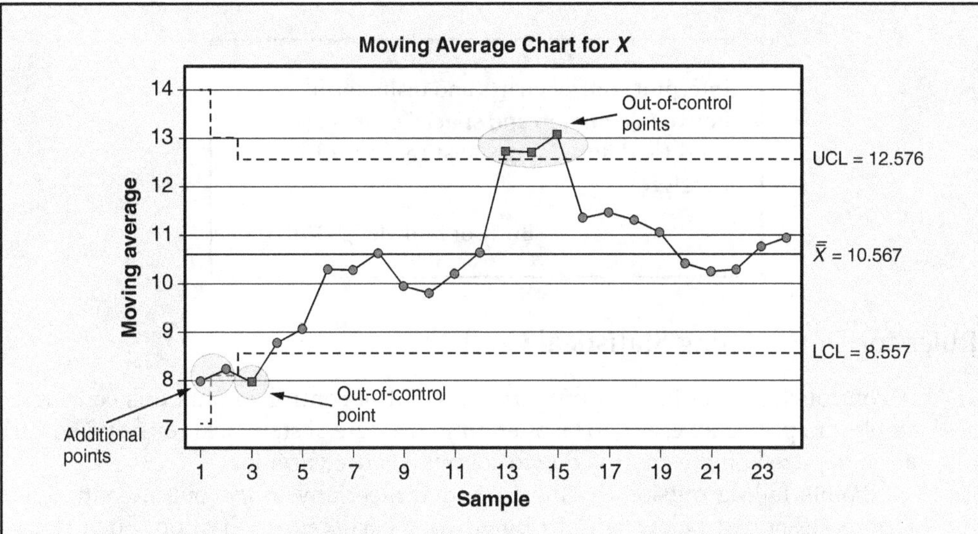

Figure 27.15 Moving average chart of length three for Example 27.9.

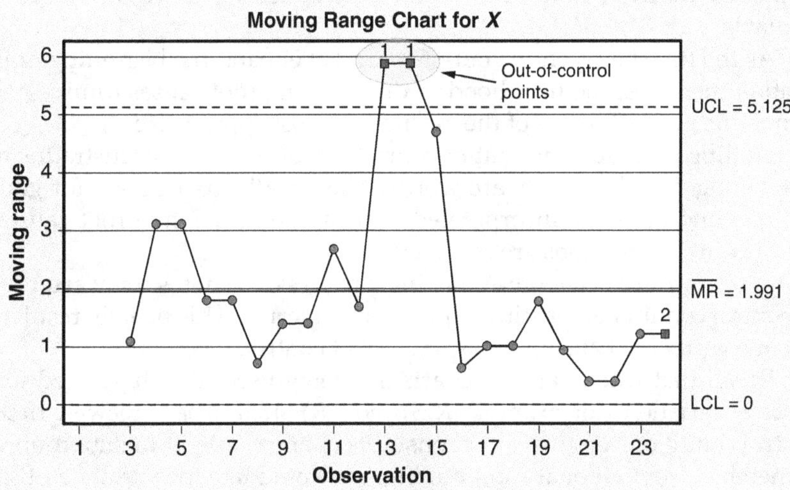

Figure 27.16 Moving range chart of length three for Example 27.9.

Let's first analyze Figure 27.15. We will note that this chart does not demonstrate statistical control. However, we will also note that the mean and the control limits do not agree with those presented in Table 27.18. This is because this chart plotted all 24 points and used the corresponding data in the calculations for the moving average and control limits, whereas this was not the case in Table 27.18. Contrast the moving average chart in Figure 27.15 to the corresponding moving range chart in Figure 27.16. Both charts are moving average charts of length three, but both calculated their averages and control limits differently. This is something readers must be aware of when using statistical software packages over which they have little control.

The moving range chart illustrated in Figure 27.16 depicts an out-of-control condition.

CONTROL CHART ANALYSIS

> Interpret control charts and distinguish between common and special causes using rules for determining statistical control. (Analyze)
>
> Body of Knowledge VIII.A.5

Rules for Determining Statistical Control

A control chart that has not triggered any out-of-control condition is considered stable and predictable, and to be operating in a state of statistical control. The variation depicted on the chart is due to common cause variation.

Points falling outside the limits or that meet any of the out-of-control conditions described below are attributed to special cause variation. Such points, regardless of whether they constitute "good" or "bad" occurrences, should be investigated immediately while the cause-and-effect relationships and individual memories are fresh, and access to documentation for process changes is readily available.

As the time between the out-of-control event and the beginning of the investigation increases, the likelihood of determining root causes diminishes greatly. Hence, the motto "time is of the essence" is most appropriate.

Finding root causes for out-of-control conditions may be frustrating and time-consuming, but the results are worthwhile. Ideally, root causes for good out-of-control conditions are incorporated into the process, while root causes for bad out-of-control conditions are removed.

Now a word of caution: Adjusting a process when it is not warranted by out-of-control conditions constitutes process tampering. This usually results in destabilizing a process, causing it to spiral out of control.

Recall that when variable charts are being used, the chart used to measure process variation (for example $\bar{R}, \bar{S}$, and $\overline{mR}$) should be reviewed first. Out-of-control conditions on this chart constitute changes in within-subgroup variation. Remember, from rational subgrouping, we would like the variation of subgroups on this chart to be as small as possible because this measure of dispersion is used to compute the control limits on the corresponding process central tendency chart (for example, $\bar{X}$ and X). The tighter the control limits on the central tendency chart, the easier it is to detect subgroup-to-subgroup variation.

Commonly used rules or tests have been devised to detect out-of-control conditions, as shown in Table 27.19.

These rules can be applied to variables control charts, while a subset of them applies to attributes and short-term control charts. Figures 27.17 through 27.24 illustrate the out-of-control conditions for rules 1–8, respectively, in Table 27.19. The out-of-control condition found in each figure is enclosed in a dotted-lined box. Note that the subgroups along the horizontal axis are for illustrative purposes only and are not intended to align to each plot point.

	Out-of-control condition	Possible reasons	Chart type							
			Variables			Attributes				Short-run
			$\bar{X}$ and R	$\bar{X}$ and s	XmR	p	np	c	u	MAMR
1	One point more than 3σ from the centerline (either side)	*Freaks*: error in plotting, calculation error, breakdown of facilities, extraneous causes	✓	✓	✓	✓	✓	✓	✓	✓
2	Nine points in a row on the same side of the centerline (Note: References to 6–9 points in a row on the same side of the centerline appear appear in the literature.)	A shift in the process means has likely occurred	✓	✓	✓	✓	✓	✓	✓	✓
3	Six points in a row, all increasing or all decreasing	*Trend*: tool wear, skill improvement, deteriorating maintenance	✓	✓	✓	✓	✓	✓	✓	✓
4	Fourteen points in a row, alternating up and down	Alternating cause systems are present, such as two suppliers, and so on. Unlike stratification, the subgroups are homogeneous	✓	✓	✓	✓	✓	✓	✓	✓
5	Two out of three points more than 2σ from the centerline (same side)	Early warning of a potential process shift	✓	✓	✓					
6	Four out of five points more than 1σ from the centerline (same side)	Early warning of a potential process shift	✓	✓	✓					
7	Fifteen points in a row than 1σ from the centerline (either side)	*Stratification*: two or more different cause systems are present in every subgroup	✓	✓	✓					
8	Eight points in a row than 1σ from the centerline (either side)	*Mixture*: two different operators being used, two machines, and so on.	✓	✓	✓					

Table 27.19 Interpreting control chart out-control conditions used by Minitab.

Rule 1: One Point Beyond Zone A, Either Side

This out-of-control condition is shown in Figure 27.17. Possible reasons for this condition include a data or plotting error, or an extraordinary cause.

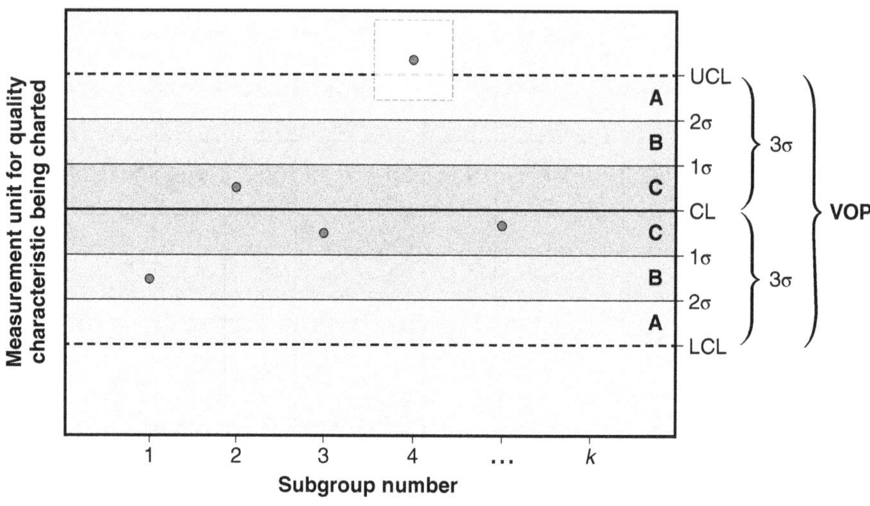

Figure 27.17 Example of Rule 1, one point outside the control limits.

Rule 2: Nine Points in a Row on One Side of the Center Line

This out-of-control condition is shown in Figure 27.18. Possible reasons for this condition include shift in the process mean.

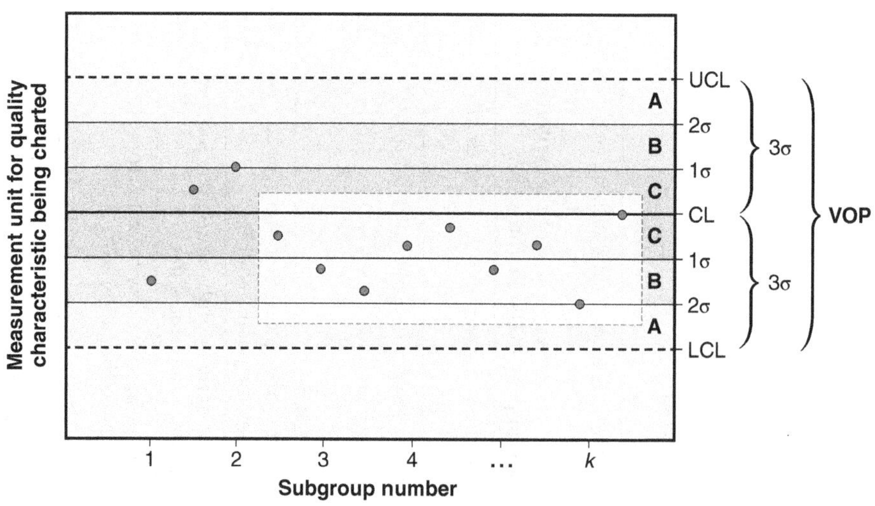

Figure 27.18 Example of Rule 2, nine points in a row on one side of the center line.

Rule 3: Six Points in a Row Steadily Increasing or Decreasing

This out-of-control condition is shown in Figure 27.19. Possible reasons for this condition include tool wear, improvement due to training, or deteriorating maintenance.

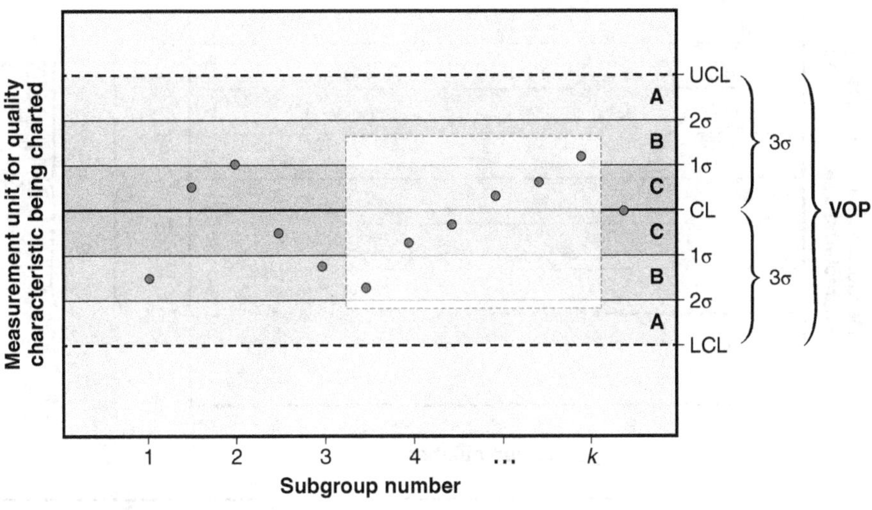

Figure 27.19 Example of Rule 3, six points in a row steadily increasing or decreasing.

Rule 4: Fourteen Points in a Row Alternating Up and Down

This out-of-control condition is shown in Figure 27.20. Possible reasons for this condition include excessive tampering, or alternating cause systems, such as two different suppliers, or machine outputs.

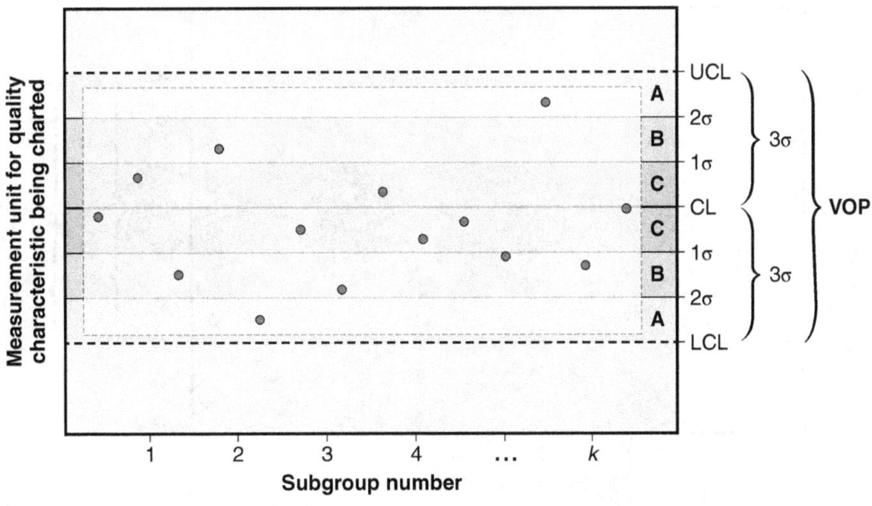

Figure 27.20 Example of Rule 4, fourteen points in a row alternating up and down.

Rule 5: Two Out of Three Points in Zone A, Same Side

This out-of-control condition is shown in Figure 27.21. A possible reason for this is a potential process mean shift.

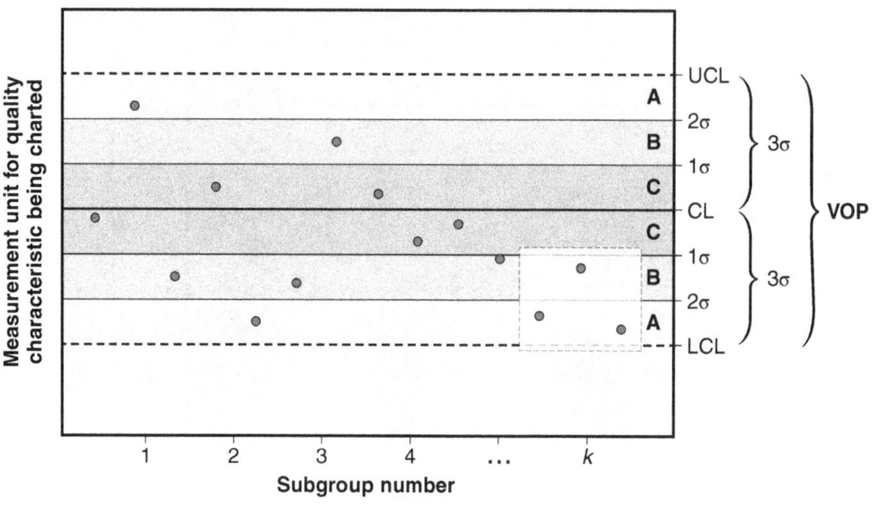

Figure 27.21 Example of Rule 5, two out of three points in a row in Zone A, same side.

Rule 6: Four Out of Five Points in Zone B or Beyond, Same Side

This out-of-control condition is shown in Figure 27.22. A possible reason for this is a potential process mean shift.

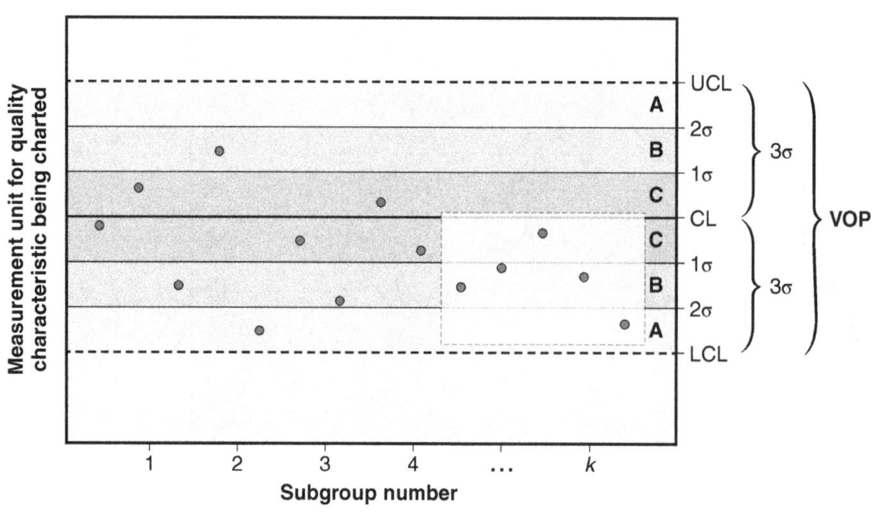

Figure 27.22 Example of Rule 6, four out of five points in Zone B or beyond, same side.

Rule 7: Fifteen Points in a Row in Zone C, Either Side

This out-of-control condition is shown in Figure 27.23. Possible reasons for this are stratification, in which subgroups are not homogeneous, or a reduction in process variability, perhaps due to a Six Sigma improvement project.

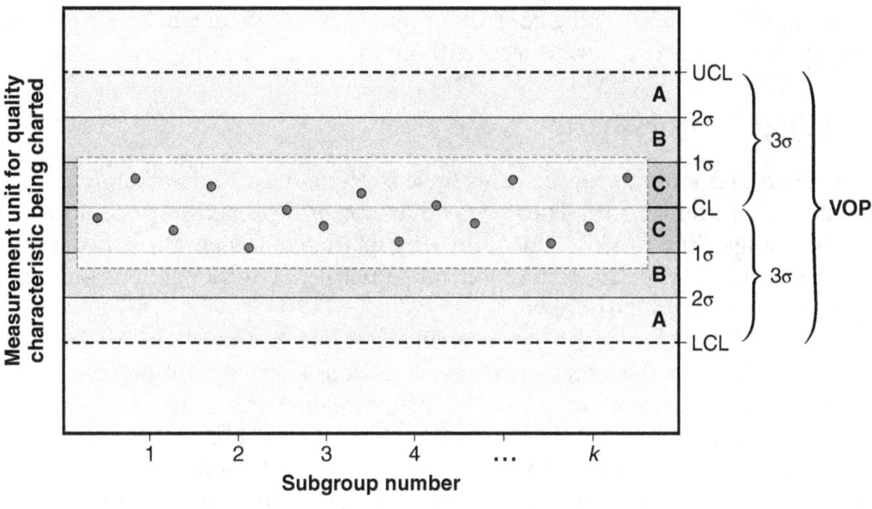

Figure 27.23 Example of Rule 7, fifteen points in a row in Zone C, either side.

Rule 8: Eight Points in Row in Zones B and A, Either Side

This out-of-control condition is shown in Figure 27.24. Possible reasons for this are a mixture of two operators, suppliers, or machines being plotted on the same chart.

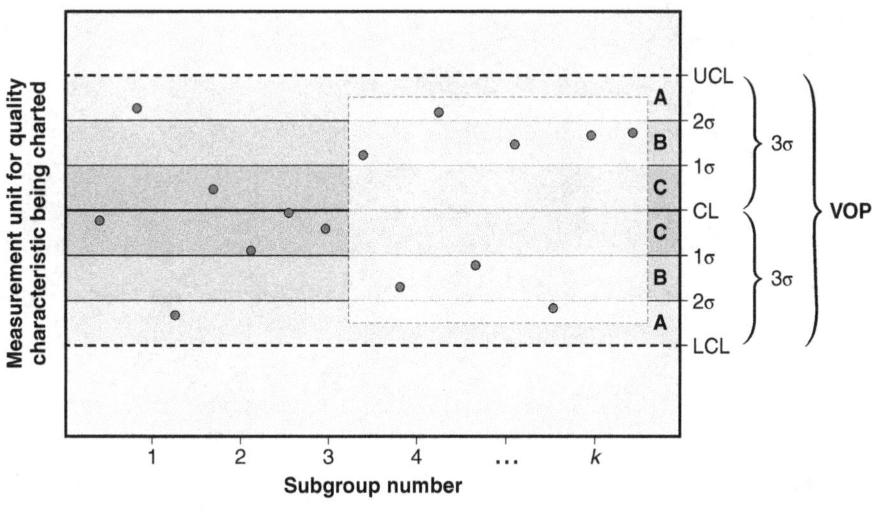

Figure 27.24 Example of Rule 8, eight points in a row in Zones B and A, either side.

The probabilities associated with the above out-of-control conditions occurring are both similar in value and relatively small. For example, for a normally distributed process, the probability of one point falling either below the lower control limit or above the upper control limit is 0.0027. The probability of nine points in a row on one side of the center line is 0.0020, and the probability of fifteen points in a row within one standard deviation of the center line is 0.0030. With the exception of points exceeding the control limits, most out-of-control conditions are subtle and would likely go unnoticed without the aid of a computerized control chart.

Interpreting Control Charts

As stated previously, specific rules have been devised to determine when out-of-control conditions occur. These rules have been designed to permit us to detect early changes in a process, thus allowing us to take systematic action to discover the root cause of the variation or permit adjustment or other actions on the process before serious damage occurs.

Control charts operating in control are stable and predictable, and operating under the influence of common cause variation. Those operating with out-of-control conditions present are under the influence of special cause variation.

A control chart is relatively easy to develop and use, and it can be a highly effective statistical tool when selected properly and used correctly. Its selection and use alone, however, is not sufficient. When so indicated, control charts must be acted on in a timely manner so that root causes may be identified and removed from the process.

One last thing: When in doubt, avoid tampering with the process.

Chapter 28
Other Controls

It is only the last turn of a bolt that tightens it; the rest is just movement.

–Shigeo Shingo

Once a process has been improved, the next, and sometimes most difficult, challenge is to hold the gains. One reason this is so difficult is that it often requires people to change the way they do things. Two tools for holding the gains are total productive maintenance and visual controls.

TOTAL PRODUCTIVE MAINTENANCE (TPM)

Define the elements of TPM and describe how it can be used to consistently control the improved process. (Understand)

Body of Knowledge VIII.B.1

Total productive maintenance (TPM) is a methodology pioneered by Nippondenso (a member of the Toyota group) that works to ensure that every machine in a production process is always able to perform its required tasks so that production is never interrupted. TPM maximizes equipment effectiveness by using a preventive maintenance program throughout the life of the equipment.

In any situation where mechanical devices are used, the working state of those devices has an impact on the control of the process. If equipment deteriorates even subtly, the process output may be affected, often in unsuspected ways. For lean systems to work, all equipment must be ready to quickly respond to customer needs. This requires a system that foresees maintenance needs and takes appropriate action. A TPM system uses historical data, manufacturer's recommendations, reports by alert operators, diagnostic tests, and other techniques to schedule maintenance activity so machine downtime can be minimized. TPM goes beyond keeping everything running. An effective TPM system includes continuous improvement initiatives as it seeks more effective and efficient ways to predict and diagnose maintenance-related problems.

EXAMPLE 28.1

A fresh and frozen distribution center of a major retailer recognized that flow disruptions and late shipments were being caused by the conveyor systems. These systems, although covered under a scheduled preventive maintenance program, were not reliable enough. A TPM initiative was launched to reduce and eliminate the unplanned downtime experienced across the center. This included reallocating duties, elevating skill sets through training, and conducting TPM audits and TPM-focused kaizen blitzes. The outcome was an improvement in overall conveyor uptime and a reduction in delayed and partial shipments.

EXAMPLE 28.2

The resolver on a pick-and-place robot was malfunctioning, causing sporadic part defects due to incorrect positioning of parts in a machine. A TPM team investigated the problem and determined that the malfunction was due to a buildup of contaminant located in and around the machine. As a result of this key learning, the team modified the robot maintenance schedule without creating any additional downtime.

An important precept of TPM is the move toward ownership of the equipment and work area by the people that work there. Machine operators become responsible for lubrication, routine adjustments, and repair of machines. This means entrusting and enabling workers to perform functions previously carried out by maintenance personnel. A significant advantage to TPM is the tendency for production personnel to suggest improvements in workstation layout and operation. If these suggestions are implemented, workers begin to recognize the connection between well-organized and maintained equipment and quality products. The performance of maintenance tasks by machine operators is called *autonomous maintenance*. Beginning steps for implementing autonomous maintenance include the following:

1. Be alert to paycheck/incentive issues. Little enthusiasm will be generated by a change that decreases take-home pay. For example, the worker may be paid at a lower rate while working on her machine than she would if maintenance personnel were working on it.
2. Make sure training, tools, and supplies are accessible. Don't ask people to perform tasks they aren't equipped to do.
3. Be alert for multi-shift tensions as in "I left this machine immaculate, now look at it." Cross-shift meetings to discuss standards will usually help. Some processes benefit from a log listing data from each shift.
4. Begin small, perhaps with daily cleaning and lubrication.
5. Determine if there are daily measurements that would help predict machine malfunction. Could a tachometer, ammeter, or recording thermostat be installed on equipment? If so, how is the output to be interpreted?

6. Be alert for, and celebrate, innovations made by workers.
7. Help maintenance department personnel understand that they are reserved for bigger things. Any slack time generated can be filled with training.

As TPM begins to work, it is possible to expand its scope to include:

- *Condition-based maintenance.* The scheduling of maintenance tasks based on operating conditions. Examples include the following:
  - Spot welding tips must be dressed or changed more frequently when used on galvanized steel.
  - Filters must be changed more frequently in summer.
  - If the patient weighs more than 300 pounds, the amps to the motor must be monitored.
- *Periodic/preventive maintenance.* The scheduling of maintenance tasks based on expected lifetime. Especially useful when multiple items are more efficiently maintained rather than one at a time, for example, light bulbs.
- *Reliability-based maintenance.* The scheduling of maintenance based on reliability data, especially if a failure is very costly. Examples include:
  - A bearing that usually fails between 1800 and 2600 hours, causing a major shutdown, might be replaced on the weekend after it has had 1500 hours of service.
  - A timing belt that has a high probability of failure at 70,000 miles might be scheduled for replacement at 60,000 miles.
- *Maintenance analytics.* The scheduling of maintenance tasks based on data from sensing devices. For example, vibration sensors and noise sensors can sometimes detect a signature signal that precedes failure. An increase in amperage drawn could imply a failing motor or failure in its load.

In addition to using TPM to minimize equipment downtime, it can also be used to maintain process control by recognizing it as one component of total process variation. When we discuss measurement systems analysis, we look at total process variation as

$$\sigma^2_{\text{Measurement}} + \sigma^2_{\text{Process}} = \sigma^2_{\text{Total}}$$

However, we can further decompose $\sigma^2_{\text{Process}}$ as follows:

$$\sigma^2_{\text{Process}} = \sigma^2_{\text{Machine}} + \sigma^2_{\text{Method}} + \sigma^2_{\text{Material}} + \cdots$$

Once the variance component due to TPM is isolated, it can be monitored and improved using a variety of tools and techniques discussed in other chapters.

Many organizations use TPM audits (similar to 5S audits) to consider the level of TPM application within a process or area of a facility. This audit can establish a baseline with which the future state can be compared.

VISUAL CONTROLS

> Define the elements of visual controls (e.g., pictures of correct procedures, color-coded components, indicator lights), and describe how they can help control the improved process. (Understand)
>
> **Body of Knowledge VIII.B.2**

Visual controls, sometimes known as visual management or the *visual factory,* are approaches and techniques that permit one to visually determine the status of a system, factory, or process at a glance and prevent or minimize process variation. These controls can be viewed as a form of mistake-proofing. Consider this: Visual controls make the process exceptions obvious.

Some examples of visual controls include:

- Signage
- Product line identification
- Color-coded items such as parts, bins, racks, documentation, walkways, and so forth
- Schedule boards
- Conspicuous posting of performance indicators

Visual controls work to provide a constant focus and attention on the process. This level of attention can help stabilize variation at the improved level of a process. Examples of visual controls are shown in Figures 28.1 through 28.8.

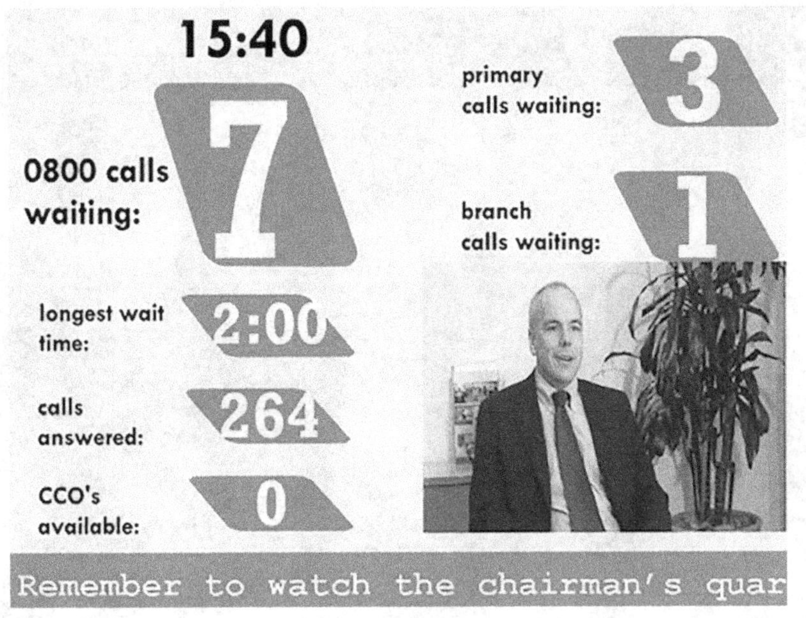

Figure 28.1 Scoreboard showing real-time performance data.

Standard Operation Sheet

faurecia	STANDARD OPERATION		FAU-F-PS-241 / EN version 02	Plant:	Washington	Document No.:	xxxx
						Revision Level:	.
Part Number	xxx	Part Name	Bolster	Line :	EQ Bolster	Work-station: Woodstock	Page No: 575

No.	Operation	✚ = SAFETY ◆ = QUALITY ● = TIP	Time: 30 Sec	Sketches / Photo's / etc.
5	Remove parts from tool		**Remove cavities 3 & 4** from the mould tool. Place parts onto left side of bench (Fig1)	Spiking Cavitie 1 0 + Fig 1.
4	Remove the spiking frame from the upper tool	●	Remove the waste then **place the frame onto the bench** **Ensure frame handle is pointing away** from you and spikes are pointing upwards.	
-	Fold waste and place onto to stand.		Fold the waste from the frame and place it onto the granulator cooling stand, using it to push the existing waste into the granulator (fig 2).	3 Granulator Cooling stand Fig 2.
.	Remove the spiked frame from the underneath bench	◆	Remove the spiked frame from underneath the bench **place it into the guides on the upper mould** tool (fig 1) Ensure that the **handle** is pointing towards you **is fully located against the censor**	
&	Place one white & green clip into cavities 3&4	●	- Take one white & green LH clip from the dispenser. - Place the green clip into the center clip position and the white into the bottom location on cavity 4. - Take one white & green RH clip from the dispencer. - Place the green clip into the center cl	White 5 White Fig 3.

Issued	Signature/Date	Checked	Signature/Date	Approved	Signature/Date	SKILLED OPERATOR	Signature/Date	Non Conforming Product:
Name:		Name:		Name:				Place rejects in reject container. Record on Process Monitor Sheet. If 3 or more rejects found with same fault call Gap Leader.
Function:		Function:		Function:		Name:		

Figure 28.2 Visual work instructions.

Figure 28.3 Visual stock control.

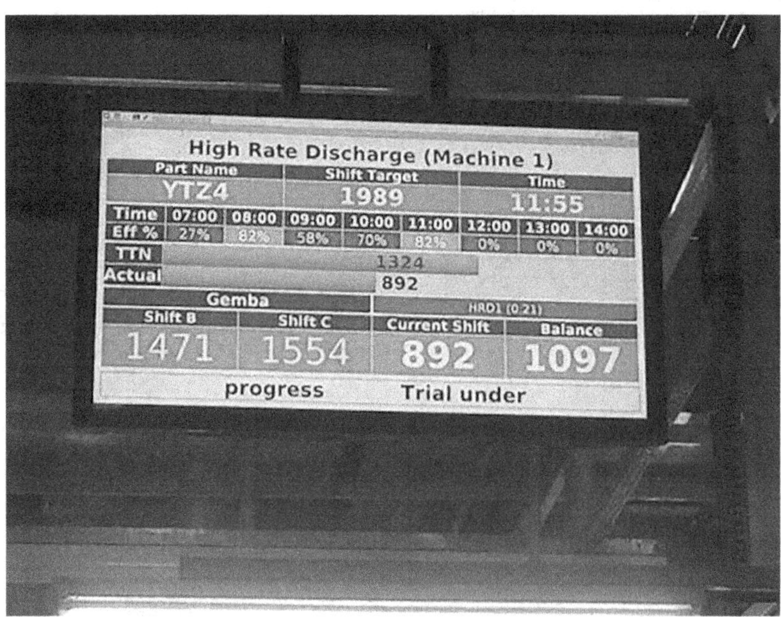

Figure 28.4 Performance data.

Figure 28.5 Floor marking.

Figure 28.6 Tool board with templates.

Figure 28.7 Floor-marked storage areas.

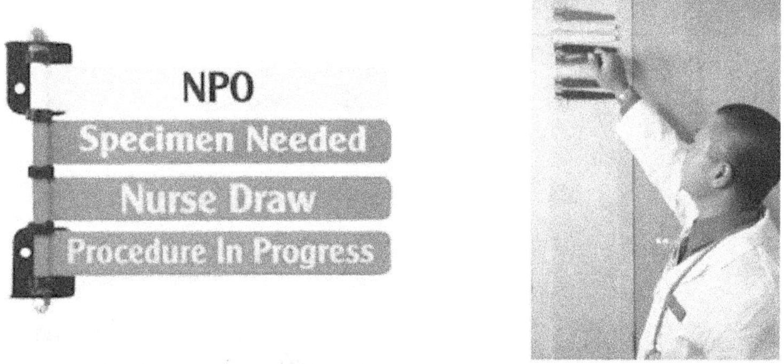

Figure 28.8 Communication flags in a medical office.

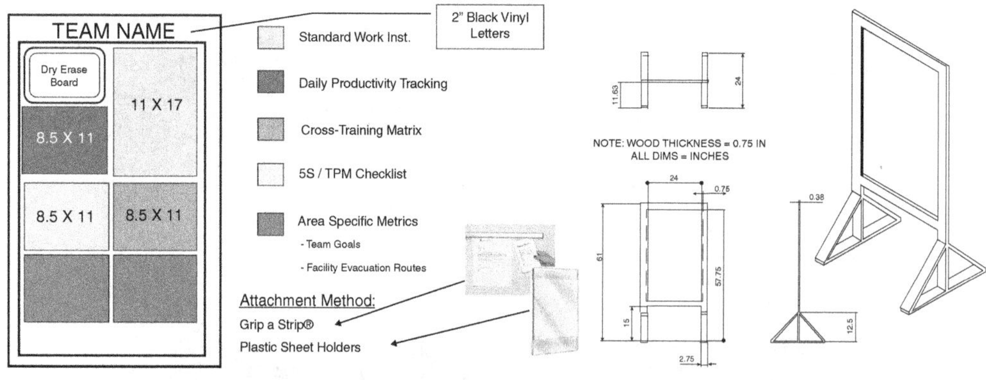

Figure 28.9 Communication board layout and design.

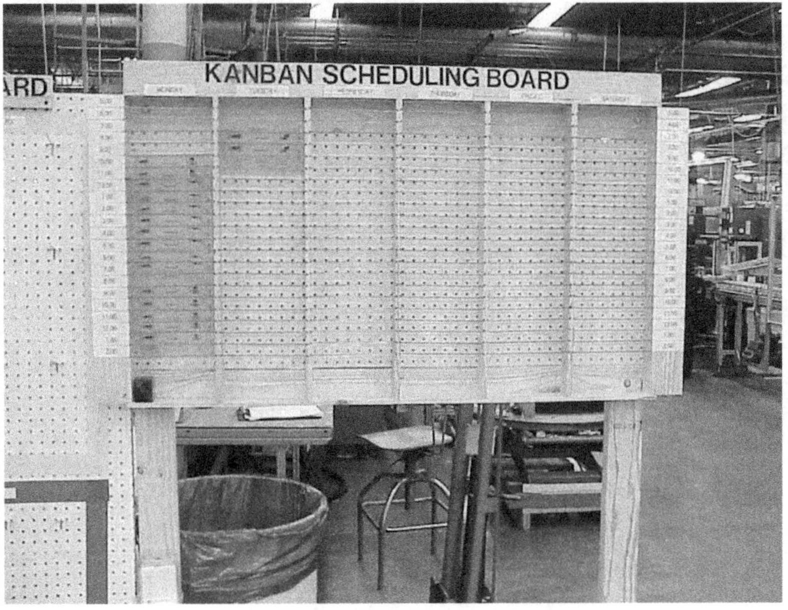

Figure 28.10 Heijunka board for sequencing and scheduling.

Chapter 29

Maintain Controls

Chance favors the prepared mind.

—Louis Pasteur

MEASUREMENT SYSTEM REANALYSIS

> Review and evaluate measurement system capability as process capability improves, and ensure that measurement capability is sufficient for its intended use. (Evaluate)
>
> Body of Knowledge VIII.C.1

There are many reasons why a reanalysis of the measurement system is required; examples include change in process, change in customer specifications, new measuring devices, equipment calibration issues, and so on. Of course, most of these reasons are obvious. One reason that is not so obvious is the impact that continuous process improvement has on the measurement system. The total observed variance in a process is made up of two components: process variation and measurement variation. We usually write this as

$$\sigma^2_{\text{Total observed}} = \sigma^2_{\text{Process}} + \sigma^2_{\text{Measurement system}}$$

Process improvement efforts can result in reduced process variance. This, in turn, results in reduced total observed variance. However, the measurement system variance remains unchanged. As a result, measurement system variance increases as a percentage of total observed variance. Depending on the percentage value, the current measurement system variance could become unacceptably large.

Measurement variation can be calculated by performing a gage repeatability and reproducibility (GR&R) analysis, as described in Chapter 16. For example, the following guidelines are typically used to determine the acceptability of a measurement system:

- < 10% study variation—The measurement system is considered acceptable.

- 10%-30% student variation—The measurement system may be considered acceptable based on importance of application, cost of gage, cost of repair, and so on. This is a gray area and depends on the situation at hand.
- > 30% study variation—The measurement system is considered unacceptable, and improvement is necessary.

Figure 29.1 depicts an acceptable measurement system using the above percentage guidelines, whereas Figure 29.2 depicts one that is unacceptable.

Other rules or standards exist for determining the acceptability of measurement system variation:

- *10:1 ratio rule.* This rule states that the measurement system discrimination should be no greater than one-tenth of the smaller of the process variation or the specification tolerance.
- *4:1 ratio (25%) rule.* This rule states that measurement uncertainty should be no greater than 25% of the specification tolerance.

EXAMPLE 29.1

An initial GR&R study determined the measurement system percentage to be 12%. In addition, the 10:1 ratio rule was met. Thus, the measurement system was judged acceptable. However, after a series of improvement projects, the part-to-part process variation was reduced by 75%. A reanalysis of the measurement system now showed that the GR&R increased to 35% and that the 10:1 ratio rule was still satisfied since the measuring devices and specification limits did not change. As a result, the organization must determine whether the measurement system is acceptable or needs improvement based on intended use, customer specification, and cost of implementation.

In Example 29.1, any future projects aimed at reducing process variation will likely fail to produce the desired results. This is due to the large amount of measurement variation. The measurement system does not have adequate resolution within the process control limits and will not be able to detect the changes in the process variation. Future activities in this area will need to address the adequacy of the measurement system before any project to further reduce process variation is undertaken.

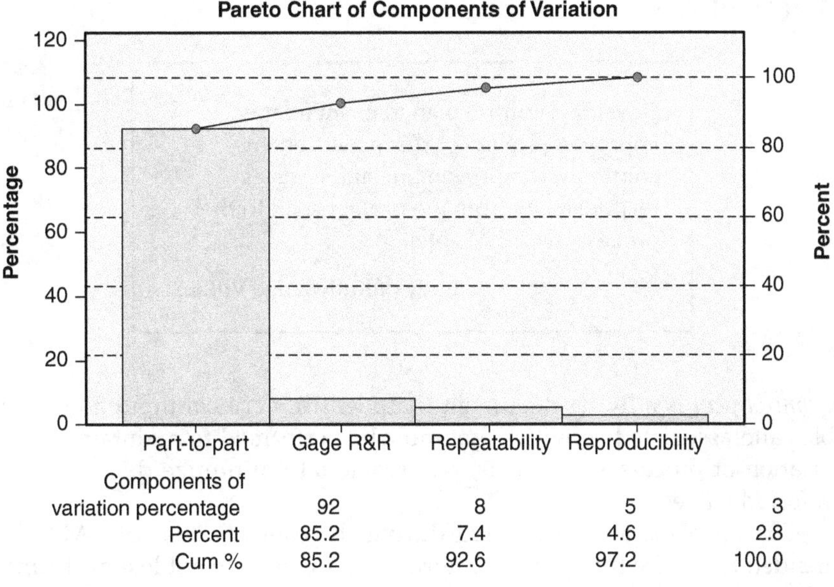

Figure 29.1 Example of an acceptable level of variation due to the measurement system.

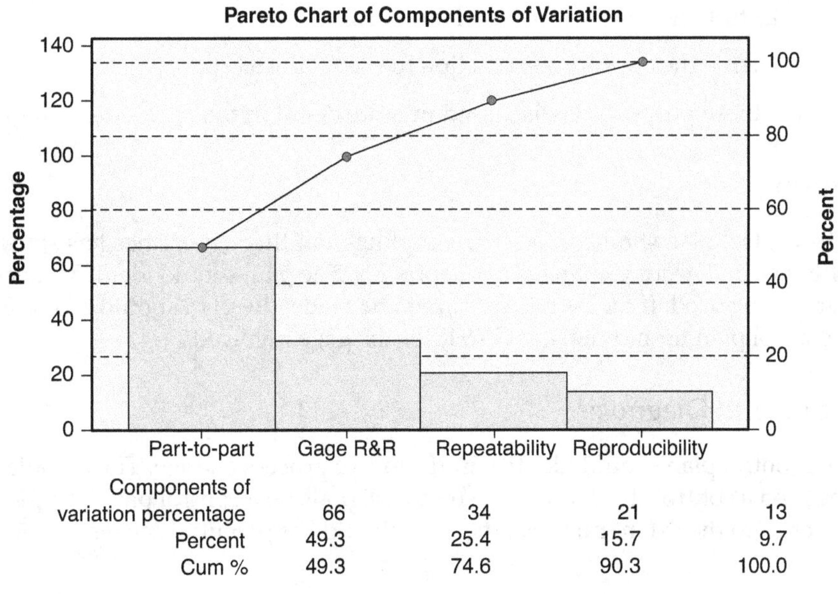

Figure 29.2 Example of an unacceptable level of variation due to the measurement system.

CONTROL PLAN

> Develop a control plan to maintain the improved process performance, enable continuous improvement, and transfer responsibility from the project team to the process owner. (Apply)
>
> Body of Knowledge VIII.C.2

A *control plan* is a living document that identifies critical input and output variables and associated activities that must be performed to maintain control of the variation of processes, products, and services to minimize deviation from their preferred values.

Control plans are formulated during the control phase of DMAIC and are intended to ensure that process improvement gains are not lost over time. A control plan is needed because, despite our best quality improvement efforts, some failure modes may occur. The control plan is designed to:

- Monitor the process
- Detect and diagnose potential failures
- Define the appropriate reaction to each failure type

Each of these purposes is discussed in more detail in the following paragraphs.

Monitoring

The control plan should specify a sampling plan that experience has shown to be effective in detecting changes to the process. The plan should identify gages or fixtures to be used. If measurements are to be made, the plan should cross-reference a control plan for monitoring GR&R for the gage involved.

Detection and Diagnosis

The control plan should identify indicators of process change. These could be patterns on a control chart, unusual sounds, signals on a control panel, or some other criteria. To the extent possible, the plan should list potential causes.

Reaction

The control plan should list the steps to be taken when a process change has been detected. This serves as an aid to the responsible personnel during what is often a stressful time. The plan should be quite specific; for example, the reaction to bulb #18 going to red should be to throw switch #4 and change filter #3A, or when seven successive points plot above the mean, the parting tool should be examined. The reaction section should cover requirements for containment and inspection of products suspected of having defects. It should also discuss disposition of parts found to be defective. Some control plans prescribe a more intense sampling protocol after certain corrective actions have been taken. Examples of control plans featuring some of these requirements are shown in Figure 29.3 and Figure 29.4.

Notice that the two plans in Figure 29.3 identify the individual responsible for taking the actions defined in the control plan, using the basic premise that things get done when accountability is assigned.

A control plan is defined as a living document and is designed to be maintained. Common triggers for updating control charts include:

- Process changes
- Specification changes
- Measurement technology changes
- Organizational changes

Control Plan for Process XYZ

Activity/ step	Input	Specification characteristic to be controlled	Control method	Control description	Responsibility
1	Copper cable	Cross-section diameter	Measure per SOP 481-4.7	$\bar{X}$ and R control chart Out-of-control condition: Do not complete operation, notify production engineer immediately	Operator
2	Resistor	Resistance	Measure per SOP 596-2.4	$\bar{X}$ and R control chart Out-of-control condition: Pull lot from production, notify supplier, draw new lot	Production engineer

Control Plan for Process XYZ

Control factor	Specification or tolerance	Measurement technique	Sample size	Sampling method/ frequency	Reaction plan	Responsibility
Cable diameter	0.5 mm ± 0.05 mm	Caliper, measure per SOP	7	$\bar{X}$ and R control chart, random sampling with a probability of 0.25	Out-of-control condition: Do not complete operation, notify production engineer immediately	Operator
Cable length	12.0 mm ± 0.10 mm	GKRD-45 optical reader, measure per SOP	5	$\bar{X}$ and R control chart, random sampling with a probability of 0.10	Out-of-control condition: Pull lot from production, notify supplier, draw new lot	Production engineer

Figure 29.3 Control plan long form (note image is wrapped to show detail).

Process	Specification	Inspection equipment See QR18 for GRR	Sampling plan	Recording medium	Discrepancy	Response action
Face and plunge	Face FIM $\leq$ 0.0008	CMM (Pgm #442)	1 every 50 parts	CMM printout	FIM > 0.0008	Stop production. Quarantine last 50 parts for inspection on CMM. Segregate any that fail flatness specification. Remove facing insert and replace. Inspect next 5 parts on CMM to make certain FIM = 0.0008 specification is met. If not, call supervisor.
Face and plunge	Slot width 0.250 ± 0.004	Caliper #Q955	5 consecutive parts once every 100	$\bar{X}$ and R chart #LA61	Point above UCL or below LCL on $\bar{X}$ 8 points one side of mean on $\bar{X}$	Stop production. Quarantine last 100 parts for inspection. Segregate any that fail width specification. Remove and replace insert on plunge tool. Inspect next 5 parts. If mean falls outside control limits, call supervisor.
					Point above UCL on R 8 points above mean on R	Stop production, call quality engineer.
Face and plunge	Slot depth 0.15 ± 0.005	Caliper #Q955	5 consecutive parts once every 100	$\bar{X}$ and R chart #LA62	Point above UCL or below LCL on $\bar{X}$	Stop production. Quarantine last 100 parts for inspection. Segregate any that fail depth specification. Remove and replace insert on plunge tool. Inspect next 5 parts. If mean falls outside control limits, call supervisor.

Figure 29.4 Another control plan format.

- Personnel turnover
- Defined period reviews

To reiterate, control plans hold the gains achieved from process improvement activities. A weak or inadequate control plan is a key failure mode for DMAIC projects. To this point, organizations with existing process or quality audit functions may want to consider adding control plans to their list of audit items.

Chapter 30

Sustain Improvements

Quality is not an act; it is a habit.

—Aristotle

LESSONS LEARNED

> Document the lessons learned and benefits realized from all phases of a project and identify strategies for reinforcing and replicating improvements. (Apply)
>
> **Body of Knowledge VIII.D.1**

Many organizations find that they solve the same problems more than once. This is often because of poor documentation, poor communication, internal employee churn, or external attrition. Moreover, the organization's memory may exist only in the minds of employees. When a problem recurs or occurs in a slightly different form, it is often solved again, particularly if the people who worked on it before are not involved. This problem is only exacerbated by organizational downsizing, whereby the bottom line may receive some short-term benefit, but the organization has been crippled due to a significant loss of its intellectual capital and organizational memory.

The recognition of the need to maintain an organization's memory has given rise to the concept of *knowledge management*. While the definition of knowledge management remains vague, it can be characterized by its requirements to identify an organization's knowledge base and intellectual capital, maintain this information, and distribute it, make it accessible, or otherwise communicate it to those in the organization who have the need to use it.

Current technologies allow organizations to maintain and distribute information rather easily. The difficulty lies in capturing it. With respect to Six Sigma, the opportunity to capture project information and related lessons learned can easily be embedded into the control phase of the methodology. Organizations can readily establish the requirement that no project can be closed out without first capturing relevant project information and lessons learned in some permanent repository. Once captured, project information can be searched and compared against future project opportunities such that decisions can be made to charter a project, replicate a past success, or even kick-start new or innovative thinking on an existing project.

The organization must recognize that projects generate knowledge, and that knowledge represents a critical resource for future projects. One approach to documentation of knowledge generated by a project is to specify a standard format for each project's final report. A suggested final report form is shown in Figure 30.1. These final reports should then be put in a searchable format for use by future project teams.

Having this information in a searchable format also provides the opportunity for future cross-project study and analysis, which could have implications for training, resource management, and project selection.

Project ID ________ **Final Report** Date ________
Six Sigma Project

Problem statement: ______________________________

____

Team members: ______________________________

____

Department/division: ______________________________

Process: ______________________________

Key steps toward problem solution: ______________________________

____

Analysis tools that were most useful: ______________________________

____

____

____

Corrective action implemented: ______________________________

____

Updates made to SOP: ______________________________

____

Updates made to work instructions: ______________________________

____

Updates made to control plan: ______________________________

____

Figure 30.1 Possible format for final report.

DOCUMENTATION

> Develop or modify documents including standard operating procedures (SOPs), work instructions, and control plans to ensure that the improvements are sustained over time. (Apply)
>
> Body of Knowledge VIII.D.2

A Six Sigma project often requires changes in processes and the way they are controlled. If these changes are not reflected in the appropriate documents, they will most likely not be sustained. When this happens, the gains achieved by the project are lost. This, unfortunately, is a common occurrence. Therefore, the format for a Six Sigma final report should include these updates, as shown in Figure 30.1.

Many organizations have found that documented standard operating procedures (SOPs) and work instructions (known in the lean manufacturing literature as "standard work") help reduce process variation. The purpose of these documents is to make certain that the activity is performed the same way over time. This is especially important when multi-skilled, cross-trained personnel move into a variety of positions.

The development and updating of these documents must involve the people who perform the work. The documentation process is begun by listing the major steps. Succeeding iterations examine the steps from the previous one and break them into smaller sub-steps. This process can continue until further deconstruction is not useful. Two main considerations include the following:

1. *Documents must be kept current.* In an era of continuous improvement, processes may be continuously changing. As a result, it is possible that different documentation releases for the same documentation may be in use simultaneously. Therefore, it is vital that employees always have access to the appropriate documentation based on the effective date of the change. It is easy to see how the complexity of managing such a documentation system can grow exponentially. With today's web-based and other technologies, documentation configuration management systems can be designed and developed to ensure that the proper documentation is available for the right process on the right part at the right time.

2. *Multiple documentation formats exist.* The right choice depends on how the documentation is to be used, by whom, and at what skill level. However, documentation best practices suggest developing documents that are color-coded; rely heavily on graphics, illustrations, and photographs; and are light on words. Photographs of acceptable and unacceptable products and procedures have been found to be especially useful. Some organizations have had success with the use of video for depicting

complex operations. As always, the level of detail provided in any set of documentation should reflect the skills and education levels of the personnel doing the actual work and the degree to which variation must be controlled. Robust processes usually require less-detailed documentation than non-robust processes.

The best and most up-to-date SOPs, work instructions, and control plans will not be impactful if they are not followed. A considerable training effort is often required, as discussed in the next section of this chapter.

TRAINING FOR PROCESS OWNERS AND STAFF

> Develop and implement training plans that are handed off to process owners to ensure consistent execution of revised process methods, KPIs to confirm sustained benefits, and standards to maintain process improvements. (Apply)
>
> Body of Knowledge VIII.D.3

A critical element for ensuring that the gains of an improved process are maintained is the training of the personnel responsible for executing the process. Training is often overlooked or viewed as an unnecessary cost or imposition on the time of already overworked employees. Training comes in two main forms:

1. *Initial.* This type is used for existing employees who have been responsible for executing the old process and will continue to be responsible for executing the new process. It also addresses the needs of employees who are new to the process. Furthermore, it may be conducted off the job or on the job, or both. The correct combination depends on the skill levels required, process complexity, and experience levels, among other factors. Initial training serves to calibrate employees and minimize variation in how the process is performed. If possible, the "starting tomorrow we're doing it this way" approach should be avoided. Instead, the rationale and methods for the change should be explained, preferably by the people closest to the process.

2. *Recurring.* This type is used to minimize deterioration in process performance over time. Deterioration usually occurs as employees become comfortable with the new process and fail to recognize minor changes or tweaks to the process either through carelessness, poor documentation, or even a system that permits obsolete documentation to remain in the process stream. In addition, on-the-job training is another factor that often adversely impacts process performance. On-the-job training can work in a manner like the children's game of "telephone" that permits the description, interpretation, and understanding of

an initial whispered message to transform itself into something entirely different after it has passed through a series of children trying to communicate the original message. Specific facts, details, and nuances are frequently left out as they pass from worker to worker. Recurring training restores process execution to its original design. The frequency of recurring training should be determined based on process metrics and employee performance. Such training may be offered at specified intervals or conducted as required to serve the needs of underperforming employees.

When developing process-related training plans, important considerations include:

- Providing employees with minimum skills and information needed to perform the functions required by the position. This goes beyond "how to turn on the screw gun." It includes how to read and interpret documentation and safety precautions, how to supply required data, and other skills as needed.
- Providing employees with additional skills and information that will ensure a broader view of what the position accomplishes for the enterprise. If the position entails installing 200 bimetallic oven controls each day, the employee should know how a bimetallic control works, which metals can be used, and some history regarding earlier models.
- Providing employees with cross-training for additional functions. This often involves training employees on the processes immediately before and after the process for which they are responsible.

Other, larger training plan considerations beyond the immediate process include:

- Providing opportunities for employees for further education outside the enterprise on topics not related to the current organization needs. This is done under the assumption that exposure to ideas outside the box is valuable.
- Providing incentives and requirements that motivate employees to continue to seek education and training opportunities.
- Providing experiences for employees that demonstrate the need the organization has for their ideas for continuous improvement.
- Providing opportunities for employees to help formulate a customized annual training plan. Such a plan should be routinely maintained, be supported by readily accessible records, and monitor progress toward plan completion.

The training plan should also convey the elements of the control plan, to include a list of key performance indicators (KPIs) to be tracked and standards to be adopted to maintain process improvement.

The KPIs wills be tracked to assure that the process improvements are sustained. These KPIs should be defined, and their connection to the process performance made clear. A plan then should be communicated to the employees listing how the KPI data will be collected, by whom and how often, and how the data will be used to assure sustainability of the improvements.

These considerations should help employees make positive contributions toward the ability of the organization to sustain process improvements over the long term.

ONGOING EVALUATION

> Identify and apply tools (e.g., control charts, control plans) for ongoing evaluation of the improved process, including monitoring leading indicators, lagging indicators, and additional opportunities for improvement. (Apply)
>
> **Body of Knowledge VIII.D.4**

Once a process has been improved, it must be monitored to ensure that the gains are maintained and to determine when additional improvements are required. The control plan, as discussed in Chapter 29, is the key tool for maintaining the gains achieved by the project. It typically specifies the use of these tools:

- *Control charts.* These are used to monitor the stability of the process, determine when a special cause is present, and decide when to take appropriate action. The choice of a particular control chart depends on the nature of the process. When out-of-control conditions occur, action is required to restore stability. Control charts represent the voice of the process.
- *Process capability studies.* These studies provide the opportunity to understand how the voice of the process (that is, control limits) compares with the voice of the customer (that is, specifications) and help determine whether the process average must be shifted or re-centered or the variation reduced.
- *Process metrics.* This includes a wide variety of in-process and end-of-process metrics that measure the overall efficiency and effectiveness of the process. Examples include cycle times, takt time, drop off rate, work-in-progress, backlog, defect rates, rework rates, and scrap rates.
- *Gage repeatability and reproducibility (GR&R) studies.* These studies monitor the measurement systems used by the process.

There is a need for a periodic formal review of completed projects to determine whether further improvements are appropriate. In fact, these measures should be incorporated into the broader management operating system to ensure that the successes and improvements sustain. Criteria that are useful in making this determination include the following:

- Leading indicators
  - Have the customer requirements changed?
  - Will they pay a higher price for an improved product?
  - Are there other customers that could be served if we had an improved product?
  - Are there changes in the regulatory environment that require process improvements?
  - Are there changes in the marketplace that require process improvements?
  - Has the market for the product reached maturity, indicating level or tapering demand?
- Lagging indicators
  - Have low-priced competitors taken market share?
  - Do data collected via the control plan indicate that process improvement would be easily achievable?
  - Has demand for the product decreased?
  - Have warranty claims decreased?
- Other indicators
  - Is the product still in alignment with enterprise goals?
  - Are new technologies/materials/processes available that might simplify improvement?

Taken collectively, these tools and methods help us gauge the overall health of a process and provide triggers for reevaluating a process for further improvement.

REPLICATION

As projects come to a close, organizations should consider the implications of the discovered root cause(s) and the application of the solution(s) to other adjacent processes. Often the projects will identify a set of new best practices that are easy to replicate elsewhere in the organization. And this is a way to leverage tight resources to really make an impact.

Part IX

Design for Six Sigma (DFSS) Framework and Methodologies

Chapter 31

Common DFSS Methodologies

Design is not just what it looks like and feels like. Design is how it works.

–Steve Jobs

> Identify and describe DMADV (define, measure, analyze, design, and validate) and DMADOV (define, measure, analyze, design, optimize, and validate). (Understand)
>
> **Body of Knowledge IX.A**

While DMAIC may be traditionally viewed as the foundation for Lean Six Sigma, its application is primarily limited to improving existing processes; it does little to address the design of new products or processes.

Fortunately, other structured methodologies exist. Each of these methodologies has its usefulness as long as the nuances of each are fully understood. The Design for Six Sigma concept was originally developed at General Electric in the late 1990s. We will cover DMADV and DMADOV, as well as DCOV, in this chapter.

DMADV

DMADV is a well-recognized DFSS methodology and an acronym for *define-measure-analyze-design-verify*. Note that the ASQ Black Belt Body of Knowledge replaces "verify" with "validate." We will explore the difference between these terms later in this section. The DMADV methodology is illustrated in Figure 31.1.

The five phases of DMADV are:

- *Define.* Unlike the Define phase in DMAIC in which we define the problem, in this Define phase, we determine the market or customer requirements of the new product or service. The project goals are set here and documented in a project charter.
- *Measure.* In the Measure phase, the Voice of the Customer (VOC) is captured. One value Lean Six Sigma technique that supports the Measure phase of the design process is quality function deployment (QFD), the details of which are presented in Chapter 10.

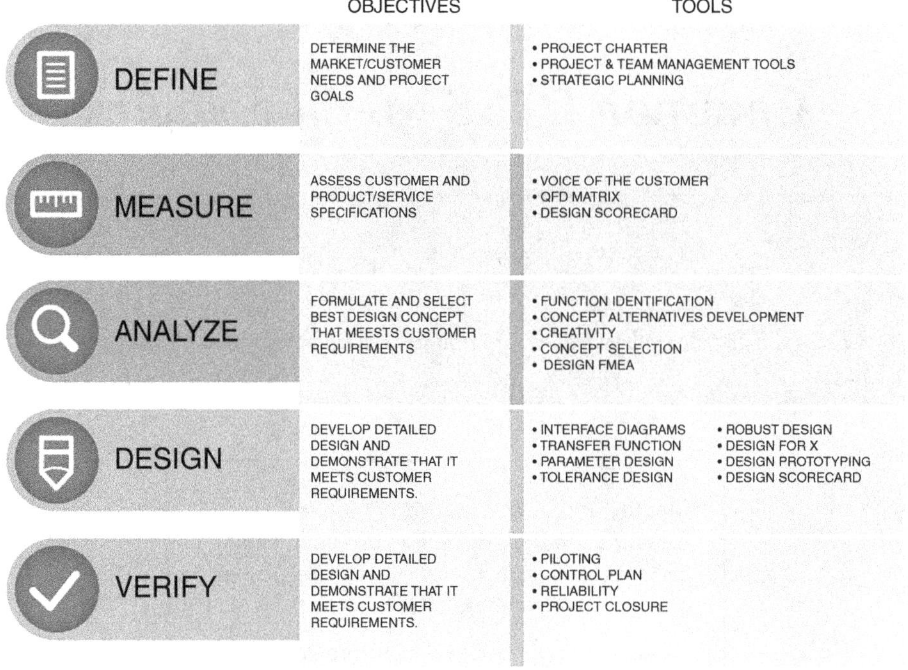

OBJECTIVES
TOOLS
DEFINE
DETERMINE THE MARKET/CUSTOMER NEEDS AND PROJECT GOALS
• PROJECT CHARTER
• PROJECT & TEAM MANAGEMENT TOOLS
• STRATEGIC PLANNING
MEASURE
ASSESS CUSTOMER AND PRODUCT/SERVICE SPECIFICATIONS
• VOICE OF THE CUSTOMER
• QFD MATRIX
• DESIGN SCORECARD
ANALYZE
FORMULATE AND SELECT BEST DESIGN CONCEPT THAT MEESTS CUSTOMER REQUIREMENTS
• FUNCTION IDENTIFICATION
• CONCEPT ALTERNATIVES DEVELOPMENT
• CREATIVITY
• CONCEPT SELECTION
• DESIGN FMEA
DESIGN
DEVELOP DETAILED DESIGN AND DEMONSTRATE THAT IT MEETS CUSTOMER REQUIREMENTS.
• INTERFACE DIAGRAMS
• TRANSFER FUNCTION
• PARAMETER DESIGN
• TOLERANCE DESIGN
• ROBUST DESIGN
• DESIGN FOR X
• DESIGN PROTOTYPING
• DESIGN SCORECARD
VERIFY
DEVELOP DETAILED DESIGN AND DEMONSTRATE THAT IT MEETS CUSTOMER REQUIREMENTS.
• PILOTING
• CONTROL PLAN
• RELIABILITY
• PROJECT CLOSURE

Figure 31.1 The DMADV methodology.

- *Analyze*. This phase is Used to formulate and select the best design concept that meets customer requirements.
- *Design*. Quite simply, this means carrying out the process of designing a product or process. Many organizations have well-established policies and procedures for their respective design processes. Tools useful in this phase include pilot runs, simulations, prototypes, and models.
- *Verify*. This phase is directed at ensuring that the design output meets the customer requirements and design specifications and is performed on the final product or process.

The term "verification" means ensuring the design meets customer requirements and that it yields the correct product or process. By contrast, the term "validation" speaks to the effectiveness of the design process itself and is intended to ensure that the output is capable of meeting the requirements of the final product or process.

Both verification and validation are necessary functions in any design process.

DMADOV

The basic difference between DMADV and DMADOV is that "O" for "optimize" has been added. This may sound like a trivial observation, but many organizations' design processes do not include this refinement action. They are intended solely to produce a minimally workable product or process. DMADOV forces attention on the need to optimize the design. Additional tools useful in this phase include design of experiments, *response surface methodology* (RSM), and *evolutionary operations* (EVOP). These methods help the design team establish and refine design parameters.

DCOV

Unlike most of the other DFSS methodologies, DCOV contains only four phases that stand for Design, Characterize, Optimize, Verify/Validate:

- *Design.* In this phase, we aim to understand the customer and identify Critical to Satisfaction drivers (CTS's) and related functional targets.
- *Characterize.* This phase is often completed using a two-step approach. First is system design in which the Critical to Satisfaction drivers are further broken down to specific outcomes (Y's), and to characterize the robustness opportunities of each Y. The second step involves functional mapping, which relates the Critical to Satisfaction drivers to Critical to Quality (CTQ) design parameters (X's) and to develop a strategy to deliver the robustness.
- *Optimize Product/Process.* This step is often performed in two stages. First, we concentrate on the product, designing for robust performance by minimizing product sensitivity to manufacturing and usage conditions. Second, we design the process for producibility by minimizing process sensitivity to product and manufacturing variation.
- *Verify/Validate.* Finally, we assess performance by running tests and conducting pilots. We can estimate process capability and product function over time by conducting pilots, and then we can verify by assessing actual performance and robustness over time.

DCOV has an increased focus on achieving customer satisfaction by improving the robustness of a product or process.

Chapter 32
Design for X (DFX)

Great design will not sell an inferior product, but it will enable a great product to achieve its maximum potential.

—Thomas Watson, Jr.

> Describe design constraints, including design for cost, design for manufacturability (producibility), design for test, and design for maintainability. (Understand)
>
> Body of Knowledge IX.B

Traditionally, the design process was conducted almost in isolation, without regard to the downstream functions that might be impacted by that design. Once the design was complete, it was handed off to manufacturing, production, or the assembly function, whose job was to translate the design from concept into reality. Unfortunately, many design functions failed to address the capability of these downstream organizations. This frequently resulted in escalating production costs and numerous engineering change orders that created a significant divergence between the "as designed" and the "as built" configurations. According to Ullman (2017), 75% of manufacturing cost is committed to by the end of the conceptual process. Decisions made after this time can influence only 25% of the manufacturing cost.

With the development of the design-by-team approach known as *concurrent engineering* or *simultaneous engineering*, for the first time, stakeholders in the design function had a voice in how a product or process was designed. With fully cross-functional design teams in place, organizations could begin improving the efficiency and effectiveness of designs to benefit both the organization and the customer.

The concept behind *design for X* (DFX), where *X* is a variable such as cost, manufacturability, producibility, testability, maintainability, and so forth, is simply that "X" becomes the focus of or constraint to the design process. Let's look at some of the more familiar "X's."

DESIGN FOR COST

The need for design for cost (DFC) usually arises when an organization establishes a fixed design budget to become more fiscally responsible, or perhaps a major customer has dictated what it is willing to spend. As a result, the design focus is shifted from "what works" to "what works within budget." The disciplines of value engineering and value analysis are keystones under a DFC scenario. This section will consider cost analysis from two viewpoints: *purchase cost* and *life cycle costs.*

Purchase Cost

In the first months after a new product is introduced, its unique features or technology may determine customers' purchase decisions. However, as a product matures, competing products tend to match technology and features. At that point cost becomes more of a determining factor in customers' decisions. Common cost-reduction efforts focus on labor and processes but often ignore cost-reduction potential related to the design cycle. Once a product and the processes that will be used to produce it have been determined, the cost has been largely determined. Trying to make major cost reductions after that point is often futile. Therefore,

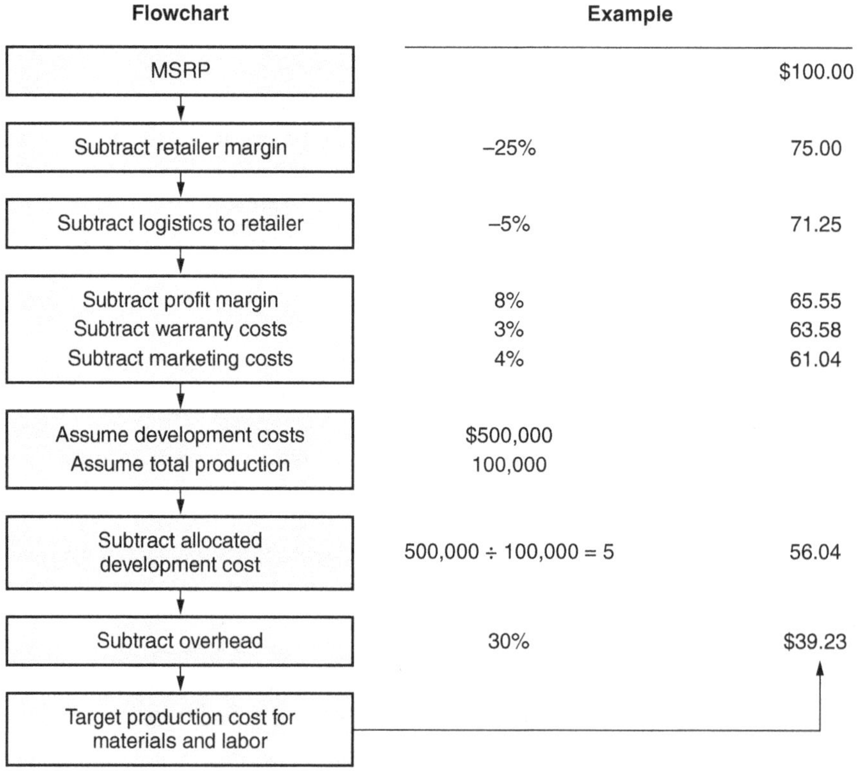

Figure 32.1 Flowchart for arriving at target cost.

significant cost reductions must start in the design stage. Figure 32.1 shows a procedure for arriving at a target production cost. Design for cost considerations during the design stage include:

1. Knowledge of the market and what customers want
2. Recognition of the trade-off between features and costs
3. Exploration of design alternatives that lower costs

Life Cycle Cost (LCC)

If the product will be used over a considerable period of time, the customer may look beyond the purchase price. Additional costs to be considered include:

- Shipping
- Other capital costs (structural changes, wiring, plumbing, and so on)
- Training costs
- Support costs (utilities, software, and so on)
- Disposal costs
- Reclamation value

Figure 32.2 illustrates how these considerations help when comparing competing products such as two machine tools, two diagnostic imaging machines, or two point-of-sale systems. In the example, time value of money is not considered.

		Option A	Option B
Acquisition costs (Purchase + Logistics)	$	1,000,000	1,000,000
Other capital costs (structural and utility changes)		+20,000	+15,000
Training costs (10 years / Operators + Maintenance)		+20,000	+10,000
Support costs (utilities, spare parts, software updates)		+5,000	+4,000
Disposal cost		0	0
Reclamation value		–100,000	–80,000
Total cost	**$**	**945,000**	**949,000**

Figure 32.2 Life cycle cost (LCC) example.

DESIGN FOR MANUFACTURING/DESIGN FOR PRODUCIBILITY/DESIGN FOR ASSEMBLY

These techniques aim to reduce material, overhead, and labor costs. Design for Manufacturing (DFM), also known as Design for Producibility, is concerned with reducing overall part-production costs and minimizing the complexity of manufacturing operations. Design for Assembly (DFA) is concerned with reducing product assembly cost and minimizing the number of assembly operations.

Key principles of DFM and DFA include:

- Reducing total number of parts
- Using modular assemblies
- Standardizing components
- Using multifunctional parts
- Minimizing handling
- Minimizing fasteners
- Using self-locating features
- Designing for ease of fabrication
- Minimizing process steps.

The design team must recognize that limitations might exist with respect to manufacturing, producing, or assembling a product. Common examples include designs calling for:

- Equipment not currently available.
- Methods unfamiliar to the manufacturing or assembly workforce. An example might be requiring an automated method of soldering when the assembly workforce is skilled only in manual soldering.
- Expensive fixtures.
- Specialized tooling.
- Workplace redesign.
- Operators/assembly workers to use asymmetrical motions.
- Limited accessibility.
- Obsolete or hard-to-find parts.
- Use of exotic material when unnecessary.
- Special manufacturing, operator, or assembly worker skills.
- Tolerances beyond that which can be achieved given the available equipment or processes.

DESIGN FOR TEST

The consideration given during the design stage to improve the testing of a product is called *design for test* (DFT) or *design for testability*.

Testing may be an integral part of ensuring quality, or it may be demanded by the customer. In such cases designs must accommodate an assemble-test-assemble type of production assembly process rather than rely entirely on functional tests of the finished product. This "no fault forward" approach can greatly decrease detection/repair of faults in final inspection. Such considerations are common with complex electromechanical equipment, including avionics and mass-market consumer electronics products.

Historically, much of the DFT literature has referred to the testing of printed circuit boards. The goal is to design a board so that every function can be tested. It is important to verify that each circuit board can handle unusual input conditions without failing. To pose a simple example, how does the arithmetic section handle division by zero? It sometimes requires extra circuitry to allow input of the scenario being tested. So, the specifications for a board include the types of tests that the board needs to pass. The design team is responsible for designing the board to facilitate those tests. Software design teams have followed this example and designed software that permits testing for specified conditions. In some cases, this requires additional code to facilitate the testing protocol.

EXAMPLE 32.1

Suppose a truck manufacturer wishes to test the braking system on each truck before releasing it for shipment. The trucks have a redundant braking system with dual master cylinders. If the system controlled by one master cylinder fails, the other will stop the truck. When testing the braking system, however, the driver has no way of determining whether the redundancy functions correctly. To thoroughly test this feature, the braking system could be designed with additional equipment that permits disabling each master cylinder in turn (but not both at the same time!) so that the redundant function can be verified. The manufacturer might recommend that vehicle users perform this check as part of a regular preventive maintenance schedule.

Other branches of manufacturing could emulate the electronics industry. Why not design a port on a valve that would permit easy pressurization for leak tests? Why not include a simple thermocouple that would facilitate testing for heat transfer? The extra cost could be more than offset by the savings in the testing function, especially in situations where 100% testing is required.

DESIGN FOR MAINTAINABILITY/DESIGN FOR SERVICE

Customer loyalty depends on long-term satisfaction. For many products, this means that the ability to perform routine maintenance and service for products must be considered during the design process. Cars that require a floor jack to remove spark plugs or a contortionist to replace a shock absorber do not inspire customer confidence in other aspects of the product. Industrial products that require minimal downtime for repair can be of paramount interest, particularly when the customer is concerned with managing the overall availability and life cycle costs of a product or process.

Some guidelines to improve maintainability are as follows:

- Use standard parts and fasteners.
- Don't require special tools to perform maintenance.
- Design self-diagnosis and/or automated testing.
- Routine maintenance should be at easily accessible points.
- Minimize time to repair.
- Design safety into the product and modules rather than depending on warning labels.
- Permit visual inspection.

Accessibility and safety for all maintenance procedures helps reduce costs and increases availability for the user. Some firms have successfully employed 3D virtual reality systems to test the degree of difficulty for various maintenance operations. This permits design modifications prior to the construction of the first model.

Customers of complex systems may list *maintainability metrics* as part of the specifications for a product. For example, a specification might state, "Hydraulics system must be replaceable in 20 minutes."

Chapter 33

Robust Designs

The signal is the truth. The noise is what distracts us from the truth.

—Nate Silver

> Describe the elements of robust product design, tolerance design, and statistical tolerancing. (Apply)
>
> **Body of Knowledge IX.C**

ROBUST PRODUCT DESIGN

Robust design results in products that perform well in the face of increased variation. A robust design will result in a product that is able to accommodate increased variation in process input while still producing the required output within defined specifications. For example, the impedance of a supplier's resistors is known to follow a normal distribution with a rather large variance. The design should be capable of accepting parts with such variation and still produce a tight output distribution.

In addition to being robust to variation in the inputs, a design needs to function when the operating environment varies. For example, some washing machines will be installed in garages, others in boiler rooms. Some products must function in salt air. Some operators will use liquid detergent, others will use powder. The design team needs to establish criteria in a host of areas as it moves through the design cycle. Product designs may need to consider variation in conditions of storage, transportation, and installation, as well as operating conditions.

Robust product design assumes uncertainty in the inputs, environment, operating conditions, and other variables. A robust design is able to function when these uncertainties stay within a stated range. For example, many automobile engines can function when the alcohol content of the fuel varies between 0% and 15%. The alcohol content for flex-fuel vehicles can range from 0% to 85%. These vehicles are robust to a wider range of variation in the alcohol content. If a vehicle engine functions in an ambient temperature ranging from –30°F to 120°F, that vehicle is robust to ambient temperature variation in that range. If the vehicle door latch functions with a slight nudge and also with a strong slam, the latch is robust to a range in operator temperament. As discussed in the next section, it is necessary to define the word "function" in each situation.

FUNCTIONAL REQUIREMENTS

The concepts of functional requirements are perhaps best understood with an example. A producer of black rubber provides door and window seals for the automotive industry. For many years, the automobile designers have specified the hardness, toughness, and elasticity of the material, the geometry of the cross section, and other specifications. As might be expected, the rubber company has struggled to meet the specifications of its customers.

More recently, the designers have been specifying such things as "will not leak under a 20 mile per hour wind and two inches of rain per hour for two hours." Such a statement is known as a *functional requirement*. It defines how the product is to perform and under what conditions. Many companies have decided that their suppliers know more about the products they supply than they do and are probably in a better position to design a product that can be manufactured efficiently.

The use of functional requirements is sometimes referred to as "black box" engineering because the customer says, in essence, "I am not going to specify the design details; here's how I want it to function." Of course, the customer typically puts some constraints on the design, perhaps providing the space available, the relationship to other components, and so on. When specifications include functional and nonfunctional requirements, it is referred to as a "gray box" design.

NOISE STRATEGIES

Noise factors were introduced in Chapter 24. Figure 33.1 illustrates a response curve with three acceptable values for the input variable P. Regardless of the value of P chosen, a certain amount of variation or noise can be expected. This noise in the input variable is represented by the normal curves sketched on the horizontal axis. Figure 32.2 illustrates the impact on the output variable Q when $P = P_1$. Figure 33.3 shows the impact of noise at each of the three values of P. It is clear that the amount of variation in Q depends on the location of P. In fact, the location of P that minimizes "transmitted noise" is the area where the response curve is flattest—P_2 in this example.

The noise strategy, then, is to conduct a designed experiment or set of experiments, as shown in Chapter 24, and when nonlinear response curves are found, locate the flattest part of the curve, as there will be a point along this section that will minimize transmitted noise.

TOLERANCE DESIGN

Tolerance design uses the concept of transmitted noise to help determine product tolerance. For example, suppose a fabricator who uses steel to produce parts finds that the hardness of the steel impacts a quality characteristic of a formed part. As a result, a hardness tolerance is applied to the steel. What should the tolerance be? The amount of acceptable variation in the quality characteristic due to hardness is reflected back through the response curve to determine the amount of acceptable

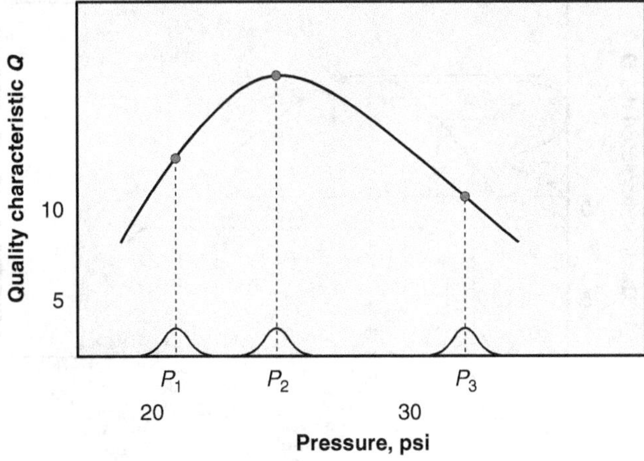

Figure 33.1 Nonlinear response curve with input noise.

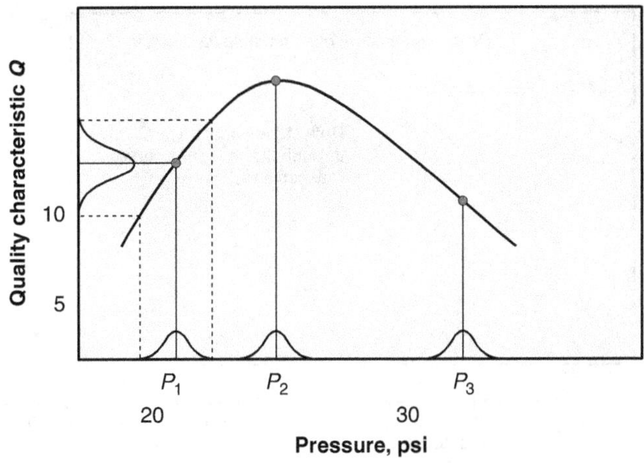

Figure 33.2 Nonlinear response curve showing the impact on Q of input noise at P_1.

variation in hardness as shown in Figure 33.4. If a designed experiment determines that it is possible to operate at a relatively flat spot on the response curve relating hardness to the quality characteristic, the hardness tolerance can be looser than it would otherwise have to be. Therefore, tolerance design is considered a cost-saving technique since loosening tolerances on a specification often reduces costs.

TOLERANCING METHODS

In this section, we will address two methods for determining tolerance:

- Conventional tolerances
- Statistical tolerances

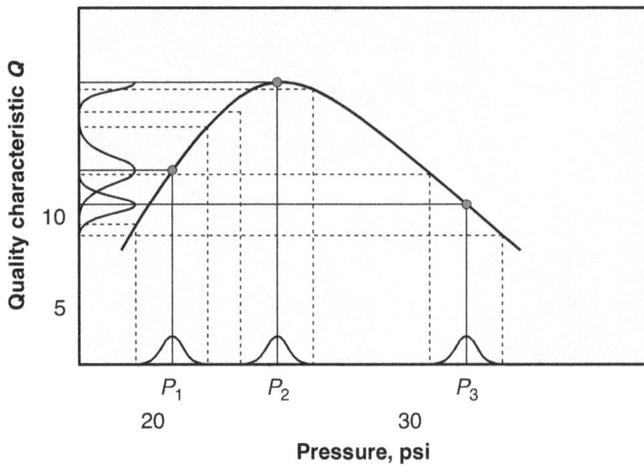

Figure 33.3 Nonlinear response curve showing the impact on Q of input noise at P_1, P_2, and P_3.

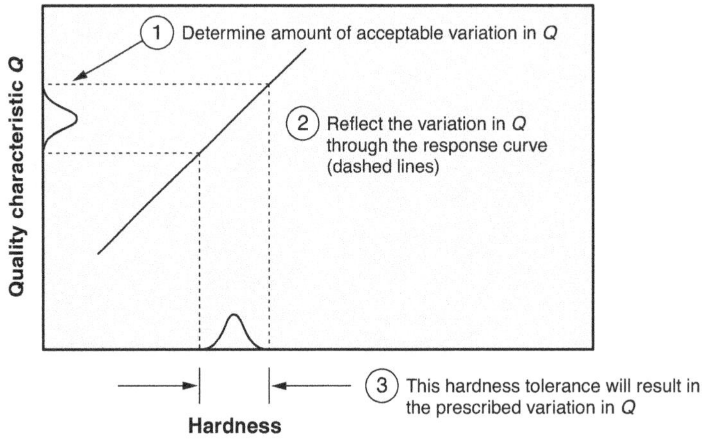

Figure 33.4 Using a response curve to determine tolerance.

Conventional Tolerances

The conventional or traditional way to determine tolerance involves a situation in which several parts are stacked together, as shown in Figure 33.5. Here, Part A has a nominal or target dimension of 1.223 with tolerance ± 0.003, resulting in a lower specification limit of 1.220 and an upper specification limit of 1.226. Likewise, Part B has specifications equal to 0.5025 ± 0.0025, and Part C has specifications equal to 0.760 ± 0.005.

The overall specifications of the assembly can be derived using stack tolerance dimensioning. The nominal or target value of the assembly is the sum of the nominal values for each part:

$$\begin{aligned} \text{Nominal}_{Total} &= \text{Nominal}_A + \text{Nominal}_B + \text{Nominal}_C \\ &= 1.223 + 0.5025 + 0.760 \\ &= 2.4855 \end{aligned}$$

And the tolerance for the assembly is the sum of the tolerances of each part, which can be calculated as:

$$\begin{aligned} Tolerance_{Total} &= Tolerance_A + Tolerance_B + Tolerance_C \\ &= 0.003 + 0.0025 + 0.005 \\ &= 0.0105 \end{aligned}$$

This approach results in the assembly having a lower specification limit of (2.4855 – 0.0105) = 2.475 and an upper specification limit of (2.4855 + 0.0105) = 2.496. We could also have obtained these values from adding the lower specifications of each part (1.220 + 0.500 + 0.755) = 2.475; and the upper specifications of each part (1.226 + 0.505 + 0.765) = 2.496.

Statistical Tolerances

In statistical tolerancing, the nominal value is once again calculated as the sum of the nominal values for each part. The tolerances, however, are based on the standard deviation of the output of the parts. If the processes producing the lengths of Parts A, B, and C are capable and the outputs follow normal distributions, the tolerances on these parts can be directly related to the standard deviations.

If we recognize that the worst-case scenario occurs when the tolerance is exactly 6 standard deviations in width (that is, ±3 standard deviations), we can write out the relationship between the tolerance and the standard deviation for each part:

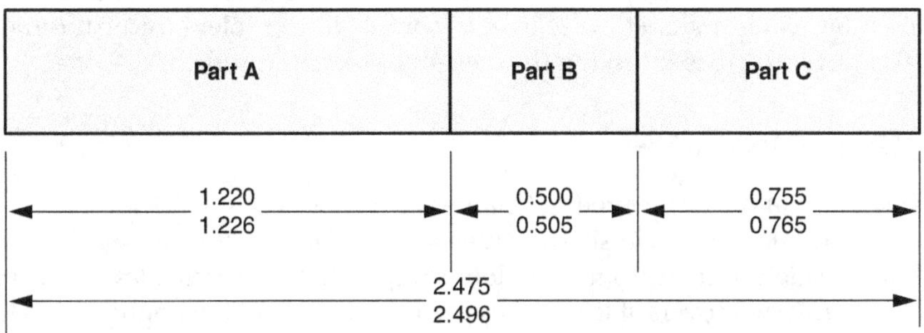

Figure 33.5 Conventional stack tolerance dimensioning.

$$Tolerance_A = 3\sigma_A = 0.003$$
$$Tolerance_B = 3\sigma_B = 0.0025$$
$$Tolerance_C = 3\sigma_C = 0.005$$

Unlike tolerances, however, standard deviations are not additive. To find the overall tolerance of the assembly using the standard deviations we must first sum the variance of each part and then take the square root as follows:

$$\begin{aligned} Tolerance_{Stack} &= \sqrt{3\sigma_A^2 + 3\sigma_B^2 + 3\sigma_C^2} \\ &= \sqrt{0.003^2 + 0.0025^2 + 0.005^2} \\ &= \sqrt{0.00004025} \\ &= 0.006344 \end{aligned}$$

Using the statistical tolerancing method, our overall tolerance is much less than the overall tolerance calculated using the conventional method (0.006344 versus 0.0105 for conventional). Given this outcome, we might want to set the statistical tolerances such that we still achieve the tolerance of the stack obtained using the conventional approach. If we assume, for the moment, that each of the statistical tolerances is equal, then our equation simplifies to:

$$\begin{aligned} Tolerance_{Stack} &= \sqrt{(Tolerance_A)^2 + (Tolerance_B)^2 + (Tolerance_C)^2} \\ &= \sqrt{3(Tolerance_{Part})^2} \end{aligned}$$

If we set the overall tolerance to be equal to the conventional tolerance of 0.0105, we can solve for the tolerance of each part:

$$\sqrt{3(Tolerance_{Part})^2} = 0.0105$$
$$Tolerance_{Part} = \frac{0.0105}{\sqrt{3}}$$
$$Tolerance_{Part} = 0.00606$$

Note that the tolerance of the part, 0.00606, is greater than any of the individual part tolerances (that is, 0.003, 0.0025, and 0.005) using the conventional approach. Thus, by using a statistical tolerance approach, the tolerance of the individual parts can be increased, giving the designer greater latitude.

TOLERANCE INTERVALS

This material is also covered in Chapter 21, BoK VI.B.4.

A *tolerance interval* (also known as a *statistical tolerance interval*) is an interval estimator determined from a random sample that provides a level of confidence that the interval covers at least a specified proportion of the population. The lower tolerance limit (LTL) and the upper tolerance limit (UTL) are given by Equation 33.1.

Equation 33.1 Lower and upper tolerance limits

$$LTL = \bar{X} - Ks$$
$$UTL = \bar{X} + Ks$$

where $\bar{X}$ is the sample mean, s is the sample standard deviation, and K is the tolerance factor table value based on the confidence level, the proportion of the population to be covered, and the sample size n. The tolerance factors for one-sided and two-sided intervals can be found in Appendices J.1 and J.2, respectively.

EXAMPLE 33.1

A 15-piece sample from a process has a mean equal to 10.821 and a standard deviation equal to 0.027. Find the tolerance interval so that there is 95% confidence that the interval will contain 99% of the population.

Here, $\bar{X} = 10.821$, $s = 0.027$, and $n = 15$. The confidence level is 0.95, and the proportion is 0.99. We find $K = 3.867$ based on the confidence level, proportion, and sample size from the two-sided tolerance factor table in Appendix J.2. Using Equation 33.1:

$$\begin{aligned} LTL &= \bar{X} - Ks \\ &= 10.821 - 3.867(0.027) \\ &= 10.7166 \end{aligned}$$

$$\begin{aligned} UTL &= \bar{X} + Ks \\ &= 10.821 + 3.867(0.027) \\ &= 10.9254 \end{aligned}$$

We are 95% confident that the interval (10.7166, 10.9254) will cover 99% of the population.

THE TAGUCHI LOSS FUNCTION

Conventionally, quality costs have been based on conformance to specifications, using scrap and rework costs. Therefore, tolerances become go/no-go limits, where any part meeting specifications is as good as any other part that does. Dr. Genichi Taguchi argued that parts near the nominal dimension have more value than others that are in specification but further away from the nominal value. Thus, the conventional way to interpret specification or tolerances assumes that all parts that meet the specification are good and all that do not are bad. In fact, all that meet the specification are usually considered equally good and all that do not are considered equally bad. This interpretation is shown by the loss curve in Figure 33.6, where LSL and USL refer to the lower and upper specification limits. This loss curve, shown as a heavy dashed line, is a step function with the vertical "riser" located at the specification limits and at a height equal to the scrap or rework cost. This is sometimes referred to as *goal post analysis* because a football kicked between goal posts is worth the same number of points, regardless of how close it is to the posts.

Taguchi maintained that any deviation from nominal makes the product less valuable. This loss increases as the dimension gets further from the nominal or "target" value. The loss that is incurred for dimensions that are in specification may not occur immediately because they will be sold to the customer at full price. Taguchi believed that the product would assemble and function in a less than perfect way, however, and therefore would be less valuable. The loss may appear in the form of a less useful product and therefore a less satisfied customer. Over time, these losses represent decrease in sales, market share, and so on.

The exact shape of the loss function varies with product and within a product. Taguchi adapted a second-degree function as a generic approximation. This loss function is illustrated in Figure 33.7.

The heavy dashed curve is a second-degree curve, a parabola, of the form $y = (x - a)^2$. If a dimension is exactly at nominal, the part has zero loss. The more the dimension deviates from nominal, the greater the loss until it violates the specification limits, at which point the loss levels off at the scrap (or rework) cost.

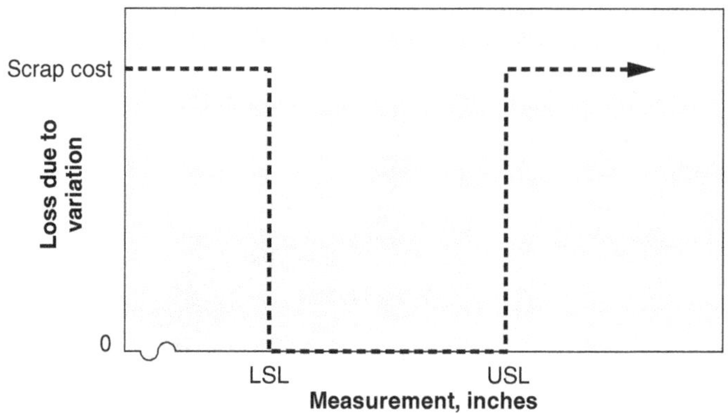

Figure 33.6 Conventional interpretation of loss.

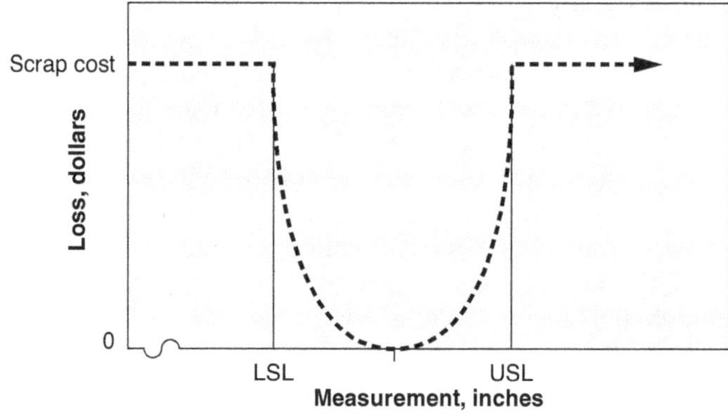

Figure 33.7 Taguchi loss function.

Part X

Appendices

Appendix A	ASQ Code of Ethics
Appendix B.1	Binomial Distribution Table
Appendix B.2	Cumulative Binomial Distribution Table
Appendix C.1	Poisson Distribution Table
Appendix C.2	Cumulative Poisson Distribution Table
Appendix D	Cumulative Standard Normal Distribution Table
Appendix E	Student's *t* Distribution Table
Appendix F	Chi-Square Distribution Table
Appendix G.1	*F*(0.01) Distribution Table
Appendix G.2	*F*(0.025) Distribution Table
Appendix G.3	*F*(0.05) Distribution Table
Appendix G.4	*F*(0.10) Distribution Table
Appendix G.5	*F*(0.90) Distribution Table
Appendix G.6	*F*(0.95) Distribution Table
Appendix G.7	*F*(0.975) Distribution Table
Appendix G.8	*F*(0.99) Distribution Table
Appendix H	Normal Scores Table
Appendix I	Equivalent Sigma Levels, Percent Defective, and ppm
Appendix J.1	Factors for One-Sided Tolerance Limits
Appendix J.2	Factors for Two-Sided Tolerance Limits
Appendix K.1	Control Limits for Variables Charts
Appendix K.2	Control Limits for Attributes Charts
Appendix K.3	Control Limits for Short-run Charts
Appendix K.4	Control Chart Constants

Appendix A
ASQ Code of Ethics

FUNDAMENTAL PRINCIPLES

ASQ requires its representatives to be honest and transparent. Avoid conflicts of interest and plagiarism. Do not harm others. Treat them with respect, dignity, and fairness. Be professional and socially responsible. Advance the role and perception of the Quality professional.

EXPECTATIONS OF A QUALITY PROFESSIONAL

1. **Act with Integrity and Honesty**
    1. Strive to uphold and advance the integrity, honor, and dignity of the Quality profession.
    2. Be truthful and transparent in all professional interactions and activities.
    3. Execute professional responsibilities and make decisions in an objective, factual, and fully informed manner.
    4. Accurately represent and do not mislead others regarding professional qualifications, including education, titles, affiliations, and certifications.
    5. Offer services, provide advice, and undertake assignments only in your areas of competence, expertise, and training.
2. **Demonstrate Responsibility, Respect, and Fairness**
    1. Hold paramount the safety, health, and welfare of individuals, the public, and the environment.
    2. Avoid conduct that unjustly harms or threatens the reputation of the Society, its members, or the Quality profession.
    3. Do not intentionally cause harm to others through words or deeds. Treat others fairly, courteously, with dignity, and without prejudice or discrimination.
    4. Act and conduct business in a professional and socially responsible manner.
    5. Allow diversity in the opinions and personal lives of others.

3. **Safeguard Proprietary Information and Avoid Conflicts of Interest**
    1. Ensure the protection and integrity of confidential information.
    2. Do not use confidential information for personal gain.
    3. Fully disclose and avoid any real or perceived conflicts of interest that could reasonably impair objectivity or independence in the service of clients, customers, employers, or the Society.
    4. Give credit where it is due.
    5. Do not plagiarize. Do not use the intellectual property of others without permission. Document the permission as it is obtained.

Appendix B.1

Binomial Distribution Table

$$\Pr(X = x) = f(n; x, p) = \binom{n}{k} p^k (1-p)^{n-k}$$

		Probability of *x* occurrences in a sample of size *n*																			
n	*x*	0.05	0.10	0.15	0.20	0.25	0.30	0.35	0.40	0.45	0.50	0.55	0.60	0.65	0.70	0.75	0.80	0.85	0.90	0.95	*n*	*x*
1	0	0.9500	0.9000	0.8500	0.8000	0.7500	0.7000	0.6500	0.6000	0.5500	0.5000	0.4500	0.4000	0.3500	0.3000	0.2500	0.2000	0.1500	0.1000	0.0500	1	0
	1	0.0500	0.1000	0.1500	0.2000	0.2500	0.3000	0.3500	0.4000	0.4500	0.5000	0.5500	0.6000	0.6500	0.7000	0.7500	0.8000	0.8500	0.9000	0.9500		1
2	0	0.9025	0.8100	0.7225	0.6400	0.5625	0.4900	0.4225	0.3600	0.3025	0.2500	0.2025	0.1600	0.1225	0.0900	0.0625	0.0400	0.0225	0.0100	0.0025	2	0
	1	0.0950	0.1800	0.2550	0.3200	0.3750	0.4200	0.4550	0.4800	0.4950	0.5000	0.4950	0.4800	0.4550	0.4200	0.3750	0.3200	0.2550	0.1800	0.0950		1
	2	0.0025	0.0100	0.0225	0.0400	0.0625	0.0900	0.1225	0.1600	0.2025	0.2500	0.3025	0.3600	0.4225	0.4900	0.5625	0.6400	0.7225	0.8100	0.9025		2
3	0	0.8574	0.7290	0.6141	0.5120	0.4219	0.3430	0.2746	0.2160	0.1664	0.1250	0.0911	0.0640	0.0429	0.0270	0.0156	0.0080	0.0034	0.0010	0.0001	3	0
	1	0.1354	0.2430	0.3251	0.3840	0.4219	0.4410	0.4436	0.4320	0.4084	0.3750	0.3341	0.2880	0.2389	0.1890	0.1406	0.0960	0.0574	0.0270	0.0071		1
	2	0.0071	0.0270	0.0574	0.0960	0.1406	0.1890	0.2389	0.2880	0.3341	0.3750	0.4084	0.4320	0.4436	0.4410	0.4219	0.3840	0.3251	0.2430	0.1354		2
	3	0.0001	0.0010	0.0034	0.0080	0.0156	0.0270	0.0429	0.0640	0.0911	0.1250	0.1664	0.2160	0.2746	0.3430	0.4219	0.5120	0.6141	0.7290	0.8574		3
4	0	0.8145	0.6561	0.5220	0.4096	0.3164	0.2401	0.1785	0.1296	0.0915	0.0625	0.0410	0.0256	0.0150	0.0081	0.0039	0.0016	0.0005	0.0001	0.0000	4	0
	1	0.1715	0.2916	0.3685	0.4096	0.4219	0.4116	0.3845	0.3456	0.2995	0.2500	0.2005	0.1536	0.1115	0.0756	0.0469	0.0256	0.0115	0.0036	0.0005		1
	2	0.0135	0.0486	0.0975	0.1536	0.2109	0.2646	0.3105	0.3456	0.3675	0.3750	0.3675	0.3456	0.3105	0.2646	0.2109	0.1536	0.0975	0.0486	0.0135		2
	3	0.0005	0.0036	0.0115	0.0256	0.0469	0.0756	0.1115	0.1536	0.2005	0.2500	0.2995	0.3456	0.3845	0.4116	0.4219	0.4096	0.3685	0.2916	0.1715		3
	4	0.0000	0.0001	0.0005	0.0016	0.0039	0.0081	0.0150	0.0256	0.0410	0.0625	0.0915	0.1296	0.1785	0.2401	0.3164	0.4096	0.5220	0.6561	0.8145		4
5	0	0.7738	0.5905	0.4437	0.3277	0.2373	0.1681	0.1160	0.0778	0.0503	0.0313	0.0185	0.0102	0.0053	0.0024	0.0010	0.0003	0.0001	0.0000	0.0000	5	0
	1	0.2036	0.3281	0.3915	0.4096	0.3955	0.3602	0.3124	0.2592	0.2059	0.1563	0.1128	0.0768	0.0488	0.0284	0.0146	0.0064	0.0022	0.0005	0.0000		1
	2	0.0214	0.0729	0.1382	0.2048	0.2637	0.3087	0.3364	0.3456	0.3369	0.3125	0.2757	0.2304	0.1811	0.1323	0.0879	0.0512	0.0244	0.0081	0.0011		2
	3	0.0011	0.0081	0.0244	0.0512	0.0879	0.1323	0.1811	0.2304	0.2757	0.3125	0.3369	0.3456	0.3364	0.3087	0.2637	0.2048	0.1382	0.0729	0.0214		3
	4	0.0000	0.0005	0.0022	0.0064	0.0146	0.0284	0.0488	0.0768	0.1128	0.1563	0.2059	0.2592	0.3124	0.3602	0.3955	0.4096	0.3915	0.3281	0.2036		4
	5	0.0000	0.0000	0.0001	0.0003	0.0010	0.0024	0.0053	0.0102	0.0185	0.0313	0.0503	0.0778	0.1160	0.1681	0.2373	0.3277	0.4437	0.5905	0.7738		5

$$\Pr(X = x) = f(n;x,p) = \binom{n}{k} p^k (1-p)^{n-k}$$

		Probability of *x* occurrences in a sample of size *n*																			
n	***x***	**0.05**	**0.10**	**0.15**	**0.20**	**0.25**	**0.30**	**0.35**	**0.40**	**0.45**	**0.50**	**0.55**	**0.60**	**0.65**	**0.70**	**0.75**	**0.80**	**0.85**	**0.90**	**0.95**	***n***	***x***
6	0	0.7351	0.5314	0.3771	0.2621	0.1780	0.1176	0.0754	0.0467	0.0277	0.0156	0.0083	0.0041	0.0018	0.0007	0.0002	0.0001	0.0000	0.0000	0.0000	6	0
	1	0.2321	0.3543	0.3993	0.3932	0.3560	0.3025	0.2437	0.1866	0.1359	0.0938	0.0609	0.0369	0.0205	0.0102	0.0044	0.0015	0.0004	0.0001	0.0000		1
	2	0.0305	0.0984	0.1762	0.2458	0.2966	0.3241	0.3280	0.3110	0.2780	0.2344	0.1861	0.1382	0.0951	0.0595	0.0330	0.0154	0.0055	0.0012	0.0001		2
	3	0.0021	0.0146	0.0415	0.0819	0.1318	0.1852	0.2355	0.2765	0.3032	0.3125	0.3032	0.2765	0.2355	0.1852	0.1318	0.0819	0.0415	0.0146	0.0021		3
	4	0.0001	0.0012	0.0055	0.0154	0.0330	0.0595	0.0951	0.1382	0.1861	0.2344	0.2780	0.3110	0.3280	0.3241	0.2966	0.2458	0.1762	0.0984	0.0305		4
	5	0.0000	0.0001	0.0004	0.0015	0.0044	0.0102	0.0205	0.0369	0.0609	0.0938	0.1359	0.1866	0.2437	0.3025	0.3560	0.3932	0.3993	0.3543	0.2321		5
	6	0.0000	0.0000	0.0000	0.0001	0.0002	0.0007	0.0018	0.0041	0.0083	0.0156	0.0277	0.0467	0.0754	0.1176	0.1780	0.2621	0.3771	0.5314	0.7351		6
7	0	0.6983	0.4783	0.3206	0.2097	0.1335	0.0824	0.0490	0.0280	0.0152	0.0078	0.0037	0.0016	0.0006	0.0002	0.0001	0.0000	0.0000	0.0000	0.0000	7	0
	1	0.2573	0.3720	0.3960	0.3670	0.3115	0.2471	0.1848	0.1306	0.0872	0.0547	0.0320	0.0172	0.0084	0.0036	0.0013	0.0004	0.0001	0.0000	0.0000		1
	2	0.0406	0.1240	0.2097	0.2753	0.3115	0.3177	0.2985	0.2613	0.2140	0.1641	0.1172	0.0774	0.0466	0.0250	0.0115	0.0043	0.0012	0.0002	0.0000		2
	3	0.0036	0.0230	0.0617	0.1147	0.1730	0.2269	0.2679	0.2903	0.2918	0.2734	0.2388	0.1935	0.1442	0.0972	0.0577	0.0287	0.0109	0.0026	0.0002		3
	4	0.0002	0.0026	0.0109	0.0287	0.0577	0.0972	0.1442	0.1935	0.2388	0.2734	0.2918	0.2903	0.2679	0.2269	0.1730	0.1147	0.0617	0.0230	0.0036		4
	5	0.0000	0.0002	0.0012	0.0043	0.0115	0.0250	0.0466	0.0774	0.1172	0.1641	0.2140	0.2613	0.2985	0.3177	0.3115	0.2753	0.2097	0.1240	0.0406		5
	6	0.0000	0.0000	0.0001	0.0004	0.0013	0.0036	0.0084	0.0172	0.0320	0.0547	0.0872	0.1306	0.1848	0.2471	0.3115	0.3670	0.3960	0.3720	0.2573		6
	7	0.0000	0.0000	0.0000	0.0000	0.0001	0.0002	0.0006	0.0016	0.0037	0.0078	0.0152	0.0280	0.0490	0.0824	0.1335	0.2097	0.3206	0.4783	0.6983		7
8	0	0.6634	0.4305	0.2725	0.1678	0.1001	0.0576	0.0319	0.0168	0.0084	0.0039	0.0017	0.0007	0.0002	0.0001	0.0000	0.0000	0.0000	0.0000	0.0000	8	0
	1	0.2793	0.3826	0.3847	0.3355	0.2670	0.1977	0.1373	0.0896	0.0548	0.0313	0.0164	0.0079	0.0033	0.0012	0.0004	0.0001	0.0000	0.0000	0.0000		1
	2	0.0515	0.1488	0.2376	0.2936	0.3115	0.2965	0.2587	0.2090	0.1569	0.1094	0.0703	0.0413	0.0217	0.0100	0.0038	0.0011	0.0002	0.0000	0.0000		2
	3	0.0054	0.0331	0.0839	0.1468	0.2076	0.2541	0.2786	0.2787	0.2568	0.2188	0.1719	0.1239	0.0808	0.0467	0.0231	0.0092	0.0026	0.0004	0.0000		3
	4	0.0004	0.0046	0.0185	0.0459	0.0865	0.1361	0.1875	0.2322	0.2627	0.2734	0.2627	0.2322	0.1875	0.1361	0.0865	0.0459	0.0185	0.0046	0.0004		4
	5	0.0000	0.0004	0.0026	0.0092	0.0231	0.0467	0.0808	0.1239	0.1719	0.2188	0.2568	0.2787	0.2786	0.2541	0.2076	0.1468	0.0839	0.0331	0.0054		5
	6	0.0000	0.0000	0.0002	0.0011	0.0038	0.0100	0.0217	0.0413	0.0703	0.1094	0.1569	0.2090	0.2587	0.2965	0.3115	0.2936	0.2376	0.1488	0.0515		6
	7	0.0000	0.0000	0.0000	0.0001	0.0004	0.0012	0.0033	0.0079	0.0164	0.0313	0.0548	0.0896	0.1373	0.1977	0.2670	0.3355	0.3847	0.3826	0.2793		7
	8	0.0000	0.0000	0.0000	0.0000	0.0000	0.0001	0.0002	0.0007	0.0017	0.0039	0.0084	0.0168	0.0319	0.0576	0.1001	0.1678	0.2725	0.4305	0.6634		8

$$\Pr(X = x) = f(n; x, p) = \binom{n}{k} p^k (1-p)^{n-k}$$

		Probability of *x* occurrences in a sample of size *n*																				
n	*x*	0.05	0.10	0.15	0.20	0.25	0.30	0.35	0.40	0.45	0.50	0.55	0.60	0.65	0.70	0.75	0.80	0.85	0.90	0.95	*n*	*x*
9	0	0.6302	0.3874	0.2316	0.1342	0.0751	0.0404	0.0207	0.0101	0.0046	0.0020	0.0008	0.0003	0.0001	0.0000	0.0000	0.0000	0.0000	0.0000	0.0000	9	0
	1	0.2985	0.3874	0.3679	0.3020	0.2253	0.1556	0.1004	0.0605	0.0339	0.0176	0.0083	0.0035	0.0013	0.0004	0.0001	0.0000	0.0000	0.0000	0.0000		1
	2	0.0629	0.1722	0.2597	0.3020	0.3003	0.2668	0.2162	0.1612	0.1110	0.0703	0.0407	0.0212	0.0098	0.0039	0.0012	0.0003	0.0000	0.0000	0.0000		2
	3	0.0077	0.0446	0.1069	0.1762	0.2336	0.2668	0.2716	0.2508	0.2119	0.1641	0.1160	0.0743	0.0424	0.0210	0.0087	0.0028	0.0006	0.0001	0.0000		3
	4	0.0006	0.0074	0.0283	0.0661	0.1168	0.1715	0.2194	0.2508	0.2600	0.2461	0.2128	0.1672	0.1181	0.0735	0.0389	0.0165	0.0050	0.0008	0.0000		4
	5	0.0000	0.0008	0.0050	0.0165	0.0389	0.0735	0.1181	0.1672	0.2128	0.2461	0.2600	0.2508	0.2194	0.1715	0.1168	0.0661	0.0283	0.0074	0.0006		5
	6	0.0000	0.0001	0.0006	0.0028	0.0087	0.0210	0.0424	0.0743	0.1160	0.1641	0.2119	0.2508	0.2716	0.2668	0.2336	0.1762	0.1069	0.0446	0.0077		6
	7	0.0000	0.0000	0.0000	0.0003	0.0012	0.0039	0.0098	0.0212	0.0407	0.0703	0.1110	0.1612	0.2162	0.2668	0.3003	0.3020	0.2597	0.1722	0.0629		7
	8	0.0000	0.0000	0.0000	0.0000	0.0001	0.0004	0.0013	0.0035	0.0083	0.0176	0.0339	0.0605	0.1004	0.1556	0.2253	0.3020	0.3679	0.3874	0.2985		8
	9	0.0000	0.0000	0.0000	0.0000	0.0000	0.0000	0.0001	0.0003	0.0008	0.0020	0.0046	0.0101	0.0207	0.0404	0.0751	0.1342	0.2316	0.3874	0.6302		9
10	0	0.5987	0.3487	0.1969	0.1074	0.0563	0.0282	0.0135	0.0060	0.0025	0.0010	0.0003	0.0001	0.0000	0.0000	0.0000	0.0000	0.0000	0.0000	0.0000	10	0
	1	0.3151	0.3874	0.3474	0.2684	0.1877	0.1211	0.0725	0.0403	0.0207	0.0098	0.0042	0.0016	0.0005	0.0001	0.0000	0.0000	0.0000	0.0000	0.0000		1
	2	0.0746	0.1937	0.2759	0.3020	0.2816	0.2335	0.1757	0.1209	0.0763	0.0439	0.0229	0.0106	0.0043	0.0014	0.0004	0.0001	0.0000	0.0000	0.0000		2
	3	0.0105	0.0574	0.1298	0.2013	0.2503	0.2668	0.2522	0.2150	0.1665	0.1172	0.0746	0.0425	0.0212	0.0090	0.0031	0.0008	0.0001	0.0000	0.0000		3
	4	0.0010	0.0112	0.0401	0.0881	0.1460	0.2001	0.2377	0.2508	0.2384	0.2051	0.1596	0.1115	0.0689	0.0368	0.0162	0.0055	0.0012	0.0001	0.0000		4
	5	0.0001	0.0015	0.0085	0.0264	0.0584	0.1029	0.1536	0.2007	0.2340	0.2461	0.2340	0.2007	0.1536	0.1029	0.0584	0.0264	0.0085	0.0015	0.0001		5
	6	0.0000	0.0001	0.0012	0.0055	0.0162	0.0368	0.0689	0.1115	0.1596	0.2051	0.2384	0.2508	0.2377	0.2001	0.1460	0.0881	0.0401	0.0112	0.0010		6
	7	0.0000	0.0000	0.0001	0.0008	0.0031	0.0090	0.0212	0.0425	0.0746	0.1172	0.1665	0.2150	0.2522	0.2668	0.2503	0.2013	0.1298	0.0574	0.0105		7
	8	0.0000	0.0000	0.0000	0.0001	0.0004	0.0014	0.0043	0.0106	0.0229	0.0439	0.0763	0.1209	0.1757	0.2335	0.2816	0.3020	0.2759	0.1937	0.0746		8
	9	0.0000	0.0000	0.0000	0.0000	0.0000	0.0001	0.0005	0.0016	0.0042	0.0098	0.0207	0.0403	0.0725	0.1211	0.1877	0.2684	0.3474	0.3874	0.3151		9
	10	0.0000	0.0000	0.0000	0.0000	0.0000	0.0000	0.0000	0.0001	0.0003	0.0010	0.0025	0.0060	0.0135	0.0282	0.0563	0.1074	0.1969	0.3487	0.5987		10

Appendix B.2

Cumulative Binomial Distribution Table

$$\Pr(X \le x) = F(n; x, p) = \sum_{k=0}^{x} \binom{n}{x} p^k (1-p)^{n-k}$$

		Probability of ≤*x* occurrences in a sample of size *n*																				
n	*x*	0.05	0.10	0.15	0.20	0.25	0.30	0.35	0.40	0.45	0.50	0.55	0.60	0.65	0.70	0.75	0.80	0.85	0.90	0.95	*n*	*x*
1	0	0.9500	0.9000	0.8500	0.8000	0.7500	0.7000	0.6500	0.6000	0.5500	0.5000	0.4500	0.4000	0.3500	0.3000	0.2500	0.2000	0.1500	0.1000	0.0500	1	0
	1	1.0000	1.0000	1.0000	1.0000	1.0000	1.0000	1.0000	1.0000	1.0000	1.0000	1.0000	1.0000	1.0000	1.0000	1.0000	1.0000	1.0000	1.0000	1.0000		1
2	0	0.9025	0.8100	0.7225	0.6400	0.5625	0.4900	0.4225	0.3600	0.3025	0.2500	0.2025	0.1600	0.1225	0.0900	0.0625	0.0400	0.0225	0.0100	0.0025	2	0
	1	0.9975	0.9900	0.9775	0.9600	0.9375	0.9100	0.8775	0.8400	0.7975	0.7500	0.6975	0.6400	0.5775	0.5100	0.4375	0.3600	0.2775	0.1900	0.0975		1
	2	1.0000	1.0000	1.0000	1.0000	1.0000	1.0000	1.0000	1.0000	1.0000	1.0000	1.0000	1.0000	1.0000	1.0000	1.0000	1.0000	1.0000	1.0000	1.0000		2
3	0	0.8574	0.7290	0.6141	0.5120	0.4219	0.3430	0.2746	0.2160	0.1664	0.1250	0.0911	0.0640	0.0429	0.0270	0.0156	0.0080	0.0034	0.0010	0.0001	3	0
	1	0.9928	0.9720	0.9393	0.8960	0.8438	0.7840	0.7183	0.6480	0.5748	0.5000	0.4253	0.3520	0.2818	0.2160	0.1563	0.1040	0.0608	0.0280	0.0073		1
	2	0.9999	0.9990	0.9966	0.9920	0.9844	0.9730	0.9571	0.9360	0.9089	0.8750	0.8336	0.7840	0.7254	0.6570	0.5781	0.4880	0.3859	0.2710	0.1426		2
	3	1.0000	1.0000	1.0000	1.0000	1.0000	1.0000	1.0000	1.0000	1.0000	1.0000	1.0000	1.0000	1.0000	1.0000	1.0000	1.0000	1.0000	1.0000	1.0000		3
4	0	0.8145	0.6561	0.5220	0.4096	0.3164	0.2401	0.1785	0.1296	0.0915	0.0625	0.0410	0.0256	0.0150	0.0081	0.0039	0.0016	0.0005	0.0001	0.0000	4	0
	1	0.9860	0.9477	0.8905	0.8192	0.7383	0.6517	0.5630	0.4752	0.3910	0.3125	0.2415	0.1792	0.1265	0.0837	0.0508	0.0272	0.0120	0.0037	0.0005		1
	2	0.9995	0.9963	0.9880	0.9728	0.9492	0.9163	0.8735	0.8208	0.7585	0.6875	0.6090	0.5248	0.4370	0.3483	0.2617	0.1808	0.1095	0.0523	0.0140		2
	3	1.0000	0.9999	0.9995	0.9984	0.9961	0.9919	0.9850	0.9744	0.9590	0.9375	0.9085	0.8704	0.8215	0.7599	0.6836	0.5904	0.4780	0.3439	0.1855		3
	4	1.0000	1.0000	1.0000	1.0000	1.0000	1.0000	1.0000	1.0000	1.0000	1.0000	1.0000	1.0000	1.0000	1.0000	1.0000	1.0000	1.0000	1.0000	1.0000		4
5	0	0.7738	0.5905	0.4437	0.3277	0.2373	0.1681	0.1160	0.0778	0.0503	0.0313	0.0185	0.0102	0.0053	0.0024	0.0010	0.0003	0.0001	0.0000	0.0000	5	0
	1	0.9774	0.9185	0.8352	0.7373	0.6328	0.5282	0.4284	0.3370	0.2562	0.1875	0.1312	0.0870	0.0540	0.0308	0.0156	0.0067	0.0022	0.0005	0.0000		1
	2	0.9988	0.9914	0.9734	0.9421	0.8965	0.8369	0.7648	0.6826	0.5931	0.5000	0.4069	0.3174	0.2352	0.1631	0.1035	0.0579	0.0266	0.0086	0.0012		2
	3	1.0000	0.9995	0.9978	0.9933	0.9844	0.9692	0.9460	0.9130	0.8688	0.8125	0.7438	0.6630	0.5716	0.4718	0.3672	0.2627	0.1648	0.0815	0.0226		3
	4	1.0000	1.0000	0.9999	0.9997	0.9990	0.9976	0.9947	0.9898	0.9815	0.9688	0.9497	0.9222	0.8840	0.8319	0.7627	0.6723	0.5563	0.4095	0.2262		4
	5	1.0000	1.0000	1.0000	1.0000	1.0000	1.0000	1.0000	1.0000	1.0000	1.0000	1.0000	1.0000	1.0000	1.0000	1.0000	1.0000	1.0000	1.0000	1.0000		5

$$\Pr(X \le x) = F(n;x,p) = \sum_{k=0}^{x} \binom{n}{x} p^k (1-p)^{n-k}$$

		Probability of ≤*x* occurrences in a sample of size *n*																				
n	*x*	0.05	0.10	0.15	0.20	0.25	0.30	0.35	0.40	0.45	0.50	0.55	0.60	0.65	0.70	0.75	0.80	0.85	0.90	0.95	*n*	*x*
6	0	0.7351	0.5314	0.3771	0.2621	0.1780	0.1176	0.0754	0.0467	0.0277	0.0156	0.0083	0.0041	0.0018	0.0007	0.0002	0.0001	0.0000	0.0000	0.0000	6	0
	1	0.9672	0.8857	0.7765	0.6554	0.5339	0.4202	0.3191	0.2333	0.1636	0.1094	0.0692	0.0410	0.0223	0.0109	0.0046	0.0016	0.0004	0.0001	0.0000		1
	2	0.9978	0.9842	0.9527	0.9011	0.8306	0.7443	0.6471	0.5443	0.4415	0.3438	0.2553	0.1792	0.1174	0.0705	0.0376	0.0170	0.0059	0.0013	0.0001		2
	3	0.9999	0.9987	0.9941	0.9830	0.9624	0.9295	0.8826	0.8208	0.7447	0.6563	0.5585	0.4557	0.3529	0.2557	0.1694	0.0989	0.0473	0.0159	0.0022		3
	4	1.0000	0.9999	0.9996	0.9984	0.9954	0.9891	0.9777	0.9590	0.9308	0.8906	0.8364	0.7667	0.6809	0.5798	0.4661	0.3446	0.2235	0.1143	0.0328		4
	5	1.0000	1.0000	1.0000	0.9999	0.9998	0.9993	0.9982	0.9959	0.9917	0.9844	0.9723	0.9533	0.9246	0.8824	0.8220	0.7379	0.6229	0.4686	0.2649		5
	6	1.0000	1.0000	1.0000	1.0000	1.0000	1.0000	1.0000	1.0000	1.0000	1.0000	1.0000	1.0000	1.0000	1.0000	1.0000	1.0000	1.0000	1.0000	1.0000		6
7	0	0.6983	0.4783	0.3206	0.2097	0.1335	0.0824	0.0490	0.0280	0.0152	0.0078	0.0037	0.0016	0.0006	0.0002	0.0001	0.0000	0.0000	0.0000	0.0000	7	0
	1	0.9556	0.8503	0.7166	0.5767	0.4449	0.3294	0.2338	0.1586	0.1024	0.0625	0.0357	0.0188	0.0090	0.0038	0.0013	0.0004	0.0001	0.0000	0.0000		1
	2	0.9962	0.9743	0.9262	0.8520	0.7564	0.6471	0.5323	0.4199	0.3164	0.2266	0.1529	0.0963	0.0556	0.0288	0.0129	0.0047	0.0012	0.0002	0.0000		2
	3	0.9998	0.9973	0.9879	0.9667	0.9294	0.8740	0.8002	0.7102	0.6083	0.5000	0.3917	0.2898	0.1998	0.1260	0.0706	0.0333	0.0121	0.0027	0.0002		3
	4	1.0000	0.9998	0.9988	0.9953	0.9871	0.9712	0.9444	0.9037	0.8471	0.7734	0.6836	0.5801	0.4677	0.3529	0.2436	0.1480	0.0738	0.0257	0.0038		4
	5	1.0000	1.0000	0.9999	0.9996	0.9987	0.9962	0.9910	0.9812	0.9643	0.9375	0.8976	0.8414	0.7662	0.6706	0.5551	0.4233	0.2834	0.1497	0.0444		5
	6	1.0000	1.0000	1.0000	1.0000	0.9999	0.9998	0.9994	0.9984	0.9963	0.9922	0.9848	0.9720	0.9510	0.9176	0.8665	0.7903	0.6794	0.5217	0.3017		6
	7	1.0000	1.0000	1.0000	1.0000	1.0000	1.0000	1.0000	1.0000	1.0000	1.0000	1.0000	1.0000	1.0000	1.0000	1.0000	1.0000	1.0000	1.0000	1.0000		7
8	0	0.6634	0.4305	0.2725	0.1678	0.1001	0.0576	0.0319	0.0168	0.0084	0.0039	0.0017	0.0007	0.0002	0.0001	0.0000	0.0000	0.0000	0.0000	0.0000	8	0
	1	0.9428	0.8131	0.6572	0.5033	0.3671	0.2553	0.1691	0.1064	0.0632	0.0352	0.0181	0.0085	0.0036	0.0013	0.0004	0.0001	0.0000	0.0000	0.0000		1
	2	0.9942	0.9619	0.8948	0.7969	0.6785	0.5518	0.4278	0.3154	0.2201	0.1445	0.0885	0.0498	0.0253	0.0113	0.0042	0.0012	0.0002	0.0000	0.0000		2
	3	0.9996	0.9950	0.9786	0.9437	0.8862	0.8059	0.7064	0.5941	0.4770	0.3633	0.2604	0.1737	0.1061	0.0580	0.0273	0.0104	0.0029	0.0004	0.0000		3
	4	1.0000	0.9996	0.9971	0.9896	0.9727	0.9420	0.8939	0.8263	0.7396	0.6367	0.5230	0.4059	0.2936	0.1941	0.1138	0.0563	0.0214	0.0050	0.0004		4
	5	1.0000	1.0000	0.9998	0.9988	0.9958	0.9887	0.9747	0.9502	0.9115	0.8555	0.7799	0.6846	0.5722	0.4482	0.3215	0.2031	0.1052	0.0381	0.0058		5
	6	1.0000	1.0000	1.0000	0.9999	0.9996	0.9987	0.9964	0.9915	0.9819	0.9648	0.9368	0.8936	0.8309	0.7447	0.6329	0.4967	0.3428	0.1869	0.0572		6
	7	1.0000	1.0000	1.0000	1.0000	1.0000	0.9999	0.9998	0.9993	0.9983	0.9961	0.9916	0.9832	0.9681	0.9424	0.8999	0.8322	0.7275	0.5695	0.3366		7
	8	1.0000	1.0000	1.0000	1.0000	1.0000	1.0000	1.0000	1.0000	1.0000	1.0000	1.0000	1.0000	1.0000	1.0000	1.0000	1.0000	1.0000	1.0000	1.0000		8

$$\Pr(X \le x) = F(n;x,p) = \sum_{k=0}^{x} \binom{n}{x} p^k (1-p)^{n-k}$$

		Probability of ≤x occurrences in a sample of size n																				
n	x	0.05	0.10	0.15	0.20	0.25	0.30	0.35	0.40	0.45	0.50	0.55	0.60	0.65	0.70	0.75	0.80	0.85	0.90	0.95	n	x
9	0	0.6302	0.3874	0.2316	0.1342	0.0751	0.0404	0.0207	0.0101	0.0046	0.0020	0.0008	0.0003	0.0001	0.0000	0.0000	0.0000	0.0000	0.0000	0.0000	9	0
	1	0.9288	0.7748	0.5995	0.4362	0.3003	0.1960	0.1211	0.0705	0.0385	0.0195	0.0091	0.0038	0.0014	0.0004	0.0001	0.0000	0.0000	0.0000	0.0000		1
	2	0.9916	0.9470	0.8591	0.7382	0.6007	0.4628	0.3373	0.2318	0.1495	0.0898	0.0498	0.0250	0.0112	0.0043	0.0013	0.0003	0.0000	0.0000	0.0000		2
	3	0.9994	0.9917	0.9661	0.9144	0.8343	0.7297	0.6089	0.4826	0.3614	0.2539	0.1658	0.0994	0.0536	0.0253	0.0100	0.0031	0.0006	0.0001	0.0000		3
	4	1.0000	0.9991	0.9944	0.9804	0.9511	0.9012	0.8283	0.7334	0.6214	0.5000	0.3786	0.2666	0.1717	0.0988	0.0489	0.0196	0.0056	0.0009	0.0000		4
	5	1.0000	0.9999	0.9994	0.9969	0.9900	0.9747	0.9464	0.9006	0.8342	0.7461	0.6386	0.5174	0.3911	0.2703	0.1657	0.0856	0.0339	0.0083	0.0006		5
	6	1.0000	1.0000	1.0000	0.9997	0.9987	0.9957	0.9888	0.9750	0.9502	0.9102	0.8505	0.7682	0.6627	0.5372	0.3993	0.2618	0.1409	0.0530	0.0084		6
	7	1.0000	1.0000	1.0000	1.0000	0.9999	0.9996	0.9986	0.9962	0.9909	0.9805	0.9615	0.9295	0.8789	0.8040	0.6997	0.5638	0.4005	0.2252	0.0712		7
	8	1.0000	1.0000	1.0000	1.0000	1.0000	1.0000	0.9999	0.9997	0.9992	0.9980	0.9954	0.9899	0.9793	0.9596	0.9249	0.8658	0.7684	0.6126	0.3698		8
	9	1.0000	1.0000	1.0000	1.0000	1.0000	1.0000	1.0000	1.0000	1.0000	1.0000	1.0000	1.0000	1.0000	1.0000	1.0000	1.0000	1.0000	1.0000	1.0000		9
10	0	0.5987	0.3487	0.1969	0.1074	0.0563	0.0282	0.0135	0.0060	0.0025	0.0010	0.0003	0.0001	0.0000	0.0000	0.0000	0.0000	0.0000	0.0000	0.0000	10	0
	1	0.9139	0.7361	0.5443	0.3758	0.2440	0.1493	0.0860	0.0464	0.0233	0.0107	0.0045	0.0017	0.0005	0.0001	0.0000	0.0000	0.0000	0.0000	0.0000		1
	2	0.9885	0.9298	0.8202	0.6778	0.5256	0.3828	0.2616	0.1673	0.0996	0.0547	0.0274	0.0123	0.0048	0.0016	0.0004	0.0001	0.0000	0.0000	0.0000		2
	3	0.9990	0.9872	0.9500	0.8791	0.7759	0.6496	0.5138	0.3823	0.2660	0.1719	0.1020	0.0548	0.0260	0.0106	0.0035	0.0009	0.0001	0.0000	0.0000		3
	4	0.9999	0.9984	0.9901	0.9672	0.9219	0.8497	0.7515	0.6331	0.5044	0.3770	0.2616	0.1662	0.0949	0.0473	0.0197	0.0064	0.0014	0.0001	0.0000		4
	5	1.0000	0.9999	0.9986	0.9936	0.9803	0.9527	0.9051	0.8338	0.7384	0.6230	0.4956	0.3669	0.2485	0.1503	0.0781	0.0328	0.0099	0.0016	0.0001		5
	6	1.0000	1.0000	0.9999	0.9991	0.9965	0.9894	0.9740	0.9452	0.8980	0.8281	0.7340	0.6177	0.4862	0.3504	0.2241	0.1209	0.0500	0.0128	0.0010		6
	7	1.0000	1.0000	1.0000	0.9999	0.9996	0.9984	0.9952	0.9877	0.9726	0.9453	0.9004	0.8327	0.7384	0.6172	0.4744	0.3222	0.1798	0.0702	0.0115		7
	8	1.0000	1.0000	1.0000	1.0000	1.0000	0.9999	0.9995	0.9983	0.9955	0.9893	0.9767	0.9536	0.9140	0.8507	0.7560	0.6242	0.4557	0.2639	0.0861		8
	9	1.0000	1.0000	1.0000	1.0000	1.0000	1.0000	1.0000	0.9999	0.9997	0.9990	0.9975	0.9940	0.9865	0.9718	0.9437	0.8926	0.8031	0.6513	0.4013		9
	10	1.0000	1.0000	1.0000	1.0000	1.0000	1.0000	1.0000	1.0000	1.0000	1.0000	1.0000	1.0000	1.0000	1.0000	1.0000	1.0000	1.0000	1.0000	1.0000		10

Appendix C.1

Poisson Distribution Table

$$\Pr(X = x) = f(x;\lambda) = \frac{\lambda^x}{x!}e^{-\lambda}$$

	Probability of x occurrences													
λ	0	1	2	3	4	5	6	7	8	9	10	11	12	λ
0.05	0.9512	0.0476	0.0012	0.0000	0.0000	0.0000	0.0000	0.0000	0.0000	0.0000	0.0000	0.0000	0.0000	**0.05**
0.10	0.9048	0.0905	0.0045	0.0002	0.0000	0.0000	0.0000	0.0000	0.0000	0.0000	0.0000	0.0000	0.0000	**0.10**
0.15	0.8607	0.1291	0.0097	0.0005	0.0000	0.0000	0.0000	0.0000	0.0000	0.0000	0.0000	0.0000	0.0000	**0.15**
0.20	0.8187	0.1637	0.0164	0.0011	0.0001	0.0000	0.0000	0.0000	0.0000	0.0000	0.0000	0.0000	0.0000	**0.20**
0.25	0.7788	0.1947	0.0243	0.0020	0.0001	0.0000	0.0000	0.0000	0.0000	0.0000	0.0000	0.0000	0.0000	**0.25**
0.30	0.7408	0.2222	0.0333	0.0033	0.0003	0.0000	0.0000	0.0000	0.0000	0.0000	0.0000	0.0000	0.0000	**0.30**
0.35	0.7047	0.2466	0.0432	0.0050	0.0004	0.0000	0.0000	0.0000	0.0000	0.0000	0.0000	0.0000	0.0000	**0.35**
0.40	0.6703	0.2681	0.0536	0.0072	0.0007	0.0001	0.0000	0.0000	0.0000	0.0000	0.0000	0.0000	0.0000	**0.40**
0.45	0.6376	0.2869	0.0646	0.0097	0.0011	0.0001	0.0000	0.0000	0.0000	0.0000	0.0000	0.0000	0.0000	**0.45**
0.50	0.6065	0.3033	0.0758	0.0126	0.0016	0.0002	0.0000	0.0000	0.0000	0.0000	0.0000	0.0000	0.0000	**0.50**
0.55	0.5769	0.3173	0.0873	0.0160	0.0022	0.0002	0.0000	0.0000	0.0000	0.0000	0.0000	0.0000	0.0000	**0.55**
0.60	0.5488	0.3293	0.0988	0.0198	0.0030	0.0004	0.0000	0.0000	0.0000	0.0000	0.0000	0.0000	0.0000	**0.60**
0.65	0.5220	0.3393	0.1103	0.0239	0.0039	0.0005	0.0001	0.0000	0.0000	0.0000	0.0000	0.0000	0.0000	**0.65**
0.70	0.4966	0.3476	0.1217	0.0284	0.0050	0.0007	0.0001	0.0000	0.0000	0.0000	0.0000	0.0000	0.0000	**0.70**
0.75	0.4724	0.3543	0.1329	0.0332	0.0062	0.0009	0.0001	0.0000	0.0000	0.0000	0.0000	0.0000	0.0000	**0.75**
0.80	0.4493	0.3595	0.1438	0.0383	0.0077	0.0012	0.0002	0.0000	0.0000	0.0000	0.0000	0.0000	0.0000	**0.80**
0.85	0.4274	0.3633	0.1544	0.0437	0.0093	0.0016	0.0002	0.0000	0.0000	0.0000	0.0000	0.0000	0.0000	**0.85**
0.90	0.4066	0.3659	0.1647	0.0494	0.0111	0.0020	0.0003	0.0000	0.0000	0.0000	0.0000	0.0000	0.0000	**0.90**
0.95	0.3867	0.3674	0.1745	0.0553	0.0131	0.0025	0.0004	0.0001	0.0000	0.0000	0.0000	0.0000	0.0000	**0.95**
1.00	0.3679	0.3679	0.1839	0.0613	0.0153	0.0031	0.0005	0.0001	0.0000	0.0000	0.0000	0.0000	0.0000	**1.00**
1.10	0.3329	0.3662	0.2014	0.0738	0.0203	0.0045	0.0008	0.0001	0.0000	0.0000	0.0000	0.0000	0.0000	**1.10**
1.20	0.3012	0.3614	0.2169	0.0867	0.0260	0.0062	0.0012	0.0002	0.0000	0.0000	0.0000	0.0000	0.0000	**1.20**
1.30	0.2725	0.3543	0.2303	0.0998	0.0324	0.0084	0.0018	0.0003	0.0001	0.0000	0.0000	0.0000	0.0000	**1.30**
1.40	0.2466	0.3452	0.2417	0.1128	0.0395	0.0111	0.0026	0.0005	0.0001	0.0000	0.0000	0.0000	0.0000	**1.40**
1.50	0.2231	0.3347	0.2510	0.1255	0.0471	0.0141	0.0035	0.0008	0.0001	0.0000	0.0000	0.0000	0.0000	**1.50**
1.60	0.2019	0.3230	0.2584	0.1378	0.0551	0.0176	0.0047	0.0011	0.0002	0.0000	0.0000	0.0000	0.0000	**1.60**
1.70	0.1827	0.3106	0.2640	0.1496	0.0636	0.0216	0.0061	0.0015	0.0003	0.0001	0.0000	0.0000	0.0000	**1.70**
1.80	0.1653	0.2975	0.2678	0.1607	0.0723	0.0260	0.0078	0.0020	0.0005	0.0001	0.0000	0.0000	0.0000	**1.80**
1.90	0.1496	0.2842	0.2700	0.1710	0.0812	0.0309	0.0098	0.0027	0.0006	0.0001	0.0000	0.0000	0.0000	**1.90**
2.00	0.1353	0.2707	0.2707	0.1804	0.0902	0.0361	0.0120	0.0034	0.0009	0.0002	0.0000	0.0000	0.0000	**2.00**
2.10	0.1225	0.2572	0.2700	0.1890	0.0992	0.0417	0.0146	0.0044	0.0011	0.0003	0.0001	0.0000	0.0000	**2.10**
2.20	0.1108	0.2438	0.2681	0.1966	0.1082	0.0476	0.0174	0.0055	0.0015	0.0004	0.0001	0.0000	0.0000	**2.20**
2.30	0.1003	0.2306	0.2652	0.2033	0.1169	0.0538	0.0206	0.0068	0.0019	0.0005	0.0001	0.0000	0.0000	**2.30**
2.40	0.0907	0.2177	0.2613	0.2090	0.1254	0.0602	0.0241	0.0083	0.0025	0.0007	0.0002	0.0000	0.0000	**2.40**
2.50	0.0821	0.2052	0.2565	0.2138	0.1336	0.0668	0.0278	0.0099	0.0031	0.0009	0.0002	0.0000	0.0000	**2.50**
2.60	0.0743	0.1931	0.2510	0.2176	0.1414	0.0735	0.0319	0.0118	0.0038	0.0011	0.0003	0.0001	0.0000	**2.60**
2.70	0.0672	0.1815	0.2450	0.2205	0.1488	0.0804	0.0362	0.0139	0.0047	0.0014	0.0004	0.0001	0.0000	**2.70**

$$\Pr(X = x) = f(x;\lambda) = \frac{\lambda^x}{x!} e^{-\lambda}$$

	Probability of *x* occurrences													
λ	13	14	15	16	17	18	19	20	21	22	23	24	25	λ
0.05	0.0000	0.0000	0.0000	0.0000	0.0000	0.0000	0.0000	0.0000	0.0000	0.0000	0.0000	0.0000	0.0000	**0.05**
0.10	0.0000	0.0000	0.0000	0.0000	0.0000	0.0000	0.0000	0.0000	0.0000	0.0000	0.0000	0.0000	0.0000	**0.10**
0.15	0.0000	0.0000	0.0000	0.0000	0.0000	0.0000	0.0000	0.0000	0.0000	0.0000	0.0000	0.0000	0.0000	**0.15**
0.20	0.0000	0.0000	0.0000	0.0000	0.0000	0.0000	0.0000	0.0000	0.0000	0.0000	0.0000	0.0000	0.0000	**0.20**
0.25	0.0000	0.0000	0.0000	0.0000	0.0000	0.0000	0.0000	0.0000	0.0000	0.0000	0.0000	0.0000	0.0000	**0.25**
0.30	0.0000	0.0000	0.0000	0.0000	0.0000	0.0000	0.0000	0.0000	0.0000	0.0000	0.0000	0.0000	0.0000	**0.30**
0.35	0.0000	0.0000	0.0000	0.0000	0.0000	0.0000	0.0000	0.0000	0.0000	0.0000	0.0000	0.0000	0.0000	**0.35**
0.40	0.0000	0.0000	0.0000	0.0000	0.0000	0.0000	0.0000	0.0000	0.0000	0.0000	0.0000	0.0000	0.0000	**0.40**
0.45	0.0000	0.0000	0.0000	0.0000	0.0000	0.0000	0.0000	0.0000	0.0000	0.0000	0.0000	0.0000	0.0000	**0.45**
0.50	0.0000	0.0000	0.0000	0.0000	0.0000	0.0000	0.0000	0.0000	0.0000	0.0000	0.0000	0.0000	0.0000	**0.50**
0.55	0.0000	0.0000	0.0000	0.0000	0.0000	0.0000	0.0000	0.0000	0.0000	0.0000	0.0000	0.0000	0.0000	**0.55**
0.60	0.0000	0.0000	0.0000	0.0000	0.0000	0.0000	0.0000	0.0000	0.0000	0.0000	0.0000	0.0000	0.0000	**0.60**
0.65	0.0000	0.0000	0.0000	0.0000	0.0000	0.0000	0.0000	0.0000	0.0000	0.0000	0.0000	0.0000	0.0000	**0.65**
0.70	0.0000	0.0000	0.0000	0.0000	0.0000	0.0000	0.0000	0.0000	0.0000	0.0000	0.0000	0.0000	0.0000	**0.70**
0.75	0.0000	0.0000	0.0000	0.0000	0.0000	0.0000	0.0000	0.0000	0.0000	0.0000	0.0000	0.0000	0.0000	**0.75**
0.80	0.0000	0.0000	0.0000	0.0000	0.0000	0.0000	0.0000	0.0000	0.0000	0.0000	0.0000	0.0000	0.0000	**0.80**
0.85	0.0000	0.0000	0.0000	0.0000	0.0000	0.0000	0.0000	0.0000	0.0000	0.0000	0.0000	0.0000	0.0000	**0.85**
0.90	0.0000	0.0000	0.0000	0.0000	0.0000	0.0000	0.0000	0.0000	0.0000	0.0000	0.0000	0.0000	0.0000	**0.90**
0.95	0.0000	0.0000	0.0000	0.0000	0.0000	0.0000	0.0000	0.0000	0.0000	0.0000	0.0000	0.0000	0.0000	**0.95**
1.00	0.0000	0.0000	0.0000	0.0000	0.0000	0.0000	0.0000	0.0000	0.0000	0.0000	0.0000	0.0000	0.0000	**1.00**
1.10	0.0000	0.0000	0.0000	0.0000	0.0000	0.0000	0.0000	0.0000	0.0000	0.0000	0.0000	0.0000	0.0000	**1.10**
1.20	0.0000	0.0000	0.0000	0.0000	0.0000	0.0000	0.0000	0.0000	0.0000	0.0000	0.0000	0.0000	0.0000	**1.20**
1.30	0.0000	0.0000	0.0000	0.0000	0.0000	0.0000	0.0000	0.0000	0.0000	0.0000	0.0000	0.0000	0.0000	**1.30**
1.40	0.0000	0.0000	0.0000	0.0000	0.0000	0.0000	0.0000	0.0000	0.0000	0.0000	0.0000	0.0000	0.0000	**1.40**
1.50	0.0000	0.0000	0.0000	0.0000	0.0000	0.0000	0.0000	0.0000	0.0000	0.0000	0.0000	0.0000	0.0000	**1.50**
1.60	0.0000	0.0000	0.0000	0.0000	0.0000	0.0000	0.0000	0.0000	0.0000	0.0000	0.0000	0.0000	0.0000	**1.60**
1.70	0.0000	0.0000	0.0000	0.0000	0.0000	0.0000	0.0000	0.0000	0.0000	0.0000	0.0000	0.0000	0.0000	**1.70**
1.80	0.0000	0.0000	0.0000	0.0000	0.0000	0.0000	0.0000	0.0000	0.0000	0.0000	0.0000	0.0000	0.0000	**1.80**
1.90	0.0000	0.0000	0.0000	0.0000	0.0000	0.0000	0.0000	0.0000	0.0000	0.0000	0.0000	0.0000	0.0000	**1.90**
2.00	0.0000	0.0000	0.0000	0.0000	0.0000	0.0000	0.0000	0.0000	0.0000	0.0000	0.0000	0.0000	0.0000	**2.00**
2.10	0.0000	0.0000	0.0000	0.0000	0.0000	0.0000	0.0000	0.0000	0.0000	0.0000	0.0000	0.0000	0.0000	**2.10**
2.20	0.0000	0.0000	0.0000	0.0000	0.0000	0.0000	0.0000	0.0000	0.0000	0.0000	0.0000	0.0000	0.0000	**2.20**
2.30	0.0000	0.0000	0.0000	0.0000	0.0000	0.0000	0.0000	0.0000	0.0000	0.0000	0.0000	0.0000	0.0000	**2.30**
2.40	0.0000	0.0000	0.0000	0.0000	0.0000	0.0000	0.0000	0.0000	0.0000	0.0000	0.0000	0.0000	0.0000	**2.40**
2.50	0.0000	0.0000	0.0000	0.0000	0.0000	0.0000	0.0000	0.0000	0.0000	0.0000	0.0000	0.0000	0.0000	**2.50**
2.60	0.0000	0.0000	0.0000	0.0000	0.0000	0.0000	0.0000	0.0000	0.0000	0.0000	0.0000	0.0000	0.0000	**2.60**
2.70	0.0000	0.0000	0.0000	0.0000	0.0000	0.0000	0.0000	0.0000	0.0000	0.0000	0.0000	0.0000	0.0000	**2.70**

$$\Pr(X = x) = f(x;\lambda) = \frac{\lambda^x}{x!}e^{-\lambda}$$

	Probability of *x* occurrences													
λ	**0**	**1**	**2**	**3**	**4**	**5**	**6**	**7**	**8**	**9**	**10**	**11**	**12**	λ
2.80	0.0608	0.1703	0.2384	0.2225	0.1557	0.0872	0.0407	0.0163	0.0057	0.0018	0.0005	0.0001	0.0000	**2.80**
2.90	0.0550	0.1596	0.2314	0.2237	0.1622	0.0940	0.0455	0.0188	0.0068	0.0022	0.0006	0.0002	0.0000	**2.90**
3.00	0.0498	0.1494	0.2240	0.2240	0.1680	0.1008	0.0504	0.0216	0.0081	0.0027	0.0008	0.0002	0.0001	**3.00**
3.10	0.0450	0.1397	0.2165	0.2237	0.1733	0.1075	0.0555	0.0246	0.0095	0.0033	0.0010	0.0003	0.0001	**3.10**
3.20	0.0408	0.1304	0.2087	0.2226	0.1781	0.1140	0.0608	0.0278	0.0111	0.0040	0.0013	0.0004	0.0001	**3.20**
3.30	0.0369	0.1217	0.2008	0.2209	0.1823	0.1203	0.0662	0.0312	0.0129	0.0047	0.0016	0.0005	0.0001	**3.30**
3.40	0.0334	0.1135	0.1929	0.2186	0.1858	0.1264	0.0716	0.0348	0.0148	0.0056	0.0019	0.0006	0.0002	**3.40**
3.50	0.0302	0.1057	0.1850	0.2158	0.1888	0.1322	0.0771	0.0385	0.0169	0.0066	0.0023	0.0007	0.0002	**3.50**
3.60	0.0273	0.0984	0.1771	0.2125	0.1912	0.1377	0.0826	0.0425	0.0191	0.0076	0.0028	0.0009	0.0003	**3.60**
3.70	0.0247	0.0915	0.1692	0.2087	0.1931	0.1429	0.0881	0.0466	0.0215	0.0089	0.0033	0.0011	0.0003	**3.70**
3.80	0.0224	0.0850	0.1615	0.2046	0.1944	0.1477	0.0936	0.0508	0.0241	0.0102	0.0039	0.0013	0.0004	**3.80**
3.90	0.0202	0.0789	0.1539	0.2001	0.1951	0.1522	0.0989	0.0551	0.0269	0.0116	0.0045	0.0016	0.0005	**3.90**
4.00	0.0183	0.0733	0.1465	0.1954	0.1954	0.1563	0.1042	0.0595	0.0298	0.0132	0.0053	0.0019	0.0006	**4.00**
4.10	0.0166	0.0679	0.1393	0.1904	0.1951	0.1600	0.1093	0.0640	0.0328	0.0150	0.0061	0.0023	0.0008	**4.10**
4.20	0.0150	0.0630	0.1323	0.1852	0.1944	0.1633	0.1143	0.0686	0.0360	0.0168	0.0071	0.0027	0.0009	**4.20**
4.30	0.0136	0.0583	0.1254	0.1798	0.1933	0.1662	0.1191	0.0732	0.0393	0.0188	0.0081	0.0032	0.0011	**4.30**
4.40	0.0123	0.0540	0.1188	0.1743	0.1917	0.1687	0.1237	0.0778	0.0428	0.0209	0.0092	0.0037	0.0013	**4.40**
4.50	0.0111	0.0500	0.1125	0.1687	0.1898	0.1708	0.1281	0.0824	0.0463	0.0232	0.0104	0.0043	0.0016	**4.50**
4.60	0.0101	0.0462	0.1063	0.1631	0.1875	0.1725	0.1323	0.0869	0.0500	0.0255	0.0118	0.0049	0.0019	**4.60**
4.70	0.0091	0.0427	0.1005	0.1574	0.1849	0.1738	0.1362	0.0914	0.0537	0.0281	0.0132	0.0056	0.0022	**4.70**
4.80	0.0082	0.0395	0.0948	0.1517	0.1820	0.1747	0.1398	0.0959	0.0575	0.0307	0.0147	0.0064	0.0026	**4.80**
4.90	0.0074	0.0365	0.0894	0.1460	0.1789	0.1753	0.1432	0.1002	0.0614	0.0334	0.0164	0.0073	0.0030	**4.90**
5.00	0.0067	0.0337	0.0842	0.1404	0.1755	0.1755	0.1462	0.1044	0.0653	0.0363	0.0181	0.0082	0.0034	**5.00**
5.10	0.0061	0.0311	0.0793	0.1348	0.1719	0.1753	0.1490	0.1086	0.0692	0.0392	0.0200	0.0093	0.0039	**5.10**
5.20	0.0055	0.0287	0.0746	0.1293	0.1681	0.1748	0.1515	0.1125	0.0731	0.0423	0.0220	0.0104	0.0045	**5.20**
5.30	0.0050	0.0265	0.0701	0.1239	0.1641	0.1740	0.1537	0.1163	0.0771	0.0454	0.0241	0.0116	0.0051	**5.30**
5.40	0.0045	0.0244	0.0659	0.1185	0.1600	0.1728	0.1555	0.1200	0.0810	0.0486	0.0262	0.0129	0.0058	**5.40**
5.50	0.0041	0.0225	0.0618	0.1133	0.1558	0.1714	0.1571	0.1234	0.0849	0.0519	0.0285	0.0143	0.0065	**5.50**
5.60	0.0037	0.0207	0.0580	0.1082	0.1515	0.1697	0.1584	0.1267	0.0887	0.0552	0.0309	0.0157	0.0073	**5.60**
5.70	0.0033	0.0191	0.0544	0.1033	0.1472	0.1678	0.1594	0.1298	0.0925	0.0586	0.0334	0.0173	0.0082	**5.70**
5.80	0.0030	0.0176	0.0509	0.0985	0.1428	0.1656	0.1601	0.1326	0.0962	0.0620	0.0359	0.0190	0.0092	**5.80**
5.90	0.0027	0.0162	0.0477	0.0938	0.1383	0.1632	0.1605	0.1353	0.0998	0.0654	0.0386	0.0207	0.0102	**5.90**
6.00	0.0025	0.0149	0.0446	0.0892	0.1339	0.1606	0.1606	0.1377	0.1033	0.0688	0.0413	0.0225	0.0113	**6.00**
6.10	0.0022	0.0137	0.0417	0.0848	0.1294	0.1579	0.1605	0.1399	0.1066	0.0723	0.0441	0.0244	0.0124	**6.10**
6.20	0.0020	0.0126	0.0390	0.0806	0.1249	0.1549	0.1601	0.1418	0.1099	0.0757	0.0469	0.0265	0.0137	**6.20**
6.30	0.0018	0.0116	0.0364	0.0765	0.1205	0.1519	0.1595	0.1435	0.1130	0.0791	0.0498	0.0285	0.0150	**6.30**
6.40	0.0017	0.0106	0.0340	0.0726	0.1162	0.1487	0.1586	0.1450	0.1160	0.0825	0.0528	0.0307	0.0164	**6.40**

$$\Pr(X = x) = f(x;\lambda) = \frac{\lambda^x}{x!} e^{-\lambda}$$

	Probability of *x* occurrences													
λ	13	14	15	16	17	18	19	20	21	22	23	24	25	λ
2.80	0.0000	0.0000	0.0000	0.0000	0.0000	0.0000	0.0000	0.0000	0.0000	0.0000	0.0000	0.0000	0.0000	**2.80**
2.90	0.0000	0.0000	0.0000	0.0000	0.0000	0.0000	0.0000	0.0000	0.0000	0.0000	0.0000	0.0000	0.0000	**2.90**
3.00	0.0000	0.0000	0.0000	0.0000	0.0000	0.0000	0.0000	0.0000	0.0000	0.0000	0.0000	0.0000	0.0000	**3.00**
3.10	0.0000	0.0000	0.0000	0.0000	0.0000	0.0000	0.0000	0.0000	0.0000	0.0000	0.0000	0.0000	0.0000	**3.10**
3.20	0.0000	0.0000	0.0000	0.0000	0.0000	0.0000	0.0000	0.0000	0.0000	0.0000	0.0000	0.0000	0.0000	**3.20**
3.30	0.0000	0.0000	0.0000	0.0000	0.0000	0.0000	0.0000	0.0000	0.0000	0.0000	0.0000	0.0000	0.0000	**3.30**
3.40	0.0000	0.0000	0.0000	0.0000	0.0000	0.0000	0.0000	0.0000	0.0000	0.0000	0.0000	0.0000	0.0000	**3.40**
3.50	0.0001	0.0000	0.0000	0.0000	0.0000	0.0000	0.0000	0.0000	0.0000	0.0000	0.0000	0.0000	0.0000	**3.50**
3.60	0.0001	0.0000	0.0000	0.0000	0.0000	0.0000	0.0000	0.0000	0.0000	0.0000	0.0000	0.0000	0.0000	**3.60**
3.70	0.0001	0.0000	0.0000	0.0000	0.0000	0.0000	0.0000	0.0000	0.0000	0.0000	0.0000	0.0000	0.0000	**3.70**
3.80	0.0001	0.0000	0.0000	0.0000	0.0000	0.0000	0.0000	0.0000	0.0000	0.0000	0.0000	0.0000	0.0000	**3.80**
3.90	0.0002	0.0000	0.0000	0.0000	0.0000	0.0000	0.0000	0.0000	0.0000	0.0000	0.0000	0.0000	0.0000	**3.90**
4.00	0.0002	0.0001	0.0000	0.0000	0.0000	0.0000	0.0000	0.0000	0.0000	0.0000	0.0000	0.0000	0.0000	**4.00**
4.10	0.0002	0.0001	0.0000	0.0000	0.0000	0.0000	0.0000	0.0000	0.0000	0.0000	0.0000	0.0000	0.0000	**4.10**
4.20	0.0003	0.0001	0.0000	0.0000	0.0000	0.0000	0.0000	0.0000	0.0000	0.0000	0.0000	0.0000	0.0000	**4.20**
4.30	0.0004	0.0001	0.0000	0.0000	0.0000	0.0000	0.0000	0.0000	0.0000	0.0000	0.0000	0.0000	0.0000	**4.30**
4.40	0.0005	0.0001	0.0000	0.0000	0.0000	0.0000	0.0000	0.0000	0.0000	0.0000	0.0000	0.0000	0.0000	**4.40**
4.50	0.0006	0.0002	0.0001	0.0000	0.0000	0.0000	0.0000	0.0000	0.0000	0.0000	0.0000	0.0000	0.0000	**4.50**
4.60	0.0007	0.0002	0.0001	0.0000	0.0000	0.0000	0.0000	0.0000	0.0000	0.0000	0.0000	0.0000	0.0000	**4.60**
4.70	0.0008	0.0003	0.0001	0.0000	0.0000	0.0000	0.0000	0.0000	0.0000	0.0000	0.0000	0.0000	0.0000	**4.70**
4.80	0.0009	0.0003	0.0001	0.0000	0.0000	0.0000	0.0000	0.0000	0.0000	0.0000	0.0000	0.0000	0.0000	**4.80**
4.90	0.0011	0.0004	0.0001	0.0000	0.0000	0.0000	0.0000	0.0000	0.0000	0.0000	0.0000	0.0000	0.0000	**4.90**
5.00	0.0013	0.0005	0.0002	0.0000	0.0000	0.0000	0.0000	0.0000	0.0000	0.0000	0.0000	0.0000	0.0000	**5.00**
5.10	0.0015	0.0006	0.0002	0.0001	0.0000	0.0000	0.0000	0.0000	0.0000	0.0000	0.0000	0.0000	0.0000	**5.10**
5.20	0.0018	0.0007	0.0002	0.0001	0.0000	0.0000	0.0000	0.0000	0.0000	0.0000	0.0000	0.0000	0.0000	**5.20**
5.30	0.0021	0.0008	0.0003	0.0001	0.0000	0.0000	0.0000	0.0000	0.0000	0.0000	0.0000	0.0000	0.0000	**5.30**
5.40	0.0024	0.0009	0.0003	0.0001	0.0000	0.0000	0.0000	0.0000	0.0000	0.0000	0.0000	0.0000	0.0000	**5.40**
5.50	0.0028	0.0011	0.0004	0.0001	0.0000	0.0000	0.0000	0.0000	0.0000	0.0000	0.0000	0.0000	0.0000	**5.50**
5.60	0.0032	0.0013	0.0005	0.0002	0.0001	0.0000	0.0000	0.0000	0.0000	0.0000	0.0000	0.0000	0.0000	**5.60**
5.70	0.0036	0.0015	0.0006	0.0002	0.0001	0.0000	0.0000	0.0000	0.0000	0.0000	0.0000	0.0000	0.0000	**5.70**
5.80	0.0041	0.0017	0.0007	0.0002	0.0001	0.0000	0.0000	0.0000	0.0000	0.0000	0.0000	0.0000	0.0000	**5.80**
5.90	0.0046	0.0019	0.0008	0.0003	0.0001	0.0000	0.0000	0.0000	0.0000	0.0000	0.0000	0.0000	0.0000	**5.90**
6.00	0.0052	0.0022	0.0009	0.0003	0.0001	0.0000	0.0000	0.0000	0.0000	0.0000	0.0000	0.0000	0.0000	**6.00**
6.10	0.0058	0.0025	0.0010	0.0004	0.0001	0.0000	0.0000	0.0000	0.0000	0.0000	0.0000	0.0000	0.0000	**6.10**
6.20	0.0065	0.0029	0.0012	0.0005	0.0002	0.0001	0.0000	0.0000	0.0000	0.0000	0.0000	0.0000	0.0000	**6.20**
6.30	0.0073	0.0033	0.0014	0.0005	0.0002	0.0001	0.0000	0.0000	0.0000	0.0000	0.0000	0.0000	0.0000	**6.30**
6.40	0.0081	0.0037	0.0016	0.0006	0.0002	0.0001	0.0000	0.0000	0.0000	0.0000	0.0000	0.0000	0.0000	**6.40**

$$\Pr(X = x) = f(x;\lambda) = \frac{\lambda^x}{x!}e^{-\lambda}$$

	Probability of x occurrences													
λ	0	1	2	3	4	5	6	7	8	9	10	11	12	λ
6.50	0.0015	0.0098	0.0318	0.0688	0.1118	0.1454	0.1575	0.1462	0.1188	0.0858	0.0558	0.0330	0.0179	**6.50**
6.60	0.0014	0.0090	0.0296	0.0652	0.1076	0.1420	0.1562	0.1472	0.1215	0.0891	0.0588	0.0353	0.0194	**6.60**
6.70	0.0012	0.0082	0.0276	0.0617	0.1034	0.1385	0.1546	0.1480	0.1240	0.0923	0.0618	0.0377	0.0210	**6.70**
6.80	0.0011	0.0076	0.0258	0.0584	0.0992	0.1349	0.1529	0.1486	0.1263	0.0954	0.0649	0.0401	0.0227	**6.80**
6.90	0.0010	0.0070	0.0240	0.0552	0.0952	0.1314	0.1511	0.1489	0.1284	0.0985	0.0679	0.0426	0.0245	**6.90**
7.00	0.0009	0.0064	0.0223	0.0521	0.0912	0.1277	0.1490	0.1490	0.1304	0.1014	0.0710	0.0452	0.0263	**7.00**
7.10	0.0008	0.0059	0.0208	0.0492	0.0874	0.1241	0.1468	0.1489	0.1321	0.1042	0.0740	0.0478	0.0283	**7.10**
7.20	0.0007	0.0054	0.0194	0.0464	0.0836	0.1204	0.1445	0.1486	0.1337	0.1070	0.0770	0.0504	0.0303	**7.20**
7.30	0.0007	0.0049	0.0180	0.0438	0.0799	0.1167	0.1420	0.1481	0.1351	0.1096	0.0800	0.0531	0.0323	**7.30**
7.40	0.0006	0.0045	0.0167	0.0413	0.0764	0.1130	0.1394	0.1474	0.1363	0.1121	0.0829	0.0558	0.0344	**7.40**
7.50	0.0006	0.0041	0.0156	0.0389	0.0729	0.1094	0.1367	0.1465	0.1373	0.1144	0.0858	0.0585	0.0366	**7.50**
7.60	0.0005	0.0038	0.0145	0.0366	0.0696	0.1057	0.1339	0.1454	0.1381	0.1167	0.0887	0.0613	0.0388	**7.60**
7.70	0.0005	0.0035	0.0134	0.0345	0.0663	0.1021	0.1311	0.1442	0.1388	0.1187	0.0914	0.0640	0.0411	**7.70**
7.80	0.0004	0.0032	0.0125	0.0324	0.0632	0.0986	0.1282	0.1428	0.1392	0.1207	0.0941	0.0667	0.0434	**7.80**
7.90	0.0004	0.0029	0.0116	0.0305	0.0602	0.0951	0.1252	0.1413	0.1395	0.1224	0.0967	0.0695	0.0457	**7.90**
8.00	0.0003	0.0027	0.0107	0.0286	0.0573	0.0916	0.1221	0.1396	0.1396	0.1241	0.0993	0.0722	0.0481	**8.00**
8.10	0.0003	0.0025	0.0100	0.0269	0.0544	0.0882	0.1191	0.1378	0.1395	0.1256	0.1017	0.0749	0.0505	**8.10**
8.20	0.0003	0.0023	0.0092	0.0252	0.0517	0.0849	0.1160	0.1358	0.1392	0.1269	0.1040	0.0776	0.0530	**8.20**
8.30	0.0002	0.0021	0.0086	0.0237	0.0491	0.0816	0.1128	0.1338	0.1388	0.1280	0.1063	0.0802	0.0555	**8.30**
8.40	0.0002	0.0019	0.0079	0.0222	0.0466	0.0784	0.1097	0.1317	0.1382	0.1290	0.1084	0.0828	0.0579	**8.40**
8.50	0.0002	0.0017	0.0074	0.0208	0.0443	0.0752	0.1066	0.1294	0.1375	0.1299	0.1104	0.0853	0.0604	**8.50**
8.60	0.0002	0.0016	0.0068	0.0195	0.0420	0.0722	0.1034	0.1271	0.1366	0.1306	0.1123	0.0878	0.0629	**8.60**
8.70	0.0002	0.0014	0.0063	0.0183	0.0398	0.0692	0.1003	0.1247	0.1356	0.1311	0.1140	0.0902	0.0654	**8.70**
8.80	0.0002	0.0013	0.0058	0.0171	0.0377	0.0663	0.0972	0.1222	0.1344	0.1315	0.1157	0.0925	0.0679	**8.80**
8.90	0.0001	0.0012	0.0054	0.0160	0.0357	0.0635	0.0941	0.1197	0.1332	0.1317	0.1172	0.0948	0.0703	**8.90**
9.00	0.0001	0.0011	0.0050	0.0150	0.0337	0.0607	0.0911	0.1171	0.1318	0.1318	0.1186	0.0970	0.0728	**9.00**
9.10	0.0001	0.0010	0.0046	0.0140	0.0319	0.0581	0.0881	0.1145	0.1302	0.1317	0.1198	0.0991	0.0752	**9.10**
9.20	0.0001	0.0009	0.0043	0.0131	0.0302	0.0555	0.0851	0.1118	0.1286	0.1315	0.1210	0.1012	0.0776	**9.20**
9.30	0.0001	0.0009	0.0040	0.0123	0.0285	0.0530	0.0822	0.1091	0.1269	0.1311	0.1219	0.1031	0.0799	**9.30**
9.40	0.0001	0.0008	0.0037	0.0115	0.0269	0.0506	0.0793	0.1064	0.1251	0.1306	0.1228	0.1049	0.0822	**9.40**
9.50	0.0001	0.0007	0.0034	0.0107	0.0254	0.0483	0.0764	0.1037	0.1232	0.1300	0.1235	0.1067	0.0844	**9.50**
9.60	0.0001	0.0007	0.0031	0.0100	0.0240	0.0460	0.0736	0.1010	0.1212	0.1293	0.1241	0.1083	0.0866	**9.60**
9.70	0.0001	0.0006	0.0029	0.0093	0.0226	0.0439	0.0709	0.0982	0.1191	0.1284	0.1245	0.1098	0.0888	**9.70**
9.80	0.0001	0.0005	0.0027	0.0087	0.0213	0.0418	0.0682	0.0955	0.1170	0.1274	0.1249	0.1112	0.0908	**9.80**
9.90	0.0001	0.0005	0.0025	0.0081	0.0201	0.0398	0.0656	0.0928	0.1148	0.1263	0.1250	0.1125	0.0928	**9.90**
10.00	0.0000	0.0005	0.0023	0.0076	0.0189	0.0378	0.0631	0.0901	0.1126	0.1251	0.1251	0.1137	0.0948	**10.00**

$$\Pr(X = x) = f(x;\lambda) = \frac{\lambda^x}{x!} e^{-\lambda}$$

	Probability of *x* occurrences													
λ	**13**	**14**	**15**	**16**	**17**	**18**	**19**	**20**	**21**	**22**	**23**	**24**	**25**	λ
6.50	0.0089	0.0041	0.0018	0.0007	0.0003	0.0001	0.0000	0.0000	0.0000	0.0000	0.0000	0.0000	0.0000	**6.50**
6.60	0.0099	0.0046	0.0020	0.0008	0.0003	0.0001	0.0000	0.0000	0.0000	0.0000	0.0000	0.0000	0.0000	**6.60**
6.70	0.0108	0.0052	0.0023	0.0010	0.0004	0.0001	0.0001	0.0000	0.0000	0.0000	0.0000	0.0000	0.0000	**6.70**
6.80	0.0119	0.0058	0.0026	0.0011	0.0004	0.0002	0.0001	0.0000	0.0000	0.0000	0.0000	0.0000	0.0000	**6.80**
6.90	0.0130	0.0064	0.0029	0.0013	0.0005	0.0002	0.0001	0.0000	0.0000	0.0000	0.0000	0.0000	0.0000	**6.90**
7.00	0.0142	0.0071	0.0033	0.0014	0.0006	0.0002	0.0001	0.0000	0.0000	0.0000	0.0000	0.0000	0.0000	**7.00**
7.10	0.0154	0.0078	0.0037	0.0016	0.0007	0.0003	0.0001	0.0000	0.0000	0.0000	0.0000	0.0000	0.0000	**7.10**
7.20	0.0168	0.0086	0.0041	0.0019	0.0008	0.0003	0.0001	0.0000	0.0000	0.0000	0.0000	0.0000	0.0000	**7.20**
7.30	0.0181	0.0095	0.0046	0.0021	0.0009	0.0004	0.0001	0.0001	0.0000	0.0000	0.0000	0.0000	0.0000	**7.30**
7.40	0.0196	0.0104	0.0051	0.0024	0.0010	0.0004	0.0002	0.0001	0.0000	0.0000	0.0000	0.0000	0.0000	**7.40**
7.50	0.0211	0.0113	0.0057	0.0026	0.0012	0.0005	0.0002	0.0001	0.0000	0.0000	0.0000	0.0000	0.0000	**7.50**
7.60	0.0227	0.0123	0.0062	0.0030	0.0013	0.0006	0.0002	0.0001	0.0000	0.0000	0.0000	0.0000	0.0000	**7.60**
7.70	0.0243	0.0134	0.0069	0.0033	0.0015	0.0006	0.0003	0.0001	0.0000	0.0000	0.0000	0.0000	0.0000	**7.70**
7.80	0.0260	0.0145	0.0075	0.0037	0.0017	0.0007	0.0003	0.0001	0.0000	0.0000	0.0000	0.0000	0.0000	**7.80**
7.90	0.0278	0.0157	0.0083	0.0041	0.0019	0.0008	0.0003	0.0001	0.0001	0.0000	0.0000	0.0000	0.0000	**7.90**
8.00	0.0296	0.0169	0.0090	0.0045	0.0021	0.0009	0.0004	0.0002	0.0001	0.0000	0.0000	0.0000	0.0000	**8.00**
8.10	0.0315	0.0182	0.0098	0.0050	0.0024	0.0011	0.0005	0.0002	0.0001	0.0000	0.0000	0.0000	0.0000	**8.10**
8.20	0.0334	0.0196	0.0107	0.0055	0.0026	0.0012	0.0005	0.0002	0.0001	0.0000	0.0000	0.0000	0.0000	**8.20**
8.30	0.0354	0.0210	0.0116	0.0060	0.0029	0.0014	0.0006	0.0002	0.0001	0.0000	0.0000	0.0000	0.0000	**8.30**
8.40	0.0374	0.0225	0.0126	0.0066	0.0033	0.0015	0.0007	0.0003	0.0001	0.0000	0.0000	0.0000	0.0000	**8.40**
8.50	0.0395	0.0240	0.0136	0.0072	0.0036	0.0017	0.0008	0.0003	0.0001	0.0001	0.0000	0.0000	0.0000	**8.50**
8.60	0.0416	0.0256	0.0147	0.0079	0.0040	0.0019	0.0009	0.0004	0.0002	0.0001	0.0000	0.0000	0.0000	**8.60**
8.70	0.0438	0.0272	0.0158	0.0086	0.0044	0.0021	0.0010	0.0004	0.0002	0.0001	0.0000	0.0000	0.0000	**8.70**
8.80	0.0459	0.0289	0.0169	0.0093	0.0048	0.0024	0.0011	0.0005	0.0002	0.0001	0.0000	0.0000	0.0000	**8.80**
8.90	0.0481	0.0306	0.0182	0.0101	0.0053	0.0026	0.0012	0.0005	0.0002	0.0001	0.0000	0.0000	0.0000	**8.90**
9.00	0.0504	0.0324	0.0194	0.0109	0.0058	0.0029	0.0014	0.0006	0.0003	0.0001	0.0000	0.0000	0.0000	**9.00**
9.10	0.0526	0.0342	0.0208	0.0118	0.0063	0.0032	0.0015	0.0007	0.0003	0.0001	0.0000	0.0000	0.0000	**9.10**
9.20	0.0549	0.0361	0.0221	0.0127	0.0069	0.0035	0.0017	0.0008	0.0003	0.0001	0.0001	0.0000	0.0000	**9.20**
9.30	0.0572	0.0380	0.0235	0.0137	0.0075	0.0039	0.0019	0.0009	0.0004	0.0002	0.0001	0.0000	0.0000	**9.30**
9.40	0.0594	0.0399	0.0250	0.0147	0.0081	0.0042	0.0021	0.0010	0.0004	0.0002	0.0001	0.0000	0.0000	**9.40**
9.50	0.0617	0.0419	0.0265	0.0157	0.0088	0.0046	0.0023	0.0011	0.0005	0.0002	0.0001	0.0000	0.0000	**9.50**
9.60	0.0640	0.0439	0.0281	0.0168	0.0095	0.0051	0.0026	0.0012	0.0006	0.0002	0.0001	0.0000	0.0000	**9.60**
9.70	0.0662	0.0459	0.0297	0.0180	0.0103	0.0055	0.0028	0.0014	0.0006	0.0003	0.0001	0.0000	0.0000	**9.70**
9.80	0.0685	0.0479	0.0313	0.0192	0.0111	0.0060	0.0031	0.0015	0.0007	0.0003	0.0001	0.0001	0.0000	**9.80**
9.90	0.0707	0.0500	0.0330	0.0204	0.0119	0.0065	0.0034	0.0017	0.0008	0.0004	0.0002	0.0001	0.0000	**9.90**
10.00	0.0729	0.0521	0.0347	0.0217	0.0128	0.0071	0.0037	0.0019	0.0009	0.0004	0.0002	0.0001	0.0000	**10.00**

Appendix C.2

Cumulative Poisson Distribution Table

$$\Pr(X \le x) = F(x;\lambda) = \sum_{x=0}^{n} \frac{\lambda^x}{x!} e^{-\lambda}$$

	Probability of ≤ x occurrences													
λ	**0**	**1**	**2**	**3**	**4**	**5**	**6**	**7**	**8**	**9**	**10**	**11**	**12**	λ
0.05	0.9512	0.9988	1.0000	1.0000	1.0000	1.0000	1.0000	1.0000	1.0000	1.0000	1.0000	1.0000	1.0000	**0.05**
0.10	0.9048	0.9953	0.9998	1.0000	1.0000	1.0000	1.0000	1.0000	1.0000	1.0000	1.0000	1.0000	1.0000	**0.10**
0.15	0.8607	0.9898	0.9995	1.0000	1.0000	1.0000	1.0000	1.0000	1.0000	1.0000	1.0000	1.0000	1.0000	**0.15**
0.20	0.8187	0.9825	0.9989	0.9999	1.0000	1.0000	1.0000	1.0000	1.0000	1.0000	1.0000	1.0000	1.0000	**0.20**
0.25	0.7788	0.9735	0.9978	0.9999	1.0000	1.0000	1.0000	1.0000	1.0000	1.0000	1.0000	1.0000	1.0000	**0.25**
0.30	0.7408	0.9631	0.9964	0.9997	1.0000	1.0000	1.0000	1.0000	1.0000	1.0000	1.0000	1.0000	1.0000	**0.30**
0.35	0.7047	0.9513	0.9945	0.9995	1.0000	1.0000	1.0000	1.0000	1.0000	1.0000	1.0000	1.0000	1.0000	**0.35**
0.40	0.6703	0.9384	0.9921	0.9992	0.9999	1.0000	1.0000	1.0000	1.0000	1.0000	1.0000	1.0000	1.0000	**0.40**
0.45	0.6376	0.9246	0.9891	0.9988	0.9999	1.0000	1.0000	1.0000	1.0000	1.0000	1.0000	1.0000	1.0000	**0.45**
0.50	0.6065	0.9098	0.9856	0.9982	0.9998	1.0000	1.0000	1.0000	1.0000	1.0000	1.0000	1.0000	1.0000	**0.50**
0.55	0.5769	0.8943	0.9815	0.9975	0.9997	1.0000	1.0000	1.0000	1.0000	1.0000	1.0000	1.0000	1.0000	**0.55**
0.60	0.5488	0.8781	0.9769	0.9966	0.9996	1.0000	1.0000	1.0000	1.0000	1.0000	1.0000	1.0000	1.0000	**0.60**
0.65	0.5220	0.8614	0.9717	0.9956	0.9994	0.9999	1.0000	1.0000	1.0000	1.0000	1.0000	1.0000	1.0000	**0.65**
0.70	0.4966	0.8442	0.9659	0.9942	0.9992	0.9999	1.0000	1.0000	1.0000	1.0000	1.0000	1.0000	1.0000	**0.70**
0.75	0.4724	0.8266	0.9595	0.9927	0.9989	0.9999	1.0000	1.0000	1.0000	1.0000	1.0000	1.0000	1.0000	**0.75**
0.80	0.4493	0.8088	0.9526	0.9909	0.9986	0.9998	1.0000	1.0000	1.0000	1.0000	1.0000	1.0000	1.0000	**0.80**
0.85	0.4274	0.7907	0.9451	0.9889	0.9982	0.9997	1.0000	1.0000	1.0000	1.0000	1.0000	1.0000	1.0000	**0.85**
0.90	0.4066	0.7725	0.9371	0.9865	0.9977	0.9997	1.0000	1.0000	1.0000	1.0000	1.0000	1.0000	1.0000	**0.90**
0.95	0.3867	0.7541	0.9287	0.9839	0.9971	0.9995	0.9999	1.0000	1.0000	1.0000	1.0000	1.0000	1.0000	**0.95**
1.00	0.3679	0.7358	0.9197	0.9810	0.9963	0.9994	0.9999	1.0000	1.0000	1.0000	1.0000	1.0000	1.0000	**1.00**
1.10	0.3329	0.6990	0.9004	0.9743	0.9946	0.9990	0.9999	1.0000	1.0000	1.0000	1.0000	1.0000	1.0000	**1.10**
1.20	0.3012	0.6626	0.8795	0.9662	0.9923	0.9985	0.9997	1.0000	1.0000	1.0000	1.0000	1.0000	1.0000	**1.20**
1.30	0.2725	0.6268	0.8571	0.9569	0.9893	0.9978	0.9996	0.9999	1.0000	1.0000	1.0000	1.0000	1.0000	**1.30**
1.40	0.2466	0.5918	0.8335	0.9463	0.9857	0.9968	0.9994	0.9999	1.0000	1.0000	1.0000	1.0000	1.0000	**1.40**
1.50	0.2231	0.5578	0.8088	0.9344	0.9814	0.9955	0.9991	0.9998	1.0000	1.0000	1.0000	1.0000	1.0000	**1.50**
1.60	0.2019	0.5249	0.7834	0.9212	0.9763	0.9940	0.9987	0.9997	1.0000	1.0000	1.0000	1.0000	1.0000	**1.60**
1.70	0.1827	0.4932	0.7572	0.9068	0.9704	0.9920	0.9981	0.9996	0.9999	1.0000	1.0000	1.0000	1.0000	**1.70**
1.80	0.1653	0.4628	0.7306	0.8913	0.9636	0.9896	0.9974	0.9994	0.9999	1.0000	1.0000	1.0000	1.0000	**1.80**
1.90	0.1496	0.4337	0.7037	0.8747	0.9559	0.9868	0.9966	0.9992	0.9998	1.0000	1.0000	1.0000	1.0000	**1.90**
2.00	0.1353	0.4060	0.6767	0.8571	0.9473	0.9834	0.9955	0.9989	0.9998	1.0000	1.0000	1.0000	1.0000	**2.00**
2.10	0.1225	0.3796	0.6496	0.8386	0.9379	0.9796	0.9941	0.9985	0.9997	0.9999	1.0000	1.0000	1.0000	**2.10**
2.20	0.1108	0.3546	0.6227	0.8194	0.9275	0.9751	0.9925	0.9980	0.9995	0.9999	1.0000	1.0000	1.0000	**2.20**
2.30	0.1003	0.3309	0.5960	0.7993	0.9162	0.9700	0.9906	0.9974	0.9994	0.9999	1.0000	1.0000	1.0000	**2.30**
2.40	0.0907	0.3084	0.5697	0.7787	0.9041	0.9643	0.9884	0.9967	0.9991	0.9998	1.0000	1.0000	1.0000	**2.40**
2.50	0.0821	0.2873	0.5438	0.7576	0.8912	0.9580	0.9858	0.9958	0.9989	0.9997	0.9999	1.0000	1.0000	**2.50**
2.60	0.0743	0.2674	0.5184	0.7360	0.8774	0.9510	0.9828	0.9947	0.9985	0.9996	0.9999	1.0000	1.0000	**2.60**
2.70	0.0672	0.2487	0.4936	0.7141	0.8629	0.9433	0.9794	0.9934	0.9981	0.9995	0.9999	1.0000	1.0000	**2.70**

$$\Pr(X \leq x) = F(x;\lambda) = \sum_{x=0}^{n} \frac{\lambda^x}{x!} e^{-\lambda}$$

	Probability of ≤ *x* occurrences													
λ	13	14	15	16	17	18	19	20	21	22	23	24	25	λ
0.05	1.0000	1.0000	1.0000	1.0000	1.0000	1.0000	1.0000	1.0000	1.0000	1.0000	1.0000	1.0000	1.0000	**0.05**
0.10	1.0000	1.0000	1.0000	1.0000	1.0000	1.0000	1.0000	1.0000	1.0000	1.0000	1.0000	1.0000	1.0000	**0.10**
0.15	1.0000	1.0000	1.0000	1.0000	1.0000	1.0000	1.0000	1.0000	1.0000	1.0000	1.0000	1.0000	1.0000	**0.15**
0.20	1.0000	1.0000	1.0000	1.0000	1.0000	1.0000	1.0000	1.0000	1.0000	1.0000	1.0000	1.0000	1.0000	**0.20**
0.25	1.0000	1.0000	1.0000	1.0000	1.0000	1.0000	1.0000	1.0000	1.0000	1.0000	1.0000	1.0000	1.0000	**0.25**
0.30	1.0000	1.0000	1.0000	1.0000	1.0000	1.0000	1.0000	1.0000	1.0000	1.0000	1.0000	1.0000	1.0000	**0.30**
0.35	1.0000	1.0000	1.0000	1.0000	1.0000	1.0000	1.0000	1.0000	1.0000	1.0000	1.0000	1.0000	1.0000	**0.35**
0.40	1.0000	1.0000	1.0000	1.0000	1.0000	1.0000	1.0000	1.0000	1.0000	1.0000	1.0000	1.0000	1.0000	**0.40**
0.45	1.0000	1.0000	1.0000	1.0000	1.0000	1.0000	1.0000	1.0000	1.0000	1.0000	1.0000	1.0000	1.0000	**0.45**
0.50	1.0000	1.0000	1.0000	1.0000	1.0000	1.0000	1.0000	1.0000	1.0000	1.0000	1.0000	1.0000	1.0000	**0.50**
0.55	1.0000	1.0000	1.0000	1.0000	1.0000	1.0000	1.0000	1.0000	1.0000	1.0000	1.0000	1.0000	1.0000	**0.55**
0.60	1.0000	1.0000	1.0000	1.0000	1.0000	1.0000	1.0000	1.0000	1.0000	1.0000	1.0000	1.0000	1.0000	**0.60**
0.65	1.0000	1.0000	1.0000	1.0000	1.0000	1.0000	1.0000	1.0000	1.0000	1.0000	1.0000	1.0000	1.0000	**0.65**
0.70	1.0000	1.0000	1.0000	1.0000	1.0000	1.0000	1.0000	1.0000	1.0000	1.0000	1.0000	1.0000	1.0000	**0.70**
0.75	1.0000	1.0000	1.0000	1.0000	1.0000	1.0000	1.0000	1.0000	1.0000	1.0000	1.0000	1.0000	1.0000	**0.75**
0.80	1.0000	1.0000	1.0000	1.0000	1.0000	1.0000	1.0000	1.0000	1.0000	1.0000	1.0000	1.0000	1.0000	**0.80**
0.85	1.0000	1.0000	1.0000	1.0000	1.0000	1.0000	1.0000	1.0000	1.0000	1.0000	1.0000	1.0000	1.0000	**0.85**
0.90	1.0000	1.0000	1.0000	1.0000	1.0000	1.0000	1.0000	1.0000	1.0000	1.0000	1.0000	1.0000	1.0000	**0.90**
0.95	1.0000	1.0000	1.0000	1.0000	1.0000	1.0000	1.0000	1.0000	1.0000	1.0000	1.0000	1.0000	1.0000	**0.95**
1.00	1.0000	1.0000	1.0000	1.0000	1.0000	1.0000	1.0000	1.0000	1.0000	1.0000	1.0000	1.0000	1.0000	**1.00**
1.10	1.0000	1.0000	1.0000	1.0000	1.0000	1.0000	1.0000	1.0000	1.0000	1.0000	1.0000	1.0000	1.0000	**1.10**
1.20	1.0000	1.0000	1.0000	1.0000	1.0000	1.0000	1.0000	1.0000	1.0000	1.0000	1.0000	1.0000	1.0000	**1.20**
1.30	1.0000	1.0000	1.0000	1.0000	1.0000	1.0000	1.0000	1.0000	1.0000	1.0000	1.0000	1.0000	1.0000	**1.30**
1.40	1.0000	1.0000	1.0000	1.0000	1.0000	1.0000	1.0000	1.0000	1.0000	1.0000	1.0000	1.0000	1.0000	**1.40**
1.50	1.0000	1.0000	1.0000	1.0000	1.0000	1.0000	1.0000	1.0000	1.0000	1.0000	1.0000	1.0000	1.0000	**1.50**
1.60	1.0000	1.0000	1.0000	1.0000	1.0000	1.0000	1.0000	1.0000	1.0000	1.0000	1.0000	1.0000	1.0000	**1.60**
1.70	1.0000	1.0000	1.0000	1.0000	1.0000	1.0000	1.0000	1.0000	1.0000	1.0000	1.0000	1.0000	1.0000	**1.70**
1.80	1.0000	1.0000	1.0000	1.0000	1.0000	1.0000	1.0000	1.0000	1.0000	1.0000	1.0000	1.0000	1.0000	**1.80**
1.90	1.0000	1.0000	1.0000	1.0000	1.0000	1.0000	1.0000	1.0000	1.0000	1.0000	1.0000	1.0000	1.0000	**1.90**
2.00	1.0000	1.0000	1.0000	1.0000	1.0000	1.0000	1.0000	1.0000	1.0000	1.0000	1.0000	1.0000	1.0000	**2.00**
2.10	1.0000	1.0000	1.0000	1.0000	1.0000	1.0000	1.0000	1.0000	1.0000	1.0000	1.0000	1.0000	1.0000	**2.10**
2.20	1.0000	1.0000	1.0000	1.0000	1.0000	1.0000	1.0000	1.0000	1.0000	1.0000	1.0000	1.0000	1.0000	**2.20**
2.30	1.0000	1.0000	1.0000	1.0000	1.0000	1.0000	1.0000	1.0000	1.0000	1.0000	1.0000	1.0000	1.0000	**2.30**
2.40	1.0000	1.0000	1.0000	1.0000	1.0000	1.0000	1.0000	1.0000	1.0000	1.0000	1.0000	1.0000	1.0000	**2.40**
2.50	1.0000	1.0000	1.0000	1.0000	1.0000	1.0000	1.0000	1.0000	1.0000	1.0000	1.0000	1.0000	1.0000	**2.50**
2.60	1.0000	1.0000	1.0000	1.0000	1.0000	1.0000	1.0000	1.0000	1.0000	1.0000	1.0000	1.0000	1.0000	**2.60**
2.70	1.0000	1.0000	1.0000	1.0000	1.0000	1.0000	1.0000	1.0000	1.0000	1.0000	1.0000	1.0000	1.0000	**2.70**

$$\Pr(X \le x) = F(x;\lambda) = \sum_{x=0}^{n} \frac{\lambda^x}{x!} e^{-\lambda}$$

	Probability of ≤ *x* occurrences													
λ	0	1	2	3	4	5	6	7	8	9	10	11	12	λ
2.80	0.0608	0.2311	0.4695	0.6919	0.8477	0.9349	0.9756	0.9919	0.9976	0.9993	0.9998	1.0000	1.0000	**2.80**
2.90	0.0550	0.2146	0.4460	0.6696	0.8318	0.9258	0.9713	0.9901	0.9969	0.9991	0.9998	0.9999	1.0000	**2.90**
3.00	0.0498	0.1991	0.4232	0.6472	0.8153	0.9161	0.9665	0.9881	0.9962	0.9989	0.9997	0.9999	1.0000	**3.00**
3.10	0.0450	0.1847	0.4012	0.6248	0.7982	0.9057	0.9612	0.9858	0.9953	0.9986	0.9996	0.9999	1.0000	**3.10**
3.20	0.0408	0.1712	0.3799	0.6025	0.7806	0.8946	0.9554	0.9832	0.9943	0.9982	0.9995	0.9999	1.0000	**3.20**
3.30	0.0369	0.1586	0.3594	0.5803	0.7626	0.8829	0.9490	0.9802	0.9931	0.9978	0.9994	0.9998	1.0000	**3.30**
3.40	0.0334	0.1468	0.3397	0.5584	0.7442	0.8705	0.9421	0.9769	0.9917	0.9973	0.9992	0.9998	0.9999	**3.40**
3.50	0.0302	0.1359	0.3208	0.5366	0.7254	0.8576	0.9347	0.9733	0.9901	0.9967	0.9990	0.9997	0.9999	**3.50**
3.60	0.0273	0.1257	0.3027	0.5152	0.7064	0.8441	0.9267	0.9692	0.9883	0.9960	0.9987	0.9996	0.9999	**3.60**
3.70	0.0247	0.1162	0.2854	0.4942	0.6872	0.8301	0.9182	0.9648	0.9863	0.9952	0.9984	0.9995	0.9999	**3.70**
3.80	0.0224	0.1074	0.2689	0.4735	0.6678	0.8156	0.9091	0.9599	0.9840	0.9942	0.9981	0.9994	0.9998	**3.80**
3.90	0.0202	0.0992	0.2531	0.4532	0.6484	0.8006	0.8995	0.9546	0.9815	0.9931	0.9977	0.9993	0.9998	**3.90**
4.00	0.0183	0.0916	0.2381	0.4335	0.6288	0.7851	0.8893	0.9489	0.9786	0.9919	0.9972	0.9991	0.9997	**4.00**
4.10	0.0166	0.0845	0.2238	0.4142	0.6093	0.7693	0.8786	0.9427	0.9755	0.9905	0.9966	0.9989	0.9997	**4.10**
4.20	0.0150	0.0780	0.2102	0.3954	0.5898	0.7531	0.8675	0.9361	0.9721	0.9889	0.9959	0.9986	0.9996	**4.20**
4.30	0.0136	0.0719	0.1974	0.3772	0.5704	0.7367	0.8558	0.9290	0.9683	0.9871	0.9952	0.9983	0.9995	**4.30**
4.40	0.0123	0.0663	0.1851	0.3594	0.5512	0.7199	0.8436	0.9214	0.9642	0.9851	0.9943	0.9980	0.9993	**4.40**
4.50	0.0111	0.0611	0.1736	0.3423	0.5321	0.7029	0.8311	0.9134	0.9597	0.9829	0.9933	0.9976	0.9992	**4.50**
4.60	0.0101	0.0563	0.1626	0.3257	0.5132	0.6858	0.8180	0.9049	0.9549	0.9805	0.9922	0.9971	0.9990	**4.60**
4.70	0.0091	0.0518	0.1523	0.3097	0.4946	0.6684	0.8046	0.8960	0.9497	0.9778	0.9910	0.9966	0.9988	**4.70**
4.80	0.0082	0.0477	0.1425	0.2942	0.4763	0.6510	0.7908	0.8867	0.9442	0.9749	0.9896	0.9960	0.9986	**4.80**
4.90	0.0074	0.0439	0.1333	0.2793	0.4582	0.6335	0.7767	0.8769	0.9382	0.9717	0.9880	0.9953	0.9983	**4.90**
5.00	0.0067	0.0404	0.1247	0.2650	0.4405	0.6160	0.7622	0.8666	0.9319	0.9682	0.9863	0.9945	0.9980	**5.00**
5.10	0.0061	0.0372	0.1165	0.2513	0.4231	0.5984	0.7474	0.8560	0.9252	0.9644	0.9844	0.9937	0.9976	**5.10**
5.20	0.0055	0.0342	0.1088	0.2381	0.4061	0.5809	0.7324	0.8449	0.9181	0.9603	0.9823	0.9927	0.9972	**5.20**
5.30	0.0050	0.0314	0.1016	0.2254	0.3895	0.5635	0.7171	0.8335	0.9106	0.9559	0.9800	0.9916	0.9967	**5.30**
5.40	0.0045	0.0289	0.0948	0.2133	0.3733	0.5461	0.7017	0.8217	0.9027	0.9512	0.9775	0.9904	0.9962	**5.40**
5.50	0.0041	0.0266	0.0884	0.2017	0.3575	0.5289	0.6860	0.8095	0.8944	0.9462	0.9747	0.9890	0.9955	**5.50**
5.60	0.0037	0.0244	0.0824	0.1906	0.3422	0.5119	0.6703	0.7970	0.8857	0.9409	0.9718	0.9875	0.9949	**5.60**
5.70	0.0033	0.0224	0.0768	0.1800	0.3272	0.4950	0.6544	0.7841	0.8766	0.9352	0.9686	0.9859	0.9941	**5.70**
5.80	0.0030	0.0206	0.0715	0.1700	0.3127	0.4783	0.6384	0.7710	0.8672	0.9292	0.9651	0.9841	0.9932	**5.80**
5.90	0.0027	0.0189	0.0666	0.1604	0.2987	0.4619	0.6224	0.7576	0.8574	0.9228	0.9614	0.9821	0.9922	**5.90**
6.00	0.0025	0.0174	0.0620	0.1512	0.2851	0.4457	0.6063	0.7440	0.8472	0.9161	0.9574	0.9799	0.9912	**6.00**
6.10	0.0022	0.0159	0.0577	0.1425	0.2719	0.4298	0.5902	0.7301	0.8367	0.9090	0.9531	0.9776	0.9900	**6.10**
6.20	0.0020	0.0146	0.0536	0.1342	0.2592	0.4141	0.5742	0.7160	0.8259	0.9016	0.9486	0.9750	0.9887	**6.20**
6.30	0.0018	0.0134	0.0498	0.1264	0.2469	0.3988	0.5582	0.7017	0.8148	0.8939	0.9437	0.9723	0.9873	**6.30**
6.40	0.0017	0.0123	0.0463	0.1189	0.2351	0.3837	0.5423	0.6873	0.8033	0.8858	0.9386	0.9693	0.9857	**6.40**
6.50	0.0015	0.0113	0.0430	0.1118	0.2237	0.3690	0.5265	0.6728	0.7916	0.8774	0.9332	0.9661	0.9840	**6.50**

$$\Pr(X \leq x) = F(x;\lambda) = \sum_{x=0}^{n} \frac{\lambda^x}{x!} e^{-\lambda}$$

	Probability of ≤ *x* occurrences													
λ	13	14	15	16	17	18	19	20	21	22	23	24	25	λ
2.80	1.0000	1.0000	1.0000	1.0000	1.0000	1.0000	1.0000	1.0000	1.0000	1.0000	1.0000	1.0000	1.0000	**2.80**
2.90	1.0000	1.0000	1.0000	1.0000	1.0000	1.0000	1.0000	1.0000	1.0000	1.0000	1.0000	1.0000	1.0000	**2.90**
3.00	1.0000	1.0000	1.0000	1.0000	1.0000	1.0000	1.0000	1.0000	1.0000	1.0000	1.0000	1.0000	1.0000	**3.00**
3.10	1.0000	1.0000	1.0000	1.0000	1.0000	1.0000	1.0000	1.0000	1.0000	1.0000	1.0000	1.0000	1.0000	**3.10**
3.20	1.0000	1.0000	1.0000	1.0000	1.0000	1.0000	1.0000	1.0000	1.0000	1.0000	1.0000	1.0000	1.0000	**3.20**
3.30	1.0000	1.0000	1.0000	1.0000	1.0000	1.0000	1.0000	1.0000	1.0000	1.0000	1.0000	1.0000	1.0000	**3.30**
3.40	1.0000	1.0000	1.0000	1.0000	1.0000	1.0000	1.0000	1.0000	1.0000	1.0000	1.0000	1.0000	1.0000	**3.40**
3.50	1.0000	1.0000	1.0000	1.0000	1.0000	1.0000	1.0000	1.0000	1.0000	1.0000	1.0000	1.0000	1.0000	**3.50**
3.60	1.0000	1.0000	1.0000	1.0000	1.0000	1.0000	1.0000	1.0000	1.0000	1.0000	1.0000	1.0000	1.0000	**3.60**
3.70	1.0000	1.0000	1.0000	1.0000	1.0000	1.0000	1.0000	1.0000	1.0000	1.0000	1.0000	1.0000	1.0000	**3.70**
3.80	1.0000	1.0000	1.0000	1.0000	1.0000	1.0000	1.0000	1.0000	1.0000	1.0000	1.0000	1.0000	1.0000	**3.80**
3.90	0.9999	1.0000	1.0000	1.0000	1.0000	1.0000	1.0000	1.0000	1.0000	1.0000	1.0000	1.0000	1.0000	**3.90**
4.00	0.9999	1.0000	1.0000	1.0000	1.0000	1.0000	1.0000	1.0000	1.0000	1.0000	1.0000	1.0000	1.0000	**4.00**
4.10	0.9999	1.0000	1.0000	1.0000	1.0000	1.0000	1.0000	1.0000	1.0000	1.0000	1.0000	1.0000	1.0000	**4.10**
4.20	0.9999	1.0000	1.0000	1.0000	1.0000	1.0000	1.0000	1.0000	1.0000	1.0000	1.0000	1.0000	1.0000	**4.20**
4.30	0.9998	1.0000	1.0000	1.0000	1.0000	1.0000	1.0000	1.0000	1.0000	1.0000	1.0000	1.0000	1.0000	**4.30**
4.40	0.9998	0.9999	1.0000	1.0000	1.0000	1.0000	1.0000	1.0000	1.0000	1.0000	1.0000	1.0000	1.0000	**4.40**
4.50	0.9997	0.9999	1.0000	1.0000	1.0000	1.0000	1.0000	1.0000	1.0000	1.0000	1.0000	1.0000	1.0000	**4.50**
4.60	0.9997	0.9999	1.0000	1.0000	1.0000	1.0000	1.0000	1.0000	1.0000	1.0000	1.0000	1.0000	1.0000	**4.60**
4.70	0.9996	0.9999	1.0000	1.0000	1.0000	1.0000	1.0000	1.0000	1.0000	1.0000	1.0000	1.0000	1.0000	**4.70**
4.80	0.9995	0.9999	1.0000	1.0000	1.0000	1.0000	1.0000	1.0000	1.0000	1.0000	1.0000	1.0000	1.0000	**4.80**
4.90	0.9994	0.9998	0.9999	1.0000	1.0000	1.0000	1.0000	1.0000	1.0000	1.0000	1.0000	1.0000	1.0000	**4.90**
5.00	0.9993	0.9998	0.9999	1.0000	1.0000	1.0000	1.0000	1.0000	1.0000	1.0000	1.0000	1.0000	1.0000	**5.00**
5.10	0.9992	0.9997	0.9999	1.0000	1.0000	1.0000	1.0000	1.0000	1.0000	1.0000	1.0000	1.0000	1.0000	**5.10**
5.20	0.9990	0.9997	0.9999	1.0000	1.0000	1.0000	1.0000	1.0000	1.0000	1.0000	1.0000	1.0000	1.0000	**5.20**
5.30	0.9988	0.9996	0.9999	1.0000	1.0000	1.0000	1.0000	1.0000	1.0000	1.0000	1.0000	1.0000	1.0000	**5.30**
5.40	0.9986	0.9995	0.9998	0.9999	1.0000	1.0000	1.0000	1.0000	1.0000	1.0000	1.0000	1.0000	1.0000	**5.40**
5.50	0.9983	0.9994	0.9998	0.9999	1.0000	1.0000	1.0000	1.0000	1.0000	1.0000	1.0000	1.0000	1.0000	**5.50**
5.60	0.9980	0.9993	0.9998	0.9999	1.0000	1.0000	1.0000	1.0000	1.0000	1.0000	1.0000	1.0000	1.0000	**5.60**
5.70	0.9977	0.9991	0.9997	0.9999	1.0000	1.0000	1.0000	1.0000	1.0000	1.0000	1.0000	1.0000	1.0000	**5.70**
5.80	0.9973	0.9990	0.9996	0.9999	1.0000	1.0000	1.0000	1.0000	1.0000	1.0000	1.0000	1.0000	1.0000	**5.80**
5.90	0.9969	0.9988	0.9996	0.9999	1.0000	1.0000	1.0000	1.0000	1.0000	1.0000	1.0000	1.0000	1.0000	**5.90**
6.00	0.9964	0.9986	0.9995	0.9998	0.9999	1.0000	1.0000	1.0000	1.0000	1.0000	1.0000	1.0000	1.0000	**6.00**
6.10	0.9958	0.9984	0.9994	0.9998	0.9999	1.0000	1.0000	1.0000	1.0000	1.0000	1.0000	1.0000	1.0000	**6.10**
6.20	0.9952	0.9981	0.9993	0.9997	0.9999	1.0000	1.0000	1.0000	1.0000	1.0000	1.0000	1.0000	1.0000	**6.20**
6.30	0.9945	0.9978	0.9992	0.9997	0.9999	1.0000	1.0000	1.0000	1.0000	1.0000	1.0000	1.0000	1.0000	**6.30**
6.40	0.9937	0.9974	0.9990	0.9996	0.9999	1.0000	1.0000	1.0000	1.0000	1.0000	1.0000	1.0000	1.0000	**6.40**
6.50	0.9929	0.9970	0.9988	0.9996	0.9998	0.9999	1.0000	1.0000	1.0000	1.0000	1.0000	1.0000	1.0000	**6.50**

$$\Pr(X \le x) = F(x;\lambda) = \sum_{x=0}^{n} \frac{\lambda^x}{x!} e^{-\lambda}$$

	Probability of ≤ *x* occurrences													
λ	**0**	**1**	**2**	**3**	**4**	**5**	**6**	**7**	**8**	**9**	**10**	**11**	**12**	λ
6.60	0.0014	0.0103	0.0400	0.1052	0.2127	0.3547	0.5108	0.6581	0.7796	0.8686	0.9274	0.9627	0.9821	**6.60**
6.70	0.0012	0.0095	0.0371	0.0988	0.2022	0.3406	0.4953	0.6433	0.7673	0.8596	0.9214	0.9591	0.9801	**6.70**
6.80	0.0011	0.0087	0.0344	0.0928	0.1920	0.3270	0.4799	0.6285	0.7548	0.8502	0.9151	0.9552	0.9779	**6.80**
6.90	0.0010	0.0080	0.0320	0.0871	0.1823	0.3137	0.4647	0.6136	0.7420	0.8405	0.9084	0.9510	0.9755	**6.90**
7.00	0.0009	0.0073	0.0296	0.0818	0.1730	0.3007	0.4497	0.5987	0.7291	0.8305	0.9015	0.9467	0.9730	**7.00**
7.10	0.0008	0.0067	0.0275	0.0767	0.1641	0.2881	0.4349	0.5838	0.7160	0.8202	0.8942	0.9420	0.9703	**7.10**
7.20	0.0007	0.0061	0.0255	0.0719	0.1555	0.2759	0.4204	0.5689	0.7027	0.8096	0.8867	0.9371	0.9673	**7.20**
7.30	0.0007	0.0056	0.0236	0.0674	0.1473	0.2640	0.4060	0.5541	0.6892	0.7988	0.8788	0.9319	0.9642	**7.30**
7.40	0.0006	0.0051	0.0219	0.0632	0.1395	0.2526	0.3920	0.5393	0.6757	0.7877	0.8707	0.9265	0.9609	**7.40**
7.50	0.0006	0.0047	0.0203	0.0591	0.1321	0.2414	0.3782	0.5246	0.6620	0.7764	0.8622	0.9208	0.9573	**7.50**
7.60	0.0005	0.0043	0.0188	0.0554	0.1249	0.2307	0.3646	0.5100	0.6482	0.7649	0.8535	0.9148	0.9536	**7.60**
7.70	0.0005	0.0039	0.0174	0.0518	0.1181	0.2203	0.3514	0.4956	0.6343	0.7531	0.8445	0.9085	0.9496	**7.70**
7.80	0.0004	0.0036	0.0161	0.0485	0.1117	0.2103	0.3384	0.4812	0.6204	0.7411	0.8352	0.9020	0.9454	**7.80**
7.90	0.0004	0.0033	0.0149	0.0453	0.1055	0.2006	0.3257	0.4670	0.6065	0.7290	0.8257	0.8952	0.9409	**7.90**
8.00	0.0003	0.0030	0.0138	0.0424	0.0996	0.1912	0.3134	0.4530	0.5925	0.7166	0.8159	0.8881	0.9362	**8.00**
8.10	0.0003	0.0028	0.0127	0.0396	0.0940	0.1822	0.3013	0.4391	0.5786	0.7041	0.8058	0.8807	0.9313	**8.10**
8.20	0.0003	0.0025	0.0118	0.0370	0.0887	0.1736	0.2896	0.4254	0.5647	0.6915	0.7955	0.8731	0.9261	**8.20**
8.30	0.0002	0.0023	0.0109	0.0346	0.0837	0.1653	0.2781	0.4119	0.5507	0.6788	0.7850	0.8652	0.9207	**8.30**
8.40	0.0002	0.0021	0.0100	0.0323	0.0789	0.1573	0.2670	0.3987	0.5369	0.6659	0.7743	0.8571	0.9150	**8.40**
8.50	0.0002	0.0019	0.0093	0.0301	0.0744	0.1496	0.2562	0.3856	0.5231	0.6530	0.7634	0.8487	0.9091	**8.50**
8.60	0.0002	0.0018	0.0086	0.0281	0.0701	0.1422	0.2457	0.3728	0.5094	0.6400	0.7522	0.8400	0.9029	**8.60**
8.70	0.0002	0.0016	0.0079	0.0262	0.0660	0.1352	0.2355	0.3602	0.4958	0.6269	0.7409	0.8311	0.8965	**8.70**
8.80	0.0002	0.0015	0.0073	0.0244	0.0621	0.1284	0.2256	0.3478	0.4823	0.6137	0.7294	0.8220	0.8898	**8.80**
8.90	0.0001	0.0014	0.0068	0.0228	0.0584	0.1219	0.2160	0.3357	0.4689	0.6006	0.7178	0.8126	0.8829	**8.90**
9.00	0.0001	0.0012	0.0062	0.0212	0.0550	0.1157	0.2068	0.3239	0.4557	0.5874	0.7060	0.8030	0.8758	**9.00**
9.10	0.0001	0.0011	0.0058	0.0198	0.0517	0.1098	0.1978	0.3123	0.4426	0.5742	0.6941	0.7932	0.8684	**9.10**
9.20	0.0001	0.0010	0.0053	0.0184	0.0486	0.1041	0.1892	0.3010	0.4296	0.5611	0.6820	0.7832	0.8607	**9.20**
9.30	0.0001	0.0009	0.0049	0.0172	0.0456	0.0986	0.1808	0.2900	0.4168	0.5479	0.6699	0.7730	0.8529	**9.30**
9.40	0.0001	0.0009	0.0045	0.0160	0.0429	0.0935	0.1727	0.2792	0.4042	0.5349	0.6576	0.7626	0.8448	**9.40**
9.50	0.0001	0.0008	0.0042	0.0149	0.0403	0.0885	0.1649	0.2687	0.3918	0.5218	0.6453	0.7520	0.8364	**9.50**
9.60	0.0001	0.0007	0.0038	0.0138	0.0378	0.0838	0.1574	0.2584	0.3796	0.5089	0.6329	0.7412	0.8279	**9.60**
9.70	0.0001	0.0007	0.0035	0.0129	0.0355	0.0793	0.1502	0.2485	0.3676	0.4960	0.6205	0.7303	0.8191	**9.70**
9.80	0.0001	0.0006	0.0033	0.0120	0.0333	0.0750	0.1433	0.2388	0.3558	0.4832	0.6080	0.7193	0.8101	**9.80**
9.90	0.0001	0.0005	0.0030	0.0111	0.0312	0.0710	0.1366	0.2294	0.3442	0.4705	0.5955	0.7081	0.8009	**9.90**
10.00	0.0000	0.0005	0.0028	0.0103	0.0293	0.0671	0.1301	0.2202	0.3328	0.4579	0.5830	0.6968	0.7916	**10.00**

$$\Pr(X \le x) = F(x;\lambda) = \sum_{x=0}^{n} \frac{\lambda^x}{x!} e^{-\lambda}$$

	Probability of ≤ x occurrences													
λ	13	14	15	16	17	18	19	20	21	22	23	24	25	λ
6.60	0.9920	0.9966	0.9986	0.9995	0.9998	0.9999	1.0000	1.0000	1.0000	1.0000	1.0000	1.0000	1.0000	**6.60**
6.70	0.9909	0.9961	0.9984	0.9994	0.9998	0.9999	1.0000	1.0000	1.0000	1.0000	1.0000	1.0000	1.0000	**6.70**
6.80	0.9898	0.9956	0.9982	0.9993	0.9997	0.9999	1.0000	1.0000	1.0000	1.0000	1.0000	1.0000	1.0000	**6.80**
6.90	0.9885	0.9950	0.9979	0.9992	0.9997	0.9999	1.0000	1.0000	1.0000	1.0000	1.0000	1.0000	1.0000	**6.90**
7.00	0.9872	0.9943	0.9976	0.9990	0.9996	0.9999	1.0000	1.0000	1.0000	1.0000	1.0000	1.0000	1.0000	**7.00**
7.10	0.9857	0.9935	0.9972	0.9989	0.9996	0.9998	0.9999	1.0000	1.0000	1.0000	1.0000	1.0000	1.0000	**7.10**
7.20	0.9841	0.9927	0.9969	0.9987	0.9995	0.9998	0.9999	1.0000	1.0000	1.0000	1.0000	1.0000	1.0000	**7.20**
7.30	0.9824	0.9918	0.9964	0.9985	0.9994	0.9998	0.9999	1.0000	1.0000	1.0000	1.0000	1.0000	1.0000	**7.30**
7.40	0.9805	0.9908	0.9959	0.9983	0.9993	0.9997	0.9999	1.0000	1.0000	1.0000	1.0000	1.0000	1.0000	**7.40**
7.50	0.9784	0.9897	0.9954	0.9980	0.9992	0.9997	0.9999	1.0000	1.0000	1.0000	1.0000	1.0000	1.0000	**7.50**
7.60	0.9762	0.9886	0.9948	0.9978	0.9991	0.9996	0.9999	1.0000	1.0000	1.0000	1.0000	1.0000	1.0000	**7.60**
7.70	0.9739	0.9873	0.9941	0.9974	0.9989	0.9996	0.9998	0.9999	1.0000	1.0000	1.0000	1.0000	1.0000	**7.70**
7.80	0.9714	0.9859	0.9934	0.9971	0.9988	0.9995	0.9998	0.9999	1.0000	1.0000	1.0000	1.0000	1.0000	**7.80**
7.90	0.9687	0.9844	0.9926	0.9967	0.9986	0.9994	0.9998	0.9999	1.0000	1.0000	1.0000	1.0000	1.0000	**7.90**
8.00	0.9658	0.9827	0.9918	0.9963	0.9984	0.9993	0.9997	0.9999	1.0000	1.0000	1.0000	1.0000	1.0000	**8.00**
8.10	0.9628	0.9810	0.9908	0.9958	0.9982	0.9992	0.9997	0.9999	1.0000	1.0000	1.0000	1.0000	1.0000	**8.10**
8.20	0.9595	0.9791	0.9898	0.9953	0.9979	0.9991	0.9997	0.9999	1.0000	1.0000	1.0000	1.0000	1.0000	**8.20**
8.30	0.9561	0.9771	0.9887	0.9947	0.9977	0.9990	0.9996	0.9998	0.9999	1.0000	1.0000	1.0000	1.0000	**8.30**
8.40	0.9524	0.9749	0.9875	0.9941	0.9973	0.9989	0.9995	0.9998	0.9999	1.0000	1.0000	1.0000	1.0000	**8.40**
8.50	0.9486	0.9726	0.9862	0.9934	0.9970	0.9987	0.9995	0.9998	0.9999	1.0000	1.0000	1.0000	1.0000	**8.50**
8.60	0.9445	0.9701	0.9848	0.9926	0.9966	0.9985	0.9994	0.9998	0.9999	1.0000	1.0000	1.0000	1.0000	**8.60**
8.70	0.9403	0.9675	0.9832	0.9918	0.9962	0.9983	0.9993	0.9997	0.9999	1.0000	1.0000	1.0000	1.0000	**8.70**
8.80	0.9358	0.9647	0.9816	0.9909	0.9957	0.9981	0.9992	0.9997	0.9999	1.0000	1.0000	1.0000	1.0000	**8.80**
8.90	0.9311	0.9617	0.9798	0.9899	0.9952	0.9978	0.9991	0.9996	0.9998	0.9999	1.0000	1.0000	1.0000	**8.90**
9.00	0.9261	0.9585	0.9780	0.9889	0.9947	0.9976	0.9989	0.9996	0.9998	0.9999	1.0000	1.0000	1.0000	**9.00**
9.10	0.9210	0.9552	0.9760	0.9878	0.9941	0.9973	0.9988	0.9995	0.9998	0.9999	1.0000	1.0000	1.0000	**9.10**
9.20	0.9156	0.9517	0.9738	0.9865	0.9934	0.9969	0.9986	0.9994	0.9998	0.9999	1.0000	1.0000	1.0000	**9.20**
9.30	0.9100	0.9480	0.9715	0.9852	0.9927	0.9966	0.9985	0.9993	0.9997	0.9999	1.0000	1.0000	1.0000	**9.30**
9.40	0.9042	0.9441	0.9691	0.9838	0.9919	0.9962	0.9983	0.9992	0.9997	0.9999	1.0000	1.0000	1.0000	**9.40**
9.50	0.8981	0.9400	0.9665	0.9823	0.9911	0.9957	0.9980	0.9991	0.9996	0.9999	0.9999	1.0000	1.0000	**9.50**
9.60	0.8919	0.9357	0.9638	0.9806	0.9902	0.9952	0.9978	0.9990	0.9996	0.9998	0.9999	1.0000	1.0000	**9.60**
9.70	0.8853	0.9312	0.9609	0.9789	0.9892	0.9947	0.9975	0.9989	0.9995	0.9998	0.9999	1.0000	1.0000	**9.70**
9.80	0.8786	0.9265	0.9579	0.9770	0.9881	0.9941	0.9972	0.9987	0.9995	0.9998	0.9999	1.0000	1.0000	**9.80**
9.90	0.8716	0.9216	0.9546	0.9751	0.9870	0.9935	0.9969	0.9986	0.9994	0.9997	0.9999	1.0000	1.0000	**9.90**
10.00	0.8645	0.9165	0.9513	0.9730	0.9857	0.9928	0.9965	0.9984	0.9993	0.9997	0.9999	1.0000	1.0000	**10.00**

Appendix D

Cumulative Standard Normal Distribution Table

Standard Normal Z Table

Table values give φ(z) = Pr(Z < z) for negative values of z

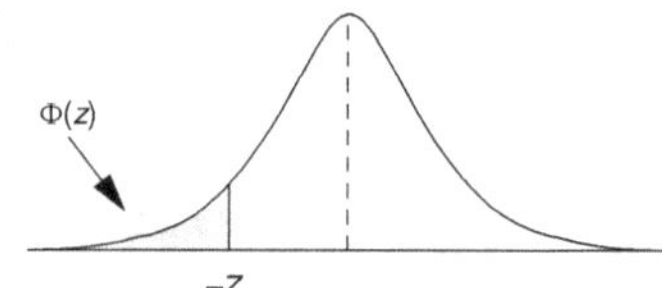

z	0.0	0.01	0.02	0.03	0.04	0.05	0.06	0.07	0.08	0.09
–4.0	0.0000	0.0000	0.0000	0.0000	0.0000	0.0000	0.0000	0.0000	0.0000	0.0000
–3.9	0.0000	0.0000	0.0000	0.0000	0.0000	0.0000	0.0000	0.0000	0.0000	0.0000
–3.8	0.0001	0.0001	0.0001	0.0001	0.0001	0.0001	0.0001	0.0001	0.0001	0.0001
–3.7	0.0001	0.0001	0.0001	0.0001	0.0001	0.0001	0.0001	0.0001	0.0001	0.0001
–3.6	0.0002	0.0002	0.0001	0.0001	0.0001	0.0001	0.0001	0.0001	0.0001	0.0001
–3.5	0.0002	0.0002	0.0002	0.0002	0.0002	0.0002	0.0002	0.0002	0.0002	0.0002
–3.4	0.0003	0.0003	0.0003	0.0003	0.0003	0.0003	0.0003	0.0003	0.0003	0.0002
–3.3	0.0005	0.0005	0.0005	0.0004	0.0004	0.0004	0.0004	0.0004	0.0004	0.0003
–3.2	0.0007	0.0007	0.0006	0.0006	0.0006	0.0006	0.0006	0.0005	0.0005	0.0005
–3.1	0.0010	0.0009	0.0009	0.0009	0.0008	0.0008	0.0008	0.0008	0.0007	0.0007
–3.0	0.0013	0.0013	0.0013	0.0012	0.0012	0.0011	0.0011	0.0011	0.0010	0.0010
–2.9	0.0019	0.0018	0.0018	0.0017	0.0016	0.0016	0.0015	0.0015	0.0014	0.0014
–2.8	0.0026	0.0025	0.0024	0.0023	0.0023	0.0022	0.0021	0.0021	0.0020	0.0019
–2.7	0.0035	0.0034	0.0033	0.0032	0.0031	0.0030	0.0029	0.0028	0.0027	0.0026
–2.6	0.0047	0.0045	0.0044	0.0043	0.0041	0.0040	0.0039	0.0038	0.0037	0.0036
–2.5	0.0062	0.0060	0.0059	0.0057	0.0055	0.0054	0.0052	0.0051	0.0049	0.0048
–2.4	0.0082	0.0080	0.0078	0.0075	0.0073	0.0071	0.0069	0.0068	0.0066	0.0064
–2.3	0.0107	0.0104	0.0102	0.0099	0.0096	0.0094	0.0091	0.0089	0.0087	0.0084
–2.2	0.0139	0.0136	0.0132	0.0129	0.0125	0.0122	0.0119	0.0116	0.0113	0.0110
–2.1	0.0179	0.0174	0.0170	0.0166	0.0162	0.0158	0.0154	0.0150	0.0146	0.0143
–2.0	0.0228	0.0222	0.0217	0.0212	0.0207	0.0202	0.0197	0.0192	0.0188	0.0183
–1.9	0.0287	0.0281	0.0274	0.0268	0.0262	0.0256	0.0250	0.0244	0.0239	0.0233
–1.8	0.0359	0.0351	0.0344	0.0336	0.0329	0.0322	0.0314	0.0307	0.0301	0.0294
–1.7	0.0446	0.0436	0.0427	0.0418	0.0409	0.0401	0.0392	0.0384	0.0375	0.0367
–1.6	0.0548	0.0537	0.0526	0.0516	0.0505	0.0495	0.0485	0.0475	0.0465	0.0455
–1.5	0.0668	0.0655	0.0643	0.0630	0.0618	0.0606	0.0594	0.0582	0.0571	0.0559
–1.4	0.0808	0.0793	0.0778	0.0764	0.0749	0.0735	0.0721	0.0708	0.0694	0.0681
–1.3	0.0968	0.0951	0.0934	0.0918	0.0901	0.0885	0.0869	0.0853	0.0838	0.0823
–1.2	0.1151	0.1131	0.1112	0.1093	0.1075	0.1056	0.1038	0.1020	0.1003	0.0985
–1.1	0.1357	0.1335	0.1314	0.1292	0.1271	0.1251	0.1230	0.1210	0.1190	0.1170
–1.0	0.1587	0.1562	0.1539	0.1515	0.1492	0.1469	0.1446	0.1423	0.1401	0.1379
–0.9	0.1841	0.1814	0.1788	0.1762	0.1736	0.1711	0.1685	0.1660	0.1635	0.1611
–0.8	0.2119	0.2090	0.2061	0.2033	0.2005	0.1977	0.1949	0.1922	0.1894	0.1867
–0.7	0.2420	0.2389	0.2358	0.2327	0.2296	0.2266	0.2236	0.2206	0.2177	0.2148
–0.6	0.2743	0.2709	0.2676	0.2643	0.2611	0.2578	0.2546	0.2514	0.2483	0.2451
–0.5	0.3085	0.3050	0.3015	0.2981	0.2946	0.2912	0.2877	0.2843	0.2810	0.2776
–0.4	0.3446	0.3409	0.3372	0.3336	0.3300	0.3264	0.3228	0.3192	0.3156	0.3121
–0.3	0.3821	0.3783	0.3745	0.3707	0.3669	0.3632	0.3594	0.3557	0.3520	0.3483
–0.2	0.4207	0.4168	0.4129	0.4090	0.4052	0.4013	0.3974	0.3936	0.3897	0.3859
–0.1	0.4602	0.4562	0.4522	0.4483	0.4443	0.4404	0.4364	0.4325	0.4286	0.4247
–0	0.5000	0.4960	0.4920	0.4880	0.4840	0.4801	0.4761	0.4721	0.4681	0.4641

Standard Normal Z Table

Table values give ϕ(z) = Pr(Z < z) for positive values of z

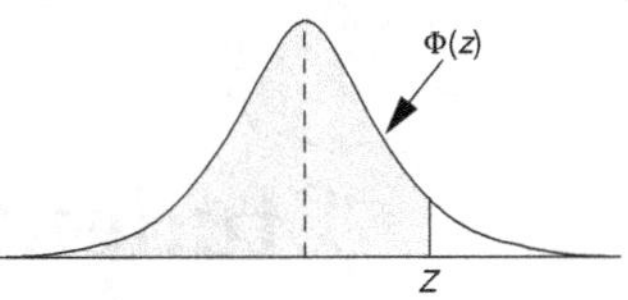

z	0.0	0.01	0.02	0.03	0.04	0.05	0.06	0.07	0.08	0.09
0.0	0.5000	0.5040	0.5080	0.5120	0.5160	0.5199	0.5239	0.5279	0.5319	0.5359
0.1	0.5398	0.5438	0.5478	0.5517	0.5557	0.5596	0.5636	0.5675	0.5714	0.5753
0.2	0.5793	0.5832	0.5871	0.5910	0.5948	0.5987	0.6026	0.6064	0.6103	0.6141
0.3	0.6179	0.6217	0.6255	0.6293	0.6331	0.6368	0.6406	0.6443	0.6480	0.6517
0.4	0.6554	0.6591	0.6628	0.6664	0.6700	0.6736	0.6772	0.6808	0.6844	0.6879
0.5	0.6915	0.6950	0.6985	0.7019	0.7054	0.7088	0.7123	0.7157	0.7190	0.7224
0.6	0.7257	0.7291	0.7324	0.7357	0.7389	0.7422	0.7454	0.7486	0.7517	0.7549
0.7	0.7580	0.7611	0.7642	0.7673	0.7704	0.7734	0.7764	0.7794	0.7823	0.7852
0.8	0.7881	0.7910	0.7939	0.7967	0.7995	0.8023	0.8051	0.8078	0.8106	0.8133
0.9	0.8159	0.8186	0.8212	0.8238	0.8264	0.8289	0.8315	0.8340	0.8365	0.8389
1.0	0.8413	0.8438	0.8461	0.8485	0.8508	0.8531	0.8554	0.8577	0.8599	0.8621
1.1	0.8643	0.8665	0.8686	0.8708	0.8729	0.8749	0.8770	0.8790	0.8810	0.8830
1.2	0.8849	0.8869	0.8888	0.8907	0.8925	0.8944	0.8962	0.8980	0.8997	0.9015
1.3	0.9032	0.9049	0.9066	0.9082	0.9099	0.9115	0.9131	0.9147	0.9162	0.9177
1.4	0.9192	0.9207	0.9222	0.9236	0.9251	0.9265	0.9279	0.9292	0.9306	0.9319
1.5	0.9332	0.9345	0.9357	0.9370	0.9382	0.9394	0.9406	0.9418	0.9429	0.9441
1.6	0.9452	0.9463	0.9474	0.9484	0.9495	0.9505	0.9515	0.9525	0.9535	0.9545
1.7	0.9554	0.9564	0.9573	0.9582	0.9591	0.9599	0.9608	0.9616	0.9625	0.9633
1.8	0.9641	0.9649	0.9656	0.9664	0.9671	0.9678	0.9686	0.9693	0.9699	0.9706
1.9	0.9713	0.9719	0.9726	0.9732	0.9738	0.9744	0.9750	0.9756	0.9761	0.9767
2.0	0.9772	0.9778	0.9783	0.9788	0.9793	0.9798	0.9803	0.9808	0.9812	0.9817
2.1	0.9821	0.9826	0.9830	0.9834	0.9838	0.9842	0.9846	0.9850	0.9854	0.9857
2.2	0.9861	0.9864	0.9868	0.9871	0.9875	0.9878	0.9881	0.9884	0.9887	0.9890
2.3	0.9893	0.9896	0.9898	0.9901	0.9904	0.9906	0.9909	0.9911	0.9913	0.9916
2.4	0.9918	0.9920	0.9922	0.9925	0.9927	0.9929	0.9931	0.9932	0.9934	0.9936
2.5	0.9938	0.9940	0.9941	0.9943	0.9945	0.9946	0.9948	0.9949	0.9951	0.9952
2.6	0.9953	0.9955	0.9956	0.9957	0.9959	0.9960	0.9961	0.9962	0.9963	0.9964
2.7	0.9965	0.9966	0.9967	0.9968	0.9969	0.9970	0.9971	0.9972	0.9973	0.9974
2.8	0.9974	0.9975	0.9976	0.9977	0.9977	0.9978	0.9979	0.9979	0.9980	0.9981
2.9	0.9981	0.9982	0.9982	0.9983	0.9984	0.9984	0.9985	0.9985	0.9986	0.9986
3.0	0.9987	0.9987	0.9987	0.9988	0.9988	0.9989	0.9989	0.9989	0.9990	0.9990
3.1	0.9990	0.9991	0.9991	0.9991	0.9992	0.9992	0.9992	0.9992	0.9993	0.9993
3.2	0.9993	0.9993	0.9994	0.9994	0.9994	0.9994	0.9994	0.9995	0.9995	0.9995
3.3	0.9995	0.9995	0.9995	0.9996	0.9996	0.9996	0.9996	0.9996	0.9996	0.9997
3.4	0.9997	0.9997	0.9997	0.9997	0.9997	0.9997	0.9997	0.9997	0.9997	0.9998
3.5	0.9998	0.9998	0.9998	0.9998	0.9998	0.9998	0.9998	0.9998	0.9998	0.9998
3.6	0.9998	0.9998	0.9999	0.9999	0.9999	0.9999	0.9999	0.9999	0.9999	0.9999
3.7	0.9999	0.9999	0.9999	0.9999	0.9999	0.9999	0.9999	0.9999	0.9999	0.9999
3.8	0.9999	0.9999	0.9999	0.9999	0.9999	0.9999	0.9999	0.9999	0.9999	0.9999
3.9	1.0000	1.0000	1.0000	1.0000	1.0000	1.0000	1.0000	1.0000	1.0000	1.0000
4.0	1.0000	1.0000	1.0000	1.0000	1.0000	1.0000	1.0000	1.0000	1.0000	1.0000

Appendix E

Student's *t* Distribution Table

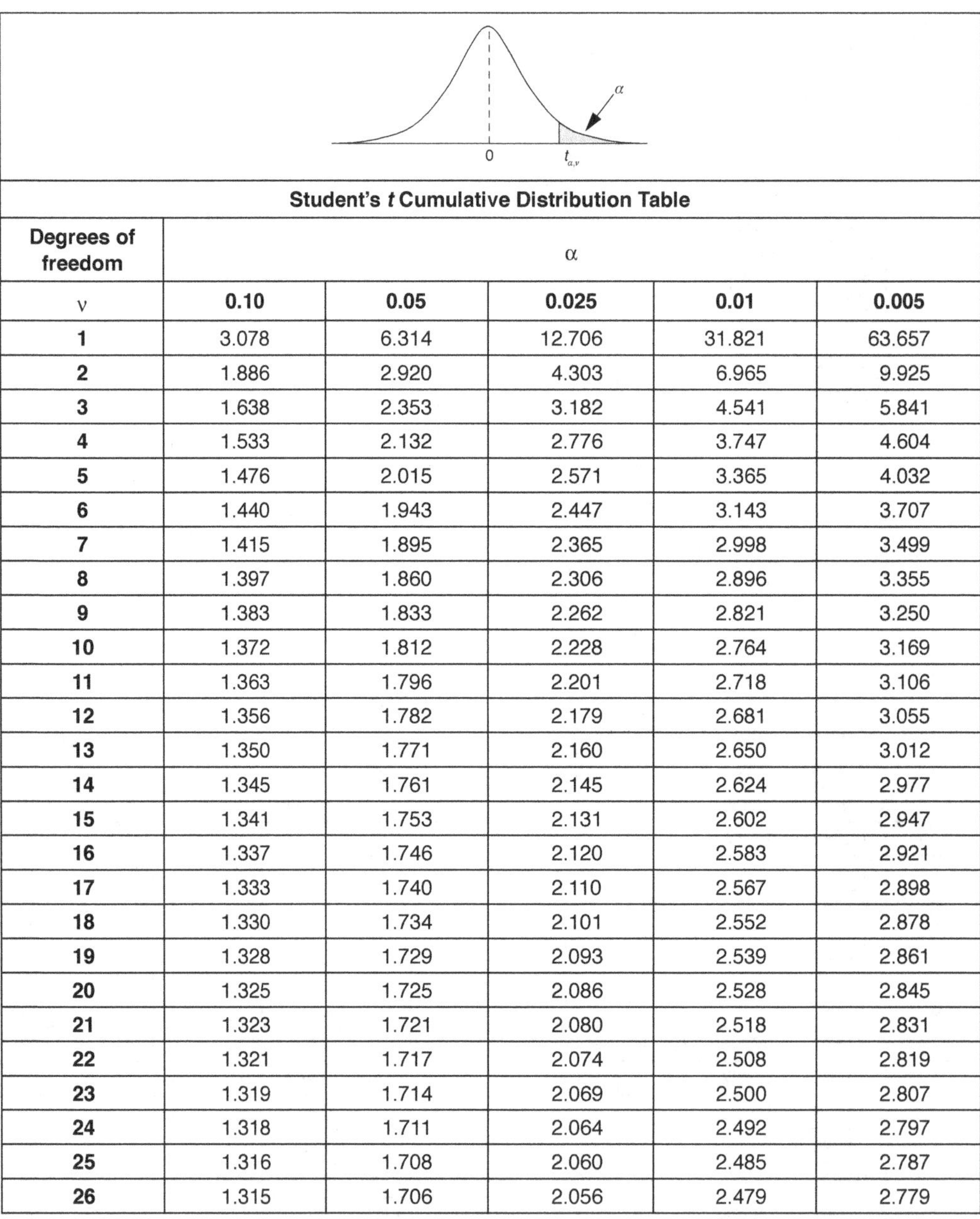

Student's *t* Cumulative Distribution Table					
Degrees of freedom	α				
ν	**0.10**	**0.05**	**0.025**	**0.01**	**0.005**
1	3.078	6.314	12.706	31.821	63.657
2	1.886	2.920	4.303	6.965	9.925
3	1.638	2.353	3.182	4.541	5.841
4	1.533	2.132	2.776	3.747	4.604
5	1.476	2.015	2.571	3.365	4.032
6	1.440	1.943	2.447	3.143	3.707
7	1.415	1.895	2.365	2.998	3.499
8	1.397	1.860	2.306	2.896	3.355
9	1.383	1.833	2.262	2.821	3.250
10	1.372	1.812	2.228	2.764	3.169
11	1.363	1.796	2.201	2.718	3.106
12	1.356	1.782	2.179	2.681	3.055
13	1.350	1.771	2.160	2.650	3.012
14	1.345	1.761	2.145	2.624	2.977
15	1.341	1.753	2.131	2.602	2.947
16	1.337	1.746	2.120	2.583	2.921
17	1.333	1.740	2.110	2.567	2.898
18	1.330	1.734	2.101	2.552	2.878
19	1.328	1.729	2.093	2.539	2.861
20	1.325	1.725	2.086	2.528	2.845
21	1.323	1.721	2.080	2.518	2.831
22	1.321	1.717	2.074	2.508	2.819
23	1.319	1.714	2.069	2.500	2.807
24	1.318	1.711	2.064	2.492	2.797
25	1.316	1.708	2.060	2.485	2.787
26	1.315	1.706	2.056	2.479	2.779

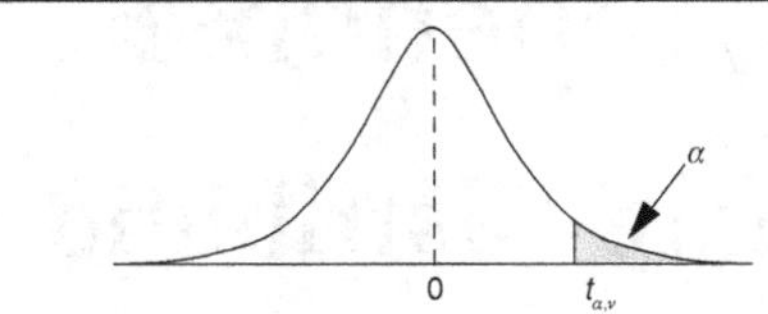

Student's t Cumulative Distribution Table

Degrees of freedom	α				
ν	**0.10**	**0.05**	**0.025**	**0.01**	**0.005**
27	1.314	1.703	2.052	2.473	2.771
28	1.313	1.701	2.048	2.467	2.763
29	1.311	1.699	2.045	2.462	2.756
30	1.310	1.697	2.042	2.457	2.750
31	1.309	1.696	2.040	2.453	2.744
32	1.309	1.694	2.037	2.449	2.738
33	1.308	1.692	2.035	2.445	2.733
34	1.307	1.691	2.032	2.441	2.728
35	1.306	1.690	2.030	2.438	2.724
36	1.306	1.688	2.028	2.434	2.719
37	1.305	1.687	2.026	2.431	2.715
38	1.304	1.686	2.024	2.429	2.712
39	1.304	1.685	2.023	2.426	2.708
40	1.303	1.684	2.021	2.423	2.704
41	1.303	1.683	2.020	2.421	2.701
42	1.302	1.682	2.018	2.418	2.698
43	1.302	1.681	2.017	2.416	2.695
44	1.301	1.680	2.015	2.414	2.692
45	1.301	1.679	2.014	2.412	2.690
46	1.300	1.679	2.013	2.410	2.687
47	1.300	1.678	2.012	2.408	2.685
48	1.299	1.677	2.011	2.407	2.682
49	1.299	1.677	2.010	2.405	2.680
50	1.299	1.676	2.009	2.403	2.678
55	1.297	1.673	2.004	2.396	2.668
60	1.296	1.671	2.000	2.390	2.660
65	1.295	1.669	1.997	2.385	2.654
70	1.294	1.667	1.994	2.381	2.648
75	1.293	1.665	1.992	2.377	2.643
80	1.292	1.664	1.990	2.374	2.639
85	1.292	1.663	1.988	2.371	2.635
90	1.291	1.662	1.987	2.368	2.632
95	1.291	1.661	1.985	2.366	2.629
100	1.290	1.660	1.984	2.364	2.626
120	1.289	1.658	1.980	2.358	2.617
∞	1.282	1.645	1.960	2.326	2.576

Appendix F

Chi-Square Distribution Table

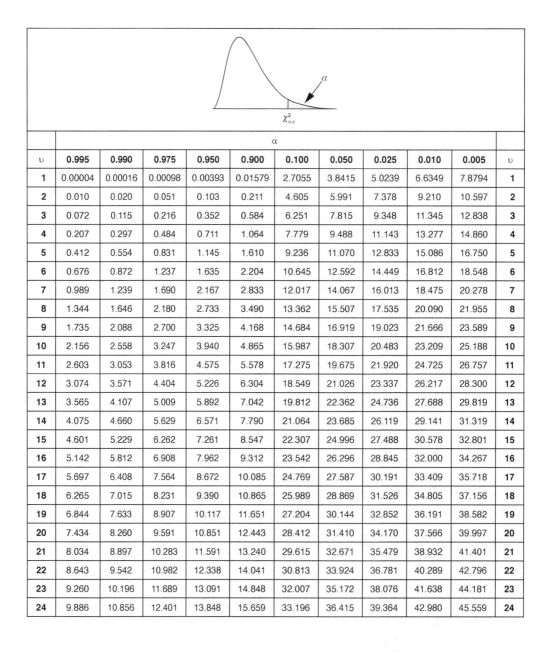

	α										
υ	**0.995**	**0.990**	**0.975**	**0.950**	**0.900**	**0.100**	**0.050**	**0.025**	**0.010**	**0.005**	υ
1	0.00004	0.00016	0.00098	0.00393	0.01579	2.7055	3.8415	5.0239	6.6349	7.8794	**1**
2	0.010	0.020	0.051	0.103	0.211	4.605	5.991	7.378	9.210	10.597	**2**
3	0.072	0.115	0.216	0.352	0.584	6.251	7.815	9.348	11.345	12.838	**3**
4	0.207	0.297	0.484	0.711	1.064	7.779	9.488	11.143	13.277	14.860	**4**
5	0.412	0.554	0.831	1.145	1.610	9.236	11.070	12.833	15.086	16.750	**5**
6	0.676	0.872	1.237	1.635	2.204	10.645	12.592	14.449	16.812	18.548	**6**
7	0.989	1.239	1.690	2.167	2.833	12.017	14.067	16.013	18.475	20.278	**7**
8	1.344	1.646	2.180	2.733	3.490	13.362	15.507	17.535	20.090	21.955	**8**
9	1.735	2.088	2.700	3.325	4.168	14.684	16.919	19.023	21.666	23.589	**9**
10	2.156	2.558	3.247	3.940	4.865	15.987	18.307	20.483	23.209	25.188	**10**
11	2.603	3.053	3.816	4.575	5.578	17.275	19.675	21.920	24.725	26.757	**11**
12	3.074	3.571	4.404	5.226	6.304	18.549	21.026	23.337	26.217	28.300	**12**
13	3.565	4.107	5.009	5.892	7.042	19.812	22.362	24.736	27.688	29.819	**13**
14	4.075	4.660	5.629	6.571	7.790	21.064	23.685	26.119	29.141	31.319	**14**
15	4.601	5.229	6.262	7.261	8.547	22.307	24.996	27.488	30.578	32.801	**15**
16	5.142	5.812	6.908	7.962	9.312	23.542	26.296	28.845	32.000	34.267	**16**
17	5.697	6.408	7.564	8.672	10.085	24.769	27.587	30.191	33.409	35.718	**17**
18	6.265	7.015	8.231	9.390	10.865	25.989	28.869	31.526	34.805	37.156	**18**
19	6.844	7.633	8.907	10.117	11.651	27.204	30.144	32.852	36.191	38.582	**19**
20	7.434	8.260	9.591	10.851	12.443	28.412	31.410	34.170	37.566	39.997	**20**
21	8.034	8.897	10.283	11.591	13.240	29.615	32.671	35.479	38.932	41.401	**21**
22	8.643	9.542	10.982	12.338	14.041	30.813	33.924	36.781	40.289	42.796	**22**
23	9.260	10.196	11.689	13.091	14.848	32.007	35.172	38.076	41.638	44.181	**23**
24	9.886	10.856	12.401	13.848	15.659	33.196	36.415	39.364	42.980	45.559	**24**

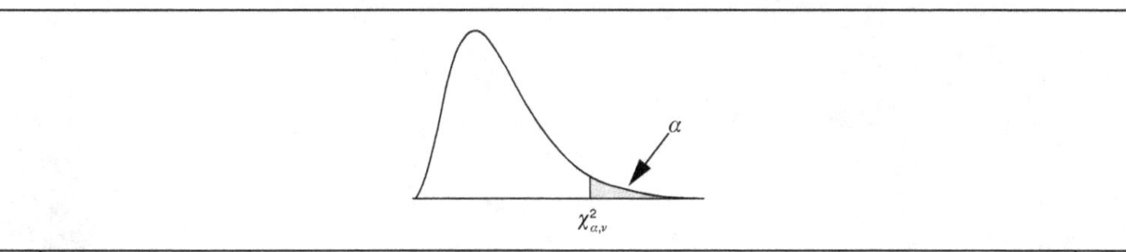

	α										
υ	**0.995**	**0.990**	**0.975**	**0.950**	**0.900**	**0.100**	**0.050**	**0.025**	**0.010**	**0.005**	υ
25	10.520	11.524	13.120	14.611	16.473	34.382	37.652	40.646	44.314	46.928	**25**
26	11.160	12.198	13.844	15.379	17.292	35.563	38.885	41.923	45.642	48.290	**26**
27	11.808	12.879	14.573	16.151	18.114	36.741	40.113	43.195	46.963	49.645	**27**
28	12.461	13.565	15.308	16.928	18.939	37.916	41.337	44.461	48.278	50.993	**28**
29	13.121	14.256	16.047	17.708	19.768	39.087	42.557	45.722	49.588	52.336	**29**
30	13.787	14.953	16.791	18.493	20.599	40.256	43.773	46.979	50.892	53.672	**30**
35	17.192	18.509	20.569	22.465	24.797	46.059	49.802	53.203	57.342	60.275	**35**
40	20.707	22.164	24.433	26.509	29.051	51.805	55.758	59.342	63.691	66.766	**40**
45	24.311	25.901	28.366	30.612	33.350	57.505	61.656	65.410	69.957	73.166	**45**
50	27.991	29.707	32.357	34.764	37.689	63.167	67.505	71.420	76.154	79.490	**50**
55	31.735	33.570	36.398	38.958	42.060	68.796	73.311	77.380	82.292	85.749	**55**
60	35.534	37.485	40.482	43.188	46.459	74.397	79.082	83.298	88.379	91.952	**60**
65	39.383	41.444	44.603	47.450	50.883	79.973	84.821	89.177	94.422	98.105	**65**
70	43.275	45.442	48.758	51.739	55.329	85.527	90.531	95.023	100.425	104.215	**70**
75	47.206	49.475	52.942	56.054	59.795	91.061	96.217	100.839	106.393	110.286	**75**
80	51.172	53.540	57.153	60.391	64.278	96.578	101.879	106.629	112.329	116.321	**80**
85	55.170	57.634	61.389	64.749	68.777	102.079	107.522	112.393	118.236	122.325	**85**
90	59.196	61.754	65.647	69.126	73.291	107.565	113.145	118.136	124.116	128.299	**90**
95	63.250	65.898	69.925	73.520	77.818	113.038	118.752	123.858	129.973	134.247	**95**
100	67.328	70.065	74.222	77.929	82.358	118.498	124.342	129.561	135.807	140.169	**100**

Appendix G

Cumulative *F* Distribution

The following eight appendices contain the critical values for the *F* distribution based on numerator and denominator degrees of freedom and alpha value. The tables are arranged so that the upper tail (F_{α}) tables appear first, since these are the most common look-up values. Then the tables for the lower tails ($F_{1-\alpha}$) are presented:

Upper Tails:

Appendix G.1: $F_{0.01}$
Appendix G.2: $F_{0.025}$
Appendix G.3: $F_{0.05}$
Appendix G.4: $F_{0.10}$

Lower Tails:
Appendix G.5: $F_{0.90}$
Appendix G.6: $F_{0.95}$
Appendix G.7: $F_{0.975}$
Appendix G.8: $F_{0.99}$

Appendix G.1

F(0.01) Distribution Table

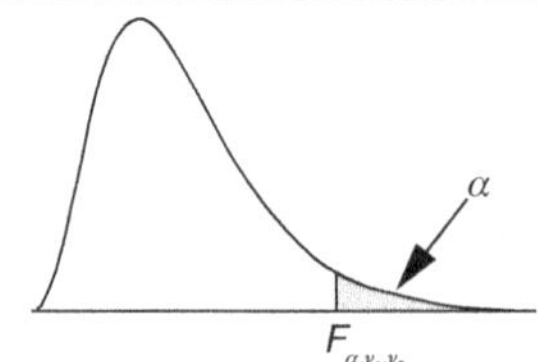

	Degrees of freedom for the numerator (ν_1)																	
(ν_2)	**1**	**2**	**3**	**4**	**5**	**6**	**7**	**8**	**9**	**10**	**11**	**12**	**13**	**14**	**15**	**16**	**17**	(ν_2)
1	4052.18	4999.50	5403.35	5624.58	5763.65	5858.99	5928.36	5981.07	6022.47	6055.85	6083.32	6106.32	6125.86	6142.67	6157.28	6170.10	6181.43	**1**
2	98.50	99.00	99.17	99.25	99.30	99.33	99.36	99.37	99.39	99.40	99.41	99.42	99.42	99.43	99.43	99.44	99.44	**2**
3	34.12	30.82	29.46	28.71	28.24	27.91	27.67	27.49	27.35	27.23	27.13	27.05	26.98	26.92	26.87	26.83	26.79	**3**
4	21.20	18.00	16.69	15.98	15.52	15.21	14.98	14.80	14.66	14.55	14.45	14.37	14.31	14.25	14.20	14.15	14.11	**4**
5	16.26	13.27	12.06	11.39	10.97	10.67	10.46	10.29	10.16	10.05	9.96	9.89	9.82	9.77	9.72	9.68	9.64	**5**
6	13.75	10.92	9.78	9.15	8.75	8.47	8.26	8.10	7.98	7.87	7.79	7.72	7.66	7.60	7.56	7.52	7.48	**6**
7	12.25	9.55	8.45	7.85	7.46	7.19	6.99	6.84	6.72	6.62	6.54	6.47	6.41	6.36	6.31	6.28	6.24	**7**
8	11.26	8.65	7.59	7.01	6.63	6.37	6.18	6.03	5.91	5.81	5.73	5.67	5.61	5.56	5.52	5.48	5.44	**8**
9	10.56	8.02	6.99	6.42	6.06	5.80	5.61	5.47	5.35	5.26	5.18	5.11	5.05	5.01	4.96	4.92	4.89	**9**
10	10.04	7.56	6.55	5.99	5.64	5.39	5.20	5.06	4.94	4.85	4.77	4.71	4.65	4.60	4.56	4.52	4.49	**10**
11	9.65	7.21	6.22	5.67	5.32	5.07	4.89	4.74	4.63	4.54	4.46	4.40	4.34	4.29	4.25	4.21	4.18	**11**
12	9.33	6.93	5.95	5.41	5.06	4.82	4.64	4.50	4.39	4.30	4.22	4.16	4.10	4.05	4.01	3.97	3.94	**12**
13	9.07	6.70	5.74	5.21	4.86	4.62	4.44	4.30	4.19	4.10	4.02	3.96	3.91	3.86	3.82	3.78	3.75	**13**
14	8.86	6.51	5.56	5.04	4.69	4.46	4.28	4.14	4.03	3.94	3.86	3.80	3.75	3.70	3.66	3.62	3.59	**14**
15	8.68	6.36	5.42	4.89	4.56	4.32	4.14	4.00	3.89	3.80	3.73	3.67	3.61	3.56	3.52	3.49	3.45	**15**
16	8.53	6.23	5.29	4.77	4.44	4.20	4.03	3.89	3.78	3.69	3.62	3.55	3.50	3.45	3.41	3.37	3.34	**16**
17	8.40	6.11	5.18	4.67	4.34	4.10	3.93	3.79	3.68	3.59	3.52	3.46	3.40	3.35	3.31	3.27	3.24	**17**
18	8.29	6.01	5.09	4.58	4.25	4.01	3.84	3.71	3.60	3.51	3.43	3.37	3.32	3.27	3.23	3.19	3.16	**18**
19	8.18	5.93	5.01	4.50	4.17	3.94	3.77	3.63	3.52	3.43	3.36	3.30	3.24	3.19	3.15	3.12	3.08	**19**
20	8.10	5.85	4.94	4.43	4.10	3.87	3.70	3.56	3.46	3.37	3.29	3.23	3.18	3.13	3.09	3.05	3.02	**20**
21	8.02	5.78	4.87	4.37	4.04	3.81	3.64	3.51	3.40	3.31	3.24	3.17	3.12	3.07	3.03	2.99	2.96	**21**
22	7.95	5.72	4.82	4.31	3.99	3.76	3.59	3.45	3.35	3.26	3.18	3.12	3.07	3.02	2.98	2.94	2.91	**22**
23	7.88	5.66	4.76	4.26	3.94	3.71	3.54	3.41	3.30	3.21	3.14	3.07	3.02	2.97	2.93	2.89	2.86	**23**
24	7.82	5.61	4.72	4.22	3.90	3.67	3.50	3.36	3.26	3.17	3.09	3.03	2.98	2.93	2.89	2.85	2.82	**24**
25	7.77	5.57	4.68	4.18	3.85	3.63	3.46	3.32	3.22	3.13	3.06	2.99	2.94	2.89	2.85	2.81	2.78	**25**
26	7.72	5.53	4.64	4.14	3.82	3.59	3.42	3.29	3.18	3.09	3.02	2.96	2.90	2.86	2.81	2.78	2.75	**26**
27	7.68	5.49	4.60	4.11	3.78	3.56	3.39	3.26	3.15	3.06	2.99	2.93	2.87	2.82	2.78	2.75	2.71	**27**
28	7.64	5.45	4.57	4.07	3.75	3.53	3.36	3.23	3.12	3.03	2.96	2.90	2.84	2.79	2.75	2.72	2.68	**28**
29	7.60	5.42	4.54	4.04	3.73	3.50	3.33	3.20	3.09	3.00	2.93	2.87	2.81	2.77	2.73	2.69	2.66	**29**
30	7.56	5.39	4.51	4.02	3.70	3.47	3.30	3.17	3.07	2.98	2.91	2.84	2.79	2.74	2.70	2.66	2.63	**30**
40	7.31	5.18	4.31	3.83	3.51	3.29	3.12	2.99	2.89	2.80	2.73	2.66	2.61	2.56	2.52	2.48	2.45	**40**
60	7.08	4.98	4.13	3.65	3.34	3.12	2.95	2.82	2.72	2.63	2.56	2.50	2.44	2.39	2.35	2.31	2.28	**60**
100	6.90	4.82	3.98	3.51	3.21	2.99	2.82	2.69	2.59	2.50	2.43	2.37	2.31	2.27	2.22	2.19	2.15	**100**
∞	6.63	4.61	3.78	3.32	3.02	2.80	2.64	2.51	2.41	2.32	2.25	2.18	2.13	2.08	2.04	2.00	1.97	∞

Degrees of freedom for the denominator

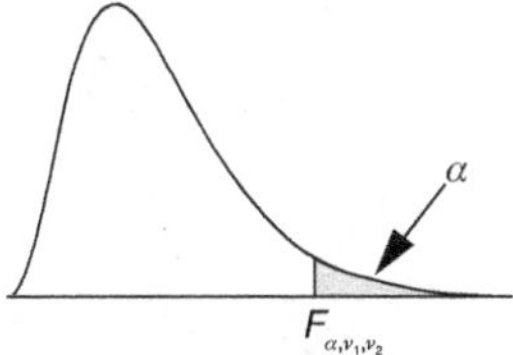

	Degrees of freedom for the numerator (ν_1)																	
(ν_2)	18	19	20	21	22	23	24	25	26	27	28	29	30	40	60	100	∞	(ν_2)
1	6191.53	6200.58	6208.73	6216.12	6222.84	6228.99	6234.63	6239.83	6244.62	6249.07	6253.20	6257.05	6260.65	6286.78	6313.03	6334.11	6365.86	1
2	99.44	99.45	99.45	99.45	99.45	99.46	99.46	99.46	99.46	99.46	99.46	99.46	99.47	99.47	99.48	99.49	99.50	2
3	26.75	26.72	26.69	26.66	26.64	26.62	26.60	26.58	26.56	26.55	26.53	26.52	26.50	26.41	26.32	26.24	26.13	3
4	14.08	14.05	14.02	13.99	13.97	13.95	13.93	13.91	13.89	13.88	13.86	13.85	13.84	13.75	13.65	13.58	13.46	4
5	9.61	9.58	9.55	9.53	9.51	9.49	9.47	9.45	9.43	9.42	9.40	9.39	9.38	9.29	9.20	9.13	9.02	5
6	7.45	7.42	7.40	7.37	7.35	7.33	7.31	7.30	7.28	7.27	7.25	7.24	7.23	7.14	7.06	6.99	6.88	6
7	6.21	6.18	6.16	6.13	6.11	6.09	6.07	6.06	6.04	6.03	6.02	6.00	5.99	5.91	5.82	5.75	5.65	7
8	5.41	5.38	5.36	5.34	5.32	5.30	5.28	5.26	5.25	5.23	5.22	5.21	5.20	5.12	5.03	4.96	4.86	8
9	4.86	4.83	4.81	4.79	4.77	4.75	4.73	4.71	4.70	4.68	4.67	4.66	4.65	4.57	4.48	4.41	4.31	9
10	4.46	4.43	4.41	4.38	4.36	4.34	4.33	4.31	4.30	4.28	4.27	4.26	4.25	4.17	4.08	4.01	3.91	10
11	4.15	4.12	4.10	4.08	4.06	4.04	4.02	4.01	3.99	3.98	3.96	3.95	3.94	3.86	3.78	3.71	3.60	11
12	3.91	3.88	3.86	3.84	3.82	3.80	3.78	3.76	3.75	3.74	3.72	3.71	3.70	3.62	3.54	3.47	3.36	12
13	3.72	3.69	3.66	3.64	3.62	3.60	3.59	3.57	3.56	3.54	3.53	3.52	3.51	3.43	3.34	3.27	3.17	13
14	3.56	3.53	3.51	3.48	3.46	3.44	3.43	3.41	3.40	3.38	3.37	3.36	3.35	3.27	3.18	3.11	3.00	14
15	3.42	3.40	3.37	3.35	3.33	3.31	3.29	3.28	3.26	3.25	3.24	3.23	3.21	3.13	3.05	2.98	2.87	15
16	3.31	3.28	3.26	3.24	3.22	3.20	3.18	3.16	3.15	3.14	3.12	3.11	3.10	3.02	2.93	2.86	2.75	16
17	3.21	3.19	3.16	3.14	3.12	3.10	3.08	3.07	3.05	3.04	3.03	3.01	3.00	2.92	2.83	2.76	2.65	17
18	3.13	3.10	3.08	3.05	3.03	3.02	3.00	2.98	2.97	2.95	2.94	2.93	2.92	2.84	2.75	2.68	2.57	18
19	3.05	3.03	3.00	2.98	2.96	2.94	2.92	2.91	2.89	2.88	2.87	2.86	2.84	2.76	2.67	2.60	2.49	19
20	2.99	2.96	2.94	2.92	2.90	2.88	2.86	2.84	2.83	2.81	2.80	2.79	2.78	2.69	2.61	2.54	2.42	20
21	2.93	2.90	2.88	2.86	2.84	2.82	2.80	2.79	2.77	2.76	2.74	2.73	2.72	2.64	2.55	2.48	2.36	21
22	2.88	2.85	2.83	2.81	2.78	2.77	2.75	2.73	2.72	2.70	2.69	2.68	2.67	2.58	2.50	2.42	2.31	22
23	2.83	2.80	2.78	2.76	2.74	2.72	2.70	2.69	2.67	2.66	2.64	2.63	2.62	2.54	2.45	2.37	2.26	23
24	2.79	2.76	2.74	2.72	2.70	2.68	2.66	2.64	2.63	2.61	2.60	2.59	2.58	2.49	2.40	2.33	2.21	24
25	2.75	2.72	2.70	2.68	2.66	2.64	2.62	2.60	2.59	2.58	2.56	2.55	2.54	2.45	2.36	2.29	2.17	25
26	2.72	2.69	2.66	2.64	2.62	2.60	2.58	2.57	2.55	2.54	2.53	2.51	2.50	2.42	2.33	2.25	2.13	26
27	2.68	2.66	2.63	2.61	2.59	2.57	2.55	2.54	2.52	2.51	2.49	2.48	2.47	2.38	2.29	2.22	2.10	27
28	2.65	2.63	2.60	2.58	2.56	2.54	2.52	2.51	2.49	2.48	2.46	2.45	2.44	2.35	2.26	2.19	2.06	28
29	2.63	2.60	2.57	2.55	2.53	2.51	2.49	2.48	2.46	2.45	2.44	2.42	2.41	2.33	2.23	2.16	2.03	29
30	2.60	2.57	2.55	2.53	2.51	2.49	2.47	2.45	2.44	2.42	2.41	2.40	2.39	2.30	2.21	2.13	2.01	30
40	2.42	2.39	2.37	2.35	2.33	2.31	2.29	2.27	2.26	2.24	2.23	2.22	2.20	2.11	2.02	1.94	1.80	40
60	2.25	2.22	2.20	2.17	2.15	2.13	2.12	2.10	2.08	2.07	2.05	2.04	2.03	1.94	1.84	1.75	1.60	60
100	2.12	2.09	2.07	2.04	2.02	2.00	1.98	1.97	1.95	1.93	1.92	1.91	1.89	1.80	1.69	1.60	1.43	100
∞	1.93	1.90	1.88	1.85	1.83	1.81	1.79	1.77	1.76	1.74	1.72	1.71	1.70	1.59	1.47	1.36	1.00	∞

Degrees of freedom for the denominator

Appendix G.2

F(0.025) Distribution Table

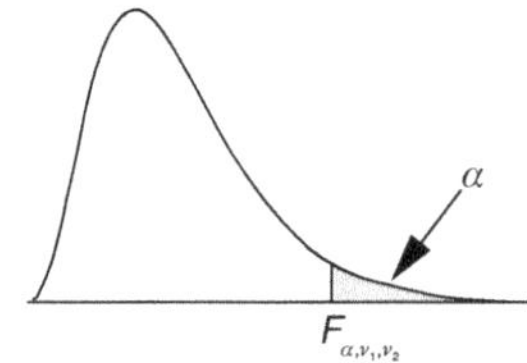

	Degrees of freedom for the numerator (ν_1)																	
Degrees of freedom for the denominator (ν_2)	**1**	**2**	**3**	**4**	**5**	**6**	**7**	**8**	**9**	**10**	**11**	**12**	**13**	**14**	**15**	**16**	**17**	(ν_2)
1	647.79	799.50	864.16	899.58	921.85	937.11	948.22	956.66	963.28	968.63	973.03	976.71	979.84	982.53	984.87	986.92	988.73	**1**
2	38.51	39.00	39.17	39.25	39.30	39.33	39.36	39.37	39.39	39.40	39.41	39.41	39.42	39.43	39.43	39.44	39.44	**2**
3	17.44	16.04	15.44	15.10	14.88	14.73	14.62	14.54	14.47	14.42	14.37	14.34	14.30	14.28	14.25	14.23	14.21	**3**
4	12.22	10.65	9.98	9.60	9.36	9.20	9.07	8.98	8.90	8.84	8.79	8.75	8.71	8.68	8.66	8.63	8.61	**4**
5	10.01	8.43	7.76	7.39	7.15	6.98	6.85	6.76	6.68	6.62	6.57	6.52	6.49	6.46	6.43	6.40	6.38	**5**
6	8.81	7.26	6.60	6.23	5.99	5.82	5.70	5.60	5.52	5.46	5.41	5.37	5.33	5.30	5.27	5.24	5.22	**6**
7	8.07	6.54	5.89	5.52	5.29	5.12	4.99	4.90	4.82	4.76	4.71	4.67	4.63	4.60	4.57	4.54	4.52	**7**
8	7.57	6.06	5.42	5.05	4.82	4.65	4.53	4.43	4.36	4.30	4.24	4.20	4.16	4.13	4.10	4.08	4.05	**8**
9	7.21	5.71	5.08	4.72	4.48	4.32	4.20	4.10	4.03	3.96	3.91	3.87	3.83	3.80	3.77	3.74	3.72	**9**
10	6.94	5.46	4.83	4.47	4.24	4.07	3.95	3.85	3.78	3.72	3.66	3.62	3.58	3.55	3.52	3.50	3.47	**10**
11	6.72	5.26	4.63	4.28	4.04	3.88	3.76	3.66	3.59	3.53	3.47	3.43	3.39	3.36	3.33	3.30	3.28	**11**
12	6.55	5.10	4.47	4.12	3.89	3.73	3.61	3.51	3.44	3.37	3.32	3.28	3.24	3.21	3.18	3.15	3.13	**12**
13	6.41	4.97	4.35	4.00	3.77	3.60	3.48	3.39	3.31	3.25	3.20	3.15	3.12	3.08	3.05	3.03	3.00	**13**
14	6.30	4.86	4.24	3.89	3.66	3.50	3.38	3.29	3.21	3.15	3.09	3.05	3.01	2.98	2.95	2.92	2.90	**14**
15	6.20	4.77	4.15	3.80	3.58	3.41	3.29	3.20	3.12	3.06	3.01	2.96	2.92	2.89	2.86	2.84	2.81	**15**
16	6.12	4.69	4.08	3.73	3.50	3.34	3.22	3.12	3.05	2.99	2.93	2.89	2.85	2.82	2.79	2.76	2.74	**16**
17	6.04	4.62	4.01	3.66	3.44	3.28	3.16	3.06	2.98	2.92	2.87	2.82	2.79	2.75	2.72	2.70	2.67	**17**
18	5.98	4.56	3.95	3.61	3.38	3.22	3.10	3.01	2.93	2.87	2.81	2.77	2.73	2.70	2.67	2.64	2.62	**18**
19	5.92	4.51	3.90	3.56	3.33	3.17	3.05	2.96	2.88	2.82	2.76	2.72	2.68	2.65	2.62	2.59	2.57	**19**
20	5.87	4.46	3.86	3.51	3.29	3.13	3.01	2.91	2.84	2.77	2.72	2.68	2.64	2.60	2.57	2.55	2.52	**20**
21	5.83	4.42	3.82	3.48	3.25	3.09	2.97	2.87	2.80	2.73	2.68	2.64	2.60	2.56	2.53	2.51	2.48	**21**
22	5.79	4.38	3.78	3.44	3.22	3.05	2.93	2.84	2.76	2.70	2.65	2.60	2.56	2.53	2.50	2.47	2.45	**22**
23	5.75	4.35	3.75	3.41	3.18	3.02	2.90	2.81	2.73	2.67	2.62	2.57	2.53	2.50	2.47	2.44	2.42	**23**
24	5.72	4.32	3.72	3.38	3.15	2.99	2.87	2.78	2.70	2.64	2.59	2.54	2.50	2.47	2.44	2.41	2.39	**24**
25	5.69	4.29	3.69	3.35	3.13	2.97	2.85	2.75	2.68	2.61	2.56	2.51	2.48	2.44	2.41	2.38	2.36	**25**
26	5.66	4.27	3.67	3.33	3.10	2.94	2.82	2.73	2.65	2.59	2.54	2.49	2.45	2.42	2.39	2.36	2.34	**26**
27	5.63	4.24	3.65	3.31	3.08	2.92	2.80	2.71	2.63	2.57	2.51	2.47	2.43	2.39	2.36	2.34	2.31	**27**
28	5.61	4.22	3.63	3.29	3.06	2.90	2.78	2.69	2.61	2.55	2.49	2.45	2.41	2.37	2.34	2.32	2.29	**28**
29	5.59	4.20	3.61	3.27	3.04	2.88	2.76	2.67	2.59	2.53	2.48	2.43	2.39	2.36	2.32	2.30	2.27	**29**
30	5.57	4.18	3.59	3.25	3.03	2.87	2.75	2.65	2.57	2.51	2.46	2.41	2.37	2.34	2.31	2.28	2.26	**30**
40	5.42	4.05	3.46	3.13	2.90	2.74	2.62	2.53	2.45	2.39	2.33	2.29	2.25	2.21	2.18	2.15	2.13	**40**
60	5.29	3.93	3.34	3.01	2.79	2.63	2.51	2.41	2.33	2.27	2.22	2.17	2.13	2.09	2.06	2.03	2.01	**60**
100	5.18	3.83	3.25	2.92	2.70	2.54	2.42	2.32	2.24	2.18	2.12	2.08	2.04	2.00	1.97	1.94	1.91	**100**
∞	5.02	3.69	3.12	2.79	2.57	2.41	2.29	2.19	2.11	2.05	1.99	1.94	1.90	1.87	1.83	1.80	1.78	∞

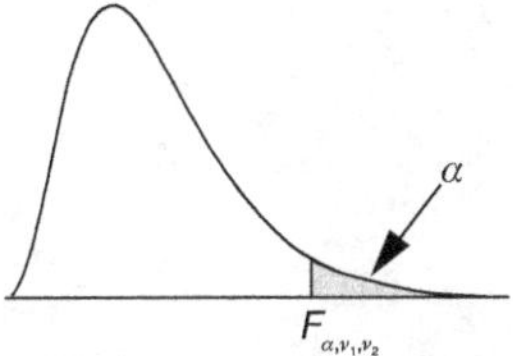

	Degrees of freedom for the numerator (ν_1)																	
(ν_2)	**18**	**19**	**20**	**21**	**22**	**23**	**24**	**25**	**26**	**27**	**28**	**29**	**30**	**40**	**60**	**100**	∞	(ν_2)
1	990.35	991.80	993.10	994.29	995.36	996.35	997.25	998.08	998.85	999.56	1000.22	1000.84	1001.41	1005.60	1009.80	1013.17	1018.26	**1**
2	39.44	39.45	39.45	39.45	39.45	39.45	39.46	39.46	39.46	39.46	39.46	39.46	39.46	39.47	39.48	39.49	39.50	**2**
3	14.20	14.18	14.17	14.16	14.14	14.13	14.12	14.12	14.11	14.10	14.09	14.09	14.08	14.04	13.99	13.96	13.90	**3**
4	8.59	8.58	8.56	8.55	8.53	8.52	8.51	8.50	8.49	8.48	8.48	8.47	8.46	8.41	8.36	8.32	8.26	**4**
5	6.36	6.34	6.33	6.31	6.30	6.29	6.28	6.27	6.26	6.25	6.24	6.23	6.23	6.18	6.12	6.08	6.02	**5**
6	5.20	5.18	5.17	5.15	5.14	5.13	5.12	5.11	5.10	5.09	5.08	5.07	5.07	5.01	4.96	4.92	4.85	**6**
7	4.50	4.48	4.47	4.45	4.44	4.43	4.41	4.40	4.39	4.39	4.38	4.37	4.36	4.31	4.25	4.21	4.14	**7**
8	4.03	4.02	4.00	3.98	3.97	3.96	3.95	3.94	3.93	3.92	3.91	3.90	3.89	3.84	3.78	3.74	3.67	**8**
9	3.70	3.68	3.67	3.65	3.64	3.63	3.61	3.60	3.59	3.58	3.58	3.57	3.56	3.51	3.45	3.40	3.33	**9**
10	3.45	3.44	3.42	3.40	3.39	3.38	3.37	3.35	3.34	3.34	3.33	3.32	3.31	3.26	3.20	3.15	3.08	**10**
11	3.26	3.24	3.23	3.21	3.20	3.18	3.17	3.16	3.15	3.14	3.13	3.13	3.12	3.06	3.00	2.96	2.88	**11**
12	3.11	3.09	3.07	3.06	3.04	3.03	3.02	3.01	3.00	2.99	2.98	2.97	2.96	2.91	2.85	2.80	2.72	**12**
13	2.98	2.96	2.95	2.93	2.92	2.91	2.89	2.88	2.87	2.86	2.85	2.85	2.84	2.78	2.72	2.67	2.60	**13**
14	2.88	2.86	2.84	2.83	2.81	2.80	2.79	2.78	2.77	2.76	2.75	2.74	2.73	2.67	2.61	2.56	2.49	**14**
15	2.79	2.77	2.76	2.74	2.73	2.71	2.70	2.69	2.68	2.67	2.66	2.65	2.64	2.59	2.52	2.47	2.40	**15**
16	2.72	2.70	2.68	2.67	2.65	2.64	2.63	2.61	2.60	2.59	2.58	2.58	2.57	2.51	2.45	2.40	2.32	**16**
17	2.65	2.63	2.62	2.60	2.59	2.57	2.56	2.55	2.54	2.53	2.52	2.51	2.50	2.44	2.38	2.33	2.25	**17**
18	2.60	2.58	2.56	2.54	2.53	2.52	2.50	2.49	2.48	2.47	2.46	2.45	2.44	2.38	2.32	2.27	2.19	**18**
19	2.55	2.53	2.51	2.49	2.48	2.46	2.45	2.44	2.43	2.42	2.41	2.40	2.39	2.33	2.27	2.22	2.13	**19**
20	2.50	2.48	2.46	2.45	2.43	2.42	2.41	2.40	2.39	2.38	2.37	2.36	2.35	2.29	2.22	2.17	2.09	**20**
21	2.46	2.44	2.42	2.41	2.39	2.38	2.37	2.36	2.34	2.33	2.33	2.32	2.31	2.25	2.18	2.13	2.04	**21**
22	2.43	2.41	2.39	2.37	2.36	2.34	2.33	2.32	2.31	2.30	2.29	2.28	2.27	2.21	2.14	2.09	2.00	**22**
23	2.39	2.37	2.36	2.34	2.33	2.31	2.30	2.29	2.28	2.27	2.26	2.25	2.24	2.18	2.11	2.06	1.97	**23**
24	2.36	2.35	2.33	2.31	2.30	2.28	2.27	2.26	2.25	2.24	2.23	2.22	2.21	2.15	2.08	2.02	1.94	**24**
25	2.34	2.32	2.30	2.28	2.27	2.26	2.24	2.23	2.22	2.21	2.20	2.19	2.18	2.12	2.05	2.00	1.91	**25**
26	2.31	2.29	2.28	2.26	2.24	2.23	2.22	2.21	2.19	2.18	2.17	2.17	2.16	2.09	2.03	1.97	1.88	**26**
27	2.29	2.27	2.25	2.24	2.22	2.21	2.19	2.18	2.17	2.16	2.15	2.14	2.13	2.07	2.00	1.94	1.85	**27**
28	2.27	2.25	2.23	2.22	2.20	2.19	2.17	2.16	2.15	2.14	2.13	2.12	2.11	2.05	1.98	1.92	1.83	**28**
29	2.25	2.23	2.21	2.20	2.18	2.17	2.15	2.14	2.13	2.12	2.11	2.10	2.09	2.03	1.96	1.90	1.81	**29**
30	2.23	2.21	2.20	2.18	2.16	2.15	2.14	2.12	2.11	2.10	2.09	2.08	2.07	2.01	1.94	1.88	1.79	**30**
40	2.11	2.09	2.07	2.05	2.03	2.02	2.01	1.99	1.98	1.97	1.96	1.95	1.94	1.88	1.80	1.74	1.64	**40**
60	1.98	1.96	1.94	1.93	1.91	1.90	1.88	1.87	1.86	1.85	1.83	1.82	1.82	1.74	1.67	1.60	1.48	**60**
100	1.89	1.87	1.85	1.83	1.81	1.80	1.78	1.77	1.76	1.75	1.74	1.72	1.71	1.64	1.56	1.48	1.35	**100**
∞	1.75	1.73	1.71	1.69	1.67	1.66	1.64	1.63	1.61	1.60	1.59	1.58	1.57	1.48	1.39	1.30	1.00	∞

Degrees of freedom for the denominator

Appendix G.3

F(0.05) Distribution Table

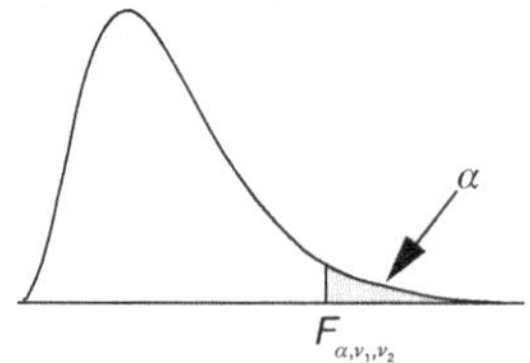

Degrees of freedom for the numerator (ν_1)

Degrees of freedom for the denominator

(ν_2)	1	2	3	4	5	6	7	8	9	10	11	12	13	14	15	16	17	(ν_2)
1	161.45	199.50	215.71	224.58	230.16	233.99	236.77	238.88	240.54	241.88	242.98	243.91	244.69	245.36	245.95	246.46	246.92	**1**
2	18.51	19.00	19.16	19.25	19.30	19.33	19.35	19.37	19.38	19.40	19.40	19.41	19.42	19.42	19.43	19.43	19.44	**2**
3	10.13	9.55	9.28	9.12	9.01	8.94	8.89	8.85	8.81	8.79	8.76	8.74	8.73	8.71	8.70	8.69	8.68	**3**
4	7.71	6.94	6.59	6.39	6.26	6.16	6.09	6.04	6.00	5.96	5.94	5.91	5.89	5.87	5.86	5.84	5.83	**4**
5	6.61	5.79	5.41	5.19	5.05	4.95	4.88	4.82	4.77	4.74	4.70	4.68	4.66	4.64	4.62	4.60	4.59	**5**
6	5.99	5.14	4.76	4.53	4.39	4.28	4.21	4.15	4.10	4.06	4.03	4.00	3.98	3.96	3.94	3.92	3.91	**6**
7	5.59	4.74	4.35	4.12	3.97	3.87	3.79	3.73	3.68	3.64	3.60	3.57	3.55	3.53	3.51	3.49	3.48	**7**
8	5.32	4.46	4.07	3.84	3.69	3.58	3.50	3.44	3.39	3.35	3.31	3.28	3.26	3.24	3.22	3.20	3.19	**8**
9	5.12	4.26	3.86	3.63	3.48	3.37	3.29	3.23	3.18	3.14	3.10	3.07	3.05	3.03	3.01	2.99	2.97	**9**
10	4.96	4.10	3.71	3.48	3.33	3.22	3.14	3.07	3.02	2.98	2.94	2.91	2.89	2.86	2.85	2.83	2.81	**10**
11	4.84	3.98	3.59	3.36	3.20	3.09	3.01	2.95	2.90	2.85	2.82	2.79	2.76	2.74	2.72	2.70	2.69	**11**
12	4.75	3.89	3.49	3.26	3.11	3.00	2.91	2.85	2.80	2.75	2.72	2.69	2.66	2.64	2.62	2.60	2.58	**12**
13	4.67	3.81	3.41	3.18	3.03	2.92	2.83	2.77	2.71	2.67	2.63	2.60	2.58	2.55	2.53	2.51	2.50	**13**
14	4.60	3.74	3.34	3.11	2.96	2.85	2.76	2.70	2.65	2.60	2.57	2.53	2.51	2.48	2.46	2.44	2.43	**14**
15	4.54	3.68	3.29	3.06	2.90	2.79	2.71	2.64	2.59	2.54	2.51	2.48	2.45	2.42	2.40	2.38	2.37	**15**
16	4.49	3.63	3.24	3.01	2.85	2.74	2.66	2.59	2.54	2.49	2.46	2.42	2.40	2.37	2.35	2.33	2.32	**16**
17	4.45	3.59	3.20	2.96	2.81	2.70	2.61	2.55	2.49	2.45	2.41	2.38	2.35	2.33	2.31	2.29	2.27	**17**
18	4.41	3.55	3.16	2.93	2.77	2.66	2.58	2.51	2.46	2.41	2.37	2.34	2.31	2.29	2.27	2.25	2.23	**18**
19	4.38	3.52	3.13	2.90	2.74	2.63	2.54	2.48	2.42	2.38	2.34	2.31	2.28	2.26	2.23	2.21	2.20	**19**
20	4.35	3.49	3.10	2.87	2.71	2.60	2.51	2.45	2.39	2.35	2.31	2.28	2.25	2.22	2.20	2.18	2.17	**20**
21	4.32	3.47	3.07	2.84	2.68	2.57	2.49	2.42	2.37	2.32	2.28	2.25	2.22	2.20	2.18	2.16	2.14	**21**
22	4.30	3.44	3.05	2.82	2.66	2.55	2.46	2.40	2.34	2.30	2.26	2.23	2.20	2.17	2.15	2.13	2.11	**22**
23	4.28	3.42	3.03	2.80	2.64	2.53	2.44	2.37	2.32	2.27	2.24	2.20	2.18	2.15	2.13	2.11	2.09	**23**
24	4.26	3.40	3.01	2.78	2.62	2.51	2.42	2.36	2.30	2.25	2.22	2.18	2.15	2.13	2.11	2.09	2.07	**24**
25	4.24	3.39	2.99	2.76	2.60	2.49	2.40	2.34	2.28	2.24	2.20	2.16	2.14	2.11	2.09	2.07	2.05	**25**
26	4.23	3.37	2.98	2.74	2.59	2.47	2.39	2.32	2.27	2.22	2.18	2.15	2.12	2.09	2.07	2.05	2.03	**26**
27	4.21	3.35	2.96	2.73	2.57	2.46	2.37	2.31	2.25	2.20	2.17	2.13	2.10	2.08	2.06	2.04	2.02	**27**
28	4.20	3.34	2.95	2.71	2.56	2.45	2.36	2.29	2.24	2.19	2.15	2.12	2.09	2.06	2.04	2.02	2.00	**28**
29	4.18	3.33	2.93	2.70	2.55	2.43	2.35	2.28	2.22	2.18	2.14	2.10	2.08	2.05	2.03	2.01	1.99	**29**
30	4.17	3.32	2.92	2.69	2.53	2.42	2.33	2.27	2.21	2.16	2.13	2.09	2.06	2.04	2.01	1.99	1.98	**30**
40	4.08	3.23	2.84	2.61	2.45	2.34	2.25	2.18	2.12	2.08	2.04	2.00	1.97	1.95	1.92	1.90	1.89	**40**
60	4.00	3.15	2.76	2.53	2.37	2.25	2.17	2.10	2.04	1.99	1.95	1.92	1.89	1.86	1.84	1.82	1.80	**60**
100	3.94	3.09	2.70	2.46	2.31	2.19	2.10	2.03	1.97	1.93	1.89	1.85	1.82	1.79	1.77	1.75	1.73	**100**
∞	3.84	3.00	2.60	2.37	2.21	2.10	2.01	1.94	1.88	1.83	1.79	1.75	1.72	1.69	1.67	1.64	1.62	∞

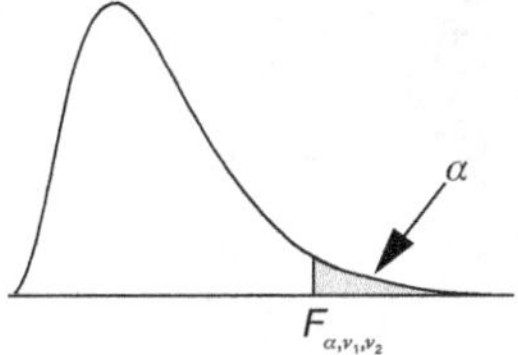

	Degrees of freedom for the numerator (ν_1)																	
(ν_2)	**18**	**19**	**20**	**21**	**22**	**23**	**24**	**25**	**26**	**27**	**28**	**29**	**30**	**40**	**60**	**100**	∞	(ν_2)
1	247.32	247.69	248.01	248.31	248.58	248.83	249.05	249.26	249.45	249.63	249.80	249.95	250.10	251.14	252.20	253.04	254.31	**1**
2	19.44	19.44	19.45	19.45	19.45	19.45	19.45	19.46	19.46	19.46	19.46	19.46	19.46	19.47	19.48	19.49	9.49	**2**
3	8.67	8.67	8.66	8.65	8.65	8.64	8.64	8.63	8.63	8.63	8.62	8.62	8.62	8.59	8.57	8.55	5.13	**3**
4	5.82	5.81	5.80	5.79	5.79	5.78	5.77	5.77	5.76	5.76	5.75	5.75	5.75	5.72	5.69	5.66	3.76	**4**
5	4.58	4.57	4.56	4.55	4.54	4.53	4.53	4.52	4.52	4.51	4.50	4.50	4.50	4.46	4.43	4.41	3.10	**5**
6	3.90	3.88	3.87	3.86	3.86	3.85	3.84	3.83	3.83	3.82	3.82	3.81	3.81	3.77	3.74	3.71	2.72	**6**
7	3.47	3.46	3.44	3.43	3.43	3.42	3.41	3.40	3.40	3.39	3.39	3.38	3.38	3.34	3.30	3.27	2.47	**7**
8	3.17	3.16	3.15	3.14	3.13	3.12	3.12	3.11	3.10	3.10	3.09	3.08	3.08	3.04	3.01	2.97	2.29	**8**
9	2.96	2.95	2.94	2.93	2.92	2.91	2.90	2.89	2.89	2.88	2.87	2.87	2.86	2.83	2.79	2.76	2.16	**9**
10	2.80	2.79	2.77	2.76	2.75	2.75	2.74	2.73	2.72	2.72	2.71	2.70	2.70	2.66	2.62	2.59	2.06	**10**
11	2.67	2.66	2.65	2.64	2.63	2.62	2.61	2.60	2.59	2.59	2.58	2.58	2.57	2.53	2.49	2.46	1.97	**11**
12	2.57	2.56	2.54	2.53	2.52	2.51	2.51	2.50	2.49	2.48	2.48	2.47	2.47	2.43	2.38	2.35	1.90	**12**
13	2.48	2.47	2.46	2.45	2.44	2.43	2.42	2.41	2.41	2.40	2.39	2.39	2.38	2.34	2.30	2.26	1.85	**13**
14	2.41	2.40	2.39	2.38	2.37	2.36	2.35	2.34	2.33	2.33	2.32	2.31	2.31	2.27	2.22	2.19	1.80	**14**
15	2.35	2.34	2.33	2.32	2.31	2.30	2.29	2.28	2.27	2.27	2.26	2.25	2.25	2.20	2.16	2.12	1.76	**15**
16	2.30	2.29	2.28	2.26	2.25	2.24	2.24	2.23	2.22	2.21	2.21	2.20	2.19	2.15	2.11	2.07	1.72	**16**
17	2.26	2.24	2.23	2.22	2.21	2.20	2.19	2.18	2.17	2.17	2.16	2.15	2.15	2.10	2.06	2.02	1.69	**17**
18	2.22	2.20	2.19	2.18	2.17	2.16	2.15	2.14	2.13	2.13	2.12	2.11	2.11	2.06	2.02	1.98	1.66	**18**
19	2.18	2.17	2.16	2.14	2.13	2.12	2.11	2.11	2.10	2.09	2.08	2.08	2.07	2.03	1.98	1.94	1.63	**19**
20	2.15	2.14	2.12	2.11	2.10	2.09	2.08	2.07	2.07	2.06	2.05	2.05	2.04	1.99	1.95	1.91	1.61	**20**
21	2.12	2.11	2.10	2.08	2.07	2.06	2.05	2.05	2.04	2.03	2.02	2.02	2.01	1.96	1.92	1.88	1.59	**21**
22	2.10	2.08	2.07	2.06	2.05	2.04	2.03	2.02	2.01	2.00	2.00	1.99	1.98	1.94	1.89	1.85	1.57	**22**
23	2.08	2.06	2.05	2.04	2.02	2.01	2.01	2.00	1.99	1.98	1.97	1.97	1.96	1.91	1.86	1.82	1.55	**23**
24	2.05	2.04	2.03	2.01	2.00	1.99	1.98	1.97	1.97	1.96	1.95	1.95	1.94	1.89	1.84	1.80	1.53	**24**
25	2.04	2.02	2.01	2.00	1.98	1.97	1.96	1.96	1.95	1.94	1.93	1.93	1.92	1.87	1.82	1.78	1.52	**25**
26	2.02	2.00	1.99	1.98	1.97	1.96	1.95	1.94	1.93	1.92	1.91	1.91	1.90	1.85	1.80	1.76	1.50	**26**
27	2.00	1.99	1.97	1.96	1.95	1.94	1.93	1.92	1.91	1.90	1.90	1.89	1.88	1.84	1.79	1.74	1.49	**27**
28	1.99	1.97	1.96	1.95	1.93	1.92	1.91	1.91	1.90	1.89	1.88	1.88	1.87	1.82	1.77	1.73	1.48	**28**
29	1.97	1.96	1.94	1.93	1.92	1.91	1.90	1.89	1.88	1.88	1.87	1.86	1.85	1.81	1.75	1.71	1.47	**29**
30	1.96	1.95	1.93	1.92	1.91	1.90	1.89	1.88	1.87	1.86	1.85	1.85	1.84	1.79	1.74	1.70	1.46	**30**
40	1.87	1.85	1.84	1.83	1.81	1.80	1.79	1.78	1.77	1.77	1.76	1.75	1.74	1.69	1.64	1.59	1.38	**40**
60	1.78	1.76	1.75	1.73	1.72	1.71	1.70	1.69	1.68	1.67	1.66	1.66	1.65	1.59	1.53	1.48	1.29	**60**
100	1.71	1.69	1.68	1.66	1.65	1.64	1.63	1.62	1.61	1.60	1.59	1.58	1.57	1.52	1.45	1.39	1.21	**100**
∞	1.60	1.59	1.57	1.56	1.54	1.53	1.52	1.51	1.50	1.49	1.48	1.47	1.46	1.39	1.32	1.24	1.00	∞

Degrees of freedom for the denominator

Appendix G.4

F(0.10) Distribution Table

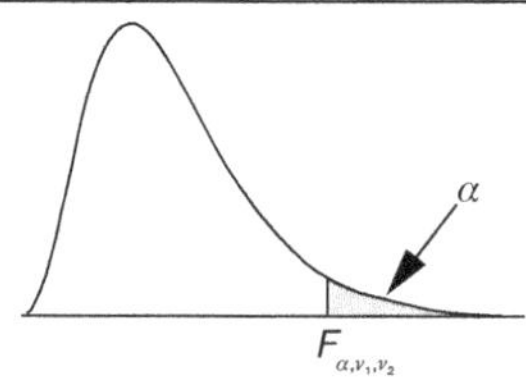

Degrees of freedom for the numerator (ν_1)

Degrees of freedom for the denominator (ν_2)

(ν_2)	1	2	3	4	5	6	7	8	9	10	11	12	13	14	15	16	17	(ν_2)
1	39.86	49.50	53.59	55.83	57.24	58.20	58.91	59.44	59.86	60.19	60.47	60.71	60.90	61.07	61.22	61.35	61.46	**1**
2	8.53	9.00	9.16	9.24	9.29	9.33	9.35	9.37	9.38	9.39	9.40	9.41	9.41	9.42	9.42	9.43	9.43	**2**
3	5.54	5.46	5.39	5.34	5.31	5.28	5.27	5.25	5.24	5.23	5.22	5.22	5.21	5.20	5.20	5.20	5.19	**3**
4	4.54	4.32	4.19	4.11	4.05	4.01	3.98	3.95	3.94	3.92	3.91	3.90	3.89	3.88	3.87	3.86	3.86	**4**
5	4.06	3.78	3.62	3.52	3.45	3.40	3.37	3.34	3.32	3.30	3.28	3.27	3.26	3.25	3.24	3.23	3.22	**5**
6	3.78	3.46	3.29	3.18	3.11	3.05	3.01	2.98	2.96	2.94	2.92	2.90	2.89	2.88	2.87	2.86	2.85	**6**
7	3.59	3.26	3.07	2.96	2.88	2.83	2.78	2.75	2.72	2.70	2.68	2.67	2.65	2.64	2.63	2.62	2.61	**7**
8	3.46	3.11	2.92	2.81	2.73	2.67	2.62	2.59	2.56	2.54	2.52	2.50	2.49	2.48	2.46	2.45	2.45	**8**
9	3.36	3.01	2.81	2.69	2.61	2.55	2.51	2.47	2.44	2.42	2.40	2.38	2.36	2.35	2.34	2.33	2.32	**9**
10	3.29	2.92	2.73	2.61	2.52	2.46	2.41	2.38	2.35	2.32	2.30	2.28	2.27	2.26	2.24	2.23	2.22	**10**
11	3.23	2.86	2.66	2.54	2.45	2.39	2.34	2.30	2.27	2.25	2.23	2.21	2.19	2.18	2.17	2.16	2.15	**11**
12	3.18	2.81	2.61	2.48	2.39	2.33	2.28	2.24	2.21	2.19	2.17	2.15	2.13	2.12	2.10	2.09	2.08	**12**
13	3.14	2.76	2.56	2.43	2.35	2.28	2.23	2.20	2.16	2.14	2.12	2.10	2.08	2.07	2.05	2.04	2.03	**13**
14	3.10	2.73	2.52	2.39	2.31	2.24	2.19	2.15	2.12	2.10	2.07	2.05	2.04	2.02	2.01	2.00	1.99	**14**
15	3.07	2.70	2.49	2.36	2.27	2.21	2.16	2.12	2.09	2.06	2.04	2.02	2.00	1.99	1.97	1.96	1.95	**15**
16	3.05	2.67	2.46	2.33	2.24	2.18	2.13	2.09	2.06	2.03	2.01	1.99	1.97	1.95	1.94	1.93	1.92	**16**
17	3.03	2.64	2.44	2.31	2.22	2.15	2.10	2.06	2.03	2.00	1.98	1.96	1.94	1.93	1.91	1.90	1.89	**17**
18	3.01	2.62	2.42	2.29	2.20	2.13	2.08	2.04	2.00	1.98	1.95	1.93	1.92	1.90	1.89	1.87	1.86	**18**
19	2.99	2.61	2.40	2.27	2.18	2.11	2.06	2.02	1.98	1.96	1.93	1.91	1.89	1.88	1.86	1.85	1.84	**19**
20	2.97	2.59	2.38	2.25	2.16	2.09	2.04	2.00	1.96	1.94	1.91	1.89	1.87	1.86	1.84	1.83	1.82	**20**
21	2.96	2.57	2.36	2.23	2.14	2.08	2.02	1.98	1.95	1.92	1.90	1.87	1.86	1.84	1.83	1.81	1.80	**21**
22	2.95	2.56	2.35	2.22	2.13	2.06	2.01	1.97	1.93	1.90	1.88	1.86	1.84	1.83	1.81	1.80	1.79	**22**
23	2.94	2.55	2.34	2.21	2.11	2.05	1.99	1.95	1.92	1.89	1.87	1.84	1.83	1.81	1.80	1.78	1.77	**23**
24	2.93	2.54	2.33	2.19	2.10	2.04	1.98	1.94	1.91	1.88	1.85	1.83	1.81	1.80	1.78	1.77	1.76	**24**
25	2.92	2.53	2.32	2.18	2.09	2.02	1.97	1.93	1.89	1.87	1.84	1.82	1.80	1.79	1.77	1.76	1.75	**25**
26	2.91	2.52	2.31	2.17	2.08	2.01	1.96	1.92	1.88	1.86	1.83	1.81	1.79	1.77	1.76	1.75	1.73	**26**
27	2.90	2.51	2.30	2.17	2.07	2.00	1.95	1.91	1.87	1.85	1.82	1.80	1.78	1.76	1.75	1.74	1.72	**27**
28	2.89	2.50	2.29	2.16	2.06	2.00	1.94	1.90	1.87	1.84	1.81	1.79	1.77	1.75	1.74	1.73	1.71	**28**
29	2.89	2.50	2.28	2.15	2.06	1.99	1.93	1.89	1.86	1.83	1.80	1.78	1.76	1.75	1.73	1.72	1.71	**29**
30	2.88	2.49	2.28	2.14	2.05	1.98	1.93	1.88	1.85	1.82	1.79	1.77	1.75	1.74	1.72	1.71	1.70	**30**
40	2.84	2.44	2.23	2.09	2.00	1.93	1.87	1.83	1.79	1.76	1.74	1.71	1.70	1.68	1.66	1.65	1.64	**40**
60	2.79	2.39	2.18	2.04	1.95	1.87	1.82	1.77	1.74	1.71	1.68	1.66	1.64	1.62	1.60	1.59	1.58	**60**
100	2.76	2.36	2.14	2.00	1.91	1.83	1.78	1.73	1.69	1.66	1.64	1.61	1.59	1.57	1.56	1.54	1.53	**100**
∞	2.71	2.30	2.08	1.94	1.85	1.77	1.72	1.67	1.63	1.60	1.57	1.55	1.52	1.50	1.49	1.47	1.46	∞

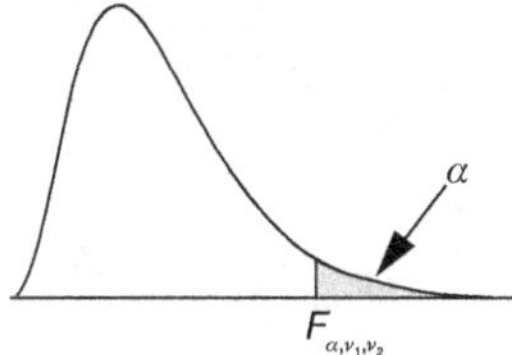

	Degrees of freedom for the numerator (ν_1)																	
(ν_2)	**18**	**19**	**20**	**21**	**22**	**23**	**24**	**25**	**26**	**27**	**28**	**29**	**30**	**40**	**60**	**100**	∞	(ν_2)
1	61.57	61.66	61.74	61.81	61.88	61.95	62.00	62.05	62.10	62.15	62.19	62.23	62.26	62.53	62.79	63.01	63.33	**1**
2	9.44	9.44	9.44	9.44	9.45	9.45	9.45	9.45	9.45	9.45	9.46	9.46	9.46	9.47	9.47	9.48	9.49	**2**
3	5.19	5.19	5.18	5.18	5.18	5.18	5.18	5.17	5.17	5.17	5.17	5.17	5.17	5.16	5.15	5.14	5.13	**3**
4	3.85	3.85	3.84	3.84	3.84	3.83	3.83	3.83	3.83	3.82	3.82	3.82	3.82	3.80	3.79	3.78	3.76	**4**
5	3.22	3.21	3.21	3.20	3.20	3.19	3.19	3.19	3.18	3.18	3.18	3.18	3.17	3.16	3.14	3.13	3.10	**5**
6	2.85	2.84	2.84	2.83	2.83	2.82	2.82	2.81	2.81	2.81	2.81	2.80	2.80	2.78	2.76	2.75	2.72	**6**
7	2.61	2.60	2.59	2.59	2.58	2.58	2.58	2.57	2.57	2.56	2.56	2.56	2.56	2.54	2.51	2.50	2.47	**7**
8	2.44	2.43	2.42	2.42	2.41	2.41	2.40	2.40	2.40	2.39	2.39	2.39	2.38	2.36	2.34	2.32	2.29	**8**
9	2.31	2.30	2.30	2.29	2.29	2.28	2.28	2.27	2.27	2.26	2.26	2.26	2.25	2.23	2.21	2.19	2.16	**9**
10	2.22	2.21	2.20	2.19	2.19	2.18	2.18	2.17	2.17	2.17	2.16	2.16	2.16	2.13	2.11	2.09	2.06	**10**
11	2.14	2.13	2.12	2.12	2.11	2.11	2.10	2.10	2.09	2.09	2.08	2.08	2.08	2.05	2.03	2.01	1.97	**11**
12	2.08	2.07	2.06	2.05	2.05	2.04	2.04	2.03	2.03	2.02	2.02	2.01	2.01	1.99	1.96	1.94	1.90	**12**
13	2.02	2.01	2.01	2.00	1.99	1.99	1.98	1.98	1.97	1.97	1.96	1.96	1.96	1.93	1.90	1.88	1.85	**13**
14	1.98	1.97	1.96	1.96	1.95	1.94	1.94	1.93	1.93	1.92	1.92	1.92	1.91	1.89	1.86	1.83	1.80	**14**
15	1.94	1.93	1.92	1.92	1.91	1.90	1.90	1.89	1.89	1.88	1.88	1.88	1.87	1.85	1.82	1.79	1.76	**15**
16	1.91	1.90	1.89	1.88	1.88	1.87	1.87	1.86	1.86	1.85	1.85	1.84	1.84	1.81	1.78	1.76	1.72	**16**
17	1.88	1.87	1.86	1.86	1.85	1.84	1.84	1.83	1.83	1.82	1.82	1.81	1.81	1.78	1.75	1.73	1.69	**17**
18	1.85	1.84	1.84	1.83	1.82	1.82	1.81	1.80	1.80	1.80	1.79	1.79	1.78	1.75	1.72	1.70	1.66	**18**
19	1.83	1.82	1.81	1.81	1.80	1.79	1.79	1.78	1.78	1.77	1.77	1.76	1.76	1.73	1.70	1.67	1.63	**19**
20	1.81	1.80	1.79	1.79	1.78	1.77	1.77	1.76	1.76	1.75	1.75	1.74	1.74	1.71	1.68	1.65	1.61	**20**
21	1.79	1.78	1.78	1.77	1.76	1.75	1.75	1.74	1.74	1.73	1.73	1.72	1.72	1.69	1.66	1.63	1.59	**21**
22	1.78	1.77	1.76	1.75	1.74	1.74	1.73	1.73	1.72	1.72	1.71	1.71	1.70	1.67	1.64	1.61	1.57	**22**
23	1.76	1.75	1.74	1.74	1.73	1.72	1.72	1.71	1.70	1.70	1.69	1.69	1.69	1.66	1.62	1.59	1.55	**23**
24	1.75	1.74	1.73	1.72	1.71	1.71	1.70	1.70	1.69	1.69	1.68	1.68	1.67	1.64	1.61	1.58	1.53	**24**
25	1.74	1.73	1.72	1.71	1.70	1.70	1.69	1.68	1.68	1.67	1.67	1.66	1.66	1.63	1.59	1.56	1.52	**25**
26	1.72	1.71	1.71	1.70	1.69	1.68	1.68	1.67	1.67	1.66	1.66	1.65	1.65	1.61	1.58	1.55	1.50	**26**
27	1.71	1.70	1.70	1.69	1.68	1.67	1.67	1.66	1.65	1.65	1.64	1.64	1.64	1.60	1.57	1.54	1.49	**27**
28	1.70	1.69	1.69	1.68	1.67	1.66	1.66	1.65	1.64	1.64	1.63	1.63	1.63	1.59	1.56	1.53	1.48	**28**
29	1.69	1.68	1.68	1.67	1.66	1.65	1.65	1.64	1.63	1.63	1.62	1.62	1.62	1.58	1.55	1.52	1.47	**29**
30	1.69	1.68	1.67	1.66	1.65	1.64	1.64	1.63	1.63	1.62	1.62	1.61	1.61	1.57	1.54	1.51	1.46	**30**
40	1.62	1.61	1.61	1.60	1.59	1.58	1.57	1.57	1.56	1.56	1.55	1.55	1.54	1.51	1.47	1.43	1.38	**40**
60	1.56	1.55	1.54	1.53	1.53	1.52	1.51	1.50	1.50	1.49	1.49	1.48	1.48	1.44	1.40	1.36	1.29	**60**
100	1.52	1.50	1.49	1.48	1.48	1.47	1.46	1.45	1.45	1.44	1.43	1.43	1.42	1.38	1.34	1.29	1.21	**100**
∞	1.44	1.43	1.42	1.41	1.40	1.39	1.38	1.38	1.37	1.36	1.35	1.35	1.34	1.30	1.24	1.18	1.00	∞

Degrees of freedom for the denominator

Appendix G.5

$F(0.90)$ Distribution Table

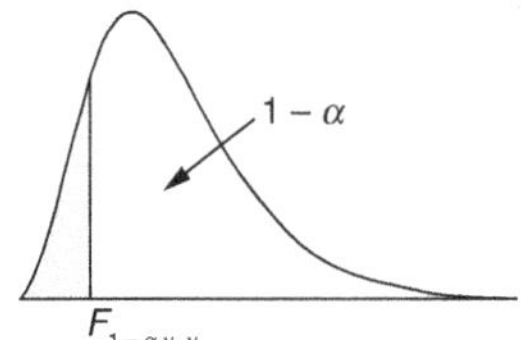

Degrees of freedom for the denominator		Degrees of freedom for the numerator (ν_1)																	
	(ν_2)	1	2	3	4	5	6	7	8	9	10	11	12	13	14	15	16	17	(ν_2)
	1	0.03	0.12	0.18	0.22	0.25	0.26	0.28	0.29	0.30	0.30	0.31	0.31	0.32	0.32	0.33	0.33	0.33	**1**
	2	0.02	0.11	0.18	0.23	0.26	0.29	0.31	0.32	0.33	0.34	0.35	0.36	0.36	0.37	0.37	0.37	0.38	**2**
	3	0.02	0.11	0.19	0.24	0.28	0.30	0.33	0.34	0.36	0.37	0.38	0.38	0.39	0.40	0.40	0.41	0.41	**3**
	4	0.02	0.11	0.19	0.24	0.28	0.31	0.34	0.36	0.37	0.38	0.39	0.40	0.41	0.42	0.42	0.43	0.43	**4**
	5	0.02	0.11	0.19	0.25	0.29	0.32	0.35	0.37	0.38	0.40	0.41	0.42	0.43	0.43	0.44	0.45	0.45	**5**
	6	0.02	0.11	0.19	0.25	0.29	0.33	0.35	0.37	0.39	0.41	0.42	0.43	0.44	0.45	0.45	0.46	0.46	**6**
	7	0.02	0.11	0.19	0.25	0.30	0.33	0.36	0.38	0.40	0.41	0.43	0.44	0.45	0.46	0.46	0.47	0.48	**7**
	8	0.02	0.11	0.19	0.25	0.30	0.34	0.36	0.39	0.40	0.42	0.43	0.45	0.46	0.46	0.47	0.48	0.49	**8**
	9	0.02	0.11	0.19	0.25	0.30	0.34	0.37	0.39	0.41	0.43	0.44	0.45	0.46	0.47	0.48	0.49	0.49	**9**
	10	0.02	0.11	0.19	0.26	0.30	0.34	0.37	0.39	0.41	0.43	0.44	0.46	0.47	0.48	0.49	0.49	0.50	**10**
	11	0.02	0.11	0.19	0.26	0.30	0.34	0.37	0.40	0.42	0.43	0.45	0.46	0.47	0.48	0.49	0.50	0.51	**11**
	12	0.02	0.11	0.19	0.26	0.31	0.34	0.37	0.40	0.42	0.44	0.45	0.47	0.48	0.49	0.50	0.50	0.51	**12**
	13	0.02	0.11	0.19	0.26	0.31	0.35	0.38	0.40	0.42	0.44	0.46	0.47	0.48	0.49	0.50	0.51	0.52	**13**
	14	0.02	0.11	0.19	0.26	0.31	0.35	0.38	0.40	0.43	0.44	0.46	0.47	0.48	0.49	0.50	0.51	0.52	**14**
	15	0.02	0.11	0.19	0.26	0.31	0.35	0.38	0.41	0.43	0.45	0.46	0.48	0.49	0.50	0.51	0.52	0.52	**15**
	16	0.02	0.11	0.19	0.26	0.31	0.35	0.38	0.41	0.43	0.45	0.46	0.48	0.49	0.50	0.51	0.52	0.53	**16**
	17	0.02	0.11	0.19	0.26	0.31	0.35	0.38	0.41	0.43	0.45	0.47	0.48	0.49	0.50	0.51	0.52	0.53	**17**
	18	0.02	0.11	0.19	0.26	0.31	0.35	0.38	0.41	0.43	0.45	0.47	0.48	0.49	0.51	0.52	0.52	0.53	**18**
	19	0.02	0.11	0.19	0.26	0.31	0.35	0.38	0.41	0.43	0.45	0.47	0.48	0.50	0.51	0.52	0.53	0.53	**19**
	20	0.02	0.11	0.19	0.26	0.31	0.35	0.39	0.41	0.44	0.45	0.47	0.49	0.50	0.51	0.52	0.53	0.54	**20**
	21	0.02	0.11	0.19	0.26	0.31	0.35	0.39	0.41	0.44	0.46	0.47	0.49	0.50	0.51	0.52	0.53	0.54	**21**
	22	0.02	0.11	0.19	0.26	0.31	0.35	0.39	0.41	0.44	0.46	0.47	0.49	0.50	0.51	0.52	0.53	0.54	**22**
	23	0.02	0.11	0.19	0.26	0.31	0.35	0.39	0.42	0.44	0.46	0.48	0.49	0.50	0.51	0.53	0.53	0.54	**23**
	24	0.02	0.11	0.19	0.26	0.31	0.35	0.39	0.42	0.44	0.46	0.48	0.49	0.50	0.52	0.53	0.54	0.54	**24**
	25	0.02	0.11	0.19	0.26	0.31	0.36	0.39	0.42	0.44	0.46	0.48	0.49	0.51	0.52	0.53	0.54	0.55	**25**
	26	0.02	0.11	0.19	0.26	0.31	0.36	0.39	0.42	0.44	0.46	0.48	0.49	0.51	0.52	0.53	0.54	0.55	**26**
	27	0.02	0.11	0.19	0.26	0.31	0.36	0.39	0.42	0.44	0.46	0.48	0.49	0.51	0.52	0.53	0.54	0.55	**27**
	28	0.02	0.11	0.19	0.26	0.31	0.36	0.39	0.42	0.44	0.46	0.48	0.50	0.51	0.52	0.53	0.54	0.55	**28**
	29	0.02	0.11	0.19	0.26	0.31	0.36	0.39	0.42	0.44	0.46	0.48	0.50	0.51	0.52	0.53	0.54	0.55	**29**
	30	0.02	0.11	0.19	0.26	0.32	0.36	0.39	0.42	0.44	0.46	0.48	0.50	0.51	0.52	0.53	0.54	0.55	**30**
	40	0.02	0.11	0.19	0.26	0.32	0.36	0.39	0.42	0.45	0.47	0.49	0.50	0.52	0.53	0.54	0.55	0.56	**40**
	60	0.02	0.11	0.19	0.26	0.32	0.36	0.40	0.43	0.45	0.47	0.49	0.51	0.53	0.54	0.55	0.56	0.57	**60**
	100	0.02	0.11	0.19	0.26	0.32	0.36	0.40	0.43	0.46	0.48	0.50	0.52	0.53	0.55	0.56	0.57	0.58	**100**
	∞	0.02	0.11	0.19	0.27	0.32	0.37	0.40	0.44	0.46	0.49	0.51	0.53	0.54	0.56	0.57	0.58	0.59	∞

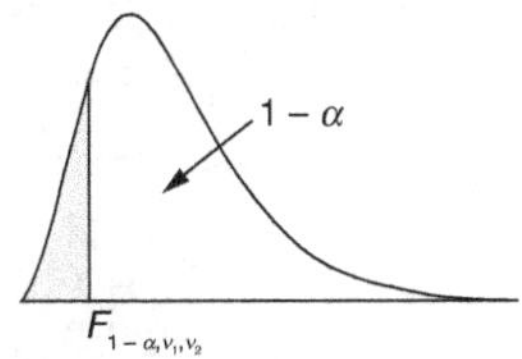

	Degrees of freedom for the numerator (ν_1)																	
(ν_2)	18	19	20	21	22	23	24	25	26	27	28	29	30	40	60	100	∞	(ν_2)
1	0.33	0.33	0.34	0.34	0.34	0.34	0.34	0.34	0.34	0.34	0.35	0.35	0.35	0.35	0.36	0.36	0.37	1
2	0.38	0.38	0.39	0.39	0.39	0.39	0.39	0.40	0.40	0.40	0.40	0.40	0.40	0.41	0.42	0.42	0.43	2
3	0.41	0.42	0.42	0.42	0.43	0.43	0.43	0.43	0.43	0.44	0.44	0.44	0.44	0.45	0.46	0.47	0.48	3
4	0.44	0.44	0.44	0.45	0.45	0.45	0.46	0.46	0.46	0.46	0.46	0.47	0.47	0.48	0.49	0.50	0.51	4
5	0.46	0.46	0.46	0.47	0.47	0.47	0.48	0.48	0.48	0.48	0.48	0.49	0.49	0.50	0.51	0.52	0.54	5
6	0.47	0.47	0.48	0.48	0.49	0.49	0.49	0.49	0.50	0.50	0.50	0.50	0.50	0.52	0.53	0.55	0.56	6
7	0.48	0.49	0.49	0.49	0.50	0.50	0.50	0.51	0.51	0.51	0.51	0.52	0.52	0.53	0.55	0.56	0.58	7
8	0.49	0.50	0.50	0.50	0.51	0.51	0.52	0.52	0.52	0.52	0.53	0.53	0.53	0.55	0.56	0.58	0.60	8
9	0.50	0.50	0.51	0.51	0.52	0.52	0.52	0.53	0.53	0.53	0.54	0.54	0.54	0.56	0.58	0.59	0.61	9
10	0.51	0.51	0.52	0.52	0.53	0.53	0.53	0.54	0.54	0.54	0.54	0.55	0.55	0.57	0.59	0.60	0.63	10
11	0.51	0.52	0.52	0.53	0.53	0.54	0.54	0.54	0.55	0.55	0.55	0.55	0.56	0.58	0.60	0.61	0.64	11
12	0.52	0.52	0.53	0.53	0.54	0.54	0.55	0.55	0.55	0.56	0.56	0.56	0.56	0.58	0.60	0.62	0.65	12
13	0.52	0.53	0.53	0.54	0.54	0.55	0.55	0.56	0.56	0.56	0.56	0.57	0.57	0.59	0.61	0.63	0.66	13
14	0.53	0.53	0.54	0.54	0.55	0.55	0.56	0.56	0.56	0.57	0.57	0.57	0.58	0.60	0.62	0.64	0.66	14
15	0.53	0.54	0.54	0.55	0.55	0.56	0.56	0.56	0.57	0.57	0.57	0.58	0.58	0.60	0.62	0.64	0.67	15
16	0.53	0.54	0.55	0.55	0.56	0.56	0.56	0.57	0.57	0.58	0.58	0.58	0.59	0.61	0.63	0.65	0.68	16
17	0.54	0.54	0.55	0.55	0.56	0.56	0.57	0.57	0.58	0.58	0.58	0.59	0.59	0.61	0.63	0.65	0.69	17
18	0.54	0.55	0.55	0.56	0.56	0.57	0.57	0.58	0.58	0.58	0.59	0.59	0.59	0.62	0.64	0.66	0.69	18
19	0.54	0.55	0.55	0.56	0.57	0.57	0.58	0.58	0.58	0.59	0.59	0.59	0.60	0.62	0.64	0.66	0.70	19
20	0.54	0.55	0.56	0.56	0.57	0.57	0.58	0.58	0.59	0.59	0.59	0.60	0.60	0.62	0.65	0.67	0.70	20
21	0.55	0.55	0.56	0.57	0.57	0.58	0.58	0.58	0.59	0.59	0.60	0.60	0.60	0.63	0.65	0.67	0.71	21
22	0.55	0.56	0.56	0.57	0.57	0.58	0.58	0.59	0.59	0.60	0.60	0.60	0.61	0.63	0.66	0.68	0.71	22
23	0.55	0.56	0.56	0.57	0.58	0.58	0.59	0.59	0.59	0.60	0.60	0.60	0.61	0.63	0.66	0.68	0.72	23
24	0.55	0.56	0.57	0.57	0.58	0.58	0.59	0.59	0.60	0.60	0.60	0.61	0.61	0.64	0.66	0.68	0.72	24
25	0.55	0.56	0.57	0.57	0.58	0.58	0.59	0.59	0.60	0.60	0.61	0.61	0.61	0.64	0.66	0.69	0.73	25
26	0.56	0.56	0.57	0.58	0.58	0.59	0.59	0.60	0.60	0.60	0.61	0.61	0.62	0.64	0.67	0.69	0.73	26
27	0.56	0.56	0.57	0.58	0.58	0.59	0.59	0.60	0.60	0.61	0.61	0.61	0.62	0.64	0.67	0.69	0.73	27
28	0.56	0.57	0.57	0.58	0.58	0.59	0.59	0.60	0.60	0.61	0.61	0.62	0.62	0.64	0.67	0.70	0.74	28
29	0.56	0.57	0.57	0.58	0.59	0.59	0.60	0.60	0.61	0.61	0.61	0.62	0.62	0.65	0.68	0.70	0.74	29
30	0.56	0.57	0.58	0.58	0.59	0.59	0.60	0.60	0.61	0.61	0.62	0.62	0.62	0.65	0.68	0.70	0.75	30
40	0.57	0.58	0.59	0.59	0.60	0.60	0.61	0.61	0.62	0.62	0.63	0.63	0.64	0.66	0.70	0.72	0.77	40
60	0.58	0.59	0.60	0.60	0.61	0.62	0.62	0.63	0.63	0.64	0.64	0.65	0.65	0.68	0.72	0.75	0.81	60
100	0.59	0.60	0.61	0.61	0.62	0.63	0.63	0.64	0.64	0.65	0.65	0.66	0.66	0.70	0.74	0.77	0.84	100
∞	0.60	0.61	0.62	0.63	0.64	0.65	0.65	0.66	0.67	0.67	0.68	0.68	0.69	0.73	0.77	0.82	1.00	∞

Degrees of freedom for the denominator

Appendix G.6

F(0.95) Distribution Table

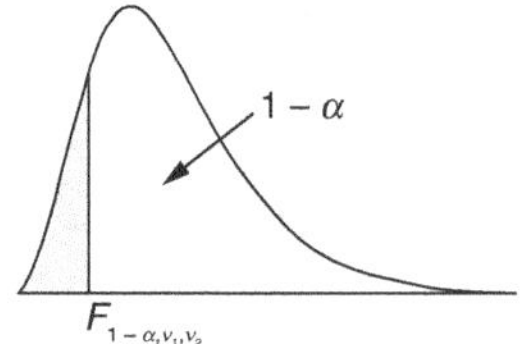

Degrees of freedom for the denominator

	Degrees of freedom for the numerator (ν_1)																	
(ν_2)	**1**	**2**	**3**	**4**	**5**	**6**	**7**	**8**	**9**	**10**	**11**	**12**	**13**	**14**	**15**	**16**	**17**	**(ν_2)**
1	0.01	0.05	0.10	0.13	0.15	0.17	0.18	0.19	0.20	0.20	0.21	0.21	0.21	0.22	0.22	0.22	0.22	**1**
2	0.01	0.05	0.10	0.14	0.17	0.19	0.21	0.22	0.23	0.24	0.25	0.26	0.26	0.27	0.27	0.28	0.28	**2**
3	0.00	0.05	0.11	0.15	0.18	0.21	0.23	0.25	0.26	0.27	0.28	0.29	0.29	0.30	0.30	0.31	0.31	**3**
4	0.00	0.05	0.11	0.16	0.19	0.22	0.24	0.26	0.28	0.29	0.30	0.31	0.31	0.32	0.33	0.33	0.34	**4**
5	0.00	0.05	0.11	0.16	0.19	0.23	0.25	0.27	0.29	0.30	0.31	0.32	0.33	0.34	0.34	0.35	0.36	**5**
6	0.00	0.05	0.11	0.16	0.20	0.23	0.26	0.28	0.30	0.31	0.32	0.33	0.34	0.35	0.36	0.36	0.37	**6**
7	0.00	0.05	0.11	0.16	0.21	0.24	0.26	0.29	0.30	0.32	0.33	0.34	0.35	0.36	0.37	0.38	0.38	**7**
8	0.00	0.05	0.11	0.17	0.21	0.24	0.27	0.29	0.31	0.33	0.34	0.35	0.36	0.37	0.38	0.39	0.39	**8**
9	0.00	0.05	0.11	0.17	0.21	0.24	0.27	0.30	0.31	0.33	0.35	0.36	0.37	0.38	0.39	0.39	0.40	**9**
10	0.00	0.05	0.11	0.17	0.21	0.25	0.27	0.30	0.32	0.34	0.35	0.36	0.37	0.38	0.39	0.40	0.41	**10**
11	0.00	0.05	0.11	0.17	0.21	0.25	0.28	0.30	0.32	0.34	0.35	0.37	0.38	0.39	0.40	0.41	0.41	**11**
12	0.00	0.05	0.11	0.17	0.21	0.25	0.28	0.30	0.33	0.34	0.36	0.37	0.38	0.39	0.40	0.41	0.42	**12**
13	0.00	0.05	0.11	0.17	0.21	0.25	0.28	0.31	0.33	0.35	0.36	0.38	0.39	0.40	0.41	0.42	0.42	**13**
14	0.00	0.05	0.11	0.17	0.22	0.25	0.28	0.31	0.33	0.35	0.37	0.38	0.39	0.40	0.41	0.42	0.43	**14**
15	0.00	0.05	0.11	0.17	0.22	0.25	0.28	0.31	0.33	0.35	0.37	0.38	0.39	0.41	0.42	0.43	0.43	**15**
16	0.00	0.05	0.12	0.17	0.22	0.25	0.29	0.31	0.33	0.35	0.37	0.38	0.40	0.41	0.42	0.43	0.44	**16**
17	0.00	0.05	0.12	0.17	0.22	0.26	0.29	0.31	0.34	0.36	0.37	0.39	0.40	0.41	0.42	0.43	0.44	**17**
18	0.00	0.05	0.12	0.17	0.22	0.26	0.29	0.32	0.34	0.36	0.37	0.39	0.40	0.41	0.42	0.43	0.44	**18**
19	0.00	0.05	0.12	0.17	0.22	0.26	0.29	0.32	0.34	0.36	0.38	0.39	0.40	0.42	0.43	0.44	0.45	**19**
20	0.00	0.05	0.12	0.17	0.22	0.26	0.29	0.32	0.34	0.36	0.38	0.39	0.41	0.42	0.43	0.44	0.45	**20**
21	0.00	0.05	0.12	0.17	0.22	0.26	0.29	0.32	0.34	0.36	0.38	0.39	0.41	0.42	0.43	0.44	0.45	**21**
22	0.00	0.05	0.12	0.17	0.22	0.26	0.29	0.32	0.34	0.36	0.38	0.40	0.41	0.42	0.43	0.44	0.45	**22**
23	0.00	0.05	0.12	0.17	0.22	0.26	0.29	0.32	0.34	0.36	0.38	0.40	0.41	0.42	0.44	0.45	0.45	**23**
24	0.00	0.05	0.12	0.17	0.22	0.26	0.29	0.32	0.34	0.37	0.38	0.40	0.41	0.43	0.44	0.45	0.46	**24**
25	0.00	0.05	0.12	0.17	0.22	0.26	0.29	0.32	0.35	0.37	0.38	0.40	0.41	0.43	0.44	0.45	0.46	**25**
26	0.00	0.05	0.12	0.17	0.22	0.26	0.29	0.32	0.35	0.37	0.39	0.40	0.42	0.43	0.44	0.45	0.46	**26**
27	0.00	0.05	0.12	0.17	0.22	0.26	0.29	0.32	0.35	0.37	0.39	0.40	0.42	0.43	0.44	0.45	0.46	**27**
28	0.00	0.05	0.12	0.17	0.22	0.26	0.30	0.32	0.35	0.37	0.39	0.40	0.42	0.43	0.44	0.45	0.46	**28**
29	0.00	0.05	0.12	0.17	0.22	0.26	0.30	0.32	0.35	0.37	0.39	0.40	0.42	0.43	0.44	0.45	0.46	**29**
30	0.00	0.05	0.12	0.17	0.22	0.26	0.30	0.32	0.35	0.37	0.39	0.41	0.42	0.43	0.45	0.46	0.47	**30**
40	0.00	0.05	0.12	0.17	0.22	0.26	0.30	0.33	0.35	0.38	0.40	0.41	0.43	0.44	0.45	0.46	0.48	**40**
60	0.00	0.05	0.12	0.18	0.23	0.27	0.30	0.33	0.36	0.38	0.40	0.42	0.44	0.45	0.46	0.47	0.49	**60**
100	0.00	0.05	0.12	0.18	0.23	0.27	0.31	0.34	0.36	0.39	0.41	0.43	0.44	0.46	0.47	0.48	0.49	**100**
∞	0.00	0.05	0.12	0.18	0.23	0.27	0.31	0.34	0.37	0.39	0.42	0.44	0.45	0.47	0.48	0.50	0.51	∞

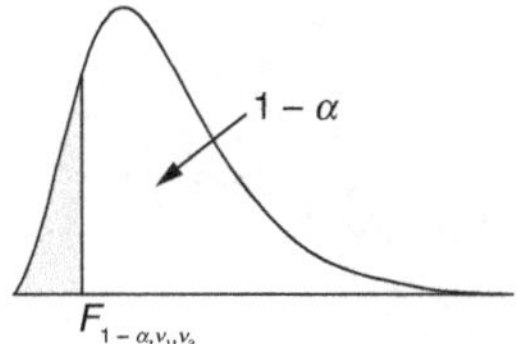

	Degrees of freedom for the numerator (ν_1)																	
(ν_2)	**18**	**19**	**20**	**21**	**22**	**23**	**24**	**25**	**26**	**27**	**28**	**29**	**30**	**40**	**60**	**100**	∞	(ν_2)
1	0.23	0.23	0.23	0.23	0.23	0.23	0.23	0.24	0.24	0.24	0.24	0.24	0.24	0.24	0.25	0.25	0.26	**1**
2	0.28	0.28	0.29	0.29	0.29	0.29	0.29	0.30	0.30	0.30	0.30	0.30	0.30	0.31	0.32	0.32	0.33	**2**
3	0.32	0.32	0.32	0.33	0.33	0.33	0.33	0.33	0.34	0.34	0.34	0.34	0.34	0.35	0.36	0.37	0.38	**3**
4	0.34	0.35	0.35	0.35	0.36	0.36	0.36	0.36	0.36	0.37	0.37	0.37	0.37	0.38	0.40	0.41	0.42	**4**
5	0.36	0.36	0.37	0.37	0.38	0.38	0.38	0.38	0.39	0.39	0.39	0.39	0.39	0.41	0.42	0.43	0.45	**5**
6	0.38	0.38	0.38	0.39	0.39	0.40	0.40	0.40	0.40	0.41	0.41	0.41	0.41	0.43	0.44	0.46	0.48	**6**
7	0.39	0.39	0.40	0.40	0.41	0.41	0.41	0.42	0.42	0.42	0.42	0.43	0.43	0.44	0.46	0.48	0.50	**7**
8	0.40	0.40	0.41	0.41	0.42	0.42	0.42	0.43	0.43	0.43	0.44	0.44	0.44	0.46	0.48	0.49	0.52	**8**
9	0.41	0.41	0.42	0.42	0.43	0.43	0.43	0.44	0.44	0.44	0.45	0.45	0.45	0.47	0.49	0.51	0.53	**9**
10	0.41	0.42	0.43	0.43	0.44	0.44	0.44	0.45	0.45	0.45	0.46	0.46	0.46	0.48	0.50	0.52	0.55	**10**
11	0.42	0.43	0.43	0.44	0.44	0.45	0.45	0.45	0.46	0.46	0.46	0.47	0.47	0.49	0.51	0.53	0.56	**11**
12	0.43	0.43	0.44	0.44	0.45	0.45	0.46	0.46	0.47	0.47	0.47	0.48	0.48	0.50	0.52	0.54	0.57	**12**
13	0.43	0.44	0.44	0.45	0.46	0.46	0.46	0.47	0.47	0.48	0.48	0.48	0.48	0.51	0.53	0.55	0.58	**13**
14	0.44	0.44	0.45	0.46	0.46	0.47	0.47	0.47	0.48	0.48	0.48	0.49	0.49	0.51	0.54	0.56	0.59	**14**
15	0.44	0.45	0.45	0.46	0.46	0.47	0.47	0.48	0.48	0.49	0.49	0.49	0.50	0.52	0.54	0.57	0.60	**15**
16	0.44	0.45	0.46	0.46	0.47	0.47	0.48	0.48	0.49	0.49	0.49	0.50	0.50	0.53	0.55	0.57	0.61	**16**
17	0.45	0.46	0.46	0.47	0.47	0.48	0.48	0.49	0.49	0.50	0.50	0.50	0.51	0.53	0.56	0.58	0.62	**17**
18	0.45	0.46	0.46	0.47	0.48	0.48	0.49	0.49	0.50	0.50	0.50	0.51	0.51	0.54	0.56	0.59	0.62	**18**
19	0.45	0.46	0.47	0.47	0.48	0.49	0.49	0.49	0.50	0.50	0.51	0.51	0.51	0.54	0.57	0.59	0.63	**19**
20	0.46	0.46	0.47	0.48	0.48	0.49	0.49	0.50	0.50	0.51	0.51	0.51	0.52	0.54	0.57	0.60	0.64	**20**
21	0.46	0.47	0.47	0.48	0.49	0.49	0.50	0.50	0.51	0.51	0.51	0.52	0.52	0.55	0.58	0.60	0.64	**21**
22	0.46	0.47	0.48	0.48	0.49	0.49	0.50	0.50	0.51	0.51	0.52	0.52	0.52	0.55	0.58	0.61	0.65	**22**
23	0.46	0.47	0.48	0.48	0.49	0.50	0.50	0.51	0.51	0.52	0.52	0.52	0.53	0.55	0.58	0.61	0.65	**23**
24	0.47	0.47	0.48	0.49	0.49	0.50	0.50	0.51	0.51	0.52	0.52	0.53	0.53	0.56	0.59	0.61	0.66	**24**
25	0.47	0.47	0.48	0.49	0.50	0.50	0.51	0.51	0.52	0.52	0.52	0.53	0.53	0.56	0.59	0.62	0.66	**25**
26	0.47	0.48	0.48	0.49	0.50	0.50	0.51	0.51	0.52	0.52	0.53	0.53	0.53	0.56	0.59	0.62	0.67	**26**
27	0.47	0.48	0.49	0.49	0.50	0.50	0.51	0.52	0.52	0.52	0.53	0.53	0.54	0.57	0.60	0.63	0.67	**27**
28	0.47	0.48	0.49	0.49	0.50	0.51	0.51	0.52	0.52	0.53	0.53	0.54	0.54	0.57	0.60	0.63	0.68	**28**
29	0.47	0.48	0.49	0.50	0.50	0.51	0.51	0.52	0.52	0.53	0.53	0.54	0.54	0.57	0.60	0.63	0.68	**29**
30	0.47	0.48	0.49	0.50	0.50	0.51	0.52	0.52	0.53	0.53	0.54	0.54	0.54	0.57	0.61	0.64	0.69	**30**
40	0.48	0.49	0.50	0.51	0.52	0.52	0.53	0.53	0.54	0.54	0.55	0.55	0.56	0.59	0.63	0.66	0.72	**40**
60	0.50	0.51	0.51	0.52	0.53	0.54	0.54	0.55	0.55	0.56	0.57	0.57	0.57	0.61	0.65	0.69	0.76	**60**
100	0.51	0.52	0.52	0.53	0.54	0.55	0.56	0.56	0.57	0.57	0.58	0.58	0.59	0.63	0.68	0.72	0.80	**100**
∞	0.52	0.53	0.54	0.55	0.56	0.57	0.58	0.58	0.59	0.60	0.60	0.61	0.62	0.66	0.72	0.78	1.00	∞

Degrees of freedom for the denominator

Appendix G.7

$F(0.975)$ Distribution Table

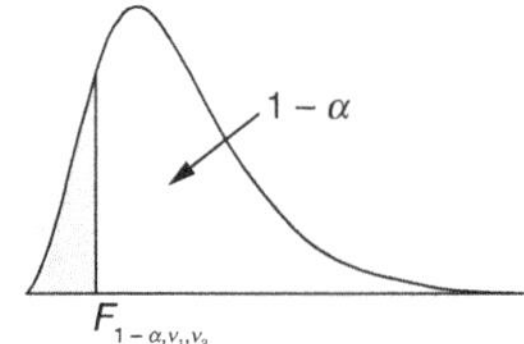

Degrees of freedom for the numerator (ν_1); Degrees of freedom for the denominator (ν_2)

(ν_2)	1	2	3	4	5	6	7	8	9	10	11	12	13	14	15	16	17	(ν_2)
1	0.00	0.03	0.06	0.08	0.10	0.11	0.12	0.13	0.14	0.14	0.15	0.15	0.16	0.16	0.16	0.16	0.17	**1**
2	0.00	0.03	0.06	0.09	0.12	0.14	0.15	0.17	0.17	0.18	0.19	0.20	0.20	0.21	0.21	0.21	0.22	**2**
3	0.00	0.03	0.06	0.10	0.13	0.15	0.17	0.18	0.20	0.21	0.22	0.22	0.23	0.24	0.24	0.25	0.25	**3**
4	0.00	0.03	0.07	0.10	0.14	0.16	0.18	0.20	0.21	0.22	0.23	0.24	0.25	0.26	0.26	0.27	0.27	**4**
5	0.00	0.03	0.07	0.11	0.14	0.17	0.19	0.21	0.22	0.24	0.25	0.26	0.27	0.27	0.28	0.29	0.29	**5**
6	0.00	0.03	0.07	0.11	0.14	0.17	0.20	0.21	0.23	0.25	0.26	0.27	0.28	0.29	0.29	0.30	0.31	**6**
7	0.00	0.03	0.07	0.11	0.15	0.18	0.20	0.22	0.24	0.25	0.27	0.28	0.29	0.30	0.30	0.31	0.32	**7**
8	0.00	0.03	0.07	0.11	0.15	0.18	0.20	0.23	0.24	0.26	0.27	0.28	0.30	0.30	0.31	0.32	0.33	**8**
9	0.00	0.03	0.07	0.11	0.15	0.18	0.21	0.23	0.25	0.26	0.28	0.29	0.30	0.31	0.32	0.33	0.34	**9**
10	0.00	0.03	0.07	0.11	0.15	0.18	0.21	0.23	0.25	0.27	0.28	0.30	0.31	0.32	0.33	0.33	0.34	**10**
11	0.00	0.03	0.07	0.11	0.15	0.18	0.21	0.24	0.26	0.27	0.29	0.30	0.31	0.32	0.33	0.34	0.35	**11**
12	0.00	0.03	0.07	0.11	0.15	0.19	0.21	0.24	0.26	0.28	0.29	0.31	0.32	0.33	0.34	0.35	0.35	**12**
13	0.00	0.03	0.07	0.11	0.15	0.19	0.22	0.24	0.26	0.28	0.29	0.31	0.32	0.33	0.34	0.35	0.36	**13**
14	0.00	0.03	0.07	0.12	0.15	0.19	0.22	0.24	0.26	0.28	0.30	0.31	0.32	0.34	0.35	0.35	0.36	**14**
15	0.00	0.03	0.07	0.12	0.16	0.19	0.22	0.24	0.27	0.28	0.30	0.31	0.33	0.34	0.35	0.36	0.37	**15**
16	0.00	0.03	0.07	0.12	0.16	0.19	0.22	0.25	0.27	0.29	0.30	0.32	0.33	0.34	0.35	0.36	0.37	**16**
17	0.00	0.03	0.07	0.12	0.16	0.19	0.22	0.25	0.27	0.29	0.30	0.32	0.33	0.34	0.36	0.37	0.37	**17**
18	0.00	0.03	0.07	0.12	0.16	0.19	0.22	0.25	0.27	0.29	0.31	0.32	0.34	0.35	0.36	0.37	0.38	**18**
19	0.00	0.03	0.07	0.12	0.16	0.19	0.22	0.25	0.27	0.29	0.31	0.32	0.34	0.35	0.36	0.37	0.38	**19**
20	0.00	0.03	0.07	0.12	0.16	0.19	0.22	0.25	0.27	0.29	0.31	0.33	0.34	0.35	0.36	0.37	0.38	**20**
21	0.00	0.03	0.07	0.12	0.16	0.19	0.22	0.25	0.27	0.29	0.31	0.33	0.34	0.35	0.36	0.38	0.38	**21**
22	0.00	0.03	0.07	0.12	0.16	0.19	0.23	0.25	0.27	0.30	0.31	0.33	0.34	0.36	0.37	0.38	0.39	**22**
23	0.00	0.03	0.07	0.12	0.16	0.19	0.23	0.25	0.28	0.30	0.31	0.33	0.34	0.36	0.37	0.38	0.39	**23**
24	0.00	0.03	0.07	0.12	0.16	0.20	0.23	0.25	0.28	0.30	0.32	0.33	0.35	0.36	0.37	0.38	0.39	**24**
25	0.00	0.03	0.07	0.12	0.16	0.20	0.23	0.25	0.28	0.30	0.32	0.33	0.35	0.36	0.37	0.38	0.39	**25**
26	0.00	0.03	0.07	0.12	0.16	0.20	0.23	0.25	0.28	0.30	0.32	0.33	0.35	0.36	0.37	0.38	0.39	**26**
27	0.00	0.03	0.07	0.12	0.16	0.20	0.23	0.26	0.28	0.30	0.32	0.33	0.35	0.36	0.37	0.39	0.40	**27**
28	0.00	0.03	0.07	0.12	0.16	0.20	0.23	0.26	0.28	0.30	0.32	0.34	0.35	0.36	0.38	0.39	0.40	**28**
29	0.00	0.03	0.07	0.12	0.16	0.20	0.23	0.26	0.28	0.30	0.32	0.34	0.35	0.36	0.38	0.39	0.40	**29**
30	0.00	0.03	0.07	0.12	0.16	0.20	0.23	0.26	0.28	0.30	0.32	0.34	0.35	0.37	0.38	0.39	0.40	**30**
40	0.00	0.03	0.07	0.12	0.16	0.20	0.23	0.26	0.29	0.31	0.33	0.34	0.36	0.37	0.39	0.40	0.41	**40**
60	0.00	0.03	0.07	0.12	0.16	0.20	0.24	0.26	0.29	0.31	0.33	0.35	0.37	0.38	0.40	0.41	0.42	**60**
100	0.00	0.03	0.07	0.12	0.16	0.20	0.24	0.27	0.29	0.32	0.34	0.36	0.37	0.39	0.40	0.42	0.43	**100**
∞	0.00	0.03	0.07	0.12	0.17	0.21	0.24	0.27	0.30	0.32	0.35	0.37	0.39	0.40	0.42	0.43	0.44	∞

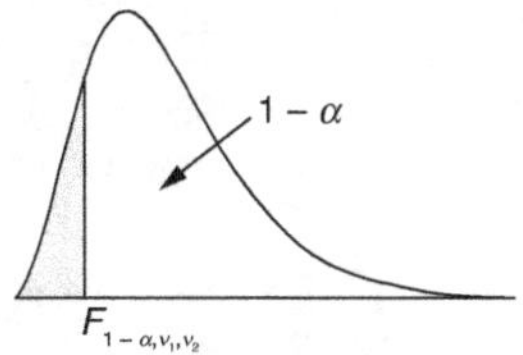

	Degrees of freedom for the numerator (ν_1)																	
(ν_2)	**18**	**19**	**20**	**21**	**22**	**23**	**24**	**25**	**26**	**27**	**28**	**29**	**30**	**40**	**60**	**100**	**∞**	**(ν_2)**
1	0.17	0.17	0.17	0.17	0.17	0.17	0.17	0.18	0.18	0.18	0.18	0.18	0.18	0.18	0.19	0.19	0.20	**1**
2	0.22	0.22	0.22	0.23	0.23	0.23	0.23	0.23	0.23	0.24	0.24	0.24	0.24	0.25	0.25	0.26	0.27	**2**
3	0.25	0.26	0.26	0.26	0.26	0.27	0.27	0.27	0.27	0.27	0.28	0.28	0.28	0.29	0.30	0.31	0.32	**3**
4	0.28	0.28	0.28	0.29	0.29	0.29	0.30	0.30	0.30	0.30	0.30	0.31	0.31	0.32	0.33	0.34	0.36	**4**
5	0.30	0.30	0.30	0.31	0.31	0.31	0.32	0.32	0.32	0.32	0.33	0.33	0.33	0.34	0.36	0.37	0.39	**5**
6	0.31	0.32	0.32	0.32	0.33	0.33	0.33	0.34	0.34	0.34	0.34	0.35	0.35	0.36	0.38	0.39	0.42	**6**
7	0.32	0.33	0.33	0.34	0.34	0.34	0.35	0.35	0.35	0.36	0.36	0.36	0.36	0.38	0.40	0.41	0.44	**7**
8	0.33	0.34	0.34	0.35	0.35	0.36	0.36	0.36	0.37	0.37	0.37	0.37	0.38	0.40	0.41	0.43	0.46	**8**
9	0.34	0.35	0.35	0.36	0.36	0.37	0.37	0.37	0.38	0.38	0.38	0.39	0.39	0.41	0.43	0.45	0.47	**9**
10	0.35	0.35	0.36	0.37	0.37	0.37	0.38	0.38	0.39	0.39	0.39	0.40	0.40	0.42	0.44	0.46	0.49	**10**
11	0.36	0.36	0.37	0.37	0.38	0.38	0.39	0.39	0.39	0.40	0.40	0.40	0.41	0.43	0.45	0.47	0.50	**11**
12	0.36	0.37	0.37	0.38	0.38	0.39	0.39	0.40	0.40	0.41	0.41	0.41	0.41	0.44	0.46	0.48	0.51	**12**
13	0.37	0.37	0.38	0.38	0.39	0.40	0.40	0.40	0.41	0.41	0.42	0.42	0.42	0.44	0.47	0.49	0.53	**13**
14	0.37	0.38	0.38	0.39	0.40	0.40	0.41	0.41	0.41	0.42	0.42	0.42	0.43	0.45	0.48	0.50	0.54	**14**
15	0.37	0.38	0.39	0.39	0.40	0.41	0.41	0.41	0.42	0.42	0.43	0.43	0.43	0.46	0.49	0.51	0.55	**15**
16	0.38	0.39	0.39	0.40	0.40	0.41	0.41	0.42	0.42	0.43	0.43	0.44	0.44	0.46	0.49	0.52	0.55	**16**
17	0.38	0.39	0.40	0.40	0.41	0.41	0.42	0.42	0.43	0.43	0.44	0.44	0.44	0.47	0.50	0.52	0.56	**17**
18	0.39	0.39	0.40	0.41	0.41	0.42	0.42	0.43	0.43	0.44	0.44	0.44	0.45	0.47	0.50	0.53	0.57	**18**
19	0.39	0.40	0.40	0.41	0.42	0.42	0.43	0.43	0.44	0.44	0.44	0.45	0.45	0.48	0.51	0.54	0.58	**19**
20	0.39	0.40	0.41	0.41	0.42	0.42	0.43	0.43	0.44	0.44	0.45	0.45	0.46	0.48	0.51	0.54	0.59	**20**
21	0.39	0.40	0.41	0.42	0.42	0.43	0.43	0.44	0.44	0.45	0.45	0.46	0.46	0.49	0.52	0.55	0.59	**21**
22	0.40	0.40	0.41	0.42	0.42	0.43	0.44	0.44	0.45	0.45	0.45	0.46	0.46	0.49	0.52	0.55	0.60	**22**
23	0.40	0.41	0.41	0.42	0.43	0.43	0.44	0.44	0.45	0.45	0.46	0.46	0.47	0.49	0.53	0.56	0.60	**23**
24	0.40	0.41	0.42	0.42	0.43	0.43	0.44	0.45	0.45	0.46	0.46	0.46	0.47	0.50	0.53	0.56	0.61	**24**
25	0.40	0.41	0.42	0.42	0.43	0.44	0.44	0.45	0.45	0.46	0.46	0.47	0.47	0.50	0.54	0.56	0.62	**25**
26	0.40	0.41	0.42	0.43	0.43	0.44	0.45	0.45	0.46	0.46	0.47	0.47	0.47	0.50	0.54	0.57	0.62	**26**
27	0.40	0.41	0.42	0.43	0.44	0.44	0.45	0.45	0.46	0.46	0.47	0.47	0.48	0.51	0.54	0.57	0.63	**27**
28	0.41	0.41	0.42	0.43	0.44	0.44	0.45	0.45	0.46	0.46	0.47	0.47	0.48	0.51	0.55	0.58	0.63	**28**
29	0.41	0.42	0.42	0.43	0.44	0.44	0.45	0.46	0.46	0.47	0.47	0.48	0.48	0.51	0.55	0.58	0.63	**29**
30	0.41	0.42	0.43	0.43	0.44	0.45	0.45	0.46	0.46	0.47	0.47	0.48	0.48	0.51	0.55	0.58	0.64	**30**
40	0.42	0.43	0.44	0.45	0.45	0.46	0.47	0.47	0.48	0.48	0.49	0.49	0.50	0.53	0.57	0.61	0.67	**40**
60	0.43	0.44	0.45	0.46	0.47	0.47	0.48	0.49	0.49	0.50	0.51	0.51	0.52	0.55	0.60	0.64	0.72	**60**
100	0.44	0.45	0.46	0.47	0.48	0.49	0.49	0.50	0.51	0.51	0.52	0.53	0.53	0.57	0.63	0.67	0.77	**100**
∞	0.46	0.47	0.48	0.49	0.50	0.51	0.52	0.52	0.53	0.54	0.55	0.55	0.56	0.61	0.67	0.74	1.00	**∞**

Degrees of freedom for the denominator

Appendix G.8

F(0.99) Distribution Table

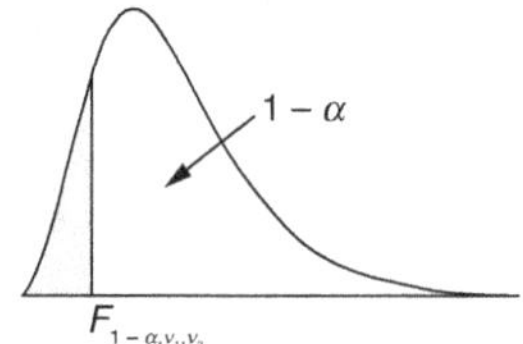

Degrees of freedom for the denominator (ν_2)	Degrees of freedom for the numerator (ν_1)																	
(ν_2)	1	2	3	4	5	6	7	8	9	10	11	12	13	14	15	16	17	(ν_2)
1	0.00	0.01	0.03	0.05	0.06	0.07	0.08	0.09	0.09	0.10	0.10	0.11	0.11	0.11	0.12	0.12	0.12	1
2	0.00	0.01	0.03	0.06	0.08	0.09	0.10	0.12	0.12	0.13	0.14	0.14	0.15	0.15	0.16	0.16	0.16	2
3	0.00	0.01	0.03	0.06	0.08	0.10	0.12	0.13	0.14	0.15	0.16	0.17	0.17	0.18	0.18	0.19	0.19	3
4	0.00	0.01	0.03	0.06	0.09	0.11	0.13	0.14	0.16	0.17	0.18	0.18	0.19	0.20	0.20	0.21	0.21	4
5	0.00	0.01	0.04	0.06	0.09	0.11	0.13	0.15	0.17	0.18	0.19	0.20	0.21	0.21	0.22	0.23	0.23	5
6	0.00	0.01	0.04	0.07	0.09	0.12	0.14	0.16	0.17	0.19	0.20	0.21	0.22	0.22	0.23	0.24	0.24	6
7	0.00	0.01	0.04	0.07	0.10	0.12	0.14	0.16	0.18	0.19	0.20	0.22	0.23	0.23	0.24	0.25	0.25	7
8	0.00	0.01	0.04	0.07	0.10	0.12	0.15	0.17	0.18	0.20	0.21	0.22	0.23	0.24	0.25	0.26	0.26	8
9	0.00	0.01	0.04	0.07	0.10	0.13	0.15	0.17	0.19	0.20	0.22	0.23	0.24	0.25	0.26	0.26	0.27	9
10	0.00	0.01	0.04	0.07	0.10	0.13	0.15	0.17	0.19	0.21	0.22	0.23	0.24	0.25	0.26	0.27	0.28	10
11	0.00	0.01	0.04	0.07	0.10	0.13	0.15	0.17	0.19	0.21	0.22	0.24	0.25	0.26	0.27	0.28	0.28	11
12	0.00	0.01	0.04	0.07	0.10	0.13	0.15	0.18	0.20	0.21	0.23	0.24	0.25	0.26	0.27	0.28	0.29	12
13	0.00	0.01	0.04	0.07	0.10	0.13	0.16	0.18	0.20	0.22	0.23	0.24	0.26	0.27	0.28	0.29	0.29	13
14	0.00	0.01	0.04	0.07	0.10	0.13	0.16	0.18	0.20	0.22	0.23	0.25	0.26	0.27	0.28	0.29	0.30	14
15	0.00	0.01	0.04	0.07	0.10	0.13	0.16	0.18	0.20	0.22	0.24	0.25	0.26	0.27	0.28	0.29	0.30	15
16	0.00	0.01	0.04	0.07	0.10	0.13	0.16	0.18	0.20	0.22	0.24	0.25	0.26	0.28	0.29	0.30	0.31	16
17	0.00	0.01	0.04	0.07	0.10	0.13	0.16	0.18	0.20	0.22	0.24	0.25	0.27	0.28	0.29	0.30	0.31	17
18	0.00	0.01	0.04	0.07	0.10	0.13	0.16	0.18	0.21	0.22	0.24	0.26	0.27	0.28	0.29	0.30	0.31	18
19	0.00	0.01	0.04	0.07	0.10	0.13	0.16	0.19	0.21	0.23	0.24	0.26	0.27	0.28	0.29	0.30	0.31	19
20	0.00	0.01	0.04	0.07	0.10	0.14	0.16	0.19	0.21	0.23	0.24	0.26	0.27	0.29	0.30	0.31	0.32	20
21	0.00	0.01	0.04	0.07	0.10	0.14	0.16	0.19	0.21	0.23	0.25	0.26	0.27	0.29	0.30	0.31	0.32	21
22	0.00	0.01	0.04	0.07	0.11	0.14	0.16	0.19	0.21	0.23	0.25	0.26	0.28	0.29	0.30	0.31	0.32	22
23	0.00	0.01	0.04	0.07	0.11	0.14	0.16	0.19	0.21	0.23	0.25	0.26	0.28	0.29	0.30	0.31	0.32	23
24	0.00	0.01	0.04	0.07	0.11	0.14	0.16	0.19	0.21	0.23	0.25	0.26	0.28	0.29	0.30	0.31	0.32	24
25	0.00	0.01	0.04	0.07	0.11	0.14	0.17	0.19	0.21	0.23	0.25	0.27	0.28	0.29	0.31	0.32	0.33	25
26	0.00	0.01	0.04	0.07	0.11	0.14	0.17	0.19	0.21	0.23	0.25	0.27	0.28	0.29	0.31	0.32	0.33	26
27	0.00	0.01	0.04	0.07	0.11	0.14	0.17	0.19	0.21	0.23	0.25	0.27	0.28	0.30	0.31	0.32	0.33	27
28	0.00	0.01	0.04	0.07	0.11	0.14	0.17	0.19	0.21	0.23	0.25	0.27	0.28	0.30	0.31	0.32	0.33	28
29	0.00	0.01	0.04	0.07	0.11	0.14	0.17	0.19	0.21	0.23	0.25	0.27	0.28	0.30	0.31	0.32	0.33	29
30	0.00	0.01	0.04	0.07	0.11	0.14	0.17	0.19	0.22	0.24	0.25	0.27	0.29	0.30	0.31	0.32	0.33	30
40	0.00	0.01	0.04	0.07	0.11	0.14	0.17	0.20	0.22	0.24	0.26	0.28	0.29	0.31	0.32	0.33	0.34	40
60	0.00	0.01	0.04	0.07	0.11	0.14	0.17	0.20	0.22	0.24	0.26	0.28	0.30	0.31	0.33	0.34	0.35	60
100	0.00	0.01	0.04	0.07	0.11	0.14	0.17	0.20	0.23	0.25	0.27	0.29	0.31	0.32	0.34	0.35	0.36	100
∞	0.00	0.01	0.04	0.07	0.11	0.15	0.18	0.21	0.23	0.26	0.28	0.30	0.32	0.33	0.35	0.36	0.38	∞

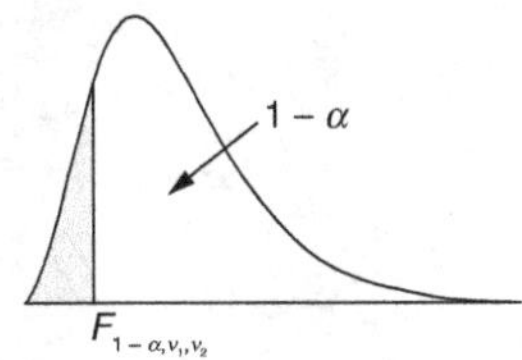

	Degrees of freedom for the numerator (ν_1)																	
(ν_2)	18	19	20	21	22	23	24	25	26	27	28	29	30	40	60	100	∞	(ν_2)
1	0.12	0.12	0.12	0.12	0.13	0.13	0.13	0.13	0.13	0.13	0.13	0.13	0.13	0.14	0.14	0.15	0.15	1
2	0.17	0.17	0.17	0.17	0.17	0.18	0.18	0.18	0.18	0.18	0.18	0.18	0.19	0.19	0.20	0.21	0.22	2
3	0.20	0.20	0.20	0.21	0.21	0.21	0.21	0.21	0.22	0.22	0.22	0.22	0.22	0.23	0.24	0.25	0.26	3
4	0.22	0.22	0.23	0.23	0.23	0.23	0.24	0.24	0.24	0.24	0.25	0.25	0.25	0.26	0.27	0.28	0.30	4
5	0.24	0.24	0.24	0.25	0.25	0.25	0.26	0.26	0.26	0.26	0.27	0.27	0.27	0.28	0.30	0.31	0.33	5
6	0.25	0.25	0.26	0.26	0.27	0.27	0.27	0.28	0.28	0.28	0.28	0.29	0.29	0.30	0.32	0.33	0.36	6
7	0.26	0.27	0.27	0.27	0.28	0.28	0.29	0.29	0.29	0.30	0.30	0.30	0.30	0.32	0.34	0.35	0.38	7
8	0.27	0.28	0.28	0.29	0.29	0.29	0.30	0.30	0.30	0.31	0.31	0.31	0.32	0.33	0.35	0.37	0.40	8
9	0.28	0.28	0.29	0.29	0.30	0.30	0.31	0.31	0.31	0.32	0.32	0.32	0.33	0.35	0.37	0.39	0.42	9
10	0.29	0.29	0.30	0.30	0.31	0.31	0.32	0.32	0.32	0.33	0.33	0.33	0.34	0.36	0.38	0.40	0.43	10
11	0.29	0.30	0.30	0.31	0.31	0.32	0.32	0.33	0.33	0.33	0.34	0.34	0.34	0.37	0.39	0.41	0.44	11
12	0.30	0.30	0.31	0.32	0.32	0.33	0.33	0.33	0.34	0.34	0.35	0.35	0.35	0.38	0.40	0.42	0.46	12
13	0.30	0.31	0.31	0.32	0.33	0.33	0.34	0.34	0.34	0.35	0.35	0.36	0.36	0.38	0.41	0.43	0.47	13
14	0.31	0.31	0.32	0.33	0.33	0.34	0.34	0.35	0.35	0.35	0.36	0.36	0.36	0.39	0.42	0.44	0.48	14
15	0.31	0.32	0.32	0.33	0.34	0.34	0.35	0.35	0.36	0.36	0.36	0.37	0.37	0.40	0.43	0.45	0.49	15
16	0.31	0.32	0.33	0.33	0.34	0.35	0.35	0.36	0.36	0.36	0.37	0.37	0.38	0.40	0.43	0.46	0.50	16
17	0.32	0.32	0.33	0.34	0.34	0.35	0.35	0.36	0.36	0.37	0.37	0.38	0.38	0.41	0.44	0.46	0.51	17
18	0.32	0.33	0.33	0.34	0.35	0.35	0.36	0.36	0.37	0.37	0.38	0.38	0.38	0.41	0.44	0.47	0.52	18
19	0.32	0.33	0.34	0.34	0.35	0.36	0.36	0.37	0.37	0.38	0.38	0.38	0.39	0.42	0.45	0.48	0.52	19
20	0.32	0.33	0.34	0.35	0.35	0.36	0.37	0.37	0.38	0.38	0.38	0.39	0.39	0.42	0.45	0.48	0.53	20
21	0.33	0.34	0.34	0.35	0.36	0.36	0.37	0.37	0.38	0.38	0.39	0.39	0.40	0.43	0.46	0.49	0.54	21
22	0.33	0.34	0.35	0.35	0.36	0.37	0.37	0.38	0.38	0.39	0.39	0.40	0.40	0.43	0.46	0.49	0.55	22
23	0.33	0.34	0.35	0.35	0.36	0.37	0.37	0.38	0.38	0.39	0.39	0.40	0.40	0.43	0.47	0.50	0.55	23
24	0.33	0.34	0.35	0.36	0.36	0.37	0.38	0.38	0.39	0.39	0.40	0.40	0.41	0.44	0.47	0.50	0.56	24
25	0.34	0.34	0.35	0.36	0.37	0.37	0.38	0.38	0.39	0.39	0.40	0.40	0.41	0.44	0.48	0.51	0.56	25
26	0.34	0.35	0.35	0.36	0.37	0.37	0.38	0.39	0.39	0.40	0.40	0.41	0.41	0.44	0.48	0.51	0.57	26
27	0.34	0.35	0.36	0.36	0.37	0.38	0.38	0.39	0.39	0.40	0.40	0.41	0.41	0.45	0.48	0.52	0.57	27
28	0.34	0.35	0.36	0.36	0.37	0.38	0.38	0.39	0.40	0.40	0.41	0.41	0.41	0.45	0.49	0.52	0.58	28
29	0.34	0.35	0.36	0.37	0.37	0.38	0.39	0.39	0.40	0.40	0.41	0.41	0.42	0.45	0.49	0.52	0.58	29
30	0.34	0.35	0.36	0.37	0.37	0.38	0.39	0.39	0.40	0.40	0.41	0.41	0.42	0.45	0.49	0.53	0.59	30
40	0.35	0.36	0.37	0.38	0.39	0.39	0.40	0.41	0.41	0.42	0.42	0.43	0.43	0.47	0.52	0.56	0.63	40
60	0.36	0.37	0.38	0.39	0.40	0.41	0.42	0.42	0.43	0.44	0.44	0.45	0.45	0.50	0.54	0.59	0.68	60
100	0.37	0.38	0.39	0.40	0.41	0.42	0.43	0.44	0.44	0.45	0.46	0.46	0.47	0.52	0.57	0.63	0.74	100
∞	0.39	0.40	0.41	0.42	0.43	0.44	0.45	0.46	0.47	0.48	0.48	0.49	0.50	0.55	0.62	0.70	1.00	∞

Degrees of freedom for the denominator

Appendix H

Normal Scores Table

	n															
n	**1**	**2**	**3**	**4**	**5**	**6**	**7**	**8**	**9**	**10**	**11**	**12**	**13**	**14**	**15**	***n***
1	0.000	−0.545	−0.819	−0.998	−1.129	−1.231	−1.315	−1.385	−1.446	−1.499	−1.546	−1.588	−1.626	−1.662	−1.694	**1**
2		0.545	0.000	−0.291	−0.486	−0.630	−0.744	−0.838	−0.917	−0.985	−1.045	−1.098	−1.146	−1.189	−1.229	**2**
3			0.819	0.291	0.000	−0.198	−0.347	−0.466	−0.564	−0.647	−0.719	−0.783	−0.839	−0.890	−0.936	**3**
4				0.998	0.486	0.198	0.000	−0.150	−0.271	−0.371	−0.456	−0.531	−0.596	−0.655	−0.707	**4**
5					1.129	0.630	0.347	0.150	0.000	−0.121	−0.222	−0.309	−0.384	−0.451	−0.511	**5**
6						1.231	0.744	0.466	0.271	0.121	0.000	−0.102	−0.189	−0.265	−0.332	**6**
7							1.315	0.838	0.564	0.371	0.222	0.102	0.000	−0.087	−0.164	**7**
8								1.385	0.917	0.647	0.456	0.309	0.189	0.087	0.000	**8**
9									1.446	0.985	0.719	0.531	0.384	0.265	0.164	**9**
10										1.499	1.045	0.783	0.596	0.451	0.332	**10**
11											1.546	1.098	0.839	0.655	0.511	**11**
12												1.588	1.146	0.890	0.707	**12**
13													1.626	1.189	0.936	**13**
14														1.662	1.229	**14**
15															1.694	**15**
16																**16**
17																**17**
18																**18**
19																**19**
20																**20**
21																**21**
22																**22**
23																**23**
24																**24**
25																**25**
26																**26**
27																**27**
28																**28**
29																**29**
30																**30**

	n															
n	**16**	**17**	**18**	**19**	**20**	**21**	**22**	**23**	**24**	**25**	**26**	**27**	**28**	**29**	**30**	**n**
1	−1.724	−1.751	−1.777	−1.801	−1.824	−1.846	−1.866	−1.885	−1.904	−1.921	−1.938	−1.954	−1.969	−1.984	−1.998	**1**
2	−1.266	−1.299	−1.331	−1.360	−1.388	−1.414	−1.438	−1.461	−1.483	−1.504	−1.524	−1.542	−1.561	−1.578	−1.595	**2**
3	−0.978	−1.017	−1.053	−1.087	−1.118	−1.148	−1.175	−1.201	−1.226	−1.249	−1.272	−1.293	−1.313	−1.332	−1.351	**3**
4	−0.755	−0.799	−0.840	−0.877	−0.912	−0.945	−0.976	−1.004	−1.032	−1.057	−1.082	−1.105	−1.127	−1.148	−1.169	**4**
5	−0.565	−0.614	−0.659	−0.701	−0.739	−0.775	−0.809	−0.840	−0.870	−0.898	−0.925	−0.950	−0.974	−0.997	−1.019	**5**
6	−0.393	−0.448	−0.497	−0.543	−0.586	−0.625	−0.662	−0.696	−0.728	−0.759	−0.787	−0.815	−0.840	−0.865	−0.888	**6**
7	−0.232	−0.293	−0.348	−0.399	−0.445	−0.488	−0.528	−0.565	−0.600	−0.633	−0.664	−0.693	−0.721	−0.747	−0.772	**7**
8	−0.077	−0.145	−0.206	−0.262	−0.313	−0.360	−0.403	−0.443	−0.481	−0.516	−0.549	−0.581	−0.610	−0.638	−0.665	**8**
9	0.077	0.000	−0.068	−0.130	−0.186	−0.237	−0.284	−0.328	−0.368	−0.406	−0.442	−0.475	−0.507	−0.537	−0.565	**9**
10	0.232	0.145	0.068	0.000	−0.062	−0.118	−0.169	−0.216	−0.260	−0.301	−0.339	−0.375	−0.409	−0.441	−0.471	**10**
11	0.393	0.293	0.206	0.130	0.062	0.000	−0.056	−0.107	−0.155	−0.199	−0.240	−0.278	−0.314	−0.348	−0.380	**11**
12	0.565	0.448	0.348	0.262	0.186	0.118	0.056	0.000	−0.051	−0.099	−0.143	−0.184	−0.223	−0.259	−0.293	**12**
13	0.755	0.614	0.497	0.399	0.313	0.237	0.169	0.107	0.051	0.000	−0.048	−0.092	−0.133	−0.172	−0.208	**13**
14	0.978	0.799	0.659	0.543	0.445	0.360	0.284	0.216	0.155	0.099	0.048	0.000	−0.044	−0.085	−0.124	**14**
15	1.266	1.017	0.840	0.701	0.586	0.488	0.403	0.328	0.260	0.199	0.143	0.092	0.044	0.000	−0.041	**15**
16	1.724	1.299	1.053	0.877	0.739	0.625	0.528	0.443	0.368	0.301	0.240	0.184	0.133	0.085	0.041	**16**
17		1.751	1.331	1.087	0.912	0.775	0.662	0.565	0.481	0.406	0.339	0.278	0.223	0.172	0.124	**17**
18			1.777	1.360	1.118	0.945	0.809	0.696	0.600	0.516	0.442	0.375	0.314	0.259	0.208	**18**
19				1.801	1.388	1.148	0.976	0.840	0.728	0.633	0.549	0.475	0.409	0.348	0.293	**19**
20					1.824	1.414	1.175	1.004	0.870	0.759	0.664	0.581	0.507	0.441	0.380	**20**
21						1.846	1.438	1.201	1.032	0.898	0.787	0.693	0.610	0.537	0.471	**21**
22							1.866	1.461	1.226	1.057	0.925	0.815	0.721	0.638	0.565	**22**
23								1.885	1.483	1.249	1.082	0.950	0.840	0.747	0.665	**23**
24									1.904	1.504	1.272	1.105	0.974	0.865	0.772	**24**
25										1.921	1.524	1.293	1.127	0.997	0.888	**25**
26											1.938	1.542	1.313	1.148	1.019	**26**
27												1.954	1.561	1.332	1.169	**27**
28													1.969	1.578	1.351	**28**
29														1.984	1.595	**29**
30															1.998	**30**

Appendix I

Equivalent Sigma Levels, Percent Yield, Percent Defective, and ppm

With no sigma shift (centered)				With 1.5 sigma shift			
Sigma level	Percent in specification	Percent defective	ppm	Sigma level	Percent in specification	Percent defective	ppm
0.10	7.9656	92.0344	920344	0.10	2.5957	97.40426	974043
0.20	15.8519	84.1481	841481	0.20	5.2235	94.77650	947765
0.30	23.5823	76.4177	764177	0.30	7.9139	92.08606	920861
0.40	31.0843	68.9157	689157	0.40	10.6950	89.30505	893050
0.50	38.2925	61.7075	617075	0.50	13.5905	86.40949	864095
0.60	45.1494	54.8506	548506	0.60	16.6196	83.38043	833804
0.70	51.6073	48.3927	483927	0.70	19.7952	80.20480	802048
0.80	57.6289	42.3711	423711	0.80	23.1240	76.87605	768760
0.90	63.1880	36.8120	368120	0.90	26.6056	73.39444	733944
1.00	68.2689	31.7311	317311	1.00	30.2328	69.76721	697672
1.10	72.8668	27.1332	271332	1.10	33.9917	66.00829	660083
1.20	76.9861	23.0139	230139	1.20	37.8622	62.13784	621378
1.30	80.6399	19.3601	193601	1.30	41.8185	58.18148	581815
1.40	83.8487	16.1513	161513	1.40	45.8306	54.16937	541694
1.50	86.6386	13.3614	133614	1.50	49.8650	50.13499	501350
1.60	89.0401	10.9599	109599	1.60	53.8860	46.11398	461140
1.70	91.0869	8.9131	89131	1.70	57.8573	42.14274	421427
1.80	92.8139	7.1861	71861	1.80	61.7428	38.25720	382572
1.90	94.2567	5.7433	57433	1.90	65.5085	34.49152	344915
2.00	95.4500	4.5500	45500	2.00	69.1230	30.87702	308770
2.10	96.4271	3.5729	35729	2.10	72.5588	27.44122	274412
2.20	97.2193	2.7807	27807	2.20	75.7929	24.20715	242071
2.30	97.8552	2.1448	21448	2.30	78.8072	21.19277	211928
2.40	98.3605	1.6395	16395	2.40	81.5892	18.41082	184108
2.50	98.7581	1.2419	12419	2.50	84.1313	15.86869	158687
2.60	99.0678	0.9322	9322	2.60	86.4313	13.56867	135687
2.70	99.3066	0.6934	6934	2.70	88.4917	11.50830	115083
2.80	99.4890	0.5110	5110	2.80	90.3191	9.68090	96809

With no sigma shift (centered)				With 1.5 sigma shift			
Sigma level	**Percent in specification**	**Percent defective**	**ppm**	**Sigma level**	**Percent in specification**	**Percent defective**	**ppm**
2.90	99.6268	0.3732	3732	2.90	91.9238	8.07621	80762
3.00	99.7300	0.2700	2700	3.00	93.3189	6.68106	66811
3.10	99.8065	0.1935	1935	3.10	94.5199	5.48014	54801
3.20	99.8626	0.1374	1374	3.20	95.5433	4.45668	44567
3.30	99.9033	0.0967	967	3.30	96.4069	3.59311	35931
3.40	99.9326	0.0674	674	3.40	97.1283	2.87170	28717
3.50	99.9535	0.0465	465	3.50	97.7250	2.27504	22750
3.60	99.9682	0.0318	318	3.60	98.2135	1.78646	17865
3.70	99.9784	0.0216	216	3.70	98.6096	1.39035	13904
3.80	99.9855	0.0145	145	3.80	98.9276	1.07242	10724
3.90	99.9904	0.0096	96.2	3.90	99.1802	0.81976	8198
4.00	99.9937	0.0063	63.3	4.00	99.3790	0.62097	6210
4.10	99.9959	0.0041	41.3	4.10	99.5339	0.46612	4661
4.20	99.9973	0.0027	26.7	4.20	99.6533	0.34670	3467
4.30	99.9983	0.0017	17.1	4.30	99.7445	0.25551	2555
4.40	99.9989	0.0011	10.8	4.40	99.8134	0.18658	1866
4.50	99.9993	0.0007	6.8	4.50	99.8650	0.13499	1350
4.60	99.9996	0.0004	4.2	4.60	99.9032	0.09676	968
4.70	99.9997	0.0003	2.6	4.70	99.9313	0.06871	687
4.80	99.9998	0.0002	1.6	4.80	99.9517	0.04834	483
4.90	99.99990	0.00010	1.0	4.90	99.9663	0.03369	337
5.00	99.99994	0.00006	0.6	5.00	99.9767	0.02326	233
5.10	99.99997	0.00003	0.3	5.10	99.9841	0.01591	159
5.20	99.99998	0.00002	0.2	5.20	99.9892	0.01078	108
5.30	99.999988	0.000012	0.12	5.30	99.9928	0.00723	72.3
5.40	99.999993	0.000007	0.07	5.40	99.9952	0.00481	48.1
5.50	99.999996	0.000004	0.04	5.50	99.9968	0.00317	31.7
5.60	99.999998	0.000002	0.02	5.60	99.9979	0.00207	20.7
5.70	99.9999988	0.0000012	0.012	5.70	99.9987	0.00133	13.3
5.80	99.9999993	0.0000007	0.007	5.80	99.9991	0.00085	8.5
5.90	99.9999996	0.0000004	0.004	5.90	99.9995	0.00054	5.4
6.00	99.9999998	0.0000002	0.002	**6.00**	**99.9997**	**0.00034**	**3.4**

Appendix J.1

Factors for One-Sided Tolerance Limits

	Confidence level								
	0.90			0.95			0.99		
	Proportion			Proportion			Proportion		
n	0.90	0.95	0.99	0.90	0.95	0.99	0.90	0.95	0.99
4	2.955	3.668	5.040	4.255	5.293	7.291	26.036	33.146	46.579
5	2.586	3.207	4.401	3.381	4.190	5.750	7.698	9.649	13.382
6	2.378	2.950	4.048	2.962	3.667	5.025	5.281	6.572	9.055
7	2.242	2.783	3.820	2.711	3.355	4.595	4.300	5.332	7.321
8	2.145	2.663	3.659	2.541	3.145	4.307	3.759	4.652	6.373
9	2.071	2.573	3.538	2.416	2.992	4.099	3.412	4.217	5.771
10	2.012	2.503	3.442	2.321	2.875	3.940	3.168	3.913	5.352
11	1.964	2.445	3.365	2.245	2.782	3.814	2.986	3.687	5.041
12	1.924	2.397	3.301	2.182	2.706	3.712	2.844	3.511	4.800
13	1.891	2.356	3.247	2.130	2.642	3.627	2.729	3.371	4.607
14	1.861	2.321	3.201	2.085	2.589	3.554	2.635	3.255	4.449
15	1.836	2.291	3.160	2.046	2.542	3.492	2.556	3.157	4.317
16	1.813	2.264	3.125	2.013	2.501	3.438	2.488	3.074	4.204
17	1.793	2.240	3.093	1.983	2.465	3.390	2.429	3.002	4.107
18	1.775	2.218	3.065	1.956	2.433	3.347	2.377	2.939	4.022
19	1.759	2.199	3.039	1.932	2.404	3.309	2.331	2.884	3.947
20	1.744	2.181	3.016	1.910	2.378	3.274	2.290	2.834	3.880
21	1.730	2.165	2.994	1.890	2.355	3.243	2.254	2.790	3.821
22	1.717	2.150	2.975	1.872	2.333	3.214	2.220	2.749	3.766
23	1.706	2.137	2.957	1.855	2.313	3.188	2.190	2.713	3.717
24	1.695	2.124	2.940	1.840	2.295	3.164	2.162	2.679	3.673
25	1.685	2.112	2.925	1.826	2.278	3.142	2.137	2.649	3.631
26	1.676	2.101	2.911	1.812	2.262	3.121	2.113	2.620	3.594
27	1.667	2.091	2.897	1.800	2.247	3.101	2.091	2.594	3.559
28	1.659	2.081	2.885	1.788	2.234	3.083	2.071	2.569	3.526
29	1.651	2.072	2.873	1.777	2.221	3.066	2.052	2.547	3.496
30	1.644	2.064	2.862	1.767	2.209	3.050	2.034	2.525	3.468

	Confidence level								
	0.90			0.95			0.99		
	Proportion			Proportion			Proportion		
n	**0.90**	**0.95**	**0.99**	**0.90**	**0.95**	**0.99**	**0.90**	**0.95**	**0.99**
31	1.637	2.056	2.851	1.758	2.197	3.035	2.018	2.506	3.441
32	1.630	2.048	2.841	1.748	2.186	3.021	2.002	2.487	3.416
33	1.624	2.041	2.832	1.740	2.176	3.008	1.987	2.469	3.393
34	1.618	2.034	2.823	1.732	2.166	2.995	1.973	2.453	3.371
35	1.613	2.027	2.814	1.724	2.157	2.983	1.960	2.437	3.350
36	1.608	2.021	2.806	1.716	2.148	2.972	1.948	2.422	3.330
37	1.602	2.015	2.799	1.709	2.140	2.961	1.936	2.408	3.312
38	1.598	2.009	2.791	1.702	2.132	2.950	1.924	2.394	3.294
39	1.593	2.004	2.784	1.696	2.124	2.941	1.914	2.381	3.277
40	1.588	1.999	2.777	1.690	2.117	2.931	1.903	2.369	3.261
41	1.584	1.994	2.771	1.684	2.110	2.922	1.894	2.358	3.245
42	1.580	1.989	2.765	1.678	2.104	2.913	1.884	2.346	3.231
43	1.576	1.984	2.759	1.673	2.097	2.905	1.875	2.336	3.217
44	1.572	1.980	2.753	1.668	2.091	2.897	1.867	2.326	3.203
45	1.569	1.976	2.748	1.662	2.085	2.889	1.858	2.316	3.190
46	1.565	1.971	2.742	1.658	2.079	2.882	1.850	2.306	3.178
47	1.562	1.967	2.737	1.653	2.074	2.875	1.843	2.297	3.166
48	1.558	1.964	2.732	1.648	2.069	2.868	1.835	2.288	3.154
49	1.555	1.960	2.727	1.644	2.063	2.861	1.828	2.280	3.143
50	1.552	1.956	2.723	1.640	2.058	2.855	1.821	2.272	3.133
51	1.549	1.953	2.718	1.636	2.054	2.848	1.815	2.264	3.122
52	1.546	1.949	2.714	1.632	2.049	2.842	1.808	2.257	3.113
53	1.543	1.946	2.710	1.628	2.045	2.837	1.802	2.249	3.103
54	1.541	1.943	2.706	1.624	2.040	2.831	1.796	2.242	3.094
55	1.538	1.940	2.702	1.621	2.036	2.826	1.791	2.235	3.085
56	1.536	1.937	2.698	1.617	2.032	2.820	1.785	2.229	3.076
57	1.533	1.934	2.694	1.614	2.028	2.815	1.780	2.222	3.068
58	1.531	1.931	2.690	1.610	2.024	2.810	1.774	2.216	3.060
59	1.528	1.929	2.687	1.607	2.020	2.805	1.769	2.210	3.052
60	1.526	1.926	2.684	1.604	2.017	2.801	1.764	2.204	3.044
61	1.524	1.923	2.680	1.601	2.013	2.796	1.759	2.199	3.037
62	1.522	1.921	2.677	1.598	2.010	2.792	1.755	2.193	3.029
63	1.520	1.918	2.674	1.595	2.007	2.787	1.750	2.188	3.022
64	1.518	1.916	2.671	1.593	2.003	2.783	1.746	2.183	3.016
65	1.516	1.914	2.668	1.590	2.000	2.779	1.741	2.178	3.009
66	1.514	1.911	2.665	1.587	1.997	2.775	1.737	2.173	3.003

	Confidence level								
	0.90			0.95			0.99		
	Proportion			Proportion			Proportion		
n	**0.90**	**0.95**	**0.99**	**0.90**	**0.95**	**0.99**	**0.90**	**0.95**	**0.99**
67	1.512	1.909	2.662	1.585	1.994	2.771	1.733	2.168	2.996
68	1.510	1.907	2.659	1.582	1.991	2.767	1.729	2.163	2.990
69	1.508	1.905	2.657	1.580	1.988	2.764	1.725	2.159	2.984
70	1.506	1.903	2.654	1.577	1.985	2.760	1.721	2.154	2.978
71	1.504	1.901	2.651	1.575	1.983	2.756	1.718	2.150	2.973
72	1.503	1.899	2.649	1.573	1.980	2.753	1.714	2.145	2.967
73	1.501	1.897	2.646	1.570	1.977	2.750	1.711	2.141	2.962
74	1.499	1.895	2.644	1.568	1.975	2.746	1.707	2.137	2.957
75	1.498	1.893	2.642	1.566	1.972	2.743	1.704	2.133	2.951
76	1.496	1.891	2.639	1.564	1.970	2.740	1.701	2.129	2.946
77	1.495	1.890	2.637	1.562	1.967	2.737	1.697	2.126	2.941
78	1.493	1.888	2.635	1.560	1.965	2.734	1.694	2.122	2.937
79	1.492	1.886	2.633	1.558	1.963	2.731	1.691	2.118	2.932
80	1.490	1.885	2.630	1.556	1.961	2.728	1.688	2.115	2.927
81	1.489	1.883	2.628	1.554	1.958	2.725	1.685	2.111	2.923
82	1.488	1.881	2.626	1.552	1.956	2.722	1.682	2.108	2.918
83	1.486	1.880	2.624	1.550	1.954	2.720	1.679	2.105	2.914
84	1.485	1.878	2.622	1.549	1.952	2.717	1.677	2.101	2.910
85	1.484	1.877	2.620	1.547	1.950	2.714	1.674	2.098	2.906
86	1.482	1.875	2.618	1.545	1.948	2.712	1.671	2.095	2.902
87	1.481	1.874	2.617	1.543	1.946	2.709	1.669	2.092	2.898
88	1.480	1.872	2.615	1.542	1.944	2.707	1.666	2.089	2.894
89	1.479	1.871	2.613	1.540	1.942	2.704	1.664	2.086	2.890
90	1.477	1.870	2.611	1.539	1.940	2.702	1.661	2.083	2.886
91	1.476	1.868	2.610	1.537	1.938	2.700	1.659	2.080	2.882
92	1.475	1.867	2.608	1.535	1.937	2.697	1.656	2.077	2.879
93	1.474	1.866	2.606	1.534	1.935	2.695	1.654	2.075	2.875
94	1.473	1.864	2.605	1.532	1.933	2.693	1.652	2.072	2.872
95	1.472	1.863	2.603	1.531	1.932	2.691	1.649	2.069	2.868
96	1.471	1.862	2.601	1.530	1.930	2.688	1.647	2.067	2.865
97	1.470	1.861	2.600	1.528	1.928	2.686	1.645	2.064	2.862
98	1.469	1.859	2.598	1.527	1.927	2.684	1.643	2.062	2.858
99	1.468	1.858	2.597	1.525	1.925	2.682	1.641	2.059	2.855
100	1.467	1.857	2.595	1.524	1.923	2.680	1.639	2.057	2.852
200	1.410	1.791	2.511	1.448	1.836	2.568	1.524	1.923	2.679
300	1.385	1.763	2.476	1.416	1.799	2.521	1.476	1.868	2.609

	Confidence level								
	0.90			0.95			0.99		
	Proportion			Proportion			Proportion		
n	**0.90**	**0.95**	**0.99**	**0.90**	**0.95**	**0.99**	**0.90**	**0.95**	**0.99**
400	1.371	1.747	2.455	1.397	1.777	2.493	1.448	1.836	2.568
500	1.361	1.736	2.441	1.385	1.762	2.475	1.430	1.814	2.540
600	1.354	1.727	2.430	1.375	1.752	2.461	1.416	1.799	2.521
700	1.349	1.721	2.422	1.368	1.744	2.451	1.406	1.787	2.505
800	1.344	1.716	2.416	1.362	1.737	2.442	1.397	1.777	2.493
900	1.340	1.712	2.411	1.358	1.732	2.436	1.390	1.769	2.483
1000	1.337	1.708	2.406	1.354	1.727	2.430	1.385	1.762	2.475

Appendix J.2

Factors for Two-Sided Tolerance Limits

	Confidence level								
	0.90			0.95			0.99		
	Proportion			Proportion			Proportion		
n	**0.90**	**0.95**	**0.99**	**0.90**	**0.95**	**0.99**	**0.90**	**0.95**	**0.99**
4	4.166	4.930	6.420	5.368	6.353	8.274	9.397	11.121	14.483
5	3.494	4.141	5.407	4.274	5.065	6.614	6.611	7.834	10.230
6	3.131	3.713	4.856	3.712	4.402	5.757	5.336	6.328	8.277
7	2.901	3.443	4.507	3.368	3.997	5.232	4.612	5.473	7.165
8	2.742	3.255	4.265	3.135	3.722	4.876	4.147	4.922	6.449
9	2.625	3.117	4.086	2.967	3.522	4.617	3.822	4.538	5.948
10	2.535	3.010	3.948	2.838	3.371	4.420	3.582	4.254	5.578
11	2.463	2.925	3.837	2.737	3.251	4.264	3.397	4.034	5.292
12	2.404	2.856	3.747	2.655	3.153	4.137	3.249	3.860	5.064
13	2.355	2.798	3.671	2.586	3.073	4.032	3.129	3.717	4.878
14	2.313	2.748	3.607	2.529	3.005	3.943	3.029	3.599	4.723
15	2.277	2.706	3.552	2.480	2.946	3.867	2.944	3.498	4.592
16	2.246	2.669	3.503	2.437	2.895	3.801	2.871	3.412	4.479
17	2.218	2.636	3.461	2.399	2.851	3.743	2.808	3.337	4.380
18	2.194	2.607	3.423	2.366	2.812	3.691	2.752	3.271	4.294
19	2.172	2.581	3.389	2.336	2.776	3.645	2.703	3.212	4.218
20	2.152	2.558	3.358	2.310	2.745	3.604	2.659	3.160	4.149
21	2.134	2.536	3.331	2.285	2.716	3.566	2.619	3.113	4.088
22	2.118	2.517	3.305	2.264	2.690	3.532	2.584	3.071	4.032
23	2.103	2.499	3.282	2.243	2.666	3.501	2.551	3.032	3.981
24	2.089	2.483	3.261	2.225	2.644	3.473	2.521	2.996	3.935
25	2.077	2.468	3.241	2.208	2.624	3.446	2.494	2.964	3.892
26	2.065	2.454	3.223	2.192	2.606	3.422	2.469	2.934	3.853
27	2.054	2.441	3.206	2.178	2.588	3.399	2.445	2.906	3.817
28	2.044	2.429	3.190	2.164	2.572	3.378	2.424	2.881	3.783
29	2.034	2.418	3.175	2.151	2.557	3.358	2.403	2.857	3.752
30	2.025	2.407	3.161	2.140	2.543	3.340	2.385	2.834	3.722

	Confidence level								
	0.90			0.95			0.99		
	Proportion			Proportion			Proportion		
n	**0.90**	**0.95**	**0.99**	**0.90**	**0.95**	**0.99**	**0.90**	**0.95**	**0.99**
31	2.017	2.397	3.148	2.128	2.530	3.323	2.367	2.813	3.695
32	2.009	2.387	3.136	2.118	2.517	3.306	2.350	2.794	3.669
33	2.001	2.379	3.124	2.108	2.505	3.291	2.335	2.775	3.645
34	1.994	2.370	3.113	2.099	2.494	3.276	2.320	2.757	3.622
35	1.987	2.362	3.103	2.090	2.484	3.262	2.306	2.741	3.600
36	1.981	2.355	3.093	2.081	2.474	3.249	2.293	2.725	3.580
37	1.975	2.347	3.083	2.073	2.464	3.237	2.280	2.711	3.560
38	1.969	2.341	3.074	2.066	2.455	3.225	2.269	2.696	3.542
39	1.964	2.334	3.066	2.058	2.447	3.214	2.257	2.683	3.524
40	1.958	2.328	3.058	2.051	2.438	3.203	2.246	2.670	3.507
41	1.953	2.322	3.050	2.045	2.431	3.193	2.236	2.658	3.491
42	1.948	2.316	3.042	2.038	2.423	3.183	2.226	2.646	3.476
43	1.944	2.311	3.035	2.032	2.416	3.173	2.217	2.635	3.462
44	1.939	2.305	3.028	2.027	2.409	3.164	2.208	2.625	3.448
45	1.935	2.300	3.022	2.021	2.402	3.156	2.200	2.615	3.434
46	1.931	2.295	3.015	2.016	2.396	3.147	2.191	2.605	3.421
47	1.927	2.291	3.009	2.010	2.390	3.139	2.183	2.595	3.409
48	1.923	2.286	3.003	2.006	2.384	3.131	2.176	2.586	3.397
49	1.920	2.282	2.998	2.001	2.378	3.124	2.168	2.578	3.386
50	1.916	2.278	2.992	1.996	2.373	3.117	2.161	2.569	3.375
51	1.913	2.274	2.987	1.992	2.367	3.110	2.155	2.561	3.364
52	1.910	2.270	2.982	1.987	2.362	3.103	2.148	2.553	3.354
53	1.906	2.266	2.977	1.983	2.357	3.097	2.142	2.546	3.344
54	1.903	2.262	2.972	1.979	2.353	3.090	2.136	2.538	3.334
55	1.900	2.259	2.967	1.975	2.348	3.084	2.130	2.531	3.325
56	1.897	2.256	2.963	1.972	2.344	3.078	2.124	2.525	3.316
57	1.895	2.252	2.958	1.968	2.339	3.073	2.118	2.518	3.308
58	1.892	2.249	2.954	1.964	2.335	3.067	2.113	2.512	3.299
59	1.889	2.246	2.950	1.961	2.331	3.062	2.108	2.505	3.291
60	1.887	2.243	2.946	1.958	2.327	3.057	2.103	2.499	3.283
61	1.884	2.240	2.942	1.954	2.323	3.052	2.098	2.494	3.276
62	1.882	2.237	2.939	1.951	2.319	3.047	2.093	2.488	3.268
63	1.880	2.234	2.935	1.948	2.316	3.042	2.088	2.482	3.261
64	1.877	2.232	2.931	1.945	2.312	3.037	2.084	2.477	3.254
65	1.875	2.229	2.928	1.942	2.309	3.033	2.080	2.472	3.247
66	1.873	2.226	2.925	1.939	2.305	3.029	2.075	2.467	3.241

	Confidence level								
	0.90			0.95			0.99		
	Proportion			Proportion			Proportion		
n	**0.90**	**0.95**	**0.99**	**0.90**	**0.95**	**0.99**	**0.90**	**0.95**	**0.99**
67	1.871	2.224	2.921	1.937	2.302	3.024	2.071	2.462	3.234
68	1.869	2.221	2.918	1.934	2.299	3.020	2.067	2.457	3.228
69	1.867	2.219	2.915	1.931	2.296	3.016	2.063	2.453	3.222
70	1.865	2.217	2.912	1.929	2.293	3.012	2.059	2.448	3.216
71	1.863	2.214	2.909	1.926	2.290	3.008	2.056	2.444	3.210
72	1.861	2.212	2.906	1.924	2.287	3.004	2.052	2.439	3.204
73	1.859	2.210	2.903	1.922	2.284	3.001	2.048	2.435	3.199
74	1.857	2.208	2.900	1.919	2.282	2.997	2.045	2.431	3.193
75	1.856	2.206	2.898	1.917	2.279	2.994	2.042	2.427	3.188
76	1.854	2.204	2.895	1.915	2.276	2.990	2.038	2.423	3.183
77	1.852	2.202	2.893	1.913	2.274	2.987	2.035	2.419	3.178
78	1.851	2.200	2.890	1.911	2.271	2.984	2.032	2.415	3.173
79	1.849	2.198	2.888	1.909	2.269	2.980	2.029	2.412	3.168
80	1.848	2.196	2.885	1.907	2.266	2.977	2.026	2.408	3.163
81	1.846	2.195	2.883	1.905	2.264	2.974	2.023	2.405	3.159
82	1.845	2.193	2.880	1.903	2.262	2.971	2.020	2.401	3.154
83	1.843	2.191	2.878	1.901	2.259	2.968	2.017	2.398	3.150
84	1.842	2.189	2.876	1.899	2.257	2.965	2.014	2.394	3.145
85	1.840	2.188	2.874	1.897	2.255	2.962	2.012	2.391	3.141
86	1.839	2.186	2.872	1.895	2.253	2.960	2.009	2.388	3.137
87	1.838	2.184	2.870	1.894	2.251	2.957	2.006	2.385	3.133
88	1.836	2.183	2.868	1.892	2.249	2.954	2.004	2.382	3.129
89	1.835	2.181	2.866	1.890	2.247	2.952	2.001	2.379	3.125
90	1.834	2.180	2.864	1.889	2.245	2.949	1.999	2.376	3.121
91	1.833	2.178	2.862	1.887	2.243	2.947	1.996	2.373	3.117
92	1.831	2.177	2.860	1.885	2.241	2.944	1.994	2.370	3.114
93	1.830	2.176	2.858	1.884	2.239	2.942	1.992	2.368	3.110
94	1.829	2.174	2.856	1.882	2.237	2.939	1.989	2.365	3.107
95	1.828	2.173	2.854	1.881	2.236	2.937	1.987	2.362	3.103
96	1.827	2.171	2.852	1.879	2.234	2.935	1.985	2.360	3.100
97	1.826	2.170	2.851	1.878	2.232	2.932	1.983	2.357	3.096
98	1.824	2.169	2.849	1.876	2.231	2.930	1.981	2.355	3.093
99	1.823	2.167	2.847	1.875	2.229	2.928	1.979	2.352	3.090
100	1.822	2.166	2.846	1.874	2.227	2.926	1.977	2.350	3.087
200	1.764	2.097	2.754	1.798	2.137	2.808	1.865	2.217	2.912
300	1.740	2.068	2.842	1.767	2.100	2.922	1.820	2.163	3.080

	Confidence level								
	0.90			0.95			0.99		
	Proportion			Proportion			Proportion		
n	**0.90**	**0.95**	**0.99**	**0.90**	**0.95**	**0.99**	**0.90**	**0.95**	**0.99**
400	1.726	2.052	2.841	1.749	2.079	2.920	1.794	2.132	3.077
500	1.717	2.041	2.839	1.737	2.065	2.918	1.777	2.112	3.074
600	1.710	2.033	2.838	1.728	2.055	2.916	1.764	2.097	3.071
700	1.705	2.027	2.836	1.722	2.047	2.914	1.755	2.086	3.069
800	1.701	2.022	2.835	1.717	2.041	2.912	1.747	2.077	3.066
900	1.697	2.018	2.833	1.712	2.035	2.910	1.741	2.069	3.063
1000	1.694	2.014	2.832	1.709	2.031	2.908	1.736	2.063	3.060

Appendix K.1

Control Limits for Variables Charts

Chart	Centerlines	LCLs	UCLs	Plot Points
$\bar{X}$	$\bar{\bar{X}} = \frac{\sum_{i=1}^{k} \bar{X}_i}{k}$	$\bar{\bar{X}} - A_2\bar{R}$	$\bar{\bar{X}} + A_2\bar{R}$	$\bar{X}_i = \frac{\sum_{j=1}^{n} x_{ij}}{n}$
R	$\bar{R} = \frac{\sum_{i=1}^{k} R_i}{k}$	$D_3\bar{R}$	$D_4\bar{R}$	$R_i = \max(x_{ij}) - \min(x_{ij})$
	k is the number of subgroups	Use *n* as the lookup value	Use *n* as the lookup value	*n* is the subgroup size
$\bar{X}$	$\bar{\bar{X}} = \frac{\sum_{i=1}^{k} \bar{X}_i}{k}$	$\bar{\bar{X}} - A_3\bar{s}$	$\bar{\bar{X}} + A_3\bar{s}$	$\bar{X}_i = \frac{\sum_{j=1}^{n} x_{ij}}{n}$
S	$\bar{s} = \frac{\sum_{i=1}^{k} s_i}{k}$	$B_3\bar{s}$	$B_4\bar{s}$	$s_i = \sqrt{\frac{\sum_{j=1}^{n} x_{ij}^2 - n\bar{x}_i^2}{n-1}}$
	k is the number of subgroups	Use *n* as the lookup value	Use *n* as the lookup value	*n* is the subgroup size
I	$\bar{X} = \frac{\sum_{i=1}^{n} x_i}{k}$	$\bar{X} - E_2\overline{mR}$	$\bar{X} + E_2\overline{mR}$	X_i
mR	$\overline{mR} = \frac{\sum_{i=2}^{k} mR_i}{k-1}$	$D_3\overline{mR}$	$D_4\overline{mR}$	$mR_i = \lvert x_i - x_{i-1} \rvert$
	k is the number of data points plotted	Use $n = 2$ as the lookup value	Use $n = 2$ as the lookup value	

Note: A_2, A_3, B_3, B_4, D_3, D_4, and E_2 can be found in Appendix K.4.

Appendix K.2

Control Limits for Attributes Charts

Chart	Centerline	LCL	UCL	Plot point
p	$\bar{p} = \dfrac{\sum_{i=1}^{k} D_i}{\sum_{i=1}^{k} n_i}$	$LCL_p = \bar{p} - 3\sqrt{\dfrac{\bar{p}(1-\bar{p})}{n_i}}$	$UCL_p = \bar{p} + 3\sqrt{\dfrac{\bar{p}(1-\bar{p})}{n_i}}$	$p_i = \dfrac{D_i}{n_i}$
np	$n\bar{p} = n\dfrac{\sum_{i=1}^{k} D_i}{\sum_{i=1}^{k} n_i}$	$LCL_{np} = n\bar{p} - 3\sqrt{n\bar{p}(1-\bar{p})}$	$UCL_{np} = n\bar{p} + 3\sqrt{n\bar{p}(1-\bar{p})}$	D_i
c	$\bar{c} = \dfrac{\sum_{i=1}^{k} c_i}{k}$	$LCL_c = \bar{c} - 3\sqrt{\bar{c}}$	$UCL_c = \bar{c} + 3\sqrt{\bar{c}}$	c_i
u	$\bar{u} = \dfrac{\sum_{i=1}^{k} c_i}{\sum_{i=1}^{k} n_i}$	$LCL_U = \bar{u} - 3\sqrt{\dfrac{\bar{u}}{n_i}}$	$UCL_u = \bar{u} + 3\sqrt{\dfrac{\bar{u}}{n_i}}$	$u_i = \dfrac{c_i}{n_i}$

Notes:

1. n = Constant sample size of each subgroup
2. n_i = Sample size of the *ith* subgroup
3. k = Number of subgroups
4. D_i = Number of *defective* (nonconforming) units in the *ith* subgroup
5. c_i = Number of *defects* in the *ith* subgroup
6. u_i = Number of *defects*/unit in the *ith* subgroup

Appendix K.3

Control Limits for Short-run Charts

Charts for non-subgrouped data

	Paired charts		Paired charts		Paired charts	
Chart type	Difference (*X*-nominal, *X*-target)	mR	Z	W	Z^*	W^*
Plot points	$X - Nom$	mR	$Z = \frac{X - Nom}{Sigma(X)}$	$W = mR_W$	$Z^* = \frac{X - Nom}{\overline{R}}$	$W^* = mR_W$
CL	0.0	$\overline{mR}$	0.0	d_2	0.0	1.0
UCL	$+A_3\overline{mR}$	$D_4\overline{mR}$	+3.0	$d_2 + 3d_3$	$+A_3$	D_4
LCL	$-A_3\overline{mR}$	$D_3\overline{mR}$	-3.0	0	$-A_3$	D_3

Where *Nom* = *Nominal* or *Target* and $Sigma\,(X) = \frac{\overline{R}}{d_2}$ and $n = 2$.

See Appendix K.4 for A_3, D_3, and D_4 values.

See Appendix K.5 for d_2 and d_3 values.

Charts for subgrouped data

	Paired charts		Paired charts		Paired charts	
Chart type	Difference	R	$\overline{Z}$	W	$\overline{Z}^*$	W^*
Plot points	$\overline{X} - Nom$	R	$\overline{Z} = \frac{\overline{X} - Nom}{Sigma(\overline{X})}$	$W = \frac{R}{Sigma(X)}$	$\overline{Z}^* = \frac{\overline{X} - Nom}{\overline{R}}$	$W^* = \frac{R}{\overline{R}}$
CL	0.0	$\overline{\overline{R}}$	0.0	d_2	0.0	1.0
UCL	$+A_2\overline{\overline{R}}$	$D_4\overline{\overline{R}}$	+3.0	$d_2 + 3d_3$	$+A_2$	D_4
LCL	$-A_2\overline{\overline{R}}$	$D_3\overline{\overline{R}}$	-3.0	$d_2 - 3d_3$	$-A_2$	D_3

Where *Nom* = *Nominal* or *Target* and $Sigma\,(\overline{X}) = \frac{\overline{R}}{d_2\sqrt{n}}$ and $n = 2$.

See Appendix K.4 for A_3, D_3, and D_4 values.

See Appendix K.5 for d_2 and d_3 values.

Standardized attributes charts

Chart type	p	np	c	u
Plot points	$Z_i = \frac{p_i - \overline{p}}{\sqrt{\overline{p}(1-\overline{p})/n}}$	$Z_i = \frac{np_i - n\overline{p}}{\sqrt{n\overline{p}(1-\overline{p})/n}}$	$Z_i = \frac{c_i - \overline{c}}{\sqrt{\overline{c}}}$	$Z_i = \frac{u_i - \overline{u}}{\sqrt{\overline{u}/n}}$
CL	0.0	0.0	0.0	0.0
UCL	+3.0	+3.0	+3.0	+3.0
LCL	-3.0	-3.0	-3.0	-3.0

Appendix K.4

Control Chart Constants

n	A_2	A_3	B_3	B_4	n
2	1.881	2.659	0.000	3.266	2
3	1.023	1.954	0.000	2.568	3
4	0.729	1.628	0.000	2.266	4
5	0.577	1.427	0.000	2.089	5
6	0.483	1.287	0.030	1.970	6
7	0.419	1.182	0.118	1.882	7
8	0.373	1.099	0.185	1.815	8
9	0.337	1.032	0.239	1.761	9
10	0.308	0.975	0.284	1.716	10
11	0.285	0.927	0.322	1.678	11
12	0.266	0.886	0.354	1.646	12
13	0.249	0.850	0.381	1.619	13
14	0.235	0.817	0.407	1.593	14
15	0.223	0.789	0.428	1.572	15
16	0.212	0.763	0.448	1.552	16
17	0.203	0.739	0.466	1.534	17
18	0.194	0.718	0.482	1.518	18
19	0.187	0.698	0.496	1.504	19
20	0.180	0.680	0.510	1.490	20
21	0.173	0.663	0.523	1.477	21
22	0.167	0.647	0.535	1.465	22
23	0.162	0.633	0.545	1.455	23
24	0.157	0.619	0.555	1.445	24
25	0.153	0.606	0.564	1.436	25

Notes: Only odd values of n are given for A_6, A_8, and A_9. Otherwise, the median for an even n is simply the average of the two middle values of the subgroup.

n	D_3	D_4	E_2	n
2	0.000	3.267	2.660	2
3	0.000	2.574	1.772	3
4	0.000	2.282	1.457	4
5	0.000	2.114	1.290	5
6	0.000	2.004	1.184	6
7	0.076	1.924	1.109	7
8	0.136	1.864	1.054	8
9	0.184	1.816	1.010	9
10	0.223	1.777	0.975	10
11	0.256	1.744	0.945	11
12	0.283	1.717	0.921	12
13	0.307	1.693	0.899	13
14	0.328	1.672	0.881	14
15	0.347	1.653	0.864	15
16	0.363	1.637	0.849	16
17	0.378	1.622	0.836	17
18	0.391	1.609	0.824	18
19	0.403	1.597	0.813	19
20	0.415	1.585	0.803	20
21	0.423	1.577	0.794	21
22	0.434	1.566	0.786	22
23	0.443	1.557	0.778	23
24	0.452	1.548	0.770	24
25	0.459	1.541	0.763	25

Notes: Only odd values of n are given for A_6, A_8, and A_9. Otherwise, the median for an even n is simply the average of the two middle values of the subgroup.

Appendix K.5

Factors for Estimating σ_X

n	c_4	d_2	d_3
2	0.7979	1.128	0.8525
3	0.8862	1.693	0.8884
4	0.9213	2.059	0.8798
5	0.9400	2.326	0.8641
6	0.9515	2.534	0.8480
7	0.9594	2.704	0.8332
8	0.9650	2.847	0.8198
9	0.9693	2.970	0.8078
10	0.9727	3.078	0.7971
11	0.9754	3.173	0.7873
12	0.9776	3.258	0.7785
13	0.9794	3.336	0.7704
14	0.9810	3.407	0.7630
15	0.9823	3.472	0.7562
16	0.9835	3.532	0.7499
17	0.9845	3.588	0.7441
18	0.9854	3.640	0.7386
19	0.9862	3.689	0.7335
20	0.9869	3.735	0.7287
21	0.9876	3.778	0.7272
22	0.9882	3.819	0.7199
23	0.9887	3.858	0.7159
24	0.9892	3.895	0.7121
25	0.9896	3.931	0.7084

Note: σ_x may be estimated from k subgroups of size n:

$$\frac{\bar{s}}{c_4}$$

$$\frac{\bar{R}}{d_2} \qquad \frac{\overline{mR}}{d_2}$$

Appendix L

Glossary of Lean Six Sigma and Related Terms

α—*See* alpha.

β—*See* beta.

C_p (process capability index)—An index describing process capability in relation to specified tolerance of a characteristic divided by the natural process variation for a process in a state of statistical control:

$$C_p = \frac{USL - LSL}{6\sigma}$$

where USL = upper specification limit, LSL = lower specification limit, and 6σ = CAP = the natural tolerance. Note: When the index is estimated using values from a control chart, σ is estimated by $\hat{\sigma}$.

See also P_p (process performance index), a similar term, except that the process may not be in a state of statistical control; process capability index.

C_{pk} (minimum process capability index)—The smaller of the upper process capability index C_{pk_U} and the lower process capability index C_{pk_L}. The C_{pk} considers the mean of the process with respect to the upper and lower specifications. The C_{pk} can be converted to a sigma level using sigma level = $3C_{pk}$.

$$C_{pk} = \min\,(C_{pkL,}\ C_{pkU})$$

C_{pk_L} (lower process capability index; CPL)—An index describing process capability in relation to the lower specification limit. The index is defined as

$$C_{pk_L} = \frac{\mu - LSL}{3\sigma}$$

where μ = the process average, LSL = lower specification limit, and 3σ = half of the natural tolerance. Note: When the index is estimated using values from a control chart, μ is estimated by $\overline{\overline{x}}$ and σ is estimated by $\hat{\sigma}$.

C_{pk_U} (upper process capability index; CPU)—An index describing process capability in relation to the upper specification limit. The index is defined as

$$C_{pk_U} = \frac{USL - \mu}{3\sigma}$$

where μ = the process average, USL = upper specification limit, and 3σ = half of the natural tolerance. Note: When the index is estimated using values from a control chart, μ is estimated by $\bar{x}$ and σ is estimated by $\hat{\sigma}$.

C_{pm} (process capability index of the mean)—An index that takes into account the location of the process average relative to a target value and is defined as

$$C_{pm} = \frac{(USL - LSL)/2}{3\sqrt{\sigma^2 + (\mu - T)^2}}$$

where USL = upper specification limit, LSL = lower specification limit, σ = standard deviation, μ = process average, and T = target value. When the process average and the target value are the same, the $C_{pm} = C_{pk}$. When the process average drifts from the target value, the $C_{pm} < C_{pk}$. Note: When the index is estimated using values from a control chart, μ is estimated by $\bar{x}$ and σ is estimated by $\hat{\sigma}$.

n—*See* sample size.

1 – α—*See* confidence level.

1 – β—*See* power.

ρ—The population correlation coefficient. *See also* correlation coefficient.

***p*-value**—The probability of obtaining the statistical result or something more extreme assuming the null hypothesis is true. When the *p*-value is less than the chosen α level, we reject the null hypothesis.

P_p (process performance index)—An index describing process performance in relation to specified tolerance. It is estimated as:

$$\hat{P}_p = \frac{USL - LSL}{6s}$$

s is used for standard deviation since both random and special causes may be present. Note: A state of statistical control is not required. Also note the similarity to the formula for C_p.

P_{pk} (minimum process performance index)—The smaller of the upper process performance index P_{pk_U} and the lower process performance index P_{pk_L}. The P_{pk}, similar to the C_{pk}, considers the mean of the process with respect to the upper and lower specifications. The P_{pk} is known as the potential process capability and is used in the validation stage of a new product launch. A state of statistical control is not required. It is estimated by:

$$\hat{P}_{pk} = \min\left(\hat{P}_{pkL}, \hat{P}_{pkU}\right)$$

P_{pk_L} (process performance index, lower; PPL)—An index describing process performance in relation to the lower specification limit. The index is estimated as:

$$\hat{P}_{pkL} = \frac{\bar{x} - LSL}{3s}$$

where $\bar{x}$ = process average, LSL = lower specification limit, and 3s = half of the process capability. Note: When the process average is obtained from a control chart, $\bar{x}$ is replaced by $\bar{\bar{x}}$.

P_{pk_U} (process performance index, upper; PPU)—An index describing process performance in relation to the upper specification limit. The index is estimated as:

$$\hat{P}_{pkL} = \frac{USL - \bar{x}}{3s}$$

where $\bar{x}$ = process average, USL = upper specification limit, and 3s = half of the process capability. Note: When the process average is obtained from a control chart, $\bar{x}$ is replaced by $\bar{\bar{x}}$.

r—*See* correlation coefficient.

R—*See* correlation coefficient.

r^2—*See* coefficient of determination.

R^2—*See* coefficient of determination.

r^2_{adj}—*See* adjusted coefficient of determination.

R^2_{adj}—*See* adjusted coefficient of determination.

t_k—This is the *t* statistic at lag *k*. The formula is:

$$t_k = \frac{r_k}{SE(r_k)}$$

where $SE(r_k)$ = standard error of the autocorrelation at lag *k*.

$Y = f(X)$—A foundational concept of Six Sigma, this equation represents the idea that process outputs are a function of process inputs.

5S (Five S)—A term that derives its name from the five terms beginning with "s" that are used to create a workplace suited for visual control and lean production. Collectively, 5S is about how to create a workplace that is visibly organized, free of clutter, neatly arranged, and sparkling clean. The 5S's are defined as follows: *seiri* (sort; also sifting) means to separate needed tools, parts, and instructions from unneeded materials and to remove the latter; *seiton* (set in order) means to neatly arrange and identify parts and tools for ease of use; *seiso* (shine; also sanitize or scrub) means to conduct a cleanup campaign; *seiketsu* (standardize) means to conduct seiri, seiton, and seiso at frequent, indeed daily, intervals to maintain a workplace in perfect condition; and *shitsuke* (sustain; also self-discipline) means to form the habit of always following the first four S's. *See also* individual listing for each of the 5S's.

5 whys—A persistent questioning technique to probe deeper to reach the root cause of a problem. *See also* 5Ws & 1H.

5Ws & 1H—Addressing the *who, what, where, when, why,* and *how* questions is a useful technique to help develop an objective and a concise statement of a problem. *See also* 5 whys.

6Ms—Typically the primary categories of the cause-and-effect diagram: machines, manpower, materials, measurements, methods, and Mother Nature. Using these categories as a structured approach provides some assurance that few causes will be overlooked. *See also* 7Ms.

7Ms—The 6Ms with the addition of management. *See also* 6Ms.

A

ABC—*See* activity-based costing.

acceptance control chart—A control chart intended primarily to evaluate whether the plotted measure can be expected to satisfy specified tolerances.

acceptance quality limit (AQL)—The quality level that is the worst tolerable product average when a continuing series of lots is submitted for acceptance sampling. Note the following: (1) This concept applies only when an acceptance sampling scheme with rules for switching and discontinuation is used. (2) Although individual lots with quality as bad as the AQL can be accepted with fairly high probability, the designation of an AQL does not suggest that this is a desirable quality level. (3) Acceptance sampling schemes found in standards with their rules for switching and discontinuation of sampling inspection are designed to encourage suppliers to have process averages consistently better than the AQL. If suppliers fail to do so, there is a high probability of being switched from normal inspection to tightened inspection, where lot acceptance becomes more difficult. Once on tightened inspection, unless corrective action is taken to improve product quality, it is very likely that the rule requiring discontinuation of sampling inspection pending such improvement will be invoked unless action is taken to improve the process. (4) The use of the abbreviation AQL to mean *acceptable quality level* is no longer recommended since modern thinking is that no fraction defective is really acceptable. Using "acceptance quality limit" rather than "acceptable quality level" indicates a technical value where acceptance occurs.

accuracy—The closeness of agreement between a test result or measurement result and the true or reference value.

ACF—*See* sample autocorrelation function.

action plan—*See* operational plan.

activity—An action of some type that requires a time duration for accomplishment.

activity network diagram (AND)—A tool used to illustrate a sequence of events or activities (nodes) and the interconnectivity of such nodes. It is used for scheduling and especially for determining the critical path through nodes. It is also known as an *arrow diagram*. The activity network diagram is one of the seven management and planning tools.

activity-based costing (ABC)—A cost allocation method that allocates overhead expenses to the activities based on the proportion of use, rather than proportion of costs.

actual cost of work performed (ACWP)—*See* actual value.

actual value (AV)—The actual cost incurred for work completed by a specific date. It is also known as the *actual cost of work performed* (ACWP).

ACWP—*See* actual value.

ADDIE model—an instructional design model comprised of the steps Analysis, Design, Development, Implementation, and Evaluation.

adjusted coefficient of determination (R^2_{adj})—A statistic that takes into consideration the number of predictor variables in the model and is helpful when comparing models with a different number of predictor variables. It is computed as follows:

$$R^2_{adj} = 1 - \left(\frac{\sum_{i=1}^{n} (y_i - \hat{y}_i)^2}{\left(\sum_{i=1}^{n} y_i - \bar{y} \right)^2} \right) \left(\frac{n-1}{n-p-1} \right)$$

where:

n = Number of observations

y_i = ith observed response value

$\bar{y}_i$ = Mean observed response value

$\hat{y}_i$ = ith fitted value

p = Number of terms in the model including the constant term

Notice when $p = 2$ (that is, simple linear regression), R^2 equals R^2_{adj}. For simple linear regression, sometimes R^2_{adj} is written as r^2_{adj}.

affinity diagram—A tool used to organize information and help achieve order out of the chaos that can develop in a brainstorming session. Large amounts of data, concepts, and ideas are grouped based on their natural relationship to one another. It is more a creative process than a logical process. Also known as the *KJ method,* the affinity diagram is one of the seven management and planning tools.

agile approach—*See* lean.

AIAG—Automotive Industry Action Group.

alias—An effect that is completely confounded with another effect due to the nature of the designed experiment. Aliases are the result of confounding, which may or may not be deliberate.

alpha (α)—(1) The maximum probability or risk of making a Type I error when dealing with the significance level of a test. (2) The probability or risk of incorrectly deciding that a shift in the process mean has occurred when in fact the process has not changed (when referring to α in general or the *p*-value obtained in the test). (3) *α* is usually designated as producer's risk.

alpha (α) risk—*See* Type I error.

alternative hypothesis—A hypothesis formulated from new information.

analysis of means (ANOM)—A statistical procedure for troubleshooting industrial processes and analyzing the results of experimental designs with factors at fixed levels. It provides a graphical display of data. Ellis R. Ott developed the procedure in 1967 because he observed that non-statisticians had difficulty understanding analysis of variance. Analysis of means is easier for quality practitioners to use because it is an extension of the control chart. In 1973, Edward G. Schilling further extended the concept, enabling analysis of means to be used with non-normal distributions and attributes data where the normal approximation to the binomial distribution does not apply. This is referred to as *analysis of means for treatment effects.*

analysis of variance (ANOVA)—A basic statistical technique for analyzing experimental data. It subdivides the total variation of a data set into meaningful component parts associated with specific sources of variation to test a hypothesis on the parameters of the model or to estimate variance components. There are three model types: fixed, random, and mixed.

analytical thinking—Breaking down a problem or situation into discrete parts to understand how each part contributes to the whole.

AND—*See* activity network diagram.

Andon board—A visual device (usually lights) displaying status alerts that can easily be seen by those who should respond.

ANOM—*See* analysis of means.

ANOVA—*See* analysis of variance.

ANSI—American National Standards Institute.

APC—*See* automated process control.

appraisal costs—The costs associated with measuring, evaluating, or auditing products or services to ensure conformance to quality standards and performance requirements. These include costs such as incoming and source inspection/test of purchased material; in-process and final inspection/test; product, process, or service audit; calibration of measuring and test equipment; and the cost of associated supplies and materials.

AQL—*See* acceptance quality limit.

ARIMA—*See* autoregressive integrated moving average.

arrow diagram—*See* activity network diagram.

AS-9100—A standard for the aeronautics industry embracing the ISO 9001 standard.

ASQ—American Society for Quality.

assessment of training effectiveness—According to the Manpower Services Commission (MSC) Glossary of Training Terms: "A general term for the process of ascertaining whether training is efficient or effective in achieving prescribed objectives. It covers both evaluation and validation."

assignable cause—A specifically identified factor that contributes to variation and is detectable. Eliminating assignable causes so that the points plotted on the control chart remain within the control limits helps achieve a state of statistical control. Note: Although assignable cause is sometimes considered synonymous with special cause, a special cause is assignable only when it is specifically identified. *See also* special cause.

assumption—A condition that must be true for a statistical procedure to be valid.

attribute data—Data that are categorized for analysis or evaluation. (Attribute data may involve measurements as long as they are used only to place given data in a category for further analysis or evaluation. Contrast with variables data.)

attrition—Refers to loss of people to jobs outside the organization.

autocorrelation—The internal correlation between members of series observations ordered in time.

automated process control (APC)—The application of automation to effect process control by maintaining manipulated variables at set point levels such that controlled variables are maintained at specified levels. Generally, automation allows for a greater number of manipulated variables to be controlled with greater speed and accuracy than possible by human intervention.

autonomation—*See* jidoka.

autoregressive integrated moving average (ARIMA)—According to the SAS Institute, Inc. "an ARIMA model predicts a value in a response time series as a linear combination of its own past values, past errors (also called *shocks* or *innovations*), and current and past values of other time series."

AV—*See* actual value.

avoidance, risk—Refers to the practice of eliminating the risk factor.

axiomatic design—A theory by Dr. Nam Pyo Suh that stresses each functional requirement be designed to achieve robustness without affecting other functional requirements.

B

BAC—*See* budget at completion.

baka-yoke—A Japanese term for a manufacturing technique for preventing mistakes by designing the manufacturing process, equipment, and tools so that an operation literally cannot be performed incorrectly. In addition to preventing incorrect operation, the technique usually provides a warning signal of some sort for incorrect performance.

balanced design—A design where all treatment combinations have the same number of observations. If replication in a design exists, it would be balanced only if the replication was consistent across all treatment combinations. In other words, the number of replicates of each treatment combination is the same.

balanced incomplete block design—Incomplete block design in which each block contains the same number k of different levels from the l levels of the principal factor arranged so that every pair of levels occurs in the same number l of blocks from the b blocks. Note: This design implies that every level of the principal factor will appear the same number of times in the experiment.

balanced scorecard—Translates an organization's mission and strategy into a comprehensive set of performance measures to provide a basis for strategic measurement and management, utilizing four balanced views: financial, customers, internal business processes, and learning and growth.

batch processing—Running large batches of a single product through the process at one time, resulting in queues awaiting the next steps in the process.

bathtub curve—A graphic representation of the relationship of the life of a product versus the probable failure rate. The curve contains three phases: early or infant failure (break-in), a stable rate during normal use, and wear-out. The bathtub curve is also known as the life-history curve.

BB—*See* Black Belt.

BCWP—*See* budgeted cost of work performed.

BCWS—*See* budgeted cost of work scheduled.

behavior, directive—Establishes a clear path to the goal by specifying what is to be done, how it is to be done, and who is going to do it.

behavior, supportive—Involves two-way communication and focuses on emotional and social support.

benchmark—An organization, a part of an organization, or a measurement that serves as a reference point or point of comparison.

benchmarking—An improvement process in which an organization measures its performance against that of best-in-class organizations (or others that are good performers), determines how those organizations achieved their performance levels, and uses the information to improve its own performance. Areas that can be benchmarked include strategies, operations, processes, and procedures.

benefit–cost analysis—A collection of the dollar value of benefits derived from an initiative divided by the associated costs incurred. A benefit–cost analysis is also known as a cost–benefit analysis.

benefit–cost ratio—The formula for computing a benefit–cost is:

$$\frac{\sum \text{NPV of all benefits anticipated}}{\sum \text{NPV of all cost anticipated}}.$$

Occasionally it is referred to as a *cost–benefit ratio*, which is the reciprocal.

best subsets—A very useful tool to help select a regression model among many other viable models. It is based on the concept that for a model comprising *m* predictor variables, there are $2^m - 1$ possible subsets of predictor variables possible. Each model can be compared using such measures as VIF, Mallows' C_p, PRESS, R^2_{adj}, and squared error to aid in the model selection.

beta (β)—(1) The maximum probability or risk of making a Type II error. (2) The probability or risk of incorrectly deciding that a shift in the process mean has not occurred when in fact the process has changed. (3) β is usually designated as consumer's risk.

beta (β) risk—*See* Type II error.

bias—A systematic difference between the mean of the test result or measurement result and a true or reference value. For example, if one measures the lengths of 10 pieces of rope that range from 1 foot to 10 feet and always concludes that the length of each piece is 2 inches shorter than the true length, then the individual is exhibiting a bias of 2 inches. Bias is a component of accuracy.

Black Belt (BB)—A Six Sigma role associated with an individual who is typically assigned full time to train and mentor Green Belts as well as lead improvement projects using specified methodologies such as define, measure, analyze, improve, and control (DMAIC) and design for Six Sigma (DFSS).

block—A collection of experimental units more homogeneous than the full set of experimental units. Blocks are usually selected to allow for special causes, in addition to those introduced as factors to be studied. These special causes may be avoidable within blocks, thus providing a more homogeneous experimental subspace.

block diagram—A diagram that describes the operation, interrelationships, and interdependencies of components in a system. Boxes, or blocks (hence the name), represent the components; connecting lines between the blocks represent interfaces. There are two types of block diagrams: a functional block diagram, which shows a system's subsystems and lower-level products, their interrelationships, and interfaces with other systems; and a reliability block diagram, which is similar to the functional block diagram except that it is modified to emphasize those aspects influencing reliability.

block effect—An effect resulting from a block in an experimental design. Existence of a block effect generally means that the method of blocking was appropriate and that an assignable cause has been found.

blocking—Including blocks in an experiment in order to broaden the applicability of the conclusions or minimize the impact of selected assignable causes. The randomization of the experiment is restricted and occurs within blocks.

BPM—*See* business process management.

brainstorming—A problem-solving tool that teams use to generate as many ideas as possible that are related to a particular subject. Team members begin by offering all their ideas; the ideas are not discussed or reviewed until after the brainstorming session.

break-even point—Conducted as an analysis, it is a useful approach when there are multiple alternatives each of which may be economical under its own set of conditions. The break-even point is determined by altering one variable while holding all others constant. The variable generally represents some passage of time or number of units processed and can be calculated or determined graphically to identify where the alternatives are equal from an economical viewpoint. This point of equality is known as the break-even point.

budget at completion (BAC)—This is the total planned value for a given task at the end of the project.

budgeted cost of work performed (BCWP)—*See* earned value.

budgeted cost of work scheduled (BCWS)—*See* planned value.

bullwhip effect—Whenever an organization changes the schedule or the demand for product frequently, these perturbations are rippled upstream throughout the value chain and amplified along the way, sending the supply chain into turmoil. This is known as the bullwhip effect. Some organizations have minimized the bullwhip effect by batching changes and releasing the changes at less frequent intervals. This introduces stability into the value chain.

business process management (BPM)—A set of activities an organization implements to optimize its processes. Business process management encompasses both software tools and manual processes designed to assist organizations in achieving process optimization.

C

calibration—The comparison of a measurement instrument or system of unverified accuracy to a measurement instrument or system of known accuracy to detect any variation from the true value.

capability—The performance of a process demonstrated to be in a state of statistical control. *See also* process capability; process performance.

capability index—*See* process capability index.

causal factor—A variable that when changed or manipulated in some manner serves to influence a given effect or result.

cause-and-effect analysis—The process of identifying the likely causes of any outcome. Some cause-and-effect analyses produce an output like a fishbone diagram. Others produce a cause-and-effect tree with multiple sub-branches.

cause-and-effect diagram—A diagram resembling a fish skeleton that is used to illustrate the main causes and sub-causes leading to an effect. One of the seven basic tools of quality, the cause-and-effect diagram is also known as the *Ishikawa diagram* or the *fishbone diagram*.

central limit theorem (CLT)—A theorem that states that irrespective of the shape of the distribution of a population, the distribution of sample means is approximately normal when the sample size is large.

central tendency—The propensity of data collected on a process to concentrate around a value situated approximately midway between the lowest and highest values. Three common measures of central tendency include (arithmetic) mean, median, and mode. *See also* mean, median, mode.

centralization versus decentralization—In the context of organizational design refers to how much decision-making authority has been delegated to lower management levels.

Certified Six Sigma Black Belt (CSSBB)—An ASQ certification.

Certified Six Sigma Green Belt (CSSGB)—An ASQ certification.

CFM—*See* continuous flow manufacturing.

chaku-chaku—A Japanese term meaning "load-load" in a cell layout where a part is taken from one machine and loaded into the next.

champion—A Six Sigma role associated with a senior manager who ensures that their projects are aligned with the organization's strategic goals and priorities, provides the Six Sigma team with resources, removes organizational barriers for the team, participates in project tollgate reviews, and essentially serves as the team's backer. Although many organizations define the terms "champion" and "sponsor" differently, they are frequently used interchangeably. *See also* sponsor.

chance cause—*See* random cause.

chance variation—Variation due to chance causes. *See also* random variation or noise.

change agent—According to Hutton (1994), a change agent is an individual who play a specific role in the planning and implementation of the change management process. They may be members of the organization or may be outsiders.

changeover time—The time interval between the last good piece off the current run and the first good piece off the next run.

characteristic—A property that helps differentiate between items of a given sample or population.

charter—A documented statement officially initiating the formation of a committee, team, project, or other effort in which a clearly stated purpose and approval are conferred.

check sheet—A simple data recording device typically used to collect the frequency of occurrences of nominal data by category. Whenever the user observes the occurrence of one of the categories, they place a mark next to the category. When the observation process is complete, final counts by category can then be obtained. The user custom designs the check sheet so that they can readily interpret the results. The check sheet is occasionally considered to be one of the seven basic tools of quality. Note: Check sheets are often confused with checklists. *See also* checklist.

checklist—A quality tool that is used for processes where there is a large human element. Examples are audit checklists and an airplane pilot's preflight checklist. Checklists serve as reminders and, depending on design, evidence that important items have been observed or appropriate actions have been taken. A well-designed checklist helps gather information to support findings and observations and serves as a guide and a place to record information. Note: Checklists are often confused with check sheets. *See also* check sheet.

churn—The movement of people to different job positions within the organization.

circle diagram—A tool used to show linkages between various items. The circle diagram is constructed by evenly placing item descriptors around a circle. Such item descriptors might include products, services, organizations, individuals, and so forth. Arrows are drawn from each item to other items where a flow exists. Circle diagrams are highly useful in that they readily depict predecessor and successor relationships as well as potential bottlenecks. Too many inputs or outputs from any given descriptor around the circumference of the circle may indicate a limiting function. A circle diagram is also known as a *hand-off map.*

closed-loop feedback system—When the manipulated variable is adjusted by the final control element, and that variable, in turn, affects the next measurement, the system is said to be a closed-loop feedback system.

CLT—*See* central limit theorem.

CMM—Capability maturity model.

CMMI—Capability maturity model integration.

coaching—A process by which a more experienced individual helps enhance the existing skills and capabilities that reside in a less experienced individual. Coaching is about listening, observing, and providing constructive, practical, and meaningful feedback. Typically, coaching is used on a one-to-one basis, or for a small group or team, and conducted at the job site or during the training process. During training, coaching helps the trainee translate the theoretical learning into applied learning while helping the trainee developing confidence in their newly developing knowledge and skills. Post training, coaches help projects stay on track and advance toward completion in a timely manner.

coefficient of determination (R^2)—A statistic that indicates how much variation in the response variable is accounted for by the regression model. $0 \le R^2 \le 1$. It is computed as follows:

$$R^2 = 1 - \frac{\sum_{i=1}^{n}(y_i - \hat{y}_i)^2}{\sum_{i=1}^{n}(y_i - \bar{y}_i)^2}$$

where:

n = Number of observations

y_i = ith observed response value

$\bar{y}_i$ = Mean observed response value

$\hat{y}_i$ = ith fitted value

For simple linear regression, R^2 is often written as r^2. The coefficient of determination is known as the *coefficient of multiple determination* when used in multiple regression.

coefficient of multiple determination—*See* coefficient of determination.

communication plan—A document that defines what will be communicated, to whom, how often, and by what means.

complete block—A block that accommodates a complete set of treatment combinations.

completely randomized design—A design in which the treatments are randomly assigned to the full set of experimental units. No blocks are involved.

completely randomized factorial design—A factorial design in which all the treatments are randomly assigned to the full set of experimental units. *See also* completely randomized design.

compliance—An affirmative indication or judgment that the supplier of a product or service has met the requirements of the relevant specifications, contract, or regulation; also the state of meeting the requirements.

components of variation (COV)—A statistical technique that allows us to separate process variation by the inputs. Components of variation is useful in the situation where our problem can be formulated as a nested hierarchal structure.

concurrent engineering—A way to reduce cost, improve quality, and shrink cycle time by simplifying a product's system of life-cycle tasks during the early concept stages. Concurrent engineering is a process to get all departments including engineering, purchasing, marketing, manufacturing, and finance to work on a new design at once to speed development. The emphasis is on upstream prevention versus downstream correction. Concurrent engineering is also known as *simultaneous engineering*.

confidence coefficient (1 – α)—*See* confidence level.

confidence interval—An estimate of the interval between two statistics that includes the true value of the parameter with some probability. This probability is called the *confidence level* of the estimate. Confidence levels typically used are 90%, 95%, and 99%. Either the interval contains the parameter or it does not.

confidence level (1 – α)—The probability that (1) the confidence interval described by a set of confidence limits actually includes the population parameter, and (2) an interval about a sample statistic actually includes the population parameter. The confidence level is also known as the *confidence coefficient*.

confidence limits—The endpoints of the interval about the sample statistic that is believed, with a specified confidence level, to include the population parameter. *See also* confidence interval.

conflict resolution—A process for resolving disagreements in a manner acceptable to all parties.

confounding—Indistinguishably combining an effect with other effects or blocks. When done deliberately, higher-order effects are systematically aliased so as to allow estimation of lower-order effects. Sometimes, confounding results from inadvertent changes to a design during the running of an experiment or from poor planning of the design. This can diminish or even invalidate the effectiveness of the experiment.

consensus—Finding a proposal acceptable enough that all team members support the decision and no member opposes it.

constraint—A bottleneck or limitation of the throughput of a process.

constraint management—Pertains to identifying a constraint and working to remove or diminish it, while dealing with resistance to change.

consumer's risk (β)—The probability of acceptance when the quality level has a value stated by the acceptance sampling plan as unsatisfactory. Note: (1) such acceptance is a Type II error; (2) consumer's risk is usually designated as beta (β). Consumer's risk is also known as *beta* (β) *risk, beta* (β) *error, error of the second kind, type 2 error,* and *type II error.*

continuous flow manufacturing (CFM)—A method in which items are produced and moved from one processing step to the next, one piece at a time. Each process makes only the one piece that the next process needs, and the transfer batch size is one. CFM is sometimes known as *one-piece flow* or *single-piece flow.*

continuous variable—A variable whose possible values form an interval set of numbers such that between each two values in the set another member of the set occurs.

control chart—A chart that plots a statistical measure of a series of samples in a particular order to steer the process regarding that measure and to control and reduce variation. The control chart comprises the plotted points, a set of upper and lower control limits, and a centerline. Specific rules are used to determine when the control chart goes out of control. Note: (1) the order is either time or sample number order based, and (2) the control chart operates most effectively when the measure is a process characteristic correlated with an ultimate product or service characteristic. The control chart is one of the seven basic tools of quality.

control chart, acceptance—*See* acceptance control chart.

control limit—A line on a control chart used for judging the stability of a process. Note: (1) control limits provide statistically determined boundaries for the deviations from the centerline of the statistic plotted on a Shewhart control chart due to random causes alone; (2) control limits (with the exception of the acceptance control chart) are based on actual process data, not on specification limits; (3) other than points outside the control limits, "out-of-control" criteria can include runs, trends, cycles, periodicity, and unusual patterns within the control limits; (4) the calculation of control limits depends on the type of control chart.

control plan—A living document that identifies critical input or output variables and associated activities that must be performed to maintain control of the variation of processes, products, and services in order to minimize deviation from their preferred values.

controlled variable—In the context of automated process control, the controlled variable is a variable that must be maintained at a set or specified level. The control variable is also known as the *process variable* or simply the *measurement*. In Lean Six Sigma terminology, it is the "Y" variable.

controller—In the context of automated process control, the controller is considered the brain of the system since it compares the value of the signal to the set value (that is, nominal or desired value) and sends a signal to the final control element for action. Essentially, the controller makes a decision. The basic operation performed is "decide."

COPQ—*See* cost of poor quality.

COQ—*See* cost of quality.

corrective action—Action taken to eliminate the root cause(s) and symptom(s) of an existing deviation or nonconformity to prevent recurrence.

correlation coefficient (*r*)—A statistic that measures the degree of linear relationship between two sets of numbers and is computed as

$$r = \frac{\sum x_i y_i - n\bar{x}\bar{y}}{\sqrt{\left(\sum x_i^2 - n\bar{x}^2\right)\left(\sum y_i^2 - n\bar{y}^2\right)}}$$

where $-1 \leq r \leq 1$. Also, r is used to estimate the population correlation coefficient ρ. Correlation values of –1 and +1 represent perfect linear agreement between two independent and dependent variables. An $r = 0$ means there is no linear relationship at all. If r is positive, the relationship between the variables is said to be positive. Hence, when x increases, y increases. If r is negative, the relationship is said to be negative. Hence, when x increases, y decreases.

The correlation coefficient is also known as the *sample correlation coefficient* and is sometimes written as *R*.

cost avoidance (budget impacting)—This type of cost avoidance eliminates or reduces items in the budget marked for future spending. For example, three engineers are budgeted for hire in the fourth quarter. The cost of the three engineers is not in the baseline, nor has any spending for these engineers occurred. Eliminating these planned expenses has an impact on the future budget and is thus cost avoidance.

cost avoidance (non-budget impacting)—This type of cost avoidance results from productivity or efficiencies gained in a process (i.e., reduction of non-value-added activities) without a headcount reduction. For example, the process cycle time that involved two workers was reduced by 10%. Assuming the 10% amounts to two hours per worker per week, the two workers save four hours per week. These four hours are allocated to other tasks.

cost avoidance savings—Are, by exclusion, everything that is not hard dollar savings. Cost avoidance savings are also known as soft dollar savings. There are two types of cost avoidance savings: budget impacting, and non-budget impacting.

cost of poor quality (COPQ)—The costs associated with the production of non-conforming material. These costs include both external and internal failure costs. *See also* external failure costs; internal failure costs.

cost of quality (COQ)—The costs specifically associated with the achievement or nonachievement of product or service quality, including all product or service requirements established by the organization and its contracts with customers and society. More specifically, quality costs are the total costs incurred by (1) investing in the prevention of nonconformances to requirements, (2) appraising a product or service for conformance to requirements, and (3) failing to meet requirements. These can then be categorized as prevention, appraisal, and failure. *See also* appraisal costs; failure costs; prevention costs.

cost performance index (CPI)—This is a dimensionless index used to measure the project's cost efficiency. It is calculated as

$$\mathrm{CPI} = \frac{\mathrm{EV}}{\mathrm{AC}} = \frac{\mathrm{BCWP}}{\mathrm{ACWP}}.$$

If the CPI is greater than 1, the project is under budget. If the CPI is equal to 1, the project is on budget. If the CPI is less than 1, the project is over budget and corrective action must be taken.

cost savings—For project savings to generate real cost savings, a prior baseline of spending must be established; the dollars must have been planned and in the budget; and the savings must affect the bottom line (that is, the profit and loss statement or balance sheet). Cost savings are also known as *hard dollar savings*.

cost variance (CV)—The cost variance is the difference between the amount budgeted for the work performed and the actual cost of the work performed. It is calculated as

$$CV = EV - AC.$$

If the CV is positive, the project is under budget. If the CV is zero, the project is on budget. If the CV is negative, the project is over budget and corrective action must be taken.

cost–benefit analysis—*See* benefit–cost analysis.

COV—*See* components of variation.

CPI—*See* cost performance index.

CPL—*See* C_{pk_L}.

CPM—*See* critical path method.

CPU—*See* C_{pk_U}.

creativity—The mental capability to generate ideas.

critical path—The sequence of tasks that takes the longest time and determines a project's completion date.

critical path method (CPM)—An activity-oriented project management technique that uses arrow-diagramming methods to demonstrate both the time and the cost required to complete a project. It provides one time estimate: normal time.

critical success factor (CSF)—*See* key business drivers.

criticality—An indication of the consequences expected to result from a failure.

critical-to-quality (CTQ)—A characteristic of a product or service that is essential to ensure customer satisfaction.

cross-functional team—A group consisting of members from more than one department that is organized to accomplish a project.

CSF—*See* critical success factor.

CSSBB—*See* Certified Six Sigma Black Belt.

CSSGB—*See* Certified Six Sigma Green Belt.

CSSYB—Certified Six Sigma Yellow Belt.

CSSWB—Certified Six Sigma White Belt.

CTQ—*See* critical-to-quality.

culture—Westcott (2006) refers to culture as "the collective beliefs, values, attitudes, manners, customs, behaviors, and artifacts unique to an organization."

cumulative sum (CUSUM) control chart—A control chart on which the plotted value is the cumulative sum of deviations of successive samples from a target value. The ordinate of each plotted point represents the algebraic sum of the previous ordinate and the most recent deviations from the target.

customer loyalty—A term used to describe the behavior of customers—in particular, customers who exhibit a high level of satisfaction, conduct repeat business, or provide referrals and testimonials. It is the result of an organization's processes, practices, and efforts designed to deliver its services or products in ways that drive such behavior.

CUSUM—*See* cumulative sum (CUSUM) control chart.

CV—*See* cost variance.

cycle time—The time required to complete one cycle of an operation. If cycle time for every operation in a complete process can be reduced to equal takt time, products can be made in single-piece flow. *See also* takt time.

cycle-time reduction—A method for reducing the amount of time it takes to execute a process or build a specific product. Elimination of duplicate or unnecessary tasks also reduces the time that is necessary to execute a process. Improving hand-offs, which tend to be points of substantial discontinuity, also eliminates rework or duplicate efforts.

D

decentralization versus centralization—In the context of organizational design, refers to how much decision-making authority has been delegated to lower management levels.

decision matrix—*See* Pugh matrix.

defect—The nonfulfillment of a requirement related to an intended or specified use for a product or service. In simpler terms, a defect is anything not done correctly the first time. Note: The distinction between the concepts *defect* and *nonconformity* is important because it has legal connotations, particularly those associated with product liability issues. Consequently, the term "defect" should be used with extreme caution.

defective—A unit of product that contains one or more defects with respect to the quality characteristic(s) under consideration.

defects per million opportunities (DPMO)—A measure of capability for discrete (attribute) data found by dividing the number of defects by the opportunities for defects multiplied by a million. DPMO allows for comparison of different types of product. *See also* parts per million.

defects per unit (DPU)—A measure of capability for discrete (attribute) data found by dividing the number of defects by the number of units.

Deming cycle—*See* plan–do–study–act (PDSA) cycle.

Deming Prize—Award given annually to organizations that, according to the award guidelines, have successfully applied organization-wide quality control based on statistical quality control and will keep up with it in the future.

Although the award is named in honor of W. Edwards Deming, its criteria are not specifically related to Deming's teachings. There are three separate divisions for the award: the Deming Application Prize, the Deming Prize for Individuals, and the Deming Prize for Overseas Companies. The award process is overseen by the Deming Prize Committee of the Union of Japanese Scientists and Engineers in Tokyo.

Deming wheel—*See* plan–do–study–act (PDSA) cycle.

dependability—The degree to which a product is operable and capable of performing its required function at any randomly chosen time during its specified operating time, provided that the product is available at the start of that period. (Non-operation-related influences are not included.) Dependability can be expressed by the ratio

$$\frac{\text{Time available}}{\text{Time available} + \text{Time required}}.$$

dependent events—Two events, *A* and *B*, are dependent if the probability of one event occurring is higher given the occurrence of the other event.

derating—The practice of using components at lower stress levels than those stated by the component specifications.

descriptive statistics—The collection of tools and techniques for displaying and summarizing data.

design failure mode and effects analysis (DFMEA)—An analysis process used to identify and evaluate the relative risk associated with a particular design.

design for Six Sigma (DFSS)—A structured methodology that focuses on designing new products or services with the intent of achieving Six Sigma quality levels. *See also* DMADV, DMADOV, DMEDI, and IDOV.

design for X (DFX)—An umbrella term whereby X is a variable that can assume multiple descriptions such as maintainability, manufacturability, producibility, quality, testability, or whatever component of design, logistics, production, quality, and so forth, of the product needs to be emphasized. The various components of the product are collectively referred to as the "ilities." Design for X involves the principle of designing products so that they are cost-effective and achieve the objectives set forth for whatever "ilities" are of concern.

design of experiments (DOE, DOX)—The arrangement in which an experimental program is to be conducted, including the selection of factor combinations and their levels. Note: The purpose of designing an experiment is to provide the most efficient and economical methods of reaching valid and relevant conclusions from the experiment. The selection of the design is a function of many considerations, such as the type of questions to be answered, the applicability of the conclusions, the homogeneity of experimental units, the randomization scheme, and the cost to run the experiment. A properly designed experiment will permit simple interpretation of valid results.

design review—Documented, comprehensive, and systematic examination of a design to evaluate its capability to fulfill the requirements for quality.

design space—The multidimensional region of possible treatment combinations formed by the selected factors and their levels.

design for cost (DFC)—*See* design-to-cost.

design to cost (DTC)—A set of tools, techniques, or methods used to set and achieve product cost goals through design trade-off analysis. Design to cost is also known as *design for cost.*

detection—The likelihood of finding a failure once it has occurred. Detection may be evaluated based on a ten-point scale. On the lowest end of the scale (1), it is assumed that a design control will detect a failure with certainty. On the highest end of the scale (10), it is assumed that a design control will not detect a failure when a failure occurs.

DFC—An acronym for design for cost. *See* design to cost.

DFM—An acronym for design for manufacturability. *See* design for X.

DFMaint—An acronym for design for maintainability. *See* design for X.

DFMEA—*See* design failure mode and effects analysis.

DFP—An acronym for design for producibility. *See* design for X.

DFQ—An acronym for design for quality. *See* design for X.

DFSS—*See* design for Six Sigma.

DFT—An acronym for design for testability. *See* design for X.

DFX—*See* design for X.

differences—Difference between data values for a specified lag value k. For example, for a given set of ordered data, there is a lag k between values xt and $xt + k$. Differencing is used to introduce stationarity to a time series. Data transformation can also be used to stabilize the variance.

discrete scale—A scale with only a set or sequence of distinct values. Examples include defects per unit, events in a given time period, types of defects, and number of orders on a truck.

discrete variable—A variable whose possible values form a finite or, at most, countably infinite set.

discriminant analysis—A statistical technique that is used "to classify observations into two or more groups if you have a sample with known groups. Discriminant analysis can also be used to investigate how variables contribute to group separation" (Minitab 15).

discrimination—The capability of the measurement system to detect and indicate small changes in the characteristic measured. Discrimination is also known as *resolution*. For example, a tape measure with gradations of one inch would be unable to distinguish between lengths of objects that fall in between the inch marks. Hence, we would say the measurement system could not properly discriminate between the objects. If an object to be measured is 2.5 inches, the measurement system (that is, tape measure) would produce a value of 2 or 3 inches depending on how the individual decided to round. Therefore, to measure an object that is 2.5 inches, a tape measure with finer gradations would be required.

dispersion effect—The influence of a single factor on the variance of the response variable.

dissatisfiers—Those features or functions that the customer or employee has come to expect, and if they are no longer present, the customer will be dissatisfied.

disturbance—In the context of automated process control, these variables cause the controlled variable to deviate from the set point. In Lean Six Sigma terminology, these are noise variables. A disturbance is also known as an *upset.*

DMADOV—A structured DFSS methodology. DMADOV stands for define, measure, analyze, design, optimize, and verify.

DMADV—A structured DFSS methodology. DMADV is an acronym for define, measure, analyze, design, and verify. Variations of DMADV exist. *See also* design for Six Sigma, DMADOV, DMEDI, IDOV.

DMAIC—A structured methodology that focuses on improving existing processes with the intent of achieving Six Sigma quality levels. DMAIC is an acronym for define, measure, analyze, improve, and control. *See also* design for Six Sigma, DMADV, DMADOV, DMEDI, IDOV.

DMEDI—A structured DFSS methodology. DMEDI stands for define, measure, explore, develop, and implement.

DOE—*See* design of experiments.

DOX—*See* design of experiments.

DPMO—*See* defects per million opportunities.

DPU—*See* defects per unit.

driving forces—In the context of a force-field analysis, driving forces are those forces that aid in achieving the objective.

DTC—*See* design to cost.

E

EAC—Estimate at completion

earned value (EV)—This is the approved budget for the work actually completed by a specific date. It is also known as the *budgeted cost of work performed* (BCWP).

education—Focuses on broadening an individual's knowledge base and expands thinking processes. Furthermore, it helps employees understand concepts and accept increased job responsibilities, and prepares them for future jobs and leadership roles. Simply, education helps individuals learn how to think.

effect—A relationship between factor(s) and response variable(s) based on cause. Note that there can be many factors and response variables. Specific types include main effect, dispersion effect, and interaction effect.

efficiency—An unbiased estimator is considered to be more efficient than another unbiased estimator if it has a smaller variance.

eight types of waste—The seven types of waste plus an additional waste: people. The eighth category was added by Taiichi Ohno, as he saw the underutilization of employees (for example, brainpower, skills, experience, and talents) as a waste. *See also* seven types of waste.

eighty-twenty (80-20) rule—A term referring to the Pareto principle, which was first defined by J. M. Juran in 1950. The principle suggests that most effects come from relatively few causes; that is, 80% of the effects come from 20% of the possible causes. *See also* Pareto principle.

entity—An item that can be individually described and considered.

error—(1) Error in measurement is the difference between the indicated value and the true value of a measured quantity. (2) A fault resulting from defective judgment, deficient knowledge, or carelessness. It is not to be confused with measurement error, which is the difference between a computed or measured value and the true or reference value.

error detection—A hybrid form of error-proofing whereby a bad part can still be made but will be caught immediately, and corrective action will be taken to prevent another bad part from being produced. An error-detection device is used to spot the error and stop the process when a bad part is made. This is used when error-proofing is too expensive or not easily implemented.

error of the first kind—*See* type I error.

error of the second kind—*See* type II error.

error-proofing—The use of process or design features to prevent the acceptance or further processing of nonconforming products. *See also* fool-proofing, mistake-proofing, and poka-yoke.

estimate at completion (EAC)—This can be simply an estimate or it can be calculated as:

1. Assuming cost performance for the remainder of the project will revert to what was originally planned:

   EAC = Approved budget for the entire task — Cost variance for work performed to date on task

   = BAC + AC – EV

2. Assuming cost performance for the remainder of the project will continue as it has for the work performed to date:

$$\text{EAC} = \frac{\text{BAC}}{\text{Cumulative CPI}}.$$

estimate to complete (ETC)—This can be simply an estimate or it can be calculated as ETC = BAC – AC to date.

ETC—*See* estimate to complete.

EV—*See* earned value.

evolutionary operations (EVOP)—The procedure of adjusting variables in a process in small increments in search of a more optimal point on the response surface.

EVOP—*See* evolutionary operations.

executive—*See* the section on Roles and Responsibilities in Chapter 2 for a detailed discussion.

expected value—The mean of a random variable.

experiential training—The focus of this form of training is on having the learner experience the effects typically encountered in a real-life situation. The experiential approach employs many types of structured experiences (for example, games, simulations, role-plays) to facilitate learning. Typically, participants assume roles within a stated scenario designed to surface one or more learning points.

experimental design—A formal plan that details the specifics for conducting an experiment, such as which responses, factors, levels, blocks, treatments, and tools are to be used. *See also* design of experiments.

experimental error—Variation in the response variable beyond that accounted for by the factors, blocks, or other assignable sources in the conduct of the experiment.

experimental run—A single performance of the experiment for a specific set of treatment combinations.

experimental unit—The smallest entity receiving a particular treatment, subsequently yielding a value of the response variable.

explanatory variable—*See* predictor variable.

external customer—A person or organization that receives a product, service, or information but is not part of the organization supplying it. *See also* internal customer.

external failure costs—The failure costs occurring after delivery or shipment of the product, and during or after furnishing of a service, to the customer. Examples are the costs of processing customer complaints, customer returns, warranty claims, and product recalls.

F

facilitator—An individual responsible for creating favorable conditions that will enable a team to reach its purpose or achieve its goals by bringing together the necessary tools, information, and resources to get the job done.

factor—An independent variable or assignable cause that may affect the responses and of which different levels are included in the experiment. Factors are also known as *explanatory, independent, regressor,* or *predictor* variables.

factor analysis—A statistical technique used "to determine the underlying factors responsible for correlations in the data" (Minitab 15).

factor relationship diagram—A visual tool that assists in the planning of experiment designs. Typically, a factor relationship diagram is composed of two structures: the design structure and the unit structure. The design structure contains those factors that are deliberately manipulated during the experimental design. The unit structure is determined by how we manage noise and other un-manipulated sources of variation during the experimental design. In addition to these two structures, we have the inference space. Hild (2009) states, "The inference space represents the range of conditions over which the experiment's results can expect to repeat."

failure—The termination, due to one or more defects, of the ability of an item, product, or service to perform its required function when called upon to do so. A failure may be partial, complete, or intermittent.

failure analysis—The process of breaking down a failure to determine its cause and to put measures in place to prevent future problems.

failure costs—The costs resulting from product or services not conforming to requirements or customer/user needs. Failure costs are further divided into internal and external categories. *See also* external failure costs, internal failure costs.

failure mode—The type of defect contributing to a failure.

failure mode and effects analysis (FMEA)—A procedure in which each potential failure mode in every subitem of an item is analyzed to determine its effect on other subitems and on the required function of the item.

failure rate—The number of failures per unit time (for equal time intervals).

final control element—In the context of automated process control, the final control element, upon receiving direction from the controller, will take action to adjust the appropriate "manipulated variable" (that is, input variable). Examples of final control elements include control values, electric motors, conveyors, and variable speed pumps. The basic operation of the final control element is "action."

first-pass yield (FPY)—The percentage of units that complete a process and meet quality guidelines without being scrapped, rerun, retested, returned, or diverted into an offline repair area. FPY is calculated by dividing the units entering the process minus the defective units by the total number of units entering the process. First-pass yield is also known as the *quality rate* or *first-time yield* (FTY).

first-time yield (FTY)—*See* first-pass yield.

fishbone diagram—*See* cause-and-effect diagram.

fitness for use—A term used to indicate that a product or service fits the customer's or user's defined purpose for that product or service.

five S—*See* 5S.

five whys—*See* 5 whys.

flowchart—A basic quality tool that uses graphical representation for the steps in a process. Effective flowcharts include decisions, inputs, and outputs as well as the sequence of process steps. The flowchart is occasionally considered to be one of the seven basic tools of quality.

FMEA—*See* failure mode and effects analysis.

fool-proofing—A method of making a product or process immune to errors on the part of the user or operator. Although fool-proofing is synonymous with error-proofing, it can carry negative connotations. *See also* error-proofing, mistake-proofing, poka-yoke.

force-field analysis—A technique for analyzing the forces that aid or hinder an organization in reaching an objective.

forecasting—A prediction of future values of a time series. For example, one might want to predict the next value, the next five values, or the next ten values in the series.

forming—The first stage of team growth. *See also* stages of team growth.

fourteen (14) points—W. Edwards Deming's 14 management practices to help organizations increase their quality and productivity. They are as follows: (1) create constancy of purpose for improving products and services; (2) adopt a new philosophy; (3) cease dependence on inspection to achieve quality; (4) end the practice of awarding business on price alone; instead, minimize total cost by working with a single supplier; (5) improve constantly and forever every process for planning, production, and service; (6) institute training on the job; (7) adopt and institute leadership; (8) drive out fear; (9) break down barriers between staff areas; (10) eliminate slogans, exhortations, and targets for the workforce; (11) eliminate numerical quotas for the workforce and numerical goals for management; (12) remove barriers that rob people of pride of workmanship, and eliminate the annual rating or merit system; (13) institute a vigorous program of education and self-improvement for everyone; (14) put everybody in the company to work to accomplish the transformation.

FPY—*See* first-pass yield.

FTY—*See* first-pass yield.

funnel experiment—An experiment that demonstrates the effects of tampering. Marbles are dropped through a funnel in an attempt to hit a mark on a flat surface target below. The experiment shows that adjusting a stable process to compensate for an undesirable result or an extraordinarily good result will produce output that is worse than if the process had been left alone.

G

gage repeatability and reproducibility (GR&R) study—A type of measurement system analysis done to evaluate the performance of a test method or measurement system. Such a study quantifies the capabilities and limitations of a measurement instrument, often estimating its repeatability and reproducibility. It typically involves multiple operators measuring a series of measurement items multiple times.

Gantt chart—A type of bar chart used in process/project planning and control to display planned work and finished work in relation to time. Also called a *milestone chart.*

gap analysis—A technique that compares an organization's existing state with its desired state (typically expressed by its long-term plans) to help determine what needs to be done to remove or minimize the gap.

GB—*See* Green Belt.

GD&T—*See* geometric dimensioning and tolerancing.

gemba walk—Gemba is a Japanese term that means "place of work" or "the place where the truth can be found." Still others may call it "the value proposition." A gemba walk is a method of obtaining voice of customer information that requires the design team to walk the process and observe how the customer uses the product in their environment.

general linear model (GLM)—A statistical tool that synthesizes many of the other common statistical techniques for analyzing both continuous and discrete data.

geometric dimensioning and tolerancing (GD&T)—A method to minimize production costs by considering the functions or relationships of part features in order to define dimensions and tolerances.

GLM—*See* general linear model.

goal—A statement of general intent, aim, or desire. It is the point toward which the organization (or individual) directs its efforts; goals are often non-quantitative.

governance—According to Bertin and Watson (2007), governance establishes the policy framework within which organization leaders will make strategic decisions to fulfill the organizational purpose as well as the tactical actions that they take at the level of operational management to deploy and execute the organization's guiding policy and strategic direction. Governance in the context of Lean Six Sigma deployment includes all the processes, procedures, rules, roles, and responsibilities associated with the strategic, tactical, and operational deployment of Lean Six Sigma. It also includes the authoritative, decision-making body charged with the responsibility of providing the required governance.

GR&R study—*See* gage repeatability and reproducibility (GR&R) study.

Green Belt (GB)—A Six Sigma role associated with an individual who retains their regular position within the firm but is trained in the tools, methods, and skills necessary to conduct Six Sigma improvement projects either individually or as part of larger teams.

H

hard dollar savings—*See* cost savings.

heijunka—A Japanese term referring to the act of leveling the variety or volume of items produced at a process over a period of time. Heijunka is used to avoid excessive batching of product types and volume fluctuations, especially at a pacemaker process.

histogram—A plot of a frequency distribution in the form of rectangles (cells) whose bases are equal to the class interval and whose areas are proportional to the frequencies. A histogram is a graphic summary of variation in a set of data. The graphical nature of the histogram permits easier visualization of patterns of variation that are difficult to detect in a simple table of numbers. The histogram is one of the seven basic tools of quality.

hoshin kanri—A Japanese term referring to a top-down, bottom-up, systematic and structured strategic planning process that engages all levels of the organization while creating measurable and aligned goals that imbue the concept of continuous improvement through use of the plan–do–check–act cycle. (Note: Some sources will cite the PDSA cycle.) Hoshin kanri is also known as *hoshin planning, policy deployment, policy management, policy control,* and *management by policy.*

hoshin planning—A term meaning "breakthrough planning." Hoshin planning is a Japanese term for the strategic planning process in which an organization develops up to four vision statements that indicate where the company should be in the next five years. Company goals and work plans are developed on the basis of the vision statements. Periodic audits are then conducted to monitor progress. *See also* hoshin kanri.

house of quality—A diagram named for its house-shaped appearance that clarifies the relationship between customer needs and product features. It helps correlate market or customer requirements and analysis of competitive products with higher-level technical and product characteristics and makes it possible to bring several factors into a single figure. The house of quality is also known as *quality function deployment* (QFD).

hygiene factors—A term used by Frederick Herzberg to label "dissatisfiers." *See also* dissatisfiers.

hypothesis—A statement about a population or the form of a probability distribution to be tested.

hypothesis test—According to Montgomery (2006), a hypothesis test is any procedure used to test a statistical hypothesis.

I

ICC—*See* intra-class correlation coefficient.

ID—*See* interrelationship digraph.

ideation—According to Jonson (2005) it is "the creative process of generating, developing, and communicating new ideas, where an idea is understood as a basic element of thought that can be visual, concrete, or abstract."

IDOV—A structured methodology as an alternative to design for Six Sigma. IDOV is an acronym for identify, design, optimize, and validate. *See also* design for Six Sigma.

imprecision—A measure of precision computed as a standard deviation of the test or measurement results. Less precision is reflected by a larger standard deviation.

incomplete block—A block that accommodates only a subset of treatment combinations.

incomplete block design—A design in which the design space is subdivided into blocks in which there are insufficient experimental units available to run a complete replicate of the experiment.

in-control process—A condition where the existence of special causes is no longer indicated by a Shewhart control chart. This does not indicate that only random causes remain, nor does it imply that the distribution of the remaining values is normal (Gaussian). It indicates (within limits) a predictable and stable process.

independent events—Two events, *A* and *B*, are called independent if the probability that they both occur is the product of the probabilities of their individual occurrences. That is:

$$P(A \cap B) = P(A)P(B).$$

independent variable—*See* predictor variable.

inferential statistics—Techniques for reaching conclusions about a population on the basis of analysis of data from a sample.

inherent process variation—The variation in a process when the process is operating in a state of statistical control.

innovation—The ability to not only be creative, but to put idea into practice.

inspection—The process of measuring, examining, testing, gauging, or otherwise comparing the unit with the applicable requirements.

interaction effect—The effect for which the apparent influence of one factor on the response variable depends on one or more other factors. Existence of an interaction effect means that the factors cannot be changed independently of each other.

interaction plot—A plot providing the average responses at the combinations of levels of two distinct factors.

internal customer—The recipient, person, or department of another person's or department's output (product, service, or information) within an organization. *See also* external customer.

internal failure costs—The failure costs occurring prior to delivery or shipment of the product, or the furnishing of a service, to the customer. Examples are the costs of scrap, rework, re-inspection, retesting, material review, and downgrading.

internal rate of return (IRR)—The discount rate that causes the sum of NPV of the costs (negative cash flows) plus the sum of the NPV of the savings (positive cash flows) to equal zero.

interrelationship digraph (ID)—A tool that displays the cause-and-effect relationships between ideas or factors in a complex situation. It identifies meaningful categories from a mass of ideas and is useful when relationships are difficult to determine. Also known as a *relations diagram*, the interrelationship digraph is one of the seven management and planning tools.

interval scale—A quantitative scale in which meaningful differences exist, but where multiplication and division are not allowed since there is not absolute zero. An example is temperature measured in °F, because 20°F isn't twice as warm as 10°F.

intervention—An action taken by a leader or a facilitator to support the effective functioning of a team or work group.

intra-class correlation coefficient (ICC)—The intra-class correlation coefficient helps gauge the effectiveness of attribute (discrete) measurement systems and is used under the following conditions or assumptions: There is the need to classify things in order, rank, or scale, ranges are equally distributed such as –2, –1, 0, 1, 2, there are consequences for misclassifying, units must be independent, raters make their classifications independently of other raters, and the categories are mutually exclusive and collectively exhaustive. There are six forms of the intra-class correlation coefficient.

IRR—*See* internal rate of return.

Ishikawa diagram—*See* cause-and-effect diagram.

ISO—"Equal" (Greek). A prefix for a series of standards published by the International Organization for Standardization.

ISO 9000 series—A set of individual, but related, international standards and guidelines on quality management and quality assurance developed to help organizations effectively document the quality system elements to be implemented to maintain an efficient quality system. The standards were developed by the International Organization for Standardization, a specialized international agency for standardization composed of the national standards bodies of nearly 100 countries.

ISO 14000 series—A set of individual, but related, international standards and guidelines relevant to developing and sustaining an environmental management system.

ITIL—Information technology infrastructure library.

J

jidoka—A Japanese term for the method of autonomous control involving the adding of intelligent features to machines to start or stop operations as control parameters are reached, and to signal operators when necessary. Jidoka is also known as *autonomation.*

JIT—*See* just-in-time manufacturing.

job aids—Virtually any type of media that can either substitute for formal training and/or provide reinforcement or reference after training.

job analysis—A process for collecting information about duties, responsibilities, skills, and outcomes. Also, a description of the work environment may be included if it is unique or extraordinary in some manner. An example of such an environment might be a manufacturing clean room.

job description—A job analysis, task analysis, and skills analysis are components of the job description. Once completed, these three aspects will be used to draft a job description and a job specification. Job descriptions, according to Rae (1997) "are statements of the outline of the whole job and show the duties and responsibilities involved in the job." It also "details the skills, knowledge, and attitudes which are required by the individual in order to carry out the duties involved in the job."

job specification—A subset of the job description, the job specification, according to Rae (1997), defines "what the job holder should do and be capable of doing." Bee and Bee (1994) add that the job specification also includes carrying out the job to a prescribed standard. The greater the detail of the job specification, the easier it will be to determine performance gaps.

just-in-time manufacturing (JIT manufacturing)—A material requirement planning system for a manufacturing process in which there is little or no manufacturing material inventory on hand at the manufacturing site and little or no incoming inspection.

K

kaikaku—A Japanese term meaning a breakthrough improvement in eliminating waste.

kaizen—A Japanese term that means gradual unending improvement by doing little things better and setting and achieving increasingly higher standards. The kaizen approach is usually implemented as a small, intensive event or project over a relatively short duration, such as a week.

kaizen blitz/event—An intense team approach to employ the concepts and techniques of continuous improvement in a short time frame (for example, to reduce cycle time, increase throughput).

kanban—A Japanese term for a system that signals the need to replenish stock or materials or to produce more of an item. Kanban is also known as a "pull" approach. Kanban systems need not be elaborate, sophisticated, or even computerized to be effective. Taiichi Ohno of Toyota developed the concept of a kanban system after a visit to a U.S. supermarket.

Kano model—A representation of the three levels of customer satisfaction, defined as dissatisfaction, neutrality, and delight.

kappa (K)—Futrell (1995) defines kappa as "the proportion of agreement between rates after agreement by chance has been removed." Kappa techniques help gauge the effectiveness of attribute (discrete) measurement systems and are used under the following conditions or assumptions: There is the need to classify things in a nominal manner, some categories can be used more frequently than others, units must be independent, raters make their classifications independently of other raters, and the categories are mutually exclusive and collectively exhaustive. The formula for kappa is:

$$K = \frac{P_{\text{Observed}} - P_{\text{Chance}}}{1 - P_{\text{Chance}}}$$

When multiple raters are involved, we must be concerned with two types of kappa statistics: K_{Overall} and K_{Category}. The overall kappa assesses the rater agreement across all of the categories, while the category kappa is used to compute individual kappa values for each category. This provides an indication regarding where each rater has trouble. These formulas are

$$K_{\text{Overall}} = 1 - \frac{nm^2 - \sum_{i=1}^{n}\sum_{j=1}^{k} x_{ij}^2}{nm(m-1)\sum_{j=1}^{k}(\bar{p}_j)(1-\bar{p}_j)}$$

$$K_{\text{Category}} = 1 - \frac{\sum_{i=1}^{n} x_{ij}(m - x_{ij})}{nm(m-1)(\bar{p}_j)(1-\bar{p}_j)}$$

where

m = Number of raters

n = Number of units

k = Number of categories

$$\bar{p} = \frac{\text{Ratings within category}}{nm}$$

KBD—See key business drivers.

Kendall's coefficient of concordance—This coefficient measures the association between appraisers and the association within appraisers and is used with attributed (discrete) measurement system. Kendall's coefficient of concordance ranges between –1 and 1. A positive value of –1 indicates positive association. Similarly, a negative value indicates negative association. A value of zero indicates no agreement or association. The formula for computing Kendall's coefficient of concordance is given by:

$$W = \frac{12\sum_{i=1}^{N} R_i^2 - 3k^2N(N+1)^2}{k^2N(N+1) - k\sum_{j=1}^{k} T_j}$$

where:

N = The number of units

$\sum_{i=1}^{N} R_i$ = The sum of the squared sums of ranks for each of the ranked N units

k = The number of appraisers

T_j = Assigns the average of ratings to tied observation = $T_j = \sum_{i=1}^{g_j} \left(t_i^3 - t_i\right)$

t = The number of tied ranks in the ith grouping of ties

g_j = The number of groups of ties in the jth set of ranks

Kendall's correlation coefficient—This coefficient measures the association between all appraisers and the known standard and each appraiser and the known standard and is used in with attribute (discrete) measurement system. Kendall's correlations coefficient is also known as Kendall's rank-order correlation coefficient, Kendall's Tau correlation coefficient, and Kendall's Tau-b correlation coefficient. Kendall's correlation coefficient ranges between –1 and 1. A positive value of –1 indicates positive association. Similarly, a negative value indicates negative association. A value of zero indicates no agreement or association. The formula for computing Kendall's correlation coefficient is given by:

$$\tau = \frac{C-D}{\sqrt{\left[N_{\text{Total}}\left(N_{\text{Total}}-1\right)(0.5)-T_X\right]}\sqrt{\left[N_{\text{Total}}\left(N_{\text{Total}}-1\right)(0.5)-T_Y\right]}}$$

where:

C = Number of concordant pairs = $\sum_{i<k}\sum_{j<i} n_{ij}n_{ki}$

D = Number of discordant pairs = $\sum_{i<k}\sum_{j>i} n_{ij}n_{ki}$

n_{+i} = Number of observations in the *i*th row

n_{+j} = Number of observations in the *j*th column

n_{ij} = Number of observations in the cell in the *i*th row and *j*th column

n_{ki} = Number of observations in the cell in the *k*th row and *i*th column

N = Total number of observations

T_X = Number of pairs tied on $X = 0.5\sum_i n_{+i}\left(n_{+i}-1\right)$

T_Y = Number of pairs tied on $Y = 0.5\sum_j n_{+j}\left(n_{+j}-1\right)$

k = Number of appraisers

Kendall's rank-order correlation coefficient—*See* Kendall's correlation coefficient.

Kendall's tau correlation coefficient—*See* Kendall's correlation coefficient.

Kendall's tau-b correlation coefficient—*See* Kendall's correlation coefficient.

key business drivers (KBDs)—Those few things that must be done well for the organization to succeed. KBDs should reflect the organization's goals and are vital for its strategies to be successful. Key business drivers are also known as *critical success factors* (CSFs).

key performance indicator (KPI)—Quantifiable financial and nonfinancial measurements that reflect an organization's key business drivers (KBDs) and are usually long term.

KJ method—*See* affinity diagram.

KPI—*See* key performance indicator.

L

lag—The number of time units between differenced values.

latent defects—Are hidden defects in either material and/or workmanship that may cause a component to malfunction or fail, but is not discoverable through inspection.

law of unintended consequences—Named by sociologist Robert K. Merton, is meant to describe outcomes not intended by purposeful actions. "Unintended consequences" is sometimes known as unanticipated consequences, unforeseen consequences, or even side effects.

LBQ—*See* Ljung-Box Q (statistics).

LCI—*See* learner-controlled instruction.

lean—A comprehensive approach complemented by a collection of tools and techniques that focus on reducing cycle time, standardizing work, and reducing waste. Lean is also known as "lean approach" or "lean thinking."

lean approach—*See* lean.

lean manufacturing—Applying the lean approach to improving manufacturing operations.

Lean Six Sigma—A fact-based, data-driven philosophy of improvement that values defect prevention over defect detection. It drives customer satisfaction and bottom-line results by reducing variation, waste, and cycle time, while promoting the use of work standardization and flow, thereby creating a competitive advantage. It applies anywhere variation and waste exist, and every employee should be involved. Note: In the first edition of *The Certified Six Sigma Black Belt Handbook*, this definition was attributed to Six Sigma. However, through experience and empirical evidence, it has become clear that Lean and Six Sigma are different sides of the same coin. Both concepts are required to effectively drive sustained breakthrough improvement. Subsequently, the definition is being changed to reflect the symbiotic relationship that must exist between Lean and Six Sigma to ensure lasting and positive change.

lean thinking—*See* lean.

learner-controlled instruction (LCI)—*See* self-directed learning.

learning—According to Rothwell (2008) "learning gives individuals the potential to get results."

level—The setting or assignment of a factor at a specific value.

linear programming—A constrained optimization technique comprising both a linear objective function and linear constraints.

linear regression coefficients—Values associated with each predictor variable in a linear regression equation that tell how the response variable changes with each unit increase in the predictor variable. The term linear refers to the fact that the estimated coefficients are linear combinations of the responses. It does not refer to the form of the regression model: for example, a linear regression model can be a quadratic function.

linear regression equation—A mathematical function or model that indicates the predictive relationship between a set of predictor variables and a response variable.

linearity (general sense)—The degree to which a pair of variables follows a straight-line relationship. Linearity can be measured by the correlation coefficient.

linearity (measurement system sense)—The difference in bias through the range of measurement. A measurement system that has good linearity will have a constant bias no matter the magnitude of measurement. If one views the relation between the observed measurement result on the *y*-axis and the true value on the *x*-axis, an ideal measurement system would have a line of slope = 1. Linearity is a component of accuracy.

link function—A function that transforms probabilities of a response variable from the closed interval, (0,1), to a continuous scale that is unbounded. Once the transformation is complete, the relationship between the predictor and response variable can be modeled with linear regression.

Ljung-Box Q statistics—A statistic that tests the null hypothesis that autocorrelations up to lag $k = 0$. The statistic is computed as

$$Q_k = n(n+2)\sum_{m=1}^{k}\frac{r_m^2}{n-m}$$

where

n = Number of observations

r_m = Autocorrelation at lag m; $m = 1,2,\ldots,k$

k = Lag j; $k = 1,2,\ldots$

Q is distributed as $\chi^2_{\alpha,k}$ and tests the hypothesis of model adequacy. If the value of Q exceeds the chi-square value, the hypothesis is rejected.

logistic regression—A type of regression that is used when the response variable is discrete. Although there are many types of logistic regression, three common types include binary, nominal, and ordinal.

M

MAD—*See* mean absolute deviation.

main effect—The influence of a single factor on the mean of the response variable.

main effects plot—The plot giving the average responses at the various levels of individual factors.

maintainability—The measure of the ability of an item to be retained or restored to a specified condition when maintenance is performed by personnel having specified skill levels, using prescribed procedures and resources, at each prescribed level of maintenance and repair.

Malcolm Baldrige National Quality Award (MBNQA)—An award established by Congress in 1987 to raise awareness of quality management and to recognize U.S. organizations that have implemented successful quality management systems. A Criteria for Performance Excellence is published each year. Three awards may be given annually in each of five categories: manufacturing businesses, service businesses, small businesses, education institutions, and healthcare organizations. The award is named after the late secretary of commerce Malcolm Baldrige, a proponent of quality management. The U.S. Commerce Department's National Institute of Standards and Technology manages the award, and ASQ administers it. The major emphasis in determining success is achieving results driven by effective processes.

Mallows's C_p—A statistic used to measure the goodness of a prediction. It is computed by using

$$\text{Mallows's } C_p = \frac{SSE_p}{MSE_m} - (n - 2p)$$

where

SSE_p = Sum of the squared error for the model under consideration

MSE_m = Mean squared error for the model with all predictors included

n = Number of observations

p = Number of terms in the model including the constant term

manipulated variable—In the context of automated process control, the manipulated variable is the variable used to maintain the controlled variable at the set point. In Lean Six Sigma terminology, it is the "X" variable. There can be many manipulated variables. In the event there are, the APC system becomes more complex. Examples of such variables include concentration, temperature, pressure, and flow rate.

MANOVA—*See* multiple analysis of variance.

MAPE —*See* mean absolute percentage error.

margin—Refers to the difference between income and cost.

market share—An organization's market share of a particular product or service is that percentage of the dollar value that is sold relative to the total dollar value sold by all organizations in a given market.

Master Black Belt (MBB)—A Six Sigma role associated with an individual typically assigned full time to train and coach Black Belts to ensure improvement projects chartered are the right strategic projects for the organization. Master Black Belts are usually the authorizing body to certify lower-level belts within an organization.

materials review board (MRB)—A quality control committee or team usually employed in manufacturing or other materials-processing installations that has the responsibility and authority to deal with items or materials that do not conform to fitness-for-use specifications.

matrix chart—*See* matrix diagram.

matrix diagram—A tool that identifies the relationships that exist between groups of data. It can be also used to identify the strength of that relationship as well.

The matrix diagram does not use a singular format. Instead, there are six different forms including the C, L, T, X, Y, and roof-shaped format. The different shapes can be selected depending on the number of variables to be compared. The matrix diagram is one of the seven management and planning tools.

MBB—*See* Master Black Belt.

MBNQA—*See* Malcolm Baldrige National Quality Award.

mean—A measure of central tendency and the arithmetic average of all measurements in a data set.

mean absolute deviation (MAD)—A measure of accuracy of the fitted time series values, computed as

$$MAD = \sum_{t=1}^{n} \left| \left(Y_t - \hat{Y}_t \right) \right|$$

where

n = Number of observations

Y_t = Actual value at time t

$\hat{Y}_t$ = Fitted value at time t

mean absolute percentage error (MAPE)—A measure of accuracy of the fitted time series values, computed as

$$MAPE = \frac{\left(\sum_{t=1}^{n} \frac{\left| Y_t - \hat{Y}_t \right|}{Y_t} \right)(100)}{n} ; Y_t \neq 0$$

where

n = Number of observations

Y_t = Actual value at time t

$\hat{Y}_t$ = Fitted value at time t

MSD—*See* mean squared deviation.

mean squared deviation (MSD)—A measure of accuracy of the fitted time series values, computed as

$$MSD = \frac{\sum_{t=1}^{n} \left| Y_t - \hat{Y}_t \right|^2}{n}$$

where

n = Number of forecasted values

Y_t = Actual value at time t

$\hat{Y}_t$ = Forecast value at time t

mean time between failures (MTBF)—A basic measure of reliability for repairable items. The mean number of life units during which all parts of an item perform within their specified limits, during a particular measurement interval under stated conditions.

mean time to failure (MTTF)—A basic measure of system reliability for nonrepairable items. The total number of life units for an item divided by the total number of failures within that population, during a particular measurement interval under stated conditions.

mean time to repair (MTTR)—A basic measure of maintainability. The sum of corrective maintenance times at any specific level of repair, divided by the total number of failures within an item repaired at that level, during a particular interval under stated conditions.

measurement error—The difference between the actual value and the measured value of a quality characteristic.

median—The middle number or center value of a set of data when all the data are arranged in increasing order.

megaprojects—Projects that are so large they can't be managed effectively. Consequently, they are decomposed into smaller, more manageable projects that can be completed in shorter times with fewer resources. Megaprojects provide a focused way of advancing an organization's strategies. However, they require additional coordination among projects and functional groups to be successful.

mentoring—While coaching focuses on the individual as it relates to Lean Six Sigma, mentoring focuses on the individual from the career perspective. Mentors are usually experienced individuals (not necessarily in Lean Six Sigma) who have in-depth knowledge about the organization, as well as the individual (that is, mentee). Usually, they come from within the organization, though not necessarily the same department as their mentee. Their role is to help provide guidance, wisdom, and a possible road map to career advancement.

method of least squares—A technique for estimating a parameter that minimizes the sum of the squared differences between the observed and the predicted values derived from the model.

metrology—The science and practice of measurements.

mind mapping—A technique for creating a visual representation of a multitude of issues or concerns by forming a map of the interrelated ideas.

mistake-proofing—The use of process or design features to prevent manufacture of nonconforming product. It is typically engineering techniques that make the process or product sufficiently robust so as to avoid failing. *See also* error-proofing, fool-proofing, and poka-yoke.

mitigation—Minimizing the impact of the risk.

mode—The value that occurs most frequently in a data set.

monitoring—Continuing to observe low risks where the cost of mitigation or avoidance is too high.

motivation, extrinsic—The satisfaction of either material or psychological needs that are applied by others or the organization through pre-action (incentive) or post-action (reward).

motivation, intrinsic—The qualities of work itself or of relationships, events, or situations that satisfy basic psychological needs (for example, achievement, power, affiliation, autonomy, responsibility, creativity, and self-actualization) in a self-rewarding process.

MRB—*See* materials review board.

MSC—*See* Manpower Services Commission.

MTBF—*See* mean time between failures.

MTTF—*See* mean time to failure.

MTTR—*See* mean time to repair.

muda—A Japanese term for an activity that consumes resources but creates no value; the seven categories are correction, overprocessing, inventory, waiting, overproduction, internal transport, and motion. *See also* seven types of waste.

multicollinearity—Multicollinearity is said to occur when two or more predictor variables in a multiple regression model are correlated. Multicollinearity may cause the coefficient estimates and significance tests for each predictor variable to be underestimated and difficult to interpret.

multiphase planning—The process of dissecting the planning time frame into smaller time elements or phases to recognize or even celebrate significant events or accomplishments and to demonstrate progress.

multiple analysis of variance (MANOVA)—A statistical technique that can be used to analyze both balanced and unbalanced experimental designs. MANOVA is used to perform multivariate analysis of variance for balanced designs when there is more than one dependent variable. The advantage of MANOVA over multiple one-way ANOVAs is that MANOVA controls the family error rate. By contrast, multiple one-way ANOVAs work to increase the alpha error rate.

multiple linear regression—A linear regression equation in which multiple predictor variables are used.

multi-vari analysis—A graphical technique for viewing multiple sources of process variation. Different sources of variation are categorized into families of related causes and quantified to reveal the largest causes.

multivariate control chart—A variables control chart that allows plotting of more than one variable. These charts make use of the T^2 statistic to combine information from the dispersion and mean of several variables.

multi-voting—A decision-making tool that enables a group to sort through a long list of ideas to identify priorities.

N

natural process variation—*See* also voice of the process.

A measure of the width of a process output distribution. Note: When the index is estimated using values from a control chart, σ is estimated by $\hat{\sigma}$.

$$\text{Natural process variation} = 6\sigma$$

natural team—A work group responsible for a particular process.

natural tolerance—*See* voice of the process of CAP.

needs analysis—*See* training needs analysis

net present value—A discounted cash flow technique for finding the present value of each future year's cash flow.

net promoter score—A voice of the customer measure in the percentage of detractors is subtracted from the percentage of promoters. The score can range from a low of negative 100 (all customers are detractors) to a high of +100 (all customers are promoters).

next operation as customer—The concept that the organization is composed of service/product providers and service/product receivers or "internal customers." *See also* internal customer.

NGT—*See* nominal group technique.

NIST—National Institute of Standards and Technology (U.S.).

noise factor—In robust parameter design, a noise factor is a predictor variable that is hard to control or is not desirable to control as part of the standard experimental conditions. In general, it is not desirable to make inference on noise factors, but they are included in an experiment to broaden the conclusions regarding control factors.

nominal group technique (NGT)—A technique similar to brainstorming that is used by teams to generate ideas on a particular subject. Team members are asked to silently come up with as many ideas as possible and write them down. Each member then shares one idea, which is recorded. After all the ideas are recorded, they are discussed and prioritized by the group.

nominal scale—A scale with unordered, labeled categories, or a scale ordered by convention. Examples include type of defect, breed of dog, and complaint category. Note: It is possible to count by category but not by order or measure.

nonconformance—*See* defective.

nonconformity—*See* defect.

nonlinear regression—In nonlinear regression as with linear regression, we are talking about the form of the coefficients or parameters. In the case of nonlinear regression, the coefficients are nonlinear. With linear regression, the parameters have a closed-form solution. However, with nonlinear regression they do not. Instead, the parameters must be solved for using iterative optimization techniques that may or may not converge.

non-value-added (NVA)—Tasks or activities that can be eliminated with no deterioration in product or service functionality, performance, or quality in the eyes of the customer. Generally, customers are unwilling to pay for non-value-added activities.

norming—The third stage of team growth. *See also* stages of team growth.

norms—Behavioral expectations, mutually agreed-upon rules of conduct, protocols to be followed, or social practices.

NPS—*See* net promoter score.

NPV—*See* net present value.

null hypothesis—A hypothesis that is formulated without considering any new information or formulated based on the belief that what already exists is true.

NVA—*See* non-value-added.

O

objective—A quantitative statement of future expectations and an indication of when the expectations should be achieved; it flows from goal(s) and clarifies what people must accomplish.

observation—The process of determining the presence or absence of attributes or measuring a variable. Also, the result of the process of determining the presence or absence of attributes or measuring a variable.

observational study—Analysis of data collected from a process without imposing changes on the process.

observed value—The particular value of a response variable determined as a result of a test or measurement.

occurrence—The likelihood of a failure occurring. Occurrence is evaluated using a ten-point scale. On the lowest end of the scale (1), it is assumed the probability of a failure is unlikely. On the highest end of the scale (10), it is assumed the probability of a failure is nearly inevitable.

OOC—*See* out of control.

operational plan—A set of short-term plans that support the achievement of an organization's tactical plans. The planning horizon for operational plans is often one year or less, but may vary depending on the nature of the organization. Operational plans are sometimes called *action plans*.

order—There are two types of order used by Minitab when creating experimental designs: (1) standard order (StdOrder) shows what the order of the runs in the experiment would be if the experiment were done in standard order (also called Yates's order), and (2) run order (RunOrder) shows what the order of the runs in the experiment would be if the experiment were run in random order.

ordinal scale—A scale with ordered, labeled categories. Note: (1) The borderline between ordinal and discrete scales is sometimes blurred. When subjective opinion ratings such as excellent, very good, neutral, poor, and very poor are coded (as numbers 1–5), the apparent effect is conversion from an ordinal to a discrete scale. However, such numbers should not be treated as ordinary numbers, because the distance between 1 and 2 may not be the same as that between 2 and 3, 3 and 4, and so forth. On the other hand, some categories that are ordered objectively according to magnitude—such as the Richter scale, which ranges from 0 to 8 according to the amount of energy release—could equally well be related to a discrete scale. (2) Sometimes, nominal scales are ordered by convention. An example is the blood groups *A*, *B*, and *O*, which are always stated in this order. It's the same case if different categories are denoted by single letters; they are then ordered by convention, according to the alphabet.

organizational dynamics—A field of study that deals with the behavioral nature of organizations, specifically with regard to the following elements: organizational culture, organizational structure and alignment, theories of motivation, leadership styles, group or team dynamics, conflict management and resolution, and change management. More importantly, organizational dynamics deals with the interaction of the above elements when they are all brought together.

out of control—A process is described as operating out of control when special causes are present.

P

parameter—A constant or coefficient that describes some characteristic of a population.

Pareto chart—A graphical tool based on the Pareto principle for ranking causes from most significant to least significant. It utilizes a vertical bar graph in which the bar height reflects the frequency or impact of causes. The graph is distinguished by the inclusion of a cumulative percentage line that identifies the vital few opportunities for improvement. It is also known as the *Pareto diagram*. The Pareto chart is one of the seven basic tools of quality.

Pareto diagram—*See* Pareto chart.

Pareto principle—An empirical rule named after the nineteenth-century economist Vilfredo Pareto that suggests that most effects come from relatively few causes; that is, about 80% of the effects come from about 20% of the possible causes. The Pareto principle is also known as the *eighty-twenty (80-20) rule*.

parts per billion (ppb)—The number of times an occurrence happens in one billion chances. In a typical quality setting it usually indicates the number of times a defective part will happen in a billion parts produced; the calculation is projected into the future on the basis of past performance. Parts per billion allows for comparison of different types of product. Two ppb corresponds to a Six Sigma level of quality assuming there is not a 1.5σ shift of the mean.

parts per million (ppm)—The number of times an occurrence happens in one million chances. In a typical quality setting it usually indicates the number of times a defective part will happen in a million parts produced; the calculation is often projected into the future on the basis of past performance. Parts per million allows for comparison of different types of product. A ppm of 3.4 corresponds to a Six Sigma level of quality assuming a 1.5σ shift of the mean.

payback period—The number of units it will take the results of a project or capital investment to recover the investment from net cash flows. (Units may refer to the amount of product, passage of time, or other meaningful component of measure.)

payout period—*See* payback period.

PDCA cycle—*See* plan–do–check–act (PDCA) cycle.

PDPC—*See* process decision program chart.

PDSA cycle—*See* plan–do–study–act (PDSA) cycle.

percent agreement—The percentage of time in an attribute GR&R study that appraisers agree with (1) themselves (that is, repeatability), (2) other appraisers (that is, reproducibility), or (3) a known standard (that is, bias) when classifying or rating items using nominal or ordinal scales, respectively.

performance—According to Rothwell (2008) "performance is the actual realization of that potential" (gained by learning).

performing—The fourth stage of team growth. *See also* stages of team growth.

PERT—*See* program evaluation and review technique.

PEST—*See* PEST analysis.

PEST analysis—An analysis similar to SWOT, the PEST analysis brings together four environmental scanning perspectives that serve as useful input into an organization's strategic planning process. PEST stands for *political, economic, social,* and *technological*.

PFMEA—*See* process failure mode and effects analysis.

pipeline—A term applied to where projects "reside" that have been selected and/or prioritized and are waiting to be assigned.

PIT—*See* process improvement team.

plan–do–check–act (PDCA) cycle—A four-step process for quality improvement. In the first step (plan), a plan to effect improvement is developed. In the second step (do), the plan is carried out, preferably on a small scale. In the third step (check), the effects of the plan are observed. In the last step (act), the results are studied to determine what was learned and what can be predicted. The plan–do–check–act cycle is sometimes referred to as the *Shewhart cycle*, after Walter A. Shewhart.

plan–do–study–act (PDSA) cycle—A variation on the plan–do–check–act (PDCA) cycle, with the variation indicating that additional study is required after a change is made. The PDSA cycle is attributed to W. Edwards Deming.

planned value (PV)—This is the approved budget for work scheduled for completion by a specific date. It is also known as the *budgeted cost of work scheduled* (BCWS).

point estimate—The single value used to estimate a population parameter. Point estimates are commonly referred to as the points at which the interval estimates are centered; these estimates give information about how much uncertainty is associated with the estimate.

poka-yoke—A Japanese term that means to mistake-proof a process by building safeguards into the system that avoids or immediately finds errors. A poka-yoke device prevents incorrect parts from being made or assembled and easily identifies a flaw or error. The term comes from the Japanese *poka,* which means "error," and *yokeru,* which means "to avoid." *See also* baka-yoke, error-proofing, fool-proofing, mistake-proofing.

policy—A high-level overall statement embracing the general goals and acceptable practices of a group.

policy control—*See* hoshin kanri.

policy deployment—*See* hoshin kanri.

policy management—*See* hoshin kanri.

PONC—*See* price of nonconformance.

population—The totality of items or units of material under consideration.

portfolio management—The process of managing both active (assigned) and inactive (pipeline) projects.

potential process capability—*See* P_{pk}.

power (1 – β)—The probability of correctly rejecting the null hypothesis when the alternative is true. We write this as P(rejecting $H_0 \mid H_0$ is not true) = 1 – β. The stronger the power of a hypothesis test, the more sensitive the test is to detecting small differences.

ppb—*See* parts per billion.

PPL—*See* P_{pk_L}.

ppm—*See* parts per million.

PPU—*See* P_{pk_U}.

precision—The closeness of agreement among randomly selected individual measurements or test results. It is that aspect of measure that addresses repeatability or consistency when an identical item is measured several times.

precision-to-tolerance ratio (PTR)—A measure of the capability of the measurement system. It can be calculated by

$$PTR = \frac{5.15\hat{\sigma}_{ms}}{\text{USL} - \text{LSL}}$$

where $\hat{\sigma}_{ms}$ is the estimated standard deviation of the total measurement system variability. In general, reducing the PTR will yield an improved measurement system.

prediction interval—Similar to a confidence interval, it is based on the predicted value that is likely to contain the values of future observations. It will be wider than the confidence interval because it contains bounds on individual observations rather than a bound on the mean of a group of observations. The 100(1 – α)% prediction interval for a single future observation from a normal distribution is given by

$$\bar{X} - t_{\alpha/2}s\sqrt{1+\frac{1}{n}} \le X_{n+1} \le \bar{X} + t_{\alpha/2}s\sqrt{1+\frac{1}{n}}$$

prediction sum of squares—*See* PRESS.

pre dictor variable—A variable that can contribute to the explanation of the outcome of an experiment. A predictor variable is also known as an *independent variable, explanatory variable,* or *regressor variable.*

PRESS—A statistic is used to assess the fit of a regression model for a given set of observations that were not used to estimate the model's parameters. The smaller the PRESS value the better. The PRESS statistic is computed as:

$$PRESS = \sum_{i=1}^{n}(y_i - \hat{y}_i)^2$$

where:

n = Number of observations

y_i = ith observed value

$\hat{y}_i$ = ith predicted value based on a model fitted to the remaining n – 1 points

prevention costs—The cost of all activities specifically designed to prevent poor quality in products or services. Examples are the cost of new product review, quality planning, supplier capability surveys, process capability evaluations, quality improvement team meetings, quality improvement projects, and quality education and training.

prevention versus detection—A phrase used to contrast two types of quality activities. Prevention refers to those activities designed to prevent nonconformances in products and services. Detection refers to those activities designed to find nonconformances already in products and services. Another phrase used to describe this distinction is "designing in quality versus inspecting in quality."

price of nonconformance (PONC)—The cost of not doing things right the first time.

principal components—Used "to form a smaller number of uncorrelated variables from a large set of data. The goal of principal components analysis is to explain the maximum amount of variance with the fewest number of principal components" (Minitab 15). Principal components have wide applicability in the social sciences and market research.

principles—Covey (1989) defines as "guidelines for human conduct that are proven to have enduring, permanent value. They're fundamental. They're essentially unarguable because they are self-evident. One way to quickly grasp the self-evident nature of principles is to simply consider the absurdity of attempting to live an effective life based on their opposites. I doubt that anyone would seriously consider unfairness, deceit, baseness, uselessness, mediocrity, or degeneration to be a solid foundation for lasting happiness and success."

prioritization matrix—A tool used to choose between several options that have many useful benefits, but where not all of them are of equal value. The choices are prioritized according to known weighted criteria and then narrowed down to the most desirable or effective one(s) to accomplish the task or problem at hand. The prioritization matrix is one of the seven management and planning tools.

process—A series of interrelated steps consisting of resources and activities that transform inputs into outputs and work together to a common end. A process can be graphically represented using a flowchart. A process may or may not add value.

process capability—The calculated inherent variability of a characteristic of a product. It represents the best performance of the process over a period of stable operations. Process capability is expressed as $6\hat{\sigma}$, where $\hat{\sigma}$ is the sample standard deviation (short-term component of variation) of the process under a state of statistical control. Note: $\hat{\sigma}$ is often shown as σ in most process capability formulas. A process is said to be "capable" when the output of the process always conforms to the process specifications.

process capability index—A single-number assessment of ability to meet specification limits on a quality characteristic of interest. This index compares the variability of the characteristic to the specification limits. Three basic process capability indices are C_p, C_{pk}, and C_{pm}. *See also* C_p, C_{pk}, C_{pm}.

process decision program chart (PDPC)—A tool that identifies all events that can go wrong and the appropriate countermeasures for these events. It graphically represents all sequences that lead to a desirable effect. It is one of the seven management and planning tools.

process failure mode and effects analysis (PFMEA)—An analysis process used to identify and evaluate the relative risks associated with a particular process.

process improvement team (PIT)—A natural work group or cross-functional team whose responsibility is to achieve needed improvements in existing processes. The lifespan of the team is based on the completion of the team purpose and specific tasks.

process management—The set of techniques and tools applied to a process to implement and improve process effectiveness, hold the gains, and ensure process integrity in fulfilling customer requirements.

process mapping—The flowcharting of a process in detail that includes the identification of inputs and outputs.

process owner—A Six Sigma role associated with an individual who coordinates the various functions and work activities at all levels of a process, has the authority or ability to make changes in the process as required, and manages the entire process cycle so as to ensure performance efficiency and effectiveness.

process performance—A statistical measure of the outcome of a characteristic from a process that may not have demonstrated to be in a state of statistical control. Note: Use this measure cautiously since it may contain a component of variability from special causes of unpredictable value. It differs from process capability because a state of statistical control is not required.

process performance index—A single-number assessment of ability to meet specification limits on a quality characteristic of interest. The index compares the variability of the characteristic with the specification limits. Three basic process performance indices are P_p, P_{pk}, and P_{pm}. The P_{pm} is analogous to the C_{pm}. *See also* P_p, P_{pk}.

producer's risk (α)—The probability of nonacceptance when the quality level has a value stated by the acceptance sampling plan as acceptable. Note: (1) such nonacceptance is a Type I error; (2) producer's risk is usually designated as alpha (α); (3) quality level could relate to fraction nonconforming and acceptable to AQL; (4) interpretation of producer's risk requires knowledge of the stated quality level. Producer's risk is also known as *alpha* (α) *risk, alpha* (α) *error, error of the first kind,* and *Type 1 error.*

product identification—A means of marking parts with a label, etching, engraving, ink, or other means so that part numbers and other key attributes can be identified.

program evaluation and review technique (PERT)—An event-oriented project management planning and measurement technique that utilizes an arrow diagram or road map to identify all major project events and demonstrates the amount of time (critical path) needed to complete a project. It provides three time estimates: optimistic, most likely, and pessimistic.

program management—Occasionally, project management is used interchangeably with program management. However, program management is actually a higher-level activity often involving the management of multiple projects with common goal.

project—A project exists for producing results. Three components must be present for an activity to be defined as a project: scope, schedule, and resources.

project, active—Projects that have been assigned and are under way.

project, inactive—Projects that currently reside in the pipeline. These include both selected and prioritized projects.

project assignment—A prioritized project and a resource (that is, Black Belt or Black Belt candidate) are available to be matched. If the matching is successful, the resource is assigned to the project and the project gets under way.

project closure—A project has been terminated for one of two reasons: successful completion or no longer viable.

project identification—The delineation of clear and specific improvement opportunities that is required in the organization.

project life cycle—A typical project life cycle consists of five sequential phases in project management: concept, planning, design, implementation, and evaluation.

project management—The discipline of planning, organizing, and managing resources to bring about the successful completion of specific project goals and objectives, categorized into five component processes (sometimes called life cycle phases): initiating, planning, executing, controlling, and closing. The Project Management Institute notes that project management is the "application of knowledge, skills, tools, and techniques" to activities to meet the requirements of a specific project.

project plan—Documents that contain the details of why the project is to be initiated, what the project is to accomplish, when and where it is to be implemented, who will be responsible, how implementation will be carried out, how much it will cost, what resources are required, and how the project's progress and results will be measured.

project portfolio—The totality of the projects that have been selected and prioritized and waiting in the pipeline plus those that have been assigned and currently under way.

project prioritization—A selected project will be independently assessed against specific criteria in order to establish a rank score. Rank scores of other selected projects will be compared and a final ranking of the projects will be established. This final ranking will set the precedence and order for project assignment.

project qualification—Translation of an identified improvement opportunity into Lean Six Sigma charter format for recognizing its completeness and the ability to assess its potential as a viable project.

project reserve budget—In instances where doubt exists, it may be possible to establish a project reserve budget. Such budgets may be set as a percentage (for example, 10%, 15%, 20%) of the actual dollar budget. These budgets are typically set aside as contingency dollars to help mitigate project risk.

project selection—To select a project means that it has met the criteria of being a Lean Six Sigma project (that is, it has been qualified) and now must be judged to determine whether it is sufficiently worthy such that the organization is willing to invest time and resources to achieve the expected benefits of the project.

propagation of error—Also known as *transmission of error;* has application in two major areas of Lean Six Sigma: (1) response model analysis where the analysis will address how random noise in the x_i values affects the predicted value of y and (2) tolerance stack-up analysis where the analysis will address tolerance stack-up problems.

PTR—*See* precision-to-tolerance ratio.

Pugh matrix—Also known as a *decision matrix;* appropriate to use when a single option must be selected from several and when multiple criteria are to be used.

PV—*See* planned value.

Q

QFD—*See* quality function deployment.

quality assurance—The planned or systematic actions necessary to provide adequate confidence that a product or service will satisfy given needs.

quality control—The operational techniques and the activities that sustain a quality of product or service that will satisfy given needs; also the use of such techniques and activities.

quality council—A group within an organization that drives the quality improvement effort and usually has oversight responsibility for the implementation and maintenance of the quality management system; it operates in parallel with the normal operation of the business. A quality council is sometimes referred to as a *quality steering committee.*

quality function deployment (QFD)—A method used to translate voice of customer information into product requirements/CTQs and to continue deployment (for example, cascading) of requirements to parts and process requirements. Quality function deployment is also known as the *house of quality. See also* house of quality.

quality improvement—The actions taken throughout an organization to increase the effectiveness and efficiency of activities and processes in order to provide added benefits to both the organization and its customers.

quality loss function—A parabolic approximation of the quality loss that occurs when a quality characteristic deviates from its target value. The quality loss function is expressed in monetary units. The cost of deviating from the target increases as a quadratic function the farther the quality characteristic moves from the target. The formula used to compute the quality loss function depends on the type of quality characteristic used. Genichi Taguchi first introduced the quality loss function in this form.

quality management—The totality of functions involved in organizing and leading the effort to determine and achieve quality.

quality manual—A document stating the quality policy and describing the quality system of an organization.

quality planning—The activity of establishing quality objectives and quality requirements.

quality policy—Top management's formally stated intentions and direction for the organization pertaining to quality.

quality system—The organizational structure, procedures, processes, and resources needed to implement quality management.

quality trilogy—A three-pronged approach identified by J. M. Juran for managing for quality. The three legs are quality planning (developing the products and processes required to meet customer needs); quality control (meeting product and process goals); and quality improvement (achieving unprecedented levels of performance).

queue—A waiting line.

queueing theory—The mathematical study of queues. "Queueing" is thought to be the only word in the English language that includes five consecutive vowels. Alternate spelling of "queueing" is "queuing."

R

random cause—A source of process variation that is inherent in a process over time. Note: In a process subject only to random cause variation, the variation is predictable within statistically established limits. Random cause is also known as *chance cause* and *common cause.*

random sampling—The process of selecting units for a sample in such a manner that all combinations of units under consideration have an equal or ascertainable chance of being selected for the sample.

random variable—A variable whose value depends on chance.

random variation—Variation due to random cause.

randomization—The process used to assign treatments to experimental units so that each experimental unit has an equal chance of being assigned a particular treatment.

randomized block design—An experimental design consisting of *b* blocks with *t* treatments assigned via randomization to the experimental units within each block. This is a method for controlling the variability of experimental units. For the completely randomized design, no stratification of the experimental units is made. In the randomized block design, the treatments are randomly allotted within each block; that is, the randomization is restricted.

randomized block factorial design—A factorial design run in a randomized block design where each block includes a complete set of factorial combinations.

ratio scale—A scale where meaningful differences are shown, where absolute zero exists, and where multiplication and division are permitted. One example of a ratio scale is length in inches, because zero length is defined as having no length, and 20 inches is twice as long as 10 inches.

rational subgroup—A subgroup that is expected to be as free as possible from assignable causes (usually consecutive items). In a rational subgroup, variation is presumed to be only from random cause.

red bead experiment—An experiment developed by W. Edwards Deming to illustrate that it is impossible to put employees in rank order of performance for the coming year based on their performance during the past year because performance differences must be attributed to the system, not to the employees. Four thousand red and white beads in a jar (of which 20% are red) and six people are needed for the experiment. The participants' goal is to produce white beads, as the customer will not accept red beads. One person stirs the beads and then, blindfolded, selects a sample of 50 beads. That person hands the jar to the next person, who repeats the process, and so on. When all participants have their samples, the number of red beads for each is counted. The limits of variation between employees that can be attributed to the system are calculated. Everyone will fall within the calculated limits of variation that could arise from the system. The calculations will show that there is no evidence that one person will be a better performer than another in the future. The experiment shows that it would be a waste of management's time to try to find out why, say, John produced 4 red beads and Jane produced 15; instead, management should improve the system, making it possible for everyone to produce more white beads.

reengineering—The process of completely redesigning or restructuring a whole organization, an organizational component, or a complete process. It's a "start all over again from the beginning" approach, sometimes called a *breakthrough*. In terms of improvement approaches, reengineering is contrasted with incremental improvement (kaizen).

regression analysis—A technique that typically uses continuous predictor variable(s) (that is, regressor variables) to predict the variation in a continuous response variable. Regression analysis uses the method of least squares to determine the values of the linear regression coefficients and the corresponding model.

regressor variable—*See* predictor variable.

reliability—The probability that an item can perform its intended function for a specified interval under stated conditions. In the context of training, reliability refers to the consistency and stability of the measurement process over time. For example, if an individual's skills have not been enhanced between two designated time periods, a reliable measurement process would yield the same results for the same participant.

reliability growth—The improvement in product reliability over a period of time.

repeatability—The precision under conditions where independent measurement results are obtained with the same method on identical measurement items by the same appraiser (that is, operator) using the same equipment within a short period of time. Although misleading, repeatability is often referred to as equipment variation (*EV*). It is also referred to as within-system variation when the conditions of measurement are fixed and defined (that is, equipment, appraiser, method, and environment). Repeatability is a component of precision.

repeated measures—The measurement of a response variable more than once under similar conditions. Repeated measures allow one to determine the inherent variability in the measurement system. Repeated measures are also known as *duplication* or *repetition.*

replication—The performance of an experiment more than once for a given set of predictor variables. Each repetition of the experiment is called a *replicate.* Replication differs from repeated measures in that it is a repeat of the entire experiment for a given set of predictor variables, not just a repeat of measurements on the same experiment. Note: Replication increases the precision of the estimates of the effects in an experiment. It is more effective when all elements contributing to the experimental error are included.

reproducibility—The precision under conditions where independent measurement results are obtained with the same method on identical measurement items with different operators using different equipment. Although misleading, reproducibility is often referred to as appraiser variation (*AV*). The term "appraiser variation" is used because it is common practice to have different operators with identical measuring systems. Reproducibility, however, can refer to any changes in the measurement system. For example, assume the same appraiser uses the same material, equipment, and environment, but uses two different measurement methods; the reproducibility calculation will show the variation due to change in methods. It is also known as the *average variation between systems* or *between-conditions variation of measurement.* Reproducibility is a component of precision.

resolution—(1) The smallest measurement increment that can be detected by the measurement system. (2) In the context of experimental design, resolution refers to the level of confounding in a fractional factorial design. For example, in a resolution III design, the main effects are confounded with the two-way interaction effects.

response variable—A variable that shows the observed results of an experimental treatment. It is sometimes known as the *dependent* variable or y variable. There may be multiple response variables in an experimental design.

restraining forces—In the context of a force-field analysis, restraining forces are those forces that hinder or oppose the objective.

return on equity (ROE)—The net profit after taxes, divided by last year's tangible stockholders' equity, and then multiplied by 100 to provide a percentage.

return on investment (ROI)—An umbrella term for a variety of ratios measuring an organization's business performance, the ROI metric measures the effectiveness of an organization's ability to use its resources to generate income. It is computed as:

$$\text{ROI} = \frac{\text{Income}}{\text{Cost}}(100\%).$$

In its most basic form, ROI indicates what remains from all money taken in after all expenses are paid.

revenue growth—The projected increase in income that will result from a project. This is calculated as the increase in gross income minus the cost. Revenue growth may be stated in dollars per year or as a percentage per year.

risk—The probability of not achieving a project goal or schedule, budget, or resource target because something did or didn't occur. Risk may be negative in the form of threats or positive in the form of opportunities.

risk, consumer's (β)—*See* consumer's risk.

risk, producer's (α)—*See* producer's risk.

risk assessment/management—The process of determining what risks are present in a situation and what actions might be taken to eliminate or mediate them.

robust designs—Products or processes that continue to perform as intended in spite of manufacturing variation and extreme environmental conditions during use.

robustness—The condition of a product or process design that remains relatively stable with a minimum of variation even though factors that influence operations or usage, such as environment and wear, are constantly changing.

ROE—*See* return on equity.

ROI—*See* return on investment.

rolled throughput yield (RTY)—The probability of a unit of product passing through an entire process defect-free. The rolled throughput yield is determined by multiplying first-pass yield from each subprocess of the total process.

root cause—A factor (that is, original cause) that, through a chain of cause and effect, causes a defect or nonconformance to occur. Root causes should be permanently eliminated through process improvement. Note: Several root causes may be present and may work either together or independently to cause a defect.

root cause analysis—A structured approach or process of identifying root (that is, original) causes. Many techniques and statistical tools are available for analyzing data to ultimately determine the root cause.

RTY—*See* rolled throughput yield.

run chart—A chart showing a line connecting consecutive data points collected from a process running over a period of time. The run chart is occasionally considered to be one of the seven basic tools of quality. Note: A trend is indicated when the series of collected data points head up or down.

run rates—A projection of future performance based on the assumption that the remainder of the project will continue as it has for the work performed to date. These estimates may be 12-month, year-end, or project-end projections.

S

sample—A group of units, portions of material, or observations taken from a larger collection of units, quantity of material, or observations that serves to provide information that may be used as a basis for making a decision concerning the larger quantity.

sample autocorrelation function (ACF)—The sample autocorrelation function is calculated as

$$r_k = \frac{\sum_{t=1}^{n}(x_{t-k} - \bar{x})(x_t - \bar{x})}{\sum_{t=1}^{n}(x_t - \bar{x})^2}$$

where

n = Number of observations

x_t = Value of x at time t

k = Lag j; $k = 1,2,\ldots$

sample size (n)—The number of units in a sample. Note: In a multistage sample, the sample size is the total number of units at the conclusion of the final stage of sampling.

Sarbanes-Oxley Act of 2002 (SOX)—A legislative act enacted after a series of financial scandals that mandates strict requirements for financial accounting and for top management's responsibility and accountability in disclosing the financial status of their organization.

scatter diagram—A plot of two variables, one on the *y*-axis and the other on the *x*-axis. The resulting graph allows visual examination for patterns to determine if the variables show any relationship or if there is just random "scatter." This pattern, or lack thereof, aids in choosing the appropriate type of model for estimation. Note: Evidence of a pattern does not imply that a causal relationship exists between the variables. The scatter diagram is one of the seven tools of quality.

scatter plot—*See* scatter diagram.

schedule performance index (SPI)—This is a dimensionless index used to measure the project's schedule efficiency. It is calculated as

$$SPI=\frac{EV}{PV}=\frac{BCWP}{BCWS}.$$

If the SPI is greater than 1, the project is ahead of schedule. If the SPI is equal to 1, the project is on schedule. If the SPI is less than 1, the project is behind schedule and corrective action must be taken.

schedule variance (SV)—The schedule variance is the difference between the amount budgeted for the work performed and the planned cost of the work performed. It is calculated as

$$SV = EV - PC.$$

If the SV is positive, the project is ahead of schedule. If the SV is zero, the project is on schedule. If the SV is negative, the project is behind schedule and corrective action must be taken.

scribe—The member of a team assigned to record minutes of meetings.

SDL—*See* self-directed learning.

SDWT—*See* self-directed work team.

SEI—Software Engineering Institute.

seiban—The name of a management practice taken from the Japanese words *sei*, which means "manufacturing," and *ban*, which means "number." A seiban number is assigned to all parts, materials, and purchase orders associated with a particular customer, job, or project. This enables a manufacturer to track everything related to a particular product, project, or customer and facilitates setting aside inventory for specific projects or priorities. Seiban is an effective practice for project and build-to-order manufacturing.

seiketsu—One of the 5S's in Japanese that means to conduct seiri (Sort), seiton (Set in Order), and seiso (Shine) at frequent, indeed daily, intervals to maintain a workplace in perfect condition. This activity is known as Standardize in English.

seiri—One of the 5S's that means to separate needed tools, parts, and instructions from unneeded materials and to remove the latter. Referred to as Sort in English.

seiso—One of the 5S's that means to conduct a cleanup campaign. This is also referred to as Shine in English.

seiton—One of the 5S's that means to neatly arrange and identify parts and tools for ease of use. This is often referred to as Set in Order in English.

self-directed learning (SDL)—A learning method by which students learn without an instructor and at their own pace. This permits adult learners to build toward achieving the desired competency level in the needed knowledge or skill.

self-directed work team (SDWT)—A team that requires little supervision and manages itself and the day-to-day work it does; self-directed teams are responsible for whole work processes and schedules, with each individual performing multiple tasks.

self-sustaining department—One that must promote itself to the remainder of the organization with the hope that the organization will fund its services.

sensor/transmitter—In the context of automated process control, these components are often combined. They capture the measurement, convert it to a signal, and transmit it to the controller for interpretation. These are also called the *primary* and *secondary elements*. The basic operation performed is "measurement."

set point—In the context of automated process control, the set point is the specified value of the controlled variable. This variable is equivalent to the nominal value in a specification.

seven basic tools of quality—A set of both qualitative and quantitative tools that help organizations understand and improve. Unfortunately, there is no longer a unified set of seven tools that are universally agreed on, but most authors agree that five of the seven basic tools include the cause-and-effect diagram, control charts, histogram, Pareto chart, and scatter diagram. Additional tools suggested as part of the seven basic tools of quality include the check sheet, flowchart, graphs, run chart, trend chart, and stratification. Note: (1) graphs are sometimes included with control charts and are distinct at other times; (2) run charts are sometimes included with control charts and are distinct at other times; (3) run charts are sometimes synonymous with trend charts and are distinct at other times; (4) run charts are sometimes included with graphs and are distinct at other times. Some authors are known to have eight basic tools of quality. *See also* individual entries.

seven management and planning tools—The seven commonly recognized management and planning tools are the affinity diagram, tree diagram, process decision program chart (PDPC), matrix diagram, interrelationship diagram, prioritization matrices, and the activity network diagram. *See also* individual entries.

seven tools of quality—*See* seven basic tools of quality.

seven types of waste—Taiichi Ohno proposed value as the opposite of waste and identified seven categories: (1) defects, (2) overproduction (ahead of demand), (3) overprocessing (beyond customer requirements), (4) waiting, (5) unnecessary motions, (6) transportation, and (7) inventory (in excess of the minimum).

severity—An indicator of the degree of a failure should a failure occur. Severity can be evaluated based on a ten-point scale. On the lowest end of the scale (1), it is assumed a failure will have no noticeable effect. On the highest end of the scale (10), it is assumed a failure will impact safe operation or violate compliance with regulatory mandate.

Shewhart cycle—*See* plan–do–check–act (PDCA) cycle.

shitsuke—One of the 5S's that means to form the habit of always following the first four S's. This is referred to as Sustain in English.

side effects—*See* law of unintended consequences.

simple linear regression—A linear regression equation in which one predictor variable is used.

simulation—The act of modeling the characteristics or behaviors of a physical or abstract system.

simultaneous engineering—*See* concurrent engineering.

single-minute exchange of die (SMED)—A series of techniques pioneered by Shigeo Shingo for changeovers of production machinery in less than ten minutes. The long-term objective is always zero setup, in which changeovers are instantaneous and do not interfere in any way with continuous flow. Setup in a single minute is not required but used as a reference. SMED is also known as *rapid exchange of tooling and dies* (RETAD).

SIPOC—A macro-level analysis of the suppliers, inputs, process, outputs, and customers.

Six Sigma—Can take on various definitions across a broad spectrum depending on the level of focus and implementation. (1) Philosophy—the philosophical perspective views all work as processes that can be defined, measured, analyzed, improved, and controlled (DMAIC). Processes require inputs and produce outputs. If you control the inputs, you will control the outputs. This is generally expressed as the $Y = f(X)$ concept. (2) Set of tools—Six Sigma as a set of tools includes all the qualitative and quantitative techniques used by the Six Sigma practitioner to drive process improvement through defect reduction and the minimization of variation. A few such tools include statistical process control (SPC), control charts, failure mode and effects analysis, and process mapping. There is probably little agreement among Six Sigma professionals as to what constitutes the tool set. (3) Methodology—this view of Six Sigma recognizes the underlying and rigorous approach known as DMAIC. DMAIC defines the steps a Six Sigma practitioner is expected to follow, starting with identifying the problem and ending with implementing long-lasting solutions. While DMAIC is not the only Six Sigma methodology in use, it is certainly the most widely adopted and recognized. (4) Metrics—in simple terms, six sigma quality performance means 3.4 defects per million opportunities (accounting for a 1.5-sigma shift in the mean).

skills analysis—The purpose of the skills analysis is to identify the specific skills required to perform the specific tasks identified by the task analysis. In many instances, it is likely that multiple skills will be required to perform a specific task. Examples of skills associated with the task example might be "ability to listen effectively" and "ability to write clearly."

slack time—The time an activity can be delayed without delaying the entire project; it is determined by calculating the difference between the latest allowable date and the earliest expected date.

SMART—SMART stands for *specific, measurable, achievable, relevant,* and *timely* and is used generally in regard to the creation of goal statements.

SMED—*See* single-minute exchange of die.

soft dollar savings—*See* cost avoidance savings.

SOW—*See* statement of work.

SOX—*See* Sarbanes-Oxley Act of 2002.

spaghetti chart—A before-improvement chart of existing steps in a process and the many back-and-forth interrelationships (can resemble a bowl of spaghetti); used to see the redundancies and other wasted movements of people and material.

span of control—The number of subordinates a manager can effectively and efficiently manage.

SPC—*See* statistical process control.

special cause—A source of process variation other than inherent process variation. Note: (1) sometimes special cause is considered synonymous with assignable cause, but a special cause is assignable only when it is specifically identified; (2) a special cause arises because of specific circumstances that are not always present. Therefore, in a process subject to special causes, the magnitude of the variation over time is unpredictable. *See also* assignable cause.

specification—An engineering requirement used for judging the acceptability of a particular product/service based on product characteristics such as appearance, performance, and size. In statistical analysis, specifications refer to the document that prescribes the requirements within which the product or service has to perform.

specification limits—Limiting value(s) stated for a characteristic. *See also* tolerance.

sponsor—A member of management who oversees, supports, and implements the efforts of a team or initiative. Although many organizations define the terms "champion" and "sponsor" differently, they are frequently used interchangeably. *See also* champion.

SPI—*See* schedule performance index.

SQC—*See* statistical quality control.

stability (of a measurement system)—The change in bias of a measurement system over time and usage when that system is used to measure a master part or standard. Thus, a stable measurement system is one in which the variation is in statistical control, which is typically demonstrated through the use of control charts. Stability is a component of accuracy.

stable process—A process that is predictable within limits; a process that is subject only to random causes. (This is also known as a state of statistical control.) Note: (1) a stable process will generally behave as though the results are simple random samples from the same population; (2) this state does not imply that the random variation is large or small, within or outside specification limits, but rather that the variation is predictable using statistical techniques; (3) the process capability of a stable process is usually improved by fundamental changes that reduce or remove some of the random causes present and/or adjusting the mean toward the target value.

stages of team growth—The four development stages through which groups typically progress are *forming, storming, norming,* and *performing.* Knowledge of the stages helps team members accept the normal problems that occur on the path from forming a group to becoming a team.

stakeholders—The people, departments, and groups that have an investment or interest in the success or actions taken by the organization.

standard—A statement, specification, or quantity of material against which measured outputs from a process may be judged as acceptable or unacceptable.

standard error of the ACF—The standard error of the ACF is calculated as:

$$SE(r_k)=\sqrt{\frac{\left(1+2\sum_{m=1}^{k-1}r_m^2\right)}{n}};SE(r_1)=\sqrt{\frac{1}{n}}$$

where

n = Number of observations

r_m = Autocorrelation at lag m; m = 1,2,...,k

k = Lag j; k = 1,2,...

standard work—A concept whereby each work activity is organized around human motion to minimize waste. Each work activity is precisely described and includes specifying cycle time, takt time, task sequence, and the minimum inventory of parts on hand required to conduct the activity. Standard work is also known as *standardized work.*

statement of work (SOW)—A description of the actual work to be accomplished. It is derived from the work breakdown structure and, when combined with the project specifications, becomes the basis for the contractual agreement on the project. The statement of work is also known as *scope of work.*

stationarity—The statistical characteristics of the mean, variance, and autocorrelation structure over time. Time series data are assumed stationary when the mean, variance, and autocorrelation structure are constant over the entire range of the data.

statistic—A quantity calculated from a sample of observations, most often to form an estimate of some population parameter.

statistical control—A process is considered to be in a state of statistical control if variations among the observed sampling results from it can be attributed to a constant system of chance causes.

statistical process control (SPC)—The use of statistical techniques such as control charts to reduce variation, increase knowledge about the process, and steer the process in the desired way. Note: (1) SPC operates most efficiently by controlling variation of process or in-process characteristics that correlate with a final product characteristic, and/or by increasing the robustness of the process against this variation; (2) a supplier's final product characteristic can be a process characteristic to the next downstream supplier's process.

statistical quality control (SQC)—The application of statistical techniques to control quality. The term "statistical process control" is often used interchangeably with "statistical quality control," although statistical quality control includes acceptance sampling as well as statistical process control.

statistical tolerance interval—An interval estimator determined from a random sample so as to provide a specified level of confidence that the interval covers at least a specified proportion of the sampled population.

storming—The second stage of team growth. *See also* stages of team growth.

strategic plan—A set of long-term plans generally focused on a three- to five-year planning horizon and designed to achieve an organization's goals and objectives.

strategic planning—A process to set an organization's long-range goals and identify the actions needed to reach those goals.

stratification—The layering of objects or data; also, the process of classifying data into subgroups based on characteristics or categories. Stratification is occasionally considered to be one of the seven tools of quality.

subsystem—A combination of sets, groups, and so on, that performs an operational function within a system and its major subdivision of the system.

supply chain—The series of processes and/or organizations that are involved in producing and delivering a product or service to the customer or user.

SV—*See* schedule variance.

SWOT—Strengths, weaknesses, opportunities, threats.

SWOT analysis—An assessment of an organization's key strengths, weaknesses, opportunities, and threats. It considers factors such as the organization's industry, competitive position, functional areas, and management.

system—A composite of equipment, skills, and techniques capable of performing or supporting an operational role, or both. A complete system includes all equipment, related facilities, material, software, services, and personnel required for its operation and support to the degree that it can be considered self-sufficient in its intended operating environment.

systems thinking—A problem-solving approach that expands the view of something under analysis to determine how it interacts with other elements of the system of which it is a part.

T

tactical plan—A set of mid-term plans that support the achievement of an organization's strategic plans. The planning horizon for tactical plans is often in the one- to three-year range, but may vary depending on the nature of the organization.

Taguchi methods—The American Supplier Institute's trademarked term for the quality engineering methodology developed by Genichi Taguchi. In this engineering approach to quality control, Taguchi calls for off-line quality control, online quality control, and a system of experimental designs to improve quality and reduce costs.

takt time—A term derived from the German word *taktzeit*, meaning "clock cycle." Takt time is the available production time divided by the rate of customer demand. Operating under takt time sets the production pace to customer demand.

task analysis—The purpose of the task analysis is to identify the specific tasks required to perform a particular job. Often, this is accomplished by direct observation of the individual performing the job. It is important that all tasks be identified regardless of whether or not they are observable at the time the task analysis is being performed. An example of a task might be "prepare minutes for all management meetings."

team—Two or more people who are equally accountable for the accomplishment of a purpose and specific performance goals; it is also defined as a small number of people with complementary skills who are committed to a common purpose.

team building—The process of transforming a group of people into a team and developing the team to achieve its purpose.

testing—A means of determining the capability of an item to meet specified requirements by subjecting the item to a set of physical, chemical, environmental, and operating actions and conditions.

theory of constraints (TOC)—Goldratt's theory deals with techniques and tools for identifying and eliminating the constraints (bottlenecks) in a process.

theory of knowledge—A belief that management is about prediction, and people learn not only from experience but also from theory. When people study a process and develop a theory, they can compare their predictions with their observations; profound learning results.

theory X and theory Y—A theory developed by Douglas McGregor that maintains that there are two contrasting assumptions about people, each of which is based on the manager's view of human nature. Theory X managers take a negative view and assume that most employees do not like work and try to avoid it. Theory Y managers take a positive view and believe that employees want to work, will seek and accept responsibility, and can offer creative solutions to organizational problems.

theory Z—A term coined by William G. Ouchi, theory Z refers to a Japanese style of management that is characterized by long-term employment, slow promotions, considerable job rotation, consensus-style decision making, and concern for the employee as a whole.

three-sixty-degree (360°) feedback process—An evaluation method that provides feedback from the perspectives of self, peers, direct reports, superiors, customers, and suppliers.

throughput time—The total time required (processing + queue time) from concept to launch, from order received to delivery, or from raw materials received to delivery to customer.

time series—A sequence of measurements of some quantity taken at different times, often at equally spaced intervals. Time series models often have the following components:

T_i = Long-term trend

C_i = Cyclical effect (due to business or economic downturns)

S_i = Seasonal effect

R_i = Residual or error effect

TOC—*See* theory of constraints.

tolerance—The difference between upper and lower specification limits.

tolerance design (Taguchi)—A rational grade limit for components of a system; determines which parts and processes need to be modified and to what degree it is necessary to increase their control capacity; a method for rationally determining tolerances.

tollgate review—A formal review process conducted by a champion who asks a series of focused questions aimed at ensuring that the team has performed diligently during the current phase. The end result of a tollgate is a "go" or "no-go" decision. The "go" decision allows the team to move forward to the next phase. If it is in the last phase, the "go" decision" brings about project closure. If the decision is "no-go," the team must remain in the phase or retreat to an earlier phase, or perhaps the project is terminated or suspended.

total productive maintenance (TPM)—A methodology pioneered by Nippondenso (a member of the Toyota group) that works to ensure that every machine in a production process is always able to perform its required tasks such that production is never interrupted. TPM maximizes equipment effectiveness by using a preventive maintenance program throughout the life of the equipment.

TPM—*See* total productive maintenance.

training—A subset of education that focuses on increasing proficiency in a skill. Therefore, training typically refers to skill-based instruction and addresses the specific skills employees need to perform a current job or task.

training need—Essentially, a performance gap between what people know or are able to do and what they should know or be able to do to perform their work competently. For example, consider the situation where a new piece of equipment is to be installed and an employee needs to know how to operate it.

training needs analysis—A diagnostic method to identify the gap between current performance and desired performance. A *needs analysis* is also known as a *needs assessment* or *training requirements analysis.*

training plan—A road map for meeting critical training requirements. All training plans, though, should be a result of a strategic business planning process and should provide a mechanism for ensuring that training and education build the organization's capabilities as well as enable employees to a make a positive contribution to the organization's success.

training requirements analysis—*See* training needs analysis.

training want—A training want may surface when an employee's proficiency is low in certain job tasks or behaviors. However, those tasks and behaviors may not necessarily be important to work performance outcomes. For example, consider a customer service employee who wants to learn more about an engineering topic because of a personal interest.

transfer, risk—Refers to moving the risk to another party or individual and allows them to assume the risk responsibility.

transmission of error—*See* propagation of error.

transmitter—*See* sensor/transmitter.

treatment—The specific setting or combination of factor levels for an experimental unit.

tree diagram—A tool that depicts the hierarchy of tasks and subtasks needed to complete an objective. The finished diagram resembles a tree. The tree diagram is one of the seven management and planning tools.

trend chart—A control chart in which the deviation of the subgroup average from an expected trend in the process level is used to evaluate the stability of a process. The trend chart is also known as the *trend control chart*. The trend chart is occasionally considered to be one of the seven basic tools of quality.

trend control chart—*See* trend chart.

TRIZ—A Russian acronym for "theory of inventive problem solving"; a systematic means of inventing and solving design conflicts. TRIZ involves three items to solve technical problems: (1) various tricks, (2) methods based on utilizing physical effects and phenomena, and (3) complex methods.

Type 1 error—*See* type I error.

Type 2 error—*See* type II error.

Type I error—An error that occurs when we reject the null hypothesis when it is true. We refer to the Pr(Type I error) = Pr(rejecting H_0 | H_0 is true) = α. A Type I error is also known as an *alpha* (α) *error* and *error of the first kind*. The Pr(Type I error) is also known as α – *value, producer's risk, level of significance*, and *significance level*.

Type II error—An error that occurs when we fail to reject the null hypothesis when it is false. We refer to the Pr(Type II error) = P(not rejecting H_0 | H_0 is false) = β. A Type II error is also known as a *beta* (β) *error* and *error of the second kind*. The Pr(Type II error) is also known as β – *value* and *consumer's risk*.

U

unanticipated consequences—*See* law of unintended consequences.

underwritten department—One that receives a budget and is expected to meet its objectives within the constraints of that budget.

unforeseen consequences—*See* law of unintended consequences.

upset—*See* disturbance.

V

VA—*See* value-added or value analysis.

valence—Is the value placed on achievement and reveals the "why" beneath the "what" is being asked of someone.

validation—Refers to the effectiveness of the design process itself and is intended to ensure the design process is capable of meeting the requirements of the final product or process.

validation, external—According to the Manpower Services Commission (MSC) "Glossary of Training Terms": "A series of tests and assessments designed to ascertain whether the behavioural objectives of an internally valid training programme were realistically based on an accurate initial identification of training needs in relations to the criteria of effectiveness adopted by the organization."

validation, internal—According to the Manpower Services Commission (MSC) "Glossary of Training Terms": "A series of test and assessments designed to ascertain whether a training programme has achieved the behavioural objective specified."

validity—In the context of training, a valid measurement process is one that measures what it is designed to measure. The most commonly used method for training programs is the content-validity approach. This is a highly subjective approach by which subject matter experts provide opinions regarding whether the process measures what is needed on the job.

value—The net difference between customer-perceived benefits and burdens; it is sometimes expressed as a ratio of benefits to burdens or a ratio of worth to cost.

value analysis—An analytical process that assumes a process, procedure, product, or service is of no value unless proved otherwise. Value analysis assigns a price to every step of a process and then computes the worth-to-cost ratio of that step. *See also* value-added.

value engineering (VE)—An engineering discipline responsible for analyzing the components and processes that create a product, with an emphasis on minimizing costs while maintaining standards required by the customer.

value stream—All activities, both value-added and non-value-added, required to bring a product from a raw material state into the hands of the customer, a customer requirement from order to delivery, or a design from concept to launch.

value stream analysis (VSA)—An analytical process designed to enhance the benefits of a value delivery system while reducing or eliminating all non-value-adding costs associated with value delivery.

value stream mapping—A technique for following the production path for a product or service from beginning to end while drawing a visual representation of every process in the material and information flows. Subsequently, a future state map is drawn of how value should flow.

value-added (VA)—The tasks or activities that convert resources into products or services consistent with customer requirements. The customer can be internal or external to the organization. Value-added activities add worth to the product or service from the customer's perspective and typically change form, fit, or function.

variables data—Data resulting from the measurement of a parameter or a variable. The resulting measurements may be recorded on a continuous scale.

variance inflation factor—Measures the increase in the variance of a regression coefficient when predictor variables are correlated. The formula for the VIF is given by:

$$VIF\left(\beta_j\right)=\frac{1}{1-R_j^2};j=1,2,\ldots,k$$

where: R_j^2 is the coefficient of multiple determination. It is determined by regressing the predictor variable, x_j, on the other remaining $k - 1$ predictor variables. Consequently, when R_j^2 is large, $VIF(\beta_j)$ is also large. This causes the variances of the coefficients to become inflated.

VE—*See* value engineering.

verification—Refers to the design meeting customer requirements and ensures that the design yields the correct product or process.

VIF—*See* variance inflation factor.

virtual team—A boundaryless team functioning without a commonly shared physical structure or physical contact, using technology to link the team members. Team members are typically remotely situated and affiliated with a common organization, purpose, or project.

visual controls—The collection of approaches and techniques that permit one to visually determine the status of a system, factory, or process at a glance and to prevent or minimize process variation. To some degree, it can be viewed as a minor form of mistake-proofing. *Visual controls* are sometimes referred to as the visual factory.

visual factory—*See* visual controls.

vital few, useful many—A phrase used by J. M. Juran to describe his use of the Pareto principle, which he first defined in 1950. (The principle was used much earlier in economics and inventory control methodologies.) The principle suggests that most effects come from relatively few causes; that is, 80% of the effects come from 20% of the possible causes. The 20% of the possible causes is referred to as the "vital few"; the remaining causes are referred to as the "useful many." When Juran first defined this principle, he was referring to the remaining causes as the "trivial many," but realizing that no problems are trivial in quality assurance, he changed it to "useful many."

VOC—*See* voice of the customer.

voice of the customer (VOC)—An organization's efforts to understand the customers' needs and expectations ("voice") and to provide products and services that truly meet them.

voice of the process (VOP)—The 6σ spread between the upper and lower control limits as determined from an in-control process. The VOP is also known as *natural process variation.*

VOP—*See* voice of the process.

VSA—*See* value stream analysis.

W

waste—Any activity that consumes resources but does not add value to the product or service a customer receives. Waste is also known as *muda.*

WB—*See* White Belt.

White Belt (WB)—A Six Sigma role associated with an individual who works on local problem-solving teams, but may not be part of a Six Sigma project team.

work breakdown structure—A hierarchical decomposition of the work content for a given project.

work group—A group composed of people from one functional area who work together on a daily basis and share a common purpose.

Y

YB—*See* Yellow Belt.

Yellow Belt (YB)—A Six Sigma role associated with an individual who participates as a project team member. They may review process improvements that support the project. Such individuals may have a hands-on role with the process being improved.

Bibliography

Agresti, Alan, and Brian Caffo. 2000. "Simple and Effective Confidence Intervals for Proportions and Differences of Proportions Result from Adding Two Successes and Two Failures." *The American Statistician*, Vol. 54, No. 4, pp. 280-288.

Agresti, Alan, and Brent A. Coull. 1998. "Approximate is better than 'exact' for interval estimation of binomial proportions." *The American Statistician*, Vol. 52, No. 2, pp. 199-128.

Allen, Derek R., and Tanniru R. Rao. 2000. *Analysis of Customer Satisfaction Data: A Comprehensive Guide to Multivariate Statistical Analysis in Customer Satisfaction, Loyalty, and Service Quality Research.* Milwaukee: ASQ Quality Press.

Alukal, George, and Anthony Manos. 2006. *Lean Kaizen: A Simplified Approach to Process Improvements.* Milwaukee: ASQ Quality Press.

Andersen, Bjørn. 2007. *Business Process Improvement Toolbox,* 2nd ed. Milwaukee: ASQ Quality Press.

Andersen, Bjørn, and Thomas Fagerhaug. 2006. *Root Cause Analysis: Simplified Tools and Techniques,* 2nd ed. Milwaukee: ASQ Quality Press.

Andersen, Bjørn, Tom Fagerhaug, Bjørnar Henriksen, and Lars E. Onsøyen. 2008. *Mapping Work Processes,* 2nd ed. Milwaukee: ASQ Quality Press.

Anderson-Cook, Christina Michaela, and Connie M. Borror. 2013. "Paving the Way: Seven Data Collection Strategies to Enhance Your Quality Analyses." *Quality Progress* 46 (4): 18-29.

ANSI/ASQC A1-1978 Definitions, Symbols, Formulas and Tables for Control Charts. 1978. Milwaukee: ASQC Quality Press.

ANSI/ASQC B1-1985 Guide for Quality Control Charts (set of 3 standards). 1985. Milwaukee: ASQC Quality Press.

ANSI/ASQC B2-1985 Control Chart Method of Analyzing Data. 1985. Milwaukee: ASQC Quality Press.

ANSI/ASQC B3-1985 Control Chart Method of Controlling Quality During Production. 1985. Milwaukee: ASQC Quality Press.

Ardent Learning, "What Is the Kirkpatrick Model? Learn the 4 Levels of Evaluation," *Ardent Learning* (blog), February 19, 2020. https://www.ardentlearning.com/blog/what-is-the-kirkpatrick-model.

Ashenbaum, Bryan. 2006. *Defining Cost Reduction and Cost Avoidance.* Critical issues report. Tempe, AZ: CAPS: Center for Strategic Supply Research.

ASQ Statistics Division. 2000. *Improving Performance Through Statistical Thinking.* Milwaukee: ASQ Quality Press.

———. 2005. *Glossary and Tables for Statistical Quality Control,* 4th ed. Milwaukee: ASQ Quality Press.

ASQC Standards Committee. 1994. *ANSI/ISO/ASQC A8402-1994 Quality Management and Quality Assurance—Vocabulary.* Milwaukee: ASQC Quality Press.

ASQC Statistics Division. 1996. *Glossary and Tables for Statistical Quality Control,* 3rd ed. Milwaukee: ASQC Quality Press.

AT&T Handbook Committee. 1958. *Statistical Quality Control Handbook.* Charlotte, NC: Western Electric.

Automotive Industry Action Group. 1995. *(QS-9000) Measurement Systems Analysis (MSA) Reference Manual,* 2nd ed. Southfield, MI: Chrysler, Ford, and GM.

———. 1995. *(QS-9000) Potential Failure Mode and Effects Analysis (FMEA) Reference Manual,* 2nd ed. Southfield, MI: Chrysler, Ford, and GM.

———. 1995. *(QS-9000) Statistical Process Control (SPC) Reference Manual.* Southfield, MI: Chrysler, Ford, and GM.

Bailey, Steven P. 2006. "What's All the NOISE About Statistical Assumptions?," 6th ASQ Six Sigma Conference, Palm Springs, CA, February 6-7, 2006.

Barrentine, Larry B. 2003. *Concepts for R&R Studies,* 2nd ed. Milwaukee: ASQ Quality Press.

Bauer, John E., Grace L. Duffy, and Russell T. Westcott. 2006. *The Quality Improvement Handbook,* 2nd ed. Milwaukee: ASQ Quality Press.

Beauregard, Michael R., Raymond J. Mikulak, and Robin E. McDermott. 1997. *The Basics of Mistake-Proofing.* New York: Quality Resources.

Bee, Frances, and Roland Bee. 1994. *Training Needs Analysis and Evaluation.* London: Chartered Institute of Personnel and Development.

Belair, Georgette, and John O. O'Neill. 2007. *Implementing Design for Six Sigma: A Leader's Guide.* Milwaukee: ASQ Quality Press.

Benbow, Donald W., and T. M. Kubiak. 2005. *The Certified Six Sigma Black Belt Handbook.* Milwaukee: ASQ Quality Press.

Bens, Ingrid. 2011. *Facilitating with Ease! Core Skills for Facilitators, Team Leaders and Members, Managers, Consultants, and Trainers,* 3rd ed. New Jersey: John Wiley & Sons.

Bertin, Marcos E. J., and Gregory H. Watson. 2007. *Corporate Governance: Quality at the Top.* Methuen, MA: GOAL/QPC.

Bicheno, John. 2004. *The New Lean Toolbox: Towards Fast, Flexible Flow.* Buckingham, UK: PICSIE Books.

Biech, Elaine. 2017. *The Art and Science of Training.* Alexandria, VA: ATD Press.

_______, ed. 2014. *ASTD Handbook: The Definitive Reference for Training and Development,* 2nd ed. Alexandria, VA: ASTD Press.

Blanchard, Ken, Patricia Zigarmi, and Drea Zigarmi. 1999. *Leadership and the One Minute Manager: Increasing Effectiveness Through Situational Leadership.* New York: HarperCollins.

Blazey, Mark L. 2008. *Insights to Performance Excellence 2008: An Inside Look at the 2008 Baldrige Award Criteria.* Milwaukee: ASQ Quality Press.

Bossert, James L. 1991. *Quality Function Deployment: A Practitioner's Approach.* Milwaukee: ASQC Quality Press/Marcel Dekker.

Bothe, Davis R. 1997. *Measuring Process Capability: Techniques and Calculations for Quality and Manufacturing Engineers.* New York: McGraw-Hill.

Bower, Keith M. 2001. "Process Capability Analysis Using Minitab: Part 2." Minitab.com. Accessed 12/21/11. http://www.minitab.com/en-US/training/articles.

Box, George E. P., J. Stuart Hunter, and William G. Hunter. 2005. *Statistics for Experimenters: Design, Innovation, and Discovery,* 2nd ed. Hoboken, NJ: John Wiley.

Brassard, Michael. 1989. *The Memory Jogger Plus.* Methuen, MA: Goal/QPC.

Brassard, Michael, Lynda Finn, Dana Ginn, and Diane Ritter. 2002. *The Six Sigma Memory Jogger II.* Salem, NH: Goal/QPC.

Breyfogle, Forrest W. III. 2003. *Implementing Six Sigma: Smarter Solutions Using Statistical Methods,* 2nd ed. Hoboken, NJ: John Wiley.

Breyfogle, Forrest W. III, James M. Cupello, and Becki Meadows. 2001. *Managing Six Sigma: A Practical Guide to Understanding, Assessing, and Implementing the Strategy That Yields Bottom-Line Success.* Hoboken, NJ: John Wiley.

Brown, L.D., T. T Cai, and A. DasGupta. 2001. "Interval estimation for a binomial proportion." *Statistical Science*, Vol. 16, No. 2, pp. 101-133.

Brush, Gary G. 1988. *Volume 12: How to Choose the Proper Sample Size*. Milwaukee: ASQC Quality Press.

Camp, Robert C. 1995. *Business Process Benchmarking: Finding and Implementing Best Practices*. Milwaukee: ASQC Quality Press.

Campanella, Jack, and ASQ Quality Costs Committee. 1999. *Principles of Quality Costs: Principles, Implementation, and Use*, 3rd ed. Milwaukee: ASQ Quality Press.

Cobb, Charles G. 2005. *Enterprise Process Mapping*. Milwaukee: ASQ Quality Press.

CommLab India. "What the Phillips Model Adds to the Kirkpatrick Model of Training Evaluation," *eLearning Design* (blog), September 27, 2021. https://blog.commlabindia.com/elearning-design/kirkpatrick-philips-model-part4.

Connelly, Mark. "ADKAR®: Simple, Powerful, Action Oriented Model for Change," *Change Management Coach* (blog), September 12, 2020. https://www.change-management-coach.com/adkar.html.

———. "The Kurt Lewin Change Management Model." *Change Management Coach* (blog), September 20, 2020. https://www.change-management-coach.com/kurt_lewin.html.

Covey, Stephen R. 1989. *The 7 Habits of Highly Effective People*. New York: Simon and Schuster.

Cox, Neil D. 1986. *Volume 11: How to Perform Statistical Tolerance Analysis*. Milwaukee: ASQC Quality Press.

Crossley, Mark L. 2008. *The Desk Reference of Statistical Quality Methods*, 2nd ed. Milwaukee: ASQ Quality Press.

Day, Ronald G. 1993. *Quality Function Deployment: Linking a Company with Its Customers*. Milwaukee: ASQC Quality Press.

DeGroot, Morris H. 1975. *Probability and Statistics*. Reading, MA: Addison-Wesley.

Deming, W. Edwards. 1982. *Quality, Productivity, and Competitive Position*. Cambridge, MA: MIT Press.

———. 1986. *Out of the Crisis*. Cambridge, MA: MIT Press.

Dettmer, H. William. 1997. *Goldratt's Theory of Constraints: A Systems Approach to Continuous Improvement*. Milwaukee: ASQ Quality Press.

———. 2007. *The Logical Thinking Process: A Systems Approach to Complex Problem Solving*. Milwaukee: ASQ Quality Press.

Dixon, Wilfrid, and Frank J. Massey Jr. 1983. *Introduction to Statistical Analysis*, 4th ed. New York: McGraw-Hill.

Dodson, Bryan. 2006. *The Weibull Analysis Handbook*, 2nd ed. Milwaukee: ASQ Quality Press.

Dovich, Robert A. 1990. *Reliability Statistics*. Milwaukee: ASQC Quality Press.

———. 1992. *Quality Engineering Statistics*. Milwaukee: ASQC Quality Press.

Duncan, Acheson J. 1974. *Quality Control and Industrial Statistics*, 4th ed. Homewood, IL: Richard D. Irwin.

Ginn, Dana, and Evelyn Varner. 2004. *The Design for Six Sigma Memory Jogger*. Salem, NH: Goal/QPC.

Goldratt, Eliyahu M. 1997. *Critical Chain*. Great Barrington, MA: The North River Press.

Grant, Eugene L., and Richard S. Leavenworth. 1988. *Statistical Quality Control*, 6th ed. New York: McGraw-Hill.

Griffith, Gary K. 1996. *Statistical Process Control Methods for Long and Short Runs*, 2nd ed. Milwaukee: ASQC Quality Press.

Groopman, Jerome. 2007. *How Doctors Think*. New York: Houghton Mifflin.

Gryna, Frank M., Richard C. H. Chua, and Joseph A. DeFeo. 2007. *Juran's Quality Planning & Analysis for Enterprise Quality*, 5th ed. New York: McGraw-Hill.

Gunst, Richard F., and Robert L. Mason. 1991. *Volume 14: How to Construct Fractional Factorial Experiments.* Milwaukee: ASQC Quality Press.

Gupta, Bhisham C., and H. Fred Walker. 2005. *Applied Statistics for the Green Belt.* Milwaukee: ASQ Quality Press.

Gupta, Praveen. 2005. *The Six Sigma Performance Handbook.* New York: McGraw-Hill.

Hahn, Gerry, Necip Doganaksoy, and Chris Stanard. 2001. "Statistical Tools for Six Sigma: What to Emphasize and De-emphasize in Training," *Quality Progress*, September.

Henderson, Bruce A., and Jorge Larco. 1999. *Lean Transformation: How to Change Your Business into a Lean Enterprise.* Richmond, VA: Oaklea Press.

Hogg, R. V., and E. A. Tanis. 1997. *Probability and Statistical Inference.* Upper Saddle River, NJ: Prentice-Hall.

ICAEW, "Top Five Cyber Risks," *ICAEW* (web site), 2016. Accessed 3/24/2022. https://www.icaew.com/-/media/corporate/files/technical/business-and-financial-management/smes/bas-for-pba/top-five-cyber-risks.ashx.

Imai, Masaaki. 1986. *Kaizen: The Key to Japan's Competitive Success.* New York: Random House.

John, Peter W. M. 1990. *Statistical Methods in Engineering and Quality Assurance.* New York: John Wiley & Sons.

Juran, Joseph M., and A. Blanton Godfrey. 1999. *Juran's Quality Handbook*, 5th ed. New York: McGraw-Hill.

Kanji, Gopal K. 2006. *100 Statistical Tests,* 3rd ed. London: Sage Publications.

Kaushik, Prabhakar, and Dinesh Khanduja. 2010. "Utilising six sigma for improving pass percentage of students: A technical institute case study," *Educational Research and Reviews*, Vol. 5(9), pp. 471-483.

Keats, J. Bert, and Douglas C. Montgomery. 1991. *Statistical Process Control in Manufacturing.* Milwaukee: ASQC Quality Press/Marcel Dekker.

Kenett, Ron S., and Shelemyahu Zacks. 2014. *Modern Industrial Statistics with Applications in R, MINITAB and JMP,* 2nd ed. Chichester, West Sussex, UK: Wiley.

Kessler, Sheila. 1996. *Measuring and Managing Customer Satisfaction: Going for the Gold.* Milwaukee: ASQC Quality Press.

Kirkpatrick, Donald L., James D. Kirkpatrick, and Wendy K. Kirkpatrick, "The Kirkpatrick Model," *Training Industry* (web site), February 27, 2013. https://trainingindustry.com/wiki/measurement-and-analytics/the-kirkpatrick-model/.

"Kirkpatrick's Evaluation Model." On Hertfordshire government website, undated, https://www.hertfordshire.gov.uk/Media-library/Documents/Kirkpatricks-Evaluation-Model.pdf. Accessed 3/02/2022.

Kisscorni, Edward, Ron Kaley, and Kristen Seaman. 2009. *The Control Test for a Michigan Business Tax Unitary Business Group.* Grand Rapids, MI: Echelbarger Himebaugh Tamm & Co.

Kotz, S., and N. L. Lovelace. 1998. *Process Capability Indices in Theory and Practice.* London: Arnold.

Krishnamoorthi, K. S. 1992. *Reliability Methods for Engineers.* Milwaukee: ASQC Quality Press.

Kubiak, T. M. 1986. *Practical Aids.* Milwaukee: ASQC Quality Press.

———. 2007. "Implementing Six Sigma: Lessons from the Trenches." *Six Sigma Forum Magazine,* August, pp. 12-15.

———. 2012. *The Certified Six Sigma Master Black Belt Handbook.* Milwaukee: ASQ Quality Press.

Kubiak, T. M., Andy Barnett, Jack Westfall, and I. Elaine Allen. 2008. "Outlook on Outsourcing . . . When Does Six Sigma Suffice?," *Quality Progress,* March.

Kubiak, T. M., and Donald W. Benbow. 2009. *The Certified Six Sigma Black Belt Handbook,* 2nd ed. Milwaukee: ASQ Quality Press.

———. 2017. *The Certified Six Sigma Black Belt Handbook*, 3rd ed. Milwaukee: ASQ Quality Press.

Lamprecht, James L. 2005. *Applied Data Analysis for Process Improvement: A Practical Guide to Six Sigma Black Belt Statistics*. Milwaukee: ASQ Quality Press.

Lareau, William. 2003. *Office Kaizen: Transforming Office Operations into a Strategic Competitive Advantage*. Milwaukee: ASQ Quality Press.

Limentani, Giselle B., Moira C. Ringo, Feng Ye, Mandy L. Bergquist, Ellen O. McSorley. 2005. "Beyond the t-test: statistical equivalence testing," *Analytical Chemistry*, June, pp. 2-6.

Levinson, William A., and Raymond A. Rerick. 2002. *Lean Enterprise: A Synergistic Approach to Minimizing Waste*. Milwaukee: ASQ Quality Press.

Locks, Mitchell O. 1995. *Reliability, Maintainability, and Availability Assessment*, 2nd ed. Milwaukee: ASQC Quality Press.

Lynch, Donald P., Suzanne Bertolino, and Elaine Cloutier. 2003. "How to Scope DMAIC Projects." *Quality Progress*, January, pp. 37-41.

MacInnes, Richard L. 2002. *The Lean Enterprise Memory Jogger: Create Value and Eliminate Waste Throughout Your Company*. Salem, NH: Goal/QPC.

Manos, Anthony, and Chad Vincent, eds. 2012. *The Lean Handbook*. Milwaukee: ASQ Quality Press.

Mathews, Paul G. 2005. *Design of Experiments with Minitab*. Milwaukee: ASQ Quality Press.

McDermott, Robin E., Raymond J. Mikulak, and Michael R. Beauregard. 1996. *The Basics of FMEA*. New York: Quality Resources.

McNeese, William H., and Robert A. Klein. 1991. *Statistical Methods for the Process Industries*. Milwaukee: ASQC Quality Press/Marcel Dekker.

McShane-Vaughn, Mary. 2016. *The Probability Handbook*. Milwaukee: ASQ Quality Press.

———. 2017. *The Probability Workbook*. Milwaukee: ASQ Quality Press.

———. 2021. *Lean Six Sigma Leadership Tools for Black Belts*. Folsom, CA: University Training Partners Publishing.

———. 2021. *Statistics for Black Belts Slide Book*. Folsom, CA: University Training Partners Publishing.

Miller, Irwin R., and John E. Freund. 1990. *Probability and Statistics for Engineers*, 4th ed. Englewood Cliffs, NJ: Prentice-Hall.

Miller, Ken. 2002. *The Change Agent's Guide to Radical Improvement*. Milwaukee: ASQ Quality Press.

Moen, Ronald D., Thomas W. Nolan, and Lloyd P. Provost. 1991. *Improving Quality Through Planned Experimentation*. Boston, MA: McGraw-Hill.

Montgomery, Douglas C. 2019. *Design and Analysis of Experiments*, 10th ed. Hoboken, NJ: John Wiley & Sons.

———. 2005. *Introduction to Statistical Quality Control*, 5th ed. Hoboken, NJ: John Wiley.

Montgomery, Douglas C., and George C. Runger. 2010. *Applied Statistics and Probability for Engineers*, 5th ed. Hoboken, NJ: John Wiley.

Muir, Alastair. 2006. *Lean Six Sigma Statistics: Calculating Process Efficiencies in Transactional Projects*. New York: McGraw-Hill.

Munro, Roderick A. 2002. *Six Sigma for the Shop Floor: A Pocket Guide*. Milwaukee: ASQ Quality Press.

———. 2008. *The Certified Six Sigma Green Belt Handbook*. Milwaukee: ASQ Quality Press.

Munro, Roderick A., Matthew J. Maio, Mohamed B. Nawaz, Govindarajan Ramu, and Daniel J. Zrymiak. 2008. *The Certified Six Sigma Green Belt Handbook*. Milwaukee: ASQ Quality Press.

O'Connor, Patrick D. T. 2002. *Practical Reliability Engineering*, 4th ed. Chichester, UK: John Wiley.

Olson, Matthew H., and B. R. Hergenhahn. 1997. *Introduction to the Theories of Learning,* 5th ed. Upper Saddle River, NJ: Prentice-Hall.
Ott, Ellis R., Edward G. Schilling, and Dean V. Neubauer. 2005. *Process Quality Control: Troubleshooting and Interpretation of Data,* 4th ed. Milwaukee: ASQ Quality Press.
Pearn, Michael, and Rajvinder Kandola. 1993. *Job Analysis: A Manager's Guide,* 2nd ed. New York: Hyperion.
Pennella, C. Robert. 2004. *Managing the Metrology System,* 3rd ed. Milwaukee: ASQ Quality Press.
Pestorius, Michael J. 2007. *Applying the Science of Six Sigma to the Art and Sales of Marketing.* Milwaukee: ASQ Quality Press.
Portny, Stanley E. 2010. *Project Management for Dummies.* Hoboken, NJ: Wiley.
Pries, Kim H. 2006. *Six Sigma for the Next Millennium.* Milwaukee: ASQ Quality Press.
Pyzdek, Thomas. 1990. *Pyzdek's Guide to SPC, Volume 1: Fundamentals.* Tucson, AZ: Quality Publishing/Milwaukee: ASQC Quality Press.
———. 1992. *Pyzdek's Guide to SPC, Volume 2: Applications and Special Topics.* Tucson, AZ: Quality Publishing/Milwaukee: ASQC Quality Press.
———. 1994. *Pocket Guide to Quality Tools.* Tucson, AZ: Quality Publishing, Inc.
———. 2003. *The Six Sigma Handbook: A Complete Guide for Green Belts, Black Belts, and Managers at All Levels: Revised and Expanded.* New York: McGraw-Hill.
Pyzdek, Thomas, and Paul A. Keller. 2003. *Quality Engineering Handbook,* 2nd ed. Boca Raton, FL: Taylor & Francis.
———. 2010. *Quality Engineering Handbook,* 3rd ed. Boca Raton, FL: Taylor & Francis.
Rae, Leslie. 1997. *How to Measure Training Effectiveness,* 3rd ed. Aldershot, England: Gower.
Rantanen, K., and E. Domb. 2002. *Simplified TRIZ: New Problem-Solving Applications for Engineers and Manufacturing Professionals.* Boca Raton, FL: St. Lucie Press.
Reidenbach, R. Eric, and Reginald W. Goeke. 2006. *Strategic Six Sigma for Champions: Key to Sustainable Competitive Advantage.* Milwaukee: ASQ Quality Press.
ReVelle, Jack B. 2004. *Quality Essentials: A Reference Guide from A to Z.* Milwaukee: ASQ Quality Press.
Rother, Mike, and John Shook. 2009. *Learning to See.* Version 1.4. Cambridge, MA: Lean Enterprise Institute.
Rothwell, William J. 2008. *Adult Learning Basics.* Alexandria, VA: ASTD Press.
Sall, John, and Brad Jones. 2005. "Leptokurtosiphobia: Irrational Fear of Non-normality." *Six Sigma Forum.* May.
Salvendy, Gavriel. 1992. *Handbook of Industrial Engineering,* 2nd ed. New York: John Wiley & Sons.
Sarkar, Debashis. 2006. *5S for Service Organizations and Offices: A Lean Look at Improvements.* Milwaukee: ASQ Quality Press.
———. 2008. *Lean for Service Organizations and Offices: A Holistic Approach for Achieving Operational Excellence and Improvements.* Milwaukee: ASQ Quality Press.
Scholtes, Peter R., Brian L. Joiner, and Barbara J. Streibel. 2003. *The Team Handbook,* 3rd ed. Madison, WI: Oriel.
Schuirmann, D. J. 1987. "A comparison of the two one-sided tests procedure and the power approach for assessing the equivalence of average bioavailability." *Journal of Pharmacokinet Biopharm.* Vol. 15, No. 6, pp. 657-680.
Shapiro, Samuel S. 1980. *Volume 03: How to Test Normality and Other Distributional Assumptions.* Milwaukee: ASQC Quality Press.
Sheridan, Bruce M. 1993. *Policy Deployment: The TQM Approach to Long-Range Planning.* Milwaukee: ASQC Quality Press.
Shewhart, W. A. 1980. *Economic Control of Quality of Manufactured Product.* Milwaukee: ASQC Quality Press.
Siebels, Donald L. 2004. *The Quality Improvement Glossary.* Milwaukee: ASQ Quality Press.

Spiegel, Murray R., and Larry J. Stephens. 1999. *Statistics,* 3rd ed. New York: McGraw-Hill.

Stamatis, D. H. 2003. *Failure Mode and Effect Analysis: FMEA from Theory to Execution,* 2nd ed. Milwaukee: ASQ Quality Press.

Sternstein, Martin. 2005. *Statistics,* 2nd ed. Hauppauge, NY: Barron's.

Sullivan, William G., Elin M. Wicks, and James T. Luxhoj. 2003. *Engineering Economy,* 12th ed. Upper Saddle River, NJ: Pearson Education.

Tague, Nancy R. 2005. *The Quality Toolbox,* 2nd ed. Milwaukee: ASQ Quality Press.

Tapping, Don, Tom Luyster, and Tom Shuker. 2002. *Value Stream Management: Eight Steps to Planning, Mapping, and Sustaining Lean Improvements.* New York: Productivity Press.

Tolbize, Anick. 2008. *Generational Differences in the Workplace.* Research and Training Center on Community Living. Minneapolis: University of Minnesota.

Treichler, David H., with Ronald D. Carmichael. 2004. *The Six Sigma Path to Leadership: Observations from the Trenches.* Milwaukee: ASQ Quality Press.

Triola, Mario F. 2006. *Elementary Statistics,* 10th ed. Boston: Pearson Education.

Watson, Gregory H. 2005. *Design for Six Sigma: Innovation for Enhanced Competitiveness.* Salem, NJ: Goal/QPC.

Wedgwood, Ian D. 2007. *Lean Sigma: A Practitioner's Guide.* Upper Saddle River, NJ: Prentice-Hall.

Westcott, Russell T. 2005. *Simplified Project Management for the Quality Professional.* Milwaukee: ASQ Quality Press.

———. 2006. *The Certified Manager of Quality/Organizational Excellence Handbook,* 3rd ed. Milwaukee: ASQ Quality Press.

Westcott, Russell T., and Grace L. Duffy. 2014. *The Certified Quality Improvement Associate Handbook,* 3rd ed. Milwaukee: ASQ Quality Press.

Wheeler, Donald J. 1989. *Tables of Screening Designs,* 2nd ed. Knoxville, TN: SPC Press.

———. 1991. *Short Run SPC.* Knoxville, TN: SPC Press.

———. 2000. *The Process Evaluation Handbook.* Knoxville, TN: SPC Press.

———. 2000. *Understanding Variation: The Key to Managing Chaos,* 2nd ed. Knoxville, TN: SPC Press.

Wheeler, Donald J., and David S. Chambers. 1992. *Understanding Statistical Process Control,* 2nd ed. Knoxville, TN: SPC Press.

Wheeler, Donald J., and Richard W. Lyday. 1989. *Evaluating the Measurement Process,* 2nd ed. Knoxville, TN: SPC Press.

Wilburn, Morris. 2007. *Managing the Customer Experience: A Measurement-Based Approach.* Milwaukee: ASQ Quality Press.

Williams, Meri. 2008. *The Principles of Project Management.* Collingwood, Victoria, Australia: SitePoint.

Wilson, Paul F., Larry D. Dell, and Gaylord F. Anderson. 1993. *Root Cause Analysis: A Tool for Total Quality Management.* Milwaukee: ASQC Quality Press.

Windsor, Samuel E. 2006. *Transactional Six Sigma for Green Belts.* Milwaukee: ASQ Quality Press.

Woodford, David. Undated. isixsigma.com. "Design for Six Sigma—IDOV Methodology." Accessed 9/22/16. https://www.isixsigma.com/new-to-six-sigma/design-for-six-sigma-dfss/design-six-sigma-idov-methodology/.

Womack, James P., and Daniel T. Jones. 1996. *Lean Thinking: Banish Waste and Create Wealth in Your Corporation.* New York: Simon & Schuster.

Yang, Kai, and Jayant Trewn. 2004. *Multivariate Statistical Methods in Quality Management.* New York: McGraw-Hill.

Zwillinger, Daniel, and Stephen Kokoska. 2000. *CRC Standard Probability and Statistics Tables and Formulae.* Boca Raton, FL: Chapman & Hall/CRC.

Index

D

E

G

H

I

J

K

N

O

P

Q

R

S

T

U

V

W

X

Y

Z

CPSIA information can be obtained
at www.ICGtesting.com
Printed in the USA
BVHW022051231222
654928BV00005B/7